Some Physical Constants

Quantity	Symbol	Value[a]
Atomic mass unit	u	$1.660\,538\,86\,(28) \times 10^{-27}$ kg $931.494\,043\,(80)$ MeV/c^2
Avogadro's number	N_A	$6.022\,141\,5\,(10) \times 10^{23}$ particles/mol
Bohr magneton	$\mu_B = \frac{e\hbar}{2m_e}$	$9.274\,009\,49\,(80) \times 10^{-24}$ J/T
Bohr radius	$a_0 = \frac{\hbar^2}{m_e e^2 k_e}$	$5.291\,772\,108\,(18) \times 10^{-11}$ m
Boltzmann's constant	$k_B = \frac{R}{N_A}$	$1.380\,650\,5\,(24) \times 10^{-23}$ J/K
Compton wavelength	$\lambda_C = \frac{h}{m_e c}$	$2.426\,310\,238\,(16) \times 10^{-12}$ m
Coulomb constant	$k_e = \frac{1}{4\pi\epsilon_0}$	$8.987\,551\,788\ldots \times 10^9$ N·m²/C² (exact)
Deuteron mass	m_d	$3.343\,583\,35\,(57) \times 10^{-27}$ kg $2.013\,553\,212\,70\,(35)$ u
Electron mass	m_e	$9.109\,382\,6\,(16) \times 10^{-31}$ kg $5.485\,799\,094\,5\,(24) \times 10^{-4}$ u $0.510\,998\,918\,(44)$ MeV/c^2
Electron volt	eV	$1.602\,176\,53\,(14) \times 10^{-19}$ J
Elementary charge	e	$1.602\,176\,53\,(14) \times 10^{-19}$ C
Gas constant	R	$8.314\,472\,(15)$ J/mol·K
Gravitational constant	G	$6.674\,2\,(10) \times 10^{-11}$ N·m²/kg²
Josephson frequency–voltage ratio	$\frac{2e}{h}$	$4.835\,978\,79\,(41) \times 10^{14}$ Hz/V
Magnetic flux quantum	$\Phi_0 = \frac{h}{2e}$	$2.067\,833\,72\,(18) \times 10^{-15}$ T·m²
Neutron mass	m_n	$1.674\,927\,28\,(29) \times 10^{-27}$ kg $1.008\,664\,915\,60\,(55)$ u $939.565\,360\,(81)$ MeV/c^2
Nuclear magneton	$\mu_n = \frac{e\hbar}{2m_p}$	$5.050\,783\,43\,(43) \times 10^{-27}$ J/T
Permeability of free space	μ_0	$4\pi \times 10^{-7}$ T·m/A (exact)
Permittivity of free space	$\epsilon_0 = \frac{1}{\mu_0 c^2}$	$8.854\,187\,817\ldots \times 10^{-12}$ C²/N·m² (exact)
Planck's constant	h	$6.626\,069\,3\,(11) \times 10^{-34}$ J·s
	$\hbar = \frac{h}{2\pi}$	$1.054\,571\,68\,(18) \times 10^{-34}$ J·s
Proton mass	m_p	$1.672\,621\,71\,(29) \times 10^{-27}$ kg $1.007\,276\,466\,88\,(13)$ u $938.272\,029\,(80)$ MeV/c^2
Rydberg constant	R_H	$1.097\,373\,156\,852\,5\,(73) \times 10^7$ m^{-1}
Speed of light in vacuum	c	$2.997\,924\,58 \times 10^8$ m/s (exact)

Note: These constants are the values recommended in 2002 by CODATA, based on a least-squares adjustment of data from different measurements. For a more complete list, see P. J. Mohr and B. N. Taylor, "CODATA Recommended Values of the Fundamental Physical Constants: 2002." *Rev. Mod. Phys.* **77**:1, 2005.

[a] The numbers in parentheses for the values represent the uncertainties of the last two digits.

Solar System Data

Body	Mass (kg)	Mean Radius (m)	Period (s)	Distance from the Sun (m)
Mercury	3.18×10^{23}	2.43×10^{6}	7.60×10^{6}	5.79×10^{10}
Venus	4.88×10^{24}	6.06×10^{6}	1.94×10^{7}	1.08×10^{11}
Earth	5.98×10^{24}	6.37×10^{6}	3.156×10^{7}	1.496×10^{11}
Mars	6.42×10^{23}	3.37×10^{6}	5.94×10^{7}	2.28×10^{11}
Jupiter	1.90×10^{27}	6.99×10^{7}	3.74×10^{8}	7.78×10^{11}
Saturn	5.68×10^{26}	5.85×10^{7}	9.35×10^{8}	1.43×10^{12}
Uranus	8.68×10^{25}	2.33×10^{7}	2.64×10^{9}	2.87×10^{12}
Neptune	1.03×10^{26}	2.21×10^{7}	5.22×10^{9}	4.50×10^{12}
Pluto[a]	$\approx 1.4 \times 10^{22}$	$\approx 1.5 \times 10^{6}$	7.82×10^{9}	5.91×10^{12}
Moon	7.36×10^{22}	1.74×10^{6}	—	—
Sun	1.991×10^{30}	6.96×10^{8}	—	—

[a] In August 2006, the International Astronomical Union adopted a definition of a planet that separates Pluto from the other eight planets. Pluto is now defined as a "dwarf planet" (like the asteroid Ceres).

Physical Data Often Used

Average Earth–Moon distance	3.84×10^{8} m
Average Earth–Sun distance	1.496×10^{11} m
Average radius of the Earth	6.37×10^{6} m
Density of air (20°C and 1 atm)	1.20 kg/m^3
Density of water (20°C and 1 atm)	1.00×10^{3} kg/m^3
Free-fall acceleration	9.80 m/s^2
Mass of the Earth	5.98×10^{24} kg
Mass of the Moon	7.36×10^{22} kg
Mass of the Sun	1.99×10^{30} kg
Standard atmospheric pressure	1.013×10^{5} Pa

Note: These values are the ones used in the text.

Some Prefixes for Powers of Ten

Power	Prefix	Abbreviation	Power	Prefix	Abbreviation
10^{-24}	yocto	y	10^{1}	deka	da
10^{-21}	zepto	z	10^{2}	hecto	h
10^{-18}	atto	a	10^{3}	kilo	k
10^{-15}	femto	f	10^{6}	mega	M
10^{-12}	pico	p	10^{9}	giga	G
10^{-9}	nano	n	10^{12}	tera	T
10^{-6}	micro	μ	10^{15}	peta	P
10^{-3}	milli	m	10^{18}	exa	E
10^{-2}	centi	c	10^{21}	zetta	Z
10^{-1}	deci	d	10^{24}	yotta	Y

Physics for Scientists and Engineers

University of Cincinnati Physics 202

Serway | Jewett

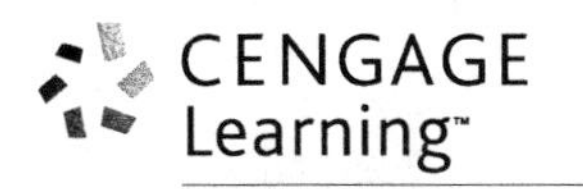

Australia • Brazil • Japan • Korea • Mexico • Singapore • Spain • United Kingdom • United States

Physics for Scientists and Engineers:
University of Cincinnati Physics 202

Serway | Jewett

Executive Editors:
Michele Baird
Maureen Staudt
Michael Stranz

Project Development Manager:
Linda deStefano

Senior Marketing Coordinators:
Sara Mercurio
Lindsay Shapiro

Production/Manufacturing Manager:
Donna M. Brown

PreMedia Services Supervisor:
Rebecca A. Walker

Rights & Permissions Specialist:
Kalina Hintz

Cover Image:
Getty Images*

* Unless otherwise noted, all cover images used by Custom Solutions, a part of Cengage Learning, have been supplied courtesy of Getty Images with the exception of the Earthview cover image, which has been supplied by the National Aeronautics and Space Administration (NASA).

ISBN-13: 978-0-495-47760-0

ISBN-10: 0-495-47760-5

Cengage Learning
5191 Natorp Boulevard
Mason, Ohio 45040
USA

Cengage Learning is a leading provider of customized learning solutions with office locations around the globe, including Singapore, the United Kingdom, Australia, Mexico, Brazil, and Japan. Locate your local office at:
international.cengage.com/region

Cengage Learning products are represented in Canada by Nelson Education, Ltd.

For your lifelong learning solutions, visit **custom.cengage.com**

Visit our corporate website at **cengage.com**

Printed in the United States of America

UNIVERSITY OF Cincinnati

WELCOME TO GENERAL PHYSICS II AT THE UNIVERSITY OF CINCINNATI

The Physics Department would like to welcome you as a student in our General Physics course. This textbook, *Physics for Scientists and Engineers with Modern Physics* by Serway and Jewett (7th Edition), has been custom published for students enrolled in General Physics II (15-PHYS-202) at the University of Cincinnati. It contains only those chapters, which will be covered during the second quarter of the one-year sequence in General Physics at the University of Cincinnati. This course is a calculus-based introduction covering the most important topics in physics. General Physics II will cover oscillatory motion and electromagnetism. Physics is the most fundamental science and provides the foundation for engineering and the other sciences. This course will emphasize the basic physics principles and concepts needed to understand the physical universe. The course will focus on developing an understanding of physical phenomena by building models and theories based on fundamental principles. Students will be expected be able to solve physics problems by using the fundamental principles and theories of physics and not just "plugging" numbers into equations or reproducing memorized facts. You may find General Physics to be a challenging course, but we hope that you will also find it to be an exciting and rewarding course that will help you in your future studies and endeavors.

Overall information about the General Physics II course is contained here for your reference. Specific information about your General Physics course will be presented on the Blackboard Course for your particular General Physics class.

GENERAL PHYSICS II COURSE INFORMATION

COURSE GOALS: The topics for General Physics II are oscillatory motion and electromagnetism. The goals for General Physics II are to achieve an understanding of the basic concepts of oscillations, electricity and magnetism, and to be able to apply these concepts to a variety of physical situations. Students are expected to acquire skills in scientific methods, critical reasoning, and problem solving. Students are also expected to learn to organize their thoughts clearly and to express them clearly in both written and oral communication.

PRE-REQUISITE OR CO-REQUISITE: Calculus II

BLACKBOARD: Students should frequently check the General Physics Blackboard course site for course information, such as assigned homework problems, practice exams, exam solutions and any updated course information. An updated course syllabus will be maintained on Blackboard.

LABORATORY: You should be co-registered in the laboratory course, 15-PHYS-212 for General Physics II, unless your program does not require the laboratory. The laboratory manual will be available through Blackboard. There will be printed laboratory manuals available only at the UC bookstore. Procedures, grading policy, etc. for the lab course will be discussed during the first laboratory class meeting.

ATTENDANCE: Students are expected to attend all classes.

ABSENCES: Except for emergencies, students are expected to inform their instructor if they cannot attend an exam. Makeup exams may be arranged at the discretion of the lecture instructor, if a student has a valid excuse for the absence.

CONDUCT: The University Rules, including the Student Code of Conduct, and other documented policies of the department, college, and university related to academic integrity will be enforced. Any violation of these regulations, including acts of plagiarism or cheating, will be dealt with on an individual basis according to the severity of the misconduct.

PHYSICS LEARNING CENTER (Room 303, Geology/Physics Building):
The Physics Learning Center, staffed by faculty and graduate students, is available to provide students help with physics problems. The schedule for the Learning Center will be posted.

SPECIAL NEEDS: If you have any special needs related to your participation in this course, including identified visual impairment, hearing impairment, physical impairment, communication disorder, and/or specific learning disability that may influence your performance in this course, you should meet with the instructor to arrange for reasonable provisions to ensure an equitable opportunity to meet all the requirements of this course. At the discretion of the instructor, some accommodations may require prior approval by Disability Services.

WITHDRAWAL: Students will be allowed to withdraw and receive a grade of "W," up to official class withdrawal date, regardless of their score in the course. However, they must obtain the signature of the lecture instructor.

REQUIREMENTS FULFILLED: This course satisfies the General Education Breadth of Knowledge Competencies in the areas of Natural Science and Quantitative Reasoning. It also satisfies the College of Arts and Sciences course requirement in Natural Sciences.

PROCEDURE FOR SOLVING GENERAL PHYSICS II PROBLEMS

Listed below is a systematic procedure and format, devised by Dr. Endorf, to help students solve General Physics II problems. The solutions should be written in the format shown in the Problem Worksheet.

1. **Read the problem carefully. Make sure you understand what is given in the problem and what you are requested to find. Write a description of the problem in your own words on the Problem Worksheet.**

2. **If applicable, draw a diagram showing all relevant features given in the problem. Label each part of the diagram, using symbols for each quantity. For vectors show their vector components, where appropriate. For kinematics problems show a motion diagram. For problems involving forces, draw all forces acting on each body under consideration. For problems involving charges or currents, draw in the relevant charges, currents, and electric and magnetic fields at the positions under consideration. For systems changing with time, show the initial, intermediate and final configurations of the system. Indicate relevant parameters that change with time, such as velocity, current, magnetic or electric flux, energy and momentum.**

3. **List all the known quantities and their values on the Problem Worksheet. Convert the values of the known quantities to a consistent set of units, usually SI units.**

4. **List the quantities to be calculated on the Problem Worksheet.**

5. **List all relevant unknown parameters on the Problem Worksheet. These may need to be eliminated from the solution or calculated before calculating the quantities requested in the problem.**

6. **List all relevant general principles, laws, equations and facts that apply to this problem.**

7. **Devise a method to solve the problem. Consider how you may use the general principles and laws that you listed above, such as Newton's Laws, the conservation of energy and momentum, Coulomb's Law, Gauss' Law, Ampere's Law, Faraday's Law, and Lenz' Law The solution may require several steps. Write an outline on the Problem Worksheet, in words, of each step that you will use in your solution.**

8. **Write the problem solution in a clear manner, using your method, on the Problem Worksheet. First solve the problem with algebraic symbols. Then, if a numerical answer is requested, input the numerical values (with units) of the known quantities and calculate the values of the requested unknown quantities. Check that the calculated quantities have the proper units. Check that the answers you have calculated make sense. For example, are the answers much too large or much too small? Do they have the correct sign? For certain very simple conditions do you get the correct answers?**

GENERAL PHYSICS PROBLEM WORKSHEET

PROBLEM #____________ DATE:______________ Sec.#__________

NAME(S)____

PROBLEM DESCRIPTION:

DIAGRAM:
(if applicable)

KNOWN QUANTITIES:

QUANTITIES TO BE CALCULATED:

RELEVANT UNKNOWN PARAMETERS:

RELEVANT GENERAL PRINCIPLES, LAWS, EQUATIONS AND FACTS:

METHOD OF SOLUTION: (general outline of solution method in words)

PROBLEM SOLUTION:
(1. First, solve algebraically; 2. check units; 3. check that the answer(s) make(s) sense.)

SUGGESTIONS FOR DOING WELL IN GENERAL PHYSICS

Listed below are a set of suggestions or strategies, complied by Dr. Robert Endorf, to help students learn physics and perform well in the General Physics.

STUDY HINTS:

1. Form a study group to discuss problems and help study for exams and quizzes. Each member of the study group should contribute and understand the material.
2. Read the entire chapter quickly to obtain the main ideas and concepts.
3. Re read each section of the chapter slowly trying to understand each idea the author presents.
4. Before going to lecture class, read the topics from the text that will be covered in class. Attend all lecture classes. For lecture sections using "clickers," participate in the class discussion and diligently answer all of the "clicker" questions.
5. Ask questions in class or after class about confusing subject matter.
6. Attend all recitation classes and participate enthusiastically in your cooperative learning group.
7. Work through all sample problems in the text and all examples given in class.
8. Read and understand the summary at the end of the each chapter.
9. Write your own review notes. Include the facts and equations you need to solve problems, but emphasize the basic principles and laws needed to solve problems. Update your notes as needed while solving the problems. Try to construct an overall model that relates the basic concepts and principles to the real world.
10. Work on all the assigned homework problems. Use the problem solving strategies and format listed in the *Procedure for Solving Physics Problems* for doing your homework problems. Focus on using general physical principles to classify and solve the problems. Complete all lecture, on-line web-based homework and recitation homework.
11. Discuss the problems in your study group. Write your own solutions for each problem.
12. Do not get behind on the scheduled material and problems. Try to spend some time, at least every other day, studying physics and working problems.
13. If help is needed, ask for help at the Physics Learning Center, in recitation, the professor's office hours or the recitation instructor's office hours.
14. For extra help, use the textbook, web-based study resources, and any student workbooks.

HINTS FOR TAKING EXAMS AND QUIZZES:

A. Before the Exam:

1. Review the summaries in the text, your class notes and your review notes.
2. Study all examples done in class.
3. Study all sample problems in the text. (Try solving the problems with the solutions covered.)
4. Study all assigned homework problems.
5. Try taking a sample exam. Pick several sample problems or assigned problems and try to solve each problem, with no aids, in a time of 20 minutes or less.
6. Take the Practice Exam and use it as a guide for additional topics that you may need to study.

B. During the Exam:

1. First, read each exam problem. Concentrate on solving the problems using general principles and problem solving strategies.
2. Begin with the problem you find the easiest.
3. Write neatly. Draw a diagram. Show all your work and explain your answers.
4. Algebraically list all equations as they are used in the problem. **Solve problems with symbols**, then insert the numbers.
5. If unable to solve one part of a problem, go to the next part.
6. Check the units of your answer. Check that your answer makes sense. Make sure all items requested are answered.
7. Allocate enough time for each problem. If stuck on one problem go to the next problem and return to where you got stuck later.
8. If time is available, recheck each problem before submitting the exam.

C. After the Exam:

1. Check the posted exam solutions.
2. Make sure that you understand the solution of each problem.
3. If any errors were made in grading your exam submit it to your instructor for a regrade.
4. Save all exams, quizzes and homework for future reference.

If you have any general questions or comments about the General Physics courses, please contact the General Physics Course Coordinator, Dr. Robert Endorf, Professor of Physics, at the email address: Robert.Endorf@UC.edu.

Brief Contents

Contents

Raymond A. Serway received his doctorate at Illinois Institute of Technology and is Professor Emeritus at James Madison University. In 1990, he received the Madison Scholar Award at James Madison University, where he taught for 17 years. Dr. Serway began his teaching career at Clarkson University, where he conducted research and taught from 1967 to 1980. He was the recipient of the Distinguished Teaching Award at Clarkson University in 1977 and of the Alumni Achievement Award from Utica College in 1985. As Guest Scientist at the IBM Research Laboratory in Zurich, Switzerland, he worked with K. Alex Müller, 1987 Nobel Prize recipient. Dr. Serway also was a visiting scientist at Argonne National Laboratory, where he collaborated with his mentor and friend, Sam Marshall. In addition to earlier editions of this textbook, Dr. Serway is the coauthor of *Principles of Physics,* fourth edition; *College Physics,* seventh edition; *Essentials of College Physics;* and *Modern Physics,* third edition. He also is the coauthor of the high school textbook *Physics,* published by Holt, Rinehart, & Winston. In addition, Dr. Serway has published more than 40 research papers in the field of condensed matter physics and has given more than 70 presentations at professional meetings. Dr. Serway and his wife, Elizabeth, enjoy traveling, golf, singing in a church choir, and spending quality time with their four children and eight grandchildren.

John W. Jewett, Jr., earned his doctorate at Ohio State University, specializing in optical and magnetic properties of condensed matter. Dr. Jewett began his academic career at Richard Stockton College of New Jersey, where he taught from 1974 to 1984. He is currently Professor of Physics at California State Polytechnic University, Pomona. Throughout his teaching career, Dr. Jewett has been active in promoting science education. In addition to receiving four National Science Foundation grants, he helped found and direct the Southern California Area Modern Physics Institute. He also directed Science IMPACT (Institute for Modern Pedagogy and Creative Teaching), which works with teachers and schools to develop effective science curricula. Dr. Jewett's honors include the Stockton Merit Award at Richard Stockton College in 1980, the Outstanding Professor Award at California State Polytechnic University for 1991–1992, and the Excellence in Undergraduate Physics Teaching Award from the American Association of Physics Teachers in 1998. He has given more than 80 presentations at professional meetings, including presentations at international conferences in China and Japan. In addition to his work on this textbook, he is coauthor of *Principles of Physics,* fourth edition, with Dr. Serway and author of *The World of Physics . . . Mysteries, Magic, and Myth.* Dr. Jewett enjoys playing keyboard with his all-physicist band, traveling, and collecting antiques that can be used as demonstration apparatus in physics lectures. Most importantly, he relishes spending time with his wife, Lisa, and their children and grandchildren.

In writing this seventh edition of *Physics for Scientists and Engineers,* we continue our ongoing efforts to improve the clarity of presentation and include new pedagogical features that help support the learning and teaching processes. Drawing on positive feedback from users of the sixth edition and reviewers' suggestions, we have refined the text to better meet the needs of students and teachers.

This textbook is intended for a course in introductory physics for students majoring in science or engineering. The entire contents of the book in its extended version could be covered in a three-semester course, but it is possible to use the material in shorter sequences with the omission of selected chapters and sections. The mathematical background of the student taking this course should ideally include one semester of calculus. If that is not possible, the student should be enrolled in a concurrent course in introductory calculus.

Objectives

This introductory physics textbook has two main objectives: to provide the student with a clear and logical presentation of the basic concepts and principles of physics and to strengthen an understanding of the concepts and principles through a broad range of interesting applications to the real world. To meet these objectives, we have placed emphasis on sound physical arguments and problem-solving methodology. At the same time, we have attempted to motivate the student through practical examples that demonstrate the role of physics in other disciplines, including engineering, chemistry, and medicine.

Changes in the Seventh Edition

A large number of changes and improvements have been made in preparing the seventh edition of this text. Some of the new features are based on our experiences and on current trends in science education. Other changes have been incorporated in response to comments and suggestions offered by users of the sixth edition and by reviewers of the manuscript. The features listed here represent the major changes in the seventh edition.

QUESTIONS AND PROBLEMS A substantial revision to the end-of-chapter questions and problems was made in an effort to improve their variety, interest, and pedagogical value, while maintaining their clarity and quality. Approximately 23% of the questions and problems are new or substantially changed. Several of the questions for each chapter are in objective format. Several problems in each chapter explicitly ask for qualitative reasoning in some parts as well as for quantitative answers in other parts:

19. ● Assume a parcel of air in a straight tube moves with a constant acceleration of $-4.00\ \mathrm{m/s^2}$ and has a velocity of 13.0 m/s at 10:05:00 a.m. on a certain date. (a) What is its velocity at 10:05:01 a.m.? (b) At 10:05:02 a.m.? (c) At 10:05:02.5 a.m.? (d) At 10:05:04 a.m.? (e) At 10:04:59 a.m.? (f) Describe the shape of a graph of velocity versus time for this parcel of air. (g) Argue for or against the statement, "Knowing the single value of an object's constant acceleration is like knowing a whole list of values for its velocity."

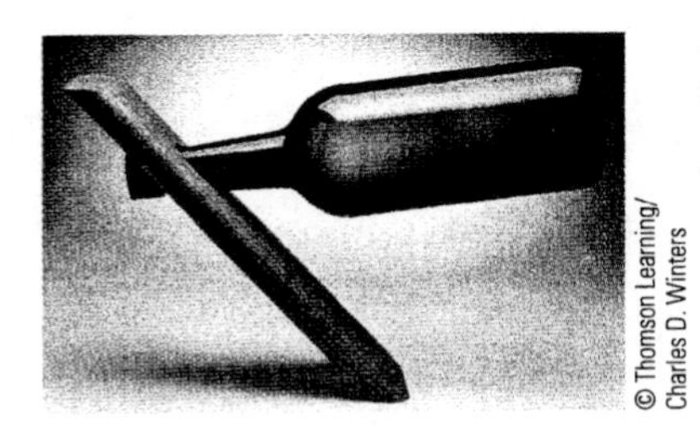
© Thomson Learning/Charles D. Winters

WORKED EXAMPLES All in-text worked examples have been recast and are now presented in a two-column format to better reinforce physical concepts. The left column shows textual information that describes the steps for solving the problem. The right column shows the mathematical manipulations and results of taking these steps. This layout facilitates matching the concept with its mathematical execution and helps students organize their work. These reconstituted examples closely follow a General Problem-Solving Strategy introduced in Chapter 2 to reinforce effective problem-solving habits. A sample of a worked example can be found on the next page.

Each solution has been reconstituted to more closely follow the General Problem-Solving Strategy as outlined in Chapter 2, to reinforce good problem-solving habits.

EXAMPLE 3.2 **A Vacation Trip**

A car travels 20.0 km due north and then 35.0 km in a direction 60.0° west of north as shown in Figure 3.11a. Find the magnitude and direction of the car's resultant displacement.

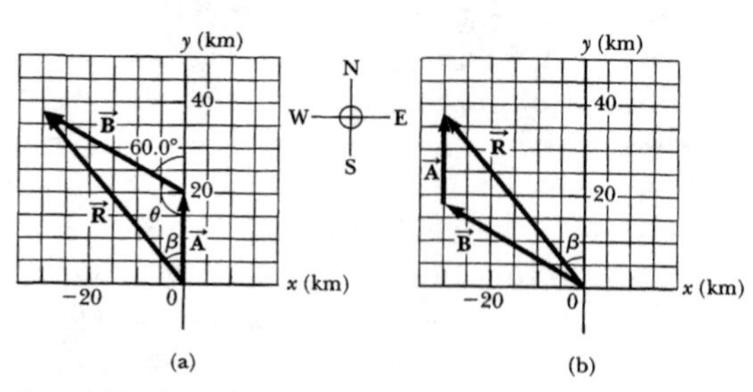

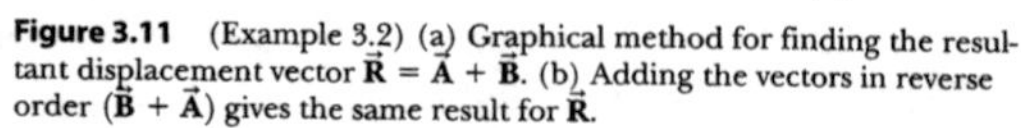

Figure 3.11 (Example 3.2) (a) Graphical method for finding the resultant displacement vector $\vec{\mathbf{R}} = \vec{\mathbf{A}} + \vec{\mathbf{B}}$. (b) Adding the vectors in reverse order $(\vec{\mathbf{B}} + \vec{\mathbf{A}})$ gives the same result for $\vec{\mathbf{R}}$.

SOLUTION

Conceptualize The vectors $\vec{\mathbf{A}}$ and $\vec{\mathbf{B}}$ drawn in Figure 3.11a help us conceptualize the problem.

Categorize We can categorize this example as a simple analysis problem in vector addition. The displacement $\vec{\mathbf{R}}$ is the resultant when the two individual displacements $\vec{\mathbf{A}}$ and $\vec{\mathbf{B}}$ are added. We can further categorize it as a problem about the analysis of triangles, so we appeal to our expertise in geometry and trigonometry.

Each step of the solution is detailed in a two-column format. The left column provides an explanation for each mathematical step in the right column, to better reinforce the physical concepts.

Analyze In this example, we show two ways to analyze the problem of finding the resultant of two vectors. The first way is to solve the problem geometrically, using graph paper and a protractor to measure the magnitude of $\vec{\mathbf{R}}$ and its direction in Figure 3.11a. (In fact, even when you know you are going to be carrying out a calculation, you should sketch the vectors to check your results.) With an ordinary ruler and protractor, a large diagram typically gives answers to two-digit but not to three-digit precision.

The second way to solve the problem is to analyze it algebraically. The magnitude of $\vec{\mathbf{R}}$ can be obtained from the law of cosines as applied to the triangle (see Appendix B.4).

Use $R^2 = A^2 + B^2 - 2AB\cos\theta$ from the law of cosines to find R:

$$R = \sqrt{A^2 + B^2 - 2AB\cos\theta}$$

Substitute numerical values, noting that $\theta = 180° - 60° = 120°$:

$$R = \sqrt{(20.0\text{ km})^2 + (35.0\text{ km})^2 - 2(20.0\text{ km})(35.0\text{ km})\cos 120°}$$

$$= 48.2\text{ km}$$

Use the law of sines (Appendix B.4) to find the direction of $\vec{\mathbf{R}}$ measured from the northerly direction:

$$\frac{\sin\beta}{B} = \frac{\sin\theta}{R}$$

$$\sin\beta = \frac{B}{R}\sin\theta = \frac{35.0\text{ km}}{48.2\text{ km}}\sin 120° = 0.629$$

$$\beta = 38.9°$$

The resultant displacement of the car is 48.2 km in a direction 38.9° west of north.

Finalize Does the angle β that we calculated agree with an estimate made by looking at Figure 3.11a or with an actual angle measured from the diagram using the graphical method? Is it reasonable that the magnitude of $\vec{\mathbf{R}}$ is larger than that of both $\vec{\mathbf{A}}$ and $\vec{\mathbf{B}}$? Are the units of $\vec{\mathbf{R}}$ correct?

Although the graphical method of adding vectors works well, it suffers from two disadvantages. First, some people find using the laws of cosines and sines to be awkward. Second, a triangle only results if you are adding two vectors. If you are adding three or more vectors, the resulting geometric shape is usually not a triangle. In Section 3.4, we explore a new method of adding vectors that will address both of these disadvantages.

What If? Suppose the trip were taken with the two vectors in reverse order: 35.0 km at 60.0° west of north first and then 20.0 km due north. How would the magnitude and the direction of the resultant vector change?

Answer They would not change. The commutative law for vector addition tells us that the order of vectors in an addition is irrelevant. Graphically, Figure 3.11b shows that the vectors added in the reverse order give us the same resultant vector.

What If? statements appear in about 1/3 of the worked examples and offer a variation on the situation posed in the text of the example. For instance, this feature might explore the effects of changing the conditions of the situation, determine what happens when a quantity is taken to a particular limiting value, or question whether additional information can be determined about the problem situation. This feature encourages students to think about the results of the example and assists in conceptual understanding of the principles.

All worked examples are also available to be assigned as interactive examples in the Enhanced WebAssign homework management system (visit **www.pse7.com** for more details).

ONLINE HOMEWORK It is now easier to assign online homework with Serway and Jewett and Enhanced WebAssign. All worked examples, end-of-chapter problems, active figures, quick quizzes, and most questions are available in WebAssign. Most problems include hints and feedback to provide instantaneous reinforcement or direction for that problem. In addition to the text content, we have also added math remediation tools to help students get up to speed in algebra, trigonometry, and calculus.

SUMMARIES Each chapter contains a summary that reviews the important concepts and equations discussed in that chapter. A marginal note next to each chapter summary directs students to additional quizzes, animations, and interactive exercises for that chapter on the book's companion Web site. The format of the end-of-chapter summary has been completely revised for this edition. The summary is divided into three sections: Definitions, Concepts and Principles, and Analysis Models for Problem-Solving. In each section, flashcard-type boxes focus on each separate definition, concept, principle, or analysis model.

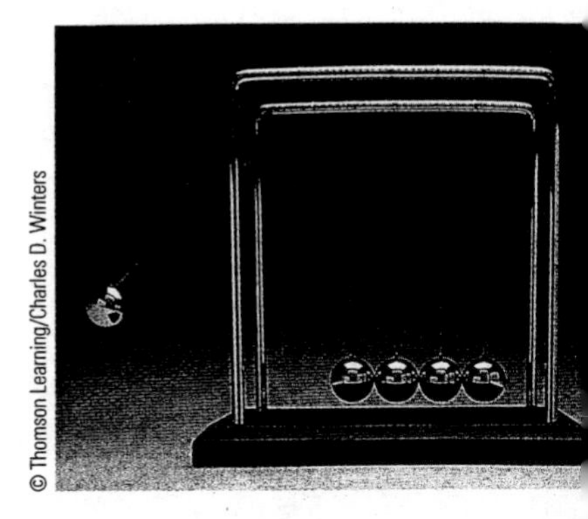

MATH APPENDIX The math appendix, a valuable tool for students, has been updated to show the math tools in a physics context. This resource is ideal for students who need a quick review on topics such as algebra, trigonometry, and calculus.

CONTENT CHANGES The content and organization of the textbook are essentially the same as in the sixth edition. Many sections in various chapters have been streamlined, deleted, or combined with other sections to allow for a more balanced presentation. Vectors are now denoted in boldface with an arrow over them (for example, $\vec{\mathbf{v}}$), making them easier to recognize. Chapters 7 and 8 have been completely reorganized to prepare students for a unified approach to energy that is used throughout the text. A new section in Chapter 9 teaches students how to analyze deformable systems with the conservation of energy equation and the impulse-momentum theorem. Chapter 34 is longer than in the sixth edition because of the movement into that chapter of the material on displacement current from Chapter 30 and Maxwell's equations from Chapter 31. A more detailed list of content changes can be found on the instructor's companion Web site.

Content

The material in this book covers fundamental topics in classical physics and provides an introduction to modern physics. The book is divided into six parts. Part 1 (Chapters 1 to 14) deals with the fundamentals of Newtonian mechanics and the physics of fluids; Part 2 (Chapters 15 to 18) covers oscillations, mechanical waves, and sound; Part 3 (Chapters 19 to 22) addresses heat and thermodynamics; Part 4 (Chapters 23 to 34) treats electricity and magnetism; Part 5 (Chapters 35 to 38) covers light and optics; and Part 6 (Chapters 39 to 46) deals with relativity and modern physics.

Text Features

Most instructors believe that the textbook selected for a course should be the student's primary guide for understanding and learning the subject matter. Furthermore, the textbook should be easily accessible and should be styled and written to facilitate instruction and learning. With these points in mind, we have included many pedagogical features, listed below, that are intended to enhance its usefulness to both students and instructors.

Problem Solving and Conceptual Understanding

GENERAL PROBLEM-SOLVING STRATEGY A general strategy outlined at the end of Chapter 2 provides students with a structured process for solving problems. In all remaining chapters, the strategy is employed explicitly in every example so that students learn how it is applied. Students are encouraged to follow this strategy when working end-of-chapter problems.

MODELING Although students are faced with hundreds of problems during their physics courses, instructors realize that a relatively small number of physical situations form the basis of these problems. When faced with a new problem, a physicist forms a *model* of the problem that can be solved in a simple way by identifying the common physical situation that occurs in the problem. For example, many problems involve particles under constant acceleration, isolated systems, or waves under refraction. Because the physicist has studied these situations extensively and understands the associated behavior, he or she can apply this knowledge as a model for solving a new problem. In certain chapters, this edition identifies Analysis Models, which are physical situations (such as the particle under constant acceleration, the isolated system, or the wave under refraction) that occur so often that they can be used as a model for solving an unfamiliar problem. These models are discussed in the chapter text, and the student is reminded of them in the end-of-chapter summary under the heading "Analysis Models for Problem-Solving."

PROBLEMS An extensive set of problems is included at the end of each chapter; in all, the text contains approximately three thousand problems. Answers to odd-numbered problems are provided at the end of the book. For the convenience of both the student and the instructor, about two-thirds of the problems are keyed to specific sections of the chapter. The remaining problems, labeled "Additional Problems," are not keyed to specific sections. The problem numbers for straightforward problems are printed in black, intermediate-level problems are in blue, and challenging problems are in magenta.

- **"Not-just-a-number" problems** Each chapter includes several marked problems that require students to think qualitatively in some parts and quantitatively in others. Instructors can assign such problems to guide students to display deeper understanding, practice good problem-solving techniques, and prepare for exams.
- **Problems for developing symbolic reasoning** Each chapter contains problems that ask for solutions in symbolic form as well as many problems asking for numerical answers. To help students develop skill in symbolic reasoning, each chapter contains a pair of otherwise identical problems, one asking for a numerical solution and one asking for a symbolic derivation. In this edition, each chapter also contains a problem giving a numerical value for every datum but one so that the answer displays how the unknown depends on the datum represented symbolically. The answer to such a problem has the form of a function of one variable. Reasoning about the behavior of this function puts emphasis on the *Finalize* step of the General Problem-Solving Strategy. All problems developing symbolic reasoning are identified by a tan background screen:

> 53. ● A light spring has an unstressed length of 15.5 cm. It is described by Hooke's law with spring constant 4.30 N/m. One end of the horizontal spring is held on a fixed vertical axle, and the other end is attached to a puck of mass m that can move without friction over a horizontal surface. The puck is set into motion in a circle with a period of 1.30 s. (a) Find the extension of the spring x as it depends on m. Evaluate x for (b) $m = 0.070\ 0$ kg, (c) $m = 0.140$ kg, (d) $m = 0.180$ kg, and (e) $m = 0.190$ kg. (f) Describe the pattern of variation of x as it depends on m.

- **Review problems** Many chapters include review problems requiring the student to combine concepts covered in the chapter with those discussed in previous chapters. These problems reflect the cohesive nature of the principles in the text and verify that physics is not a scattered set of ideas. When facing a real-world issue such as global warming or nuclear weapons, it may be necessary to call on ideas in physics from several parts of a textbook such as this one.
- **"Fermi problems"** As in previous editions, at least one problem in each chapter asks the student to reason in order-of-magnitude terms.

- **Design problems** Several chapters contain problems that ask the student to determine design parameters for a practical device so that it can function as required.
- **"*Jeopardy!*" problems** Some chapters give students practice in changing between different representations by stating equations and asking for a description of a situation to which they apply as well as for a numerical answer.
- **Calculus-based problems** Every chapter contains at least one problem applying ideas and methods from differential calculus and one problem using integral calculus.

The instructor's Web site, **www.thomsonedu.com/physics/serway,** provides lists of problems using calculus, problems encouraging or requiring computer use, problems with **"What If?"** parts, problems referred to in the chapter text, problems based on experimental data, order-of-magnitude problems, problems about biological applications, design problems, *Jeopardy!* problems, review problems, problems reflecting historical reasoning about confusing ideas, problems developing symbolic reasoning skill, problems with qualitative parts, ranking questions, and other objective questions.

QUESTIONS The questions section at the end of each chapter has been significantly revised. Multiple-choice, ranking, and true–false questions have been added. The instructor may select items to assign as homework or use in the classroom, possibly with "peer instruction" methods and possibly with "clicker" systems. More than eight hundred questions are included in this edition. Answers to selected questions are included in the *Student Solutions Manual/Study Guide,* and answers to all questions are found in the *Instructor's Solutions Manual.*

19. O (i) Rank the gravitational accelerations you would measure for (a) a 2-kg object 5 cm above the floor, (b) a 2-kg object 120 cm above the floor, (c) a 3-kg object 120 cm above the floor, and (d) a 3-kg object 80 cm above the floor. List the one with the largest-magnitude acceleration first. If two are equal, show their equality in your list. **(ii)** Rank the gravitational forces on the same four objects, largest magnitude first. **(iii)** Rank the gravitational potential energies (of the object–Earth system) for the same four objects, largest first, taking $y = 0$ at the floor.

23. O An ice cube has been given a push and slides without friction on a level table. Which is correct? (a) It is in stable equilibrium. (b) It is in unstable equilibrium. (c) It is in neutral equilibrium (d) It is not in equilibrium.

WORKED EXAMPLES Two types of worked examples are presented to aid student comprehension. All worked examples in the text may be assigned for homework in WebAssign.

The first example type presents a problem and numerical answer. As discussed earlier, solutions to these examples have been altered in this edition to feature a two-column layout to explain the physical concepts and the mathematical steps side by side. Every example follows the explicit steps of the General Problem-Solving Strategy outlined in Chapter 2.

The second type of example is conceptual in nature. To accommodate increased emphasis on understanding physical concepts, the many conceptual examples are labeled as such, set off in boxes, and designed to focus students on the physical situation in the problem.

WHAT IF? Approximately one-third of the worked examples in the text contain a **What If?** feature. At the completion of the example solution, a **What If?** question offers a variation on the situation posed in the text of the example. For instance, this feature might explore the effects of changing the conditions of the situation, determine what happens when a quantity is taken to a particular limiting value, or question whether additional information can be determined about the situation. This feature encourages students to think about the results of the example, and it also assists in conceptual understanding of the principles. **What If?** questions also prepare students to encounter novel problems that may be included on exams. Some of the end-of-chapter problems also include this feature.

QUICK QUIZZES Quick Quizzes provide students an opportunity to test their understanding of the physical concepts presented. The questions require students to make decisions on the basis of sound reasoning, and some of the questions have been written to help students overcome common misconceptions. Quick Quizzes have been cast in an objective format, including multiple-choice, true–false, and ranking. Answers to all Quick Quiz questions are found at the end of each chapter. Additional Quick Quizzes that can be used in classroom teaching are available on the instructor's companion Web site. Many instructors choose to use such questions in a "peer instruction" teaching style or with the use of personal response system "clickers," but they can be used in standard quiz format as well. Quick Quizzes are set off from the text by horizontal lines:

Quick Quiz 7.5 A dart is loaded into a spring-loaded toy dart gun by pushing the spring in by a distance x. For the next loading, the spring is compressed a distance $2x$. How much faster does the second dart leave the gun compared with the first? (a) four times as fast (b) two times as fast (c) the same (d) half as fast (e) one-fourth as fast

---

PITFALL PREVENTION 16.2
Two Kinds of Speed/Velocity

Do not confuse v, the speed of the wave as it propagates along the string, with v_y, the transverse velocity of a point on the string. The speed v is constant for a uniform medium, whereas v_y varies sinusoidally.

PITFALL PREVENTIONS More than two hundred Pitfall Preventions (such as the one to the left) are provided to help students avoid common mistakes and misunderstandings. These features, which are placed in the margins of the text, address both common student misconceptions and situations in which students often follow unproductive paths.

Helpful Features

STYLE To facilitate rapid comprehension, we have written the book in a clear, logical, and engaging style. We have chosen a writing style that is somewhat informal and relaxed so that students will find the text appealing and enjoyable to read. New terms are carefully defined, and we have avoided the use of jargon.

IMPORTANT STATEMENTS AND EQUATIONS Most important statements and definitions are set in **boldface** or are highlighted with a background screen for added emphasis and ease of review. Similarly, important equations are highlighted with a background screen to facilitate location.

MARGINAL NOTES Comments and notes appearing in the margin with a ▶ icon can be used to locate important statements, equations, and concepts in the text.

PEDAGOGICAL USE OF COLOR Readers should consult the **pedagogical color chart** (inside the front cover) for a listing of the color-coded symbols used in the text diagrams. This system is followed consistently throughout the text.

MATHEMATICAL LEVEL We have introduced calculus gradually, keeping in mind that students often take introductory courses in calculus and physics concurrently. Most steps are shown when basic equations are developed, and reference is often made to mathematical appendices near the end of the textbook. Vector products are introduced later in the text, where they are needed in physical applications. The dot product is introduced in Chapter 7, which addresses energy of a system; the cross product is introduced in Chapter 11, which deals with angular momentum.

SIGNIFICANT FIGURES Significant figures in both worked examples and end-of-chapter problems have been handled with care. Most numerical examples are worked to either two or three significant figures, depending on the precision of the data provided. End-of-chapter problems regularly state data and answers to three-digit precision.

UNITS The international system of units (SI) is used throughout the text. The U.S. customary system of units is used only to a limited extent in the chapters on mechanics and thermodynamics.

APPENDICES AND ENDPAPERS Several appendices are provided near the end of the textbook. Most of the appendix material represents a review of mathematical concepts and techniques used in the text, including scientific notation, algebra, geometry, trigonometry, differential calculus, and integral calculus. Reference to these appendices is made throughout the text. Most mathematical review sections in the appendices include worked examples and exercises with answers. In addition to the mathematical reviews, the appendices contain tables of physical data, conversion factors, and the SI units of physical quantities as well as a periodic table of the elements. Other useful information—fundamental constants and physical data, planetary data, a list of standard prefixes, mathematical symbols, the Greek alphabet, and standard abbreviations of units of measure—appears on the endpapers.

Course Solutions That Fit Your Teaching Goals and Your Students' Learning Needs

Recent advances in educational technology have made homework management systems and audience response systems powerful and affordable tools to enhance the way you teach your course. Whether you offer a more traditional text-based course, are interested in using or are currently using an online homework management system such as WebAssign, or are ready to turn your lecture into an interactive learning environment with JoinIn on TurningPoint, you can be confident that the text's proven content provides the foundation for each and every component of our technology and ancillary package.

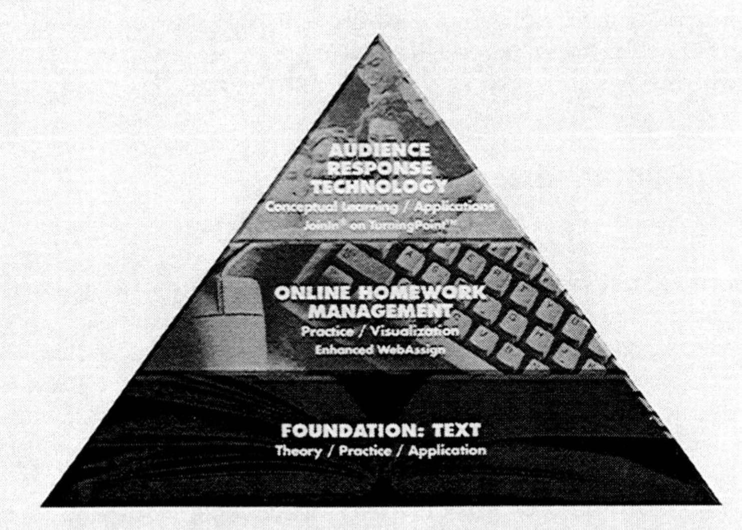

Homework Management Systems

Enhanced WebAssign Whether you're an experienced veteran or a beginner, Enhanced WebAssign is the perfect solution to fit your homework management needs. Designed by physicists for physicists, this system is a reliable and user-friendly teaching companion. Enhanced WebAssign is available for *Physics for Scientists and Engineers*, giving you the freedom to assign

- every end-of-chapter Problem and Question, enhanced with hints and feedback
- every worked example, enhanced with hints and feedback, to help strengthen students' problem-solving skills
- every Quick Quiz, giving your students ample opportunity to test their conceptual understanding.

- animated Active Figures, enhanced with hints and feedback, to help students develop their visualization skills
- a math review to help students brush up on key quantitative concepts

Please visit **www.thomsonedu.com/physics/serway** to view a live demonstration of Enhanced WebAssign.

The text also supports the following Homework Management Systems:

LON-CAPA: A Computer-Assisted Personalized Approach
http://www.lon-capa.org/

The University of Texas Homework Service
contact **moore@physics.utexas.edu**

JoinIn™ on TurningPoint®

Personal Response Systems

JoinIn on TurningPoint Pose book-specific questions and display students' answers seamlessly within the Microsoft® PowerPoint slides of your own lecture in conjunction with the "clicker" hardware of your choice. JoinIn on TurningPoint works with most infrared or radio frequency keypad systems, including Responsecard, EduCue, H-ITT, and even laptops. Contact your local sales representative to learn more about our personal response software and hardware.

Personal Response System Content Regardless of the response system you are using, we provide the tested content to support it. Our ready-to-go content includes all the questions from the Quick Quizzes, test questions, and a selection of end-of-chapter questions to provide helpful conceptual checkpoints to drop into your lecture. Our series of Active Figure animations have also been enhanced with multiple-choice questions to help test students' observational skills.

We also feature the Assessing to Learn in the Classroom content from the University of Massachusetts at Amherst. This collection of 250 advanced conceptual questions has been tested in the classroom for more than ten years and takes peer learning to a new level.

Visit **www.thomsonedu.com/physics/serway** to download samples of our personal response system content.

Lecture Presentation Resources

The following resources provide support for your presentations in lecture.

MULTIMEDIA MANAGER INSTRUCTOR'S RESOURCE CD An easy-to-use multimedia lecture tool, the Multimedia Manager Instructor's Resource CD allows you to quickly assemble art, animations, digital video, and database files with notes to create fluid lectures. The two-volume set (Volume 1: Chapters 1–22; Volume 2: Chapters 23–46) includes prebuilt PowerPoint lectures, a database of animations, video clips, and digital art from the text as well as editable electronic files of the *Instructor's Solutions Manual* and *Test Bank*.

TRANSPARENCY ACETATES Each volume contains approximately one hundred transparency acetates featuring art from the text. Volume 1 contains Chapters 1 through 22, and Volume 2 contains Chapters 23 through 46.

Assessment and Course Preparation Resources

A number of resources listed below will assist with your assessment and preparation processes.

INSTRUCTOR'S SOLUTIONS MANUAL by Ralph McGrew. This two-volume manual contains complete worked solutions to all end-of-chapter problems in the textbook as well as answers to the even-numbered problems and all the questions. The solutions to problems new to the seventh edition are marked for easy identification. Volume 1 contains

Chapters 1 through 22, and Volume 2 contains Chapters 23 through 46. Electronic files of the Instructor's Solutions are available on the Multimedia Manager CD as well.

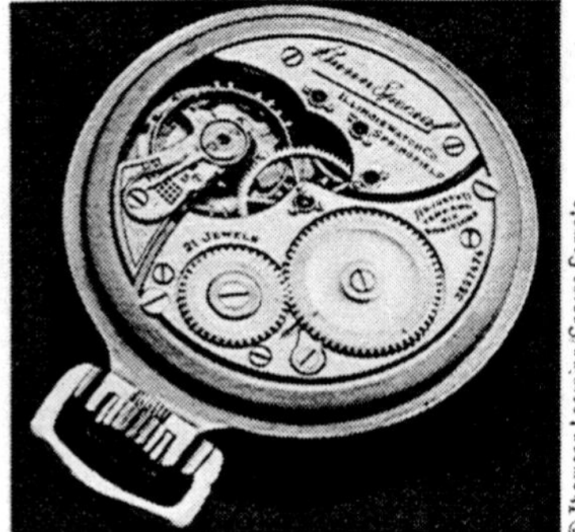
© Thomson Learning/George Semple

PRINTED TEST BANK by Edward Adelson. This two-volume test bank contains approximately 2 200 multiple-choice questions. These questions are also available in electronic format with complete answers and solutions in the ExamView test software and as editable Word® files on the Multimedia Manager CD. Volume 1 contains Chapters 1 through 22, and Volume 2 contains Chapters 23 through 46.

EXAMVIEW This easy-to-use test generator CD features all of the questions from the printed test bank in an editable format.

WEBCT AND BLACKBOARD CONTENT For users of either course management system, we provide our test bank questions in the proper format for easy upload into your online course. In addition, you can integrate the ThomsonNOW for Physics student tutorial content into your WebCT or Blackboard course, providing your students a single sign-on to all their Web-based learning resources. Contact your local sales representative to learn more about our WebCT and Blackboard resources.

INSTRUCTOR'S COMPANION WEB SITE Consult the instructor's site by pointing your browser to **www.thomsonedu.com/physics/serway** for additional Quick Quiz questions, a detailed list of content changes since the sixth edition, a problem correlation guide, images from the text, and sample PowerPoint lectures. Instructors adopting the seventh edition of *Physics for Scientists and Engineers* may download these materials after securing the appropriate password from their local Thomson•Brooks/Cole sales representative.

Student Resources

STUDENT SOLUTIONS MANUAL/STUDY GUIDE by John R. Gordon, Ralph McGrew, Raymond Serway, and John W. Jewett, Jr. This two-volume manual features detailed solutions to 20% of the end-of-chapter problems from the text. The manual also features a list of important equations, concepts, and notes from key sections of the text in addition to answers to selected end-of-chapter questions. Volume 1 contains Chapters 1 through 22, and Volume 2 contains Chapters 23 through 46.

THOMSONNOW PERSONAL STUDY This assessment-based student tutorial system provides students with a personalized learning plan based on their performance on a series of diagnostic pre-tests. Rich interactive content, including Active Figures, Coached Problems, and Interactive Examples, helps students prepare for tests and exams.

Teaching Options

The topics in this textbook are presented in the following sequence: classical mechanics, oscillations and mechanical waves, and heat and thermodynamics followed by electricity and magnetism, electromagnetic waves, optics, relativity, and modern physics. This presentation represents a traditional sequence, with the subject of mechanical waves being presented before electricity and magnetism. Some instructors may prefer to discuss both mechanical and electromagnetic waves together after completing electricity and magnetism. In this case, Chapters 16 through 18 could be covered along with Chapter 34. The chapter on relativity is placed near the end of the text because this topic often is treated as an introduction to the era of "modern physics." If time permits, instructors may choose to cover Chapter 39 after completing Chapter 13 as a conclusion to the material on Newtonian mechanics.

For those instructors teaching a two-semester sequence, some sections and chapters could be deleted without any loss of continuity. The following sections can be considered optional for this purpose:

2.8	Kinematic Equations Derived from Calculus
4.6	Relative Velocity and Relative Acceleration
6.3	Motion in Accelerated Frames
6.4	Motion in the Presence of Resistive Forces
7.9	Energy Diagrams and Equilibrium of a System
9.8	Rocket Propulsion
11.5	The Motion of Gyroscopes and Tops
14.7	Other Applications of Fluid Dynamics
15.6	Damped Oscillations
15.7	Forced Oscillations
17.5	Digital Sound Recording
17.6	Motion Picture Sound
18.6	Standing Waves in Rods and Membranes
18.8	Nonsinusoidal Wave Patterns
22.8	Entropy on a Microscopic Scale
25.7	The Millikan Oil-Drop Experiment
25.8	Applications of Electrostatics
26.7	An Atomic Description of Dielectrics
27.5	Superconductors
28.5	Electrical Meters
28.6	Household Wiring and Electrical Safety
29.3	Applications Involving Charged Particles Moving in a Magnetic Field
29.6	The Hall Effect
30.6	Magnetism in Matter
30.7	The Magnetic Field of the Earth
31.6	Eddy Currents
33.9	Rectifiers and Filters
34.6	Production of Electromagnetic Waves by an Antenna
36.5	Lens Aberrations
36.6	The Camera
36.7	The Eye
36.8	The Simple Magnifier
36.9	The Compound Microscope
36.10	The Telescope
38.5	Diffraction of X-Rays by Crystals
39.10	The General Theory of Relativity
41.6	Applications of Tunneling
42.9	Spontaneous and Stimulated Transitions
42.10	Lasers
43.7	Semiconductor Devices
43.8	Superconductivity
44.8	Nuclear Magnetic Resonance and Magnetic Resonance Imaging
45.5	Radiation Damage
45.6	Radiation Detectors
45.7	Uses of Radiation

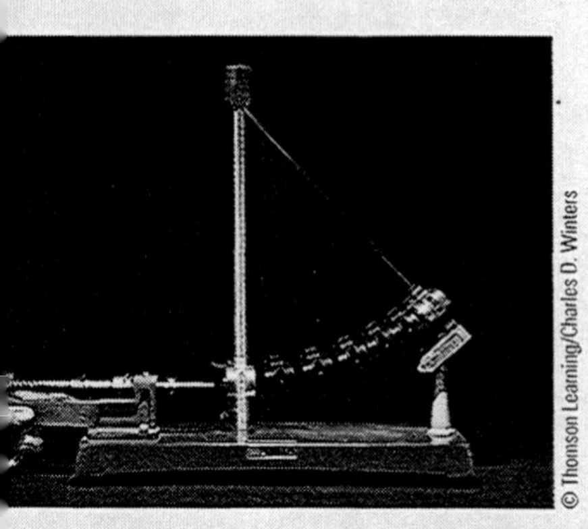

Acknowledgments

This seventh edition of *Physics for Scientists and Engineers* was prepared with the guidance and assistance of many professors who reviewed selections of the manuscript, the prerevision text, or both. We wish to acknowledge the following scholars and express our sincere appreciation for their suggestions, criticisms, and encouragement:

David P. Balogh, *Fresno City College*
Leonard X. Finegold, *Drexel University*
Raymond Hall, *California State University, Fresno*

Bob Jacobsen, *University of California, Berkeley*
Robin Jordan, *Florida Atlantic University*
Rafael Lopez-Mobilia, *University of Texas at San Antonio*
Diana Lininger Markham, *City College of San Francisco*
Steven Morris, *Los Angeles Harbor City College*
Taha Mzoughi, *Kennesaw State University*
Nobel Sanjay Rebello, *Kansas State University*
John Rosendahl, *University of California, Irvine*
Mikolaj Sawicki, *John A. Logan College*
Glenn B. Stracher, *East Georgia College*
Som Tyagi, *Drexel University*
Robert Weidman, *Michigan Technological University*
Edward A. Whittaker, *Stevens Institute of Technology*

This title was carefully checked for accuracy by Zinoviy Akkerman, *City College of New York;* Grant Hart, *Brigham Young University;* Michael Kotlarchyk, *Rochester Institute of Technology;* Andres LaRosa, *Portland State University;* Bruce Mason, *University of Oklahoma at Norman;* Peter Moeck, *Portland State University;* Brian A. Raue, *Florida International University;* James E. Rutledge, *University of California at Irvine;* Bjoern Seipel, *Portland State University;* Z. M. Stadnik, *University of Ottawa;* and Harry W. K. Tom, *University of California at Riverside.* We thank them for their diligent efforts under schedule pressure.

We are grateful to Ralph McGrew for organizing the end-of-chapter problems, writing many new problems, and suggesting improvements in the content of the textbook. Problems and questions new to this edition were written by Duane Deardorff, Thomas Grace, Francisco Izaguirre, John Jewett, Robert Forsythe, Randall Jones, Ralph McGrew, Kurt Vandervoort, and Jerzy Wrobel. Help was very kindly given by Dwight Neuenschwander, Michael Kinney, Amy Smith, Will Mackin, and the Sewer Department of Grand Forks, North Dakota. Daniel Kim, Jennifer Hoffman, Ed Oberhofer, Richard Webb, Wesley Smith, Kevin Kilty, Zinoviy Akkerman, Michael Rudmin, Paul Cox, Robert LaMontagne, Ken Menningen, and Chris Church made corrections to problems taken from previous editions. We are grateful to authors John R. Gordon and Ralph McGrew for preparing the *Student Solutions Manual/Study Guide.* Author Ralph McGrew has prepared an excellent *Instructor's Solutions Manual.* Edward Adelson has carefully edited and improved the test bank. Kurt Vandervoort prepared extra Quick Quiz questions for the instructor's companion Web site.

Special thanks and recognition go to the professional staff at the Brooks/Cole Publishing Company—in particular, Ed Dodd, Brandi Kirksey (who managed the ancillary program and so much more), Shawn Vasquez, Sam Subity, Teri Hyde, Michelle Julet, David Harris, and Chris Hall—for their fine work during the development and production of this textbook. Mark Santee is our seasoned marketing manager, and Bryan Vann coordinates our marketing communications. We recognize the skilled production service and excellent artwork provided by the staff at Lachina Publishing Services, and the dedicated photo research efforts of Jane Sanders Miller.

Finally, we are deeply indebted to our wives, children, and grandchildren for their love, support, and long-term sacrifices.

Raymond A. Serway
St. Petersburg, Florida

John W. Jewett, Jr.
Pomona, California

It is appropriate to offer some words of advice that should be of benefit to you, the student. Before doing so, we assume you have read the Preface, which describes the various features of the text and support materials that will help you through the course.

How to Study

Instructors are often asked, "How should I study physics and prepare for examinations?" There is no simple answer to this question, but we can offer some suggestions based on our own experiences in learning and teaching over the years.

First and foremost, maintain a positive attitude toward the subject matter, keeping in mind that physics is the most fundamental of all natural sciences. Other science courses that follow will use the same physical principles, so it is important that you understand and are able to apply the various concepts and theories discussed in the text.

Concepts and Principles

It is essential that you understand the basic concepts and principles before attempting to solve assigned problems. You can best accomplish this goal by carefully reading the textbook before you attend your lecture on the covered material. When reading the text, you should jot down those points that are not clear to you. Also be sure to make a diligent attempt at answering the questions in the Quick Quizzes as you come to them in your reading. We have worked hard to prepare questions that help you judge for yourself how well you understand the material. Study the **What If?** features that appear in many of the worked examples carefully. They will help you extend your understanding beyond the simple act of arriving at a numerical result. The Pitfall Preventions will also help guide you away from common misunderstandings about physics. During class, take careful notes and ask questions about those ideas that are unclear to you. Keep in mind that few people are able to absorb the full meaning of scientific material after only one reading; several readings of the text and your notes may be necessary. Your lectures and laboratory work supplement the textbook and should clarify some of the more difficult material. You should minimize your memorization of material. Successful memorization of passages from the text, equations, and derivations does not necessarily indicate that you understand the material. Your understanding of the material will be enhanced through a combination of efficient study habits, discussions with other students and with instructors, and your ability to solve the problems presented in the textbook. Ask questions whenever you believe that clarification of a concept is necessary.

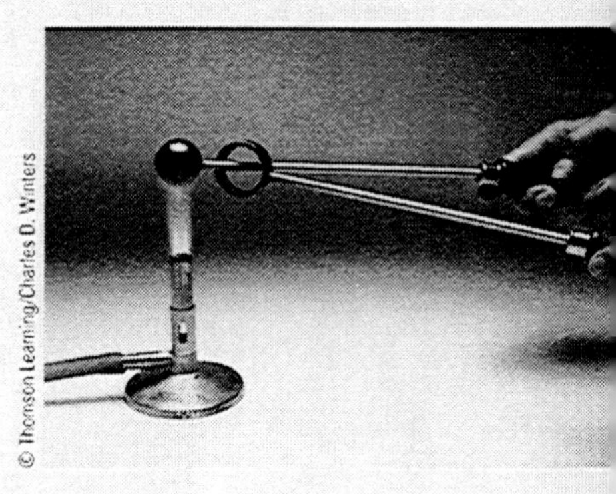

Study Schedule

It is important that you set up a regular study schedule, preferably a daily one. Make sure that you read the syllabus for the course and adhere to the schedule set by your instructor. The lectures will make much more sense if you read the corresponding text material *before* attending them. As a general rule, you should devote about two hours of study time for each hour you are in class. If you are having trouble with the course, seek the advice of the instructor or other students who have taken the course. You may find it necessary to seek further instruction from experienced students. Very often, instructors offer review sessions in addition to regular class periods. Avoid the practice of delaying study until a day or two before an exam. More often than not, this approach has disastrous results. Rather than undertake an all-night study session before a test, briefly review the basic concepts and equations, and then get a good night's rest. If you believe that you need additional help in understanding the concepts, in preparing for exams, or in problem solving, we suggest that you acquire a copy of the *Student Solutions Manual/Study Guide* that accompanies this textbook; this manual should be available at your college bookstore or through the publisher.

Use the Features

You should make full use of the various features of the text discussed in the Preface. For example, marginal notes are useful for locating and describing important equations and concepts, and **boldface** indicates important statements and definitions. Many useful tables are contained in the appendices, but most are incorporated in the text where they are most often referenced. Appendix B is a convenient review of mathematical tools used in the text.

Answers to odd-numbered problems are given at the end of the textbook, answers to Quick Quizzes are located at the end of each chapter, and solutions to selected end-of-chapter questions and problems are provided in the *Student Solutions Manual/Study Guide*. The table of contents provides an overview of the entire text, and the index enables you to locate specific material quickly. Footnotes are sometimes used to supplement the text or to cite other references on the subject discussed.

After reading a chapter, you should be able to define any new quantities introduced in that chapter and discuss the principles and assumptions that were used to arrive at certain key relations. The chapter summaries and the review sections of the *Student Solutions Manual/Study Guide* should help you in this regard. In some cases, you may find it necessary to refer to the textbook's index to locate certain topics. You should be able to associate with each physical quantity the correct symbol used to represent that quantity and the unit in which the quantity is specified. Furthermore, you should be able to express each important equation in concise and accurate prose.

Problem Solving

R. P. Feynman, Nobel laureate in physics, once said, "You do not know anything until you have practiced." In keeping with this statement, we strongly advise you to develop the skills necessary to solve a wide range of problems. Your ability to solve problems will be one of the main tests of your knowledge of physics; therefore, you should try to solve as many problems as possible. It is essential that you understand basic concepts and principles before attempting to solve problems. It is good practice to try to find alternate solutions to the same problem. For example, you can solve problems in mechanics using Newton's laws, but very often an alternative method that draws on energy considerations is more direct. You should not deceive yourself into thinking that you understand a problem merely because you have seen it solved in class. You must be able to solve the problem and similar problems on your own.

The approach to solving problems should be carefully planned. A systematic plan is especially important when a problem involves several concepts. First, read the problem several times until you are confident you understand what is being asked. Look for any key words that will help you interpret the problem and perhaps allow you to make certain assumptions. Your ability to interpret a question properly is an integral part of problem solving. Second, you should acquire the habit of writing down the information given in a problem and those quantities that need to be found; for example, you might construct a table listing both the quantities given and the quantities to be found. This procedure is sometimes used in the worked examples of the textbook. Finally, after you have decided on the method you believe is appropriate for a given problem, proceed with your solution. The General Problem-Solving Strategy will guide you through complex problems. If you follow the steps of this procedure *(Conceptualize, Categorize, Analyze, Finalize)*, you will find it easier to come up with a solution and gain more from your efforts. This Strategy, located at the end of Chapter 2, is used in all worked examples in the remaining chapters so that you can learn how to apply it. Specific problem-solving strategies for certain types of situations are included in the text and appear with a blue heading. These specific strategies follow the outline of the General Problem-Solving Strategy.

Often, students fail to recognize the limitations of certain equations or physical laws in a particular situation. It is very important that you understand and remember the assumptions that underlie a particular theory or formalism. For example, certain equations in kinematics apply only to a particle moving with constant acceleration. These equations are not valid for describing motion whose acceleration is not constant such as the motion of an object connected to a spring or the motion of an object through a fluid. Study the Analysis Models for Problem-Solving in the chapter summaries carefully so that you know how each model can be applied to a specific situation.

Experiments

Physics is a science based on experimental observations. Therefore, we recommend that you try to supplement the text by performing various types of "hands-on" experiments either at home or in the laboratory. These experiments can be used to test ideas and models discussed in class or in the textbook. For example, the common Slinky toy is excellent for studying traveling waves, a ball swinging on the end of a long string can be used to investigate pendulum motion, various masses attached to the end of a vertical spring or rubber band can be used to determine their elastic nature, an old pair of Polaroid sunglasses and some discarded lenses and a magnifying glass are the components of various experiments in optics, and an approximate measure of the free-fall acceleration can be determined simply by measuring with a stopwatch the time it takes for a ball to drop from a known height. The list of such experiments is endless. When physical models are not available, be imaginative and try to develop models of your own.

New Media

We strongly encourage you to use the **ThomsonNOW** Web-based learning system that accompanies this textbook. It is far easier to understand physics if you see it in action, and these new materials will enable you to become a part of that action. **ThomsonNOW** media described in the Preface and accessed at **www.thomsonedu.com/physics/serway** feature a three-step learning process consisting of a pre-test, a personalized learning plan, and a post-test.

It is our sincere hope that you will find physics an exciting and enjoyable experience and that you will benefit from this experience, regardless of your chosen profession. Welcome to the exciting world of physics!

The scientist does not study nature because it is useful; he studies it because he delights in it, and he delights in it because it is beautiful. If nature were not beautiful, it would not be worth knowing, and if nature were not worth knowing, life would not be worth living.

—Henri Poincaré

PART 2

Oscillations and Mechanical Waves

We begin this new part of the text by studying a special type of motion called *periodic* motion, the repeating motion of an object in which it continues to return to a given position after a fixed time interval. The repetitive movements of such an object are called *oscillations*. We will focus our attention on a special case of periodic motion called *simple harmonic motion*. All periodic motions can be modeled as combinations of simple harmonic motions.

Simple harmonic motion also forms the basis for our understanding of *mechanical waves*. Sound waves, seismic waves, waves on stretched strings, and water waves are all produced by some source of oscillation. As a sound wave travels through the air, elements of the air oscillate back and forth; as a water wave travels across a pond, elements of the water oscillate up and down and backward and forward. The motion of the elements of the medium bears a strong resemblance to the periodic motion of an oscillating pendulum or an object attached to a spring.

To explain many other phenomena in nature, we must understand the concepts of oscillations and waves. For instance, although skyscrapers and bridges appear to be rigid, they actually oscillate, something the architects and engineers who design and build them must take into account. To understand how radio and television work, we must understand the origin and nature of electromagnetic waves and how they propagate through space. Finally, much of what scientists have learned about atomic structure has come from information carried by waves. Therefore, we must first study oscillations and waves if we are to understand the concepts and theories of atomic physics.

Drops of water fall from a leaf into a pond. The disturbance caused by the falling water causes the water surface to oscillate. These oscillations are associated with waves moving away from the point at which the water fell. In Part 2 of the text, we will explore the principles related to oscillations and waves. (Don Bonsey/Getty Images)

To reduce swaying in tall buildings because of the wind, tuned dampers are placed near the top of the building. These mechanisms include an object of large mass that oscillates under computer control at the same frequency as the building, reducing the swaying. The large sphere in the photograph on the left is part of the tuned damper system of the building in the photograph on the right, called Taipei 101, in Taiwan. The building, also called the Taipei Financial Center, was completed in 2004, at which time it held the record as the world's tallest building. (left, Courtesy of Motioneering, Inc.; right, © Simon Kwang/Reuters/CORBIS)

15 Oscillatory Motion

Periodic motion **is motion of an object that regularly returns to a given position** after a fixed time interval. With a little thought, we can identify several types of periodic motion in everyday life. Your car returns to the driveway each afternoon. You return to the dinner table each night to eat. A bumped chandelier swings back and forth, returning to the same position at a regular rate. The Earth returns to the same position in its orbit around the Sun each year, resulting in the variation among the four seasons.

In addition to these everyday examples, numerous other systems exhibit periodic motion. The molecules in a solid oscillate about their equilibrium positions; electromagnetic waves, such as light waves, radar, and radio waves, are characterized by oscillating electric and magnetic field vectors; and in alternating-current electrical circuits, voltage, current, and electric charge vary periodically with time.

A special kind of periodic motion occurs in mechanical systems when the force acting on an object is proportional to the position of the object relative to some equilibrium position. If this force is always directed toward the equilibrium position, the motion is called *simple harmonic motion*, which is the primary focus of this chapter.

15.1 Motion of an Object Attached to a Spring

As a model for simple harmonic motion, consider a block of mass m attached to the end of a spring, with the block free to move on a horizontal, frictionless surface (Active Fig. 15.1). When the spring is neither stretched nor compressed, the block is at rest at the position called the **equilibrium position** of the system, which we identify as $x = 0$. We know from experience that such a system oscillates back and forth if disturbed from its equilibrium position.

We can understand the oscillating motion of the block in Active Figure 15.1 qualitatively by first recalling that when the block is displaced to a position x, the spring exerts on the block a force that is proportional to the position and given by **Hooke's law** (see Section 7.4):

$$F_s = -kx \quad (15.1)$$

◀ Hooke's law

We call F_s a **restoring force** because it is always directed toward the equilibrium position and therefore *opposite* the displacement of the block from equilibrium. That is, when the block is displaced to the right of $x = 0$ in Active Figure 15.1a, the position is positive and the restoring force is directed to the left. Figure 15.1b shows the block at $x = 0$, where the force on the block is zero. When the block is displaced to the left of $x = 0$ as in Figure 15.1c, the position is negative and the restoring force is directed to the right.

Applying Newton's second law to the motion of the block, with Equation 15.1 providing the net force in the x direction, we obtain

$$-kx = ma_x$$

$$a_x = -\frac{k}{m}x \quad (15.2)$$

That is, the acceleration of the block is proportional to its position, and the direction of the acceleration is opposite the direction of the displacement of the block from equilibrium. Systems that behave in this way are said to exhibit **simple harmonic motion.** An object moves with simple harmonic motion whenever its acceleration is proportional to its position and is oppositely directed to the displacement from equilibrium.

If the block in Active Figure 15.1 is displaced to a position $x = A$ and released from rest, its *initial* acceleration is $-kA/m$. When the block passes through the equilibrium position $x = 0$, its acceleration is zero. At this instant, its speed is a maximum because the acceleration changes sign. The block then continues to travel to the left of equilibrium with a positive acceleration and finally reaches $x = -A$, at which time its acceleration is $+kA/m$ and its speed is again zero as discussed in Sections 7.4 and 7.9. The block completes a full cycle of its motion by returning to the original position, again passing through $x = 0$ with maximum speed. Therefore,

PITFALL PREVENTION 15.1

The Orientation of the Spring

Active Figure 15.1 shows a *horizontal* spring, with an attached block sliding on a frictionless surface. Another possibility is a block hanging from a *vertical* spring. All the results we discuss for the horizontal spring are the same for the vertical spring with one exception: when the block is placed on the vertical spring, its weight causes the spring to extend. If the resting position of the block is defined as $x = 0$, the results of this chapter also apply to this vertical system.

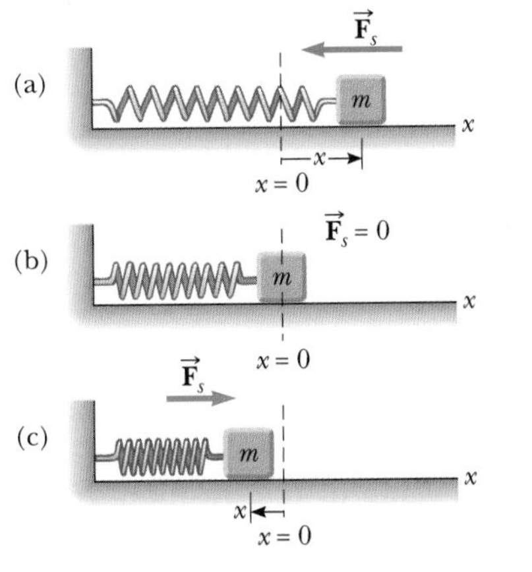

ACTIVE FIGURE 15.1

A block attached to a spring moving on a frictionless surface. (a) When the block is displaced to the right of equilibrium ($x > 0$), the force exerted by the spring acts to the left. (b) When the block is at its equilibrium position ($x = 0$), the force exerted by the spring is zero. (c) When the block is displaced to the left of equilibrium ($x < 0$), the force exerted by the spring acts to the right.

Sign in at www.thomsonedu.com and go to ThomsonNOW to choose the spring constant and the initial position and velocity of the block and see the resulting simple harmonic motion.

the block oscillates between the turning points $x = \pm A$. In the absence of friction, this idealized motion will continue forever because the force exerted by the spring is conservative. Real systems are generally subject to friction, so they do not oscillate forever. We shall explore the details of the situation with friction in Section 15.6.

Quick Quiz 15.1 A block on the end of a spring is pulled to position $x = A$ and released from rest. In one full cycle of its motion, through what total distance does it travel? (a) $A/2$ (b) A (c) $2A$ (d) $4A$

15.2 The Particle in Simple Harmonic Motion

The motion described in the preceding section occurs so often that we identify the **particle in simple harmonic motion** model to represent such situations. To develop a mathematical representation for this model, first recognize that the block is a particle under a net force as described in Equation 15.1. We will generally choose x as the axis along which the oscillation occurs; hence, we will drop the subscript-x notation in this discussion. Recall that, by definition, $a = dv/dt = d^2x/dt^2$, and so we can express Equation 15.2 as

$$\frac{d^2x}{dt^2} = -\frac{k}{m}x \qquad (15.3)$$

PITFALL PREVENTION 15.2
A Nonconstant Acceleration

The acceleration of a particle in simple harmonic motion is not constant. Equation 15.3 shows that its acceleration varies with position x. Therefore, we *cannot* apply the kinematic equations of Chapter 2 in this situation.

If we denote the ratio k/m with the symbol ω^2 (we choose ω^2 rather than ω so as to make the solution we develop below simpler in form), then

$$\omega^2 = \frac{k}{m} \qquad (15.4)$$

and Equation 15.3 can be written in the form

$$\frac{d^2x}{dt^2} = -\omega^2 x \qquad (15.5)$$

Let's now find a mathematical solution to Equation 15.5, that is, a function $x(t)$ that satisfies this second-order differential equation and is a mathematical representation of the position of the particle as a function of time. We seek a function whose second derivative is the same as the original function with a negative sign and multiplied by ω^2. The trigonometric functions sine and cosine exhibit this behavior, so we can build a solution around one or both of them. The following cosine function is a solution to the differential equation:

Position versus time for an object in simple harmonic motion ▶

$$x(t) = A\cos(\omega t + \phi) \qquad (15.6)$$

where A, ω, and ϕ are constants. To show explicitly that this solution satisfies Equation 15.5, notice that

$$\frac{dx}{dt} = A\frac{d}{dt}\cos(\omega t + \phi) = -\omega A\sin(\omega t + \phi) \qquad (15.7)$$

$$\frac{d^2x}{dt^2} = -\omega A\frac{d}{dt}\sin(\omega t + \phi) = -\omega^2 A\cos(\omega t + \phi) \qquad (15.8)$$

PITFALL PREVENTION 15.3
Where's the Triangle?

Equation 15.6 includes a trigonometric function, a *mathematical function* that can be used whether it refers to a triangle or not. In this case, the cosine function happens to have the correct behavior for representing the position of a particle in simple harmonic motion.

Comparing Equations 15.6 and 15.8, we see that $d^2x/dt^2 = -\omega^2 x$ and Equation 15.5 is satisfied.

The parameters A, ω, and ϕ are constants of the motion. To give physical significance to these constants, it is convenient to form a graphical representation of the motion by plotting x as a function of t as in Active Figure 15.2a. First, A, called the **amplitude** of the motion, is simply **the maximum value of the position of the particle in either the positive or negative x direction.** The constant ω is called the

angular frequency, and it has units[1] of rad/s. It is a measure of how rapidly the oscillations are occurring; the more oscillations per unit time, the higher the value of ω. From Equation 15.4, the angular frequency is

$$\omega = \sqrt{\frac{k}{m}} \qquad (15.9)$$

The constant angle ϕ is called the **phase constant** (or initial phase angle) and, along with the amplitude A, is determined uniquely by the position and velocity of the particle at $t = 0$. If the particle is at its maximum position $x = A$ at $t = 0$, the phase constant is $\phi = 0$ and the graphical representation of the motion is as shown in Active Figure 15.2b. The quantity $(\omega t + \phi)$ is called the **phase** of the motion. Notice that the function $x(t)$ is periodic and its value is the same each time ωt increases by 2π radians.

Equations 15.1, 15.5, and 15.6 form the basis of the mathematical representation of the particle in simple harmonic motion model. If you are analyzing a situation and find that the force on a particle is of the mathematical form of Equation 15.1, you know the motion is that of a simple harmonic oscillator and the position of the particle is described by Equation 15.6. If you analyze a system and find that it is described by a differential equation of the form of Equation 15.5, the motion is that of a simple harmonic oscillator. If you analyze a situation and find that the position of a particle is described by Equation 15.6, you know the particle undergoes simple harmonic motion.

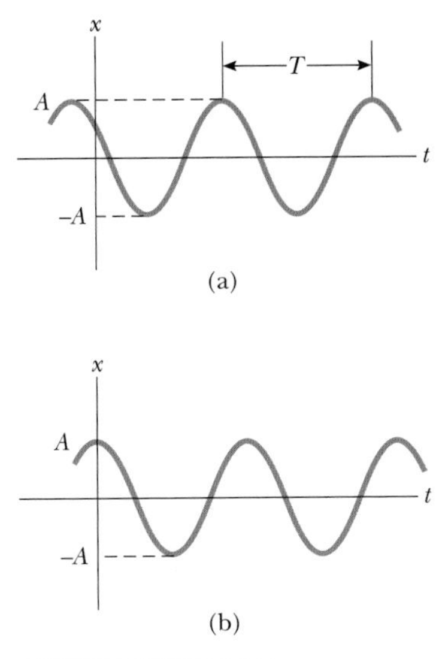

ACTIVE FIGURE 15.2

(a) An x–t graph for an object undergoing simple harmonic motion. The amplitude of the motion is A, the period (defined in Eq. 15.10) is T. (b) The x–t graph in the special case in which $x = A$ at $t = 0$ and hence $\phi = 0$.

Sign in at www.thomsonedu.com and go to ThomsonNOW to adjust the graphical representation and see the resulting simple harmonic motion of the block in Active Figure 15.1.

Quick Quiz 15.2 Consider a graphical representation (Fig. 15.3) of simple harmonic motion as described mathematically in Equation 15.6. When the object is at point Ⓐ on the graph, what can you say about its position and velocity? (a) The position and velocity are both positive. (b) The position and velocity are both negative. (c) The position is positive, and its velocity is zero. (d) The position is negative, and its velocity is zero. (e) The position is positive, and its velocity is negative. (f) The position is negative, and its velocity is positive.

Quick Quiz 15.3 Figure 15.4 shows two curves representing objects undergoing simple harmonic motion. The correct description of these two motions is that the simple harmonic motion of object B is (a) of larger angular frequency and larger amplitude than that of object A, (b) of larger angular frequency and smaller amplitude than that of object A, (c) of smaller angular frequency and larger amplitude than that of object A, or (d) of smaller angular frequency and smaller amplitude than that of object A.

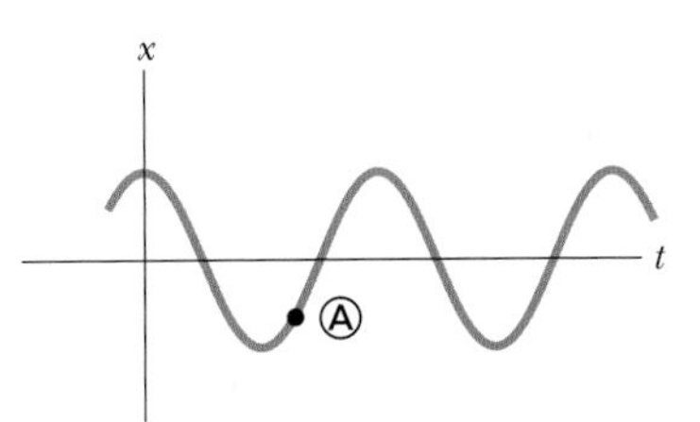

Figure 15.3 (Quick Quiz 15.2) An x–t graph for an object undergoing simple harmonic motion. At a particular time, the object's position is indicated by Ⓐ in the graph.

Let us investigate further the mathematical description of simple harmonic motion. The **period** T of the motion is the time interval required for the particle to go through one full cycle of its motion (Active Fig. 15.2a). That is, the values of x and v for the particle at time t equal the values of x and v at time $t + T$. Because the phase increases by 2π radians in a time interval of T,

$$[\omega(t + T) + \phi] - (\omega t + \phi) = 2\pi$$

Simplifying this expression gives $\omega T = 2\pi$, or

$$T = \frac{2\pi}{\omega} \qquad (15.10)$$

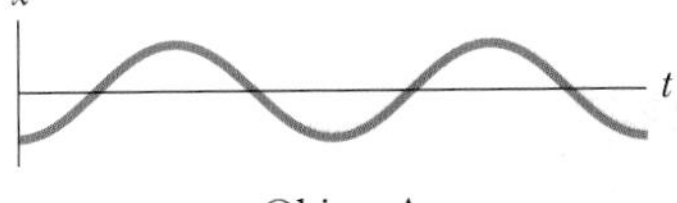

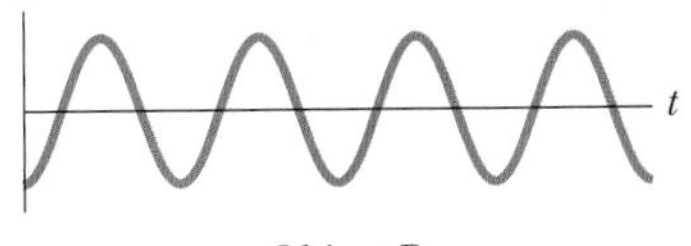

Object B

Figure 15.4 (Quick Quiz 15.3) Two x–t graphs for objects undergoing simple harmonic motion. The amplitudes and frequencies are different for the two objects.

[1] We have seen many examples in earlier chapters in which we evaluate a trigonometric function of an angle. The argument of a trigonometric function, such as sine or cosine, *must* be a pure number. The radian is a pure number because it is a ratio of lengths. Angles in degrees are pure numbers because the degree is an artificial "unit"; it is not related to measurements of lengths. The argument of the trigonometric function in Equation 15.6 must be a pure number. Therefore, ω *must* be expressed in rad/s (and not, for example, in revolutions per second) if t is expressed in seconds. Furthermore, other types of functions such as logarithms and exponential functions require arguments that are pure numbers.

PITFALL PREVENTION 15.4

Two Kinds of Frequency

We identify two kinds of frequency for a simple harmonic oscillator: f, called simply the *frequency*, is measured in hertz, and ω, the *angular frequency*, is measured in radians per second. Be sure you are clear about which frequency is being discussed or requested in a given problem. Equations 15.11 and 15.12 show the relationship between the two frequencies.

The inverse of the period is called the **frequency** f of the motion. Whereas the period is the time interval per oscillation, the frequency represents the **number of oscillations the particle undergoes per unit time interval:**

$$f = \frac{1}{T} = \frac{\omega}{2\pi} \tag{15.11}$$

The units of f are cycles per second, or **hertz** (Hz). Rearranging Equation 15.11 gives

$$\omega = 2\pi f = \frac{2\pi}{T} \tag{15.12}$$

Equations 15.9, 15.10, and 15.11 can be used to express the period and frequency of the motion for the particle in simple harmonic motion in terms of the characteristics m and k of the system as

Period ▶

$$T = \frac{2\pi}{\omega} = 2\pi\sqrt{\frac{m}{k}} \tag{15.13}$$

Frequency ▶

$$f = \frac{1}{T} = \frac{1}{2\pi}\sqrt{\frac{k}{m}} \tag{15.14}$$

That is, the period and frequency depend *only* on the mass of the particle and the force constant of the spring and *not* on the parameters of the motion, such as A or ϕ. As we might expect, the frequency is larger for a stiffer spring (larger value of k) and decreases with increasing mass of the particle.

We can obtain the velocity and acceleration[2] of a particle undergoing simple harmonic motion from Equations 15.7 and 15.8:

Velocity of an object in simple harmonic motion ▶

$$v = \frac{dx}{dt} = -\omega A \sin(\omega t + \phi) \tag{15.15}$$

Acceleration of an object in simple harmonic motion ▶

$$a = \frac{d^2x}{dt^2} = -\omega^2 A \cos(\omega t + \phi) \tag{15.16}$$

From Equation 15.15 we see that, because the sine and cosine functions oscillate between ± 1, the extreme values of the velocity v are $\pm\omega A$. Likewise, Equation 15.16 shows that the extreme values of the acceleration a are $\pm\omega^2 A$. Therefore, the *maximum* values of the magnitudes of the velocity and acceleration are

Maximum magnitudes of velocity and acceleration in simple harmonic motion ▶

$$v_{\text{max}} = \omega A = \sqrt{\frac{k}{m}}A \tag{15.17}$$

$$a_{\text{max}} = \omega^2 A = \frac{k}{m}A \tag{15.18}$$

Figure 15.5a plots position versus time for an arbitrary value of the phase constant. The associated velocity–time and acceleration–time curves are illustrated in Figures 15.5b and 15.5c. They show that the phase of the velocity differs from the phase of the position by $\pi/2$ rad, or 90°. That is, when x is a maximum or a minimum, the velocity is zero. Likewise, when x is zero, the speed is a maximum. Furthermore, notice that the phase of the acceleration differs from the phase of the position by π radians, or 180°. For example, when x is a maximum, a has a maximum magnitude in the opposite direction.

Quick Quiz 15.4 An object of mass m is hung from a spring and set into oscillation. The period of the oscillation is measured and recorded as T. The object of

[2] Because the motion of a simple harmonic oscillator takes place in one dimension, we denote velocity as v and acceleration as a, with the direction indicated by a positive or negative sign as in Chapter 2.

mass m is removed and replaced with an object of mass $2m$. When this object is set into oscillation, what is the period of the motion? (a) $2T$ (b) $\sqrt{2}T$ (c) T (d) $T/\sqrt{2}$ (e) $T/2$

Equation 15.6 describes simple harmonic motion of a particle in general. Let's now see how to evaluate the constants of the motion. The angular frequency ω is evaluated using Equation 15.9. The constants A and ϕ are evaluated from the initial conditions, that is, the state of the oscillator at $t = 0$.

Suppose the particle is set into motion by pulling it from equilibrium by a distance A and releasing it from rest at $t = 0$ as in Active Figure 15.6. We must then require our solutions for $x(t)$ and $v(t)$ (Eqs. 15.6 and 15.15) to obey the initial conditions that $x(0) = A$ and $v(0) = 0$:

$$x(0) = A\cos\phi = A$$

$$v(0) = -\omega A\sin\phi = 0$$

These conditions are met if $\phi = 0$, giving $x = A\cos\omega t$ as our solution. To check this solution, notice that it satisfies the condition that $x(0) = A$ because $\cos 0 = 1$.

The position, velocity, and acceleration versus time are plotted in Figure 15.7a for this special case. The acceleration reaches extreme values of $\mp\omega^2 A$ when the position has extreme values of $\pm A$. Furthermore, the velocity has extreme values of $\pm\omega A$, which both occur at $x = 0$. Hence, the quantitative solution agrees with our qualitative description of this system.

Let's consider another possibility. Suppose the system is oscillating and we define $t = 0$ as the instant the particle passes through the unstretched position of the spring while moving to the right (Active Fig. 15.8). In this case, our solutions for $x(t)$ and $v(t)$ must obey the initial conditions that $x(0) = 0$ and $v(0) = v_i$:

$$x(0) = A\cos\phi = 0$$

$$v(0) = -\omega A\sin\phi = v_i$$

The first of these conditions tells us that $\phi = \pm\pi/2$. With these choices for ϕ, the second condition tells us that $A = \mp v_i/\omega$. Because the initial velocity is positive and the amplitude must be positive, we must have $\phi = -\pi/2$. Hence, the solution is

$$x = \frac{v_i}{\omega}\cos\left(\omega t - \frac{\pi}{2}\right)$$

The graphs of position, velocity, and acceleration versus time for this choice of $t = 0$ are shown in Figure 15.7b. Notice that these curves are the same as those in Figure 15.7a, but shifted to the right by one fourth of a cycle. This shift is described mathematically by the phase constant $\phi = -\pi/2$, which is one fourth of a full cycle of 2π.

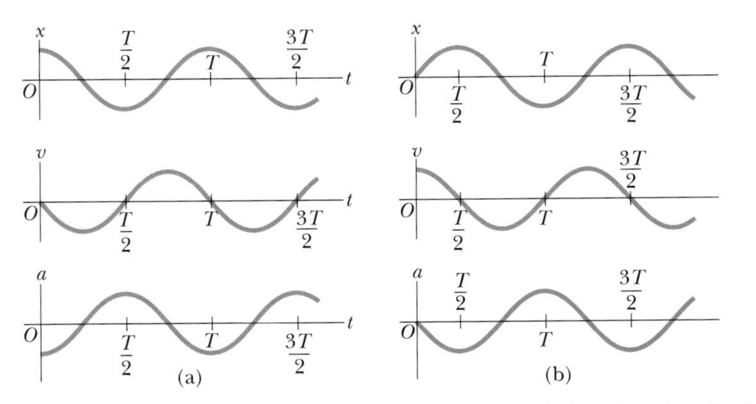

Figure 15.7 (a) Position, velocity, and acceleration versus time for a block undergoing simple harmonic motion under the initial conditions that at $t = 0$, $x(0) = A$ and $v(0) = 0$. (b) Position, velocity, and acceleration versus time for a block undergoing simple harmonic motion under the initial conditions that at $t = 0$, $x(0) = 0$ and $v(0) = v_i$.

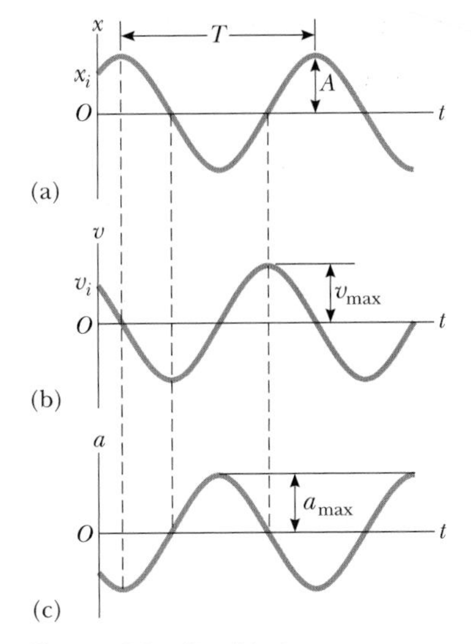

Figure 15.5 Graphical representation of simple harmonic motion. (a) Position versus time. (b) Velocity versus time. (c) Acceleration versus time. Notice that at any specified time the velocity is 90° out of phase with the position and the acceleration is 180° out of phase with the position.

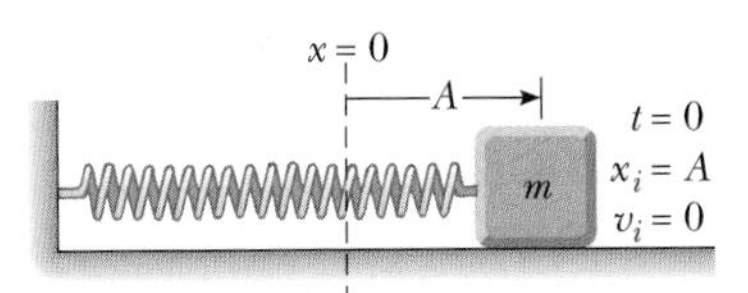

ACTIVE FIGURE 15.6

A block-spring system that begins its motion from rest with the block at $x = A$ at $t = 0$. In this case, $\phi = 0$; therefore, $x = A\cos\omega t$.

Sign in at www.thomsonedu.com and go to ThomsonNOW to compare the oscillations of two blocks starting from different initial positions and see that the frequency is independent of the amplitude.

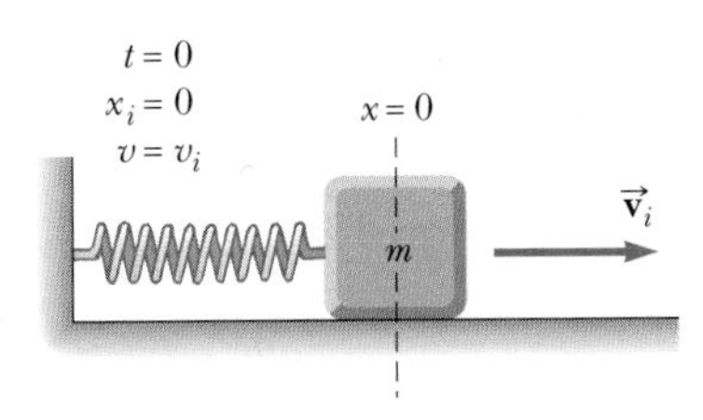

ACTIVE FIGURE 15.8

The block–spring system is undergoing oscillation, and $t = 0$ is defined at an instant when the block passes through the equilibrium position $x = 0$ and is moving to the right with speed v_i.

Sign in at www.thomsonedu.com and go to ThomsonNOW to compare the oscillations of two blocks with different velocities at $t = 0$ and see that the frequency is independent of the amplitude.

EXAMPLE 15.1 A Block-Spring System

A 200-g block connected to a light spring for which the force constant is 5.00 N/m is free to oscillate on a horizontal, frictionless surface. The block is displaced 5.00 cm from equilibrium and released from rest as in Active Figure 15.6.

(A) Find the period of its motion.

SOLUTION

Conceptualize Study Active Figure 15.6 and imagine the block moving back and forth in simple harmonic motion once it is released. Set up an experimental model in the vertical direction by hanging a heavy object such as a stapler from a strong rubber band.

Categorize The block is modeled as a particle in simple harmonic motion. We find values from equations developed in this section for the particle in simple harmonic motion model, so we categorize this example as a substitution problem.

Use Equation 15.9 to find the angular frequency of the block-spring system:

$$\omega = \sqrt{\frac{k}{m}} = \sqrt{\frac{5.00 \text{ N/m}}{200 \times 10^{-3} \text{ kg}}} = 5.00 \text{ rad/s}$$

Use Equation 15.13 to find the period of the system:

$$T = \frac{2\pi}{\omega} = \frac{2\pi}{5.00 \text{ rad/s}} = 1.26 \text{ s}$$

(B) Determine the maximum speed of the block.

SOLUTION

Use Equation 15.17 to find v_{max}:

$$v_{max} = \omega A = (5.00 \text{ rad/s})(5.00 \times 10^{-2} \text{ m}) = 0.250 \text{ m/s}$$

(C) What is the maximum acceleration of the block?

SOLUTION

Use Equation 15.18 to find a_{max}:

$$a_{max} = \omega^2 A = (5.00 \text{ rad/s})^2(5.00 \times 10^{-2} \text{ m}) = 1.25 \text{ m/s}^2$$

(D) Express the position, velocity, and acceleration as functions of time.

SOLUTION

Find the phase constant from the initial condition that $x = A$ at $t = 0$:

$$x(0) = A \cos \phi = A \quad \rightarrow \quad \phi = 0$$

Use Equation 15.6 to write an expression for $x(t)$:

$$x = A \cos (\omega t + \phi) = (0.050\,0 \text{ m}) \cos 5.00t$$

Use Equation 15.15 to write an expression for $v(t)$:

$$v = -\omega A \sin (\omega t + \phi) = -(0.250 \text{ m/s}) \sin 5.00t$$

Use Equation 15.16 to write an expression for $a(t)$:

$$a = -\omega^2 A \cos (\omega t + \phi) = -(1.25 \text{ m/s}^2) \cos 5.00t$$

What If? What if the block were released from the same initial position, $x_i = 5.00$ cm, but with an initial velocity of $v_i = -0.100$ m/s? Which parts of the solution change and what are the new answers for those that do change?

Answers Part (A) does not change because the period is independent of how the oscillator is set into motion. Parts (B), (C), and (D) will change.

Write position and velocity expressions for the initial conditions:

$$(1) \quad x(0) = A \cos \phi = x_i$$

$$(2) \quad v(0) = -\omega A \sin \phi = v_i$$

Divide Equation (2) by Equation (1) to find the phase constant:

$$\frac{-\omega A \sin \phi}{A \cos \phi} = \frac{v_i}{x_i}$$

$$\tan \phi = -\frac{v_i}{\omega x_i} = -\frac{-0.100 \text{ m/s}}{(5.00 \text{ rad/s})(0.050\,0 \text{ m})} = 0.400$$

$$\phi = 0.127\pi$$

Use Equation (1) to find A:

$$A = \frac{x_i}{\cos \phi} = \frac{0.050\,0 \text{ m}}{\cos (0.127\pi)} = 0.054\,3 \text{ m}$$

Find the new maximum speed:

$$v_{\max} = \omega A = (5.00 \text{ rad/s})(5.43 \times 10^{-2} \text{ m}) = 0.271 \text{ m/s}$$

Find the new magnitude of the maximum acceleration:

$$a_{\max} = \omega^2 A = (5.00 \text{ rad/s})^2 (5.43 \times 10^{-2} \text{ m}) = 1.36 \text{ m/s}^2$$

Find new expressions for position, velocity, and acceleration:

$$x = (0.054\,3 \text{ m}) \cos (5.00t + 0.127\pi)$$

$$v = -(0.271 \text{ m/s}) \sin (5.00t + 0.127\pi)$$

$$a = -(1.36 \text{ m/s}^2) \cos (5.00t + 0.127\pi)$$

As we saw in Chapters 7 and 8, many problems are easier to solve using an energy approach rather than one based on variables of motion. This particular **What If?** is easier to solve from an energy approach. Therefore, we shall investigate the energy of the simple harmonic oscillator in the next section.

EXAMPLE 15.2 Watch Out for Potholes!

A car with a mass of 1 300 kg is constructed so that its frame is supported by four springs. Each spring has a force constant of 20 000 N/m. Two people riding in the car have a combined mass of 160 kg. Find the frequency of vibration of the car after it is driven over a pothole in the road.

SOLUTION

Conceptualize Think about your experiences with automobiles. When you sit in a car, it moves downward a small distance because your weight is compressing the springs further. If you push down on the front bumper and release it, the front of the car oscillates a few times.

Categorize We imagine the car as being supported by a single spring and model the car as a particle in simple harmonic motion.

Analyze First, let's determine the effective spring constant of the four springs combined. For a given extension x of the springs, the combined force on the car is the sum of the forces from the individual springs.

Find an expression for the total force on the car:

$$F_{\text{total}} = \sum (-kx) = -\left(\sum k\right)x$$

In this expression, x has been factored from the sum because it is the same for all four springs. The effective spring constant for the combined springs is the sum of the individual spring constants.

Evaluate the effective spring constant:

$$k_{\text{eff}} = \sum k = 4 \times 20\,000 \text{ N/m} = 80\,000 \text{ N/m}$$

Use Equation 15.14 to find the frequency of vibration:

$$f = \frac{1}{2\pi}\sqrt{\frac{k_{\text{eff}}}{m}} = \frac{1}{2\pi}\sqrt{\frac{80\,000 \text{ N/m}}{1\,460 \text{ kg}}} = 1.18 \text{ Hz}$$

Finalize The mass we used here is that of the car plus the people because that is the total mass that is oscillating. Also notice that we have explored only up-and-down motion of the car. If an oscillation is established in which the car rocks back and forth such that the front end goes up when the back end goes down, the frequency will be different.

What If? Suppose the car stops on the side of the road and the two people exit the car. One of them pushes downward on the car and releases it so that it oscillates vertically. Is the frequency of the oscillation the same as the value we just calculated?

Answer The suspension system of the car is the same, but the mass that is oscillating is smaller: it no longer includes the mass of the two people. Therefore, the frequency should be higher. Let's calculate the new frequency taking the mass to be 1 300 kg:

$$f = \frac{1}{2\pi}\sqrt{\frac{k_{\text{eff}}}{m}} = \frac{1}{2\pi}\sqrt{\frac{80\,000\text{ N/m}}{1\,300\text{ kg}}} = 1.25\text{ Hz}$$

As predicted, the new frequency is a bit higher.

15.3 Energy of the Simple Harmonic Oscillator

Let us examine the mechanical energy of the block-spring system illustrated in Active Figure 15.1. Because the surface is frictionless, the system is isolated and we expect the total mechanical energy of the system to be constant. We assume a massless spring, so the kinetic energy of the system corresponds only to that of the block. We can use Equation 15.15 to express the kinetic energy of the block as

Kinetic energy of a simple harmonic oscillator ▶

$$K = \tfrac{1}{2}mv^2 = \tfrac{1}{2}m\omega^2 A^2 \sin^2(\omega t + \phi) \qquad \textbf{(15.19)}$$

The elastic potential energy stored in the spring for any elongation x is given by $\frac{1}{2}kx^2$ (see Eq. 7.22). Using Equation 15.6 gives

Potential energy of a simple harmonic oscillator ▶

$$U = \tfrac{1}{2}kx^2 = \tfrac{1}{2}kA^2 \cos^2(\omega t + \phi) \qquad \textbf{(15.20)}$$

We see that K and U are *always* positive quantities or zero. Because $\omega^2 = k/m$, we can express the total mechanical energy of the simple harmonic oscillator as

$$E = K + U = \tfrac{1}{2}kA^2[\sin^2(\omega t + \phi) + \cos^2(\omega t + \phi)]$$

From the identity $\sin^2\theta + \cos^2\theta = 1$, we see that the quantity in square brackets is unity. Therefore, this equation reduces to

Total energy of a simple harmonic oscillator ▶

$$E = \tfrac{1}{2}kA^2 \qquad \textbf{(15.21)}$$

That is, **the total mechanical energy of a simple harmonic oscillator is a constant of the motion and is proportional to the square of the amplitude.** The total mechanical energy is equal to the maximum potential energy stored in the spring when $x = \pm A$ because $v = 0$ at these points and there is no kinetic energy. At the equilibrium position, where $U = 0$ because $x = 0$, the total energy, all in the form of kinetic energy, is again $\frac{1}{2}kA^2$.

Plots of the kinetic and potential energies versus time appear in Active Figure 15.9a, where we have taken $\phi = 0$. At all times, the sum of the kinetic and potential energies is a constant equal to $\frac{1}{2}kA^2$, the total energy of the system.

The variations of K and U with the position x of the block are plotted in Active Figure 15.9b. Energy is continuously being transformed between potential energy stored in the spring and kinetic energy of the block.

Active Figure 15.10 illustrates the position, velocity, acceleration, kinetic energy, and potential energy of the block-spring system for one full period of the motion. Most of the ideas discussed so far are incorporated in this important figure. Study it carefully.

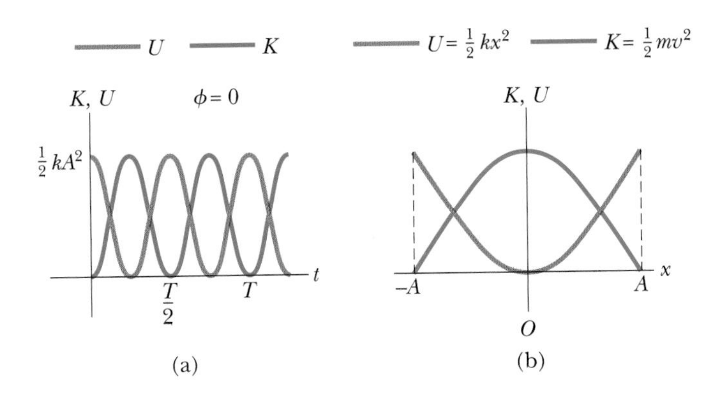

ACTIVE FIGURE 15.9

(a) Kinetic energy and potential energy versus time for a simple harmonic oscillator with $\phi = 0$. (b) Kinetic energy and potential energy versus position for a simple harmonic oscillator. In either plot, notice that $K + U =$ constant.

Sign in at www.thomsonedu.com and go to ThomsonNOW to compare the physical oscillation of a block with energy graphs in this figure as well as with energy bar graphs.

Finally, we can obtain the velocity of the block at an arbitrary position by expressing the total energy of the system at some arbitrary position x as

$$E = K + U = \tfrac{1}{2}mv^2 + \tfrac{1}{2}kx^2 = \tfrac{1}{2}kA^2$$

$$v = \pm\sqrt{\frac{k}{m}(A^2 - x^2)} = \pm\,\omega\sqrt{A^2 - x^2} \qquad \textbf{(15.22)}$$

◀ Velocity as a function of position for a simple harmonic oscillator

When you check Equation 15.22 to see whether it agrees with known cases, you find that it verifies that the speed is a maximum at $x = 0$ and is zero at the turning points $x = \pm A$.

You may wonder why we are spending so much time studying simple harmonic oscillators. We do so because they are good models of a wide variety of physical phenomena. For example, recall the Lennard–Jones potential discussed in Example 7.9. This complicated function describes the forces holding atoms together. Figure 15.11a (page 428) shows that for small displacements from the equilibrium position, the potential energy curve for this function approximates a parabola, which represents the potential energy function for a simple harmonic oscillator. Therefore, we can model the complex atomic binding forces as being due to tiny springs as depicted in Figure 15.11b.

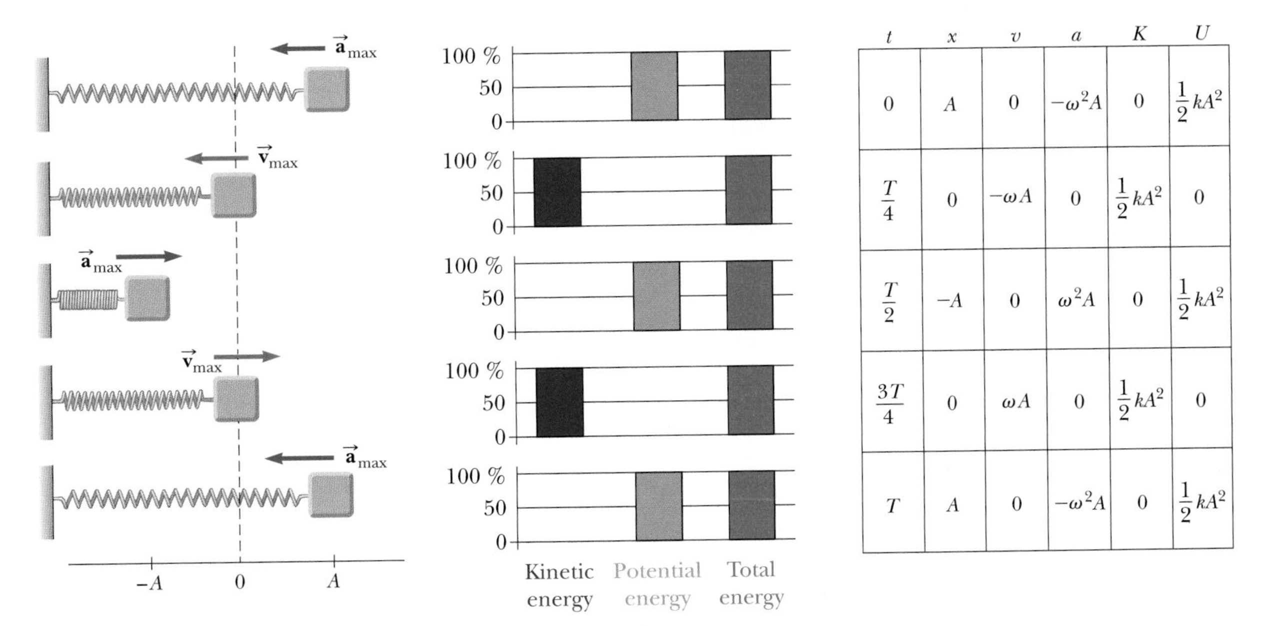

t	x	v	a	K	U
0	A	0	$-\omega^2 A$	0	$\frac{1}{2}kA^2$
$\frac{T}{4}$	0	$-\omega A$	0	$\frac{1}{2}kA^2$	0
$\frac{T}{2}$	$-A$	0	$\omega^2 A$	0	$\frac{1}{2}kA^2$
$\frac{3T}{4}$	0	ωA	0	$\frac{1}{2}kA^2$	0
T	A	0	$-\omega^2 A$	0	$\frac{1}{2}kA^2$

ACTIVE FIGURE 15.10

Several instants in the simple harmonic motion for a block–spring system. Energy bar graphs show the distribution of the energy of the system at each instant. The parameters in the table at the right refer to the block–spring system, assuming that at $t = 0$, $x = A$; hence, $x = A \cos \omega t$.

Sign in at www.thomsonedu.com and go to ThomsonNOW to set the initial position of the block and see the block–spring system and the analogous energy bar graphs.

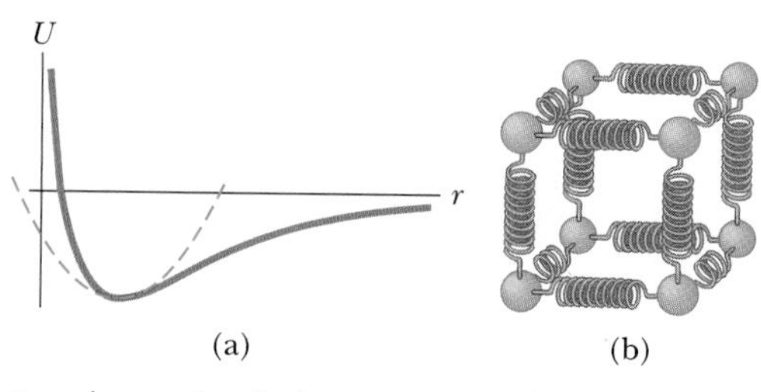

Figure 15.11 (a) If the atoms in a molecule do not move too far from their equilibrium positions, a graph of potential energy versus separation distance between atoms is similar to the graph of potential energy versus position for a simple harmonic oscillator (dashed blue curve). (b) The forces between atoms in a solid can be modeled by imagining springs between neighboring atoms.

The ideas presented in this chapter apply not only to block-spring systems and atoms, but also to a wide range of situations that include bungee jumping, tuning in a television station, and viewing the light emitted by a laser. You will see more examples of simple harmonic oscillators as you work through this book.

EXAMPLE 15.3 Oscillations on a Horizontal Surface

A 0.500-kg cart connected to a light spring for which the force constant is 20.0 N/m oscillates on a horizontal, frictionless air track.

(A) Calculate the total energy of the system and the maximum speed of the cart if the amplitude of the motion is 3.00 cm.

SOLUTION

Conceptualize The system oscillates in exactly the same way as the block in Active Figure 15.10.

Categorize The cart is modeled as a particle in simple harmonic motion.

Analyze Use Equation 15.21 to find the energy of the oscillator:

$$E = \frac{1}{2}kA^2 = \frac{1}{2}(20.0\ \text{N/m})(3.00 \times 10^{-2}\ \text{m})^2$$
$$= 9.00 \times 10^{-3}\ \text{J}$$

When the cart is at $x = 0$, the energy of the oscillator is entirely kinetic, so set $E = \frac{1}{2}mv_{\text{max}}^2$:

$$\frac{1}{2}mv_{\text{max}}^2 = 9.00 \times 10^{-3}\ \text{J}$$

Solve for the maximum speed:

$$v_{\text{max}} = \sqrt{\frac{2(9.00 \times 10^{-3}\ \text{J})}{0.500\ \text{kg}}} = 0.190\ \text{m/s}$$

(B) What is the velocity of the cart when the position is 2.00 cm?

SOLUTION

Use Equation 15.22 to evaluate the velocity:

$$v = \pm\sqrt{\frac{k}{m}(A^2 - x^2)}$$
$$= \pm\sqrt{\frac{20.0\ \text{N/m}}{0.500\ \text{kg}}[(0.030\,0\ \text{m})^2 - (0.020\,0\ \text{m})^2]}$$
$$= \pm 0.141\ \text{m/s}$$

The positive and negative signs indicate that the cart could be moving to either the right or the left at this instant.

(C) Compute the kinetic and potential energies of the system when the position is 2.00 cm.

SOLUTION

Use the result of part (B) to evaluate the kinetic energy at $x = 0.020\ 0$ m:

$$K = \tfrac{1}{2}mv^2 = \tfrac{1}{2}(0.500\text{ kg})(0.141\text{ m/s})^2 = 5.00 \times 10^{-3}\text{ J}$$

Evaluate the elastic potential energy at $x = 0.020\ 0$ m:

$$U = \tfrac{1}{2}kx^2 = \tfrac{1}{2}(20.0\text{ N/m})(0.0200\text{ m})^2 = 4.00 \times 10^{-3}\text{ J}$$

Finalize Notice that the sum of the kinetic and potential energies in part (C) is equal to the total energy found in part (A). That must be true for *any* position of the cart.

What If? The cart in this example could have been set into motion by releasing the cart from rest at $x = 3.00$ cm. What if the cart were released from the same position, but with an initial velocity of $v = -0.100$ m/s? What are the new amplitude and maximum speed of the cart?

Answer This question is of the same type we asked at the end of Example 15.1, but here we apply an energy approach.

First calculate the total energy of the system at $t = 0$:

$$E = \tfrac{1}{2}mv^2 + \tfrac{1}{2}kx^2$$

$$= \tfrac{1}{2}(0.500\text{ kg})(-0.100\text{ m/s})^2 + \tfrac{1}{2}(20.0\text{ N/m})(0.030\ 0\text{ m})^2$$

$$= 1.15 \times 10^{-2}\text{ J}$$

Equate this total energy to the potential energy when the cart is at the end point of the motion:

$$E = \tfrac{1}{2}kA^2$$

Solve for the amplitude A:

$$A = \sqrt{\frac{2E}{k}} = \sqrt{\frac{2(1.15 \times 10^{-2}\text{ J})}{20.0\text{ N/m}}} = 0.033\ 9\text{ m}$$

Find the new maximum speed by equating the total energy to the kinetic energy when the cart is at the equilibrium position:

$$E = \tfrac{1}{2}mv_{\text{max}}^2$$

Solve for the maximum speed:

$$v_{\text{max}} = \sqrt{\frac{2E}{m}} = \sqrt{\frac{2(1.15 \times 10^{-2}\text{ J})}{0.500\text{ kg}}} = 0.214\text{ m/s}$$

The amplitude and maximum velocity are larger than the previous values because the cart was given an initial velocity at $t = 0$.

15.4 Comparing Simple Harmonic Motion with Uniform Circular Motion

Some common devices in our everyday life exhibit a relationship between oscillatory motion and circular motion. For example, the pistons in an automobile engine (Fig. 15.12a, page 430) go up and down—oscillatory motion—yet the net result of this motion is circular motion of the wheels. In an old-fashioned locomotive (Fig. 15.12b), the drive shaft goes back and forth in oscillatory motion, causing a circular motion of the wheels. In this section, we explore this interesting relationship between these two types of motion.

Active Figure 15.13 (page 430) is a view of an experimental arrangement that shows this relationship. A ball is attached to the rim of a turntable of radius A, which is illuminated from the side by a lamp. The ball casts a shadow on a screen. **As the turntable rotates with constant angular speed, the shadow of the ball moves back and forth in simple harmonic motion.**

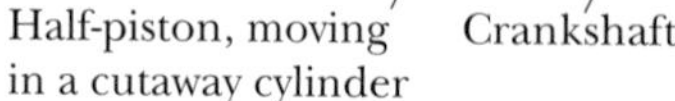

Figure 15.12 (*Left*) The pistons of an automobile engine move in periodic motion along a single dimension as shown in this cutaway view of two of these pistons. This motion is converted to circular motion of the crankshaft, at the lower right, and ultimately of the wheels of the automobile. (*Right*) The back-and-forth motion of pistons (in the curved housing at the left) in an old-fashioned locomotive is converted to circular motion of the wheels.

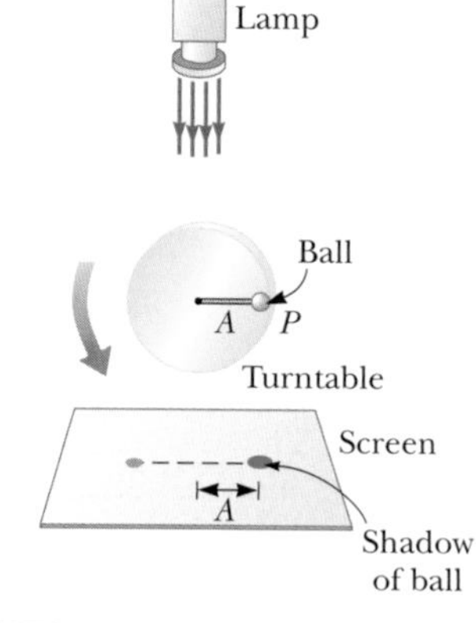

ACTIVE FIGURE 15.13

An experimental setup for demonstrating the connection between simple harmonic motion and uniform circular motion. As the ball rotates on the turntable with constant angular speed, its shadow on the screen moves back and forth in simple harmonic motion.

Sign in at www.thomsonedu.com and go to ThomsonNOW to adjust the frequency and radial position of the ball and see the resulting simple harmonic motion of the shadow.

Consider a particle located at point P on the circumference of a circle of radius A as in Figure 15.14a, with the line OP making an angle ϕ with the x axis at $t = 0$. We call this circle a *reference circle* for comparing simple harmonic motion with uniform circular motion, and we choose the position of P at $t = 0$ as our reference position. If the particle moves along the circle with constant angular speed ω until OP makes an angle θ with the x axis as in Figure 15.14b, at some time $t > 0$ the angle between OP and the x axis is $\theta = \omega t + \phi$. As the particle moves along the circle, the projection of P on the x axis, labeled point Q, moves back and forth along the x axis between the limits $x = \pm A$.

Notice that points P and Q always have the same x coordinate. From the right triangle OPQ, we see that this x coordinate is

$$x(t) = A \cos (\omega t + \phi) \qquad \textbf{(15.23)}$$

This expression is the same as Equation 15.6 and shows that the point Q moves with simple harmonic motion along the x axis. Therefore, **simple harmonic motion along a straight line can be represented by the projection of uniform circular motion along a diameter of a reference circle.**

This geometric interpretation shows that the time interval for one complete revolution of the point P on the reference circle is equal to the period of motion T for simple harmonic motion between $x = \pm A$. That is, the angular speed ω of P is the same as the angular frequency ω of simple harmonic motion along the x axis

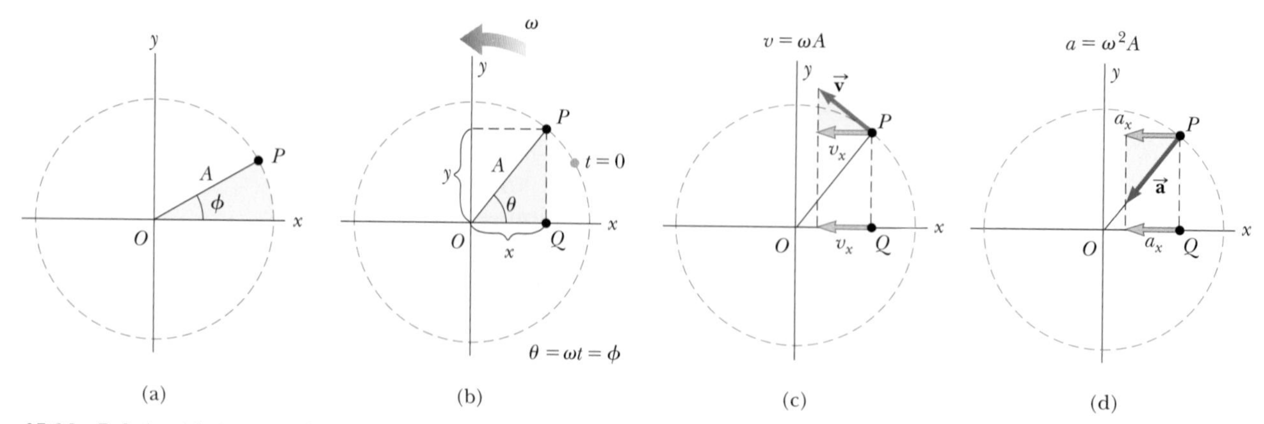

Figure 15.14 Relationship between the uniform circular motion of a point P and the simple harmonic motion of a point Q. A particle at P moves in a circle of radius A with constant angular speed ω. (a) A reference circle showing the position of P at $t = 0$. (b) The x coordinates of points P and Q are equal and vary in time according to the expression $x = A \cos (\omega t + \phi)$. (c) The x component of the velocity of P equals the velocity of Q. (d) The x component of the acceleration of P equals the acceleration of Q.

(which is why we use the same symbol). The phase constant ϕ for simple harmonic motion corresponds to the initial angle OP makes with the x axis. The radius A of the reference circle equals the amplitude of the simple harmonic motion.

Because the relationship between linear and angular speed for circular motion is $v = r\omega$ (see Eq. 10.10), the particle moving on the reference circle of radius A has a velocity of magnitude ωA. From the geometry in Figure 15.14c, we see that the x component of this velocity is $-\omega A \sin(\omega t + \phi)$. By definition, point Q has a velocity given by dx/dt. Differentiating Equation 15.23 with respect to time, we find that the velocity of Q is the same as the x component of the velocity of P.

The acceleration of P on the reference circle is directed radially inward toward O and has a magnitude $v^2/A = \omega^2 A$. From the geometry in Figure 15.14d, we see that the x component of this acceleration is $-\omega^2 A \cos(\omega t + \phi)$. This value is also the acceleration of the projected point Q along the x axis, as you can verify by taking the second derivative of Equation 15.23.

Quick Quiz 15.5 Figure 15.15 shows the position of an object in uniform circular motion at $t = 0$. A light shines from above and projects a shadow of the object on a screen below the circular motion. What are the correct values for the *amplitude* and *phase constant* (relative to an x axis to the right) of the simple harmonic motion of the shadow? (a) 0.50 m and 0 (b) 1.00 m and 0 (c) 0.50 m and π (d) 1.00 m and π

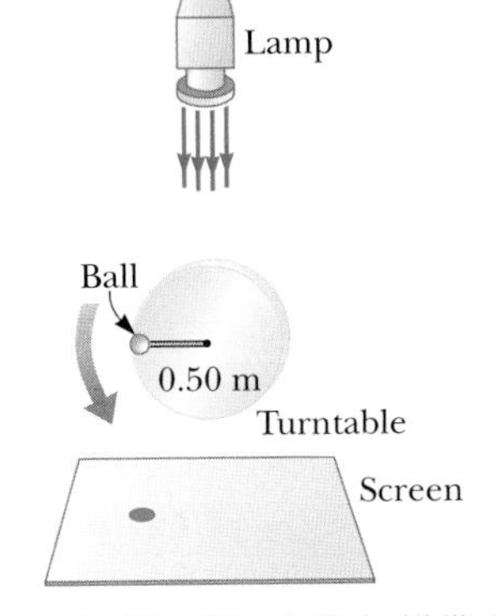

Figure 15.15 (Quick Quiz 15.5) An object moves in circular motion, casting a shadow on the screen below. Its position at an instant of time is shown.

EXAMPLE 15.4 Circular Motion with Constant Angular Speed

A particle rotates counterclockwise in a circle of radius 3.00 m with a constant angular speed of 8.00 rad/s. At $t = 0$, the particle has an x coordinate of 2.00 m and is moving to the right.

(A) Determine the x coordinate of the particle as a function of time.

SOLUTION

Conceptualize Be sure you understand the relationship between circular motion of a particle and simple harmonic motion of its shadow as described in Active Figure 15.13.

Categorize The particle on the circle is a particle under constant angular speed. The shadow is a particle in simple harmonic motion.

Analyze Use Equation 15.23 to write an expression for the x coordinate of the rotating particle with $\omega = 8.00$ rad/s:

$$x = A\cos(\omega t + \phi) = (3.00\text{ m})\cos(8.00t + \phi)$$

Evaluate ϕ by using the initial condition $x = 2.00$ m at $t = 0$:

$$2.00\text{ m} = (3.00\text{ m})\cos(0 + \phi)$$

Solve for ϕ:

$$\phi = \cos^{-1}\left(\frac{2.00\text{ m}}{3.00\text{ m}}\right) = \cos^{-1}(0.667) = \pm 48.2° = \pm 0.841\text{ rad}$$

If we were to take $\phi = +0.841$ rad as our answer, the particle would be moving to the left at $t = 0$. Because the particle is moving to the right at $t = 0$, we must choose $\phi = -0.841$ rad.

Write the x coordinate as a function of time:

$$x = (3.00\text{ m})\cos(8.00t - 0.841)$$

(B) Find the x components of the particle's velocity and acceleration at any time t.

SOLUTION

Differentiate the x coordinate with respect to time to find the velocity at any time:

$$v_x = \frac{dx}{dt} = (-3.00\text{ m})(8.00\text{ rad/s})\sin(8.00t - 0.841)$$

$$= -(24.0\text{ m/s})\sin(8.00t - 0.841)$$

Differentiate the velocity with respect to time to find the acceleration at any time:

$$a_x = \frac{dv_x}{dt} = (-24.0\text{ m/s})(8.00\text{ rad/s})\cos(8.00t - 0.841)$$

$$= -(192\text{ m/s}^2)\cos(8.00t - 0.841)$$

Finalize Although we have evaluated these results for the particle moving in the circle, remember that these same results apply to the shadow, which is moving in simple harmonic motion.

15.5 The Pendulum

The **simple pendulum** is another mechanical system that exhibits periodic motion. It consists of a particle-like bob of mass m suspended by a light string of length L that is fixed at the upper end as shown in Active Figure 15.16. The motion occurs in the vertical plane and is driven by the gravitational force. We shall show that, provided the angle θ is small (less than about 10°), the motion is very close to that of a simple harmonic oscillator.

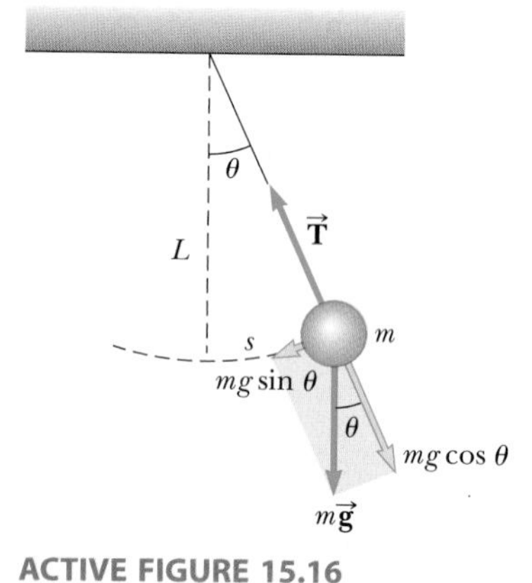

ACTIVE FIGURE 15.16

The restoring force is $-mg\sin\theta$, the component of the gravitational force tangent to the arc. When θ is small, a simple pendulum oscillates in simple harmonic motion about the equilibrium position $\theta = 0$.

Sign in at www.thomsonedu.com and go to ThomsonNOW to adjust the mass of the bob, the length of the string, and the initial angle and see the resulting oscillation of the pendulum.

The forces acting on the bob are the force $\vec{\mathbf{T}}$ exerted by the string and the gravitational force $m\vec{\mathbf{g}}$. The tangential component $mg\sin\theta$ of the gravitational force always acts toward $\theta = 0$, opposite the displacement of the bob from the lowest position. Therefore, the tangential component is a restoring force, and we can apply Newton's second law for motion in the tangential direction:

$$F_t = -mg\sin\theta = m\frac{d^2s}{dt^2}$$

where s is the bob's position measured along the arc and the negative sign indicates that the tangential force acts toward the equilibrium (vertical) position. Because $s = L\theta$ (Eq. 10.1a) and L is constant, this equation reduces to

$$\frac{d^2\theta}{dt^2} = -\frac{g}{L}\sin\theta$$

Considering θ as the position, let us compare this equation to Equation 15.3. Does it have the same mathematical form? The right side is proportional to $\sin\theta$ rather than to θ; hence, we would not expect simple harmonic motion because this expression is not of the form of Equation 15.3. If we assume θ is *small* (less than about 10° or 0.2 rad), however, we can use the **small angle approximation**, in which $\sin\theta \approx \theta$, where θ is measured in radians. Table 15.1 shows angles in degrees and radians and the sines of these angles. As long as θ is less than approximately 10°, the angle in radians and its sine are the same to within an accuracy of less than 1.0%.

PITFALL PREVENTION 15.5

Not True Simple Harmonic Motion

The pendulum *does not* exhibit true simple harmonic motion for *any* angle. If the angle is less than about 10°, the motion is close to and can be *modeled* as simple harmonic.

Therefore, for small angles, the equation of motion becomes

$$\frac{d^2\theta}{dt^2} = -\frac{g}{L}\theta \quad \text{(for small values of } \theta\text{)} \qquad \textbf{(15.24)}$$

Equation 15.24 has the same form as Equation 15.3, so we conclude that the motion for small amplitudes of oscillation can be modeled as simple harmonic motion. Therefore, the solution of Equation 15.24 is $\theta = \theta_{max}\cos(\omega t + \phi)$, where θ_{max} is the *maximum angular position* and the angular frequency ω is

Angular frequency for a simple pendulum ▶

$$\omega = \sqrt{\frac{g}{L}} \qquad \textbf{(15.25)}$$

TABLE 15.1

Angles and Sines of Angles

Angle in Degrees	Angle in Radians	Sine of Angle	Percent Difference
0°	0.000 0	0.000 0	0.0%
1°	0.017 5	0.017 5	0.0%
2°	0.034 9	0.034 9	0.0%
3°	0.052 4	0.052 3	0.0%
5°	0.087 3	0.087 2	0.1%
10°	0.174 5	0.173 6	0.5%
15°	0.261 8	0.258 8	1.2%
20°	0.349 1	0.342 0	2.1%
30°	0.523 6	0.500 0	4.7%

The period of the motion is

$$T = \frac{2\pi}{\omega} = 2\pi\sqrt{\frac{L}{g}} \quad (15.26)$$

◀ Period of a simple pendulum

In other words, **the period and frequency of a simple pendulum depend only on the length of the string and the acceleration due to gravity.** Because the period is independent of the mass, we conclude that all simple pendula that are of equal length and are at the same location (so that g is constant) oscillate with the same period.

The simple pendulum can be used as a timekeeper because its period depends only on its length and the local value of g. It is also a convenient device for making precise measurements of the free-fall acceleration. Such measurements are important because variations in local values of g can provide information on the location of oil and other valuable underground resources.

Quick Quiz 15.6 A grandfather clock depends on the period of a pendulum to keep correct time. **(i)** Suppose a grandfather clock is calibrated correctly and then a mischievous child slides the bob of the pendulum downward on the oscillating rod. Does the grandfather clock run (a) slow, (b) fast, or (c) correctly? **(ii)** Suppose a grandfather clock is calibrated correctly at sea level and is then taken to the top of a very tall mountain. Does the grandfather clock now run (a) slow, (b) fast, or (c) correctly?

EXAMPLE 15.5 A Connection Between Length and Time

Christian Huygens (1629–1695), the greatest clockmaker in history, suggested that an international unit of length could be defined as the length of a simple pendulum having a period of exactly 1 s. How much shorter would our length unit be if his suggestion had been followed?

SOLUTION

Conceptualize Imagine a pendulum that swings back and forth in exactly 1 second. Based on your experience in observing swinging objects, can you make an estimate of the required length? Hang a small object from a string and simulate the 1-s pendulum.

Categorize This example involves a simple pendulum, so we categorize it as an application of the concepts introduced in this section.

Analyze Solve Equation 15.26 for the length and substitute the known values:

$$L = \frac{T^2 g}{4\pi^2} = \frac{(1.00\text{ s})^2(9.80\text{ m/s}^2)}{4\pi^2} = 0.248\text{ m}$$

Finalize The meter's length would be slightly less than one-fourth of its current length. Also, the number of significant digits depends only on how precisely we know g because the time has been defined to be exactly 1 s.

What If? What if Huygens had been born on another planet? What would the value for g have to be on that planet such that the meter based on Huygens's pendulum would have the same value as our meter?

Answer Solve Equation 15.26 for g:

$$g = \frac{4\pi^2 L}{T^2} = \frac{4\pi^2(1.00 \text{ m})}{(1.00 \text{ s})^2} = 4\pi^2 \text{ m/s}^2 = 39.5 \text{ m/s}^2$$

No planet in our solar system has an acceleration due to gravity that large.

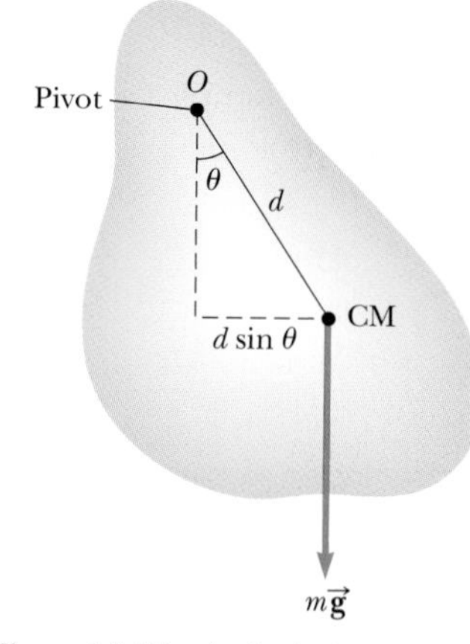

Figure 15.17 A physical pendulum pivoted at O.

Physical Pendulum

Suppose you balance a wire coat hanger so that the hook is supported by your extended index finger. When you give the hanger a small angular displacement (with your other hand) and then release it, it oscillates. If a hanging object oscillates about a fixed axis that does not pass through its center of mass and the object cannot be approximated as a point mass, we cannot treat the system as a simple pendulum. In this case, the system is called a **physical pendulum.**

Consider a rigid object pivoted at a point O that is a distance d from the center of mass (Fig. 15.17). The gravitational force provides a torque about an axis through O, and the magnitude of that torque is $mgd \sin \theta$, where θ is as shown in Figure 15.17. We model the object as a rigid object under a net torque and use the rotational form of Newton's second law, $\Sigma \tau = I\alpha$, where I is the moment of inertia of the object about the axis through O. The result is

$$-mgd \sin \theta = I \frac{d^2\theta}{dt^2}$$

The negative sign indicates that the torque about O tends to decrease θ. That is, the gravitational force produces a restoring torque. If we again assume θ is small, the approximation $\sin \theta \approx \theta$ is valid and the equation of motion reduces to

$$\frac{d^2\theta}{dt^2} = -\left(\frac{mgd}{I}\right)\theta = -\omega^2\theta \qquad \textbf{(15.27)}$$

Because this equation is of the same form as Equation 15.3, its solution is that of the simple harmonic oscillator. That is, the solution of Equation 15.27 is given by $\theta = \theta_{\text{max}} \cos(\omega t + \phi)$, where θ_{max} is the maximum angular position and

$$\omega = \sqrt{\frac{mgd}{I}}$$

The period is

Period of a physical pendulum ▶

$$T = \frac{2\pi}{\omega} = 2\pi\sqrt{\frac{I}{mgd}} \qquad \textbf{(15.28)}$$

This result can be used to measure the moment of inertia of a flat rigid object. If the location of the center of mass—and hence the value of d—is known, the moment of inertia can be obtained by measuring the period. Finally, notice that Equation 15.28 reduces to the period of a simple pendulum (Eq. 15.26) when $I = md^2$, that is, when all the mass is concentrated at the center of mass.

EXAMPLE 15.6 A Swinging Rod

A uniform rod of mass M and length L is pivoted about one end and oscillates in a vertical plane (Fig. 15.18). Find the period of oscillation if the amplitude of the motion is small.

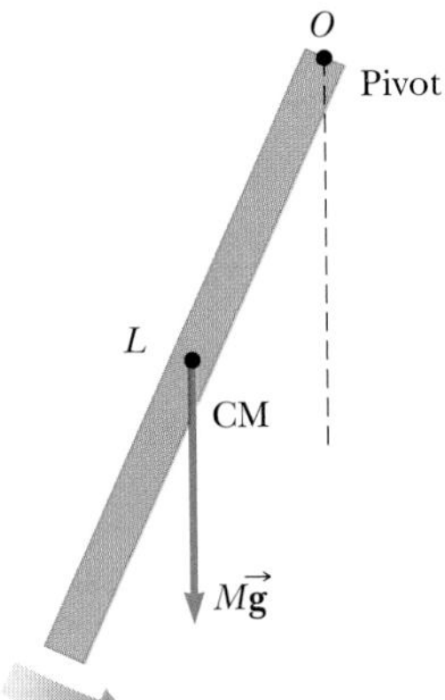

Figure 15.18 (Example 15.6) A rigid rod oscillating about a pivot through one end is a physical pendulum with $d = L/2$ and, from Table 10.2, $I = \frac{1}{3}ML^2$.

SOLUTION

Conceptualize Imagine a rod swinging back and forth when pivoted at one end. Try it with a meterstick or a scrap piece of wood.

Categorize Because the rod is not a point particle, we categorize it as a physical pendulum.

Analyze In Chapter 10, we found that the moment of inertia of a uniform rod about an axis through one end is $\frac{1}{3}ML^2$. The distance d from the pivot to the center of mass of the rod is $L/2$.

Substitute these quantities into Equation 15.28:

$$T = 2\pi\sqrt{\frac{\frac{1}{3}ML^2}{Mg(L/2)}} = 2\pi\sqrt{\frac{2L}{3g}}$$

Finalize In one of the Moon landings, an astronaut walking on the Moon's surface had a belt hanging from his space suit, and the belt oscillated as a physical pendulum. A scientist on the Earth observed this motion on television and used it to estimate the free-fall acceleration on the Moon. How did the scientist make this calculation?

Torsional Pendulum

Figure 15.19 shows a rigid object suspended by a wire attached at the top to a fixed support. When the object is twisted through some angle θ, the twisted wire exerts on the object a restoring torque that is proportional to the angular position. That is,

$$\tau = -\kappa\theta$$

where κ (Greek letter kappa) is called the *torsion constant* of the support wire. The value of κ can be obtained by applying a known torque to twist the wire through a measurable angle θ. Applying Newton's second law for rotational motion, we find that

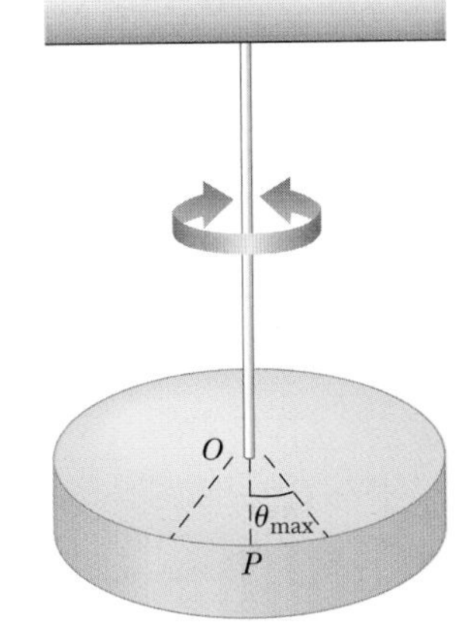

Figure 15.19 A torsional pendulum consists of a rigid object suspended by a wire attached to a rigid support. The object oscillates about the line OP with an amplitude θ_{max}.

$$\tau = -\kappa\theta = I\frac{d^2\theta}{dt^2}$$

$$\frac{d^2\theta}{dt^2} = -\frac{\kappa}{I}\theta \qquad (15.29)$$

Again, this result is the equation of motion for a simple harmonic oscillator, with $\omega = \sqrt{\kappa/I}$ and a period

$$T = 2\pi\sqrt{\frac{I}{\kappa}} \qquad (15.30)$$

◀ Period of a torsional pendulum

This system is called a *torsional pendulum*. There is no small-angle restriction in this situation as long as the elastic limit of the wire is not exceeded.

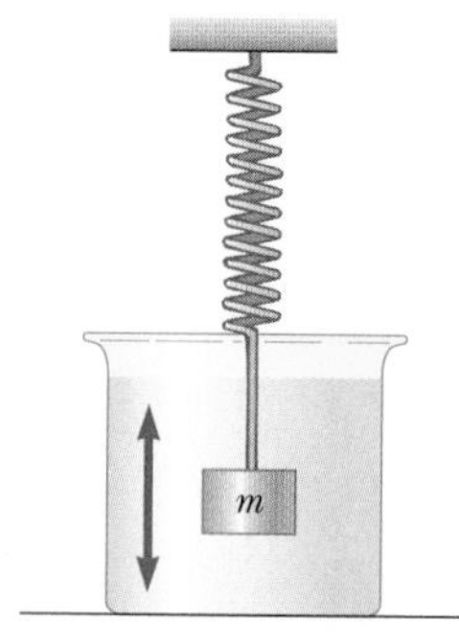

Figure 15.20 One example of a damped oscillator is an object attached to a spring and submersed in a viscous liquid.

15.6 Damped Oscillations

The oscillatory motions we have considered so far have been for ideal systems, that is, systems that oscillate indefinitely under the action of only one force, a linear restoring force. In many real systems, nonconservative forces such as friction retard the motion. Consequently, the mechanical energy of the system diminishes in time, and the motion is said to be *damped.* The lost mechanical energy is transformed into internal energy in the object and the retarding medium. Figure 15.20 depicts one such system: an object attached to a spring and submersed in a viscous liquid.

One common type of retarding force is that discussed in Section 6.4, where the force is proportional to the speed of the moving object and acts in the direction opposite the velocity of the object with respect to the medium. This retarding force is often observed when an object moves through air, for instance. Because the retarding force can be expressed as $\vec{\mathbf{R}} = -b\vec{\mathbf{v}}$ (where b is a constant called the *damping coefficient*) and the restoring force of the system is $-kx$, we can write Newton's second law as

$$\sum F_x = -kx - bv_x = ma_x$$

$$-kx - b\frac{dx}{dt} = m\frac{d^2x}{dt^2} \qquad \textbf{(15.31)}$$

The solution to this equation requires mathematics that may be unfamiliar to you; we simply state it here without proof. When the retarding force is small compared with the maximum restoring force—that is, when b is small—the solution to Equation 15.31 is

$$x = Ae^{-(b/2m)t}\cos(\omega t + \phi) \qquad \textbf{(15.32)}$$

where the angular frequency of oscillation is

$$\omega = \sqrt{\frac{k}{m} - \left(\frac{b}{2m}\right)^2} \qquad \textbf{(15.33)}$$

This result can be verified by substituting Equation 15.32 into Equation 15.31. It is convenient to express the angular frequency of a damped oscillator in the form

$$\omega = \sqrt{\omega_0^2 - \left(\frac{b}{2m}\right)^2}$$

where $\omega_0 = \sqrt{k/m}$ represents the angular frequency in the absence of a retarding force (the undamped oscillator) and is called the **natural frequency** of the system.

Active Figure 15.21 shows the position as a function of time for an object oscillating in the presence of a retarding force. **When the retarding force is small, the oscillatory character of the motion is preserved but the amplitude decreases in time, with the result that the motion ultimately ceases.** Any system that behaves in this way is known as a **damped oscillator.** The dashed blue lines in Active Figure 15.21, which define the *envelope* of the oscillatory curve, represent the exponential factor in Equation 15.32. This envelope shows that **the amplitude decays exponentially with time.** For motion with a given spring constant and object mass, the oscillations dampen more rapidly for larger values of the retarding force.

ACTIVE FIGURE 15.21

Graph of position versus time for a damped oscillator. Notice the decrease in amplitude with time.

Sign in at www.thomsonedu.com and go to ThomsonNOW to adjust the spring constant, the mass of the object, and the damping constant and see the resulting damped oscillation of the object.

When the magnitude of the retarding force is small such that $b/2m < \omega_0$, the system is said to be **underdamped.** The resulting motion is represented by the blue curve in Figure 15.22. As the value of b increases, the amplitude of the oscillations decreases more and more rapidly. When b reaches a critical value b_c such that $b_c/2m = \omega_0$, the system does not oscillate and is said to be **critically damped.** In this case, the system, once released from rest at some nonequilibrium position, approaches but does not pass through the equilibrium position. The graph of position versus time for this case is the red curve in Figure 15.22.

If the medium is so viscous that the retarding force is large compared to the restoring force—that is, if $b/2m > \omega_0$—the system is **overdamped.** Again, the displaced system, when free to move, does not oscillate but rather simply returns to its equilibrium position. As the damping increases, the time interval required for the system to approach equilibrium also increases as indicated by the black curve in Figure 15.22. For critically damped and overdamped systems, there is no angular frequency ω and the solution in Equation 15.32 is not valid.

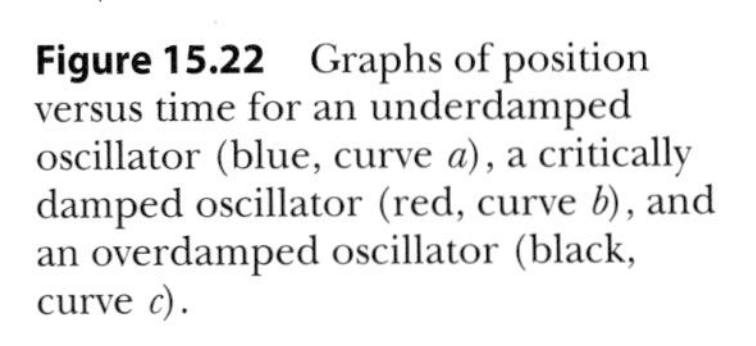

Figure 15.22 Graphs of position versus time for an underdamped oscillator (blue, curve *a*), a critically damped oscillator (red, curve *b*), and an overdamped oscillator (black, curve *c*).

15.7 Forced Oscillations

We have seen that the mechanical energy of a damped oscillator decreases in time as a result of the resistive force. It is possible to compensate for this energy decrease by applying an external force that does positive work on the system. At any instant, energy can be transferred into the system by an applied force that acts in the direction of motion of the oscillator. For example, a child on a swing can be kept in motion by appropriately timed "pushes." The amplitude of motion remains constant if the energy input per cycle of motion exactly equals the decrease in mechanical energy in each cycle that results from resistive forces.

A common example of a forced oscillator is a damped oscillator driven by an external force that varies periodically, such as $F(t) = F_0 \sin \omega t$, where F_0 is a constant and ω is the angular frequency of the driving force. In general, the frequency ω of the driving force is variable, whereas the natural frequency ω_0 of the oscillator is fixed by the values of k and m. Newton's second law in this situation gives

$$\sum F = ma \quad \rightarrow \quad F_0 \sin \omega t - b\frac{dx}{dt} - kx = m\frac{d^2x}{dt^2} \qquad \textbf{(15.34)}$$

Again, the solution of this equation is rather lengthy and will not be presented. After the driving force on an initially stationary object begins to act, the amplitude of the oscillation will increase. After a sufficiently long period of time, when the energy input per cycle from the driving force equals the amount of mechanical energy transformed to internal energy for each cycle, a steady-state condition is reached in which the oscillations proceed with constant amplitude. In this situation, the solution of Equation 15.34 is

$$x = A \cos (\omega t + \phi) \qquad \textbf{(15.35)}$$

where

$$A = \frac{F_0/m}{\sqrt{(\omega^2 - \omega_0^2)^2 + \left(\frac{b\omega}{m}\right)^2}} \qquad \textbf{(15.36)}$$

◄ Amplitude of a driven oscillator

and where $\omega_0 = \sqrt{k/m}$ is the natural frequency of the undamped oscillator ($b = 0$).

Equations 15.35 and 15.36 show that the forced oscillator vibrates at the frequency of the driving force and that the amplitude of the oscillator is constant for a given driving force because it is being driven in steady-state by an external force. For small damping, the amplitude is large when the frequency of the driving force is near the natural frequency of oscillation, or when $\omega \approx \omega_0$. The dramatic increase in amplitude near the natural frequency is called **resonance,** and the natural frequency ω_0 is also called the **resonance frequency** of the system.

The reason for large-amplitude oscillations at the resonance frequency is that energy is being transferred to the system under the most favorable conditions. We can better understand this concept by taking the first time derivative of x in Equation 15.35, which gives an expression for the velocity of the oscillator. We find that v is proportional to $\sin (\omega t + \phi)$, which is the same trigonometric function as that describing the driving force. Therefore, the applied force $\vec{\mathbf{F}}$ is in phase with the velocity. The rate at which work is done on the oscillator by $\vec{\mathbf{F}}$ equals the dot product

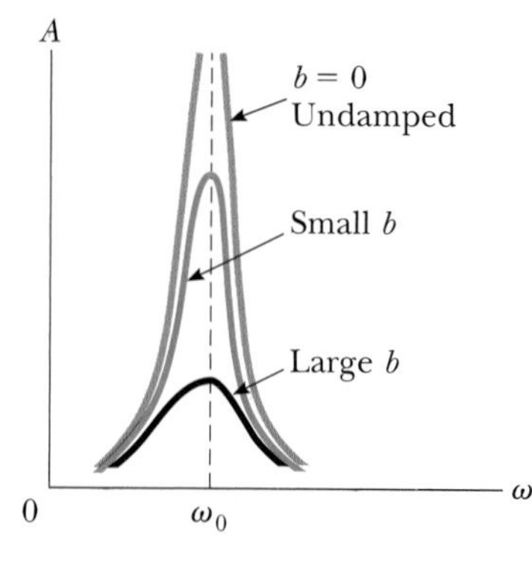

Figure 15.23 Graph of amplitude versus frequency for a damped oscillator when a periodic driving force is present. When the frequency ω of the driving force equals the natural frequency ω_0 of the oscillator, resonance occurs. Notice that the shape of the resonance curve depends on the size of the damping coefficient b.

$\vec{\mathbf{F}} \cdot \vec{\mathbf{v}}$; this rate is the power delivered to the oscillator. Because the product $\vec{\mathbf{F}} \cdot \vec{\mathbf{v}}$ is a maximum when $\vec{\mathbf{F}}$ and $\vec{\mathbf{v}}$ are in phase, we conclude that **at resonance, the applied force is in phase with the velocity and the power transferred to the oscillator is a maximum.**

Figure 15.23 is a graph of amplitude as a function of frequency for a forced oscillator with and without damping. Notice that the amplitude increases with decreasing damping ($b \rightarrow 0$) and that the resonance curve broadens as the damping increases. In the absence of a damping force ($b = 0$), we see from Equation 15.36 that the steady-state amplitude approaches infinity as ω approaches ω_0. In other words, if there are no losses in the system and we continue to drive an initially motionless oscillator with a periodic force that is in phase with the velocity, the amplitude of motion builds without limit (see the brown curve in Fig. 15.23). This limitless building does not occur in practice because some damping is always present in reality.

Later in this book we shall see that resonance appears in other areas of physics. For example, certain electric circuits have natural frequencies. A bridge has natural frequencies that can be set into resonance by an appropriate driving force. A dramatic example of such resonance occurred in 1940 when the Tacoma Narrows Bridge in the state of Washington was destroyed by resonant vibrations. Although the winds were not particularly strong on that occasion, the "flapping" of the wind across the roadway (think of the "flapping" of a flag in a strong wind) provided a periodic driving force whose frequency matched that of the bridge. The resulting oscillations of the bridge caused it to ultimately collapse (Fig. 15.24) because the bridge design had inadequate built-in safety features.

Many other examples of resonant vibrations can be cited. A resonant vibration you may have experienced is the "singing" of telephone wires in the wind. Machines often break if one vibrating part is in resonance with some other moving part. Soldiers marching in cadence across a bridge have been known to set up resonant vibrations in the structure and thereby cause it to collapse. Whenever any real physical system is driven near its resonance frequency, you can expect oscillations of very large amplitudes.

Figure 15.24 (a) In 1940, turbulent winds set up torsional vibrations in the Tacoma Narrows Bridge, causing it to oscillate at a frequency near one of the natural frequencies of the bridge structure. (b) Once established, this resonance condition led to the bridge's collapse. *(UPI/Bettmann Newsphotos)*

Summary

ThomsonNOW™ Sign in at **www.thomsonedu.com** and go to ThomsonNOW to take a practice test for this chapter.

CONCEPTS AND PRINCIPLES

The kinetic energy and potential energy for an object of mass m oscillating at the end of a spring of force constant k vary with time and are given by

$$K = \frac{1}{2}mv^2 = \frac{1}{2}m\omega^2A^2 \sin^2(\omega t + \phi) \quad \textbf{(15.19)}$$

$$U = \frac{1}{2}kx^2 = \frac{1}{2}kA^2 \cos^2(\omega t + \phi) \quad \textbf{(15.20)}$$

The total energy of a simple harmonic oscillator is a constant of the motion and is given by

$$E = \frac{1}{2}kA^2 \quad \textbf{(15.21)}$$

A **simple pendulum** of length L moves in simple harmonic motion for small angular displacements from the vertical. Its period is

$$T = 2\pi\sqrt{\frac{L}{g}} \quad \textbf{(15.26)}$$

For small angular displacements from the vertical, a **physical pendulum** moves in simple harmonic motion about a pivot that does not go through the center of mass. The period of this motion is

$$T = 2\pi\sqrt{\frac{I}{mgd}} \quad \textbf{(15.28)}$$

where I is the moment of inertia about an axis through the pivot and d is the distance from the pivot to the center of mass.

If an oscillator experiences a damping force $\vec{\mathbf{R}} = -b\vec{\mathbf{v}}$, its position for small damping is described by

$$x = Ae^{-(b/2m)t}\cos(\omega t + \phi) \quad \textbf{(15.32)}$$

where

$$\omega = \sqrt{\frac{k}{m} - \left(\frac{b}{2m}\right)^2} \quad \textbf{(15.33)}$$

If an oscillator is subject to a sinusoidal driving force $F(t) = F_0 \sin \omega t$, it exhibits **resonance,** in which the amplitude is largest when the driving frequency ω matches the natural frequency $\omega_0 = \sqrt{k/m}$ of the oscillator.

ANALYSIS MODEL FOR PROBLEM SOLVING

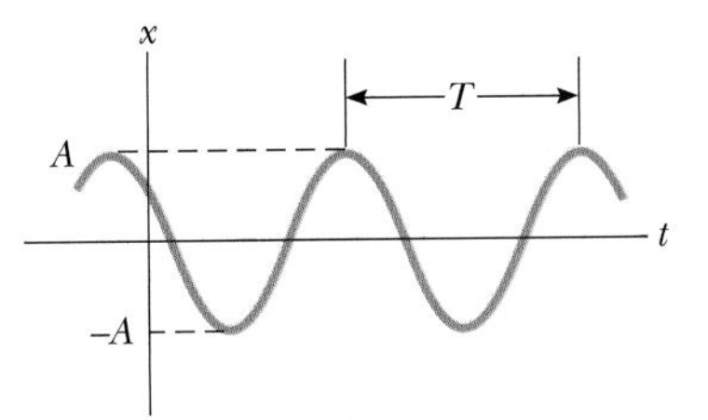

Particle in Simple Harmonic Motion If a particle is subject to a force of the form of Hooke's law $F = -kx$, the particle exhibits **simple harmonic motion**. Its position is described by

$$x(t) = A\cos(\omega t + \phi) \quad \textbf{(15.6)}$$

where A is the **amplitude** of the motion, ω is the **angular frequency,** and ϕ is the **phase constant.** The value of ϕ depends on the initial position and initial velocity of the oscillator.

The **period** of the oscillation is

$$T = \frac{2\pi}{\omega} = 2\pi\sqrt{\frac{m}{k}} \quad \textbf{(15.13)}$$

and the inverse of the period is the **frequency.**

Questions

☐ denotes answer available in *Student Solutions Manual/Study Guide;* **O** denotes objective question

1. Is a bouncing ball an example of simple harmonic motion? Is the daily movement of a student from home to school and back simple harmonic motion? Why or why not?

2. **O** A particle on a spring moves in simple harmonic motion along the x axis between turning points at $x_1 = 100$ cm and $x_2 = 140$ cm. **(i)** At which of the following positions does the particle have maximum speed? (a) 100 cm (b) 110 cm (c) 120 cm (d) some other position (e) The same greatest value occurs at multiple points. **(ii)** At which position does it have maximum acceleration? Choose from the same possibilities. **(iii)** At which position is the greatest net force exerted on the particle? **(iv)** At which position does the particle have the greatest magnitude of momentum? **(v)** At which position does the particle have greatest kinetic energy? **(vi)** At which position does the particle-spring system have the greatest total energy?

3. If the coordinate of a particle varies as $x = -A \cos \omega t$, what is the phase constant in Equation 15.6? At what position is the particle at $t = 0$?

4. **O** Rank the periods of the following oscillating systems from the greatest to the smallest. If any periods are equal, show their equality in your ranking. Each system differs in only one way from system (a), which is a 0.1-kg glider on a horizontal, frictionless surface, oscillating with amplitude 0.1 m on a spring with force constant 10 N/m. In situation (b), the amplitude is 0.2 m. In situation (c), the mass is 0.2 kg. In situation (d), the spring has stiffness constant 20 N/m. Situation (e) is just like situation (a) except for being in a gravitational field of 4.9 m/s^2 instead of 9.8 m/s^2. Situation (f) is just like situation (a) except that the object bounces in simple harmonic motion on the bottom end of the spring hanging vertically. Situation (g) is just like situation (a) except that a small resistive force makes the motion underdamped.

5. **O** For a simple harmonic oscillator, the position is measured as the displacement from equilibrium. (a) Can the quantities position and velocity be in the same direction? (b) Can velocity and acceleration be in the same direction? (c) Can position and acceleration be in the same direction?

6. **O** The top end of a spring is held fixed. A block is hung on the bottom end and the frequency f of the oscillation of the system is measured. The block, a second identical block, and the spring are carried up in a space shuttle to Earth orbit. The two blocks are attached to the ends of the spring. The spring is compressed, without making adjacent coils touch, and the system is released to oscillate while floating within the shuttle cabin. What is the frequency of oscillation for this system in terms of f? (a) $f/4$ (b) $f/2$ (c) $f/\sqrt{2}$ (d) f (e) $\sqrt{2}f$ (f) $2f$ (g) $4f$

7. **O** You attach a block to the bottom end of a spring hanging vertically. You slowly let the block move down and find that it hangs at rest with the spring stretched by 15.0 cm. Next, you lift the block back up and release it from rest with the spring unstretched. What maximum distance does it move down? (a) 7.5 cm (b) 15.0 cm (c) 30.0 cm (d) 60.0 cm (e) The distance cannot be determined without knowing the mass and spring constant.

8. The equations listed in Table 2.2 give position as a function of time, velocity as a function of time, and velocity as function of position for an object moving in a straight line with constant acceleration. The quantity v_{xi} appears in every equation. Do any of these equations apply to an object moving in a straight line with simple harmonic motion? Using a similar format, make a table of equations describing simple harmonic motion. Include equations giving acceleration as a function of time and acceleration as a function of position. State the equations in such a form that they apply equally to a block-spring system, to a pendulum, and to other vibrating systems. What quantity appears in every equation?

9. **O** A simple pendulum has a period of 2.5 s. **(i)** What is its period if its length is made four times larger? (a) 0.625 s (b) 1.25 s (c) 2.5 s (d) 3.54 s (e) 5 s (f) 10 s **(ii)** What is its period if, instead of changing its length, the mass of the suspended bob is made four times larger? Choose from the same possibilities.

10. **O** A simple pendulum is suspended from the ceiling of a stationary elevator, and the period is determined. **(i)** When the elevator accelerates upward, is the period (a) greater, (b) smaller, or (c) unchanged? **(ii)** When the elevator has a downward acceleration, is the period (a) greater, (b) smaller, or (c) unchanged? **(iii)** When the elevator moves with constant upward velocity, is the period of the pendulum (a) greater, (b) smaller, or (c) unchanged?

11. Figure Q15.11 shows graphs of the potential energy of four different systems versus the position of a particle in each system. Each particle is set into motion with a push at an arbitrarily chosen location. Describe its subsequent motion in each case (a), (b), (c), and (d).

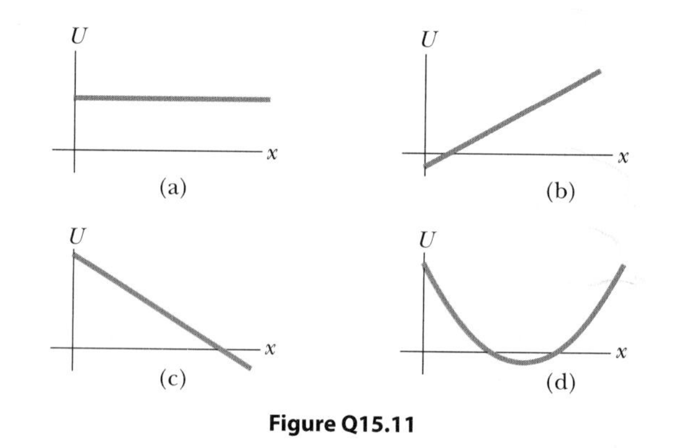

Figure Q15.11

12. A simple pendulum can be modeled as exhibiting simple harmonic motion when θ is small. Is the motion periodic when θ is large? How does the period of motion change as θ increases?

13. The mechanical energy of an undamped block-spring system is constant as kinetic energy transforms to elastic potential energy and vice versa. For comparison, explain in the same terms what happens to the energy of a damped oscillator.

14. A student thinks that any real vibration must be damped. Is the student correct? If so, give convincing reasoning. If not, give an example of a real vibration that keeps constant amplitude forever if the system is isolated.

15. Will damped oscillations occur for any values of b and k? Explain.

16. Is it possible to have damped oscillations when a system is at resonance? Explain.

17. You stand on the end of a diving board and bounce to set it into oscillation. You find a maximum response, in terms of the amplitude of oscillation of the end of the board, when you bounce at frequency f. You now move to the middle of the board and repeat the experiment. Is the resonance frequency for forced oscillations at this point higher, lower, or the same as f? Why?

18. You are looking at a small, leafy tree. You do not notice any breeze, and most of the leaves on the tree are motionless. One leaf, however, is fluttering back and forth wildly. After a while, that leaf stops moving and you notice a different leaf moving much more than all the others. Explain what could cause the large motion of one particular leaf.

19. The bob of a certain pendulum is a sphere filled with water. What would happen to the frequency of vibration of this pendulum if there were a hole in the sphere that allowed the water to leak out slowly?

Problems

WebAssign The Problems from this chapter may be assigned online in WebAssign.

ThomsonNOW Sign in at **www.thomsonedu.com** and go to ThomsonNOW to assess your understanding of this chapter's topics with additional quizzing and conceptual questions.

1, 2, 3 denotes straightforward, intermediate, challenging; ☐ denotes full solution available in *Student Solutions Manual/Study Guide;* ▲ denotes coached solution with hints available at **www.thomsonedu.com;** ▭ denotes developing symbolic reasoning; ● denotes asking for qualitative reasoning; ▪ denotes computer useful in solving problem

Note: Ignore the mass of every spring, except in Problems 62 and 64.

Section 15.1 Motion of an Object Attached to a Spring

Problems 16, 17, 18, 26, and 60 in Chapter 7 can also be assigned with this section.

1. ● A ball dropped from a height of 4.00 m makes an elastic collision with the ground. Assuming no mechanical energy is lost due to air resistance, (a) show that the ensuing motion is periodic and (b) determine the period of the motion. (c) Is the motion simple harmonic? Explain.

Section 15.2 The Particle in Simple Harmonic Motion

2. In an engine, a piston oscillates with simple harmonic motion so that its position varies according to the expression

$$x = (5.00 \text{ cm}) \cos\left(2t + \frac{\pi}{6}\right)$$

where x is in centimeters and t is in seconds. At $t = 0$, find (a) the position of the particle, (b) its velocity, and (c) its acceleration. (d) Find the period and amplitude of the motion.

3. The position of a particle is given by the expression $x = (4.00 \text{ m}) \cos(3.00\pi t + \pi)$, where x is in meters and t is in seconds. Determine (a) the frequency and period of the motion, (b) the amplitude of the motion, (c) the phase constant, and (d) the position of the particle at $t = 0.250$ s.

4. ● (a) A hanging spring stretches by 35.0 cm when an object of mass 450 g is hung on it at rest. In this situation, we define its position as $x = 0$. The object is pulled down an additional 18.0 cm and released from rest to oscillate without friction. What is its position x at a moment 84.4 s later? (b) **What If?** Another hanging spring stretches by 35.5 cm when an object of mass 440 g is hung on it at rest. We define this new position as $x = 0$. This object is also pulled down an additional 18.0 cm and released from rest to oscillate without friction. Find its position 84.4 s later. (c) Why are the answers to parts (a) and (b) different by such a large percentage when the data are so similar? Does this circumstance reveal a fundamental difficulty in calculating the future? (d) Find the distance traveled by the vibrating object in part (a). (e) Find the distance traveled by the object in part (b).

5. ▲ A particle moving along the x axis in simple harmonic motion starts from its equilibrium position, the origin, at $t = 0$ and moves to the right. The amplitude of its motion is 2.00 cm, and the frequency is 1.50 Hz. (a) Show that the position of the particle is given by

$$x = (2.00 \text{ cm}) \sin(3.00\pi t)$$

Determine (b) the maximum speed and the earliest time ($t > 0$) at which the particle has this speed, (c) the maximum acceleration and the earliest time ($t > 0$) at which the particle has this acceleration, and (d) the total distance traveled between $t = 0$ and $t = 1.00$ s.

6. A simple harmonic oscillator takes 12.0 s to undergo five complete vibrations. Find (a) the period of its motion, (b) the frequency in hertz, and (c) the angular frequency in radians per second.

7. A 7.00-kg object is hung from the bottom end of a vertical spring fastened to an overhead beam. The object is set into vertical oscillations having a period of 2.60 s. Find the force constant of the spring.

8. **Review problem.** A particle moves along the x axis. It is initially at the position 0.270 m, moving with velocity

0.140 m/s and acceleration −0.320 m/s². Suppose it moves with constant acceleration for 4.50 s. Find (a) its position and (b) its velocity at the end of this time interval. Next, assume it moves with simple harmonic motion for 4.50 s and $x = 0$ is its equilibrium position. Find (c) its position and (d) its velocity at the end of this time interval.

9. A piston in a gasoline engine is in simple harmonic motion. Taking the extremes of its position relative to its center point as ±5.00 cm, find the maximum velocity and acceleration of the piston when the engine is running at the rate of 3 600 rev/min.

10. A 1.00-kg glider attached to a spring with a force constant of 25.0 N/m oscillates on a horizontal, frictionless air track. At $t = 0$, the glider is released from rest at $x = -3.00$ cm. (That is, the spring is compressed by 3.00 cm.) Find (a) the period of its motion, (b) the maximum values of its speed and acceleration, and (c) the position, velocity, and acceleration as functions of time.

11. A 0.500-kg object attached to a spring with a force constant of 8.00 N/m vibrates in simple harmonic motion with an amplitude of 10.0 cm. Calculate (a) the maximum value of its speed and acceleration, (b) the speed and acceleration when the object is 6.00 cm from the equilibrium position, and (c) the time interval required for the object to move from $x = 0$ to $x = 8.00$ cm.

12. ● You attach an object to the bottom end of a hanging vertical spring. It hangs at rest after extending the spring 18.3 cm. You then set the object vibrating. Do you have enough information to find its period? Explain your answer and state whatever you can about its period.

13. A 1.00-kg object is attached to a horizontal spring. The spring is initially stretched by 0.100 m, and the object is released from rest there. It proceeds to move without friction. The next time the speed of the object is zero is 0.500 s later. What is the maximum speed of the object?

Section 15.3 Energy of the Simple Harmonic Oscillator

14. A 200-g block is attached to a horizontal spring and executes simple harmonic motion with a period of 0.250 s. The total energy of the system is 2.00 J. Find (a) the force constant of the spring and (b) the amplitude of the motion.

15. ▲ An automobile having a mass of 1 000 kg is driven into a brick wall in a safety test. The car's bumper behaves like a spring of constant 5.00×10^6 N/m and compresses 3.16 cm as the car is brought to rest. What was the speed of the car before impact, assuming that no mechanical energy is lost during impact with the wall?

16. A block-spring system oscillates with an amplitude of 3.50 cm. The spring constant is 250 N/m, and the mass of the block is 0.500 kg. Determine (a) the mechanical energy of the system, (b) the maximum speed of the block, and (c) the maximum acceleration.

17. A 50.0-g object connected to a spring with a force constant of 35.0 N/m oscillates on a horizontal, frictionless surface with an amplitude of 4.00 cm. Find (a) the total energy of the system and (b) the speed of the object when the position is 1.00 cm. Find (c) the kinetic energy and (d) the potential energy when the position is 3.00 cm.

18. A 2.00-kg object is attached to a spring and placed on a horizontal, smooth surface. A horizontal force of 20.0 N is required to hold the object at rest when it is pulled 0.200 m from its equilibrium position (the origin of the x axis). The object is now released from rest with an initial position of $x_i = 0.200$ m, and it subsequently undergoes simple harmonic oscillations. Find (a) the force constant of the spring, (b) the frequency of the oscillations, and (c) the maximum speed of the object. Where does this maximum speed occur? (d) Find the maximum acceleration of the object. Where does it occur? (e) Find the total energy of the oscillating system. Find (f) the speed and (g) the acceleration of the object when its position is equal to one-third of the maximum value.

19. A particle executes simple harmonic motion with an amplitude of 3.00 cm. At what position does its speed equal one half of its maximum speed?

20. A 65.0-kg bungee jumper steps off a bridge with a light bungee cord tied to her and to the bridge (Fig. P15.20). The unstretched length of the cord is 11.0 m. The jumper reaches the bottom of her motion 36.0 m below the bridge before bouncing back. Her motion can be separated into an 11.0-m free fall and a 25.0-m section of simple harmonic oscillation. (a) For what time interval is she in free fall? (b) Use the principle of conservation of energy to find the spring constant of the bungee cord. (c) What is the location of the equilibrium point where the spring force balances the gravitational force exerted on the jumper? This point is taken as the origin in our mathematical description of simple harmonic oscillation. (d) What is the angular frequency of the oscillation? (e) What time interval is required for the cord to stretch by 25.0 m? (f) What is the total time interval for the entire 36.0 m drop?

Telegraph Colour Library/FPG International

Figure P15.20 Problems 20 and 54.

21. A cart attached to a spring with constant 3.24 N/m vibrates such that its position is given by the function $x = (5.00 \text{ cm}) \cos (3.60t \text{ rad/s})$. (a) During the first cycle, for $0 < t < 1.75$ s, at what value of t is the system's potential energy changing most rapidly into kinetic energy? (b) What is the maximum rate of energy transformation?

Section 15.4 Comparing Simple Harmonic Motion with Uniform Circular Motion

22. ● Consider the simplified single-piston engine in Figure P15.22. Assuming the wheel rotates with constant angular speed, explain why the piston rod oscillates in simple harmonic motion.

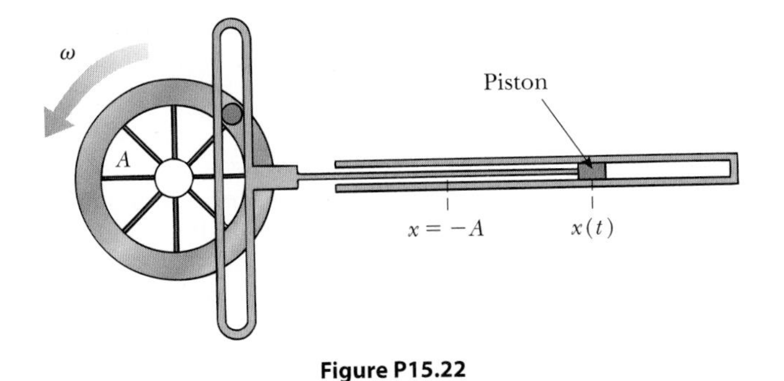

Figure P15.22

23. ● While riding behind a car traveling at 3.00 m/s, you notice that one of the car's tires has a small hemispherical bump on its rim as shown in Figure P15.23. (a) Explain why the bump, from your viewpoint behind the car, executes simple harmonic motion. (b) If the radii of the car's tires are 0.300 m, what is the bump's period of oscillation?

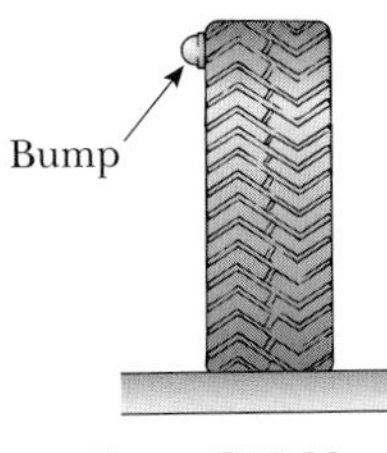

Figure P15.23

Section 15.5 The Pendulum

Problem 52 in Chapter 1 can also be assigned with this section.

24. A "seconds pendulum" is one that moves through its equilibrium position once each second. (The period of the pendulum is precisely 2 s.) The length of a seconds pendulum is 0.992 7 m at Tokyo, Japan, and 0.994 2 m at Cambridge, England. What is the ratio of the free-fall accelerations at these two locations?

25. ▲ ● A simple pendulum has a mass of 0.250 kg and a length of 1.00 m. It is displaced through an angle of 15.0° and then released. What are (a) the maximum speed, (b) the maximum angular acceleration, and (c) the maximum restoring force? **What If?** Solve this problem by using the simple harmonic motion model for the motion of the pendulum and then solve the problem by using more general principles. Compare the answers.

26. The angular position of a pendulum is represented by the equation $\theta = (0.032\ 0\ \text{rad})\cos \omega t$, where θ is in radians and $\omega = 4.43$ rad/s. Determine the period and length of the pendulum.

27. A particle of mass m slides without friction inside a hemispherical bowl of radius R. Show that if the particle starts from rest with a small displacement from equilibrium, it moves in simple harmonic motion with an angular frequency equal to that of a simple pendulum of length R. That is, $\omega = \sqrt{g/R}$.

28. **Review problem.** A simple pendulum is 5.00 m long. (a) What is the period of small oscillations for this pendulum if it is located in an elevator accelerating upward at 5.00 m/s²? (b) What is its period if the elevator is accelerating downward at 5.00 m/s²? (c) What is the period of this pendulum if it is placed in a truck that is accelerating horizontally at 5.00 m/s²?

29. A physical pendulum in the form of a planar object moves in simple harmonic motion with a frequency of 0.450 Hz. The pendulum has a mass of 2.20 kg, and the pivot is located 0.350 m from the center of mass. Determine the moment of inertia of the pendulum about the pivot point.

30. A small object is attached to the end of a string to form a simple pendulum. The period of its harmonic motion is measured for small angular displacements and three lengths. For each length, the time interval for 50 oscillations is measured with a stopwatch. For lengths of 1.000 m, 0.750 m, and 0.500 m, total time intervals of 99.8 s, 86.6 s, and 71.1 s are measured for 50 oscillations. (a) Determine the period of motion for each length. (b) Determine the mean value of g obtained from these three independent measurements and compare it with the accepted value. (c) Plot T^2 versus L and obtain a value for g from the slope of your best-fit straight-line graph. Compare this value with that obtained in part (b).

31. Consider the physical pendulum of Figure 15.17. (a) Represent its moment of inertia about an axis passing through its center of mass and parallel to the axis passing through its pivot point as I_{CM}. Show that its period is

$$T = 2\pi\sqrt{\frac{I_{\text{CM}} + md^2}{mgd}}$$

where d is the distance between the pivot point and center of mass. (b) Show that the period has a minimum value when d satisfies $md^2 = I_{\text{CM}}$.

32. A very light rigid rod with a length of 0.500 m extends straight out from one end of a meterstick. The meterstick is suspended from a pivot at the far end of the rod and is set into oscillation. (a) Determine the period of oscillation. *Suggestion:* Use the parallel-axis theorem from Section 10.5. (b) By what percentage does the period differ from the period of a simple pendulum 1.00 m long?

33. A clock balance wheel (Fig. P15.33) has a period of oscillation of 0.250 s. The wheel is constructed so that its mass of 20.0 g is concentrated around a rim of radius 0.500 cm. What are (a) the wheel's moment of inertia and (b) the torsion constant of the attached spring?

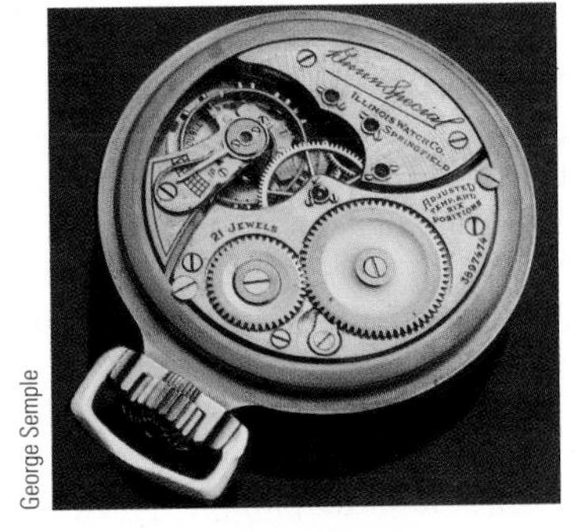

Figure P15.33

Section 15.6 Damped Oscillations

34. Show that the time rate of change of mechanical energy for a damped, undriven oscillator is given by $dE/dt = -bv^2$ and hence is always negative. To do so, differentiate the expression for the mechanical energy of an oscillator, $E = \frac{1}{2}mv^2 + \frac{1}{2}kx^2$, and use Equation 15.31.

35. A pendulum with a length of 1.00 m is released from an initial angle of 15.0°. After 1 000 s, its amplitude has been reduced by friction to 5.50°. What is the value of $b/2m$?

36. Show that Equation 15.32 is a solution of Equation 15.31 provided $b^2 < 4mk$.

37. A 10.6-kg object oscillates at the end of a vertical spring that has a spring constant of 2.05×10^4 N/m. The effect of air resistance is represented by the damping coefficient $b = 3.00$ N·s/m. (a) Calculate the frequency of the damped oscillation. (b) By what percentage does the amplitude of the oscillation decrease in each cycle? (c) Find the time interval that elapses while the energy of the system drops to 5.00% of its initial value.

Section 15.7 Forced Oscillations

38. The front of her sleeper wet from teething, a baby rejoices in the day by crowing and bouncing up and down in her crib. Her mass is 12.5 kg, and the crib mattress can be modeled as a light spring with force constant 4.30 kN/m. (a) The baby soon learns to bounce with maximum amplitude and minimum effort by bending her knees at what frequency? (b) She learns to use the mattress as a trampoline—losing contact with it for part of each cycle—when her amplitude exceeds what value?

39. A 2.00-kg object attached to a spring moves without friction and is driven by an external force given by $F = (3.00 \text{ N}) \sin (2\pi t)$. The force constant of the spring is 20.0 N/m. Determine (a) the period and (b) the amplitude of the motion.

40. Considering an undamped, forced oscillator ($b = 0$), show that Equation 15.35 is a solution of Equation 15.34, with an amplitude given by Equation 15.36.

41. A block weighing 40.0 N is suspended from a spring that has a force constant of 200 N/m. The system is undamped and is subjected to a harmonic driving force of frequency 10.0 Hz, resulting in a forced-motion amplitude of 2.00 cm. Determine the maximum value of the driving force.

42. Damping is negligible for a 0.150-kg object hanging from a light 6.30-N/m spring. A sinusoidal force with an amplitude of 1.70 N drives the system. At what frequency will the force make the object vibrate with an amplitude of 0.440 m?

43. You are a research biologist. Even though your emergency pager's batteries are getting low, you take the pager along to a fine restaurant. You switch the small pager to vibrate instead of beep, and you put it into a side pocket of your suit coat. The arm of your chair presses the light cloth against your body at one spot. Fabric with a length of 8.21 cm hangs freely below that spot, with the pager at the bottom. A coworker urgently needs instructions and pages you from the laboratory. The motion of the pager makes the hanging part of your coat swing back and forth with remarkably large amplitude. The waiter, maître d', wine steward, and nearby diners notice immediately and fall silent. Your daughter pipes up and says, accurately enough, "Daddy, look! Your cockroaches must have gotten out again!" Find the frequency at which your pager vibrates.

Additional Problems

44. ● **Review problem.** The problem extends the reasoning of Problem 54 in Chapter 9. Two gliders are set in motion on an air track. Glider one has mass $m_1 = 0.240$ kg and velocity $0.740\hat{\mathbf{i}}$ m/s. It will have a rear-end collision with glider number two, of mass $m_2 = 0.360$ kg, which has original velocity $0.120\hat{\mathbf{i}}$ m/s. A light spring of force constant 45.0 N/m is attached to the back end of glider two as shown in Figure P9.54. When glider one touches the spring, superglue instantly and permanently makes it stick to its end of the spring. (a) Find the common velocity the two gliders have when the spring compression is a maximum. (b) Find the maximum spring compression distance. (c) Argue that the motion after the gliders become attached consists of the center of mass of the two-glider system moving with the constant velocity found in part (a) while both gliders oscillate in simple harmonic motion relative to the center of mass. (d) Find the energy of the center-of-mass motion. (e) Find the energy of the oscillation.

45. ● An object of mass m moves in simple harmonic motion with amplitude 12.0 cm on a light spring. Its maximum acceleration is 108 cm/s². Regard m as a variable. (a) Find the period T of the object. (b) Find its frequency f. (c) Find the maximum speed v_{max} of the object. (d) Find the energy E of the vibration. (e) Find the force constant k of the spring. (f) Describe the pattern of dependence of each of the quantities T, f, v_{max}, E, and k on m.

46. ● **Review problem.** A rock rests on a concrete sidewalk. An earthquake strikes, making the ground move vertically in harmonic motion with a constant frequency of 2.40 Hz and with gradually increasing amplitude. (a) With what amplitude does the ground vibrate when the rock begins to lose contact with the sidewalk? Another rock is sitting on the concrete bottom of a swimming pool full of water. The earthquake produces only vertical motion, so the water does not slosh from side to side. (b) Present a convincing argument that when the ground vibrates with the amplitude found in part (a), the submerged rock also barely loses contact with the floor of the swimming pool.

47. A small ball of mass M is attached to the end of a uniform rod of equal mass M and length L that is pivoted at the top (Fig. P15.47). (a) Determine the tensions in the rod at the pivot and at the point P when the system is stationary. (b) Calculate the period of oscillation for small displacements from equilibrium and determine this period for $L = 2.00$ m. *Suggestions:* Model the object at the end of the rod as a particle and use Eq. 15.28.

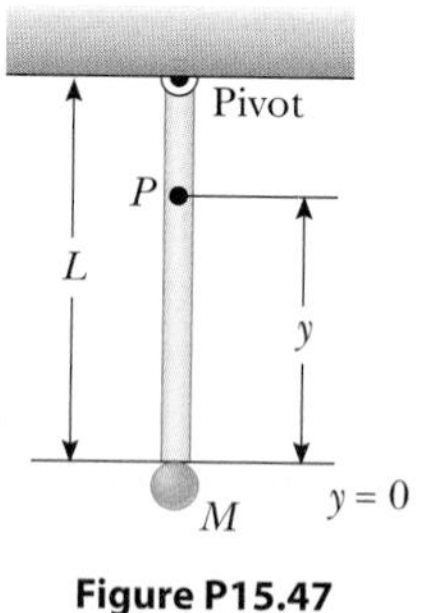

Figure P15.47

48. An object of mass $m_1 = 9.00$ kg is in equilibrium, connected to a light spring of constant $k = 100$ N/m that is fastened to a wall as shown in Figure P15.48a. A second object, $m_2 = 7.00$ kg, is slowly pushed up against m_1, compressing the spring by the amount $A = 0.200$ m (see Fig. P15.48b). The system is then released, and both objects start moving to the right on the frictionless surface. (a) When m_1 reaches the equilibrium point, m_2 loses contact with m_1 (see Fig. P15.48c) and moves to the right with speed v. Determine the value of v. (b) How far apart are the objects when the spring is fully stretched for the first time (D in Fig. P15.48d)? *Suggestion:* First determine the period of oscillation and the amplitude of the m_1–spring system after m_2 loses contact with m_1.

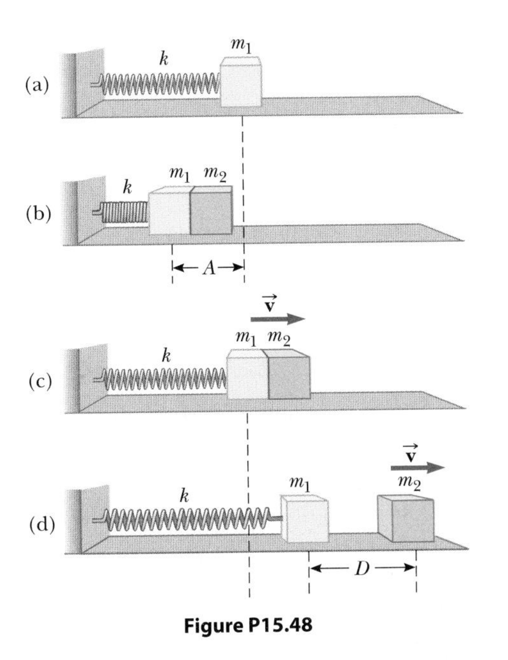

Figure P15.48

49. ▲ A large block P executes horizontal simple harmonic motion as it slides across a frictionless surface with a frequency $f = 1.50$ Hz. Block B rests on it as shown in Figure P15.49, and the coefficient of static friction between the two is $\mu_s = 0.600$. What maximum amplitude of oscillation can the system have if block B is not to slip?

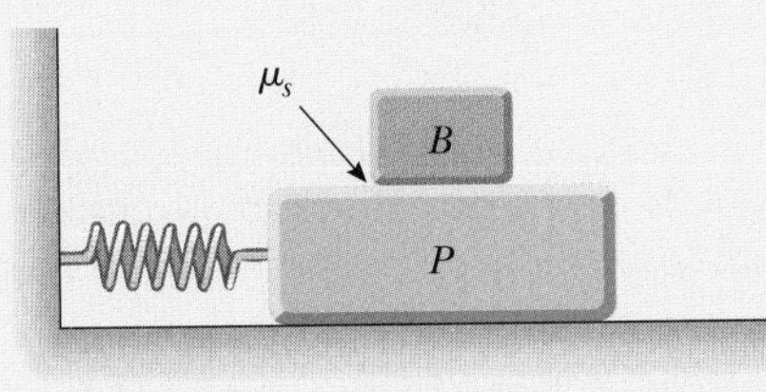

Figure P15.49 Problems 49 and 50.

50. A large block P executes horizontal simple harmonic motion as it slides across a frictionless surface with a frequency f. Block B rests on it as shown in Figure P15.49, and the coefficient of static friction between the two is μ_s. What maximum amplitude of oscillation can the system have if the upper block is not to slip?

51. The mass of the deuterium molecule (D_2) is twice that of the hydrogen molecule (H_2). If the vibrational frequency of H_2 is 1.30×10^{14} Hz, what is the vibrational frequency of D_2? Assume the "spring constant" of attracting forces is the same for the two molecules.

52. ● *You can now more completely analyze the situation in Problem 54 of Chapter 7.* Two steel balls, each of diameter 25.4 mm, move in opposite directions at 5.00 m/s. They collide head-on and bounce apart elastically. (a) Does their interaction last only for an instant or for a nonzero time interval? State your evidence. (b) One of the balls is squeezed in a vise while precise measurements are made of the resulting amount of compression. Assume Hooke's law is a good model of the ball's elastic behavior. For one datum, a force of 16.0 kN exerted by each jaw of the vise reduces the diameter by 0.200 mm. Modeling the ball as a spring, find its spring constant. (c) Assume the balls have the density of iron. Compute the kinetic energy of each ball before the balls collide. (d) Model each ball as a particle with a massless spring as its front bumper. Let the particle have the initial kinetic energy found in part (c) and the bumper have the spring constant found in part (b). Compute the maximum amount of compression each ball undergoes when the balls collide. (e) Model the motion of each ball, while the balls are in contact, as one half of a cycle of simple harmonic motion. Compute the time interval for which the balls are in contact.

53. A light, cubical container of volume a^3 is initially filled with a liquid of mass density ρ. The cube is initially supported by a light string to form a simple pendulum of length L_i, measured from the center of mass of the filled container, where $L_i >> a$. The liquid is allowed to flow from the bottom of the container at a constant rate (dM/dt). At any time t, the level of the fluid in the container is h and the length of the pendulum is L (measured relative to the instantaneous center of mass). (a) Sketch the apparatus and label the dimensions a, h, L_i, and L. (b) Find the time rate of change of the period as a function of time t. (c) Find the period as a function of time.

54. After a thrilling plunge, bungee jumpers bounce freely on the bungee cord through many cycles (Fig. P15.20). After the first few cycles, the cord does not go slack. Your younger brother can make a pest of himself by figuring out the mass of each person, using a proportion that you set up by solving this problem: An object of mass m is oscillating freely on a vertical spring with a period T. Another object of unknown mass m' on the same spring oscillates with a period T'. Determine (a) the spring constant and (b) the unknown mass.

55. A pendulum of length L and mass M has a spring of force constant k connected to it at a distance h below its point of suspension (Fig. P15.55). Find the frequency of vibration

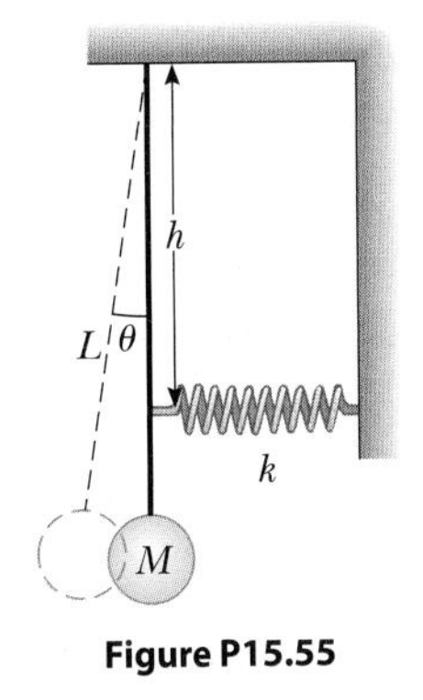

Figure P15.55

of the system for small values of the amplitude (small θ). Assume the vertical suspension rod of length L is rigid, but ignore its mass.

56. A particle with a mass of 0.500 kg is attached to a spring with a force constant of 50.0 N/m. At the moment $t = 0$, the particle has its maximum speed of 20.0 m/s and is moving to the left. (a) Determine the particle's equation of motion, specifying its position as a function of time. (b) Where in the motion is the potential energy three times the kinetic energy? (c) Find the length of a simple pendulum with the same period. (d) Find the minimum time interval required for the particle to move from $x = 0$ to $x = 1.00$ m.

57. A horizontal plank of mass m and length L is pivoted at one end. The plank's other end is supported by a spring of force constant k (Fig. P15.57). The moment of inertia of the plank about the pivot is $\frac{1}{3}mL^2$. The plank is displaced by a small angle θ from its horizontal equilibrium position and released. (a) Show that the plank moves with simple harmonic motion with an angular frequency $\omega = \sqrt{3k/m}$. (b) Evaluate the frequency, taking the mass as 5.00 kg and the spring force constant as 100 N/m.

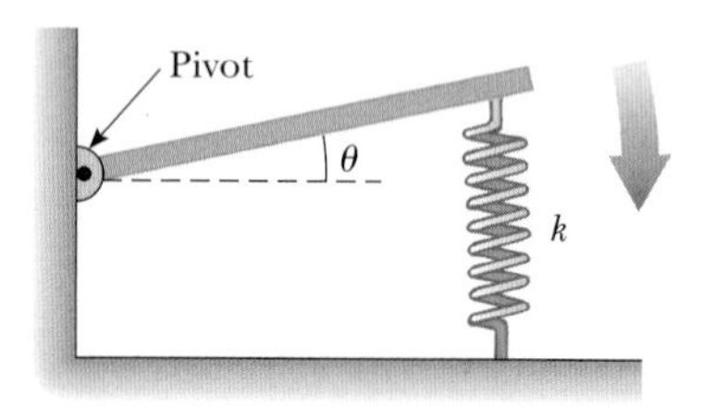

Figure P15.57

58. ● **Review problem.** A particle of mass 4.00 kg is attached to a spring with a force constant of 100 N/m. It is oscillating on a horizontal, frictionless surface with an amplitude of 2.00 m. A 6.00-kg object is dropped vertically on top of the 4.00-kg object as it passes through its equilibrium point. The two objects stick together. (a) By how much does the amplitude of the vibrating system change as a result of the collision? (b) By how much does the period change? (c) By how much does the energy change? (d) Account for the change in energy.

59. A simple pendulum with a length of 2.23 m and a mass of 6.74 kg is given an initial speed of 2.06 m/s at its equilibrium position. Assume it undergoes simple harmonic motion. Determine its (a) period, (b) total energy, and (c) maximum angular displacement.

60. **Review problem.** One end of a light spring with force constant 100 N/m is attached to a vertical wall. A light string is tied to the other end of the horizontal spring. The string changes from horizontal to vertical as it passes over a solid pulley of diameter 4.00 cm. The pulley is free to turn on a fixed, smooth axle. The vertical section of the string supports a 200-g object. The string does not slip at its contact with the pulley. Find the frequency of oscillation of the object, assuming the mass of the pulley is (a) negligible, (b) 250 g, and (c) 750 g.

61. ● People who ride motorcycles and bicycles learn to look out for bumps in the road and especially for *washboarding*, a condition in which many equally spaced ridges are worn into the road. What is so bad about washboarding? A motorcycle has several springs and shock absorbers in its suspension, but you can model it as a single spring supporting a block. You can estimate the force constant by thinking about how far the spring compresses when a heavy rider sits on the seat. A motorcyclist traveling at highway speed must be particularly careful of washboard bumps that are a certain distance apart. What is the order of magnitude of their separation distance? State the quantities you take as data and the values you measure or estimate for them.

62. A block of mass M is connected to a spring of mass m and oscillates in simple harmonic motion on a horizontal, frictionless track (Fig. P15.62). The force constant of the spring is k, and the equilibrium length is ℓ. Assume all portions of the spring oscillate in phase and the velocity of a segment dx is proportional to the distance x from the fixed end; that is, $v_x = (x/\ell)v$. Also, notice that the mass of a segment of the spring is $dm = (m/\ell)\,dx$. Find (a) the kinetic energy of the system when the block has a speed v and (b) the period of oscillation.

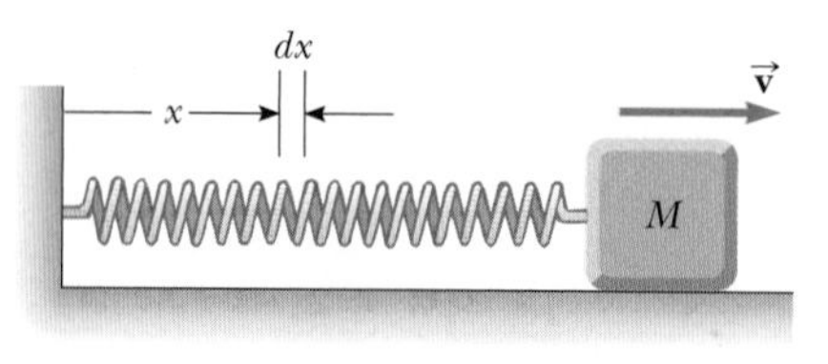

Figure P15.62

63. ▲ A ball of mass m is connected to two rubber bands of length L, each under tension T as shown in Figure P15.63. The ball is displaced by a small distance y perpendicular to the length of the rubber bands. Assuming the tension does not change, show that (a) the restoring force is $-(2T/L)y$ and (b) the system exhibits simple harmonic motion with an angular frequency $\omega = \sqrt{2T/mL}$.

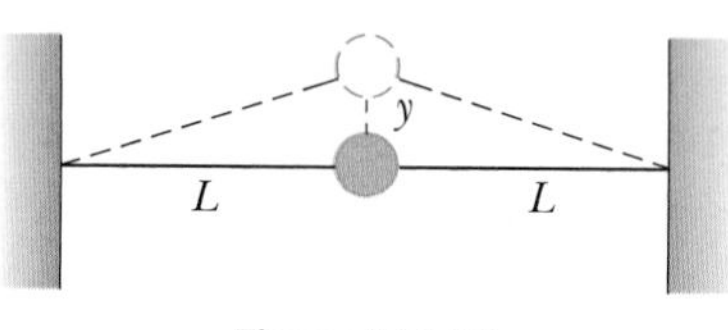

Figure P15.63

64. When a block of mass M, connected to the end of a spring of mass $m_s = 7.40$ g and force constant k, is set into simple harmonic motion, the period of its motion is

$$T = 2\pi\sqrt{\frac{M + (m_s/3)}{k}}$$

A two-part experiment is conducted with the use of blocks of various masses suspended vertically from the spring as shown in Figure P15.64. (a) Static extensions of 17.0, 29.3, 35.3, 41.3, 47.1, and 49.3 cm are measured for M values of 20.0, 40.0, 50.0, 60.0, 70.0, and 80.0 g, respectively. Construct a graph of Mg versus x and perform a linear least-squares fit to the data. From the slope of your graph, determine a value for k for this spring. (b) The system is now set into simple harmonic motion, and periods are measured with a stopwatch. With $M = 80.0$ g, the total time interval required for ten oscillations is measured to be 13.41 s. The experiment is repeated with M values of 70.0, 60.0, 50.0, 40.0, and 20.0 g, with corresponding time intervals for ten oscillations of 12.52, 11.67, 10.67, 9.62, and 7.03 s. Compute the experimental value for T from each of these measurements. Plot a graph of T^2 versus M and determine a value for k from the slope of the linear least-squares fit through the data points. Compare this value of k with that obtained in part (a). (c) Obtain a value for m_s from your graph and compare it with the given value of 7.40 g.

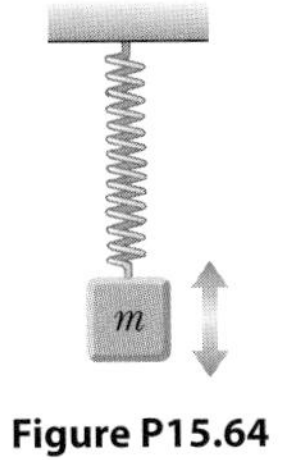

Figure P15.64

65. A smaller disk of radius r and mass m is attached rigidly to the face of a second larger disk of radius R and mass M as shown in Figure P15.65. The center of the small disk is located at the edge of the large disk. The large disk is mounted at its center on a frictionless axle. The assembly is rotated through a small angle θ from its equilibrium position and released. (a) Show that the speed of the center of the small disk as it passes through the equilibrium position is

$$v = 2\left[\frac{Rg(1 - \cos\theta)}{(M/m) + (r/R)^2 + 2}\right]^{1/2}$$

(b) Show that the period of the motion is

$$T = 2\pi\left[\frac{(M + 2m)R^2 + mr^2}{2mgR}\right]^{1/2}$$

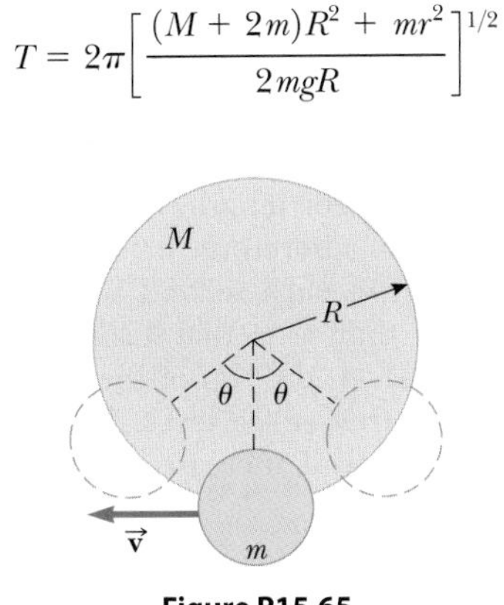

Figure P15.65

66. Consider a damped oscillator illustrated in Figures 15.20 and 15.21. The mass of the object is 375 g, the spring constant is 100 N/m, and b = 0.100 N · s/m. (a) Over what time interval does the amplitude drop to half its initial value? (b) **What If?** Over what time interval does the mechanical energy drop to half its initial value? (c) Show that, in general, the fractional rate at which the amplitude decreases in a damped harmonic oscillator is one-half the fractional rate at which the mechanical energy decreases.

67. A block of mass m is connected to two springs of force constants k_1 and k_2 in two ways as shown in Figures P15.67a and P15.67b. In both cases, the block moves on a frictionless table after it is displaced from equilibrium and released. Show that in the two cases the block exhibits simple harmonic motion with periods

$$\text{(a)}\ T = 2\pi\sqrt{\frac{m(k_1 + k_2)}{k_1 k_2}} \quad \text{and} \quad \text{(b)}\ T = 2\pi\sqrt{\frac{m}{k_1 + k_2}}$$

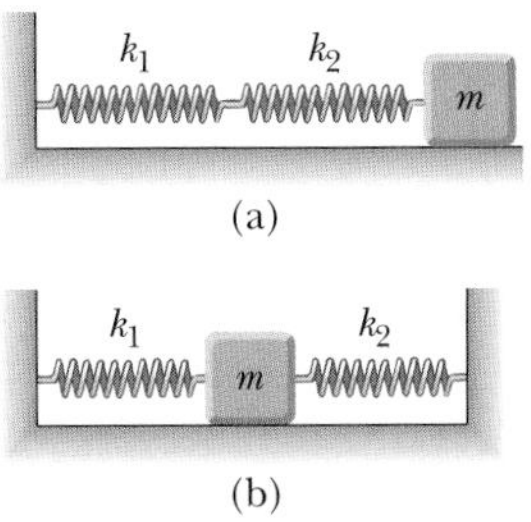

(a)

(b)

Figure P15.67

68. A lobsterman's buoy is a solid wooden cylinder of radius r and mass M. It is weighted at one end so that it floats upright in calm seawater, having density ρ. A passing shark tugs on the slack rope mooring the buoy to a lobster trap, pulling the buoy down a distance x from its equilibrium position and releasing it. Show that the buoy will execute simple harmonic motion if the resistive effects of the water are ignored and determine the period of the oscillations.

69. **Review problem.** Imagine that a hole is drilled through the center of the Earth to the other side. An object of mass m at a distance r from the center of the Earth is pulled toward the center of the Earth only by the mass within the sphere of radius r (the reddish region in Fig. P15.69). (a) Write Newton's law of gravitation for an object at the distance r from the center of the Earth and show that the force on it is of Hooke's law form, $F = -kr$, where the effective force constant is $k = \frac{4}{3}\pi\rho Gm$. Here ρ is the density of the Earth, assumed uniform, and G is the gravitational constant. (b) Show that a sack of mail dropped into the hole will execute simple harmonic motion if it moves without friction. When will it arrive at the other side of the Earth?

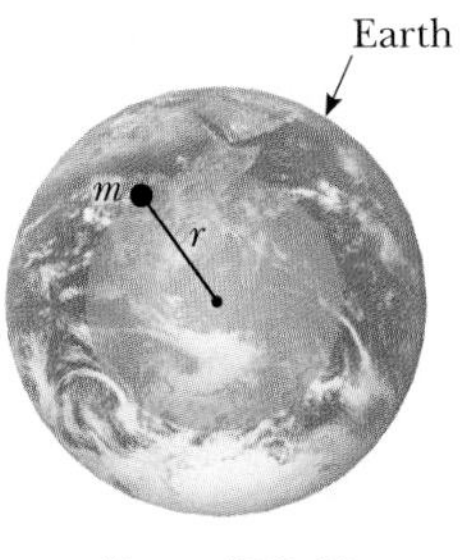

Figure P15.69

70. Your thumb squeaks on a plate you have just washed. Your sneakers squeak on the gym floor. Car tires squeal when you start or stop abruptly. Mortise joints groan in an old barn. The concertmaster's violin sings out over a full orchestra. You can make a goblet sing by wiping your moistened finger around its rim. As you slide it across the table, a Styrofoam cup may not make much sound, but it

makes the surface of some water inside it dance in a complicated resonance vibration. When chalk squeaks on a blackboard, you can see that it makes a row of regularly spaced dashes. As these examples suggest, vibration commonly results when friction acts on a moving elastic object. The oscillation is not simple harmonic motion, but is called *stick and slip*. This problem models stick-and-slip motion.

A block of mass m is attached to a fixed support by a horizontal spring with force constant k and negligible mass (Fig. P15.70). Hooke's law describes the spring both in extension and in compression. The block sits on a long horizontal board, with which it has coefficient of static friction μ_s and a smaller coefficient of kinetic friction μ_k. The board moves to the right at constant speed v. Assume the block spends most of its time sticking to the board and moving to the right, so the speed v is small in comparison to the average speed the block has as it slips back toward the left. (a) Show that the maximum extension of the spring from its unstressed position is very nearly given by $\mu_s mg/k$. (b) Show that the block oscillates around an equilibrium position at which the spring is stretched by $\mu_k mg/k$. (c) Graph the block's position versus time. (d) Show that the amplitude of the block's motion is

$$A = \frac{(\mu_s - \mu_k)mg}{k}$$

(e) Show that the period of the block's motion is

$$T = \frac{2(\mu_s - \mu_k)mg}{vk} + \pi\sqrt{\frac{m}{k}}$$

(f) Evaluate the frequency of the motion, taking $\mu_s = 0.400$, $\mu_k = 0.250$, $m = 0.300$ kg, $k = 12.0$ N/m, and $v = 2.40$ cm/s. (g) **What If?** What happens to the frequency if the mass increases? (h) If the spring constant increases? (i) If the speed of the board increases? (j) If the coefficient of static friction increases relative to the coefficient of kinetic friction? It is the excess of static over kinetic friction that is important for the vibration. "The squeaky wheel gets the grease" because even a viscous fluid cannot exert a force of static friction.

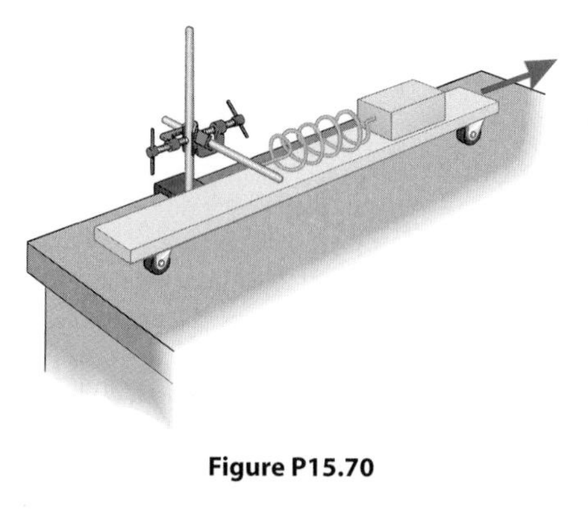

Figure P15.70

Answers to Quick Quizzes

15.1 (d). From its maximum positive position to the equilibrium position, the block travels a distance A. Next, it goes an equal distance past the equilibrium position to its maximum negative position. It then repeats these two motions in the reverse direction to return to its original position and complete one cycle.

15.2 (f). The object is in the region $x < 0$, so the position is negative. Because the object is moving back toward the origin in this region, the velocity is positive.

15.3 (a). The amplitude is larger because the curve for object B shows that the displacement from the origin (the vertical axis on the graph) is larger. The frequency is larger for object B because there are more oscillations per unit time interval.

15.4 (b). According to Equation 15.13, the period is proportional to the square root of the mass.

15.5 (c). The amplitude of the simple harmonic motion is the same as the radius of the circular motion. The initial position of the object in its circular motion is π radians from the positive x axis.

15.6 **(i)**, (a). With a longer length, the period of the pendulum will increase. Therefore, it will take longer to execute each swing, so each second according to the clock will take longer than an actual second and the clock will run slow. **(ii)**, (a). At the top of the mountain, the value of g is less than that at sea level. As a result, the period of the pendulum will increase and the clock will run slow.

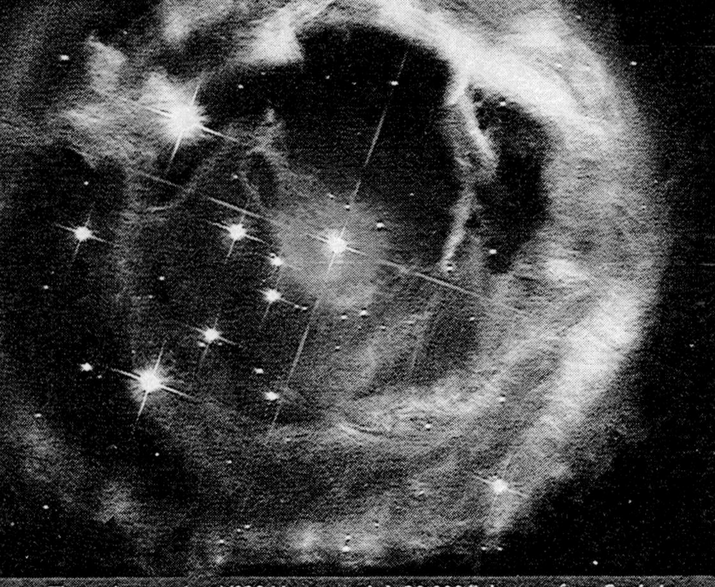

The red supergiant V838 Monocerotis is 20 000 lightyears from Earth. In 2002, the star exhibited a major outburst of energy typical of a nova event. Following the outburst, however, the variable behavior of infrared radiation from the star did not follow the typical nova pattern. Models of gravitational interaction leading to the merging of the star with a binary companion or its own planets have been proposed to explain the unusual behavior. (©STScI/NASA/Corbis)

13 Universal Gravitation

Before 1687, a large amount of data had been collected on the motions of the Moon and the planets, but a clear understanding of the forces related to these motions was not available. In that year, Isaac Newton provided the key that unlocked the secrets of the heavens. He knew, from his first law, that a net force had to be acting on the Moon because without such a force the Moon would move in a straight-line path rather than in its almost circular orbit. Newton reasoned that this force was the gravitational attraction exerted by the Earth on the Moon. He realized that the forces involved in the Earth–Moon attraction and in the Sun–planet attraction were not something special to those systems, but rather were particular cases of a general and universal attraction between objects. In other words, Newton saw that the same force of attraction that causes the Moon to follow its path around the Earth also causes an apple to fall from a tree. It was the first time that "earthly" and "heavenly" motions were unified.

In this chapter, we study the law of universal gravitation. We emphasize a description of planetary motion because astronomical data provide an important test of this law's validity. We then show that the laws of planetary motion developed by Johannes Kepler follow from the law of universal gravitation and the principle of conservation of angular momentum. We conclude by deriving a general expression for gravitational potential energy and examining the energetics of planetary and satellite motion.

13.1 Newton's Law of Universal Gravitation

You may have heard the legend that, while napping under a tree, Newton was struck on the head by a falling apple. This alleged accident supposedly prompted him to imagine that perhaps all objects in the Universe were attracted to each other in the same way the apple was attracted to the Earth. Newton analyzed astronomical data on the motion of the Moon around the Earth. From that analysis, he made the bold assertion that the force law governing the motion of planets was the *same* as the force law that attracted a falling apple to the Earth.

In 1687, Newton published his work on the law of gravity in his treatise *Mathematical Principles of Natural Philosophy.* **Newton's law of universal gravitation** states that

> every particle in the Universe attracts every other particle with a force that is directly proportional to the product of their masses and inversely proportional to the square of the distance between them.

◀ The law of universal gravitation

If the particles have masses m_1 and m_2 and are separated by a distance r, the magnitude of this gravitational force is

$$F_g = G\frac{m_1 m_2}{r^2} \tag{13.1}$$

where G is a constant, called the *universal gravitational constant.* Its value in SI units is

$$G = 6.673 \times 10^{-11}\ \text{N}\cdot\text{m}^2/\text{kg}^2 \tag{13.2}$$

Henry Cavendish (1731–1810) measured the universal gravitational constant in an important 1798 experiment. Cavendish's apparatus consists of two small spheres, each of mass m, fixed to the ends of a light, horizontal rod suspended by a fine fiber or thin metal wire as illustrated in Figure 13.1. When two large spheres, each of mass M, are placed near the smaller ones, the attractive force between smaller and larger spheres causes the rod to rotate and twist the wire suspension to a new equilibrium orientation. The angle of rotation is measured by the deflection of a light beam reflected from a mirror attached to the vertical suspension.

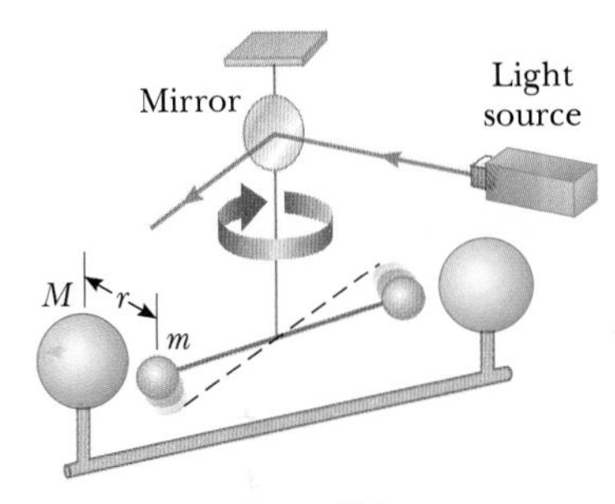

Figure 13.1 Cavendish apparatus for measuring G. The dashed line represents the original position of the rod.

The form of the force law given by Equation 13.1 is often referred to as an **inverse-square law** because the magnitude of the force varies as the inverse square of the separation of the particles.[1] We shall see other examples of this type of force law in subsequent chapters. We can express this force in vector form by defining a unit vector $\hat{\mathbf{r}}_{12}$ (Active Fig. 13.2). Because this unit vector is directed from particle 1 toward particle 2, the force exerted by particle 1 on particle 2 is

$$\vec{\mathbf{F}}_{12} = -G\frac{m_1 m_2}{r^2}\hat{\mathbf{r}}_{12} \tag{13.3}$$

where the negative sign indicates that particle 2 is attracted to particle 1; hence, the force on particle 2 must be directed toward particle 1. By Newton's third law, the force exerted by particle 2 on particle 1, designated $\vec{\mathbf{F}}_{21}$, is equal in magnitude to $\vec{\mathbf{F}}_{12}$ and in the opposite direction. That is, these forces form an action–reaction pair, and $\vec{\mathbf{F}}_{21} = -\vec{\mathbf{F}}_{12}$.

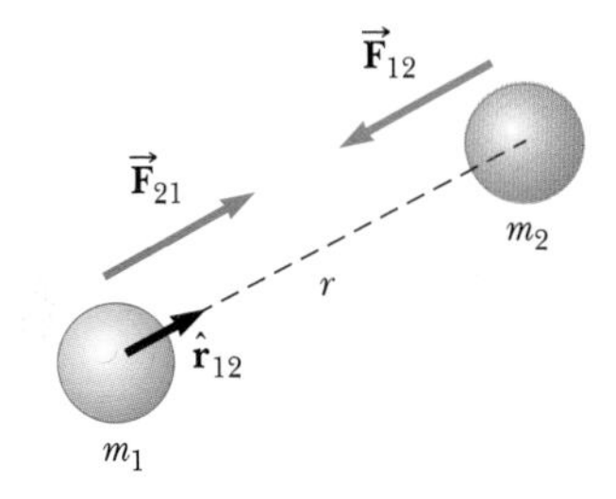

ACTIVE FIGURE 13.2

The gravitational force between two particles is attractive. The unit vector $\hat{\mathbf{r}}_{12}$ is directed from particle 1 toward particle 2. Notice that $\vec{\mathbf{F}}_{21} = -\vec{\mathbf{F}}_{12}$.

Sign in at www.thomsonedu.com and go to ThomsonNOW to change the masses of the particles and the separation distance between the particles and see the effect on the gravitational force.

Two features of Equation 13.3 deserve mention. First, the gravitational force is a field force that always exists between two particles, regardless of the medium that separates them. Because the force varies as the inverse square of the distance between the particles, it decreases rapidly with increasing separation.

Equation 13.3 can also be used to show that **the gravitational force exerted by a finite-size, spherically symmetric mass distribution on a particle outside the**

[1] An *inverse* proportionality between two quantities x and y is one in which $y = k/x$, where k is a constant. A *direct* proportion between x and y exists when $y = kx$.

PITFALL PREVENTION 13.1
Be Clear on g and G

The symbol g represents the magnitude of the free-fall acceleration near a planet. At the surface of the Earth, g has an average value of 9.80 m/s^2. On the other hand, G is a universal constant that has the same value everywhere in the Universe.

distribution is the same as if the entire mass of the distribution were concentrated at the center. For example, the magnitude of the force exerted by the Earth on a particle of mass m near the Earth's surface is

$$F_g = G\frac{M_E m}{R_E^2} \quad (13.4)$$

where M_E is the Earth's mass and R_E its radius. This force is directed toward the center of the Earth.

Quick Quiz 13.1 A planet has two moons of equal mass. Moon 1 is in a circular orbit of radius r. Moon 2 is in a circular orbit of radius $2r$. What is the magnitude of the gravitational force exerted by the planet on Moon 2? (a) four times as large as that on Moon 1 (b) twice as large as that on Moon 1 (c) equal to that on Moon 1 (d) half as large as that on Moon 1 (e) one-fourth as large as that on Moon 1

EXAMPLE 13.1 Billiards, Anyone?

Three 0.300-kg billiard balls are placed on a table at the corners of a right triangle as shown in Figure 13.3. The sides of the triangle are of lengths a = 0.400 m, b = 0.300 m, and c = 0.500 m. Calculate the gravitational force vector on the cue ball (designated m_1) resulting from the other two balls as well as the magnitude and direction of this force.

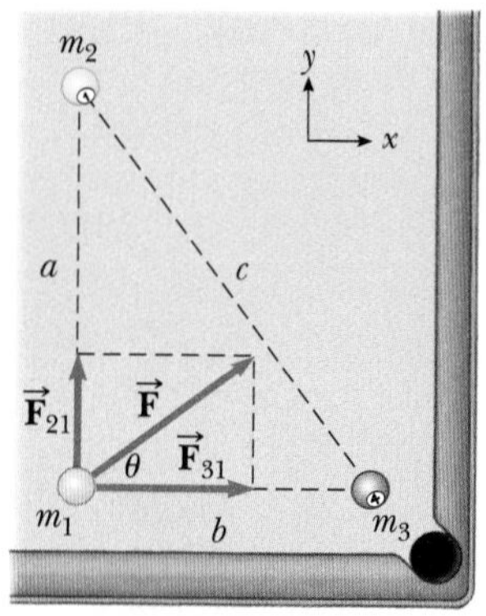

Figure 13.3 (Example 13.1) The resultant gravitational force acting on the cue ball is the vector sum $\vec{\mathbf{F}}_{21} + \vec{\mathbf{F}}_{31}$.

SOLUTION

Conceptualize Notice in Figure 13.3 that the cue ball is attracted to both other balls by the gravitational force. We can see graphically that the net force should point upward and toward the right. We locate our coordinate axes as shown in Figure 13.3, placing our origin at the position of the cue ball.

Categorize This problem involves evaluating the gravitational forces on the cue ball using Equation 13.3. Once these forces are evaluated, it becomes a vector addition problem to find the net force.

Analyze Find the force exerted by m_2 on the cue ball:

$$\vec{\mathbf{F}}_{21} = G\frac{m_2 m_1}{r_{21}^2}\,\hat{\mathbf{j}}$$

$$= (6.67 \times 10^{-11}\ \mathrm{N\cdot m^2/kg^2})\frac{(0.300\ \mathrm{kg})(0.300\ \mathrm{kg})}{(0.400\ \mathrm{m})^2}\,\hat{\mathbf{j}}$$

$$= 3.75 \times 10^{-11}\,\hat{\mathbf{j}}\ \mathrm{N}$$

Find the force exerted by m_3 on the cue ball:

$$\vec{\mathbf{F}}_{31} = G\frac{m_3 m_1}{r_{31}^2}\,\hat{\mathbf{i}}$$

$$= (6.67 \times 10^{-11}\ \mathrm{N\cdot m^2/kg^2})\frac{(0.300\ \mathrm{kg})(0.300\ \mathrm{kg})}{(0.300\ \mathrm{m})^2}\,\hat{\mathbf{i}}$$

$$= 6.67 \times 10^{-11}\,\hat{\mathbf{i}}\ \mathrm{N}$$

Find the net gravitational force on the cue ball by adding these force vectors:

$$\vec{\mathbf{F}} = \vec{\mathbf{F}}_{31} + \vec{\mathbf{F}}_{21} = (6.67\,\hat{\mathbf{i}} + 3.75\,\hat{\mathbf{j}}) \times 10^{-11}\ \mathrm{N}$$

Find the magnitude of this force:

$$F = \sqrt{F_{31}^2 + F_{21}^2} = \sqrt{(6.67)^2 + (3.75)^2} \times 10^{-11}\ \mathrm{N}$$

$$= 7.65 \times 10^{-11}\ \mathrm{N}$$

Find the tangent of the angle θ for the net force vector:

$$\tan\theta = \frac{F_y}{F_x} = \frac{F_{21}}{F_{31}} = \frac{3.75 \times 10^{-11}\text{ N}}{6.67 \times 10^{-11}\text{ N}} = 0.562$$

Evaluate the angle θ:

$$\theta = \tan^{-1}(0.562) = 29.3°$$

Finalize The result for F shows that the gravitational forces between everyday objects have extremely small magnitudes.

13.2 Free-Fall Acceleration and the Gravitational Force

Because the magnitude of the force acting on a freely falling object of mass m near the Earth's surface is given by Equation 13.4, we can equate this force to that given by Equation 5.6, $F_g = mg$, to obtain

$$mg = G\frac{M_E m}{R_E^2}$$

$$g = G\frac{M_E}{R_E^2} \quad (13.5)$$

Now consider an object of mass m located a distance h above the Earth's surface or a distance r from the Earth's center, where $r = R_E + h$. The magnitude of the gravitational force acting on this object is

$$F_g = G\frac{M_E m}{r^2} = G\frac{M_E m}{(R_E + h)^2}$$

The magnitude of the gravitational force acting on the object at this position is also $F_g = mg$, where g is the value of the free-fall acceleration at the altitude h. Substituting this expression for F_g into the last equation shows that g is given by

$$g = \frac{GM_E}{r^2} = \frac{GM_E}{(R_E + h)^2} \quad (13.6)$$

◀ Variation of g with altitude

Therefore, it follows that g *decreases* with *increasing altitude*. Values of g at various altitudes are listed in Table 13.1. Because an object's weight is mg, we see that as $r \to \infty$, the weight approaches zero.

TABLE 13.1

Free-Fall Acceleration g at Various Altitudes Above the Earth's Surface

Altitude h (km)	g (m/s^2)
1 000	7.33
2 000	5.68
3 000	4.53
4 000	3.70
5 000	3.08
6 000	2.60
7 000	2.23
8 000	1.93
9 000	1.69
10 000	1.49
50 000	0.13
∞	0

Quick Quiz 13.2 Superman stands on top of a very tall mountain and throws a baseball horizontally with a speed such that the baseball goes into a circular orbit around the Earth. While the baseball is in orbit, what is the magnitude of the acceleration of the ball? (a) It depends on how fast the baseball is thrown. (b) It is zero because the ball does not fall to the ground. (c) It is slightly less than 9.80 m/s^2. (d) It is equal to 9.80 m/s^2.

EXAMPLE 13.2 Variation of g with Altitude h

The International Space Station operates at an altitude of 350 km. Plans for the final construction show that 4.22×10^6 N of material, measured at the Earth's surface, will have been lifted off the surface by various spacecraft. What is the weight of the space station when in orbit?

SOLUTION

Conceptualize The mass of the space station is fixed; it is independent of its location. Based on the discussion in this section, we realize that the value of g will be reduced at the height of the space station's orbit. Therefore, its weight will be smaller than that at the surface of the Earth.

Categorize This example is a relatively simple substitution problem.

Find the mass of the space station from its weight at the surface of the Earth:

$$m = \frac{F_g}{g} = \frac{4.22 \times 10^6\ \text{N}}{9.80\ \text{m/s}^2} = 4.31 \times 10^5\ \text{kg}$$

Use Equation 13.6 with $h = 350$ km to find g at the orbital location:

$$g = \frac{GM_E}{(R_E + h)^2}$$

$$= \frac{(6.67 \times 10^{-11}\ \text{N}\cdot\text{m}^2/\text{kg}^2)(5.98 \times 10^{24}\ \text{kg})}{(6.37 \times 10^6\ \text{m} + 0.350 \times 10^6\ \text{m})^2} = 8.83\ \text{m/s}^2$$

Use this value of g to find the space station's weight in orbit:

$$mg = (4.31 \times 10^5\ \text{kg})(8.83\ \text{m/s}^2) = 3.80 \times 10^6\ \text{N}$$

EXAMPLE 13.3 The Density of the Earth

Using the known radius of the Earth and that $g = 9.80\ \text{m/s}^2$ at the Earth's surface, find the average density of the Earth.

SOLUTION

Conceptualize Assume the Earth is a perfect sphere. The density of material in the Earth varies, but let's adopt a simplified model in which we assume the density to be uniform throughout the Earth. The resulting density is the average density of the Earth.

Categorize This example is a relatively simple substitution problem.

Solve Equation 13.5 for the mass of the Earth:

$$M_E = \frac{gR_E^{\,2}}{G}$$

Substitute this mass into the definition of density (Eq. 1.1):

$$\rho_E = \frac{M_E}{V_E} = \frac{(gR_E^{\,2}/G)}{\frac{4}{3}\pi R_E^{\,3}} = \frac{3}{4}\frac{g}{\pi G R_E}$$

$$= \frac{3}{4}\frac{9.80\ \text{m/s}^2}{\pi(6.67 \times 10^{-11}\ \text{N}\cdot\text{m}^2/\text{kg}^2)(6.37 \times 10^6\ \text{m})} = 5.51 \times 10^3\ \text{kg/m}^3$$

What If? What if you were told that a typical density of granite at the Earth's surface were $2.75 \times 10^3\ \text{kg/m}^3$. What would you conclude about the density of the material in the Earth's interior?

Answer Because this value is about half the density we calculated as an average for the entire Earth, we would conclude that the inner core of the Earth has a density much higher than the average value. It is most amazing that the Cavendish experiment—which determines G and can be done on a tabletop—combined with simple free-fall measurements of g, provides information about the core of the Earth!

13.3 Kepler's Laws and the Motion of Planets

Humans have observed the movements of the planets, stars, and other celestial objects for thousands of years. In early history, these observations led scientists to regard the Earth as the center of the Universe. This *geocentric model* was elaborated and formalized by the Greek astronomer Claudius Ptolemy (c. 100–c. 170) in the second century and was accepted for the next 1 400 years. In 1543, Polish astronomer Nicolaus Copernicus (1473–1543) suggested that the Earth and the other planets revolved in circular orbits around the Sun (the *heliocentric model*).

Danish astronomer Tycho Brahe (1546–1601) wanted to determine how the heavens were constructed and pursued a project to determine the positions of both stars and planets. Those observations of the planets and 777 stars visible to the naked eye were carried out with only a large sextant and a compass. (The telescope had not yet been invented.)

German astronomer Johannes Kepler was Brahe's assistant for a short while before Brahe's death, whereupon he acquired his mentor's astronomical data and spent 16 years trying to deduce a mathematical model for the motion of the planets. Such data are difficult to sort out because the moving planets are observed from a moving Earth. After many laborious calculations, Kepler found that Brahe's data on the revolution of Mars around the Sun led to a successful model.

Kepler's complete analysis of planetary motion is summarized in three statements known as **Kepler's laws:**

Art Resource

JOHANNES KEPLER
German astronomer (1571–1630)
Kepler is best known for developing the laws of planetary motion based on the careful observations of Tycho Brahe.

◀ Kepler's laws

1. All planets move in elliptical orbits with the Sun at one focus.
2. The radius vector drawn from the Sun to a planet sweeps out equal areas in equal time intervals.
3. The square of the orbital period of any planet is proportional to the cube of the semimajor axis of the elliptical orbit.

Kepler's First Law

We are familiar with circular orbits of objects around gravitational force centers from our discussions in this chapter. Kepler's first law indicates that the circular orbit is a very special case and elliptical orbits are the general situation. This notion was difficult for scientists of the time to accept because they believed that perfect circular orbits of the planets reflected the perfection of heaven.

Active Figure 13.4 shows the geometry of an ellipse, which serves as our model for the elliptical orbit of a planet. An ellipse is mathematically defined by choosing two points F_1 and F_2, each of which is a called a **focus,** and then drawing a curve through points for which the sum of the distances r_1 and r_2 from F_1 and F_2, respectively, is a constant. The longest distance through the center between points on the ellipse (and passing through each focus) is called the **major axis,** and this distance is $2a$. In Active Figure 13.4, the major axis is drawn along the x direction. The distance a is called the **semimajor axis.** Similarly, the shortest distance through the center between points on the ellipse is called the **minor axis** of length $2b$, where the distance b is the **semiminor axis.** Either focus of the ellipse is located at a distance c from the center of the ellipse, where $a^2 = b^2 + c^2$. In the elliptical orbit of a planet around the Sun, the Sun is at one focus of the ellipse. There is nothing at the other focus.

The **eccentricity** of an ellipse is defined as $e = c/a$, and it describes the general shape of the ellipse. For a circle, $c = 0$, and the eccentricity is therefore zero. The smaller b is compared to a, the shorter the ellipse is along the y direction compared with its extent in the x direction in Active Figure 13.4. As b decreases, c increases and the eccentricity e increases. Therefore, higher values of eccentricity correspond to longer and thinner ellipses. The range of values of the eccentricity for an ellipse is $0 < e < 1$.

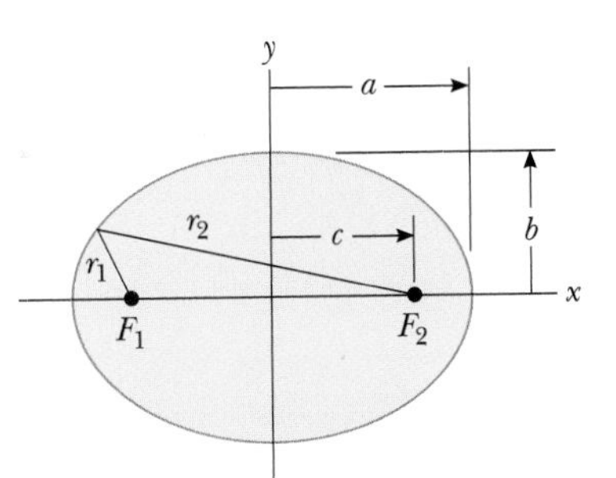

ACTIVE FIGURE 13.4

Plot of an ellipse. The semimajor axis has length a, and the semiminor axis has length b. Each focus is located at a distance c from the center on each side of the center.

Sign in at www.thomsonedu.com and go to ThomsonNOW to move the focal points or enter values for a, b, c, and the eccentricity $e = c/a$ and see the resulting elliptical shape.

PITFALL PREVENTION 13.2
Where Is the Sun?

The Sun is located at one focus of the elliptical orbit of a planet. It is *not* located at the center of the ellipse.

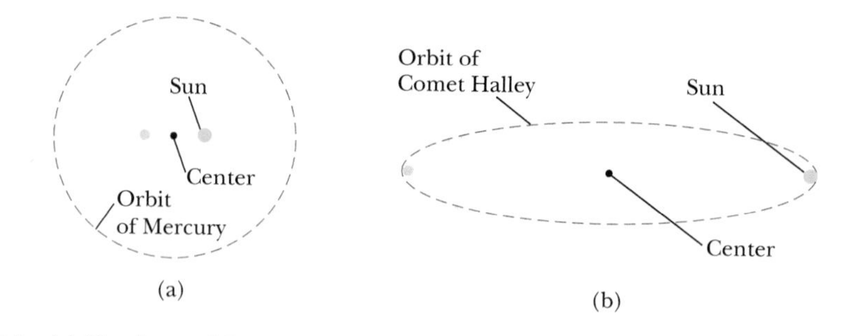

Figure 13.5 (a) The shape of the orbit of Mercury, which has the highest eccentricity ($e = 0.21$) among the eight planets in the solar system. The Sun is located at the large yellow dot, which is a focus of the ellipse. There is nothing physical located at the center (the small dot) or the other focus (the blue dot). (b) The shape of the orbit of Comet Halley.

Eccentricities for planetary orbits vary widely in the solar system. The eccentricity of the Earth's orbit is 0.017, which makes it nearly circular. On the other hand, the eccentricity of Mercury's orbit is 0.21, the highest of the eight planets. Figure 13.5a shows an ellipse with an eccentricity equal to that of Mercury's orbit. Notice that even this highest-eccentricity orbit is difficult to distinguish from a circle, which is one reason Kepler's first law is an admirable accomplishment. The eccentricity of the orbit of Comet Halley is 0.97, describing an orbit whose major axis is much longer than its minor axis, as shown in Figure 13.5b. As a result, Comet Halley spends much of its 76-year period far from the Sun and invisible from the Earth. It is only visible to the naked eye during a small part of its orbit when it is near the Sun.

Now imagine a planet in an elliptical orbit such as that shown in Active Figure 13.4, with the Sun at focus F_2. When the planet is at the far left in the diagram, the distance between the planet and the Sun is $a + c$. At this point, called the *aphelion,* the planet is at its maximum distance from the Sun. (For an object in orbit around the Earth, this point is called the *apogee.*) Conversely, when the planet is at the right end of the ellipse, the distance between the planet and the Sun is $a - c$. At this point, called the *perihelion* (for an Earth orbit, the *perigee*), the planet is at its minimum distance from the Sun.

Kepler's first law is a direct result of the inverse square nature of the gravitational force. We have already discussed circular and elliptical orbits, the allowed shapes of orbits for objects that are *bound* to the gravitational force center. These objects include planets, asteroids, and comets that move repeatedly around the Sun, as well as moons orbiting a planet. There are also *unbound* objects, such as a meteoroid from deep space that might pass by the Sun once and then never return. The gravitational force between the Sun and these objects also varies as the inverse square of the separation distance, and the allowed paths for these objects include parabolas ($e = 1$) and hyperbolas ($e > 1$).

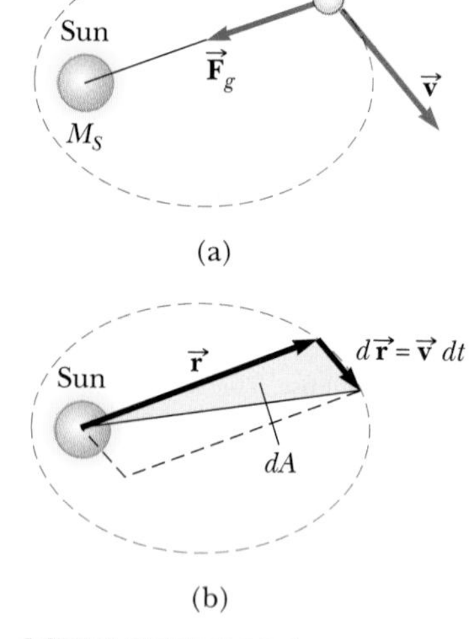

ACTIVE FIGURE 13.6

(a) The gravitational force acting on a planet is directed toward the Sun. (b) As a planet orbits the Sun, the area swept out by the radius vector in a time interval dt is equal to half the area of the parallelogram formed by the vectors $\vec{\mathbf{r}}$ and $d\vec{\mathbf{r}} = \vec{\mathbf{v}}\,dt$.

Sign in at www.thomsonedu.com and go to ThomsonNOW to assign a value of the eccentricity and see the resulting motion of the planet around the Sun.

Kepler's Second Law

Kepler's second law can be shown to be a consequence of angular momentum conservation as follows. Consider a planet of mass M_p moving about the Sun in an elliptical orbit (Active Fig. 13.6a). Let us consider the planet as a system. We model the Sun to be so much more massive than the planet that the Sun does not move. The gravitational force exerted by the Sun on the planet is a central force, always along the radius vector, directed toward the Sun (Active Fig. 13.6a). The torque on the planet due to this central force is clearly zero because $\vec{\mathbf{F}}_g$ is parallel to $\vec{\mathbf{r}}$.

Recall that the external net torque on a system equals the time rate of change of angular momentum of the system; that is, $\sum \vec{\boldsymbol{\tau}} = d\vec{\mathbf{L}}/dt$ (Eq. 11.13). Therefore, because the external torque on the planet is zero, it is modeled as an isolated system for angular momentum and **the angular momentum $\vec{\mathbf{L}}$ of the planet is a constant of the motion:**

$$\vec{\mathbf{L}} = \vec{\mathbf{r}} \times \vec{\mathbf{p}} = M_p \vec{\mathbf{r}} \times \vec{\mathbf{v}} = \text{constant}$$

We can relate this result to the following geometric consideration. In a time interval dt, the radius vector $\vec{\mathbf{r}}$ in Active Figure 13.6b sweeps out the area dA, which equals half the area $|\vec{\mathbf{r}} \times d\vec{\mathbf{r}}|$ of the parallelogram formed by the vectors $\vec{\mathbf{r}}$ and $d\vec{\mathbf{r}}$. Because the displacement of the planet in the time interval dt is given by $d\vec{\mathbf{r}} = \vec{\mathbf{v}}dt$,

$$dA = \tfrac{1}{2}|\vec{\mathbf{r}} \times d\vec{\mathbf{r}}| = \tfrac{1}{2}|\vec{\mathbf{r}} \times \vec{\mathbf{v}}\,dt| = \frac{L}{2M_p}\,dt$$

$$\frac{dA}{dt} = \frac{L}{2M_p} \tag{13.7}$$

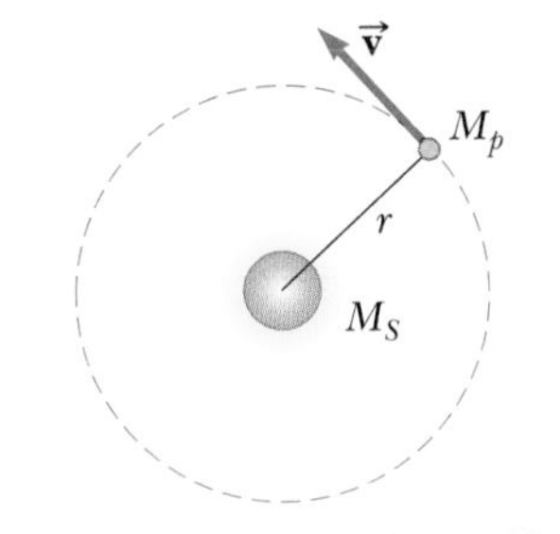

Figure 13.7 A planet of mass M_p moving in a circular orbit around the Sun. The orbits of all planets except Mercury are nearly circular.

where L and M_p are both constants. This result shows that that **the radius vector from the Sun to any planet sweeps out equal areas in equal times.**

This conclusion is a result of the gravitational force being a central force, which in turn implies that angular momentum of the planet is constant. Therefore, the law applies to *any* situation that involves a central force, whether inverse square or not.

Kepler's Third Law

Kepler's third law can be predicted from the inverse-square law for circular orbits. Consider a planet of mass M_p that is assumed to be moving about the Sun (mass M_S) in a circular orbit as in Figure 13.7. Because the gravitational force provides the centripetal acceleration of the planet as it moves in a circle, we use Newton's second law for a particle in uniform circular motion,

$$F_g = \frac{GM_SM_p}{r^2} = M_pa = \frac{M_pv^2}{r}$$

The orbital speed of the planet is $2\pi r/T$, where T is the period; therefore, the preceding expression becomes

$$\frac{GM_S}{r^2} = \frac{(2\pi r/T)^2}{r}$$

$$T^2 = \left(\frac{4\pi^2}{GM_S}\right)r^3 = K_Sr^3$$

where K_S is a constant given by

$$K_S = \frac{4\pi^2}{GM_S} = 2.97 \times 10^{-19}\ \mathrm{s^2/m^3}$$

This equation is also valid for elliptical orbits if we replace r with the length a of the semimajor axis (Active Fig. 13.4):

$$T^2 = \left(\frac{4\pi^2}{GM_S}\right)a^3 = K_Sa^3 \tag{13.8}$$

◀ Kepler's third law

Equation 13.8 is Kepler's third law. Because the semimajor axis of a circular orbit is its radius, this equation is valid for both circular and elliptical orbits. Notice that the constant of proportionality K_S is independent of the mass of the planet. Equation 13.8 is therefore valid for *any* planet.[2] If we were to consider the orbit of a satellite such as the Moon about the Earth, the constant would have a different value, with the Sun's mass replaced by the Earth's mass, that is, $K_E = 4\pi^2/GM_E$.

Table 13.2 is a collection of useful data for planets and other objects in the solar system. The far-right column verifies that the ratio T^2/r^3 is constant for all objects orbiting the Sun. The small variations in the values in this column are the result of uncertainties in the data measured for the periods and semimajor axes of the objects.

Recent astronomical work has revealed the existence of a large number of solar system objects beyond the orbit of Neptune. In general, these objects lie in the

[2] Equation 13.8 is indeed a proportion because the ratio of the two quantities T^2 and a^3 is a constant. The variables in a proportion are not required to be limited to the first power only.

TABLE 13.2

Useful Planetary Data

Body	Mass (kg)	Mean Radius (m)	Period of Revolution (s)	Mean Distance from the Sun (m)	$\frac{T^2}{r^3}$ (s²/m³)
Mercury	3.18×10^{23}	2.43×10^{6}	7.60×10^{6}	5.79×10^{10}	2.97×10^{-19}
Venus	4.88×10^{24}	6.06×10^{6}	1.94×10^{7}	1.08×10^{11}	2.99×10^{-19}
Earth	5.98×10^{24}	6.37×10^{6}	3.156×10^{7}	1.496×10^{11}	2.97×10^{-19}
Mars	6.42×10^{23}	3.37×10^{6}	5.94×10^{7}	2.28×10^{11}	2.98×10^{-19}
Jupiter	1.90×10^{27}	6.99×10^{7}	3.74×10^{8}	7.78×10^{11}	2.97×10^{-19}
Saturn	5.68×10^{26}	5.85×10^{7}	9.35×10^{8}	1.43×10^{12}	2.99×10^{-19}
Uranus	8.68×10^{25}	2.33×10^{7}	2.64×10^{9}	2.87×10^{12}	2.95×10^{-19}
Neptune	1.03×10^{26}	2.21×10^{7}	5.22×10^{9}	4.50×10^{12}	2.99×10^{-19}
Pluto[a]	$\approx 1.4 \times 10^{22}$	$\approx 1.5 \times 10^{6}$	7.82×10^{9}	5.91×10^{12}	2.96×10^{-19}
Moon	7.36×10^{22}	1.74×10^{6}	—	—	—
Sun	1.991×10^{30}	6.96×10^{8}	—	—	—

[a] In August, 2006, the International Astronomical Union adopted a definition of a planet that separates Pluto from the other eight planets. Pluto is now defined as a "dwarf planet" like the asteroid Ceres.

Kuiper belt, a region that extends from about 30 AU (the orbital radius of Neptune) to 50 AU. (An AU is an *astronomical unit,* equal to the radius of the Earth's orbit.) Current estimates identify at least 70 000 objects in this region with diameters larger than 100 km. The first Kuiper belt object (KBO) is Pluto, discovered in 1930, and formerly classified as a planet. Starting in 1992, many more have been detected, such as Varuna (diameter about 900–1 000 km, discovered in 2000), Ixion (diameter about 900–1 000 km, discovered in 2001), and Quaoar (diameter about 800 km, discovered in 2002). Others do not yet have names, but are currently indicated by their date of discovery, such as 2003 EL61, 2004 DW, and 2005 FY9. One KBO, 2003 UP313, is thought to be larger than Pluto.

A subset of about 1 400 KBOs are called "Plutinos" because, like Pluto, they exhibit a resonance phenomenon, orbiting the Sun two times in the same time interval as Neptune revolves three times. The contemporary application of Kepler's laws and such exotic proposals as planetary angular momentum exchange and migrating planets[3] suggest the excitement of this active area of current research.

Quick Quiz 13.3 An asteroid is in a highly eccentric elliptical orbit around the Sun. The period of the asteroid's orbit is 90 days. Which of the following statements is true about the possibility of a collision between this asteroid and the Earth? (a) There is no possible danger of a collision. (b) There is a possibility of a collision. (c) There is not enough information to determine whether there is danger of a collision.

EXAMPLE 13.4 The Mass of the Sun

Calculate the mass of the Sun noting that the period of the Earth's orbit around the Sun is 3.156×10^7 s and its distance from the Sun is 1.496×10^{11} m.

SOLUTION

Conceptualize Based on Kepler's third law, we realize that the mass of the Sun is related to the orbital size and period of a planet.

Categorize This example is a relatively simple substitution problem.

[3] R. Malhotra, "Migrating Planets," *Scientific American,* **281**(3): 56–63, September 1999.

Solve Equation 13.8 for the mass of the Sun:

$$M_S = \frac{4\pi^2 r^3}{GT^2}$$

Substitute the known values:

$$M_S = \frac{4\pi^2(1.496 \times 10^{11}\ \text{m})^3}{(6.67 \times 10^{-11}\ \text{N} \cdot \text{m}^2/\text{kg}^2)(3.156 \times 10^7\ \text{s})^2} = \boxed{1.99 \times 10^{30}\ \text{kg}}$$

In Example 13.3, an understanding of gravitational forces enabled us to find out something about the density of the Earth's core, and now we have used this understanding to determine the mass of the Sun!

EXAMPLE 13.5 **A Geosynchronous Satellite**

Consider a satellite of mass m moving in a circular orbit around the Earth at a constant speed v and at an altitude h above the Earth's surface as illustrated in Figure 13.8.

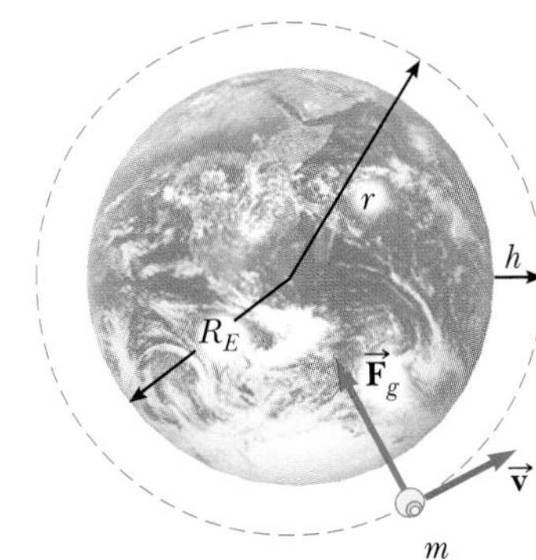

Figure 13.8 (Example 13.5) A satellite of mass m moving around the Earth in a circular orbit of radius r with constant speed v. The only force acting on the satellite is the gravitational force $\vec{F}_g$. (Not drawn to scale.)

(A) Determine the speed of the satellite in terms of G, h, R_E (the radius of the Earth), and M_E (the mass of the Earth).

SOLUTION

Conceptualize Imagine the satellite moving around the Earth in a circular orbit under the influence of the gravitational force.

Categorize The satellite must have a centripetal acceleration. Therefore, we categorize the satellite as a particle under a net force and a particle in uniform circular motion.

Analyze The only external force acting on the satellite is the gravitational force, which acts toward the center of the Earth and keeps the satellite in its circular orbit.

Apply Newton's second law to the satellite:

$$F_g = G\frac{M_E m}{r^2} = ma = m\frac{v^2}{r}$$

Solve for v, noting that the distance r from the center of the Earth to the satellite is $r = R_E + h$:

$$(1)\quad v = \sqrt{\frac{GM_E}{r}} = \boxed{\sqrt{\frac{GM_E}{R_E + h}}}$$

(B) If the satellite is to be *geosynchronous* (that is, appearing to remain over a fixed position on the Earth), how fast is it moving through space?

SOLUTION

To appear to remain over a fixed position on the Earth, the period of the satellite must be 24 h = 86 400 s and the satellite must be in orbit directly over the equator.

Solve Kepler's third law (with $a = r$ and $M_S \rightarrow M_E$) for r:

$$r = \left(\frac{GM_E T^2}{4\pi^2}\right)^{1/3}$$

Substitute numerical values:

$$r = \left[\frac{(6.67 \times 10^{-11}\ \text{N} \cdot \text{m}^2/\text{kg}^2)(5.98 \times 10^{24}\ \text{kg})(86\ 400\ \text{s})^2}{4\pi^2}\right]^{1/3}$$

$$= 4.23 \times 10^7\ \text{m}$$

Use Equation (1) to find the speed of the satellite:

$$v = \sqrt{\frac{(6.67 \times 10^{-11}\ \text{N}\cdot\text{m}^2/\text{kg}^2)(5.98 \times 10^{24}\ \text{kg})}{4.23 \times 10^{7}\ \text{m}}}$$

$$= 3.07 \times 10^{3}\ \text{m/s}$$

Finalize The value of r calculated here translates to a height of the satellite above the surface of the Earth of almost 36 000 km. Therefore, geosynchronous satellites have the advantage of allowing an earthbound antenna to be aimed in a fixed direction, but there is a disadvantage in that the signals between Earth and the satellite must travel a long distance. It is difficult to use geosynchronous satellites for optical observation of the Earth's surface because of their high altitude.

What If? What if the satellite motion in part (A) were taking place at height h above the surface of another planet more massive than the Earth but of the same radius? Would the satellite be moving at a higher speed or a lower speed than it does around the Earth?

Answer If the planet exerts a larger gravitational force on the satellite due to its larger mass, the satellite must move with a higher speed to avoid moving toward the surface. This conclusion is consistent with the predictions of Equation (1), which shows that because the speed v is proportional to the square root of the mass of the planet, the speed increases as the mass of the planet increases.

13.4 The Gravitational Field

When Newton published his theory of universal gravitation, it was considered a success because it satisfactorily explained the motion of the planets. Since 1687, the same theory has been used to account for the motions of comets, the deflection of a Cavendish balance, the orbits of binary stars, and the rotation of galaxies. Nevertheless, both Newton's contemporaries and his successors found it difficult to accept the concept of a force that acts at a distance. They asked how it was possible for two objects to interact when they were not in contact with each other. Newton himself could not answer that question.

An approach to describing interactions between objects that are not in contact came well after Newton's death. This approach enables us to look at the gravitational interaction in a different way, using the concept of a **gravitational field** that exists at every point in space. When a particle of mass m is placed at a point where the gravitational field is $\vec{\mathbf{g}}$, the particle experiences a force $\vec{\mathbf{F}}_g = m\vec{\mathbf{g}}$. In other words, we imagine that the field exerts a force on the particle rather than consider a direct interaction between two particles. The gravitational field $\vec{\mathbf{g}}$ is defined as

Gravitational field ▶

$$\vec{\mathbf{g}} \equiv \frac{\vec{\mathbf{F}}_g}{m} \qquad (13.9)$$

That is, the gravitational field at a point in space equals the gravitational force experienced by a *test particle* placed at that point divided by the mass of the test particle. We call the object creating the field the *source particle.* (Although the Earth is not a particle, it is possible to show that we can model the Earth as a particle for the purpose of finding the gravitational field that it creates.) Notice that the presence of the test particle is not necessary for the field to exist: the source particle creates the gravitational field. We can detect the presence of the field and measure its strength by placing a test particle in the field and noting the force exerted on it. In essence, we are describing the "effect" that any object (in this case, the Earth) has on the empty space around itself in terms of the force that *would* be present *if* a second object were somewhere in that space.[4]

[4] We shall return to this idea of mass affecting the space around it when we discuss Einstein's theory of gravitation in Chapter 39.

As an example of how the field concept works, consider an object of mass m near the Earth's surface. Because the gravitational force acting on the object has a magnitude GM_Em/r^2 (see Eq. 13.4), the field $\vec{\mathbf{g}}$ at a distance r from the center of the Earth is

$$\vec{\mathbf{g}} = \frac{\vec{\mathbf{F}}_g}{m} = -\frac{GM_E}{r^2}\hat{\mathbf{r}} \tag{13.10}$$

where $\hat{\mathbf{r}}$ is a unit vector pointing radially outward from the Earth and the negative sign indicates that the field points toward the center of the Earth as illustrated in Figure 13.9a. The field vectors at different points surrounding the Earth vary in both direction and magnitude. In a small region near the Earth's surface, the downward field $\vec{\mathbf{g}}$ is approximately constant and uniform as indicated in Figure 13.9b. Equation 13.10 is valid at all points *outside* the Earth's surface, assuming the Earth is spherical. At the Earth's surface, where $r = R_E$, $\vec{\mathbf{g}}$ has a magnitude of 9.80 N/kg. (The unit N/kg is the same as m/s^2.)

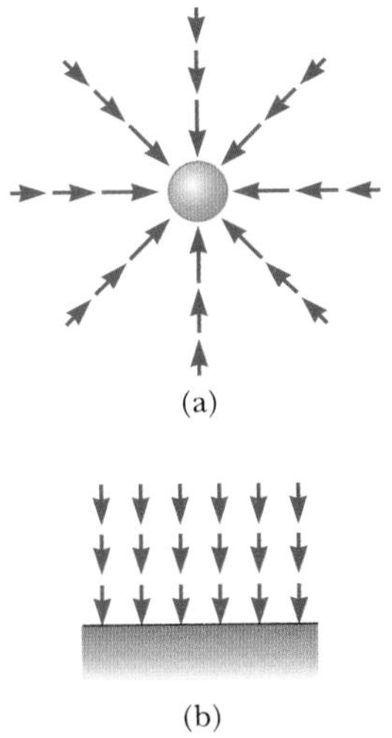

(a)

(b)

Figure 13.9 (a) The gravitational field vectors in the vicinity of a uniform spherical mass such as the Earth vary in both direction and magnitude. The vectors point in the direction of the acceleration a particle would experience if it were placed in the field. The magnitude of the field vector at any location is the magnitude of the free-fall acceleration at that location. (b) The gravitational field vectors in a small region near the Earth's surface are uniform in both direction and magnitude.

13.5 Gravitational Potential Energy

In Chapter 8, we introduced the concept of gravitational potential energy, which is the energy associated with the configuration of a system of objects interacting via the gravitational force. We emphasized that the gravitational potential energy function mgy for a particle–Earth system is valid only when the particle is near the Earth's surface, where the gravitational force is constant. Because the gravitational force between two particles varies as $1/r^2$, we expect that a more general potential energy function—one that is valid without the restriction of having to be near the Earth's surface—will be different from $U = mgy$.

Recall from Equation 7.26 that the change in the gravitational potential energy of a system associated with a given displacement of a member of the system is defined as the negative of the work done by the gravitational force on that member during the displacement:

$$\Delta U = U_f - U_i = -\int_{r_i}^{r_f} F(r)\,dr \tag{13.11}$$

We can use this result to evaluate the gravitational potential energy function. Consider a particle of mass m moving between two points Ⓐ and Ⓑ above the Earth's surface (Fig. 13.10). The particle is subject to the gravitational force given by Equation 13.1. We can express this force as

$$F(r) = -\frac{GM_Em}{r^2}$$

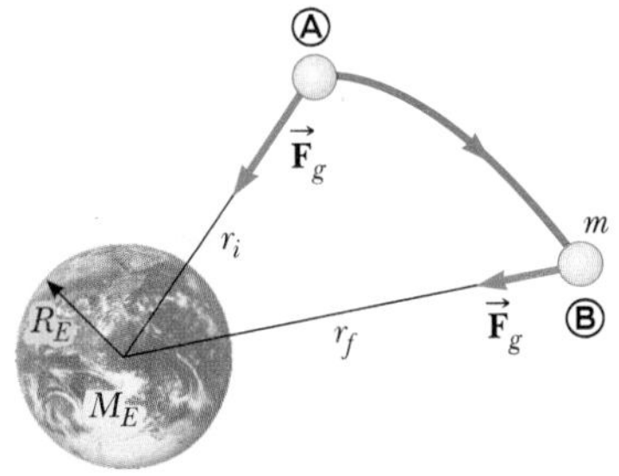

Ⓐ
$\vec{\mathbf{F}}_g$
m
r_i
R_E
r_f
$\vec{\mathbf{F}}_g$
Ⓑ
M_E

Figure 13.10 As a particle of mass m moves from Ⓐ to Ⓑ above the Earth's surface, the gravitational potential energy of the particle–Earth system changes according to Equation 13.12.

where the negative sign indicates that the force is attractive. Substituting this expression for $F(r)$ into Equation 13.11, we can compute the change in the gravitational potential energy function for the particle–Earth system:

$$U_f - U_i = GM_Em\int_{r_i}^{r_f}\frac{dr}{r^2} = GM_Em\left[-\frac{1}{r}\right]_{r_i}^{r_f}$$

$$U_f - U_i = -GM_Em\left(\frac{1}{r_f} - \frac{1}{r_i}\right) \tag{13.12}$$

As always, the choice of a reference configuration for the potential energy is completely arbitrary. It is customary to choose the reference configuration for zero potential energy to be the same as that for which the force is zero. Taking $U_i = 0$ at $r_i = \infty$, we obtain the important result

Gravitational potential energy of the Earth–particle system

$$U(r) = -\frac{GM_Em}{r} \tag{13.13}$$

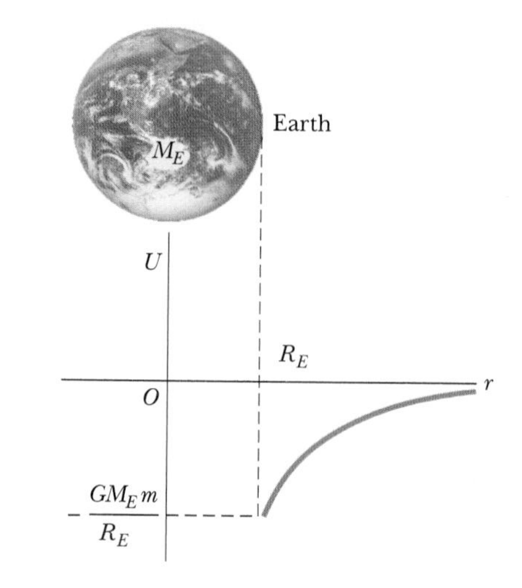

Figure 13.11 Graph of the gravitational potential energy U versus r for the system of an object above the Earth's surface. The potential energy goes to zero as r approaches infinity.

This expression applies when the particle is separated from the center of the Earth by a distance r, provided that $r \geq R_E$. The result is not valid for particles inside the Earth, where $r < R_E$. Because of our choice of U_i, the function U is always negative (Fig. 13.11).

Although Equation 13.13 was derived for the particle–Earth system, it can be applied to any two particles. That is, the gravitational potential energy associated with any pair of particles of masses m_1 and m_2 separated by a distance r is

$$U = -\frac{Gm_1 m_2}{r} \qquad (13.14)$$

This expression shows that the gravitational potential energy for any pair of particles varies as $1/r$, whereas the force between them varies as $1/r^2$. Furthermore, the potential energy is negative because the force is attractive and we have chosen the potential energy as zero when the particle separation is infinite. Because the force between the particles is attractive, an external agent must do positive work to increase the separation between them. The work done by the external agent produces an increase in the potential energy as the two particles are separated. That is, U becomes less negative as r increases.

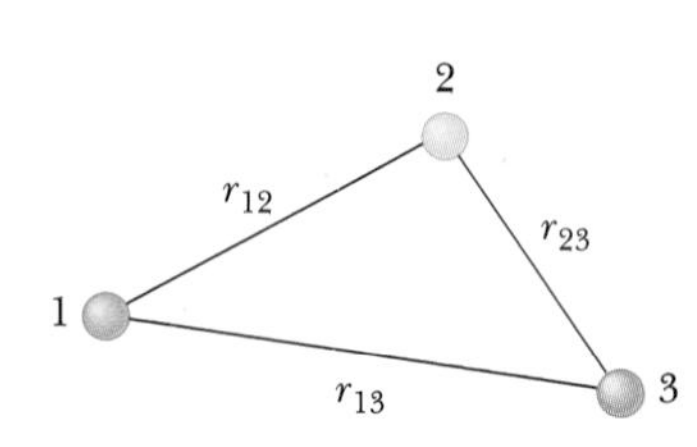

Figure 13.12 Three interacting particles.

When two particles are at rest and separated by a distance r, an external agent has to supply an energy at least equal to $+Gm_1 m_2/r$ to separate the particles to an infinite distance. It is therefore convenient to think of the absolute value of the potential energy as the *binding energy* of the system. If the external agent supplies an energy greater than the binding energy, the excess energy of the system is in the form of kinetic energy of the particles when the particles are at an infinite separation.

We can extend this concept to three or more particles. In this case, the total potential energy of the system is the sum over all pairs of particles. Each pair contributes a term of the form given by Equation 13.14. For example, if the system contains three particles as in Figure 13.12,

$$U_{\text{total}} = U_{12} + U_{13} + U_{23} = -G\left(\frac{m_1 m_2}{r_{12}} + \frac{m_1 m_3}{r_{13}} + \frac{m_2 m_3}{r_{23}}\right) \qquad (13.15)$$

The absolute value of U_{total} represents the work needed to separate the particles by an infinite distance.

EXAMPLE 13.6 The Change in Potential Energy

A particle of mass m is displaced through a small vertical distance Δy near the Earth's surface. Show that in this situation the general expression for the change in gravitational potential energy given by Equation 13.12 reduces to the familiar relationship $\Delta U = mg\,\Delta y$.

SOLUTION

Conceptualize Compare the two different situations for which we have developed expressions for gravitational potential energy: (1) a planet and an object that are far apart for which the energy expression is Equation 13.12 and (2) a small object at the surface of a planet for which the energy expression is Equation 7.19. We wish to show that these two expressions are equivalent.

Categorize This example is a substitution problem.

Combine the fractions in Equation 13.12:

$$(1) \quad \Delta U = -GM_E m\left(\frac{1}{r_f} - \frac{1}{r_i}\right) = GM_E m\left(\frac{r_f - r_i}{r_i r_f}\right)$$

Evaluate $r_f - r_i$ and $r_i r_f$ if both the initial and final positions of the particle are close to the Earth's surface:

$$r_f - r_i = \Delta y \qquad r_i r_f \approx R_E^{\,2}$$

Substitute these expressions into Equation (1):

$$\Delta U \approx \frac{GM_E m}{R_E^{\,2}}\,\Delta y = mg\,\Delta y$$

where $g = GM_E/R_E^{\,2}$ (Eq. 13.5).

What If? Suppose you are performing upper-atmosphere studies and are asked by your supervisor to find the height in the Earth's atmosphere at which the "surface equation" $\Delta U = mg\,\Delta y$ gives a 1.0% error in the change in the potential energy. What is this height?

Answer Because the surface equation assumes a constant value for g, it will give a ΔU value that is larger than the value given by the general equation, Equation 13.12.

Set up a ratio reflecting a 1.0% error:

$$\frac{\Delta U_{\text{surface}}}{\Delta U_{\text{general}}} = 1.010$$

Substitute the expressions for each of these changes ΔU:

$$\frac{mg\,\Delta y}{GM_E m(\Delta y/r_i r_f)} = \frac{g r_i r_f}{GM_E} = 1.010$$

Substitute for r_i, r_f, and g from Equation 13.5:

$$\frac{(GM_E/R_E^{\,2})R_E(R_E + \Delta y)}{GM_E} = \frac{R_E + \Delta y}{R_E} = 1 + \frac{\Delta y}{R_E} = 1.010$$

Solve for Δy:

$$\Delta y = 0.010R_E = 0.010(6.37 \times 10^6 \text{ m}) = 6.37 \times 10^4 \text{ m} = 63.7 \text{ km}$$

13.6 Energy Considerations in Planetary and Satellite Motion

Consider an object of mass m moving with a speed v in the vicinity of a massive object of mass M, where $M >> m$. The system might be a planet moving around the Sun, a satellite in orbit around the Earth, or a comet making a one-time flyby of the Sun. If we assume the object of mass M is at rest in an inertial reference frame, the total mechanical energy E of the two-object system when the objects are separated by a distance r is the sum of the kinetic energy of the object of mass m and the potential energy of the system, given by Equation 13.14:

$$E = K + U$$

$$E = \tfrac{1}{2}mv^2 - \frac{GMm}{r} \qquad \textbf{(13.16)}$$

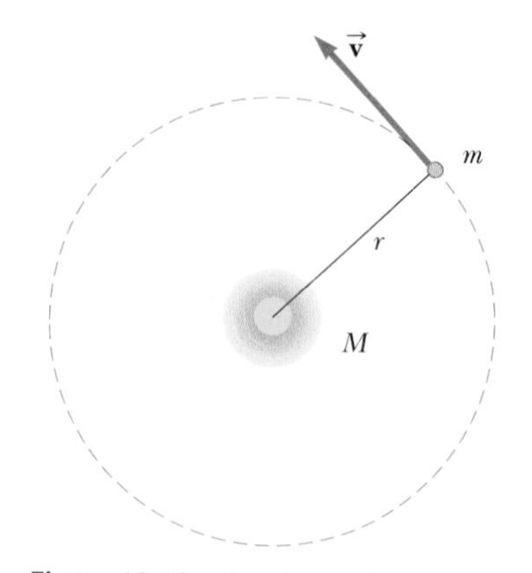

Figure 13.13 An object of mass m moving in a circular orbit about a much larger object of mass M.

Equation 13.16 shows that E may be positive, negative, or zero, depending on the value of v. For a bound system such as the Earth–Sun system, however, E is necessarily *less than zero* because we have chosen the convention that $U \rightarrow 0$ as $r \rightarrow \infty$.

We can easily establish that $E < 0$ for the system consisting of an object of mass m moving in a circular orbit about an object of mass $M >> m$ (Fig. 13.13). Newton's second law applied to the object of mass m gives

$$F_g = \frac{GMm}{r^2} = ma = \frac{mv^2}{r}$$

Multiplying both sides by r and dividing by 2 gives

$$\tfrac{1}{2}mv^2 = \frac{GMm}{2r} \qquad (13.17)$$

Substituting this equation into Equation 13.16, we obtain

$$E = \frac{GMm}{2r} - \frac{GMm}{r}$$

Total energy for circular orbits ▶

$$E = -\frac{GMm}{2r} \quad \text{(circular orbits)} \qquad (13.18)$$

This result shows that **the total mechanical energy is negative in the case of circular orbits.** Notice that **the kinetic energy is positive and equal to half the absolute value of the potential energy.** The absolute value of E is also equal to the binding energy of the system because this amount of energy must be provided to the system to move the two objects infinitely far apart.

The total mechanical energy is also negative in the case of elliptical orbits. The expression for E for elliptical orbits is the same as Equation 13.18 with r replaced by the semimajor axis length a:

Total energy for elliptical orbits ▶

$$E = -\frac{GMm}{2a} \quad \text{(elliptical orbits)} \qquad (13.19)$$

Furthermore, the total energy is constant if we assume the system is isolated. Therefore, as the object of mass m moves from Ⓐ to Ⓑ in Figure 13.10, the total energy remains constant and Equation 13.16 gives

$$E = \tfrac{1}{2}mv_i^2 - \frac{GMm}{r_i} = \tfrac{1}{2}mv_f^2 - \frac{GMm}{r_f} \qquad (13.20)$$

Combining this statement of energy conservation with our earlier discussion of conservation of angular momentum, we see that **both the total energy and the total angular momentum of a gravitationally bound, two-object system are constants of the motion.**

Quick Quiz 13.4 A comet moves in an elliptical orbit around the Sun. Which point in its orbit (perihelion or aphelion) represents the highest value of (a) the speed of the comet, (b) the potential energy of the comet–Sun system, (c) the kinetic energy of the comet, and (d) the total energy of the comet–Sun system?

EXAMPLE 13.7 Changing the Orbit of a Satellite

A space transportation vehicle releases a 470-kg communications satellite while in an orbit 280 km above the surface of the Earth. A rocket engine on the satellite boosts it into a geosynchronous orbit. How much energy does the engine have to provide?

SOLUTION

Conceptualize Notice that the height of 280 km is much lower than that for a geosynchronous satellite, 36 000 km, as mentioned in Example 13.5. Therefore, energy must be expended to raise the satellite to this much higher position.

Categorize This example is a substitution problem.

Find the initial radius of the satellite's orbit when it is still in the shuttle's cargo bay:

$$r_i = R_E + 280 \text{ km} = 6.65 \times 10^6 \text{ m}$$

Use Equation 13.18 to find the difference in energies for the satellite–Earth system with the satellite at the initial and final radii:

$$\Delta E = E_f - E_i = -\frac{GM_Em}{2r_f} - \left(-\frac{GM_Em}{2r_i}\right) = -\frac{GM_Em}{2}\left(\frac{1}{r_f} - \frac{1}{r_i}\right)$$

Substitute numerical values, using $r_f = 4.23 \times 10^7$ m from Example 13.5:

$$\Delta E = -\frac{(6.67 \times 10^{-11} \text{ N}\cdot\text{m}^2/\text{kg}^2)(5.98 \times 10^{24} \text{ kg})(470 \text{ kg})}{2}$$

$$\times \left(\frac{1}{4.23 \times 10^7 \text{ m}} - \frac{1}{6.65 \times 10^6 \text{ m}}\right)$$

$$= 1.19 \times 10^{10} \text{ J}$$

which is the energy equivalent of 89 gal of gasoline. NASA engineers must account for the changing mass of the spacecraft as it ejects burned fuel, something we have not done here. Would you expect the calculation that includes the effect of this changing mass to yield a greater or a lesser amount of energy required from the engine?

Escape Speed

Suppose an object of mass m is projected vertically upward from the Earth's surface with an initial speed v_i as illustrated in Figure 13.14. We can use energy considerations to find the minimum value of the initial speed needed to allow the object to move infinitely far away from the Earth. Equation 13.16 gives the total energy of the system at any point. At the surface of the Earth, $v = v_i$ and $r = r_i = R_E$. When the object reaches its maximum altitude, $v = v_f = 0$ and $r = r_f = r_{\text{max}}$. Because the total energy of the object–Earth system is conserved, substituting these conditions into Equation 13.20 gives

$$\tfrac{1}{2}mv_i^2 - \frac{GM_Em}{R_E} = -\frac{GM_Em}{r_{\text{max}}}$$

Solving for v_i^2 gives

$$v_i^2 = 2GM_E\left(\frac{1}{R_E} - \frac{1}{r_{\text{max}}}\right) \quad \textbf{(13.21)}$$

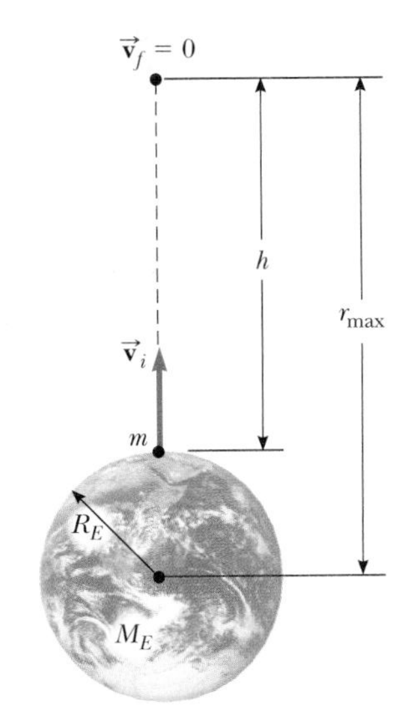

Figure 13.14 An object of mass m projected upward from the Earth's surface with an initial speed v_i reaches a maximum altitude h.

For a given maximum altitude $h = r_{\text{max}} - R_E$, we can use this equation to find the required initial speed.

We are now in a position to calculate **escape speed,** which is the minimum speed the object must have at the Earth's surface to approach an infinite separation distance from the Earth. Traveling at this minimum speed, the object continues to move farther and farther away from the Earth as its speed asymptotically approaches zero. Letting $r_{\text{max}} \to \infty$ in Equation 13.21 and taking $v_i = v_{\text{esc}}$ gives

$$v_{\text{esc}} = \sqrt{\frac{2GM_E}{R_E}} \quad \textbf{(13.22)}$$

This expression for v_{esc} is independent of the mass of the object. In other words, a spacecraft has the same escape speed as a molecule. Furthermore, the result is independent of the direction of the velocity and ignores air resistance.

If the object is given an initial speed equal to v_{esc}, the total energy of the system is equal to zero. Notice that when $r \to \infty$, the object's kinetic energy and the potential energy of the system are both zero. If v_i is greater than v_{esc}, the total energy of the system is greater than zero and the object has some residual kinetic energy as $r \to \infty$.

PITFALL PREVENTION 13.3

You Can't Really Escape

Although Equation 13.22 provides the "escape speed" from the Earth, *complete* escape from the Earth's gravitational influence is impossible because the gravitational force is of infinite range. No matter how far away you are, you will always feel some gravitational force due to the Earth.

EXAMPLE 13.8 Escape Speed of a Rocket

Calculate the escape speed from the Earth for a 5 000-kg spacecraft and determine the kinetic energy it must have at the Earth's surface to move infinitely far away from the Earth.

SOLUTION

Conceptualize Imagine projecting the spacecraft from the Earth's surface so that it moves farther and farther away, traveling more and more slowly, with its speed approaching zero. Its speed will never reach zero, however, so the object will never turn around and come back.

Categorize This example is a substitution problem.

Use Equation 13.22 to find the escape speed:

$$v_{\text{esc}} = \sqrt{\frac{2GM_E}{R_E}} = \sqrt{\frac{2(6.67 \times 10^{-11}\ \text{N} \cdot \text{m}^2/\text{kg}^2)(5.98 \times 10^{24}\ \text{kg})}{6.37 \times 10^6\ \text{m}}}$$

$$= 1.12 \times 10^4\ \text{m/s}$$

Evaluate the kinetic energy of the spacecraft from Equation 7.16:

$$K = \tfrac{1}{2}mv_{\text{esc}}^2 = \tfrac{1}{2}(5.00 \times 10^3\ \text{kg})(1.12 \times 10^4\ \text{m/s})^2$$

$$= 3.14 \times 10^{11}\ \text{J}$$

The calculated escape speed corresponds to about 25 000 mi/h. The kinetic energy of the spacecraft is equivalent to the energy released by the combustion of about 2 300 gal of gasoline.

What If? What if you want to launch a 1 000-kg spacecraft at the escape speed? How much energy would that require?

Answer In Equation 13.22, the mass of the object moving with the escape speed does not appear. Therefore, the escape speed for the 1 000-kg spacecraft is the same as that for the 5 000-kg spacecraft. The only change in the kinetic energy is due to the mass, so the 1 000-kg spacecraft requires one-fifth of the energy of the 5 000-kg spacecraft:

$$K = \tfrac{1}{5}(3.14 \times 10^{11}\ \text{J}) = 6.28 \times 10^{10}\ \text{J}$$

Equations 13.21 and 13.22 can be applied to objects projected from any planet. That is, in general, the escape speed from the surface of any planet of mass M and radius R is

$$v_{\text{esc}} = \sqrt{\frac{2GM}{R}} \qquad \textbf{(13.23)}$$

Escape speeds for the planets, the Moon, and the Sun are provided in Table 13.3. The values vary from 2.3 km/s for the Moon to about 618 km/s for the Sun. These results, together with some ideas from the kinetic theory of gases (see Chapter 21), explain why some planets have atmospheres and others do not. As we shall see later, at a given temperature the average kinetic energy of a gas molecule depends only on the mass of the molecule. Lighter molecules, such as hydrogen and helium, have a higher average speed than heavier molecules at the same temperature. When the average speed of the lighter molecules is not much less than the escape speed of a planet, a significant fraction of them have a chance to escape.

This mechanism also explains why the Earth does not retain hydrogen molecules and helium atoms in its atmosphere but does retain heavier molecules, such as oxygen and nitrogen. On the other hand, the very large escape speed for Jupiter enables that planet to retain hydrogen, the primary constituent of its atmosphere.

TABLE 13.3

Escape Speeds from the Surfaces of the Planets, Moon, and Sun

Planet	v_{esc} (km/s)
Mercury	4.3
Venus	10.3
Earth	11.2
Mars	5.0
Jupiter	60
Saturn	36
Uranus	22
Neptune	24
Moon	2.3
Sun	618

Black Holes

In Example 11.7, we briefly described a rare event called a supernova, the catastrophic explosion of a very massive star. The material that remains in the central core of such an object continues to collapse, and the core's ultimate fate depends on its mass. If the core has a mass less than 1.4 times the mass of our Sun, it gradually cools down and ends its life as a white dwarf star. If the core's mass is greater than this value, however, it may collapse further due to gravitational forces. What remains is a neutron star, discussed in Example 11.7, in which the mass of a star is compressed to a radius of about 10 km. (On the Earth, a teaspoon of this material would weigh about 5 billion tons!)

An even more unusual star death may occur when the core has a mass greater than about three solar masses. The collapse may continue until the star becomes a very small object in space, commonly referred to as a **black hole.** In effect, black holes are remains of stars that have collapsed under their own gravitational force. If an object such as a spacecraft comes close to a black hole, the object experiences an extremely strong gravitational force and is trapped forever.

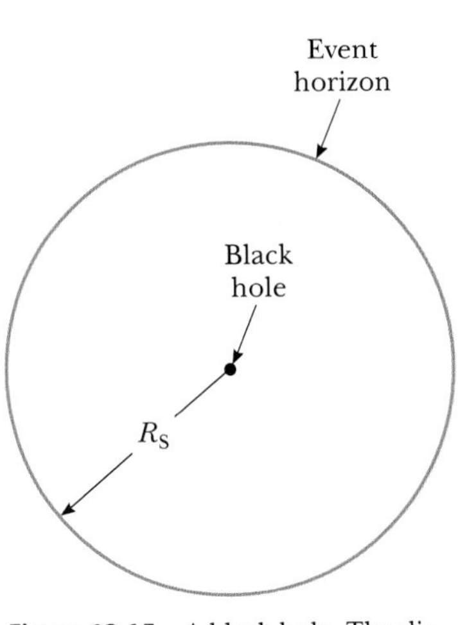

Figure 13.15 A black hole. The distance R_S equals the Schwarzschild radius. Any event occurring within the boundary of radius R_S, called the event horizon, is invisible to an outside observer.

The escape speed for a black hole is very high because of the concentration of the star's mass into a sphere of very small radius (see Eq. 13.23). If the escape speed exceeds the speed of light c, radiation from the object (such as visible light) cannot escape and the object appears to be black (hence the origin of the terminology "black hole"). The critical radius R_S at which the escape speed is c is called the **Schwarzschild radius** (Fig. 13.15). The imaginary surface of a sphere of this radius surrounding the black hole is called the **event horizon,** which is the limit of how close you can approach the black hole and hope to escape.

Although light from a black hole cannot escape, light from events taking place near the black hole should be visible. For example, it is possible for a binary star system to consist of one normal star and one black hole. Material surrounding the ordinary star can be pulled into the black hole, forming an **accretion disk** around the black hole as suggested in Figure 13.16. Friction among particles in the accretion disk results in transformation of mechanical energy into internal energy. As a result, the temperature of the material above the event horizon rises. This high-temperature material emits a large amount of radiation, extending well into the x-ray region of the electromagnetic spectrum. These x-rays are characteristic of a black hole. Several possible candidates for black holes have been identified by observation of these x-rays.

There is also evidence that supermassive black holes exist at the centers of galaxies, with masses very much larger than the Sun. (There is strong evidence of a supermassive black hole of mass 2–3 million solar masses at the center of our galaxy.) Theoretical models for these bizarre objects predict that jets of material should be evident along the rotation axis of the black hole. Figure 13.17 (page 380) shows a Hubble Space Telescope photograph of galaxy M87. The jet of material coming from this galaxy is believed to be evidence for a supermassive black hole at the center of the galaxy.

Figure 13.16 A binary star system consisting of an ordinary star on the left and a black hole on the right. Matter pulled from the ordinary star forms an accretion disk around the black hole, in which matter is raised to very high temperatures, resulting in the emission of x-rays.

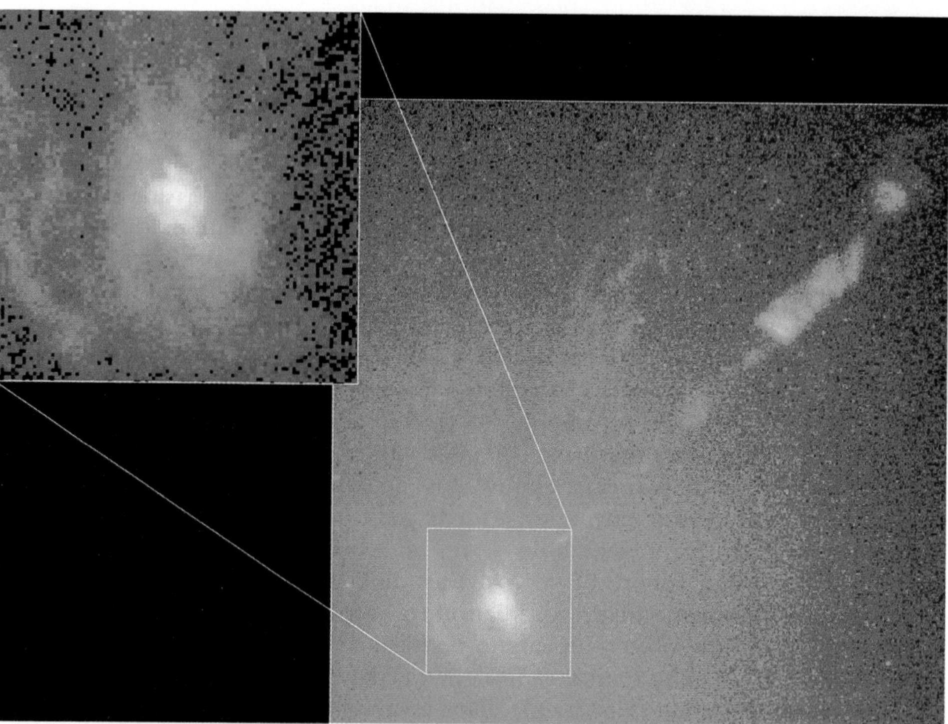

Figure 13.17 Hubble Space Telescope images of the galaxy M87. The inset shows the center of the galaxy. The wider view shows a jet of material moving away from the center of the galaxy toward the upper right of the figure at about one tenth of the speed of light. Such jets are believed to be evidence of a supermassive black hole at the galaxy center.

Summary

ThomsonNOW™ Sign in at **www.thomsonedu.com** and go to ThomsonNOW to take a practice test for this chapter.

DEFINITIONS

The **gravitational field** at a point in space is defined as the gravitational force experienced by any test particle located at that point divided by the mass of the test particle:

$$\vec{\mathbf{g}} \equiv \frac{\vec{\mathbf{F}}_g}{m} \tag{13.9}$$

CONCEPTS AND PRINCIPLES

Newton's law of universal gravitation states that the gravitational force of attraction between any two particles of masses m_1 and m_2 separated by a distance r has the magnitude

$$F_g = G\frac{m_1 m_2}{r^2} \tag{13.1}$$

where $G = 6.673 \times 10^{-11}\ \text{N}\cdot\text{m}^2/\text{kg}^2$ is the **universal gravitational constant.** This equation enables us to calculate the force of attraction between masses under many circumstances.

An object at a distance h above the Earth's surface experiences a gravitational force of magnitude mg, where g is the free-fall acceleration at that elevation:

$$g = \frac{GM_E}{r^2} = \frac{GM_E}{(R_E + h)^2} \tag{13.6}$$

In this expression, M_E is the mass of the Earth and R_E is its radius. Therefore, the weight of an object decreases as the object moves away from the Earth's surface.

(continued)

Kepler's laws of planetary motion state:

1. All planets move in elliptical orbits with the Sun at one focus.
2. The radius vector drawn from the Sun to a planet sweeps out equal areas in equal time intervals.
3. The square of the orbital period of any planet is proportional to the cube of the semimajor axis of the elliptical orbit.

Kepler's third law can be expressed as

$$T^2 = \left(\frac{4\pi^2}{GM_S}\right)a^3 \qquad (13.8)$$

where M_S is the mass of the Sun and a is the semimajor axis. For a circular orbit, a can be replaced in Equation 13.8 by the radius r. Most planets have nearly circular orbits around the Sun.

The **gravitational potential energy** associated with two particles separated by a distance r is

$$U = -\frac{Gm_1 m_2}{r} \qquad (13.14)$$

where U is taken to be zero as $r \to \infty$.

If an isolated system consists of an object of mass m moving with a speed v in the vicinity of a massive object of mass M, the total energy E of the system is the sum of the kinetic and potential energies:

$$E = \tfrac{1}{2}mv^2 - \frac{GMm}{r} \qquad (13.16)$$

The total energy of the system is a constant of the motion. If the object moves in an elliptical orbit of semimajor axis a around the massive object and $M >> m$, the total energy of the system is

$$E = -\frac{GMm}{2a} \qquad (13.19)$$

For a circular orbit, this same equation applies with $a = r$.

The **escape speed** for an object projected from the surface of a planet of mass M and radius R is

$$v_{esc} = \sqrt{\frac{2GM}{R}} \qquad (13.23)$$

Questions

☐ denotes answer available in *Student Solutions Manual/Study Guide;* **O** denotes objective question

1. O Rank the magnitudes of the following gravitational forces from largest to smallest. If two forces are equal, show their equality in your list. (a) The force exerted by a 2-kg object on a 3-kg object 1 m away. (b) The force exerted by a 2-kg object on a 9-kg object 1 m away. (c) The force exerted by a 2-kg object on a 9-kg object 2 m away. (d) The force exerted by a 9-kg object on a 2-kg object 2 m away. (e) The force exerted by a 4-kg object on another 4-kg object 2 m away.

2. O The gravitational force exerted on an astronaut on the Earth's surface is 650 N directed downward. When she is in the International Space Station, what is the gravitational force on her? (a) several times larger (b) slightly larger (c) precisely the same (d) slightly smaller (e) several times smaller (f) nearly but not exactly zero (g) precisely zero (h) up instead of down

3. O Imagine that nitrogen and other atmospheric gases were more soluble in water so that the atmosphere of the Earth were entirely absorbed by the oceans. Atmospheric pressure would then be zero, and outer space would start at the planet's surface. Would the Earth then have a gravitational field? (a) yes; at the surface it would be larger in magnitude than 9.8 N/kg (b) yes, essentially the same as the current value (c) yes, somewhat less than 9.8 N/kg (d) yes, much less than 9.8 N/kg (e) no

4. The gravitational force exerted by the Sun on you is downward into the Earth at night and upward into the sky during the day. If you had a sensitive enough bathroom scale, would you expect to weigh more at night than during the day? Note also that you are farther away from the Sun at night than during the day. Would you expect to weigh less?

5. O Suppose the gravitational acceleration at the surface of a certain satellite A of Jupiter is 2 m/s^2. Satellite B has twice the mass and twice the radius of satellite A. What is the gravitational acceleration at its surface? (a) 16 m/s^2 (b) 8 m/s^2 (c) 4 m/s^2 (d) 2 m/s^2 (e) 1 m/s^2 (f) 0.5 m/s^2 (g) 0.25 m/s^2

6. O A satellite originally moves in a circular orbit of radius R around the Earth. Suppose it is moved into a circular orbit of radius $4R$. **(i)** What does the force exerted on the satellite then become? (a) 16 times larger (b) 8 times larger (c) 4 times larger (d) 2 times larger (e) unchanged (f) 1/2 as large (g) 1/4 as large (h) 1/8 as large (i) 1/16 as large **(ii)** What happens to the speed of the satellite? Choose from the same possibilities (a) through (i). **(iii)** What happens to its period? Choose from the same possibilities (a) through (i).

7. O The vernal equinox and the autumnal equinox are associated with two points 180° apart in the Earth's orbit.

That is, the Earth is on precisely opposite sides of the Sun when it passes through these two points. From the vernal equinox, 185.4 days elapse before the autumnal equinox. Only 179.8 days elapse from the autumnal equinox until the next vernal equinox. In the year 2007, for example, the vernal equinox is 8 minutes after midnight Greenwich Mean Time on March 21, 2007, and the autumnal equinox is 9:51 p.m. September 23. Why is the interval from the March to the September equinox (which contains the summer solstice) longer than the interval from the September to the March equinox, rather than being equal to that interval? (a) They are really the same, but the Earth spins faster during the "summer" interval, so the days are shorter. (b) Over the "summer" interval the Earth moves slower because it is farther from the Sun. (c) Over the March-to-September interval the Earth moves slower because it is closer to the Sun. (d) The Earth has less kinetic energy when it is warmer. (e) The Earth has less orbital angular momentum when it is warmer. (f) Other objects do work to speed up and slow down the Earth's orbital motion.

8. A satellite in orbit around the Earth is not truly traveling through a vacuum. Rather, it moves through very thin air. Does the resulting air friction cause the satellite to slow down?

9. **O** A system consists of five particles. How many terms appear in the expression for the total gravitational potential energy? (a) 4 (b) 5 (c) 10 (d) 20 (e) 25 (f) 120

10. Explain why it takes more fuel for a spacecraft to travel from the Earth to the Moon than for the return trip. Estimate the difference.

11. **O** Rank the following quantities of energy from the largest to the smallest. State if any are equal. (a) the absolute value of the average potential energy of the Sun–Earth system (b) the average kinetic energy of the Earth in its orbital motion relative to the Sun (c) the absolute value of the total energy of the Sun–Earth system

12. Why don't we put a geosynchronous weather satellite in orbit around the 45th parallel? Wouldn't such a satellite be more useful in the United States than one in orbit around the equator?

13. Explain why the force exerted on a particle by a uniform sphere must be directed toward the center of the sphere. Would this statement be true if the mass distribution of the sphere were not spherically symmetric?

14. At what position in its elliptical orbit is the speed of a planet a maximum? At what position is the speed a minimum?

15. You are given the mass and radius of planet X. How would you calculate the free-fall acceleration on the surface of this planet?

16. If a hole could be dug to the center of the Earth, would the force on an object of mass m still obey Equation 13.1 there? What do you think the force on m would be at the center of the Earth?

17. In his 1798 experiment, Cavendish was said to have "weighed the Earth." Explain this statement.

18. Is the gravitational force a conservative or a nonconservative force? Each *Voyager* spacecraft was accelerated toward escape speed from the Sun by the gravitational force exerted by Jupiter on the spacecraft. Does the interaction of the spacecraft with Jupiter meet the definition of an elastic collision? How could the spacecraft be moving faster after the collision?

Problems

WebAssign The Problems from this chapter may be assigned online in WebAssign.

ThomsonNOW Sign in at **www.thomsonedu.com** and go to ThomsonNOW to assess your understanding of this chapter's topics with additional quizzing and conceptual questions.

1, 2, 3 denotes straightforward, intermediate, challenging; □ denotes full solution available in *Student Solutions Manual/Study Guide;* ▲ denotes coached solution with hints available at **www.thomsonedu.com;** denotes developing symbolic reasoning; ● denotes asking for qualitative reasoning; denotes computer useful in solving problem

Section 13.1 Newton's Law of Universal Gravitation

1. Determine the order of magnitude of the gravitational force that you exert on another person 2 m away. In your solution, state the quantities you measure or estimate and their values.

2. Two ocean liners, each with a mass of 40 000 metric tons, are moving on parallel courses 100 m apart. What is the magnitude of the acceleration of one of the liners toward the other due to their mutual gravitational attraction? Model the ships as particles.

3. A 200-kg object and a 500-kg object are separated by 0.400 m. (a) Find the net gravitational force exerted by these objects on a 50.0-kg object placed midway between them. (b) At what position (other than an infinitely remote one) can the 50.0-kg object be placed so as to experience a net force of zero?

4. Two objects attract each other with a gravitational force of magnitude 1.00×10^{-8} N when separated by 20.0 cm. If the total mass of the two objects is 5.00 kg, what is the mass of each?

5. Three uniform spheres of mass 2.00 kg, 4.00 kg, and 6.00 kg are placed at the corners of a right triangle as shown in Figure P13.5. Calculate the resultant gravitational force on the 4.00-kg object, assuming the spheres are isolated from the rest of the Universe.

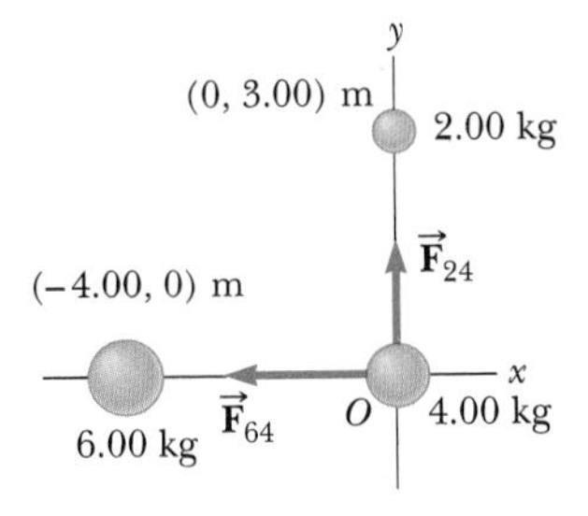

Figure P13.5

6. ● During a solar eclipse, the Moon, Earth, and Sun all lie on the same line, with the Moon between the Earth and the Sun. (a) What force is exerted by the Sun on the Moon? (b) What force is exerted by the Earth on the Moon? (c) What force is exerted by the Sun on the Earth? (d) Compare the answers to parts (a) and (b). Why doesn't the Sun capture the Moon away from the Earth?

7. ▲ In introductory physics laboratories, a typical Cavendish balance for measuring the gravitational constant G uses lead spheres with masses of 1.50 kg and 15.0 g whose centers are separated by about 4.50 cm. Calculate the gravitational force between these spheres, treating each as a particle located at the center of the sphere.

8. ● A student proposes to measure the gravitational constant G by suspending two spherical objects from the ceiling of a tall cathedral and measuring the deflection of the cables from the vertical. Draw a free-body diagram of one of the objects. Assume two 100.0-kg objects are suspended at the lower ends of cables 45.00 m long and the cables are attached to the ceiling 1.000 m apart. What is the separation of the objects? Is there more than one equilibrium separation distance? Explain.

Section 13.2 Free-Fall Acceleration and the Gravitational Force

9. ▲ When a falling meteoroid is at a distance above the Earth's surface of 3.00 times the Earth's radius, what is its acceleration due to the Earth's gravitation?

10. **Review problem.** Miranda, a satellite of Uranus, is shown in Figure P13.10a. It can be modeled as a sphere of radius 242 km and mass 6.68×10^{19} kg. (a) Find the free-fall acceleration on its surface. (b) A cliff on Miranda is 5.00 km high. It appears on the limb at the 11 o'clock position in Figure P13.10a and is magnified in Figure P13.10b. A devotee of extreme sports runs horizontally off the top of the cliff at 8.50 m/s. For what time interval is he in flight? (Or is he in orbit?) (c) How far from the base of the vertical cliff does he strike the icy surface of Miranda? (d) What is his vector impact velocity?

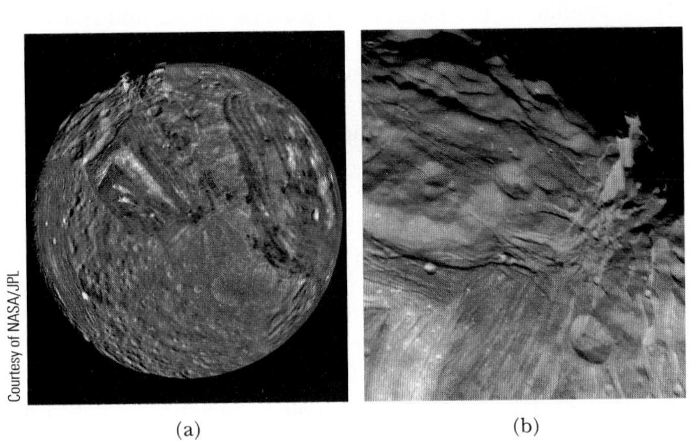

Figure P13.10

11. The free-fall acceleration on the surface of the Moon is about one-sixth that on the surface of the Earth. The radius of the Moon is about $0.250R_E$. Find the ratio of their average densities, $\rho_{\text{Moon}}/\rho_{\text{Earth}}$.

Section 13.3 Kepler's Laws and the Motion of Planets

12. ● A particle of mass m moves along a straight line with constant speed in the x direction, a distance b from the x axis (Fig. P13.12). Does the particle possess any angular momentum about the origin? Explain why the amount of its angular momentum should change or should stay constant. Show that Kepler's second law is satisfied by showing that the two shaded triangles in the figure have the same area when $t_4 - t_3 = t_2 - t_1$.

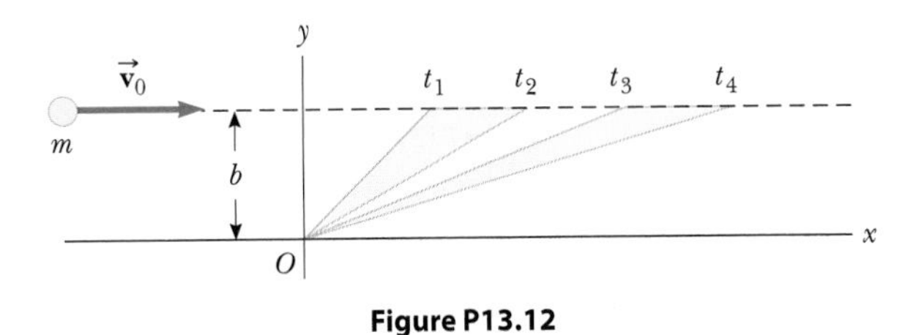

Figure P13.12

13. Plaskett's binary system consists of two stars that revolve in a circular orbit about a center of mass midway between them. This statement implies that the masses of the two stars are equal (Fig. P13.13). Assume the orbital speed of each star is 220 km/s and the orbital period of each is 14.4 days. Find the mass M of each star. (For comparison, the mass of our Sun is 1.99×10^{30} kg.)

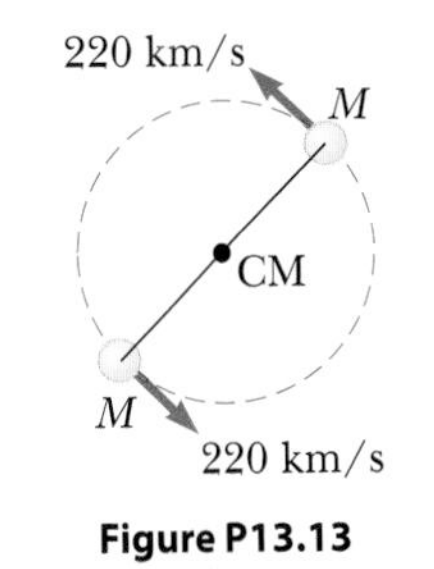

Figure P13.13

14. Comet Halley (Fig. P13.14) approaches the Sun to within 0.570 AU, and its orbital period is 75.6 years. (AU is the symbol for astronomical unit, where 1 AU = 1.50×10^{11} m is the mean Earth–Sun distance.) How far from the

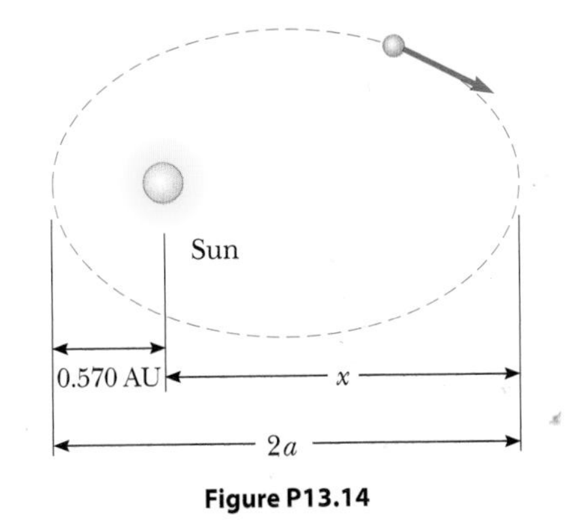

Figure P13.14

Sun will Halley's comet travel before it starts its return journey?

15. ▲ Io, a satellite of Jupiter, has an orbital period of 1.77 days and an orbital radius of 4.22×10^5 km. From these data, determine the mass of Jupiter.

16. Two planets X and Y travel counterclockwise in circular orbits about a star as shown in Figure P13.16. The radii of their orbits are in the ratio 3:1. At one moment, they are aligned as shown in Figure P13.16a, making a straight line with the star. During the next five years the angular displacement of planet X is 90.0° as shown in Figure P13.16b. Where is planet Y at this moment?

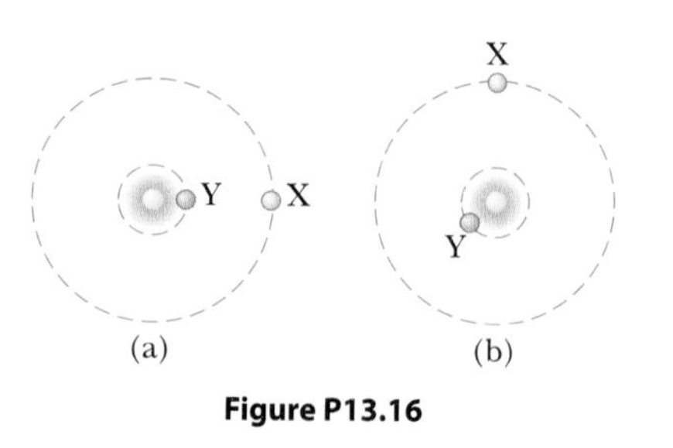

Figure P13.16

17. A synchronous satellite, which always remains above the same point on a planet's equator, is put in orbit around Jupiter to study the famous red spot. Jupiter rotates once every 9.84 h. Use the data of Table 13.2 to find the altitude of the satellite.

18. Neutron stars are extremely dense objects formed from the remnants of supernova explosions. Many rotate very rapidly. Suppose the mass of a certain spherical neutron star is twice the mass of the Sun and its radius is 10.0 km. Determine the greatest possible angular speed it can have so that the matter at the surface of the star on its equator is just held in orbit by the gravitational force.

19. Suppose the Sun's gravity were switched off. Objects in the solar system would leave their orbits and fly away in straight lines as described by Newton's first law. Would Mercury ever be farther from the Sun than Pluto? If so, find how long it would take for Mercury to achieve this passage. If not, give a convincing argument that Pluto is always farther from the Sun.

20. ● Given that the period of the Moon's orbit about the Earth is 27.32 d and the nearly constant distance between the center of the Earth and the center of the Moon is 3.84×10^8 m, use Equation 13.8 to calculate the mass of the Earth. Why is the value you calculate a bit too large?

Section 13.4 The Gravitational Field

21. Three objects of equal mass are located at three corners of a square of edge length ℓ as shown in Figure P13.21. Find the gravitational field at the fourth corner due to these objects.

Figure P13.21

22. A spacecraft in the shape of a long cylinder has a length of 100 m, and its mass with occupants is 1 000 kg. It has strayed too close to a black hole having a mass 100 times that of the Sun (Fig. P13.22). The nose of the spacecraft points toward the black hole, and the distance between the nose and the center of the black hole is 10.0 km. (a) Determine the total force on the spacecraft. (b) What is the difference in the gravitational fields acting on the occupants in the nose of the ship and on those in the rear of the ship, farthest from the black hole? This difference in accelerations grows rapidly as the ship approaches the black hole. It puts the body of the ship under extreme tension and eventually tears it apart.

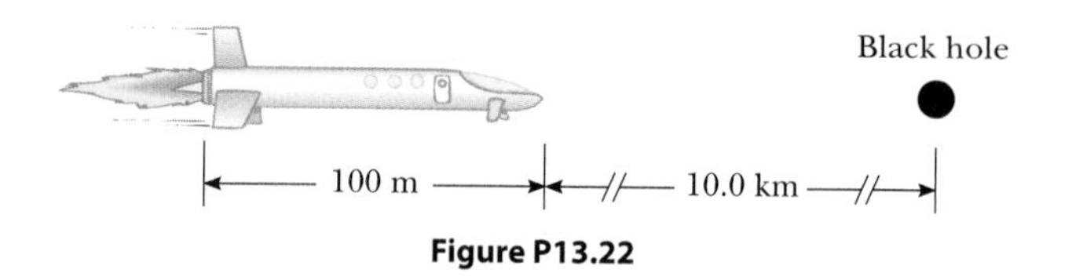

Figure P13.22

23. ● (a) Compute the vector gravitational field at a point P on the perpendicular bisector of the line joining two objects of equal mass separated by a distance $2a$ as shown in Figure P13.23. (b) Explain physically why the field should approach zero as $r \to 0$. (c) Prove mathematically that the answer to part (a) behaves in this way. (d) Explain physically why the magnitude of the field should approach $2GM/r^2$ as $r \to \infty$. (e) Prove mathematically that the answer to part (a) behaves correctly in this limit.

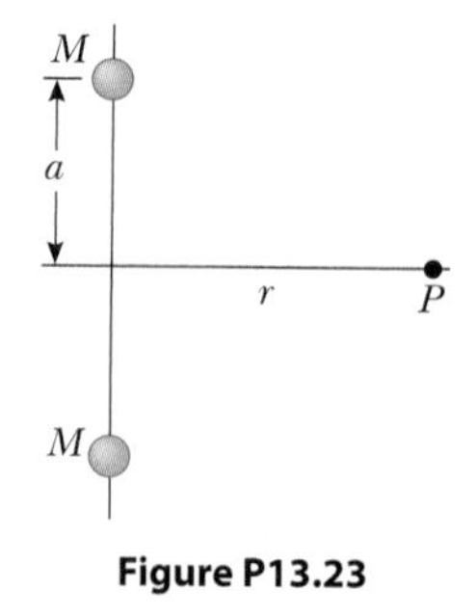

Figure P13.23

Section 13.5 Gravitational Potential Energy

In problems 24–39, assume $U = 0$ at $r = \infty$.

24. A satellite of the Earth has a mass of 100 kg and is at an altitude of 2.00×10^6 m. (a) What is the potential energy of the satellite–Earth system? (b) What is the magnitude of the gravitational force exerted by the Earth on the satellite? (c) **What If?** What force, if any, does the satellite exert on the Earth?

25. After our Sun exhausts its nuclear fuel, its ultimate fate may be to collapse to a *white dwarf* state. In this state, it would have approximately the same mass as it has now but a radius equal to the radius of the Earth. Calculate (a) the average density of the white dwarf, (b) the surface free-fall acceleration, and (c) the gravitational potential energy associated with a 1.00-kg object at its surface.

26. At the Earth's surface a projectile is launched straight up at a speed of 10.0 km/s. To what height will it rise? Ignore air resistance and the rotation of the Earth.

2 = intermediate; 3 = challenging; ☐ = SSM/SG; ▲ = ThomsonNOW; ☐ = symbolic reasoning; ● = qualitative reasoning

27. ● A system consists of three particles, each of mass 5.00 g, located at the corners of an equilateral triangle with sides of 30.0 cm. (a) Calculate the potential energy of the system. (b) Assume the particles are released simultaneously. Describe the subsequent motion of each. Will any collisions take place? Explain.

28. How much work is done by the Moon's gravitational field on a 1 000-kg meteor as it comes in from outer space and impacts on the Moon's surface?

29. An object is released from rest at an altitude h above the surface of the Earth. (a) Show that its speed at a distance r from the Earth's center, where $R_E \le r \le R_E + h$, is

$$v = \sqrt{2GM_E\left(\frac{1}{r} - \frac{1}{R_E + h}\right)}$$

(b) Assume the release altitude is 500 km. Perform the integral

$$\Delta t = \int_i^f dt = -\int_i^f \frac{dr}{v}$$

to find the time of fall as the object moves from the release point to the Earth's surface. The negative sign appears because the object is moving opposite to the radial direction, so its speed is $v = -dr/dt$. Perform the integral numerically.

Section 13.6 Energy Considerations in Planetary and Satellite Motion

30. (a) What is the minimum speed, relative to the Sun, necessary for a spacecraft to escape the solar system, if it starts at the Earth's orbit? (b) *Voyager 1* achieved a maximum speed of 125 000 km/h on its way to photograph Jupiter. Beyond what distance from the Sun is this speed sufficient to escape the solar system?

31. ▲ A space probe is fired as a projectile from the Earth's surface with an initial speed of 2.00×10^4 m/s. What will its speed be when it is very far from the Earth? Ignore friction and the rotation of the Earth.

32. ● A 1 000-kg satellite orbits the Earth at a constant altitude of 100 km. How much energy must be added to the system to move the satellite into a circular orbit with altitude 200 km? Discuss the changes in kinetic energy, potential energy, and total energy.

33. A "treetop satellite" moves in a circular orbit just above the surface of a planet, assumed to offer no air resistance. Show that its orbital speed v and the escape speed from the planet are related by the expression $v_{esc} = \sqrt{2}v$.

34. ● Ganymede is the largest of Jupiter's moons. Consider a rocket on the surface of Ganymede, at the point farthest from the planet (Fig. P13.34). Does the presence of Ganymede make Jupiter exert a larger, smaller, or same-size force on the rocket compared with the force it would exert if Ganymede were not interposed? Determine the escape speed for the rocket from the planet–satellite system. The radius of Ganymede is 2.64×10^6 m, and its mass is 1.495×10^{23} kg. The distance between Jupiter and Ganymede is 1.071×10^9 m, and the mass of Jupiter is 1.90×10^{27} kg. Ignore the motion of Jupiter and Ganymede as they revolve about their center of mass.

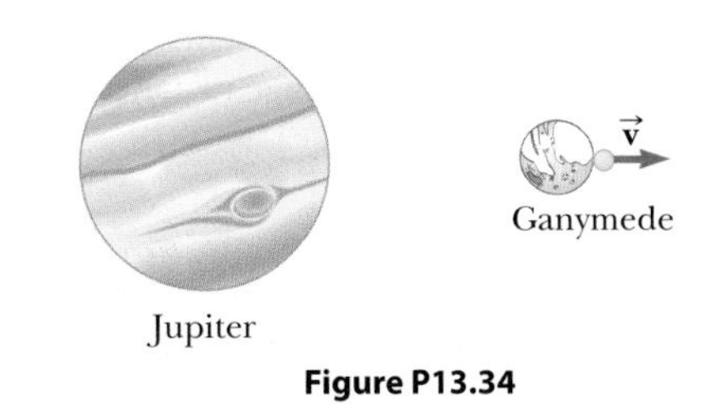

Figure P13.34

35. A satellite of mass 200 kg is placed in Earth orbit at a height of 200 km above the surface. (a) Assuming a circular orbit, how long does the satellite take to complete one orbit? (b) What is the satellite's speed? (c) Starting from the satellite on the Earth's surface, what is the minimum energy input necessary to place this satellite in orbit? Ignore air resistance, but include the effect of the planet's daily rotation.

36. ● A satellite of mass m, originally on the surface of the Earth, is placed into Earth orbit at an altitude h. (a) Assuming a circular orbit, how long does the satellite take to complete one orbit? (b) What is the satellite's speed? (c) What is the minimum energy input necessary to place this satellite in orbit? Ignore air resistance, but include the effect of the planet's daily rotation. At what location on the Earth's surface and in what direction should the satellite be launched to minimize the required energy investment? Represent the mass and radius of the Earth as M_E and R_E.

37. An object is fired vertically upward from the surface of the Earth (of radius R_E) with an initial speed v_i that is comparable to but less than the escape speed v_{esc}. (a) Show that the object attains a maximum height h given by

$$h = \frac{R_E v_i^2}{v_{esc}^2 - v_i^2}$$

(b) A space vehicle is launched vertically upward from the Earth's surface with an initial speed of 8.76 km/s, which is less than the escape speed of 11.2 km/s. What maximum height does it attain? (c) A meteorite falls toward the Earth. It is essentially at rest with respect to the Earth when it is at a height of 2.51×10^7 m. With what speed does the meteorite strike the Earth? (d) **What If?** Assume a baseball is tossed up with an initial speed that is very small compared with the escape speed. Show that the equation from part (a) is consistent with Equation 4.12.

38. A satellite moves around the Earth in a circular orbit of radius r. (a) What is the speed v_0 of the satellite? Suddenly, an explosion breaks the satellite into two pieces, with masses m and $4m$. Immediately after the explosion the smaller piece of mass m is stationary with respect to the Earth and falls directly toward the Earth. (b) What is the speed v_i of the larger piece immediately after the explosion? (c) Because of the increase in its speed, this larger piece now moves in a new elliptical orbit. Find its distance away from the center of the Earth when it reaches the other end of the ellipse.

39. A comet of mass 1.20×10^{10} kg moves in an elliptical orbit around the Sun. Its distance from the Sun ranges between 0.500 AU and 50.0 AU. (a) What is the eccentricity of its orbit? (b) What is its period? (c) At aphelion what is the

potential energy of the comet–Sun system? *Note:* 1 AU = one astronomical unit = the average distance from Sun to Earth = 1.496×10^{11} m.

Additional Problems

40. ● Assume you are agile enough to run across a horizontal surface at 8.50 m/s, independently of the value of the gravitational field. What would be (a) the radius and (b) the mass of an airless spherical asteroid of uniform density 1.10×10^3 kg/m^3 on which you could launch yourself into orbit by running? (c) What would be your period? (d) Would your running significantly affect the rotation of the asteroid? Explain.

41. The Solar and Heliospheric Observatory (SOHO) spacecraft has a special orbit, chosen so that its view of the Sun is never eclipsed and it is always close enough to the Earth to transmit data easily. It moves in a near-circle around the Sun that is smaller than the Earth's circular orbit. Its period, however, is not less than 1 yr but rather is just equal to 1 yr. It is always located between the Earth and the Sun along the line joining them. Both objects exert gravitational forces on the observatory. Show that its distance from the Earth must be between 1.47×10^9 m and 1.48×10^9 m. In 1772, Joseph Louis Lagrange determined theoretically the special location allowing this orbit. The SOHO spacecraft took this position on February 14, 1996. *Suggestion:* Use data that are precise to four digits. The mass of the Earth is 5.983×10^{24} kg.

42. Let Δg_M represent the difference in the gravitational fields produced by the Moon at the points on the Earth's surface nearest to and farthest from the Moon. Find the fraction $\Delta g_M/g$, where g is the Earth's gravitational field. (This difference is responsible for the occurrence of the *lunar tides* on the Earth.)

43. **Review problem.** Two identical hard spheres, each of mass m and radius r, are released from rest in otherwise empty space with their centers separated by the distance R. They are allowed to collide under the influence of their gravitational attraction. (a) Show that the magnitude of the impulse received by each sphere before they make contact is given by $[Gm^3(1/2r - 1/R)]^{1/2}$. (b) **What If?** Find the magnitude of the impulse each receives during their contact if they collide elastically.

44. Two spheres having masses M and $2M$ and radii R and $3R$, respectively, are released from rest when the distance between their centers is $12R$. How fast will each sphere be moving when they collide? Assume the two spheres interact only with each other.

45. A ring of matter is a familiar structure in planetary and stellar astronomy. Examples include Saturn's rings and a ring nebula. Consider a large uniform ring having a mass of 2.36×10^{20} kg and radius 1.00×10^8 m. An object of mass 1 000 kg is placed at a point A on the axis of the ring, 2.00×10^8 m from the center of the ring (Fig. P13.45). When the object is released, the attraction of the ring makes the object move along the axis toward the center of the ring (point B). (a) Calculate the gravitational potential energy of the object–ring system when the object is at A. (b) Calculate the gravitational potential energy of the system when the object is at B. (c) Calculate the object's speed as it passes through B.

Figure P13.45

46. (a) Show that the rate of change of the free-fall acceleration with distance above the Earth's surface is

$$\frac{dg}{dr} = -\frac{2GM_E}{R_E^{\,3}}$$

This rate of change over distance is called a *gradient.* (b) Assuming that h is small in comparison to the radius of the Earth, show that the difference in free-fall acceleration between two points separated by vertical distance h is

$$|\Delta g| = \frac{2GM_E h}{R_E^{\,3}}$$

(c) Evaluate this difference for h = 6.00 m, a typical height for a two-story building.

47. As an astronaut, you observe a small planet to be spherical. After landing on the planet, you set off, walking always straight ahead, and find yourself returning to your spacecraft from the opposite side after completing a lap of 25.0 km. You hold a hammer and a falcon feather at a height of 1.40 m, release them, and observe that they fall together to the surface in 29.2 s. Determine the mass of the planet.

48. A certain quaternary star system consists of three stars, each of mass m, moving in the same circular orbit of radius r about a central star of mass M. The stars orbit in the same sense and are positioned one-third of a revolution apart from one another. Show that the period of each of the three stars is

$$T = 2\pi\sqrt{\frac{r^3}{G(M + m/\sqrt{3})}}$$

49. **Review problem.** A cylindrical habitat in space 6.00 km in diameter and 30 km long has been proposed (by G. K. O'Neill, 1974). Such a habitat would have cities, land, and lakes on the inside surface and air and clouds

in the center. They would all be held in place by rotation of the cylinder about its long axis. How fast would the cylinder have to rotate to imitate the Earth's gravitational field at the walls of the cylinder?

50. ● Many people assume air resistance acting on a moving object will always make the object slow down. It can, however, actually be responsible for making the object speed up. Consider a 100-kg Earth satellite in a circular orbit at an altitude of 200 km. A small force of air resistance makes the satellite drop into a circular orbit with an altitude of 100 km. (a) Calculate its initial speed. (b) Calculate its final speed in this process. (c) Calculate the initial energy of the satellite–Earth system. (d) Calculate the final energy of the system. (e) Show that the system has lost mechanical energy and find the amount of the loss due to friction. (f) What force makes the satellite's speed increase? You will find a free-body diagram to be useful in explaining your answer.

51. ▲ Two hypothetical planets of masses m_1 and m_2 and radii r_1 and r_2, respectively, are nearly at rest when they are an infinite distance apart. Because of their gravitational attraction, they head toward each other on a collision course. (a) When their center-to-center separation is d, find expressions for the speed of each planet and for their relative speed. (b) Find the kinetic energy of each planet just before they collide, taking $m_1 = 2.00 \times 10^{24}$ kg, $m_2 = 8.00 \times 10^{24}$ kg, $r_1 = 3.00 \times 10^6$ m, and $r_2 = 5.00 \times 10^6$ m. *Note:* Both energy and momentum of the system are conserved.

52. The maximum distance from the Earth to the Sun (at aphelion) is 1.521×10^{11} m, and the distance of closest approach (at perihelion) is 1.471×10^{11} m. The Earth's orbital speed at perihelion is 3.027×10^4 m/s. Determine (a) the Earth's orbital speed at aphelion, (b) the kinetic and potential energies of the Earth–Sun system at perihelion, and (c) the kinetic and potential energies at aphelion. Is the total energy of the system constant? (Ignore the effect of the Moon and other planets.)

53. Studies of the relationship of the Sun to its galaxy—the Milky Way—have revealed that the Sun is located near the outer edge of the galactic disk, about 30 000 ly from the center. The Sun has an orbital speed of approximately 250 km/s around the galactic center. (a) What is the period of the Sun's galactic motion? (b) What is the order of magnitude of the mass of the Milky Way galaxy? Suppose the galaxy is made mostly of stars of which the Sun is typical. What is the order of magnitude of the number of stars in the Milky Way?

54. X-ray pulses from Cygnus X-1, a celestial x-ray source, have been recorded during high-altitude rocket flights. The signals can be interpreted as originating when a blob of ionized matter orbits a black hole with a period of 5.0 ms. If the blob is in a circular orbit about a black hole whose mass is $20M_{\text{Sun}}$, what is the orbit radius?

55. Astronomers detect a distant meteoroid moving along a straight line that, if extended, would pass at a distance $3R_E$ from the center of the Earth, where R_E is the radius of the Earth. What minimum speed must the meteoroid have if the Earth's gravitation is not to deflect the meteoroid to make it strike the Earth?

56. The oldest artificial satellite in orbit is *Vanguard I*, launched March 3, 1958. Its mass is 1.60 kg. In its initial orbit, its minimum distance from the center of the Earth was 7.02 Mm and its speed at this perigee point was 8.23 km/s. (a) Find the total energy of the satellite–Earth system. (b) Find the magnitude of the angular momentum of the satellite. (c) At apogee, find its speed and its distance from the center of the Earth. (d) Find the semimajor axis of its orbit. (e) Determine its period.

57. Two stars of masses M and m, separated by a distance d, revolve in circular orbits about their center of mass (Fig. P13.57). Show that each star has a period given by

$$T^2 = \frac{4\pi^2 d^3}{G(M + m)}$$

Proceed by applying Newton's second law to each star. Note that the center-of-mass condition requires that $Mr_2 = mr_1$, where $r_1 + r_2 = d$.

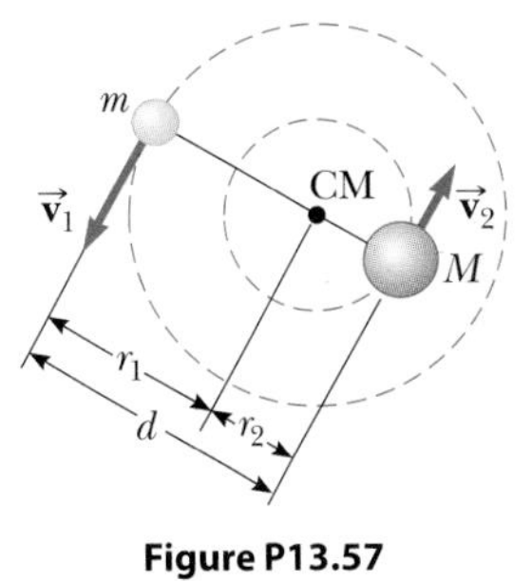

Figure P13.57

58. Show that the minimum period for a satellite in orbit around a spherical planet of uniform density ρ is

$$T_{\min} = \sqrt{\frac{3\pi}{G\rho}}$$

independent of the radius of the planet.

59. Two identical particles, each of mass 1 000 kg, are coasting in free space along the same path. At one instant their separation is 20.0 m and each has precisely the same velocity of $800\hat{\mathbf{i}}$ m/s. What are their velocities when they are 2.00 m apart?

60. (a) Consider an object of mass m, not necessarily small compared with the mass of the Earth, released at a distance of 1.20×10^7 m from the center of the Earth. Assume the objects behave as a pair of particles, isolated from the rest of the Universe. Find the magnitude of the acceleration a_{rel} with which each starts to move relative to the other. Evaluate the acceleration (b) for $m = 5.00$ kg, (c) for $m = 2\,000$ kg, and (d) for $m = 2.00 \times 10^{24}$ kg. (e) Describe the pattern of variation of a_{rel} with m.

61. As thermonuclear fusion proceeds in its core, the Sun loses mass at a rate of 3.64×10^9 kg/s. During the 5 000-yr period of recorded history, by how much has the length of the year changed due to the loss of mass from the Sun? *Suggestions:* Assume the Earth's orbit is circular. No external torque acts on the Earth–Sun system, so angular momentum is conserved. If x is small compared with 1, then $(1 + x)^n$ is nearly equal to $1 + nx$.

Answers to Quick Quizzes

13.1 (e). The gravitational force follows an inverse-square behavior, so doubling the distance causes the force to be one-fourth as large.

13.2 (c). An object in orbit is simply falling while it moves around the Earth. The acceleration of the object is that due to gravity. Because the object was launched from a very tall mountain, the value for g is slightly less than that at the surface.

13.3 (a). From Kepler's third law and the given period, the major axis of the asteroid can be calculated. It is found to be 1.2×10^{11} m. Because this value is smaller than the Earth–Sun distance, the asteroid cannot possibly collide with the Earth.

13.4 (a) Perihelion. Because of conservation of angular momentum, the speed of the comet is highest at its closest position to the Sun. (b) Aphelion. The potential energy of the comet–Sun system is highest when the comet is at its farthest distance from the Sun. (c) Perihelion. The kinetic energy is highest at the point at which the speed of the comet is highest. (d) All points. The total energy of the system is the same regardless of where the comet is in its orbit.

PART 4

Electricity and Magnetism

We now study the branch of physics concerned with electric and magnetic phenomena. The laws of electricity and magnetism play a central role in the operation of such devices as MP3 players, televisions, electric motors, computers, high-energy accelerators, and other electronic devices. More fundamentally, the interatomic and intermolecular forces responsible for the formation of solids and liquids are electric in origin.

Evidence in Chinese documents suggests magnetism was observed as early as 2000 BC. The ancient Greeks observed electric and magnetic phenomena possibly as early as 700 BC. The Greeks knew about magnetic forces from observations that the naturally occurring stone *magnetite* (Fe_3O_4) is attracted to iron. (The word *electric* comes from *elecktron*, the Greek word for "amber." The word *magnetic* comes from *Magnesia*, the name of the district of Greece where magnetite was first found.)

Not until the early part of the nineteenth century did scientists establish that electricity and magnetism are related phenomena. In 1819, Hans Oersted discovered that a compass needle is deflected when placed near a circuit carrying an electric current. In 1831, Michael Faraday and, almost simultaneously, Joseph Henry showed that when a wire is moved near a magnet (or, equivalently, when a magnet is moved near a wire), an electric current is established in the wire. In 1873, James Clerk Maxwell used these observations and other experimental facts as a basis for formulating the laws of electromagnetism as we know them today. (*Electromagnetism* is a name given to the combined study of electricity and magnetism.)

Maxwell's contributions to the field of electromagnetism were especially significant because the laws he formulated are basic to *all* forms of electromagnetic phenomena. His work is as important as Newton's work on the laws of motion and the theory of gravitation.

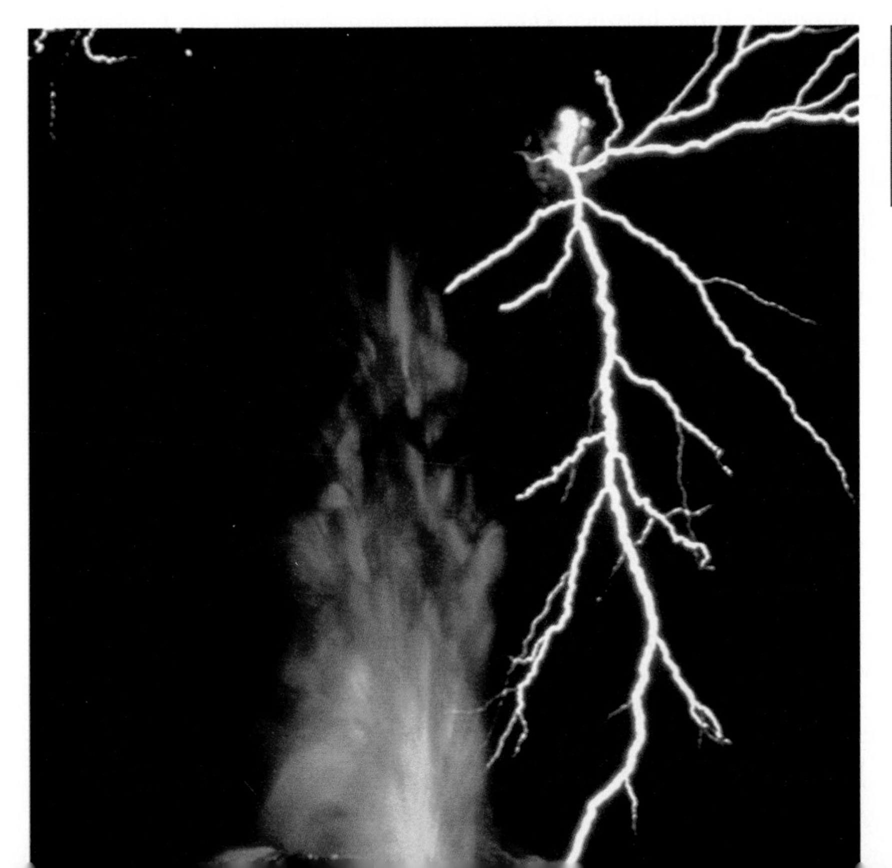

Lightning is a dramatic example of electrical phenomena occurring in nature. Although we are most familiar with lightning originating from thunderclouds, it can occur in other situations such as in a volcanic eruption (here, the Sakurajima volcano, Japan). (M. Zhilin/M. Newman/Photo Researchers, Inc.)

Mother and daughter are both enjoying the effects of electrically charging their bodies. Each individual hair on their heads becomes charged and exerts a repulsive force on the other hairs, resulting in the "stand-up" hair-dos seen here. (Courtesy of Resonance Research Corporation)

23 Electric Fields

The electromagnetic force between charged particles is one of the fundamental forces of nature. We begin this chapter by describing some basic properties of one manifestation of the electromagnetic force, the electric force. We then discuss Coulomb's law, which is the fundamental law governing the electric force between any two charged particles. Next, we introduce the concept of an electric field associated with a charge distribution and describe its effect on other charged particles. We then show how to use Coulomb's law to calculate the electric field for a given charge distribution. The chapter concludes with a discussion of the motion of a charged particle in a uniform electric field.

23.1 Properties of Electric Charges

A number of simple experiments demonstrate the existence of electric forces. For example, after rubbing a balloon on your hair on a dry day, you will find that the balloon attracts bits of paper. The attractive force is often strong enough to suspend the paper from the balloon.

When materials behave in this way, they are said to be *electrified* or to have become **electrically charged**. You can easily electrify your body by vigorously rubbing your shoes on a wool rug. Evidence of the electric charge on your body can be detected by lightly touching (and startling) a friend. Under the right conditions, you will see a spark when you touch and both of you will feel a slight tingle.

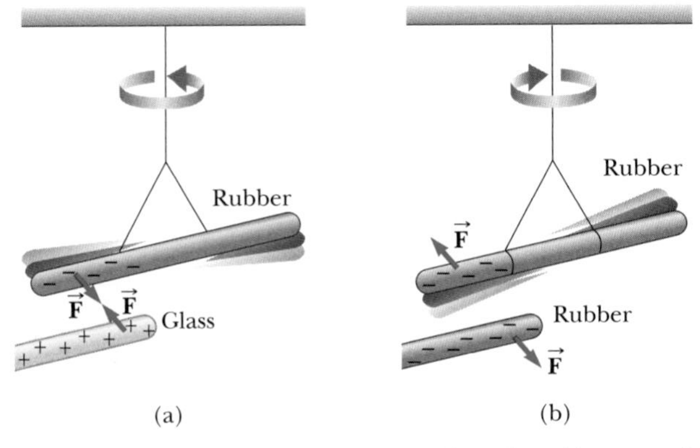

Figure 23.1 (a) A negatively charged rubber rod suspended by a thread is attracted to a positively charged glass rod. (b) A negatively charged rubber rod is repelled by another negatively charged rubber rod.

(Experiments such as these work best on a dry day because an excessive amount of moisture in the air can cause any charge you build up to "leak" from your body to the Earth.)

In a series of simple experiments, it was found that there are two kinds of electric charges, which were given the names **positive** and **negative** by Benjamin Franklin (1706–1790). Electrons are identified as having negative charge, while protons are positively charged. To verify that there are two types of charge, suppose a hard rubber rod that has been rubbed on fur is suspended by a sewing thread as shown in Figure 23.1. When a glass rod that has been rubbed on silk is brought near the rubber rod, the two attract each other (Fig. 23.1a). On the other hand, if two charged rubber rods (or two charged glass rods) are brought near each other as shown in Figure 23.1b, the two repel each other. This observation shows that the rubber and glass have two different types of charge on them. On the basis of these observations, we conclude that **charges of the same sign repel one another and charges with opposite signs attract one another.**

Using the convention suggested by Franklin, the electric charge on the glass rod is called positive and that on the rubber rod is called negative. Therefore, any charged object attracted to a charged rubber rod (or repelled by a charged glass rod) must have a positive charge, and any charged object repelled by a charged rubber rod (or attracted to a charged glass rod) must have a negative charge.

◀ Electric charge is conserved

Another important aspect of electricity that arises from experimental observations is that **electric charge is always conserved** in an isolated system. That is, when one object is rubbed against another, charge is not created in the process. The electrified state is due to a *transfer* of charge from one object to the other. One object gains some amount of negative charge while the other gains an equal amount of positive charge. For example, when a glass rod is rubbed on silk as in Figure 23.2, the silk obtains a negative charge equal in magnitude to the positive charge on the glass rod. We now know from our understanding of atomic structure that electrons are transferred in the rubbing process from the glass to the silk. Similarly, when rubber is rubbed on fur, electrons are transferred from the fur to the rubber, giving the rubber a net negative charge and the fur a net positive charge. This process is consistent with the fact that neutral, uncharged matter contains as many positive charges (protons within atomic nuclei) as negative charges (electrons).

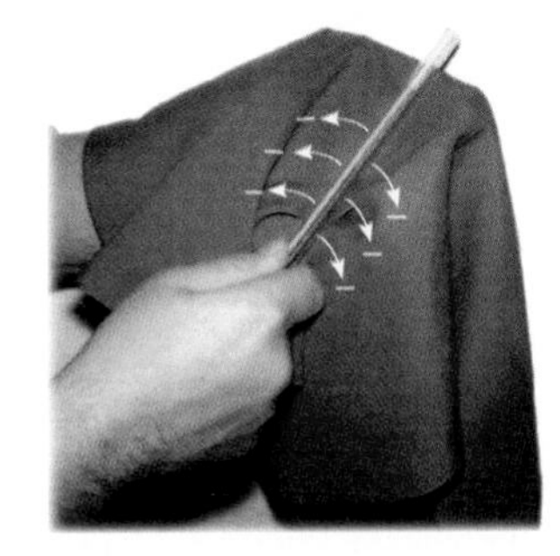

Figure 23.2 When a glass rod is rubbed with silk, electrons are transferred from the glass to the silk. Because of conservation of charge, each electron adds negative charge to the silk and an equal positive charge is left behind on the rod. Also, because the charges are transferred in discrete bundles, the charges on the two objects are $\pm e$, or $\pm 2e$, or $\pm 3e$, and so on.

In 1909, Robert Millikan (1868–1953) discovered that electric charge always occurs as integral multiples of a fundamental amount of charge e (see Section 25.7). In modern terms, the electric charge q is said to be **quantized,** where q is the standard symbol used for charge as a variable. That is, electric charge exists as discrete "packets," and we can write $q = \pm Ne$, where N is some integer. Other experiments in the same period showed that the electron has a charge $-e$ and the proton has a charge of equal magnitude but opposite sign $+e$. Some particles, such as the neutron, have no charge.

Quick Quiz 23.1 Three objects are brought close to each other, two at a time. When objects A and B are brought together, they repel. When objects B and C are brought together, they also repel. Which of the following are true? (a) Objects A and C possess charges of the same sign. (b) Objects A and C possess charges of opposite sign. (c) All three objects possess charges of the same sign. (d) One object is neutral. (e) Additional experiments must be performed to determine the signs of the charges.

23.2 Charging Objects by Induction

It is convenient to classify materials in terms of the ability of electrons to move through the material:

Electrical **conductors** are materials in which some of the electrons are free electrons[1] that are not bound to atoms and can move relatively freely through the material; electrical **insulators** are materials in which all electrons are bound to atoms and cannot move freely through the material.

Materials such as glass, rubber, and dry wood fall into the category of electrical insulators. When such materials are charged by rubbing, only the area rubbed becomes charged and the charged particles are unable to move to other regions of the material.

In contrast, materials such as copper, aluminum, and silver are good electrical conductors. When such materials are charged in some small region, the charge readily distributes itself over the entire surface of the material.

Semiconductors are a third class of materials, and their electrical properties are somewhere between those of insulators and those of conductors. Silicon and germanium are well-known examples of semiconductors commonly used in the fabrication of a variety of electronic chips used in computers, cellular telephones, and stereo systems. The electrical properties of semiconductors can be changed over many orders of magnitude by the addition of controlled amounts of certain atoms to the materials.

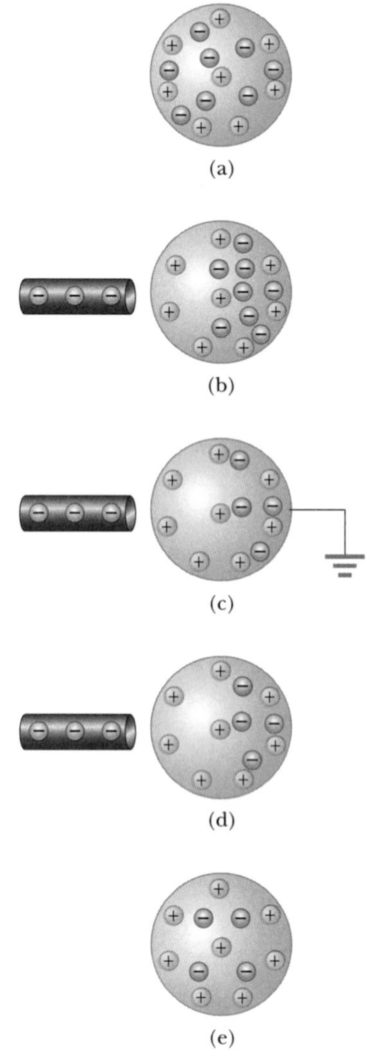

Figure 23.3 Charging a metallic object by *induction* (that is, the two objects never touch each other). (a) A neutral metallic sphere, with equal numbers of positive and negative charges. (b) The electrons on the neutral sphere are redistributed when a charged rubber rod is placed near the sphere. (c) When the sphere is grounded, some of its electrons leave through the ground wire. (d) When the ground connection is removed, the sphere has excess positive charge that is nonuniformly distributed. (e) When the rod is removed, the remaining electrons redistribute uniformly and there is a net uniform distribution of positive charge on the sphere.

To understand how to charge a conductor by a process known as **induction,** consider a neutral (uncharged) conducting sphere insulated from the ground as shown in Figure 23.3a. There are an equal number of electrons and protons in the sphere if the charge on the sphere is exactly zero. When a negatively charged rubber rod is brought near the sphere, electrons in the region nearest the rod experience a repulsive force and migrate to the opposite side of the sphere. This migration leaves the side of the sphere near the rod with an effective positive charge because of the diminished number of electrons as in Figure 23.3b. (The left side of the sphere in Figure 23.3b is positively charged *as if* positive charges moved into this region, but remember that it is only electrons that are free to move.) This process occurs even if the rod never actually touches the sphere. If the same experiment is performed with a conducting wire connected from the sphere to the Earth (Fig. 23.3c), some of the electrons in the conductor are so strongly repelled by the presence of the negative charge in the rod that they move out of the sphere through the wire and into the Earth. The symbol ⏚ at the end of the wire in Figure 23.3c indicates that the wire is connected to **ground,** which means a reservoir, such as the Earth, that can accept or provide electrons freely with negligible effect on its electrical characteristics. If the wire to ground is then removed

[1] A metal atom contains one or more outer electrons, which are weakly bound to the nucleus. When many atoms combine to form a metal, the *free electrons* are these outer electrons, which are not bound to any one atom. These electrons move about the metal in a manner similar to that of gas molecules moving in a container.

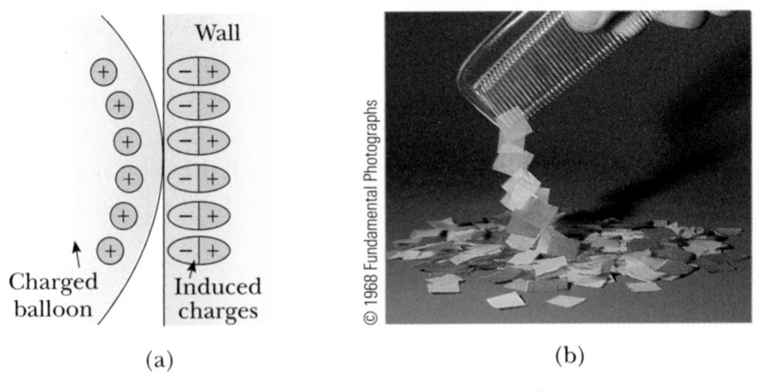

Figure 23.4 (a) The charged object on the left induces a charge distribution on the surface of an insulator due to realignment of charges in the molecules. (b) A charged comb attracts bits of paper because charges in molecules in the paper are realigned.

(Fig. 23.3d), the conducting sphere contains an excess of *induced* positive charge because it has fewer electrons than it needs to cancel out the positive charge of the protons. When the rubber rod is removed from the vicinity of the sphere (Fig. 23.3e), this induced positive charge remains on the ungrounded sphere. Notice that the rubber rod loses none of its negative charge during this process.

Charging an object by induction requires no contact with the object inducing the charge. That is in contrast to charging an object by rubbing (that is, by *conduction*), which does require contact between the two objects.

A process similar to induction in conductors takes place in insulators. In most neutral molecules, the center of positive charge coincides with the center of negative charge. In the presence of a charged object, however, these centers inside each molecule in an insulator may shift slightly, resulting in more positive charge on one side of the molecule than on the other. This realignment of charge within individual molecules produces a layer of charge on the surface of the insulator as shown in Figure 23.4a. Your knowledge of induction in insulators should help you explain why a comb that has been drawn through your hair attracts bits of electrically neutral paper as shown in Figure 23.4b.

Quick Quiz 23.2 Three objects are brought close to one another, two at a time. When objects A and B are brought together, they attract. When objects B and C are brought together, they repel. Which of the following are necessarily true? (a) Objects A and C possess charges of the same sign. (b) Objects A and C possess charges of opposite sign. (c) All three objects possess charges of the same sign. (d) One object is neutral. (e) Additional experiments must be performed to determine information about the charges on the objects.

23.3 Coulomb's Law

Charles Coulomb measured the magnitudes of the electric forces between charged objects using the torsion balance, which he invented (Fig. 23.5). The operating principle of the torsion balance is the same as that of the apparatus used by Cavendish to measure the gravitational constant (see Section 13.1), with the electrically neutral spheres replaced by charged ones. The electric force between charged spheres A and B in Figure 23.5 causes the spheres to either attract or repel each other, and the resulting motion causes the suspended fiber to twist. Because the restoring torque of the twisted fiber is proportional to the angle through which the fiber rotates, a measurement of this angle provides a quantitative measure of the electric force of attraction or repulsion. Once the spheres are charged by rubbing, the electric force between them is very large compared with the gravitational attraction, and so the gravitational force can be neglected.

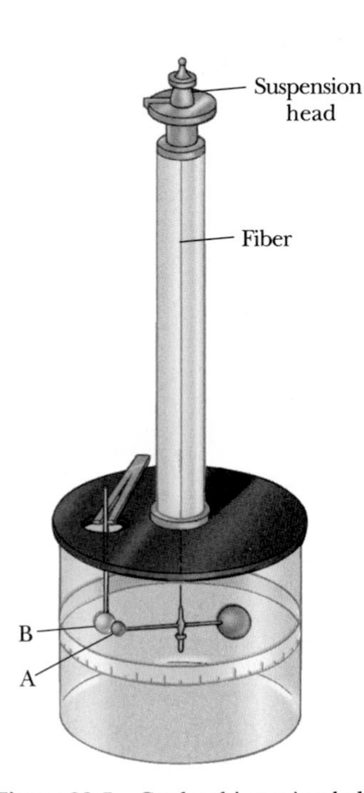

Figure 23.5 Coulomb's torsion balance, used to establish the inverse-square law for the electric force between two charges.

From Coulomb's experiments, we can generalize the properties of the **electric force** between two stationary charged particles. We use the term **point charge** to refer to a charged particle of zero size. The electrical behavior of electrons and protons is very well described by modeling them as point charges. From experimental observations, we find that the magnitude of the electric force (sometimes called the *Coulomb force*) between two point charges is given by **Coulomb's law:**

Coulomb's law ▶

$$F_e = k_e \frac{|q_1||q_2|}{r^2} \quad \textbf{(23.1)}$$

where k_e is a constant called the **Coulomb constant.** In his experiments, Coulomb was able to show that the value of the exponent of r was 2 to within an uncertainty of a few percent. Modern experiments have shown that the exponent is 2 to within an uncertainty of a few parts in 10^{16}. Experiments also show that the electric force, like the gravitational force, is conservative.

The value of the Coulomb constant depends on the choice of units. The SI unit of charge is the **coulomb** (C). The Coulomb constant k_e in SI units has the value

Coulomb constant ▶

$$k_e = 8.987\,6 \times 10^9 \text{ N}\cdot\text{m}^2/\text{C}^2 \quad \textbf{(23.2)}$$

This constant is also written in the form

$$k_e = \frac{1}{4\pi\epsilon_0} \quad \textbf{(23.3)}$$

where the constant ϵ_0 (Greek letter epsilon) is known as the **permittivity of free space** and has the value

$$\epsilon_0 = 8.854\,2 \times 10^{-12} \text{ C}^2/\text{N}\cdot\text{m}^2 \quad \textbf{(23.4)}$$

The smallest unit of free charge e known in nature,[2] the charge on an electron $(-e)$ or a proton $(+e)$, has a magnitude

$$e = 1.602\,18 \times 10^{-19} \text{ C} \quad \textbf{(23.5)}$$

Therefore, 1 C of charge is approximately equal to the charge of 6.24×10^{18} electrons or protons. This number is very small when compared with the number of free electrons in 1 cm^3 of copper, which is on the order of 10^{23}. Nevertheless, 1 C is a substantial amount of charge. In typical experiments in which a rubber or glass rod is charged by friction, a net charge on the order of 10^{-6} C is obtained. In other words, only a very small fraction of the total available charge is transferred between the rod and the rubbing material.

The charges and masses of the electron, proton, and neutron are given in Table 23.1.

Photo courtesy of AIP Niels Bohr Library/E. Scott Barr Collection

CHARLES COULOMB
French physicist (1736–1806)
Coulomb's major contributions to science were in the areas of electrostatics and magnetism. During his lifetime, he also investigated the strengths of materials and determined the forces that affect objects on beams, thereby contributing to the field of structural mechanics. In the field of ergonomics, his research provided a fundamental understanding of the ways in which people and animals can best do work.

TABLE 23.1
Charge and Mass of the Electron, Proton, and Neutron

Particle	Charge (C)	Mass (kg)
Electron (e)	$-1.602\,176\,5 \times 10^{-19}$	$9.109\,4 \times 10^{-31}$
Proton (p)	$+1.602\,176\,5 \times 10^{-19}$	$1.672\,62 \times 10^{-27}$
Neutron (n)	0	$1.674\,93 \times 10^{-27}$

[2] No unit of charge smaller than e has been detected on a free particle; current theories, however, propose the existence of particles called *quarks* having charges $-e/3$ and $2e/3$. Although there is considerable experimental evidence for such particles inside nuclear matter, *free* quarks have never been detected. We discuss other properties of quarks in Chapter 46.

EXAMPLE 23.1 The Hydrogen Atom

The electron and proton of a hydrogen atom are separated (on the average) by a distance of approximately 5.3×10^{-11} m. Find the magnitudes of the electric force and the gravitational force between the two particles.

SOLUTION

Conceptualize Think about the two particles separated by the very small distance given in the problem statement. In Chapter 13, we found the gravitational force between small objects to be weak, so we expect the gravitational force between the electron and proton to be significantly smaller than the electric force.

Categorize The electric and gravitational forces will be evaluated from universal force laws, so we categorize this example as a substitution problem.

Use Coulomb's law to find the magnitude of the electric force:

$$F_e = k_e \frac{|e||-e|}{r^2} = (8.99 \times 10^9 \text{ N}\cdot\text{m}^2/\text{C}^2)\frac{(1.60 \times 10^{-19}\text{ C})^2}{(5.3 \times 10^{-11}\text{ m})^2}$$

$$= 8.2 \times 10^{-8}\text{ N}$$

Use Newton's law of universal gravitation and Table 23.1 (for the particle masses) to find the magnitude of the gravitational force:

$$F_g = G\frac{m_e m_p}{r^2}$$

$$= (6.67 \times 10^{-11}\text{ N}\cdot\text{m}^2/\text{kg}^2)\frac{(9.11 \times 10^{-31}\text{ kg})(1.67 \times 10^{-27}\text{ kg})}{(5.3 \times 10^{-11}\text{ m})^2}$$

$$= 3.6 \times 10^{-47}\text{ N}$$

The ratio $F_e/F_g \approx 2 \times 10^{39}$. Therefore, the gravitational force between charged atomic particles is negligible when compared with the electric force. Notice the similar forms of Newton's law of universal gravitation and Coulomb's law of electric forces. Other than magnitude, what is a fundamental difference between the two forces?

When dealing with Coulomb's law, remember that force is a vector quantity and must be treated accordingly. Coulomb's law expressed in vector form for the electric force exerted by a charge q_1 on a second charge q_2, written $\vec{\mathbf{F}}_{12}$, is

$$\vec{\mathbf{F}}_{12} = k_e \frac{q_1 q_2}{r^2}\hat{\mathbf{r}}_{12} \qquad \textbf{(23.6)}$$

◀ Vector form of Coulomb's law

where $\hat{\mathbf{r}}_{12}$ is a unit vector directed from q_1 toward q_2 as shown in Active Figure 23.6a. Because the electric force obeys Newton's third law, the electric force exerted by q_2 on q_1 is equal in magnitude to the force exerted by q_1 on q_2 and in

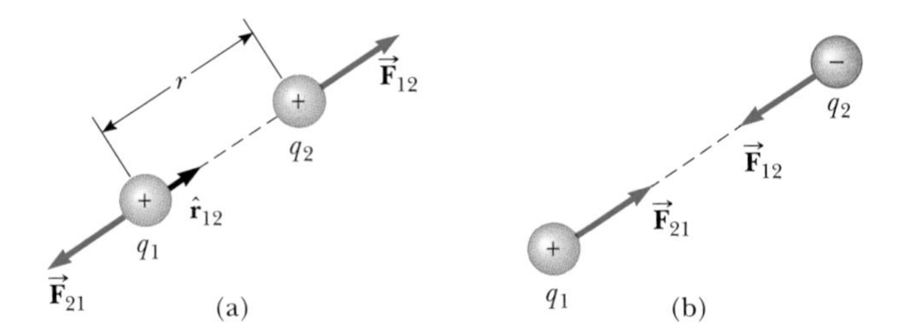

ACTIVE FIGURE 23.6

Two point charges separated by a distance r exert a force on each other that is given by Coulomb's law. The force $\vec{\mathbf{F}}_{21}$ exerted by q_2 on q_1 is equal in magnitude and opposite in direction to the force $\vec{\mathbf{F}}_{12}$ exerted by q_1 on q_2. (a) When the charges are of the same sign, the force is repulsive. (b) When the charges are of opposite signs, the force is attractive.

Sign in at www.thomsonedu.com and go to ThomsonNOW to move the charges to any position in two-dimensional space and observe the electric forces on them.

the opposite direction; that is, $\vec{\mathbf{F}}_{21} = -\vec{\mathbf{F}}_{12}$. Finally, Equation 23.6 shows that if q_1 and q_2 have the same sign as in Active Figure 23.6a, the product q_1q_2 is positive. If q_1 and q_2 are of opposite sign as shown in Active Figure 23.6b, the product q_1q_2 is negative. These signs describe the *relative* direction of the force but not the *absolute* direction. A negative product indicates an attractive force, and each charge experiences a force toward the other. A positive product indicates a repulsive force such that each charge experiences a force away from the other. The *absolute* direction of the force on a charge depends on the location of the other charge. For example, if an x axis lies along the two charges in Active Figure 23.6a, the product q_1q_2 is positive, but $\vec{\mathbf{F}}_{12}$ points in the $+x$ direction and $\vec{\mathbf{F}}_{21}$ points in the $-x$ direction.

When more than two charges are present, the force between any pair of them is given by Equation 23.6. Therefore, the resultant force on any one of them equals the vector sum of the forces exerted by the other individual charges. For example, if four charges are present, the resultant force exerted by particles 2, 3, and 4 on particle 1 is

$$\vec{\mathbf{F}}_1 = \vec{\mathbf{F}}_{21} + \vec{\mathbf{F}}_{31} + \vec{\mathbf{F}}_{41}$$

Quick Quiz 23.3 Object A has a charge of $+2\ \mu$C, and object B has a charge of $+6\ \mu$C. Which statement is true about the electric forces on the objects? (a) $\vec{\mathbf{F}}_{AB} = -3\vec{\mathbf{F}}_{BA}$ (b) $\vec{\mathbf{F}}_{AB} = -\vec{\mathbf{F}}_{BA}$ (c) $3\vec{\mathbf{F}}_{AB} = -\vec{\mathbf{F}}_{BA}$ (d) $\vec{\mathbf{F}}_{AB} = 3\vec{\mathbf{F}}_{BA}$ (e) $\vec{\mathbf{F}}_{AB} = \vec{\mathbf{F}}_{BA}$ (f) $3\vec{\mathbf{F}}_{AB} = \vec{\mathbf{F}}_{BA}$

EXAMPLE 23.2 Find the Resultant Force

Consider three point charges located at the corners of a right triangle as shown in Figure 23.7, where $q_1 = q_3 = 5.0\ \mu$C, $q_2 = -2.0\ \mu$C, and $a = 0.10$ m. Find the resultant force exerted on q_3.

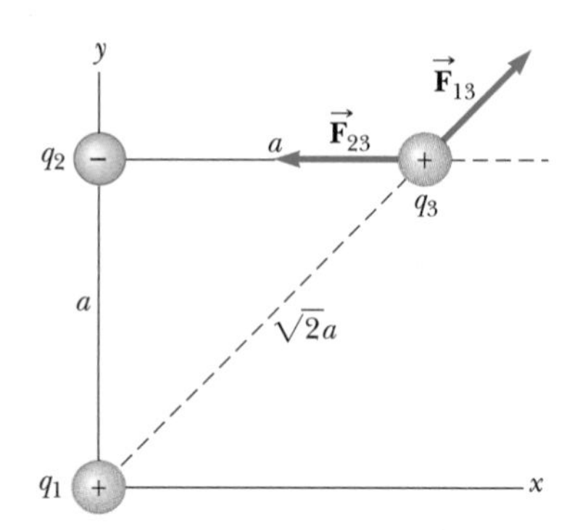

Figure 23.7 (Example 23.2) The force exerted by q_1 on q_3 is $\vec{\mathbf{F}}_{13}$. The force exerted by q_2 on q_3 is $\vec{\mathbf{F}}_{23}$. The resultant force $\vec{\mathbf{F}}_3$ exerted on q_3 is the vector sum $\vec{\mathbf{F}}_{13} + \vec{\mathbf{F}}_{23}$.

SOLUTION

Conceptualize Think about the net force on q_3. Because charge q_3 is near two other charges, it will experience two electric forces.

Categorize Because two forces are exerted on charge q_3, we categorize this example as a vector addition problem.

Analyze The directions of the individual forces exerted by q_1 and q_2 on q_3 are shown in Figure 23.7. The force $\vec{\mathbf{F}}_{23}$ exerted by q_2 on q_3 is attractive because q_2 and q_3 have opposite signs. In the coordinate system shown in Figure 23.7, the attractive force $\vec{\mathbf{F}}_{23}$ is to the left (in the negative x direction).

The force $\vec{\mathbf{F}}_{13}$ exerted by q_1 on q_3 is repulsive because both charges are positive. The repulsive force $\vec{\mathbf{F}}_{13}$ makes an angle of 45° with the x axis.

Use Equation 23.1 to find the magnitude of $\vec{\mathbf{F}}_{23}$:

$$F_{23} = k_e \frac{|q_2||q_3|}{a^2}$$

$$= (8.99 \times 10^9\ \text{N}\cdot\text{m}^2/\text{C}^2)\frac{(2.0 \times 10^{-6}\ \text{C})(5.0 \times 10^{-6}\ \text{C})}{(0.10\ \text{m})^2} = 9.0\ \text{N}$$

Find the magnitude of the force $\vec{\mathbf{F}}_{13}$:

$$F_{13} = k_e \frac{|q_1||q_3|}{(\sqrt{2}a)^2}$$

$$= (8.99 \times 10^9\ \text{N}\cdot\text{m}^2/\text{C}^2)\frac{(5.0 \times 10^{-6}\ \text{C})(5.0 \times 10^{-6}\ \text{C})}{2(0.10\ \text{m})^2} = 11\ \text{N}$$

Find the x and y components of the force $\vec{\mathbf{F}}_{13}$:

$$F_{13x} = F_{13} \cos 45° = 7.9 \text{ N}$$
$$F_{13y} = F_{13} \sin 45° = 7.9 \text{ N}$$

Find the components of the resultant force acting on q_3:

$$F_{3x} = F_{13x} + F_{23x} = 7.9 \text{ N} + (-9.0 \text{ N}) = -1.1 \text{ N}$$
$$F_{3y} = F_{13y} + F_{23y} = 7.9 \text{ N} + 0 = 7.9 \text{ N}$$

Express the resultant force acting on q_3 in unit–vector form:

$$\vec{\mathbf{F}}_3 = (-1.1\hat{\mathbf{i}} + 7.9\hat{\mathbf{j}}) \text{ N}$$

Finalize The net force on q_3 is upward and toward the left in Figure 23.7. If q_3 moves in response to the net force, the distances between q_3 and the other charges change, so the net force changes. Therefore, q_3 can be modeled as a particle under a net force as long as it is recognized that the force exerted on q_3 is *not* constant.

What If? What if the signs of all three charges were changed to the opposite signs? How would that affect the result for $\vec{\mathbf{F}}_3$?

Answer The charge q_3 would still be attracted toward q_2 and repelled from q_1 with forces of the same magnitude. Therefore, the final result for $\vec{\mathbf{F}}_3$ would be the same.

EXAMPLE 23.3 Where Is the Net Force Zero?

Three point charges lie along the x axis as shown in Figure 23.8. The positive charge $q_1 = 15.0\ \mu\text{C}$ is at $x = 2.00$ m, the positive charge $q_2 = 6.00\ \mu\text{C}$ is at the origin, and the net force acting on q_3 is zero. What is the x coordinate of q_3?

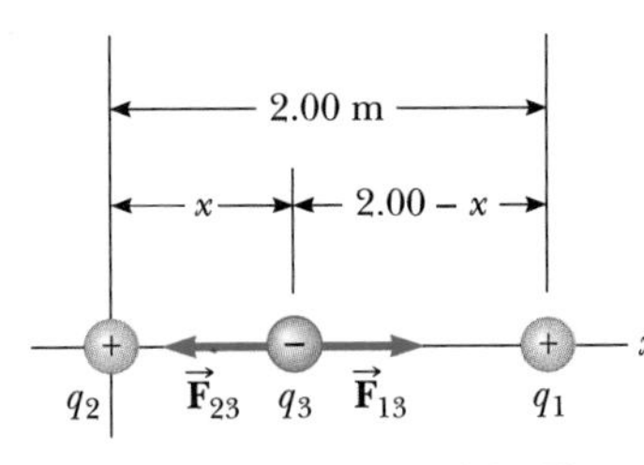

Figure 23.8 (Example 23.3) Three point charges are placed along the x axis. If the resultant force acting on q_3 is zero, the force $\vec{\mathbf{F}}_{13}$ exerted by q_1 on q_3 must be equal in magnitude and opposite in direction to the force $\vec{\mathbf{F}}_{23}$ exerted by q_2 on q_3.

SOLUTION

Conceptualize Because q_3 is near two other charges, it experiences two electric forces. Unlike the preceding example, however, the forces lie along the same line in this problem as indicated in Figure 23.8. Because q_3 is negative while q_1 and q_2 are positive, the forces $\vec{\mathbf{F}}_{13}$ and $\vec{\mathbf{F}}_{23}$ are both attractive.

Categorize Because the net force on q_3 is zero, we model the point charge as a particle in equilibrium.

Analyze Write an expression for the net force on charge q_3 when it is in equilibrium:

$$\vec{\mathbf{F}}_3 = \vec{\mathbf{F}}_{23} + \vec{\mathbf{F}}_{13} = -k_e \frac{|q_2||q_3|}{x^2}\hat{\mathbf{i}} + k_e \frac{|q_1||q_3|}{(2.00 - x)^2}\hat{\mathbf{i}} = 0$$

Move the second term to the right side of the equation and set the coefficients of the unit vector $\hat{\mathbf{i}}$ equal:

$$k_e \frac{|q_2||q_3|}{x^2} = k_e \frac{|q_1||q_3|}{(2.00 - x)^2}$$

Eliminate k_e and $|q_3|$ and rearrange the equation:

$$(2.00 - x)^2|q_2| = x^2|q_1|$$
$$(4.00 - 4.00x + x^2)(6.00 \times 10^{-6} \text{ C}) = x^2(15.0 \times 10^{-6} \text{ C})$$

Reduce the quadratic equation to a simpler form:

$$3.00x^2 + 8.00x - 8.00 = 0$$

Solve the quadratic equation for the positive root:

$$x = 0.775 \text{ m}$$

Finalize The second root to the quadratic equation is $x = -3.44$ m. That is another location where the *magnitudes* of the forces on q_3 are equal, but both forces are in the same direction.

What If? Suppose q_3 is constrained to move only along the x axis. From its initial position at $x = 0.775$ m, it is pulled a small distance along the x axis. When released, does it return to equilibrium, or is it pulled further from equilibrium? That is, is the equilibrium stable or unstable?

Answer If q_3 is moved to the right, $\vec{\mathbf{F}}_{13}$ becomes larger and $\vec{\mathbf{F}}_{23}$ becomes smaller. The result is a net force to the right, in the same direction as the displacement. Therefore, the charge q_3 would continue to move to the right and the equilibrium is *unstable.* (See Section 7.9 for a review of stable and unstable equilibrium.)

If q_3 is constrained to stay at a *fixed* x coordinate but allowed to move up and down in Figure 23.8, the equilibrium is stable. In this case, if the charge is pulled upward (or downward) and released, it moves back toward the equilibrium position and oscillates about this point.

EXAMPLE 23.4 Find the Charge on the Spheres

Two identical small charged spheres, each having a mass of 3.0×10^{-2} kg, hang in equilibrium as shown in Figure 23.9a. The length of each string is 0.15 m, and the angle θ is 5.0°. Find the magnitude of the charge on each sphere.

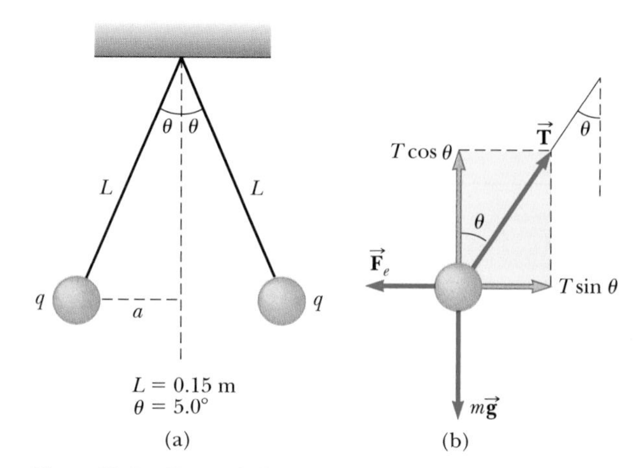

Figure 23.9 (Example 23.4) (a) Two identical spheres, each carrying the same charge q, suspended in equilibrium. (b) The free-body diagram for the sphere on the left of part (a).

SOLUTION

Conceptualize Figure 23.9a helps us conceptualize this example. The two spheres exert repulsive forces on each other. If they are held close to each other and released, they move outward from the center and settle into the configuration in Figure 23.9a after the oscillations have vanished due to air resistance.

Categorize The key phrase "in equilibrium" helps us model each sphere as a particle in equilibrium. This example is similar to the particle in equilibrium problems in Chapter 5 with the added feature that one of the forces on a sphere is an electric force.

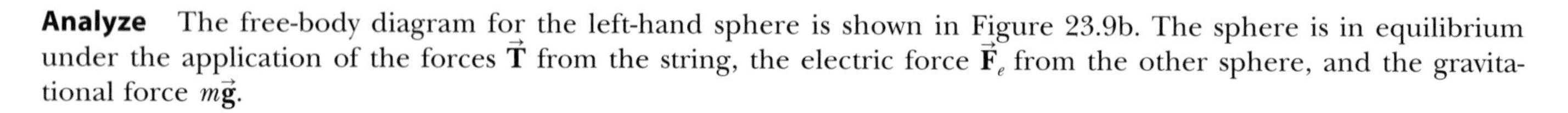

Analyze The free-body diagram for the left-hand sphere is shown in Figure 23.9b. The sphere is in equilibrium under the application of the forces $\vec{\mathbf{T}}$ from the string, the electric force $\vec{\mathbf{F}}_e$ from the other sphere, and the gravitational force $m\vec{\mathbf{g}}$.

Write Newton's second law for the left-hand sphere in component form:

$$(1)\quad \sum F_x = T\sin\theta - F_e = 0 \quad\rightarrow\quad T\sin\theta = F_e$$

$$(2)\quad \sum F_y = T\cos\theta - mg = 0 \quad\rightarrow\quad T\cos\theta = mg$$

Divide Equation (1) by Equation (2) to find F_e:

$$\tan\theta = \frac{F_e}{mg} \quad\rightarrow\quad F_e = mg\tan\theta$$

Evaluate the electric force numerically:

$$F_e = (3.0 \times 10^{-2}\ \text{kg})(9.80\ \text{m/s}^2)\tan(5.0°) = 2.6 \times 10^{-2}\ \text{N}$$

Use the geometry of the right triangle in Figure 23.9a to find a relationship between a, L, and θ:

$$\sin\theta = \frac{a}{L} \quad\rightarrow\quad a = L\sin\theta$$

Evaluate a:

$$a = (0.15\ \text{m})\sin(5.0°) = 0.013\ \text{m}$$

Solve Coulomb's law (Eq. 23.1) for the charge $|q|$ on each sphere:

$$F_e = k_e\frac{|q|^2}{r^2} \quad\rightarrow\quad |q| = \sqrt{\frac{F_e r^2}{k_e}} = \sqrt{\frac{F_e(2a)^2}{k_e}}$$

Substitute numerical values:

$$|q| = \sqrt{\frac{(2.6 \times 10^{-2}\ \text{N})[2(0.013\ \text{m})]^2}{8.99 \times 10^9\ \text{N}\cdot\text{m}^2/\text{C}^2}} = 4.4 \times 10^{-8}\ \text{C}$$

Finalize We cannot determine the sign of the charge from the information given. In fact, the sign of the charge is not important. The situation is the same whether both spheres are positively charged or negatively charged.

What If? Suppose your roommate proposes solving this problem without the assumption that the charges are of equal magnitude. She claims the symmetry of the problem is destroyed if the charges are not equal, so the strings would make two different angles with the vertical and the problem would be much more complicated. How would you respond?

Answer The symmetry is not destroyed and the angles are not different. Newton's third law requires the magnitudes of the electric forces on the two charges to be the same, regardless of the equality or nonequality of the charges. The solution to the example remains the same with one change: the value of $|q|^2$ in the solution is replaced by $|q_1 q_2|$ in the new situation, where q_1 and q_2 are the values of the charges on the two spheres. The symmetry of the problem would be destroyed if the *masses* of the spheres were not the same. In this case, the strings would make different angles with the vertical and the problem would be more complicated.

23.4 The Electric Field

Two field forces—the gravitational force in Chapter 13 and the electric force here—have been introduced into our discussions so far. As pointed out earlier, field forces can act through space, producing an effect even when no physical contact occurs between interacting objects. The gravitational field $\vec{\mathbf{g}}$ at a point in space due to a source particle was defined in Section 13.4 to be equal to the gravitational force $\vec{\mathbf{F}}_g$ acting on a test particle of mass m divided by that mass: $\vec{\mathbf{g}} \equiv \vec{\mathbf{F}}_g/m$. The concept of a field was developed by Michael Faraday (1791–1867) in the context of electric forces and is of such practical value that we shall devote much attention to it in the next several chapters. In this approach, an **electric field** is said to exist in the region of space around a charged object, the **source charge**. When another charged object—the **test charge**—enters this electric field, an electric force acts on it. As an example, consider Figure 23.10, which shows a small positive test charge q_0 placed near a second object carrying a much greater positive charge Q. We define the electric field due to the source charge at the location of the test charge to be the electric force on the test charge *per unit charge*, or, to be more specific, **the electric field vector $\vec{\mathbf{E}}$** at a point in space is defined as the electric force $\vec{\mathbf{F}}_e$ acting on a positive test charge q_0 placed at that point divided by the test charge:[3]

This dramatic photograph captures a lightning bolt striking a tree near some rural homes. Lightning is associated with very strong electric fields in the atmosphere.

$$\vec{\mathbf{E}} \equiv \frac{\vec{\mathbf{F}}_e}{q_0} \tag{23.7}$$

◀ Definition of electric field

The vector $\vec{\mathbf{E}}$ has the SI units of newtons per coulomb (N/C). Note that $\vec{\mathbf{E}}$ is the field produced by some charge or charge distribution *separate from* the test charge; it is not the field produced by the test charge itself. Also note that the existence of an electric field is a property of its source; the presence of the test charge is not necessary for the field to exist. The test charge serves as a *detector* of the electric field.

The direction of $\vec{\mathbf{E}}$ as shown in Figure 23.10 is the direction of the force a positive test charge experiences when placed in the field. **An electric field exists at a point if a test charge at that point experiences an electric force.**

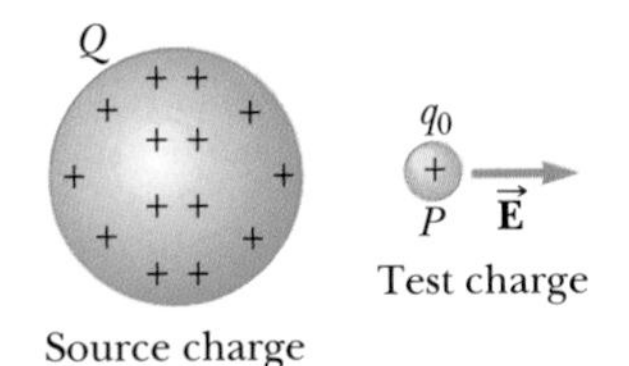

Figure 23.10 A small positive test charge q_0 placed at point P near an object carrying a much larger positive charge Q experiences an electric field $\vec{\mathbf{E}}$ at point P established by the source charge Q.

[3] When using Equation 23.7, we must assume the test charge q_0 is small enough that it does not disturb the charge distribution responsible for the electric field. If the test charge is great enough, the charge on the metallic sphere is redistributed and the electric field it sets up is different from the field it sets up in the presence of the much smaller test charge.

PITFALL PREVENTION 23.1
Particles Only

Equation 23.8 is only valid for a *particle* of charge q, that is, an object of zero size. For a charged *object* of finite size in an electric field, the field may vary in magnitude and direction over the size of the object, so the corresponding force equation may be more complicated.

Equation 23.7 can be rearranged as

$$\vec{\mathbf{F}}_e = q\vec{\mathbf{E}} \tag{23.8}$$

This equation gives us the force on a charged particle q placed in an electric field. If q is positive, the force is in the same direction as the field. If q is negative, the force and the field are in opposite directions. Notice the similarity between Equation 23.8 and the corresponding equation for a particle with mass placed in a gravitational field, $\vec{\mathbf{F}}_g = m\vec{\mathbf{g}}$ (Section 5.5). Once the magnitude and direction of the electric field are known at some point, the electric force exerted on *any* charged particle placed at that point can be calculated from Equation 23.8.

To determine the direction of an electric field, consider a point charge q as a source charge. This charge creates an electric field at all points in space surrounding it. A test charge q_0 is placed at point P, a distance r from the source charge, as in Active Figure 23.11a. We imagine using the test charge to determine the direction of the electric force and therefore that of the electric field. According to Coulomb's law, the force exerted by q on the test charge is

$$\vec{\mathbf{F}}_e = k_e \frac{qq_0}{r^2}\hat{\mathbf{r}}$$

where $\hat{\mathbf{r}}$ is a unit vector directed from q toward q_0. This force in Active Figure 23.11a is directed away from the source charge q. Because the electric field at P, the position of the test charge, is defined by $\vec{\mathbf{E}} = \vec{\mathbf{F}}_e/q_0$, the electric field at P created by q is

$$\vec{\mathbf{E}} = k_e \frac{q}{r^2}\hat{\mathbf{r}} \tag{23.9}$$

If the source charge q is positive, Active Figure 23.11b shows the situation with the test charge removed: the source charge sets up an electric field at P, directed away from q. If q is negative, as in Active Figure 23.11c, the force on the test charge is toward the source charge, so the electric field at P is directed toward the source charge as in Active Figure 23.11d.

To calculate the electric field at a point P due to a group of point charges, we first calculate the electric field vectors at P individually using Equation 23.9 and then add them vectorially. In other words, at any point P, the total electric field due to a group of source charges equals the vector sum of the electric fields of all the charges. This superposition principle applied to fields follows directly from the vector addition of electric forces. Therefore, the electric field at point P due to a group of source charges can be expressed as the vector sum

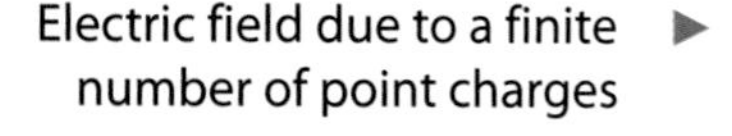

$$\vec{\mathbf{E}} = k_e \sum_i \frac{q_i}{r_i^2}\hat{\mathbf{r}}_i \tag{23.10}$$

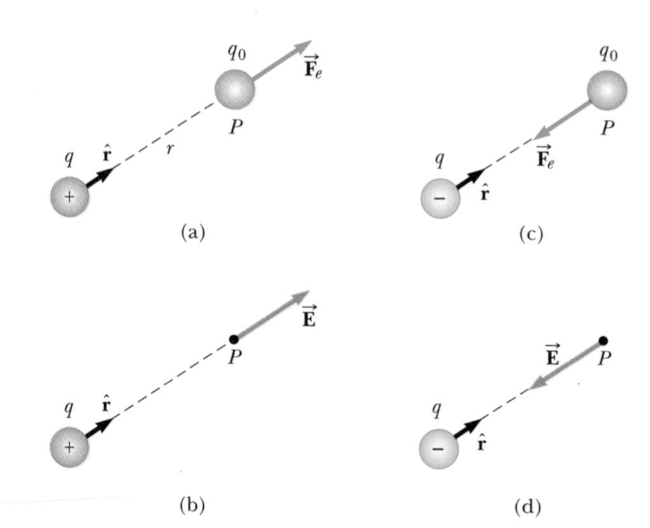

ACTIVE FIGURE 23.11

A test charge q_0 at point P is a distance r from a point charge q. (a) If q is positive, the force on the test charge is directed away from q. (b) For the positive source charge, the electric field at P points radially outward from q. (c) If q is negative, the force on the test charge is directed toward q. (d) For the negative source charge, the electric field at P points radially inward toward q.

Sign in at www.thomsonedu.com and go to ThomsonNOW to move point P to any position in two-dimensional space and observe the electric field due to q.

where r_i is the distance from the ith source charge q_i to the point P and $\hat{\mathbf{r}}_i$ is a unit vector directed from q_i toward P.

In Example 23.5, we explore the electric field due to two charges using the superposition principle. Part (B) of the example focuses on an **electric dipole**, which is defined as a positive charge q and a negative charge $-q$ separated by a distance $2a$. The electric dipole is a good model of many molecules, such as hydrochloric acid (HCl). Neutral atoms and molecules behave as dipoles when placed in an external electric field. Furthermore, many molecules, such as HCl, are permanent dipoles. The effect of such dipoles on the behavior of materials subjected to electric fields is discussed in Chapter 26.

Quick Quiz 23.4 A test charge of $+3\ \mu C$ is at a point P where an external electric field is directed to the right and has a magnitude of 4×10^6 N/C. If the test charge is replaced with another test charge of $-3\ \mu C$, what happens to the external electric field at P? (a) It is unaffected. (b) It reverses direction. (c) It changes in a way that cannot be determined.

EXAMPLE 23.5 Electric Field Due to Two Charges

Charges q_1 and q_2 are located on the x axis, at distances a and b, respectively, from the origin as shown in Figure 23.12.

(A) Find the components of the net electric field at the point P, which is on the y axis.

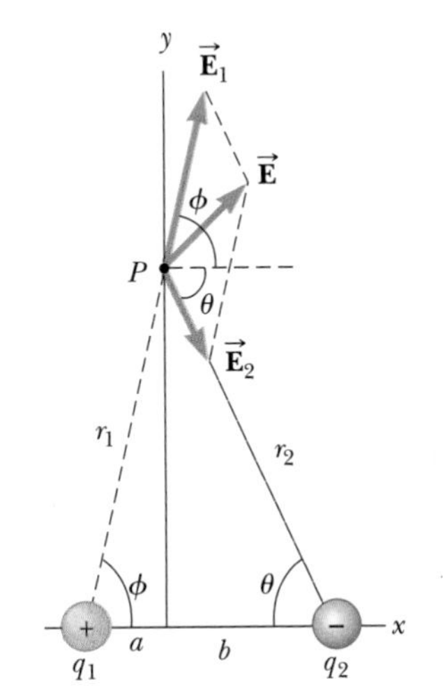

Figure 23.12 (Example 23.5) The total electric field $\vec{E}$ at P equals the vector sum $\vec{E}_1 + \vec{E}_2$, where $\vec{E}_1$ is the field due to the positive charge q_1 and $\vec{E}_2$ is the field due to the negative charge q_2.

SOLUTION

Conceptualize Compare this example to Example 23.2. There, we add vector forces to find the net force on a charged particle. Here, we add electric field vectors to find the net electric field at a point in space.

Categorize We have two source charges and wish to find the resultant electric field, so we categorize this example as one in which we can use the superposition principle represented by Equation 23.10.

Analyze Find the magnitude of the electric field at P due to charge q_1:

$$E_1 = k_e \frac{|q_1|}{r_1^{\,2}} = k_e \frac{|q_1|}{(a^2 + y^2)}$$

Find the magnitude of the electric field at P due to charge q_2:

$$E_2 = k_e \frac{|q_2|}{r_2^{\,2}} = k_e \frac{|q_2|}{(b^2 + y^2)}$$

Write the electric field vectors for each charge in unit–vector form:

$$\vec{E}_1 = k_e \frac{|q_1|}{(a^2 + y^2)} \cos\phi\,\hat{\mathbf{i}} + k_e \frac{|q_1|}{(a^2 + y^2)} \sin\phi\,\hat{\mathbf{j}}$$

$$\vec{E}_2 = k_e \frac{|q_2|}{(b^2 + y^2)} \cos\theta\,\hat{\mathbf{i}} - k_e \frac{|q_2|}{(b^2 + y^2)} \sin\theta\,\hat{\mathbf{j}}$$

Write the components of the net electric field vector:

$$(1)\quad E_x = E_{1x} + E_{2x} = k_e \frac{|q_1|}{(a^2 + y^2)} \cos\phi + k_e \frac{|q_2|}{(b^2 + y^2)} \cos\theta$$

$$(2)\quad E_y = E_{1y} + E_{2y} = k_e \frac{|q_1|}{(a^2 + y^2)} \sin\phi - k_e \frac{|q_2|}{(b^2 + y^2)} \sin\theta$$

(B) Evaluate the electric field at point P in the special case that $|q_1| = |q_2|$ and $a = b$.

SOLUTION

Conceptualize Figure 23.13 shows the situation in this special case. Notice the symmetry in the situation and that the charge distribution is now an electric dipole.

Categorize Because Figure 23.13 is a special case of the general case shown in Figure 23.12, we can categorize this example as one in which we can take the result of part (A) and substitute the appropriate values of the variables.

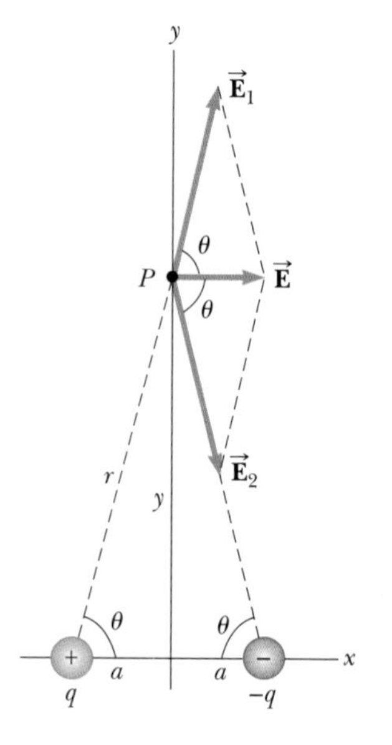

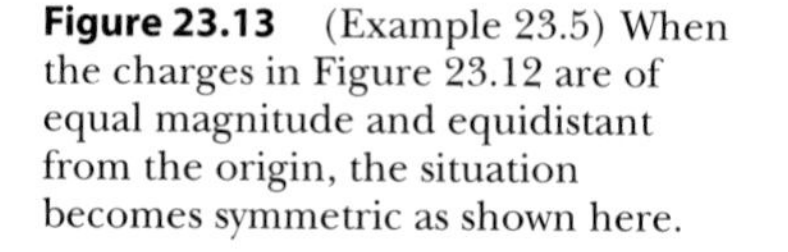
Figure 23.13 (Example 23.5) When the charges in Figure 23.12 are of equal magnitude and equidistant from the origin, the situation becomes symmetric as shown here.

Analyze Based on the symmetry in Figure 23.13, evaluate Equations (1) and (2) from part (A) with $a = b$, $|q_1| = |q_2| = q$, and $\phi = \theta$:

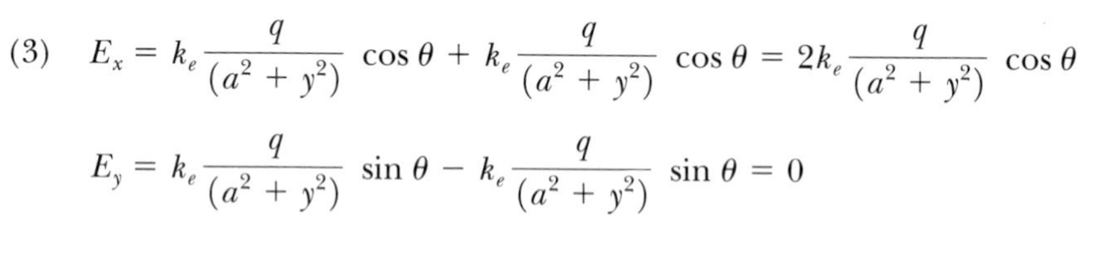

$$(3)\quad E_x = k_e \frac{q}{(a^2 + y^2)} \cos\theta + k_e \frac{q}{(a^2 + y^2)} \cos\theta = 2k_e \frac{q}{(a^2 + y^2)} \cos\theta$$

$$E_y = k_e \frac{q}{(a^2 + y^2)} \sin\theta - k_e \frac{q}{(a^2 + y^2)} \sin\theta = 0$$

From the geometry in Figure 23.13, evaluate $\cos\theta$:

$$(4)\quad \cos\theta = \frac{a}{r} = \frac{a}{(a^2 + y^2)^{1/2}}$$

Substitute Equation (4) into Equation (3):

$$E_x = 2k_e \frac{q}{(a^2 + y^2)} \frac{a}{(a^2 + y^2)^{1/2}} = k_e \frac{2qa}{(a^2 + y^2)^{3/2}}$$

(C) Find the electric field due to the electric dipole when point P is a distance $y \gg a$ from the origin.

SOLUTION

In the solution to part (B), because $y \gg a$, neglect a^2 compared with y^2 and write the expression for E in this case:

$$(5)\quad E \approx k_e \frac{2qa}{y^3}$$

Finalize From Equation (5), we see that at points far from a dipole but along the perpendicular bisector of the line joining the two charges, the magnitude of the electric field created by the dipole varies as $1/r^3$, whereas the more slowly varying field of a point charge varies as $1/r^2$ (see Eq. 23.9). That is because at distant points, the fields of the two charges of equal magnitude and opposite sign almost cancel each other. The $1/r^3$ variation in E for the dipole also is obtained for a distant point along the x axis (see Problem 18) and for any general distant point.

23.5 Electric Field of a Continuous Charge Distribution

Very often, the distances between charges in a group of charges are much smaller than the distance from the group to a point where the electric field is to be calculated. In such situations, the system of charges can be modeled as continuous. That is, the system of closely spaced charges is equivalent to a total charge that is continuously distributed along some line, over some surface, or throughout some volume.

To set up the process for evaluating the electric field created by a continuous charge distribution, let's use the following procedure. First, divide the charge distribution into small elements, each of which contains a small charge Δq as shown in Figure 23.14. Next, use Equation 23.9 to calculate the electric field due to one of these elements at a point P. Finally, evaluate the total electric field at P due to the charge distribution by summing the contributions of all the charge elements (that is, by applying the superposition principle).

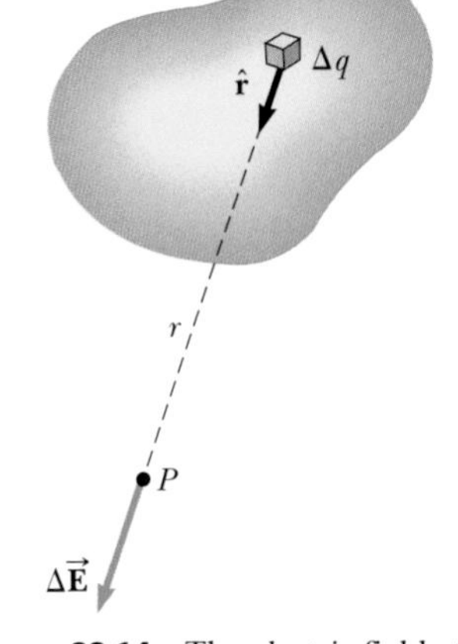

Figure 23.14 The electric field at P due to a continuous charge distribution is the vector sum of the fields $\Delta\vec{\mathbf{E}}$ due to all the elements Δq of the charge distribution.

The electric field at P due to one charge element carrying charge Δq is

$$\Delta\vec{\mathbf{E}} = k_e \frac{\Delta q}{r^2}\hat{\mathbf{r}}$$

where r is the distance from the charge element to point P and $\hat{\mathbf{r}}$ is a unit vector directed from the element toward P. The total electric field at P due to all elements in the charge distribution is approximately

$$\vec{\mathbf{E}} \approx k_e \sum_i \frac{\Delta q_i}{r_i^2}\hat{\mathbf{r}}_i$$

where the index i refers to the ith element in the distribution. Because the charge distribution is modeled as continuous, the total field at P in the limit $\Delta q_i \rightarrow 0$ is

$$\vec{\mathbf{E}} = k_e \lim_{\Delta q_i \rightarrow 0} \sum_i \frac{\Delta q_i}{r_i^2}\hat{\mathbf{r}}_i = k_e \int \frac{dq}{r^2}\hat{\mathbf{r}} \qquad (23.11)$$

◀ Electric field due to a continuous charge distribution

where the integration is over the entire charge distribution. The integration in Equation 23.11 is a vector operation and must be treated appropriately.

Let's illustrate this type of calculation with several examples in which the charge is distributed on a line, on a surface, or throughout a volume. When performing such calculations, it is convenient to use the concept of a *charge density* along with the following notations:

- If a charge Q is uniformly distributed throughout a volume V, the **volume charge density** ρ is defined by

$$\rho \equiv \frac{Q}{V}$$

◀ Volume charge density

where ρ has units of coulombs per cubic meter (C/m^3).

- If a charge Q is uniformly distributed on a surface of area A, the **surface charge density** σ (Greek letter sigma) is defined by

$$\sigma \equiv \frac{Q}{A}$$

◀ Surface charge density

where σ has units of coulombs per square meter (C/m^2).

- If a charge Q is uniformly distributed along a line of length ℓ, the **linear charge density** λ is defined by

$$\lambda \equiv \frac{Q}{\ell}$$

◀ Linear charge density

where λ has units of coulombs per meter (C/m).

- If the charge is nonuniformly distributed over a volume, surface, or line, the amounts of charge dq in a small volume, surface, or length element are

$$dq = \rho\, dV \qquad dq = \sigma\, dA \qquad dq = \lambda\, d\ell$$

PROBLEM-SOLVING STRATEGY Calculating the Electric Field

The following procedure is recommended for solving problems that involve the determination of an electric field due to individual charges or a charge distribution:

1. *Conceptualize.* Establish a mental representation of the problem: think carefully about the individual charges or the charge distribution and imagine what type of electric field they would create. Appeal to any symmetry in the arrangement of charges to help you visualize the electric field.

2. *Categorize.* Are you analyzing a group of individual charges or a continuous charge distribution? The answer to this question tells you how to proceed in the Analyze step.

3. *Analyze.*

   (a) *If you are analyzing a group of individual charge,* use the superposition principle: When several point charges are present, the resultant field at a point in space is the *vector sum* of the individual fields due to the individual charges (Eq. 23.10). Be very careful in the manipulation of vector quantities. It may be useful to review the material on vector addition in Chapter 3. Example 23.5 demonstrated this procedure.

   (b) *If you are analyzing a continuous charge distribution,* replace the vector sums for evaluating the total electric field from individual charges by vector integrals. The charge distribution is divided into infinitesimal pieces, and the vector sum is carried out by integrating over the entire charge distribution (Eq. 23.11). Examples 23.6 through 23.8 demonstrate such procedures.

   Consider symmetry when dealing with either a distribution of point charges or a continuous charge distribution. Take advantage of any symmetry in the system you observed in the Conceptualize step to simplify your calculations. The cancellation of field components perpendicular to the axis in Example 23.7 is an example of the application of symmetry.

4. *Finalize.* Check to see if your electric field expression is consistent with the mental representation and if it reflects any symmetry that you noted previously. Imagine varying parameters such as the distance of the observation point from the charges or the radius of any circular objects to see if the mathematical result changes in a reasonable way.

EXAMPLE 23.6 The Electric Field Due to a Charged Rod

A rod of length ℓ has a uniform positive charge per unit length λ and a total charge Q. Calculate the electric field at a point P that is located along the long axis of the rod and a distance a from one end (Fig. 23.15).

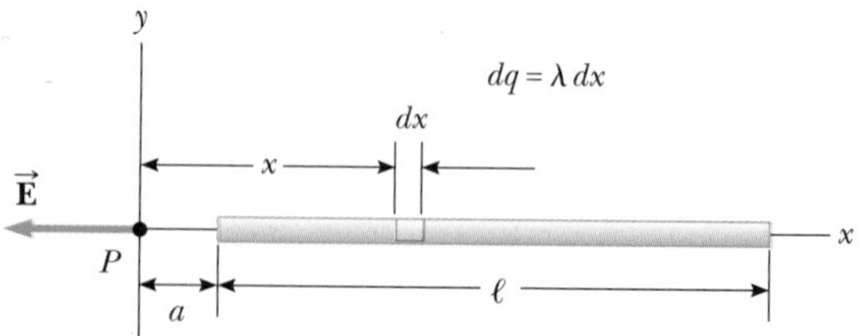

Figure 23.15 (Example 23.6) The electric field at P due to a uniformly charged rod lying along the x axis. The magnitude of the field at P due to the segment of charge dq is $k_e\, dq/x^2$. The total field at P is the vector sum over all segments of the rod.

SOLUTION

Conceptualize The field $d\vec{\mathbf{E}}$ at P due to each segment of charge on the rod is in the negative x direction because every segment carries a positive charge.

Categorize Because the rod is continuous, we are evaluating the field due to a continuous charge distribution rather than a group of individual charges. Because every segment of the rod produces an electric field in the negative x direction, the sum of their contributions can be handled without the need to add vectors.

Analyze Let's assume the rod is lying along the x axis, dx is the length of one small segment, and dq is the charge on that segment. Because the rod has a charge per unit length λ, the charge dq on the small segment is $dq = \lambda\, dx$.

Find the magnitude of the electric field at P due to one segment of the rod having a charge dq:

$$dE = k_e \frac{dq}{x^2} = k_e \frac{\lambda\, dx}{x^2}$$

Find the total field at P using[4] Equation 23.11:

$$E = \int_a^{\ell + a} k_e \lambda \frac{dx}{x^2}$$

Noting that k_e and $\lambda = Q/\ell$ are constants and can be removed from the integral, evaluate the integral:

$$E = k_e \lambda \int_a^{\ell + a} \frac{dx}{x^2} = k_e \lambda \left[-\frac{1}{x} \right]_a^{\ell + a}$$

$$(1) \quad E = k_e \frac{Q}{\ell}\left(\frac{1}{a} - \frac{1}{\ell + a} \right) = \frac{k_e Q}{a(\ell + a)}$$

Finalize If ℓ goes to zero, Equation (1) reduces to the electric field due to a point charge as given by Equation 23.9, which is what we expect because the rod has shrunk to zero size.

What If? Suppose point P is very far away from the rod. What is the nature of the electric field at such a point?

Answer If P is far from the rod ($a \gg \ell$), then ℓ in the denominator of Equation (1) can be neglected and $E \approx k_e Q/a^2$. That is exactly the form you would expect for a point charge. Therefore, at large values of a/ℓ, the charge distribution appears to be a point charge of magnitude Q; the point P is so far away from the rod we cannot distinguish that it has a size. The use of the limiting technique ($a/\ell \to \infty$) is often a good method for checking a mathematical expression.

[4]To carry out integrations such as this one, first express the charge element dq in terms of the other variables in the integral. (In this example, there is one variable, x, so we made the change $dq = \lambda\, dx$.) The integral must be over scalar quantities; therefore, express the electric field in terms of components, if necessary. (In this example, the field has only an x component, so this detail is of no concern.) Then, reduce your expression to an integral over a single variable (or to multiple integrals, each over a single variable). In examples that have spherical or cylindrical symmetry, the single variable is a radial coordinate.

EXAMPLE 23.7 The Electric Field of a Uniform Ring of Charge

A ring of radius a carries a uniformly distributed positive total charge Q. Calculate the electric field due to the ring at a point P lying a distance x from its center along the central axis perpendicular to the plane of the ring (Fig. 23.16a).

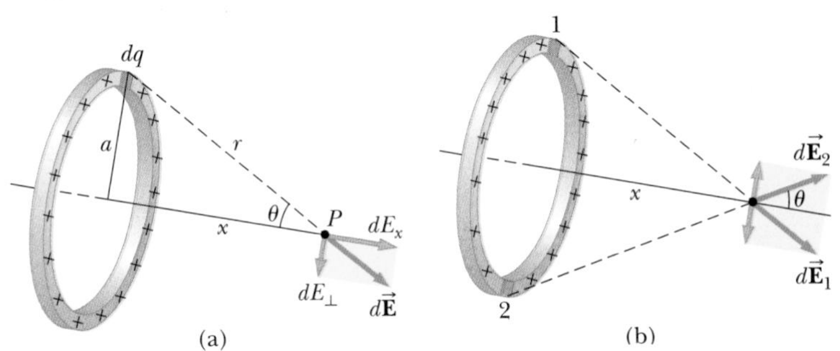

Figure 23.16 (Example 23.7) A uniformly charged ring of radius a. (a) The field at P on the x axis due to an element of charge dq. (b) The total electric field at P is along the x axis. The perpendicular component of the field at P due to segment 1 is canceled by the perpendicular component due to segment 2.

SOLUTION

Conceptualize Figure 23.16a shows the electric field contribution $d\vec{\mathbf{E}}$ at P due to a single segment of charge at the top of the ring. This field vector can be resolved into components dE_x parallel to the axis of the ring and $dE_\perp$ perpendicular to the axis. Figure 23.16b shows the electric field contributions from two segments on opposite sides of the ring. Because of the symmetry of the situation, the perpendicular components of the field cancel. That is true for all pairs of segments around the ring, so we can ignore the perpendicular component of the field and focus solely on the parallel components, which simply add.

Categorize Because the ring is continuous, we are evaluating the field due to a continuous charge distribution rather than a group of individual charges.

Analyze Evaluate the parallel component of an electric field contribution from a segment of charge dq on the ring:

$$(1)\quad dE_x = k_e \frac{dq}{r^2}\cos\theta = k_e \frac{dq}{(a^2 + x^2)}\cos\theta$$

From the geometry in Figure 23.16a, evaluate $\cos\theta$:

$$(2)\quad \cos\theta = \frac{x}{r} = \frac{x}{(a^2 + x^2)^{1/2}}$$

Substitute Equation (2) into Equation (1):

$$dE_x = k_e \frac{dq}{(a^2 + x^2)} \frac{x}{(a^2 + x^2)^{1/2}} = \frac{k_e x}{(a^2 + x^2)^{3/2}}\, dq$$

All segments of the ring make the same contribution to the field at P because they are all equidistant from this point. Integrate to obtain the total field at P:

$$E_x = \int \frac{k_e x}{(a^2 + x^2)^{3/2}}\, dq = \frac{k_e x}{(a^2 + x^2)^{3/2}} \int dq$$

$$(3)\quad E = \frac{k_e x}{(a^2 + x^2)^{3/2}}\, Q$$

Finalize This result shows that the field is zero at $x = 0$. Is that consistent with the symmetry in the problem? Furthermore, notice that Equation (3) reduces to $k_e Q/x^2$ if $x \gg a$, so the ring acts like a point charge for locations far away from the ring.

What If? Suppose a negative charge is placed at the center of the ring in Figure 23.16 and displaced slightly by a distance $x \ll a$ along the x axis. When the charge is released, what type of motion does it exhibit?

Answer In the expression for the field due to a ring of charge, let $x \ll a$, which results in

$$E_x = \frac{k_e Q}{a^3}\, x$$

Therefore, from Equation 23.8, the force on a charge $-q$ placed near the center of the ring is

$$F_x = -\frac{k_e q Q}{a^3}\, x$$

Because this force has the form of Hooke's law (Eq. 15.1), the motion of the negative charge is *simple harmonic*!

EXAMPLE 23.8 The Electric Field of a Uniformly Charged Disk

A disk of radius R has a uniform surface charge density σ. Calculate the electric field at a point P that lies along the central perpendicular axis of the disk and a distance x from the center of the disk (Fig. 23.17).

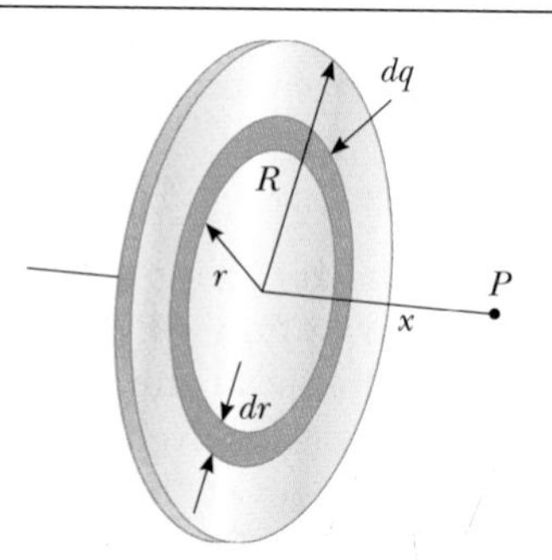

Figure 23.17 (Example 23.8) A uniformly charged disk of radius R. The electric field at an axial point P is directed along the central axis, perpendicular to the plane of the disk.

SOLUTION

Conceptualize If the disk is considered to be a set of concentric rings, we can use our result from Example 23.7—which gives the field created by a ring of radius a—and sum the contributions of all rings making up the disk. By symmetry, the field at an axial point must be along the central axis.

Categorize Because the disk is continuous, we are evaluating the field due to a continuous charge distribution rather than a group of individual charges.

Analyze Find the amount of charge dq on a ring of radius r and width dr as shown in Figure 23.17:

$$dq = \sigma\, dA = \sigma(2\pi r\, dr) = 2\pi\sigma r\, dr$$

Use this result in the equation given for E_x in Example 23.7 (with a replaced by r and Q replaced by dq) to find the field due to the ring:

$$dE_x = \frac{k_e x}{(r^2 + x^2)^{3/2}}(2\pi\sigma r\,dr)$$

To obtain the total field at P, integrate this expression over the limits $r = 0$ to $r = R$, noting that x is a constant in this situation:

$$E_x = k_e x\pi\sigma \int_0^R \frac{2r\,dr}{(r^2 + x^2)^{3/2}}$$

$$= k_e x\pi\sigma \int_0^R (r^2 + x^2)^{-3/2}\,d(r^2)$$

$$= k_e x\pi\sigma \left[\frac{(r^2 + x^2)^{-1/2}}{-1/2}\right]_0^R = 2\pi k_e\sigma\left[1 - \frac{x}{(R^2 + x^2)^{1/2}}\right]$$

Finalize This result is valid for all values of $x > 0$. We can calculate the field close to the disk along the axis by assuming that $R \gg x$; therefore, the expression in brackets reduces to unity to give us the near-field approximation

$$E_x = 2\pi k_e\sigma = \frac{\sigma}{2\epsilon_0}$$

where ϵ_0 is the permittivity of free space. In Chapter 24, we obtain the same result for the field created by an infinite plane of charge with uniform surface charge density.

23.6 Electric Field Lines

We have defined the electric field mathematically through Equation 23.7. Let's now explore a means of visualizing the electric field in a pictorial representation. A convenient way of visualizing electric field patterns is to draw lines, called **electric field lines** and first introduced by Faraday, that are related to the electric field in a region of space in the following manner:

- The electric field vector $\vec{\mathbf{E}}$ is tangent to the electric field line at each point. The line has a direction, indicated by an arrowhead, that is the same as that of the electric field vector. The direction of the line is that of the force on a positive test charge placed in the field.
- The number of lines per unit area through a surface perpendicular to the lines is proportional to the magnitude of the electric field in that region. Therefore, the field lines are close together where the electric field is strong and far apart where the field is weak.

These properties are illustrated in Figure 23.18. The density of field lines through surface A is greater than the density of lines through surface B. Therefore, the magnitude of the electric field is larger on surface A than on surface B. Furthermore, because the lines at different locations point in different directions, the field is nonuniform.

Is this relationship between strength of the electric field and the density of field lines consistent with Equation 23.9, the expression we obtained for E using Coulomb's law? To answer this question, consider an imaginary spherical surface of radius r concentric with a point charge. From symmetry, we see that the magnitude of the electric field is the same everywhere on the surface of the sphere. The number of lines N that emerge from the charge is equal to the number that penetrate the spherical surface. Hence, the number of lines per unit area on the sphere is $N/4\pi r^2$ (where the surface area of the sphere is $4\pi r^2$). Because E is proportional to the number of lines per unit area, we see that E varies as $1/r^2$; this finding is consistent with Equation 23.9.

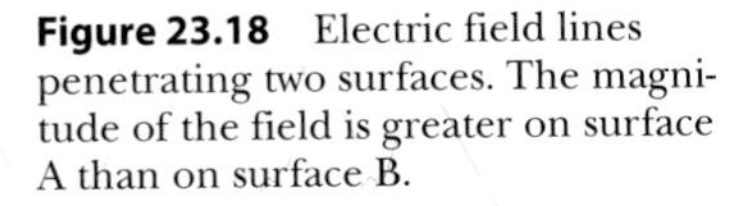

Figure 23.18 Electric field lines penetrating two surfaces. The magnitude of the field is greater on surface A than on surface B.

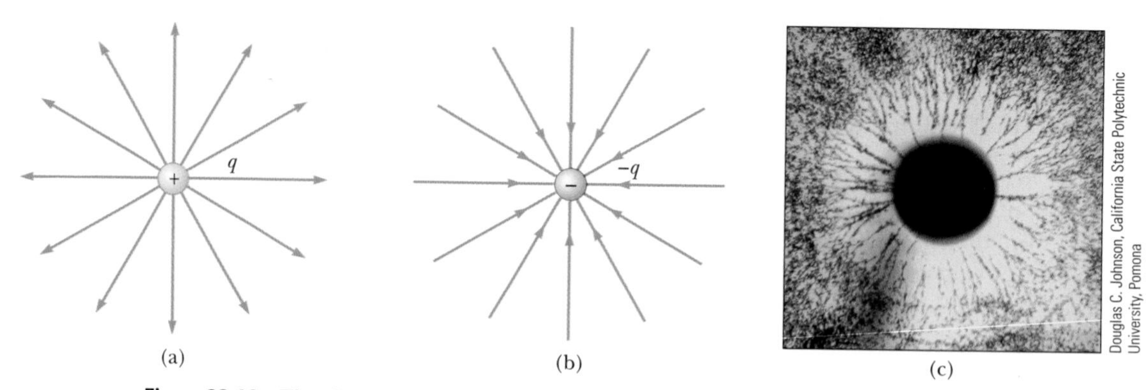

Figure 23.19 The electric field lines for a point charge. (a) For a positive point charge, the lines are directed radially outward. (b) For a negative point charge, the lines are directed radially inward. Notice that the figures show only those field lines that lie in the plane of the page. (c) The dark areas are small particles suspended in oil, which align with the electric field produced by a charged conductor at the center.

PITFALL PREVENTION 23.2
Electric Field Lines Are Not Paths of Particles!

Electric field lines represent the field at various locations. Except in very special cases, they *do not* represent the path of a charged particle moving in an electric field.

PITFALL PREVENTION 23.3
Electric Field Lines Are Not Real

Electric field lines are not material objects. They are used only as a pictorial representation to provide a qualitative description of the electric field. Only a finite number of lines from each charge can be drawn, which makes it appear as if the field were quantized and exists only in certain parts of space. The field, in fact, is continuous, existing at every point. You should avoid obtaining the wrong impression from a two-dimensional drawing of field lines used to describe a three-dimensional situation.

Representative electric field lines for the field due to a single positive point charge are shown in Figure 23.19a. This two-dimensional drawing shows only the field lines that lie in the plane containing the point charge. The lines are actually directed radially outward from the charge in all directions; therefore, instead of the flat "wheel" of lines shown, you should picture an entire spherical distribution of lines. Because a positive test charge placed in this field would be repelled by the positive source charge, the lines are directed radially away from the source charge. The electric field lines representing the field due to a single negative point charge are directed toward the charge (Fig. 23.19b). In either case, the lines are along the radial direction and extend all the way to infinity. Notice that the lines become closer together as they approach the charge, indicating that the strength of the field increases as we move toward the source charge.

The rules for drawing electric field lines are as follows:

- The lines must begin on a positive charge and terminate on a negative charge. In the case of an excess of one type of charge, some lines will begin or end infinitely far away.
- The number of lines drawn leaving a positive charge or approaching a negative charge is proportional to the magnitude of the charge.
- No two field lines can cross.

We choose the number of field lines starting from any positively charged object to be Cq and the number of lines ending on any negatively charged object to be $C|q|$, where C is an arbitrary proportionality constant. Once C is chosen, the number of lines is fixed. For example, in a two-charge system, if object 1 has charge Q_1 and object 2 has charge Q_2, the ratio of number of lines in contact with the

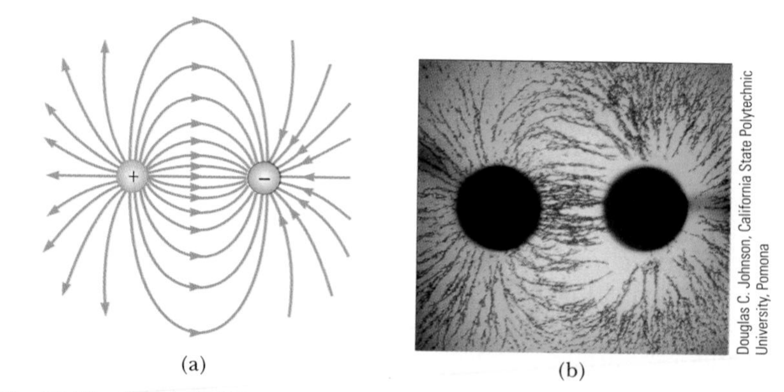

Figure 23.20 (a) The electric field lines for two point charges of equal magnitude and opposite sign (an electric dipole). The number of lines leaving the positive charge equals the number terminating at the negative charge. (b) Small particles suspended in oil align with the electric field.

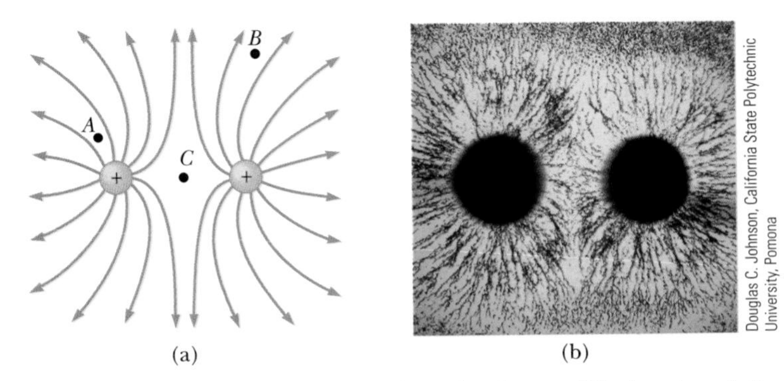

Figure 23.21 (a) The electric field lines for two positive point charges. (The locations A, B, and C are discussed in Quick Quiz 23.5.) (b) Small particles suspended in oil align with the electric field.

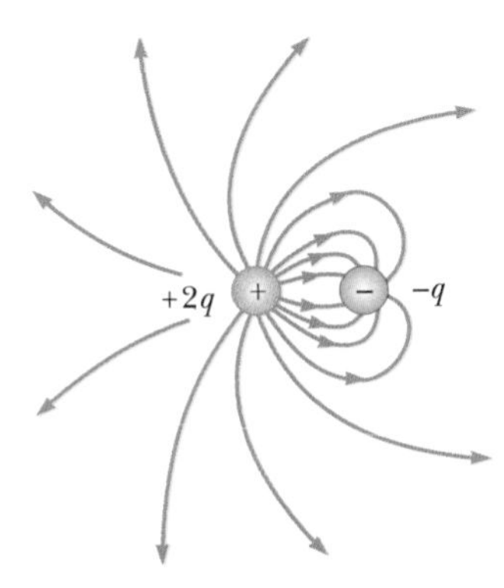

ACTIVE FIGURE 23.22

The electric field lines for a point charge $+2q$ and a second point charge $-q$. Notice that two lines leave $+2q$ for every one that terminates on $-q$.

Sign in at www.thomsonedu.com and go to ThomsonNOW to choose the values and signs for the two charges and observe the electric field lines for the configuration you have chosen.

charges is $N_2/N_1 = Q_2/Q_1$. The electric field lines for two point charges of equal magnitude but opposite signs (an electric dipole) are shown in Figure 23.20. Because the charges are of equal magnitude, the number of lines that begin at the positive charge must equal the number that terminate at the negative charge. At points very near the charges, the lines are nearly radial. The high density of lines between the charges indicates a region of strong electric field.

Figure 23.21 shows the electric field lines in the vicinity of two equal positive point charges. Again, the lines are nearly radial at points close to either charge, and the same number of lines emerge from each charge because the charges are equal in magnitude. At great distances from the charges, the field is approximately equal to that of a single point charge of magnitude $2q$.

Finally, in Active Figure 23.22, we sketch the electric field lines associated with a positive charge $+2q$ and a negative charge $-q$. In this case, the number of lines leaving $+2q$ is twice the number terminating at $-q$. Hence, only half the lines that leave the positive charge reach the negative charge. The remaining half terminate on a negative charge we assume to be at infinity. At distances much greater than the charge separation, the electric field lines are equivalent to those of a single charge $+q$.

Quick Quiz 23.5 Rank the magnitudes of the electric field at points A, B, and C shown in Figure 23.21a (greatest magnitude first).

23.7 Motion of a Charged Particle in a Uniform Electric Field

When a particle of charge q and mass m is placed in an electric field $\vec{\mathbf{E}}$, the electric force exerted on the charge is $q\vec{\mathbf{E}}$ according to Equation 23.8. If that is the only force exerted on the particle, it must be the net force and it causes the particle to accelerate according to the particle under a net force model. Therefore,

$$\vec{\mathbf{F}}_e = q\vec{\mathbf{E}} = m\vec{\mathbf{a}}$$

and the acceleration of the particle is

$$\vec{\mathbf{a}} = \frac{q\vec{\mathbf{E}}}{m} \qquad \textbf{(23.12)}$$

If $\vec{\mathbf{E}}$ is uniform (that is, constant in magnitude and direction), the electric force on the particle is constant and we can apply the particle under constant acceleration model. If the particle has a positive charge, its acceleration is in the direction of the electric field. If the particle has a negative charge, its acceleration is in the direction opposite the electric field.

PITFALL PREVENTION 23.4

Just Another Force

Electric forces and fields may seem abstract to you. Once $\vec{\mathbf{F}}_e$ is evaluated, however, it causes a particle to move according to our well-established models of forces and motion from Chapters 2 through 6. Keeping this link with the past in mind should help you solve problems in this chapter.

EXAMPLE 23.9 An Accelerating Positive Charge

A uniform electric field $\vec{\mathbf{E}}$ is directed along the x axis between parallel plates of charge separated by a distance d as shown in Figure 23.23. A positive point charge q of mass m is released from rest at a point Ⓐ next to the positive plate and accelerates to a point Ⓑ next to the negative plate.

(A) Find the speed of the particle at Ⓑ by modeling it as a particle under constant acceleration.

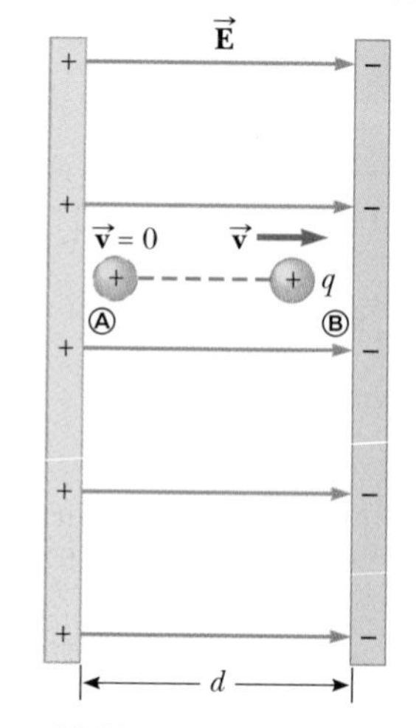

Figure 23.23 (Example 23.9) A positive point charge q in a uniform electric field $\vec{\mathbf{E}}$ undergoes constant acceleration in the direction of the field.

SOLUTION

Conceptualize When the positive charge is placed at Ⓐ, it experiences an electric force toward the right in Figure 23.23 due to the electric field directed toward the right.

Categorize Because the electric field is uniform, a constant electric force acts on the charge. Therefore, the example involves a charged particle under constant acceleration.

Analyze Use Equation 2.17 to express the velocity of the particle as a function of position:

$$v_f^2 = v_i^2 + 2a(x_f - x_i) = 0 + 2a(d - 0) = 2ad$$

Solve for v_f and substitute for the magnitude of the acceleration from Equation 23.12:

$$v_f = \sqrt{2ad} = \sqrt{2\left(\frac{qE}{m}\right)d} = \sqrt{\frac{2qEd}{m}}$$

(B) Find the speed of the particle at Ⓑ by modeling it as a nonisolated system.

SOLUTION

Categorize The problem statement tells us that the charge is a nonisolated system. Energy is transferred to this charge by work done by the electric force exerted on the charge. The initial configuration of the system is when the particle is at Ⓐ, and the final configuration is when it is at Ⓑ.

Analyze Write the appropriate reduction of the conservation of energy equation, Equation 8.2, for the system of the charged particle:

$$W = \Delta K$$

Replace the work and kinetic energies with values appropriate for this situation:

$$F_e\,\Delta x = K_{Ⓑ} - K_{Ⓐ} = \tfrac{1}{2}mv_f^2 - 0 \quad \rightarrow \quad v_f = \sqrt{\frac{2F_e\,\Delta x}{m}}$$

Substitute for the electric force F_e and the displacement Δx:

$$v_f = \sqrt{\frac{2(qE)(d)}{m}} = \sqrt{\frac{2qEd}{m}}$$

Finalize The answer to part (B) is the same as that for part (A), as we expect.

EXAMPLE 23.10 An Accelerated Electron

An electron enters the region of a uniform electric field as shown in Active Figure 23.24, with $v_i = 3.00 \times 10^6$ m/s and $E = 200$ N/C. The horizontal length of the plates is $\ell = 0.100$ m.

ACTIVE FIGURE 23.24

(Example 23.10) An electron is projected horizontally into a uniform electric field produced by two charged plates. The electron undergoes a downward acceleration (opposite $\vec{\mathbf{E}}$), and its motion is parabolic while it is between the plates.

Sign in at www.thomsonedu.com and go to ThomsonNOW to choose the strength of the electric field and the mass and charge of the projected particle.

(A) Find the acceleration of the electron while it is in the electric field.

SOLUTION

Conceptualize This example differs from the preceding one because the velocity of the charged particle is initially perpendicular to the electric field lines. In Example 23.9, the velocity of the charged particle is always parallel to the electric field lines. As a result, the electron in this example follows a curved path as shown in Active Figure 23.24.

Categorize Because the electric field is uniform, a constant electric force is exerted on the electron. To find the acceleration of the electron, we can model it as a particle under a net force.

Analyze The direction of the electron's acceleration is downward in Active Figure 23.24, opposite the direction of the electric field lines.

Combine Newton's second law with the magnitude of the electric force given by Equation 23.8 to find the y component of the acceleration of the electron:

$$\Sigma F_y = ma_y \quad \rightarrow \quad a_y = \frac{\Sigma F_y}{m} = -\frac{eE}{m_e}$$

Substitute numerical values:

$$a_y = -\frac{(1.60 \times 10^{-19}\ \mathrm{C})(200\ \mathrm{N/C})}{9.11 \times 10^{-31}\ \mathrm{kg}} = -3.51 \times 10^{13}\ \mathrm{m/s^2}$$

(B) Assuming the electron enters the field at time $t = 0$, find the time at which it leaves the field.

SOLUTION

Categorize Because the electric force acts only in the vertical direction in Active Figure 23.24, the motion of the particle in the horizontal direction can be analyzed by modeling it as a particle under constant velocity.

Analyze Solve Equation 2.7 for the time at which the electron arrives at the right edges of the plates:

$$x_f = x_i + v_x t \quad \rightarrow \quad t = \frac{x_f - x_i}{v_x}$$

Substitute numerical values:

$$t = \frac{\ell - 0}{v_x} = \frac{0.100\ \mathrm{m}}{3.00 \times 10^6\ \mathrm{m/s}} = 3.33 \times 10^{-8}\ \mathrm{s}$$

(C) Assuming the vertical position of the electron as it enters the field is $y_i = 0$, what is its vertical position when it leaves the field?

SOLUTION

Categorize Because the electric force is constant in Active Figure 23.24, the motion of the particle in the vertical direction can be analyzed by modeling it as a particle under constant acceleration.

Analyze Use Equation 2.16 to describe the position of the particle at any time t:

$$y_f = y_i + v_{yi}t + \tfrac{1}{2}a_y t^2$$

Substitute numerical values:

$$y_f = 0 + 0 + \tfrac{1}{2}(-3.51 \times 10^{13}\ \text{m/s}^2)(3.33 \times 10^{-8}\ \text{s})^2$$

$$= -0.019\,5\ \text{m} = -1.95\ \text{cm}$$

Finalize If the electron enters just below the negative plate in Active Figure 23.24 and the separation between the plates is less than the value just calculated, the electron will strike the positive plate.

We have neglected the gravitational force acting on the electron, which represents a good approximation when dealing with atomic particles. For an electric field of 200 N/C, the ratio of the magnitude of the electric force eE to the magnitude of the gravitational force mg is on the order of 10^{12} for an electron and on the order of 10^9 for a proton.

Summary

ThomsonNOW™ Sign in at **www.thomsonedu.com** and go to ThomsonNOW to take a practice test for this chapter.

DEFINITIONS

The **electric field $\vec{\mathbf{E}}$** at some point in space is defined as the electric force $\vec{\mathbf{F}}_e$ that acts on a small positive test charge placed at that point divided by the magnitude q_0 of the test charge:

$$\vec{\mathbf{E}} \equiv \frac{\vec{\mathbf{F}}_e}{q_0} \qquad (23.7)$$

CONCEPTS AND PRINCIPLES

Electric charges have the following important properties:

- Charges of opposite sign attract one another, and charges of the same sign repel one another.
- The total charge in an isolated system is conserved.
- Charge is quantized.

Conductors are materials in which electrons move freely. **Insulators** are materials in which electrons do not move freely.

Coulomb's law states that the electric force exerted by a point charge q_1 on a second point charge q_2 is

$$\vec{\mathbf{F}}_{12} = k_e \frac{q_1 q_2}{r^2}\hat{\mathbf{r}}_{12} \qquad (23.6)$$

where r is the distance between the two charges and $\hat{\mathbf{r}}_{12}$ is a unit vector directed from q_1 toward q_2. The constant k_e, which is called the **Coulomb constant,** has the value $k_e = 8.99 \times 10^9\ \text{N}\cdot\text{m}^2/\text{C}^2$.

The electric force on a charge q placed in an electric field $\vec{\mathbf{E}}$ is

$$\vec{\mathbf{F}}_e = q\vec{\mathbf{E}} \qquad (23.8)$$

At a distance r from a point charge q, the electric field due to the charge is

$$\vec{\mathbf{E}} = k_e \frac{q}{r^2}\hat{\mathbf{r}} \qquad (23.9)$$

where $\hat{\mathbf{r}}$ is a unit vector directed from the charge toward the point in question. The electric field is directed radially outward from a positive charge and radially inward toward a negative charge.

The electric field due to a group of point charges can be obtained by using the superposition principle. That is, the total electric field at some point equals the vector sum of the electric fields of all the charges:

$$\vec{\mathbf{E}} = k_e \sum_i \frac{q_i}{r_i^2}\hat{\mathbf{r}}_i \qquad (23.10)$$

The electric field at some point due to a continuous charge distribution is

$$\vec{\mathbf{E}} = k_e \int \frac{dq}{r^2}\hat{\mathbf{r}} \qquad (23.11)$$

where dq is the charge on one element of the charge distribution and r is the distance from the element to the point in question.

Questions

☐ denotes answer available in *Student Solutions Manual/Study Guide;* **O** denotes objective question

1. Explain what is meant by the term "a neutral atom." Explain what "a negatively charged atom" means.

2. O (i) A metallic coin is given a positive electric charge. Does its mass (a) increase measurably, (b) increase by an amount too small to measure directly, (c) remain unchanged, (d) decrease by an amount too small to measure directly, or (e) decrease measurably? **(ii)** Now the coin is given a negative electric charge. What happens to its mass? Choose from the same possibilities.

3. A student who grew up in a tropical country and is studying in the United States may have no experience with static electricity sparks and shocks until their first American winter. Explain.

4. Explain the similarities and differences between Newton's law of universal gravitation and Coulomb's law.

5. A balloon is negatively charged by rubbing, and then it clings to a wall. Does that mean the wall is positively charged? Why does the balloon eventually fall?

6. O In Figure 23.8, assume the objects with charges q_2 and q_3 are fixed. Notice that there is no sightline from the location of object 2 to the location of object 1. We could say that a bug standing on q_1 is unable to see q_2 because it is behind q_3. How would you calculate the force exerted on the object with charge q_1? (a) Find only the force exerted by q_2 on charge q_1. (b) Find only the force exerted by q_3 on charge q_1. (c) Add the force that q_2 would exert by itself on charge q_1 to the force that q_3 would exert by itself on charge q_1. (d) Add the force that q_3 would exert by itself to a certain fraction of the force that q_2 would exert by itself. (e) There is no definite way to find the force on charge q_1.

7. O A charged particle is at the origin of coordinates. The particle produces an electric field of $4\hat{\mathbf{i}}$ kN/C at the point with position vector $36\hat{\mathbf{i}}$ cm. **(i)** At what location does the field have the value $1\hat{\mathbf{i}}$ kN/C? (a) $9\hat{\mathbf{i}}$ cm (b) $18\hat{\mathbf{i}}$ cm (c) $72\hat{\mathbf{i}}$ cm (d) $144\hat{\mathbf{i}}$ cm (e) nowhere **(ii)** At what location is the value $16\hat{\mathbf{i}}$ kN/C? Choose from the same possibilities.

8. Is it possible for an electric field to exist in empty space? Explain. Consider point *A* in Figure 23.21a. Does charge exist at this point? Does a force exist at this point? Does a field exist at this point?

9. O (i) Rank the magnitude of the forces charged particle A exerts on charged particle B, located at distance r away from A, from the largest to the smallest in the following cases. In your ranking, note any cases of equality. (a) $q_A = 20$ nC, $q_B = 20$ nC, $r = 2$ cm (b) $q_A = 30$ nC, $q_B = 10$ nC, $r = 2$ cm (c) $q_A = 10$ nC, $q_B = 30$ nC, $r = 2$ cm (d) $q_A = 30$ nC, $q_B = 20$ nC, $r = 3$ cm (e) $q_A = 45$ nC, $q_B = 20$ nC, $r = 3$ cm **(ii)** Rank the magnitudes of the electric fields charged particle A creates at the location of charged particle B, a distance r away from A, from the largest to the smallest in the same cases. In your ranking, note any cases of equality.

10. O Three charged particles are arranged on corners of a square as shown in Figure Q23.10, with charge $-Q$ on both the particle at the upper left corner and the particle at the lower right corner, and charge $+2Q$ on the particle at the lower left corner. **(i)** What is the direction of the electric field at the upper right corner, which is a point in empty space? (a) It is upward and to the right. (b) It is straight to the right. (c) It is straight downward. (d) It is downward and to the left. (e) It is perpendicular to the plane of the picture and outward. (f) There is no direction; no field exists at that corner because no charge is there. (g) There is no direction; the total field there is zero. **(ii)** Suppose the $+2Q$ charge at the lower left corner is removed. Then does the magnitude of the field at the upper right corner (a) become larger, (b) become smaller, (c) stay the same, or (d) change unpredictably?

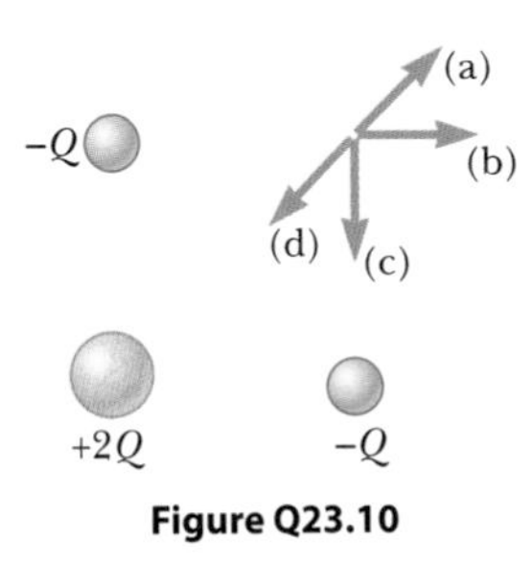

Figure Q23.10

11. O Two charged particles A and B are alone in the Universe, 8 cm apart. The charge of A is 40 nC. The net electric field at one certain point 4 cm from A is zero. What can you conclude about the charge of B? Choose every correct answer. (a) It can be 40 nC. (b) It can be 120 nC. (c) It can be 360 nC. (d) It can be -40 nC. (e) It can be -120 nC. (f) It can be -360 nC. (g) It can have any of an infinite number of values. (h) It can have any of several values. (i) It must have one of three values. (j) It must have one of two values. (k) It must have one certain value. (l) No possible value for q_B exists; the situation is impossible.

12. Explain why electric field lines never cross. *Suggestion:* Begin by explaining why the electric field at a particular point must have only one direction.

13. Figures 23.12 and 23.13 show three electric field vectors at the same point. With a little extrapolation, Figure 23.19 would show many electric field lines at the same point. Is it really true that "no two field lines can cross"? Are the diagrams drawn correctly? Explain your answers.

14. O A circular ring of charge with radius b has total charge q uniformly distributed around it. What is the magnitude of the electric field at the center of the ring? (a) 0 (b) $k_e q/b^2$ (c) $k_e q^2/b^2$ (d) $k_e q^2/b$ (c) none of these answers

15. O Assume a uniformly charged ring of radius R and charge Q produces an electric field E_{ring} at a point P on its axis, at distance x away from the center of the ring. Now the charge Q is spread uniformly over the circular area the ring encloses, forming a flat disk of charge with the same radius. How does the field E_{disk} produced by the disk at P compare to the field produced by the ring at the same point? (a) $E_{\text{disk}} < E_{\text{ring}}$ (b) $E_{\text{disk}} = E_{\text{ring}}$ (c) $E_{\text{disk}} > E_{\text{ring}}$ (d) impossible to determine

16. **O** A free electron and a free proton are released in identical electric fields. **(i)** How do the magnitudes of the electric force exerted on the two particles compare? (a) It is millions of times greater for the electron. (b) It is thousands of times greater for the electron. (c) They are equal. (d) It is thousands of times smaller for the electron. (e) It is millions of times smaller for the electron. (f) It is zero for the electron. (g) It is zero for the proton. **(ii)** Compare the magnitudes of their accelerations. Choose from the same possibilities.

17. **O** An object with negative charge is placed in a region of space where the electric field is directed vertically upward. What is the direction of the electric force exerted on this charge? (a) It is up. (b) It is down. (c) There is no force. (d) The force can be in any direction.

18. Explain the differences between linear, surface, and volume charge densities and give examples of when each would be used.

19. Would life be different if the electron were positively charged and the proton were negatively charged? Does the choice of signs have any bearing on physical and chemical interactions? Explain.

20. Consider two electric dipoles in empty space. Each dipole has zero net charge. Does an electric force exist between the dipoles; that is, can two objects with zero net charge exert electric forces on each other? If so, is the force one of attraction or of repulsion?

Problems

WebAssign The Problems from this chapter may be assigned online in WebAssign.

ThomsonNOW Sign in at **www.thomsonedu.com** and go to ThomsonNOW to assess your understanding of this chapter's topics with additional quizzing and conceptual questions.

1, 2, 3 denotes straightforward, intermediate, challenging; □ denotes full solution available in *Student Solutions Manual/Study Guide;* ▲ denotes coached solution with hints available at **www.thomsonedu.com;** denotes developing symbolic reasoning; ● denotes asking for qualitative reasoning; denotes computer useful in solving problem

Section 23.1 Properties of Electric Charges

1. (a) Find to three significant digits the charge and the mass of an ionized hydrogen atom, represented as H^+. *Suggestion:* Begin by looking up the mass of a neutral atom on the periodic table of the elements in Appendix C. (b) Find the charge and the mass of Na^+, a singly ionized sodium atom. (c) Find the charge and the average mass of a chloride ion Cl^- that joins with the Na^+ to make one molecule of table salt. (d) Find the charge and the mass of $Ca^{++} = Ca^{2+}$, a doubly ionized calcium atom. (e) You can model the center of an ammonia molecule as an N^{3-} ion. Find its charge and mass. (f) The plasma in a hot star contains quadruply ionized nitrogen atoms, N^{4+}. Find their charge and mass. (g) Find the charge and the mass of the nucleus of a nitrogen atom. (h) Find the charge and the mass of the molecular ion H_2O^-.

2. (a) Calculate the number of electrons in a small, electrically neutral silver pin that has a mass of 10.0 g. Silver has 47 electrons per atom, and its molar mass is 107.87 g/mol. (b) Imagine adding electrons to the pin until the negative charge has the very large value 1.00 mC. How many electrons are added for every 10^9 electrons already present?

Section 23.2 Charging Objects by Induction

Section 23.3 Coulomb's Law

3. ▲ Nobel laureate Richard Feynman (1918–1988) once said that if two persons stood at arm's length from each other and each person had 1% more electrons than protons, the force of repulsion between them would be enough to lift a "weight" equal to that of the entire Earth. Carry out an order-of-magnitude calculation to substantiate this assertion.

4. A charged particle A exerts a force of 2.62 μN to the right on charged particle B when the particles are 13.7 mm apart. Particle B moves straight away from A to make the distance between them 17.7 mm. What vector force does it then exert on A?

5. ● (a) Two protons in a molecule are 3.80×10^{-10} m apart. Find the electrical force exerted by one proton on the other. (b) State how the magnitude of this force compares with the magnitude of the gravitational force exerted by one proton on the other. (c) **What If?** What must be a particle's charge-to-mass ratio if the magnitude of the gravitational force between two of these particles is equal to the magnitude of electrical force between them?

6. Two small silver spheres, each with a mass of 10.0 g, are separated by 1.00 m. Calculate the fraction of the electrons in one sphere that must be transferred to the other to produce an attractive force of 1.00×10^4 N (about 1 ton) between the spheres. (The number of electrons per atom of silver is 47, and the number of atoms per gram is Avogadro's number divided by the molar mass of silver, 107.87 g/mol.)

7. Three charged particles are located at the corners of an equilateral triangle as shown in Figure P23.7. Calculate the total electric force on the 7.00-μC charge.

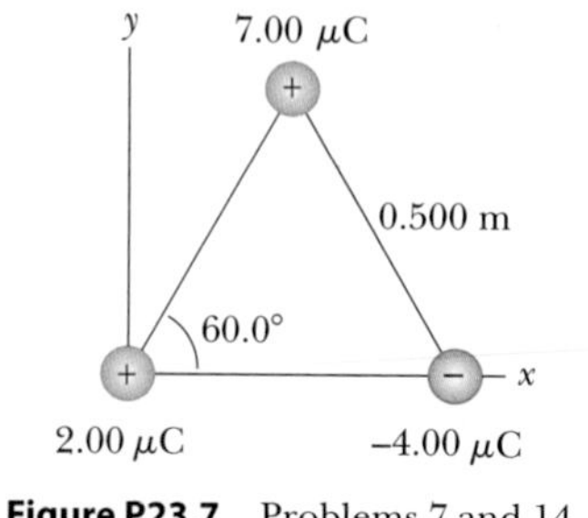

Figure P23.7 Problems 7 and 14.

8. ● Two small beads having positive charges $3q$ and q are fixed at the opposite ends of a horizontal insulating rod, extending from the origin to the point $x = d$. As shown in Figure P23.8, a third small charged bead is free to slide on the rod. At what position is the third bead in equilibrium? Explain whether it can be in stable equilibrium.

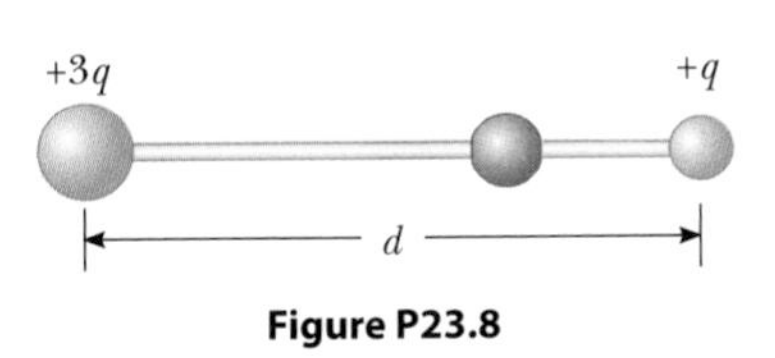

Figure P23.8

9. Two identical conducting small spheres are placed with their centers 0.300 m apart. One is given a charge of 12.0 nC and the other a charge of −18.0 nC. (a) Find the electric force exerted by one sphere on the other. (b) **What If?** The spheres are connected by a conducting wire. Find the electric force each exerts on the other after they have come to equilibrium.

10. **Review problem**. Two identical particles, each having charge $+q$, are fixed in space and separated by a distance d. A third particle with charge $-Q$ is free to move and lies initially at rest on the perpendicular bisector of the two fixed charges a distance x from the midpoint between the two fixed charges (Fig. P23.10). (a) Show that if x is small compared with d, the motion of $-Q$ is simple harmonic along the perpendicular bisector. Determine the period of that motion. (b) How fast will the charge $-Q$ be moving when it is at the midpoint between the two fixed charges if initially it is released at a distance $a \ll d$ from the midpoint?

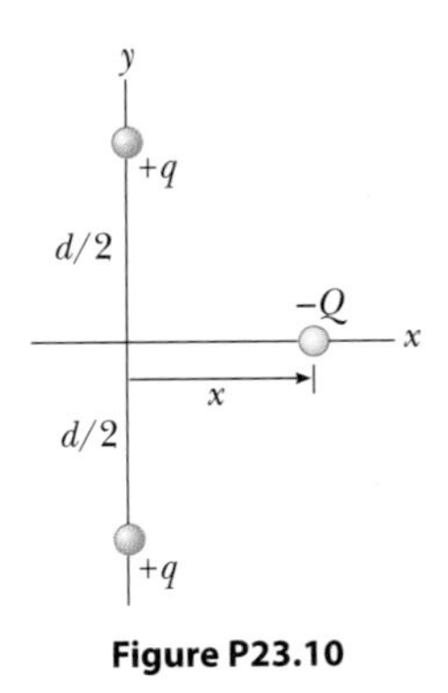

Figure P23.10

11. **Review problem**. In the Bohr theory of the hydrogen atom, an electron moves in a circular orbit about a proton, where the radius of the orbit is 0.529×10^{-10} m. (a) Find the electric force exerted on each particle. (b) If this force causes the centripetal acceleration of the electron, what is the speed of the electron?

Section 23.4 The Electric Field

12. In Figure P23.12, determine the point (other than infinity) at which the electric field is zero.

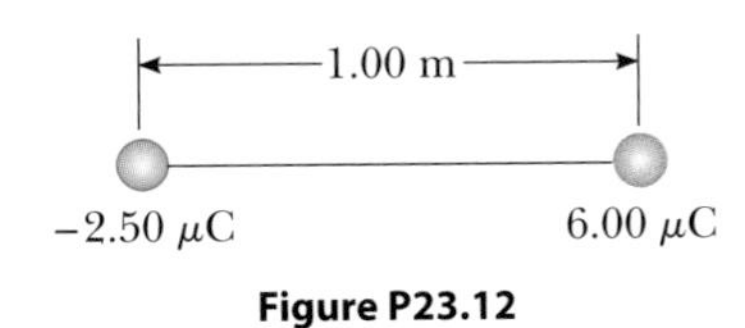

Figure P23.12

13. What are the magnitude and direction of the electric field that balances the weight of (a) an electron and (b) a proton? You may use the data in Table 23.1.

14. Three charged particles are at the corners of an equilateral triangle as shown in Figure P23.7. (a) Calculate the electric field at the position of the 2.00-μC charge due to the 7.00-μC and −4.00-μC charges. (b) Use your answer to part (a) to determine the force on the 2.00-μC charge.

15. ● Two charged particles are located on the x axis. The first is a charge $+Q$ at $x = -a$. The second is an unknown charge located at $x = +3a$. The net electric field these charges produce at the origin has a magnitude of $2k_eQ/a^2$. Explain how many values are possible for the unknown charge and find the possible values.

16. Two 2.00-μC charged particles are located on the x axis. One is at $x = 1.00$ m, and the other is at $x = -1.00$ m. (a) Determine the electric field on the y axis at $y = 0.500$ m. (b) Calculate the electric force on a −3.00-μC charge placed on the y axis at $y = 0.500$ m.

17. Four charged particles are at the corners of a square of side a as shown in Figure P23.17. (a) Determine the magnitude and direction of the electric field at the location of charge q. (b) What is the total electric force exerted on q?

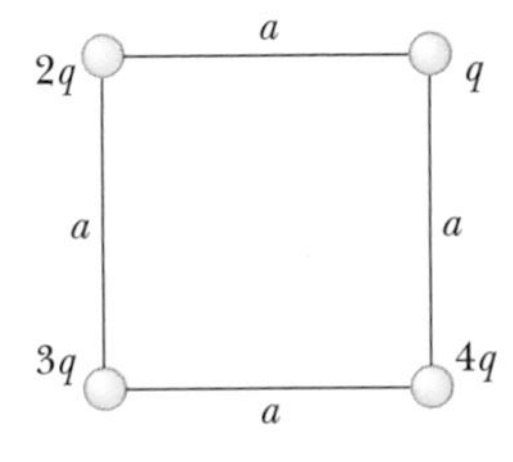

Figure P23.17

18. Consider the electric dipole shown in Figure P23.18. Show that the electric field at a *distant* point on the $+x$ axis is $E_x \approx -4k_eqa/x^3$.

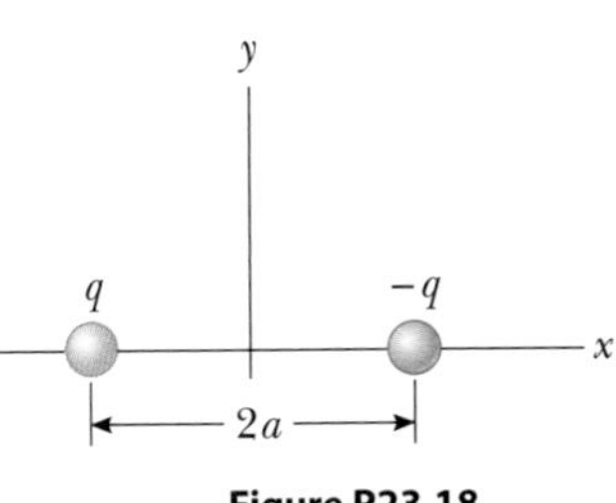

Figure P23.18

19. ● Consider n equal positive charged particles each of magnitude Q/n placed symmetrically around a circle of radius R. (a) Calculate the magnitude of the electric field at a point a distance x from the center of the circle and on the line passing through the center and perpendicular to the plane of the circle. (b) Explain why this result is identical to the result of the calculation done in Example 23.7.

Section 23.5 Electric Field of a Continuous Charge Distribution

20. A continuous line of charge lies along the x axis, extending from $x = +x_0$ to positive infinity. The line carries charge with a uniform linear charge density λ_0. What are

the magnitude and direction of the electric field at the origin?

21. A rod 14.0 cm long is uniformly charged and has a total charge of $-22.0\ \mu C$. Determine the magnitude and direction of the electric field along the axis of the rod at a point 36.0 cm from its center.

22. Show that the maximum magnitude E_{max} of the electric field along the axis of a uniformly charged ring occurs at $x = a/\sqrt{2}$ (see Fig. 23.16) and has the value $Q/(6\sqrt{3}\pi\epsilon_0 a^2)$.

23. A uniformly charged ring of radius 10.0 cm has a total charge of $75.0\ \mu C$. Find the electric field on the axis of the ring at (a) 1.00 cm, (b) 5.00 cm, (c) 30.0 cm, and (d) 100 cm from the center of the ring.

24. A uniformly charged disk of radius 35.0 cm carries charge with a density of $7.90 \times 10^{-3}\ C/m^2$. Calculate the electric field on the axis of the disk at (a) 5.00 cm, (b) 10.0 cm, (c) 50.0 cm, and (d) 200 cm from the center of the disk.

25. ● Example 23.8 derives the exact expression for the electric field at a point on the axis of a uniformly charged disk. Consider a disk of radius $R = 3.00$ cm having a uniformly distributed charge of $+5.20\ \mu C$. (a) Using the result of Example 23.8, compute the electric field at a point on the axis and 3.00 mm from the center. **What If?** Explain how this answer compares with the field computed from the near-field approximation $E = \sigma/2\epsilon_0$. (b) Using the result of Example 23.8, compute the electric field at a point on the axis and 30.0 cm from the center of the disk. **What If?** Explain how this answer compares with the electric field obtained by treating the disk as a $+5.20$-μC charged particle at a distance of 30.0 cm.

26. The electric field along the axis of a uniformly charged disk of radius R and total charge Q was calculated in Example 23.8. Show that the electric field at distances x that are large compared with R approaches that of a particle with charge $Q = \sigma\pi R^2$. *Suggestion:* First show that $x/(x^2 + R^2)^{1/2} = (1 + R^2/x^2)^{-1/2}$ and use the binomial expansion $(1 + \delta)^n \approx 1 + n\delta$ when $\delta \ll 1$.

27. ▲ A uniformly charged insulating rod of length 14.0 cm is bent into the shape of a semicircle as shown in Figure P23.27. The rod has a total charge of $-7.50\ \mu C$. Find the magnitude and direction of the electric field at O, the center of the semicircle.

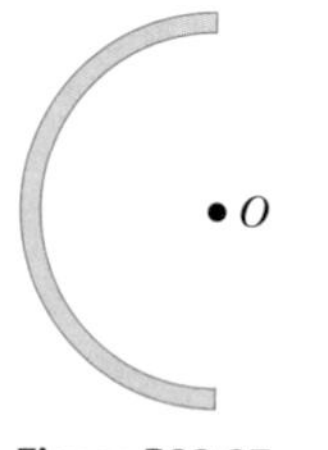

Figure P23.27

28. (a) Consider a uniformly charged thin-walled right circular cylindrical shell having total charge Q, radius R, and height h. Determine the electric field at a point a distance d from the right side of the cylinder as shown in Figure P23.28. *Suggestion:* Use the result of Example 23.7 and treat the cylinder as a collection of ring charges. (b) **What If?** Consider now a solid cylinder with the same dimensions and carrying the same charge, uniformly distributed through its volume. Use the result of Example 23.8 to find the field it creates at the same point.

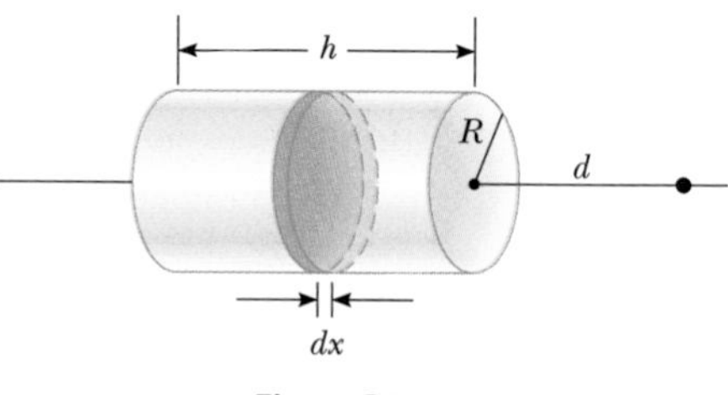

Figure P23.28

29. A thin rod of length ℓ and uniform charge per unit length λ lies along the x axis as shown in Figure P23.29. (a) Show that the electric field at P, a distance y from the rod along its perpendicular bisector, has no x component and is given by $E = 2k_e\lambda \sin\theta_0/y$. (b) **What If?** Using your result to part (a), show that the field of a rod of infinite length is $E = 2k_e\lambda/y$. *Suggestion:* First calculate the field at P due to an element of length dx, which has a charge $\lambda\,dx$. Then change variables from x to θ, using the relationships $x = y\tan\theta$ and $dx = y\sec^2\theta\,d\theta$, and integrate over θ.

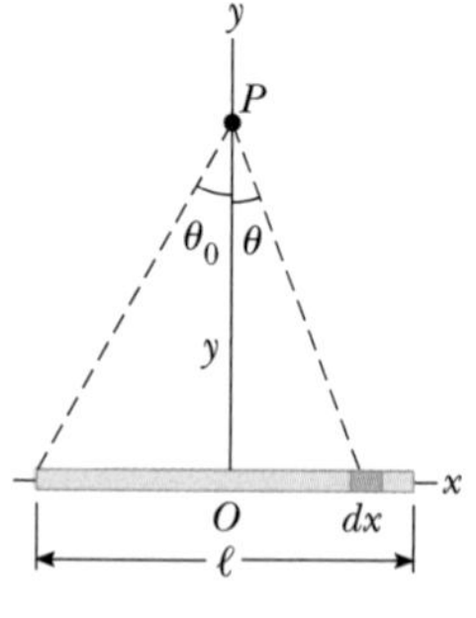

Figure P23.29

30. Three solid plastic cylinders all have radius 2.50 cm and length 6.00 cm. One (a) carries charge with uniform density $15.0\ nC/m^2$ everywhere on its surface. Another (b) carries charge with the same uniform density on its curved lateral surface only. The third (c) carries charge with uniform density $500\ nC/m^3$ throughout the plastic. Find the charge of each cylinder.

31. Eight solid plastic cubes, each 3.00 cm on each edge, are glued together to form each one of the objects (i, ii, iii, and iv) shown in Figure P23.31. (a) Assuming each object carries charge with uniform density $400\ nC/m^3$ throughout its volume, find the charge of each object. (b) Assuming each object carries charge with uniform density $15.0\ nC/m^2$ everywhere on its exposed surface, find the charge on each object. (c) Assuming charge is placed

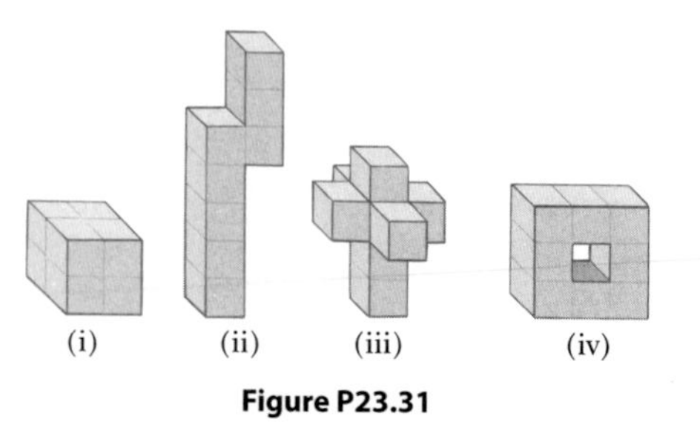

Figure P23.31

only on the edges where perpendicular surfaces meet, with uniform density 80.0 pC/m, find the charge of each object.

Section 23.6 Electric Field Lines

32. A positively charged disk has a uniform charge per unit area as described in Example 23.8. Sketch the electric field lines in a plane perpendicular to the plane of the disk passing through its center.

33. A negatively charged rod of finite length carries charge with a uniform charge per unit length. Sketch the electric field lines in a plane containing the rod.

34. Figure P23.34 shows the electric field lines for two charged particles separated by a small distance. (a) Determine the ratio q_1/q_2. (b) What are the signs of q_1 and q_2?

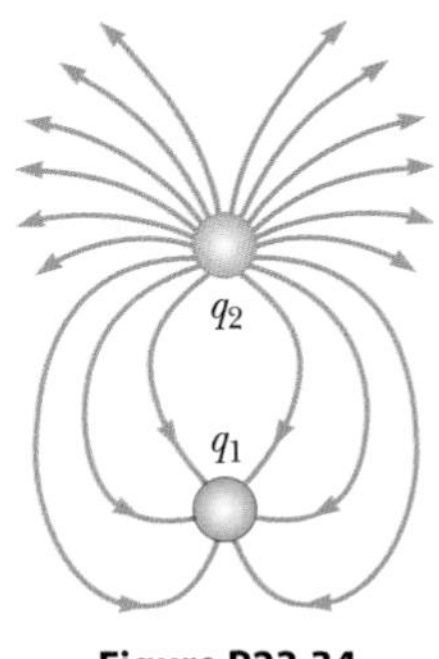

Figure P23.34

35. ▲ Three equal positive charges q are at the corners of an equilateral triangle of side a as shown in Figure P23.35. (a) Assume the three charges together create an electric field. Sketch the field lines in the plane of the charges. Find the location of one point (other than ∞) where the electric field is zero. (b) What are the magnitude and direction of the electric field at P due to the two charges at the base?

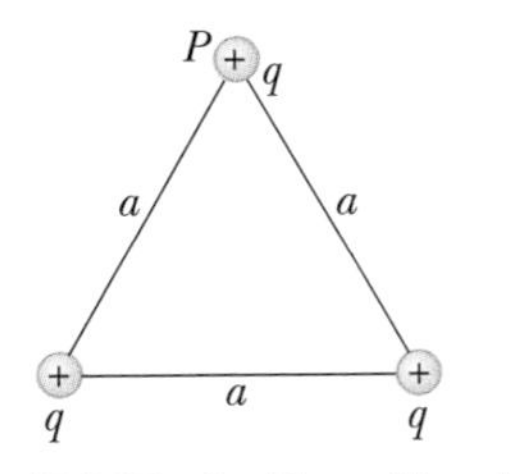

Figure P23.35 Problems 35 and 58.

Section 23.7 Motion of Charged Particles in a Uniform Electric Field

36. A proton is projected in the positive x direction into a region of a uniform electric field $\vec{\mathbf{E}} = -6.00 \times 10^5 \hat{\mathbf{i}}$ N/C at $t = 0$. The proton travels 7.00 cm as it comes to rest. Determine (a) the acceleration of the proton, (b) its initial speed, and (c) the time interval over which the proton comes to rest.

37. A proton accelerates from rest in a uniform electric field of 640 N/C. At one later moment, its speed is 1.20 Mm/s (nonrelativistic because v is much less than the speed of light). (a) Find the acceleration of the proton. (b) Over what time interval does the proton reach this speed? (c) How far does it move in this time interval? (d) What is its kinetic energy at the end of this interval?

38. ● Two horizontal metal plates, each 100 mm square, are aligned 10.0 mm apart, with one above the other. They are given equal-magnitude charges of opposite sign so that a uniform downward electric field of 2 000 N/C exists in the region between them. A particle of mass 2.00×10^{-16} kg and with a positive charge of 1.00×10^{-6} C leaves the center of the bottom negative plate with an initial speed of 1.00×10^5 m/s at an angle of 37.0° above the horizontal. Describe the trajectory of the particle. Which plate does it strike? Where does it strike, relative to its starting point?

39. ▲ The electrons in a particle beam each have a kinetic energy K. What are the magnitude and direction of the electric field that will stop these electrons in a distance d?

40. Protons are projected with initial speed $v_i = 9.55$ km/s into a region where a uniform electric field $\vec{\mathbf{E}} = (-720\hat{\mathbf{j}})$ N/C is present as shown in Figure P23.40. The protons are to hit a target that lies at a horizontal distance of 1.27 mm from the point where the protons cross the plane and enter the electric field. Find (a) the two projection angles θ that will result in a hit and (b) the time of flight (the time interval during which the proton is above the plane in Fig. P23.40) for each trajectory.

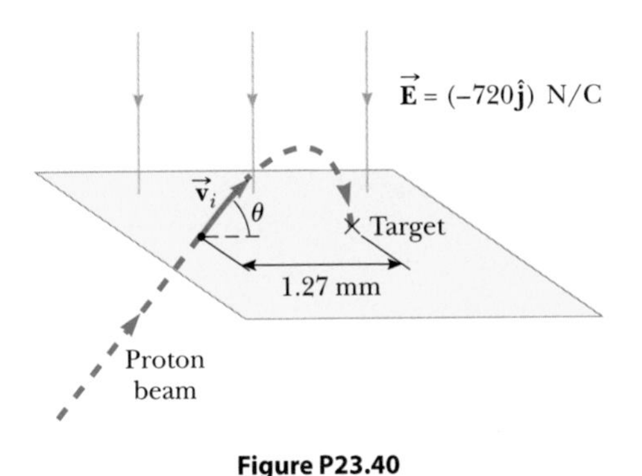

Figure P23.40

41. A proton moves at 4.50×10^5 m/s in the horizontal direction. It enters a uniform vertical electric field with a magnitude of 9.60×10^3 N/C. Ignoring any gravitational effects, find (a) the time interval required for the proton to travel 5.00 cm horizontally, (b) its vertical displacement during the time interval in which it travels 5.00 cm horizontally, and (c) the horizontal and vertical components of its velocity after it has traveled 5.00 cm horizontally.

Additional Problems

42. ● Two known charges, −12.0 μC and 45.0 μC, and a third unknown charge are located on the x axis. The charge −12.0 μC is at the origin, and the charge 45.0 μC is at $x = 15.0$ cm. The unknown charge is to be placed so that each charge is in equilibrium under the action of the electric forces exerted by the other two charges. Is this situation possible? Is it possible in more than one way? Explain. Find the required location, magnitude, and sign of the unknown charge.

43. A uniform electric field of magnitude 640 N/C exists between two parallel plates that are 4.00 cm apart. A proton is released from the positive plate at the same instant an electron is released from the negative plate. (a) Determine the distance from the positive plate at which the two pass each other. (Ignore the electrical attraction between the proton and electron.) (b) **What If?** Repeat part (a) for a sodium ion (Na^+) and a chloride ion (Cl^-).

44. Three charged particles are aligned along the x axis as shown in Figure P23.44. Find the electric field at (a) the position (2.00, 0) and (b) the position (0, 2.00).

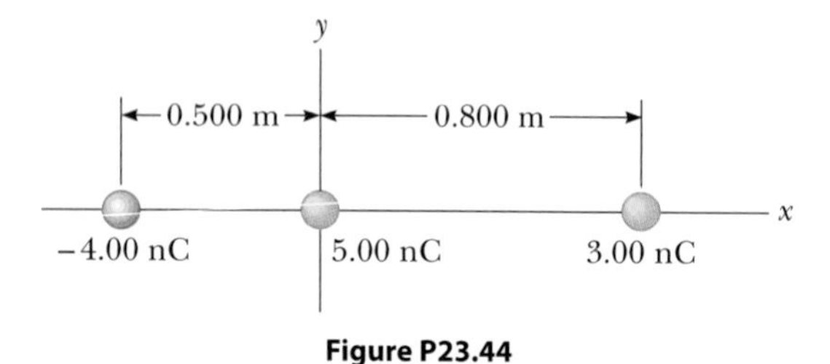

Figure P23.44

45. ▲ A charged cork ball of mass 1.00 g is suspended on a light string in the presence of a uniform electric field as shown in Figure P23.45. When $\vec{\mathbf{E}} = (3.00\hat{\mathbf{i}} + 5.00\hat{\mathbf{j}}) \times 10^5$ N/C, the ball is in equilibrium at $\theta = 37.0°$. Find (a) the charge on the ball and (b) the tension in the string.

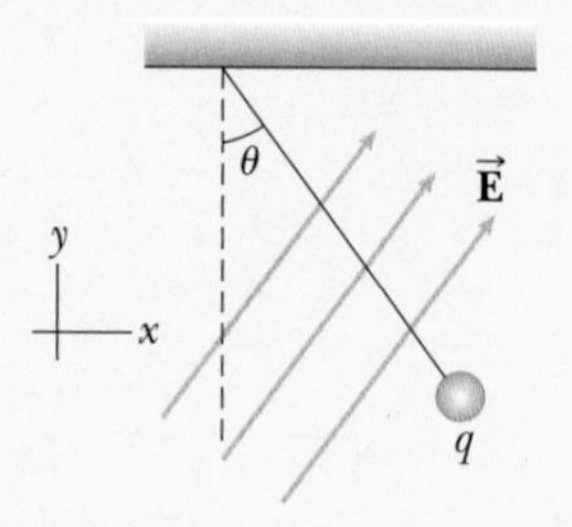

Figure P23.45 Problems 45 and 46.

46. A charged cork ball of mass m is suspended on a light string in the presence of a uniform electric field as shown in Figure P23.45. When $\vec{\mathbf{E}} = (A\hat{\mathbf{i}} + B\hat{\mathbf{j}})$ N/C, where A and B are positive numbers, the ball is in equilibrium at the angle θ. Find (a) the charge on the ball and (b) the tension in the string.

47. Four identical charged particles ($q = +10.0\ \mu$C) are located on the corners of a rectangle as shown in Figure P23.47. The dimensions of the rectangle are $L = 60.0$ cm and $W = 15.0$ cm. Calculate the magnitude and direction of the total electric force exerted on the charge at the lower left corner by the other three charges.

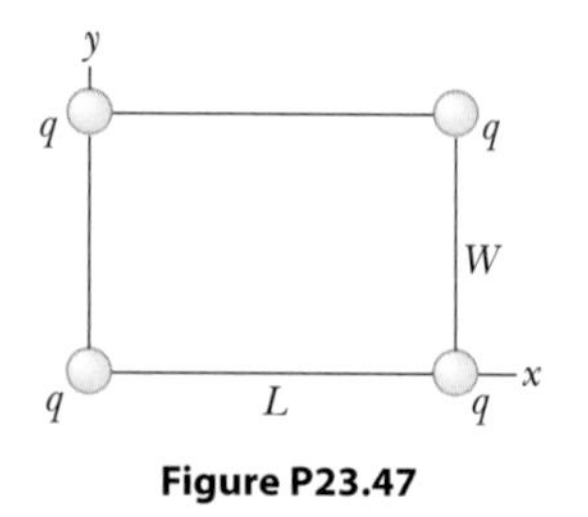

Figure P23.47

48. Inez is putting up decorations for her sister's quinceañera (fifteenth birthday party). She ties three light silk ribbons together to the top of a gateway and hangs a rubber balloon from each ribbon (Fig. P23.48). To include the effects of the gravitational and buoyant forces on it, each balloon can be modeled as a particle of mass 2.00 g, with its center 50.0 cm from the point of support. To show off the colors of the balloons, Inez rubs the whole surface of each balloon with her woolen scarf, making them hang separately with gaps between them. The centers of the hanging balloons form a horizontal equilateral triangle with sides 30.0 cm long. What is the common charge each balloon carries?

Figure P23.48

49. **Review problem.** Two identical metallic blocks resting on a frictionless horizontal surface are connected by a light metallic spring having a spring constant k and an unstretched length L_i as shown in Figure P23.49a. A total charge Q is slowly placed on the system, causing the spring to stretch to an equilibrium length L as shown in Figure P23.49b. Determine the value of Q, assuming all the charge resides on the blocks and modeling the blocks as charged particles.

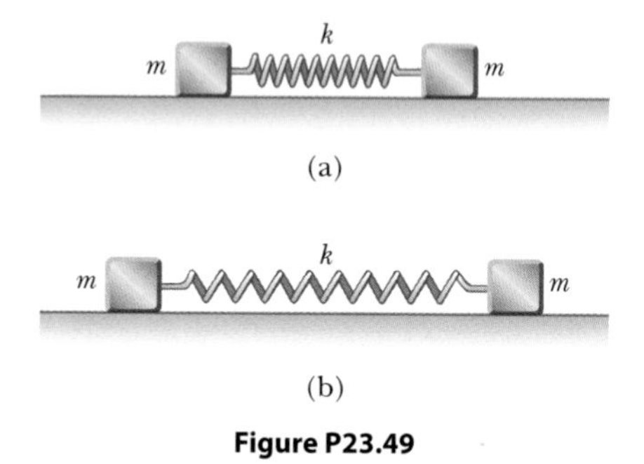

Figure P23.49

50. Consider a regular polygon with 29 sides. The distance from the center to each vertex is a. Identical charges q are placed at 28 vertices of the polygon. A single charge Q is placed at the center of the polygon. What is the magnitude and direction of the force experienced by the charge Q? *Suggestion:* You may use the result of Problem 60 in Chapter 3.

51. Identical thin rods of length $2a$ carry equal charges $+Q$ uniformly distributed along their lengths. The rods lie along the x axis with their centers separated by a distance $b > 2a$ (Fig. P23.51). Show that the magnitude of the force exerted by the left rod on the right one is

$$F = \left(\frac{k_e Q^2}{4a^2}\right) \ln\left(\frac{b^2}{b^2 - 4a^2}\right)$$

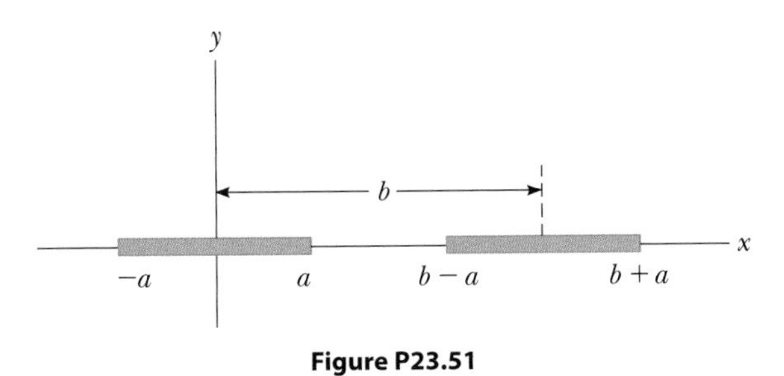

Figure P23.51

52. Two small spheres hang in equilibrium at the bottom ends of threads, 40.0 cm long, that have their top ends tied to the same fixed point. One sphere has mass 2.40 g and charge +300 nC. The other sphere has the same mass and a charge of +200 nC. Find the distance between the centers of the spheres. You will need to solve an equation numerically.

53. A line of positive charge is formed into a semicircle of radius R = 60.0 cm as shown in Figure P23.53. The charge per unit length along the semicircle is described by the expression $\lambda = \lambda_0 \cos\theta$. The total charge on the semicircle is 12.0 μC. Calculate the total force on a charge of 3.00 μC placed at the center of curvature.

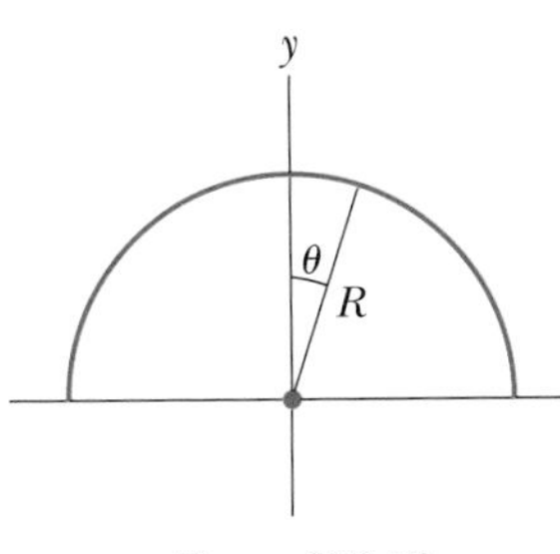

Figure P23.53

54. ● Two particles, each with charge 52.0 nC, are located on the y axis at y = 25.0 cm and y = −25.0 cm. (a) Find the vector electric field at a point on the x axis as a function of x. (b) Find the field at x = 36.0 cm. (c) At what location is the field $1.00\hat{\mathbf{i}}$ kN/C? You may need to solve an equation numerically. (d) At what location is the field $16.0\hat{\mathbf{i}}$ kN/C? (e) Compare this problem with Question 7. Describe the similarities and explain the differences.

55. ● Two small spheres of mass m are suspended from strings of length ℓ that are connected at a common point. One sphere has charge Q and the other has charge $2Q$. The strings make angles θ_1 and θ_2 with the vertical. (a) Explain how θ_1 and θ_2 are related. (b) Assume θ_1 and θ_2 are small. Show that the distance r between the spheres is approximately

$$r \approx \left(\frac{4k_eQ^2\ell}{mg}\right)^{1/3}$$

56. Two identical beads each have a mass m and charge q. When placed in a hemispherical bowl of radius R with frictionless, nonconducting walls, the beads move, and at equilibrium they are a distance R apart (Fig. P23.56). Determine the charge on each bead.

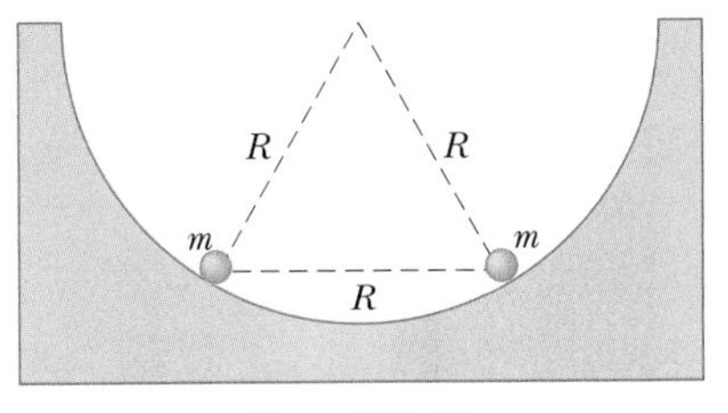

Figure P23.56

57. ● **Review problem.** A 1.00-g cork ball with charge 2.00 μC is suspended vertically on a 0.500-m-long light string in the presence of a uniform, downward-directed electric field of magnitude $E = 1.00 \times 10^5$ N/C. If the ball is displaced slightly from the vertical, it oscillates like a simple pendulum. (a) Determine the period of this oscillation. (b) Should the effect of gravitation be included in the calculation for part (a)? Explain.

58. ● Figure P23.35 shows three equal positive charges at the corners of an equilateral triangle of side a = 3.00 cm. Add a vertical line through the top charge at P, bisecting the triangle. Along this line label points A, B, C, D, E, and F, with A just below the charge at P; B at the center of the triangle; B, C, D, and E in order and close together with E at the center of the bottom side of the triangle; and F close below E. (a) Identify the direction of the total electric field at A, E, and F. Identify the electric field at B. Identify the direction of the electric field at C. (b) Argue that the answers to part (a) imply that the electric field must be zero at a point close to D. (c) Find the distance from point E on the bottom side of the triangle to the point around D where the electric field is zero. You will need to solve a transcendental equation.

59. Eight charged particles, each of magnitude q, are located on the corners of a cube of edge s as shown in Figure P23.59. (a) Determine the x, y, and z components of the total force exerted by the other charges on the charge located at point A. (b) What are the magnitude and direction of this total force?

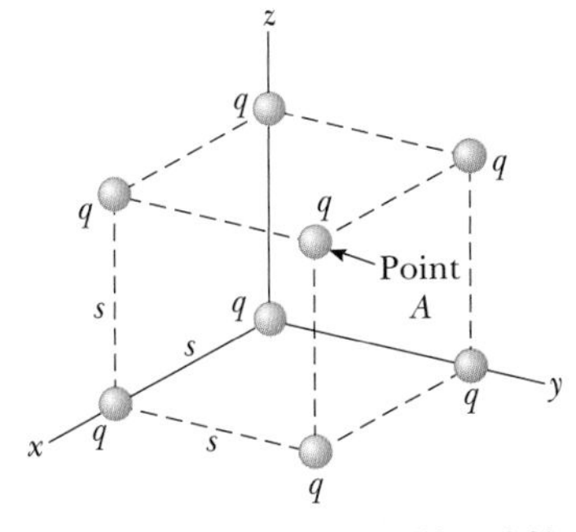

Figure P23.59 Problems 59 and 60.

60. Consider the charge distribution shown in Figure P23.59. (a) Show that the magnitude of the electric field at the center of any face of the cube has a value of $2.18k_eq/s^2$. (b) What is the direction of the electric field at the center of the top face of the cube?

61. **Review problem.** A negatively charged particle $-q$ is placed at the center of a uniformly charged ring, where the ring has a total positive charge Q as shown in Example 23.7. The particle, confined to move along the x axis,

is moved a small distance x along the axis (where $x \ll a$) and released. Show that the particle oscillates in simple harmonic motion with a frequency given by

$$f = \frac{1}{2\pi}\left(\frac{k_e qQ}{ma^3}\right)^{1/2}$$

62. A line of charge with uniform density 35.0 nC/m lies along the line $y = -15.0$ cm between the points with coordinates $x = 0$ and $x = 40.0$ cm. Find the electric field it creates at the origin.

63. **Review problem**. An electric dipole in a uniform electric field is displaced slightly from its equilibrium position as shown in Figure P23.63, where θ is small. The separation of the charges is $2a$, and the moment of inertia of the dipole is I. Assuming the dipole is released from this position, show that its angular orientation exhibits simple harmonic motion with a frequency

$$f = \frac{1}{2\pi}\sqrt{\frac{2qaE}{I}}$$

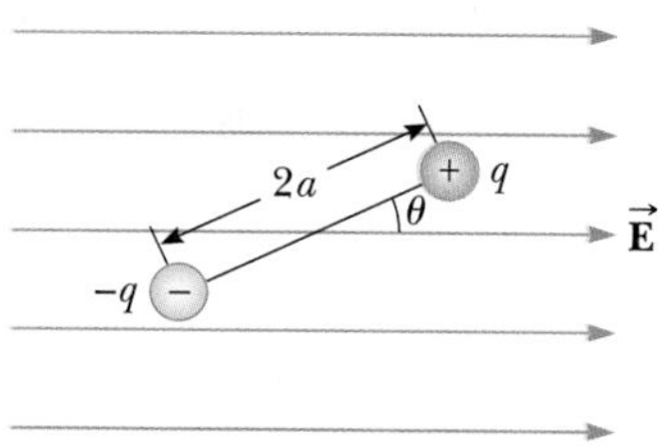

2a
q
θ
−q
$\vec{\mathbf{E}}$

Figure P23.63

64. Consider an infinite number of identical particles, each with charge q, placed along the x axis at distances a, $2a$, $3a$, $4a$, . . . , from the origin. What is the electric field at the origin due to this distribution? *Suggestion:* Use the fact that

$$1 + \frac{1}{2^2} + \frac{1}{3^2} + \frac{1}{4^2} + \cdots = \frac{\pi^2}{6}$$

65. A line of charge starts at $x = +x_0$ and extends to positive infinity. The linear charge density is $\lambda = \lambda_0 x_0/x$, where λ_0 is a constant. Determine the electric field at the origin.

Answers to Quick Quizzes

23.1 (a), (c), (e). The experiment shows that A and B have charges of the same sign, as do objects B and C. Therefore, all three objects have charges of the same sign. We cannot determine from this information, however, if the charges are positive or negative.

23.2 (e). In the first experiment, objects A and B may have charges with opposite signs or one of the objects may be neutral. The second experiment shows that B and C have charges with the same signs, so B must be charged. We still do not know, however, if A is charged or neutral.

23.3 (b). From Newton's third law, the electric force exerted by object B on object A is equal in magnitude to the force exerted by object A on object B and in the opposite direction.

23.4 (a). There is no effect on the electric field if we assume the source charge producing the field is not disturbed by our actions. Remember that the electric field is created by the source charge(s) (unseen in this case), not the test charge(s).

23.5 *A*, *B*, *C*. The field is greatest at point *A* because that is where the field lines are closest together. The absence of lines near point *C* indicates that the electric field there is zero.

In a tabletop plasma ball, the colorful lines emanating from the sphere give evidence of strong electric fields. Using Gauss's law, we show in this chapter that the electric field surrounding a uniformly charged sphere is identical to that of a point charge. (Getty Images)

24 Gauss's Law

In Chapter 23, we showed how to calculate the electric field due to a given charge distribution. In this chapter, we describe *Gauss's law* and an alternative procedure for calculating electric fields. Gauss's law is based on the inverse-square behavior of the electric force between point charges. Although Gauss's law is a consequence of Coulomb's law, it is more convenient for calculating the electric fields of highly symmetric charge distributions and makes it possible to deal with complicated problems using qualitative reasoning.

24.1 Electric Flux

The concept of electric field lines was described qualitatively in Chapter 23. We now treat electric field lines in a more quantitative way.

Consider an electric field that is uniform in both magnitude and direction as shown in Figure 24.1. The field lines penetrate a rectangular surface of area A, whose plane is oriented perpendicular to the field. Recall from Section 23.6 that the number of lines per unit area (in other words, the *line density*) is proportional to the magnitude of the electric field. Therefore, the total number of lines penetrating the surface is proportional to the product EA. This product of the magnitude of the electric field E and surface area A perpendicular to the field is called the **electric flux** Φ_E (uppercase Greek letter phi):

$$\Phi_E = EA \qquad \textbf{(24.1)}$$

Area $= A$

$\vec{\mathbf{E}}$

Figure 24.1 Field lines representing a uniform electric field penetrating a plane of area A perpendicular to the field. The electric flux Φ_E through this area is equal to EA.

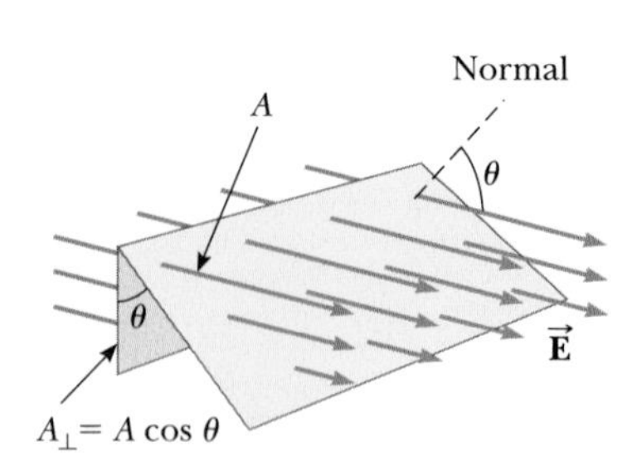

Figure 24.2 Field lines representing a uniform electric field penetrating an area A that is at an angle θ to the field. Because the number of lines that go through the area $A_\perp$ is the same as the number that go through A, the flux through $A_\perp$ is equal to the flux through A and is given by $\Phi_E = EA\cos\theta$.

From the SI units of E and A, we see that Φ_E has units of newton meters squared per coulomb ($\text{N}\cdot\text{m}^2/\text{C}$). **Electric flux is proportional to the number of electric field lines penetrating some surface.**

If the surface under consideration is not perpendicular to the field, the flux through it must be less than that given by Equation 24.1. Consider Figure 24.2, where the normal to the surface of area A is at an angle θ to the uniform electric field. Notice that the number of lines that cross this area A is equal to the number of lines that cross the area $A_\perp$, which is a projection of area A onto a plane oriented perpendicular to the field. Figure 24.2 shows that the two areas are related by $A_\perp = A\cos\theta$. Because the flux through A equals the flux through $A_\perp$, the flux through A is

$$\Phi_E = EA_\perp = EA\cos\theta \qquad \textbf{(24.2)}$$

From this result, we see that the flux through a surface of fixed area A has a maximum value EA when the surface is perpendicular to the field (when the normal to the surface is parallel to the field, that is, when $\theta = 0°$ in Fig. 24.2); the flux is zero when the surface is parallel to the field (when the normal to the surface is perpendicular to the field, that is, when $\theta = 90°$).

We assumed a uniform electric field in the preceding discussion. In more general situations, the electric field may vary over a large surface. Therefore, the definition of flux given by Equation 24.2 has meaning only for a small element of area over which the field is approximately constant. Consider a general surface divided into a large number of small elements, each of area ΔA. It is convenient to define a vector $\Delta\vec{\mathbf{A}}_i$ whose magnitude represents the area of the ith element of the large surface and whose direction is defined to be *perpendicular* to the surface element as shown in Figure 24.3. The electric field $\vec{\mathbf{E}}_i$ at the location of this element makes an angle θ_i with the vector $\Delta\vec{\mathbf{A}}_i$. The electric flux $\Delta\Phi_E$ through this element is

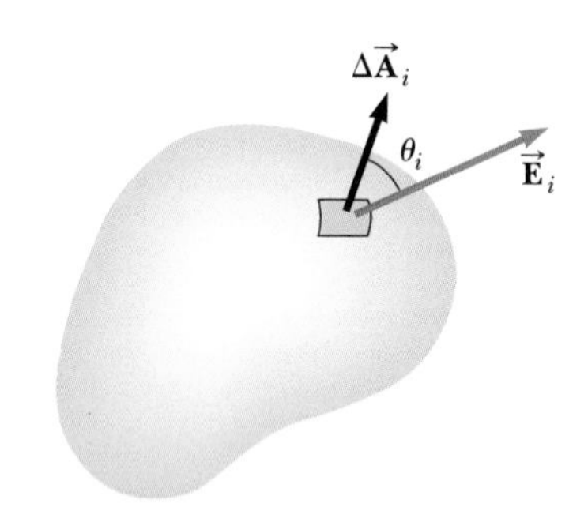

Figure 24.3 A small element of surface area ΔA_i. The electric field makes an angle θ_i with the vector $\Delta\vec{\mathbf{A}}_i$, defined as being normal to the surface element, and the flux through the element is equal to $E_i\,\Delta A_i\cos\theta_i$.

$$\Delta\Phi_E = E_i\,\Delta A_i\cos\theta_i = \vec{\mathbf{E}}_i\cdot\Delta\vec{\mathbf{A}}_i$$

where we have used the definition of the scalar product of two vectors ($\vec{\mathbf{A}}\cdot\vec{\mathbf{B}} = AB\cos\theta$; see Chapter 7). Summing the contributions of all elements gives an approximation to the total flux through the surface:

$$\Phi_E \approx \sum \vec{\mathbf{E}}_i\cdot\Delta\vec{\mathbf{A}}_i$$

If the area of each element approaches zero, the number of elements approaches infinity and the sum is replaced by an integral. Therefore, the general definition of electric flux is

Definition of electric flux ▶

$$\Phi_E \equiv \int_{\text{surface}} \vec{\mathbf{E}}\cdot d\vec{\mathbf{A}} \qquad \textbf{(24.3)}$$

Equation 24.3 is a *surface integral*, which means it must be evaluated over the surface in question. In general, the value of Φ_E depends both on the field pattern and on the surface.

We are often interested in evaluating the flux through a *closed surface*, defined as a surface that divides space into an inside and an outside region so that one cannot move from one region to the other without crossing the surface. The surface of a sphere, for example, is a closed surface.

Consider the closed surface in Active Figure 24.4. The vectors $\Delta\vec{\mathbf{A}}_i$ point in different directions for the various surface elements, but at each point they are normal to the surface and, by convention, always point outward. At the element labeled ①, the field lines are crossing the surface from the inside to the outside and $\theta < 90°$; hence, the flux $\Delta\Phi_E = \vec{\mathbf{E}}\cdot\Delta\vec{\mathbf{A}}_1$ through this element is positive. For element ②, the field lines graze the surface (perpendicular to the vector $\Delta\vec{\mathbf{A}}_2$); therefore, $\theta = 90°$ and the flux is zero. For elements such as ③, where the field lines are crossing the surface from outside to inside, $180° > \theta > 90°$ and the flux is negative because $\cos\theta$ is negative. The *net* flux through the surface is proportional to the net number of lines leaving the surface, where the net number

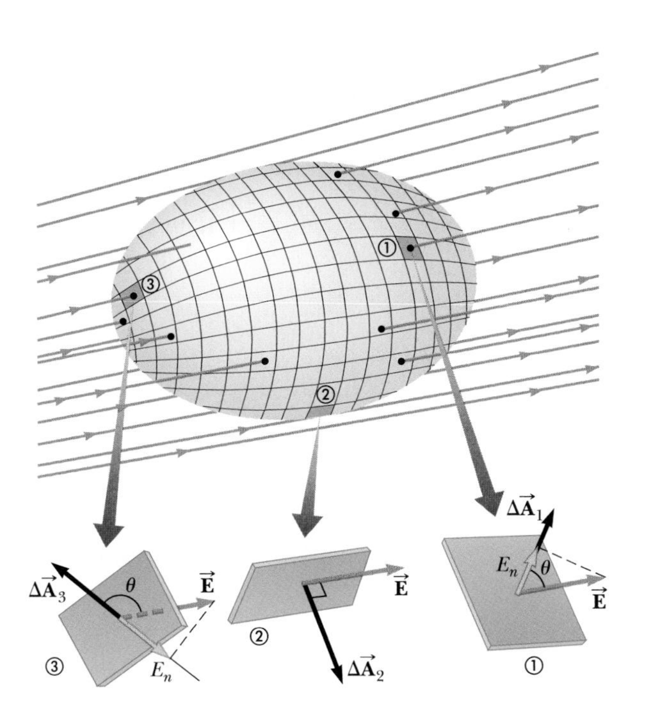

ACTIVE FIGURE 24.4

A closed surface in an electric field. The area vectors are, by convention, normal to the surface and point outward. The flux through an area element can be positive (element ①), zero (element ②), or negative (element ③).

Sign in at www.thomsonedu.com and go to ThomsonNOW to select any segment on the surface and see the relationship between the electric field vector $\vec{\mathbf{E}}$ and the area vector $\Delta\vec{\mathbf{A}}_i$.

means *the number of lines leaving the surface minus the number of lines entering the surface.* If more lines are leaving than entering, the net flux is positive. If more lines are entering than leaving, the net flux is negative. Using the symbol $\oint$ to represent an integral over a closed surface, we can write the net flux Φ_E through a closed surface as

$$\Phi_E = \oint \vec{\mathbf{E}} \cdot d\vec{\mathbf{A}} = \oint E_n \, dA \qquad \textbf{(24.4)}$$

where E_n represents the component of the electric field normal to the surface.

Quick Quiz 24.1 Suppose a point charge is located at the center of a spherical surface. The electric field at the surface of the sphere and the total flux through the sphere are determined. Now the radius of the sphere is halved. What happens to the flux through the sphere and the magnitude of the electric field at the surface of the sphere? (a) The flux and field both increase. (b) The flux and field both decrease. (c) The flux increases, and the field decreases. (d) The flux decreases, and the field increases. (e) The flux remains the same, and the field increases. (f) The flux decreases, and the field remains the same.

EXAMPLE 24.1 Flux Through a Cube

Consider a uniform electric field $\vec{\mathbf{E}}$ oriented in the x direction in empty space. Find the net electric flux through the surface of a cube of edge length ℓ, oriented as shown in Figure 24.5.

SOLUTION

Conceptualize Examine Figure 24.5 carefully. Notice that the electric field lines pass through two faces perpendicularly and are parallel to four other faces of the cube.

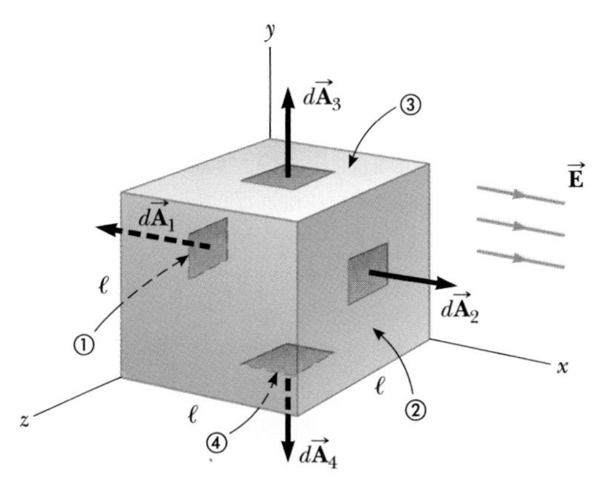

Figure 24.5 (Example 24.1) A closed surface in the shape of a cube in a uniform electric field oriented parallel to the x axis. Side ④ is the bottom of the cube, and side ① is opposite side ②.

Categorize We evaluate the flux from its definition, so we categorize this example as a substitution problem.

The flux through four of the faces (③, ④, and the unnumbered ones) is zero because $\vec{\mathbf{E}}$ is parallel to the four faces and therefore perpendicular to $d\vec{\mathbf{A}}$ on these faces.

Write the integrals for the net flux through faces ① and ②:

$$\Phi_E = \int_1 \vec{\mathbf{E}} \cdot d\vec{\mathbf{A}} + \int_2 \vec{\mathbf{E}} \cdot d\vec{\mathbf{A}}$$

For face ①, $\vec{\mathbf{E}}$ is constant and directed inward but $d\vec{\mathbf{A}}_1$ is directed outward ($\theta = 180°$). Find the flux through this face:

$$\int_1 \vec{\mathbf{E}} \cdot d\vec{\mathbf{A}} = \int_1 E(\cos 180°)\, dA = -E \int_1 dA = -EA = -E\ell^2$$

For face ②, $\vec{\mathbf{E}}$ is constant and outward and in the same direction as $d\vec{\mathbf{A}}_2$ ($\theta = 0°$). Find the flux through this face:

$$\int_2 \vec{\mathbf{E}} \cdot d\vec{\mathbf{A}} = \int_2 E(\cos 0°)\, dA = E \int_2 dA = +EA = E\ell^2$$

Find the net flux by adding the flux over all six faces:

$$\Phi_E = -E\ell^2 + E\ell^2 + 0 + 0 + 0 + 0 = \boxed{0}$$

24.2 Gauss's Law

In this section, we describe a general relationship between the net electric flux through a closed surface (often called a *gaussian surface*) and the charge enclosed by the surface. This relationship, known as *Gauss's law,* is of fundamental importance in the study of electric fields.

Consider a positive point charge q located at the center of a sphere of radius r as shown in Figure 24.6. From Equation 23.9, we know that the magnitude of the electric field everywhere on the surface of the sphere is $E = k_e q/r^2$. The field lines are directed radially outward and hence are perpendicular to the surface at every point on the surface. That is, at each surface point, $\vec{\mathbf{E}}$ is parallel to the vector $\Delta\vec{\mathbf{A}}_i$ representing a local element of area ΔA_i surrounding the surface point. Therefore,

$$\vec{\mathbf{E}} \cdot \Delta\vec{\mathbf{A}}_i = E\, \Delta A_i$$

and, from Equation 24.4, we find that the net flux through the gaussian surface is

$$\Phi_E = \oint \vec{\mathbf{E}} \cdot d\vec{\mathbf{A}} = \oint E\, dA = E \oint dA$$

where we have moved E outside of the integral because, by symmetry, E is constant over the surface. The value of E is given by $E = k_e q/r^2$. Furthermore, because the surface is spherical, $\oint dA = A = 4\pi r^2$. Hence, the net flux through the gaussian surface is

$$\Phi_E = k_e \frac{q}{r^2}(4\pi r^2) = 4\pi k_e q$$

Recalling from Section 23.3 that $k_e = 1/4\pi\epsilon_0$, we can write this equation in the form

$$\Phi_E = \frac{q}{\epsilon_0} \qquad \textbf{(24.5)}$$

Equation 24.5 shows that the net flux through the spherical surface is proportional to the charge inside the surface. The flux is independent of the radius r because the area of the spherical surface is proportional to r^2, whereas the electric field is proportional to $1/r^2$. Therefore, in the product of area and electric field, the dependence on r cancels.

KARL FRIEDRICH GAUSS
German mathematician and astronomer (1777–1855)
Gauss received a doctoral degree in mathematics from the University of Helmstedt in 1799. In addition to his work in electromagnetism, he made contributions to mathematics and science in number theory, statistics, non-Euclidean geometry, and cometary orbital mechanics. He was a founder of the German Magnetic Union, which studies the Earth's magnetic field on a continual basis.

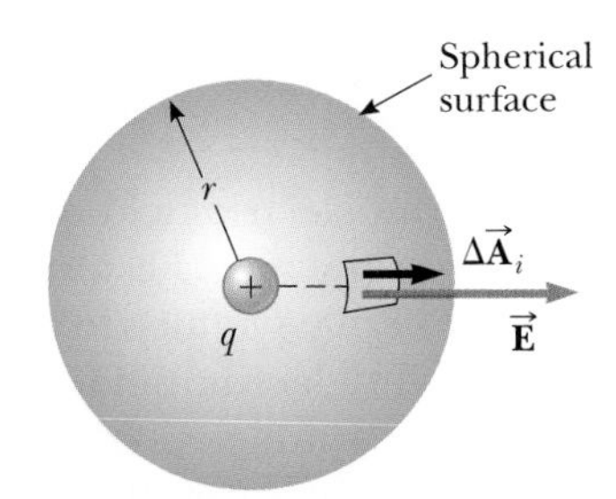

Figure 24.6 A spherical gaussian surface of radius *r* surrounding a point charge *q*. When the charge is at the center of the sphere, the electric field is everywhere normal to the surface and constant in magnitude.

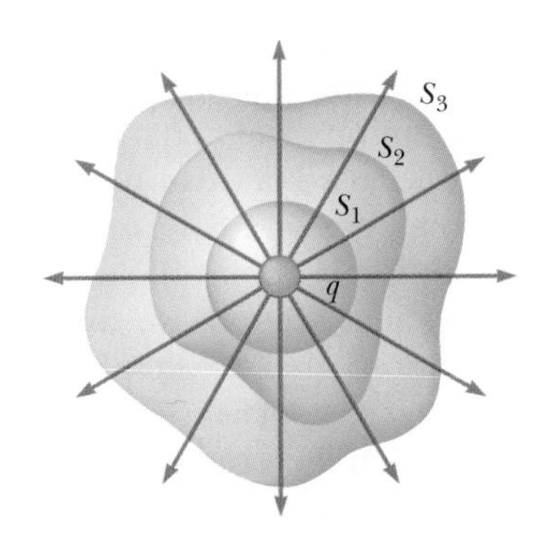

Figure 24.7 Closed surfaces of various shapes surrounding a charge *q*. The net electric flux is the same through all surfaces.

Figure 24.8 A point charge located *outside* a closed surface. The number of lines entering the surface equals the number leaving the surface.

Now consider several closed surfaces surrounding a charge q as shown in Figure 24.7. Surface S_1 is spherical, but surfaces S_2 and S_3 are not. From Equation 24.5, the flux that passes through S_1 has the value q/ϵ_0. As discussed in the preceding section, flux is proportional to the number of electric field lines passing through a surface. The construction shown in Figure 24.7 shows that the number of lines through S_1 is equal to the number of lines through the nonspherical surfaces S_2 and S_3. Therefore, **the net flux through *any* closed surface surrounding a point charge q is given by q/ϵ_0 and is independent of the shape of that surface.**

Now consider a point charge located *outside* a closed surface of arbitrary shape as shown in Figure 24.8. As can be seen from this construction, any electric field line entering the surface leaves the surface at another point. The number of electric field lines entering the surface equals the number leaving the surface. Therefore, **the net electric flux through a closed surface that surrounds no charge is zero.** Applying this result to Example 24.1, we see that the net flux through the cube is zero because there is no charge inside the cube.

Let's extend these arguments to two generalized cases: (1) that of many point charges and (2) that of a continuous distribution of charge. We once again use the superposition principle, which states that **the electric field due to many charges is the vector sum of the electric fields produced by the individual charges.** Therefore, the flux through any closed surface can be expressed as

$$\oint \vec{\mathbf{E}} \cdot d\vec{\mathbf{A}} = \oint (\vec{\mathbf{E}}_1 + \vec{\mathbf{E}}_2 + \cdots) \cdot d\vec{\mathbf{A}}$$

where $\vec{\mathbf{E}}$ is the total electric field at any point on the surface produced by the vector addition of the electric fields at that point due to the individual charges. Consider the system of charges shown in Active Figure 24.9. The surface S surrounds only one charge, q_1; hence, the net flux through S is q_1/ϵ_0. The flux through S due to charges q_2, q_3, and q_4 outside it is zero because each electric field line from these charges that enters S at one point leaves it at another. The surface S' surrounds charges q_2 and q_3; hence, the net flux through it is $(q_2 + q_3)/\epsilon_0$. Finally, the net flux through surface S'' is zero because there is no charge inside this surface. That is, *all* the electric field lines that enter S'' at one point leave at another. Charge q_4 does not contribute to the net flux through any of the surfaces because it is outside all the surfaces.

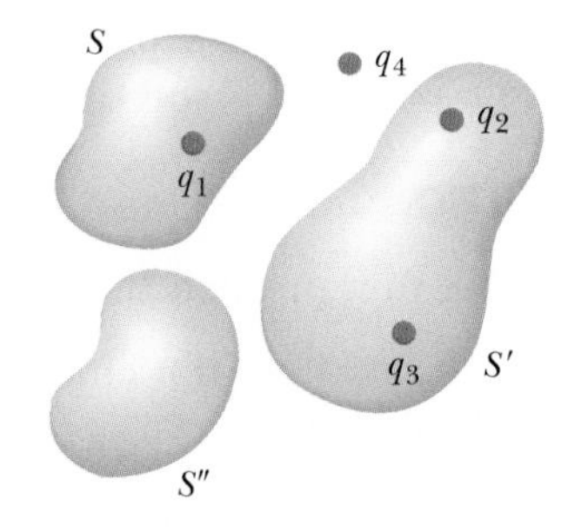

ACTIVE FIGURE 24.9

The net electric flux through any closed surface depends only on the charge *inside* that surface. The net flux through surface S is q_1/ϵ_0, the net flux through surface S' is $(q_2 + q_3)/\epsilon_0$, and the net flux through surface S'' is zero. Charge q_4 does not contribute to the flux through any surface because it is outside all surfaces.

Sign in at www.thomsonedu.com and go to ThomsonNOW to change the size and shape of a closed surface and see the effect on the electric flux of surrounding combinations of charge with that surface.

Gauss's law is a generalization of what we have just described and states that the net flux through *any* closed surface is

$$\Phi_E = \oint \vec{\mathbf{E}} \cdot d\vec{\mathbf{A}} = \frac{q_{\text{in}}}{\epsilon_0} \qquad \textbf{(24.6)}$$

◀ Gauss's law

where $\vec{\mathbf{E}}$ represents the electric field at any point on the surface and q_{in} represents the net charge inside the surface.

PITFALL PREVENTION 24.1
Zero Flux Is Not Zero Field

In two situations, there is zero flux through a closed surface: either there are no charged particles enclosed by the surface or there are charged particles enclosed, but the net charge inside the surface is zero. For either situation, it is *incorrect* to conclude that the electric field on the surface is zero. Gauss's law states that the electric *flux* is proportional to the enclosed charge, not the electric *field*.

When using Equation 24.6, you should note that although the charge q_{in} is the net charge inside the gaussian surface, $\vec{\mathbf{E}}$ represents the *total electric field*, which includes contributions from charges both inside and outside the surface.

In principle, Gauss's law can be solved for $\vec{\mathbf{E}}$ to determine the electric field due to a system of charges or a continuous distribution of charge. In practice, however, this type of solution is applicable only in a limited number of highly symmetric situations. In the next section, we use Gauss's law to evaluate the electric field for charge distributions that have spherical, cylindrical, or planar symmetry. If one chooses the gaussian surface surrounding the charge distribution carefully, the integral in Equation 24.6 can be simplified.

Quick Quiz 24.2 If the net flux through a gaussian surface is *zero*, the following four statements *could be true*. Which of the statements *must be true?* (a) There are no charges inside the surface. (b) The net charge inside the surface is zero. (c) The electric field is zero everywhere on the surface. (d) The number of electric field lines entering the surface equals the number leaving the surface.

CONCEPTUAL EXAMPLE 24.2 Flux Due to a Point Charge

A spherical gaussian surface surrounds a point charge q. Describe what happens to the total flux through the surface if **(A)** the charge is tripled, **(B)** the radius of the sphere is doubled, **(C)** the surface is changed to a cube, and **(D)** the charge is moved to another location inside the surface.

SOLUTION

(A) The flux through the surface is tripled because flux is proportional to the amount of charge inside the surface.

(B) The flux does not change because all electric field lines from the charge pass through the sphere, regardless of its radius.

(C) The flux does not change when the shape of the gaussian surface changes because all electric field lines from the charge pass through the surface, regardless of its shape.

(D) The flux does not change when the charge is moved to another location inside that surface because Gauss's law refers to the total charge enclosed, regardless of where the charge is located inside the surface.

24.3 Application of Gauss's Law to Various Charge Distributions

PITFALL PREVENTION 24.2
Gaussian Surfaces Are Not Real

A gaussian surface is an imaginary surface you construct to satisfy the conditions listed here. It does not have to coincide with a physical surface in the situation.

As mentioned earlier, Gauss's law is useful for determining electric fields when the charge distribution is highly symmetric. The following examples demonstrate ways of choosing the gaussian surface over which the surface integral given by Equation 24.6 can be simplified and the electric field determined. In choosing the surface, always take advantage of the symmetry of the charge distribution so that E can be removed from the integral. The goal in this type of calculation is to determine a surface for which each portion of the surface satisfies one or more of the following conditions:

1. The value of the electric field can be argued by symmetry to be constant over the portion of the surface.
2. The dot product in Equation 24.6 can be expressed as a simple algebraic product $E\,dA$ because $\vec{\mathbf{E}}$ and $d\vec{\mathbf{A}}$ are parallel.
3. The dot product in Equation 24.6 is zero because $\vec{\mathbf{E}}$ and $d\vec{\mathbf{A}}$ are perpendicular.
4. The electric field is zero over the portion of the surface.

Different portions of the gaussian surface can satisfy different conditions as long as every portion satisfies at least one condition. All four conditions are used in examples throughout the remainder of this chapter.

EXAMPLE 24.3 A Spherically Symmetric Charge Distribution

An insulating solid sphere of radius a has a uniform volume charge density ρ and carries a total positive charge Q (Fig. 24.10).

(A) Calculate the magnitude of the electric field at a point outside the sphere.

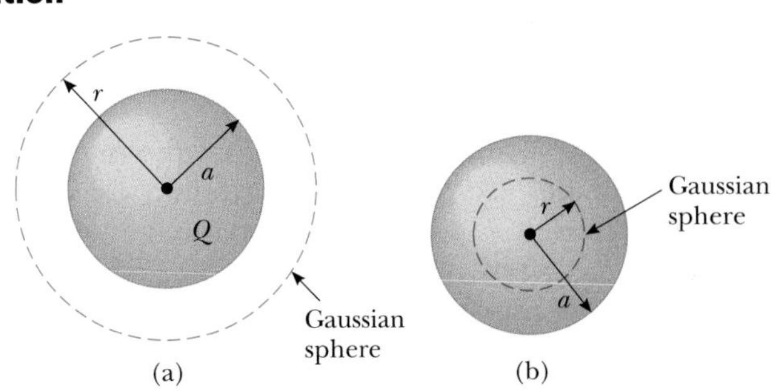

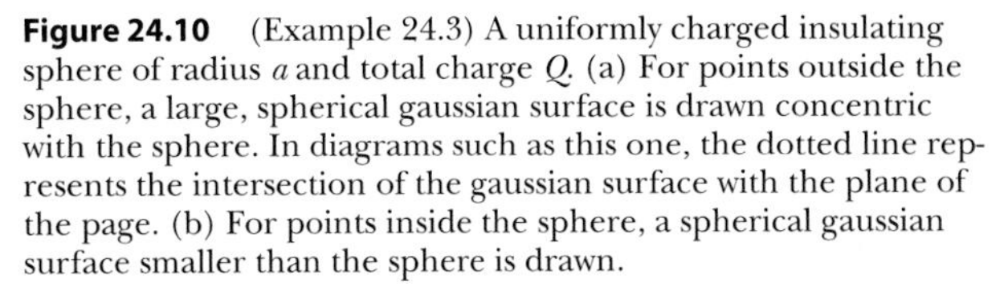

Figure 24.10 (Example 24.3) A uniformly charged insulating sphere of radius a and total charge Q. (a) For points outside the sphere, a large, spherical gaussian surface is drawn concentric with the sphere. In diagrams such as this one, the dotted line represents the intersection of the gaussian surface with the plane of the page. (b) For points inside the sphere, a spherical gaussian surface smaller than the sphere is drawn.

SOLUTION

Conceptualize Note how this problem differs from our previous discussion of Gauss's law. The electric field due to point charges was discussed in Section 24.2. Now we are considering the electric field due to a distribution of charge. We found the field for various distributions of charge in Chapter 23 by integrating over the distribution. In this chapter, we find the electric field using Gauss's law.

Categorize Because the charge is distributed uniformly throughout the sphere, the charge distribution has spherical symmetry and we can apply Gauss's law to find the electric field.

Analyze To reflect the spherical symmetry, let's choose a spherical gaussian surface of radius r, concentric with the sphere, as shown in Figure 24.10a. For this choice, condition (2) is satisfied everywhere on the surface and $\vec{\mathbf{E}} \cdot d\vec{\mathbf{A}} = E\,dA$.

Replace $\vec{\mathbf{E}} \cdot d\vec{\mathbf{A}}$ in Gauss's law with $E\,dA$:

$$\Phi_E = \oint \vec{\mathbf{E}} \cdot d\vec{\mathbf{A}} = \oint E\,dA = \frac{Q}{\epsilon_0}$$

By symmetry, E is constant everywhere on the surface, which satisfies condition (1), so we can remove E from the integral:

$$\oint E\,dA = E\oint dA = E(4\pi r^2) = \frac{Q}{\epsilon_0}$$

Solve for E:

$$(1)\quad E = \frac{Q}{4\pi\epsilon_0 r^2} = k_e\frac{Q}{r^2} \quad (\text{for } r > a)$$

Finalize This field is identical to that for a point charge. Therefore, **the electric field due to a uniformly charged sphere in the region external to the sphere is *equivalent* to that of a point charge located at the center of the sphere.**

(B) Find the magnitude of the electric field at a point inside the sphere.

SOLUTION

Analyze In this case, let's choose a spherical gaussian surface having radius $r < a$, concentric with the insulating sphere (Fig. 24.10b). Let V' be the volume of this smaller sphere. To apply Gauss's law in this situation, recognize that the charge q_{in} within the gaussian surface of volume V' is less than Q.

Calculate q_{in} by using $q_{\text{in}} = \rho V'$:

$$q_{\text{in}} = \rho V' = \rho(\tfrac{4}{3}\pi r^3)$$

Notice that conditions (1) and (2) are satisfied everywhere on the gaussian surface in Figure 24.10b. Apply Gauss's law in the region $r < a$:

$$\oint E\,dA = E\oint dA = E(4\pi r^2) = \frac{q_{\text{in}}}{\epsilon_0}$$

Solve for E and substitute for q_{in}:

$$E = \frac{q_{\text{in}}}{4\pi\epsilon_0 r^2} = \frac{\rho(\frac{4}{3}\pi r^3)}{4\pi\epsilon_0 r^2} = \frac{\rho}{3\epsilon_0}r$$

Substitute $\rho = Q/\frac{4}{3}\pi a^3$ and $\epsilon_0 = 1/4\pi k_e$:

$$(2) \quad E = \frac{(Q/\frac{4}{3}\pi a^3)}{3(1/4\pi k_e)} r = k_e \frac{Q}{a^3} r \quad (\text{for } r < a)$$

Finalize This result for E differs from the one obtained in part (A). It shows that $E \to 0$ as $r \to 0$. Therefore, the result eliminates the problem that would exist at $r = 0$ if E varied as $1/r^2$ inside the sphere as it does outside the sphere. That is, if $E \propto 1/r^2$ for $r < a$, the field would be infinite at $r = 0$, which is physically impossible.

What If? Suppose the radial position $r = a$ is approached from inside the sphere and from outside. Do we obtain the same value of the electric field from both directions?

Answer Equation (1) shows that the electric field approaches a value from the outside given by

$$E = \lim_{r \to a} \left(k_e \frac{Q}{r^2} \right) = k_e \frac{Q}{a^2}$$

From the inside, Equation (2) gives

$$E = \lim_{r \to a} \left(k_e \frac{Q}{a^3} r \right) = k_e \frac{Q}{a^3} a = k_e \frac{Q}{a^2}$$

Therefore, the value of the field is the same as the surface is approached from both directions. A plot of E versus r is shown in Figure 24.11. Notice that the magnitude of the field is continuous.

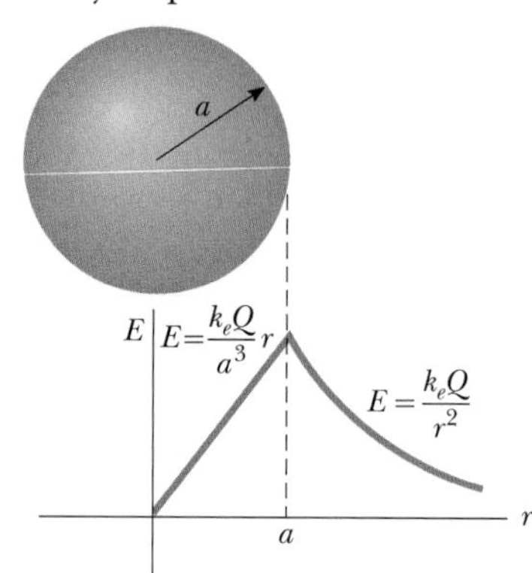

Figure 24.11 (Example 24.3) A plot of E versus r for a uniformly charged insulating sphere. The electric field inside the sphere ($r < a$) varies linearly with r. The field outside the sphere ($r > a$) is the same as that of a point charge Q located at $r = 0$.

EXAMPLE 24.4 A Cylindrically Symmetric Charge Distribution

Find the electric field a distance r from a line of positive charge of infinite length and constant charge per unit length λ (Fig. 24.12a).

SOLUTION

Conceptualize The line of charge is *infinitely* long. Therefore, the field is the same at all points equidistant from the line, regardless of the vertical position of the point in Figure 24.12a.

Categorize Because the charge is distributed uniformly along the line, the charge distribution has cylindrical symmetry and we can apply Gauss's law to find the electric field.

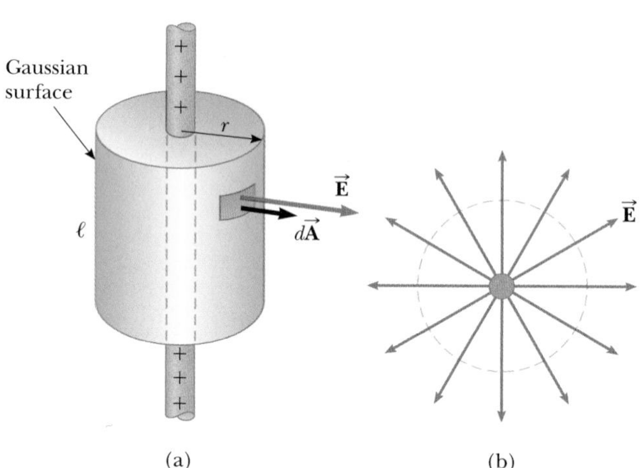

Figure 24.12 (Example 24.4) (a) An infinite line of charge surrounded by a cylindrical gaussian surface concentric with the line. (b) An end view shows that the electric field at the cylindrical surface is constant in magnitude and perpendicular to the surface.

Analyze The symmetry of the charge distribution requires that $\vec{E}$ be perpendicular to the line charge and directed outward as shown in Figures 24.12a and b. To reflect the symmetry of the charge distribution, let's choose a cylindrical gaussian surface of radius r and length ℓ that is coaxial with the line charge. For the curved part of this surface, $\vec{E}$ is constant in magnitude and perpendicular to the surface at each point, satisfying conditions (1) and (2). Furthermore, the flux through the ends of the gaussian cylinder is zero because $\vec{E}$ is parallel to these surfaces. That is the first application we have seen of condition (3).

We must take the surface integral in Gauss's law over the entire gaussian surface. Because $\vec{E} \cdot d\vec{A}$ is zero for the flat ends of the cylinder, however, we restrict our attention to only the curved surface of the cylinder.

Apply Gauss's law and conditions (1) and (2) for the curved surface, noting that the total charge inside our gaussian surface is $\lambda\ell$:

$$\Phi_E = \oint \vec{E} \cdot d\vec{A} = E \oint dA = EA = \frac{q_{in}}{\epsilon_0} = \frac{\lambda\ell}{\epsilon_0}$$

Substitute the area $A = 2\pi r\ell$ of the curved surface:

$$E(2\pi r\ell) = \frac{\lambda\ell}{\epsilon_0}$$

Solve for the magnitude of the electric field:

$$E = \frac{\lambda}{2\pi\epsilon_0 r} = 2k_e\frac{\lambda}{r} \quad \textbf{(24.7)}$$

Finalize This result shows that the electric field due to a cylindrically symmetric charge distribution varies as $1/r$, whereas the field external to a spherically symmetric charge distribution varies as $1/r^2$. Equation 24.7 can also be derived by direct integration over the charge distribution. (See Problem 29 in Chapter 23.)

What If? What if the line segment in this example were not infinitely long?

Answer If the line charge in this example were of finite length, the electric field would not be given by Equation 24.7. A finite line charge does not possess sufficient symmetry to make use of Gauss's law because the magnitude of the electric field is no longer constant over the surface of the gaussian cylinder: the field near the ends of the line would be different from that far from the ends. Therefore, condition (1) would not be satisfied in this situation. Furthermore, $\vec{\mathbf{E}}$ is not perpendicular to the cylindrical surface at all points: the field vectors near the ends would have a component parallel to the line. Therefore, condition (2) would not be satisfied. For points close to a finite line charge and far from the ends, Equation 24.7 gives a good approximation of the value of the field.

It is left for you to show (see Problem 27) that the electric field inside a uniformly charged rod of finite radius and infinite length is proportional to r.

EXAMPLE 24.5 A Plane of Charge

Find the electric field due to an infinite plane of positive charge with uniform surface charge density σ.

SOLUTION

Conceptualize Note that the plane of charge is *infinitely* large. Therefore, the electric field should be the same at all points near the plane.

Categorize Because the charge is distributed uniformly on the plane, the charge distribution is symmetric; hence, we can use Gauss's law to find the electric field.

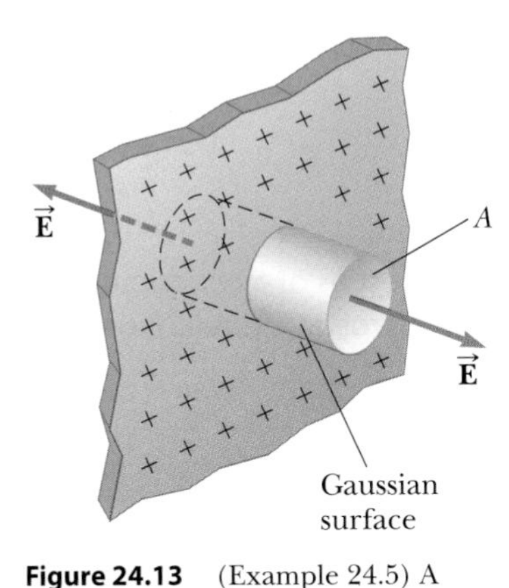

Figure 24.13 (Example 24.5) A cylindrical gaussian surface penetrating an infinite plane of charge. The flux is EA through each end of the gaussian surface and zero through its curved surface.

Analyze By symmetry, $\vec{\mathbf{E}}$ must be perpendicular to the plane at all points. The direction of $\vec{\mathbf{E}}$ is away from positive charges, indicating that the direction of $\vec{\mathbf{E}}$ on one side of the plane must be opposite its direction on the other side as shown in Figure 24.13. A gaussian surface that reflects the symmetry is a small cylinder whose axis is perpendicular to the plane and whose ends each have an area A and are equidistant from the plane. Because $\vec{\mathbf{E}}$ is parallel to the curved surface—and therefore perpendicular to $d\vec{\mathbf{A}}$ everywhere on the surface—condition (3) is satisfied and there is no contribution to the surface integral from this surface. For the flat ends of the cylinder, conditions (1) and (2) are satisfied. The flux through each end of the cylinder is EA; hence, the total flux through the entire gaussian surface is just that through the ends, $\Phi_E = 2EA$.

Write Gauss's law for this surface, noting that the enclosed charge is $q_{\text{in}} = \sigma A$:

$$\Phi_E = 2EA = \frac{q_{\text{in}}}{\epsilon_0} = \frac{\sigma A}{\epsilon_0}$$

Solve for E:

$$E = \frac{\sigma}{2\epsilon_0} \quad \textbf{(24.8)}$$

Finalize Because the distance from each flat end of the cylinder to the plane does not appear in Equation 24.8, we conclude that $E = \sigma/2\epsilon_0$ at *any* distance from the plane. That is, the field is uniform everywhere.

What If? Suppose two infinite planes of charge are parallel to each other, one positively charged and the other negatively charged. Both planes have the same surface charge density. What does the electric field look like in this situation?

Answer The electric fields due to the two planes add in the region between the planes, resulting in a uniform field of magnitude σ/ϵ_0, and cancel elsewhere to give a field of zero. This method is a practical way to achieve uniform electric fields.

CONCEPTUAL EXAMPLE 24.6 **Don't Use Gauss's Law Here!**

Explain why Gauss's law cannot be used to calculate the electric field near an electric dipole, a charged disk, or a triangle with a point charge at each corner.

SOLUTION

The charge distributions of all these configurations do not have sufficient symmetry to make the use of Gauss's law practical. We cannot find a closed surface surrounding any of these distributions that satisfies one or more of conditions (1) through (4) listed at the beginning of this section.

24.4 Conductors in Electrostatic Equilibrium

As we learned in Section 23.2, a good electrical conductor contains charges (electrons) that are not bound to any atom and therefore are free to move about within the material. When there is no net motion of charge within a conductor, the conductor is in **electrostatic equilibrium.** A conductor in electrostatic equilibrium has the following properties:

Properties of a conductor in electrostatic equilibrium ▶

1. The electric field is zero everywhere inside the conductor, whether the conductor is solid or hollow.
2. If an isolated conductor carries a charge, the charge resides on its surface.
3. The electric field just outside a charged conductor is perpendicular to the surface of the conductor and has a magnitude σ/ϵ_0, where σ is the surface charge density at that point.
4. On an irregularly shaped conductor, the surface charge density is greatest at locations where the radius of curvature of the surface is smallest.

We verify the first three properties in the discussion that follows. The fourth property is presented here (but not verified until Chapter 25) to provide a complete list of properties for conductors in electrostatic equilibrium.

We can understand the first property by considering a conducting slab placed in an external field $\vec{\mathbf{E}}$ (Fig. 24.14). The electric field inside the conductor *must* be zero assuming electrostatic equilibrium exists. If the field were not zero, free electrons in the conductor would experience an electric force ($\vec{\mathbf{F}} = q\vec{\mathbf{E}}$) and would accelerate due to this force. This motion of electrons, however, would mean that the conductor is not in electrostatic equilibrium. Therefore, the existence of electrostatic equilibrium is consistent only with a zero field in the conductor.

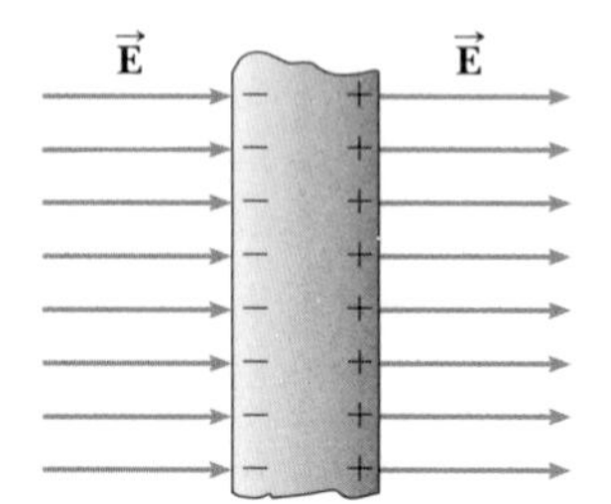

Figure 24.14 A conducting slab in an external electric field $\vec{\mathbf{E}}$. The charges induced on the two surfaces of the slab produce an electric field that opposes the external field, giving a resultant field of zero inside the slab.

Let's investigate how this zero field is accomplished. Before the external field is applied, free electrons are uniformly distributed throughout the conductor. When the external field is applied, the free electrons accelerate to the left in Figure 24.14, causing a plane of negative charge to accumulate on the left surface. The movement of electrons to the left results in a plane of positive charge on the right surface. These planes of charge create an additional electric field inside the conductor that opposes the external field. As the electrons move, the surface charge densities on the left and right surfaces increase until the magnitude of the internal field equals that of the external field, resulting in a net field of zero inside the conductor. The time it takes a good conductor to reach equilibrium is on the order of 10^{-16} s, which for most purposes can be considered instantaneous.

If the conductor is hollow, the electric field inside the conductor is also zero, whether we consider points in the conductor or in the cavity within the conductor. The zero value of the electric field in the cavity is easiest to argue with the concept of electric potential, so we will address this issue in Section 25.6.

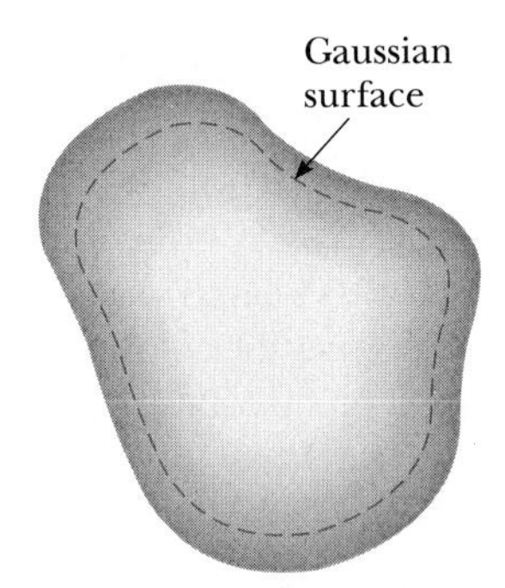

Figure 24.15 A conductor of arbitrary shape. The broken line represents a gaussian surface that can be just inside the conductor's surface.

Gauss's law can be used to verify the second property of a conductor in electrostatic equilibrium. Figure 24.15 shows an arbitrarily shaped conductor. A gaussian surface is drawn inside the conductor and can be very close to the conductor's surface. As we have just shown, the electric field everywhere inside the conductor is zero when it is in electrostatic equilibrium. Therefore, the electric field must be zero at every point on the gaussian surface, in accordance with condition (4) in Section 24.3, and the net flux through this gaussian surface is zero. From this result and Gauss's law, we conclude that the net charge inside the gaussian surface is zero. Because there can be no net charge inside the gaussian surface (which is arbitrarily close to the conductor's surface), **any net charge on the conductor must reside on its surface.** Gauss's law does not indicate how this excess charge is distributed on the conductor's surface, only that it resides exclusively on the surface.

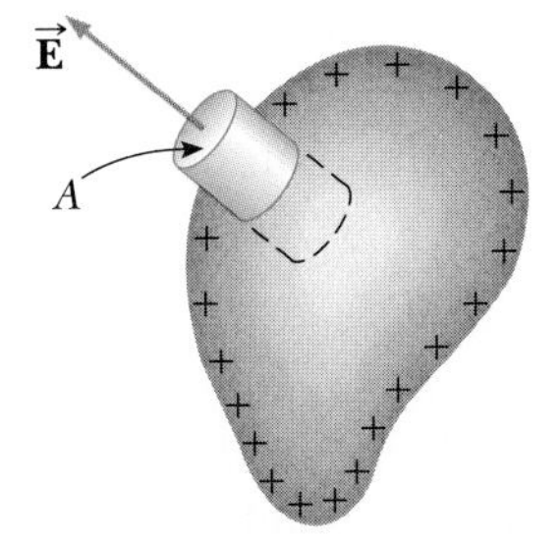

Figure 24.16 A gaussian surface in the shape of a small cylinder is used to calculate the electric field immediately outside a charged conductor. The flux through the gaussian surface is EA. Remember that $\vec{E}$ is zero inside the conductor.

Let's verify the third property. If the field vector $\vec{E}$ had a component parallel to the conductor's surface, free electrons would experience an electric force and move along the surface; in such a case, the conductor would not be in equilibrium. Therefore, the field vector must be perpendicular to the surface. To determine the magnitude of the electric field, we use Gauss's law and draw a gaussian surface in the shape of a small cylinder whose end faces are parallel to the conductor's surface (Fig. 24.16). Part of the cylinder is just outside the conductor, and part is inside. The field is perpendicular to the conductor's surface from the condition of electrostatic equilibrium. Therefore, condition (3) in Section 24.3 is satisfied for the curved part of the cylindrical gaussian surface: there is no flux through this part of the gaussian surface because $\vec{E}$ is parallel to the surface. There is no flux through the flat face of the cylinder inside the conductor because here $\vec{E} = 0$, which satisfies condition (4). Hence, the net flux through the gaussian surface is equal to that through only the flat face outside the conductor, where the field is perpendicular to the gaussian surface. Using conditions (1) and (2) for this face, the flux is EA, where E is the electric field just outside the conductor and A is the area of the cylinder's face. Applying Gauss's law to this surface gives

$$\Phi_E = \oint E\,dA = EA = \frac{q_{\text{in}}}{\epsilon_0} = \frac{\sigma A}{\epsilon_0}$$

where we have used $q_{\text{in}} = \sigma A$. Solving for E gives for the electric field immediately outside a charged conductor

$$E = \frac{\sigma}{\epsilon_0} \quad \textbf{(24.9)}$$

Quick Quiz 24.3 Your younger brother likes to rub his feet on the carpet and then touch you to give you a shock. While you are trying to escape the shock treatment, you discover a hollow metal cylinder in your basement, large enough to climb inside. In which of the following cases will you *not* be shocked? (a) You climb inside the cylinder, making contact with the inner surface, and your charged brother touches the outer metal surface. (b) Your charged brother is inside touching the inner metal surface and you are outside, touching the outer metal surface. (c) Both of you are outside the cylinder, touching its outer metal surface but not touching each other directly.

EXAMPLE 24.7 A Sphere Inside a Spherical Shell

A solid insulating sphere of radius a carries a net positive charge Q uniformly distributed throughout its volume. A conducting spherical shell of inner radius b and outer radius c is concentric with the solid sphere and carries a net charge $-2Q$. Using Gauss's law, find the electric field in the regions labeled ①, ②, ③, and ④ in Active Figure 24.17 and the charge distribution on the shell when the entire system is in electrostatic equilibrium.

ACTIVE FIGURE 24.17

(Example 24.7) An insulating sphere of radius a and carrying a charge Q surrounded by a conducting spherical shell carrying a charge $-2Q$.

Sign in at www.thomsonedu.com and go to ThomsonNOW to vary the charges on the sphere and shell and see the effect on the electric field.

SOLUTION

Conceptualize Note how this problem differs from Example 24.3. The charged sphere in Figure 24.10 is now surrounded by a shell carrying a charge of $-2Q$.

Categorize The charge is distributed uniformly throughout the sphere, and we know that the charge on the conducting shell distributes itself uniformly on the surfaces. Therefore, the system has spherical symmetry and we can apply Gauss's law to find the electric field.

Analyze In region ②—between the surface of the solid sphere and the inner surface of the shell—we construct a spherical gaussian surface of radius r, where $a < r < b$, noting that the charge inside this surface is $+Q$ (the charge on the solid sphere). Because of the spherical symmetry, the electric field lines must be directed radially outward and be constant in magnitude on the gaussian surface.

The charge on the conducting shell creates zero electric field in the region $r < b$, so the shell has no effect on the field due to the sphere. Therefore, write an expression for the field in region ② as that due to the sphere from part (A) of Example 24.3:

$$E_2 = k_e \frac{Q}{r^2} \quad (\text{for } a < r < b)$$

Because the conducting shell creates zero field inside itself, it also has no effect on the field inside the sphere. Therefore, write an expression for the field in region ① as that due to the sphere from part (B) of Example 24.3:

$$E_1 = k_e \frac{Q}{a^3} r \quad (\text{for } r < a)$$

In region ④, where $r > c$, construct a spherical gaussian surface; this surface surrounds a total charge of $q_{in} = Q + (-2Q) = -Q$. Therefore, model the charge distribution as a sphere with charge $-Q$ and write an expression for the field in region ④ from part (A) of Example 24.3:

$$E_4 = -k_e \frac{Q}{r^2} \quad (\text{for } r > c)$$

In region ③, the electric field must be zero because the spherical shell is a conductor in equilibrium:

$$E_3 = 0 \quad (\text{for } b < r < c)$$

Construct a gaussian surface of radius r, where $b < r < c$, and note that q_{in} must be zero because $E_3 = 0$. Find the amount of charge q_{inner} on the inner surface of the shell:

$$q_{in} = q_{sphere} + q_{inner}$$

$$q_{inner} = q_{in} - q_{sphere} = 0 - Q = -Q$$

Finalize The charge on the inner surface of the spherical shell must be $-Q$ to cancel the charge $+Q$ on the solid sphere and give zero electric field in the material of the shell. Because the net charge on the shell is $-2Q$, its outer surface must carry a charge $-Q$.

What If? How would the results of this problem differ if the sphere were conducting instead of insulating?

Answer The only change would be in region ①, where $r < a$. Because there can be no charge inside a conductor in electrostatic equilibrium, $q_{in} = 0$ for a gaussian surface of radius $r < a$; therefore, on the basis of Gauss's law and symmetry, $E_1 = 0$. In regions ②, ③, and ④, there would be no way to determine whether the sphere is conducting or insulating.

Summary

ThomsonNOW™ Sign in at **www.thomsonedu.com** and go to ThomsonNOW to take a practice test for this chapter.

DEFINITION

Electric flux is proportional to the number of electric field lines that penetrate a surface. If the electric field is uniform and makes an angle θ with the normal to a surface of area A, the electric flux through the surface is

$$\Phi_E = EA \cos \theta \qquad (24.2)$$

In general, the electric flux through a surface is

$$\Phi_E \equiv \int_{\text{surface}} \vec{\mathbf{E}} \cdot d\vec{\mathbf{A}} \qquad (24.3)$$

CONCEPTS AND PRINCIPLES

Gauss's law says that the net electric flux Φ_E through any closed gaussian surface is equal to the *net* charge q_{in} inside the surface divided by ϵ_0:

$$\Phi_E = \oint \vec{\mathbf{E}} \cdot d\vec{\mathbf{A}} = \frac{q_{in}}{\epsilon_0} \qquad (24.6)$$

Using Gauss's law, you can calculate the electric field due to various symmetric charge distributions.

A conductor in **electrostatic equilibrium** has the following properties:

1. The electric field is zero everywhere inside the conductor, whether the conductor is solid or hollow.
2. If an isolated conductor carries a charge, the charge resides on its surface.
3. The electric field just outside a charged conductor is perpendicular to the surface of the conductor and has a magnitude σ/ϵ_0, where σ is the surface charge density at that point.
4. On an irregularly shaped conductor, the surface charge density is greatest at locations where the radius of curvature of the surface is smallest.

Questions

☐ denotes answer available in *Student Solutions Manual/Study Guide;* **O** denotes objective question

1. The Sun is lower in the sky during the winter than it is during the summer. How does this change affect the flux of sunlight hitting a given area on the surface of the Earth? How does this change affect the weather?
2. If more electric field lines leave a gaussian surface than enter it, what can you conclude about the net charge enclosed by that surface?
3. A uniform electric field exists in a region of space containing no charges. What can you conclude about the net electric flux through a gaussian surface placed in this region of space?
4. **O** A particle with charge q is located inside a cubical gaussian surface. No other charges are nearby. **(i)** If the particle is at the center of the cube, what is the flux through each one of the faces of the cube? (a) 0 (b) q/ϵ_0 (c) $q/2\epsilon_0$ (d) $q/4\epsilon_0$ (e) $q/6\epsilon_0$ (f) $q/8\epsilon_0$ (g) depends on the size of the cube **(ii)** If the particle can be moved to any point within the cube, what maximum value can the flux through one face approach? Choose from the same possibilities. **(iii)** If the particle can be moved anywhere within the cube or on its surface, what is the minimum possible flux through one face? Choose from the same possibilities.
5. **O** A cubical gaussian surface surrounds a long, straight, charged filament that passes perpendicularly through two opposite faces. No other charges are nearby. **(i)** Over how many of the cube's faces is the electric field zero? (a) 0

(b) 2 (c) 4 (d) 6 **(ii)** Through how many of the cube's faces is the electric flux zero? Choose from the same possibilities.

6. O A cubical gaussian surface is bisected by a large sheet of charge, parallel to its top and bottom faces. No other charges are nearby. **(i)** Over how many of the cube's faces is the electric field zero? (a) 0 (b) 2 (c) 4 (d) 6 **(ii)** Through how many of the cube's faces is the electric flux zero? Choose from the same possibilities.

7. O Two solid spheres, both of radius 5 cm, carry identical total charges of 2 μC. Sphere A is a good conductor. Sphere B is an insulator, and its charge is distributed uniformly throughout its volume. **(i)** How do the magnitudes of the electric fields they separately create at a radial distance of 6 cm compare? (a) $E_A > E_B = 0$ (b) $E_A > E_B > 0$ (c) $E_A = E_B > 0$ (d) $E_A = E_B = 0$ (e) $0 < E_A < E_B$ (f) $0 = E_A < E_B$ **(ii)** How do the magnitudes of the electric fields they separately create at radius 4 cm compare? Choose from the same possibilities.

8. If the total charge inside a closed surface is known but the distribution of the charge is unspecified, can you use Gauss's law to find the electric field? Explain.

9. Explain why the electric flux through a closed surface with a given enclosed charge is independent of the size or shape of the surface.

10. On the basis of the repulsive nature of the force between like charges and the freedom of motion of charge within a conductor, explain why excess charge on an isolated conductor must reside on its surface.

11. O A solid insulating sphere of radius 5 cm carries electric charge uniformly distributed throughout its volume. Concentric with the sphere is a conducting spherical shell with no net charge as shown in Figure Q24.11. The inner radius of the shell is 10 cm, and the outer radius is 15 cm. No other charges are nearby. (a) Rank the magnitude of the electric field at points A (at radius 4 cm), B (radius 8 cm), C (radius 12 cm), and D (radius 16 cm) from largest to smallest. Display any cases of equality in your ranking. (b) Similarly rank the electric flux through concentric spherical surfaces through points A, B, C, and D.

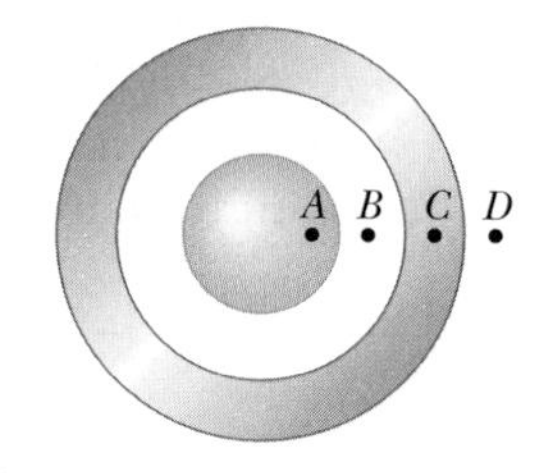

Figure Q24.11 Question 11 and Problem 44.

12. O A coaxial cable consists of a long, straight filament surrounded by a long, coaxial, cylindrical conducting shell. Assume charge Q is on the filament, zero net charge is on the shell, and the electric field is $E_1\hat{\mathbf{i}}$ at a particular point P midway between the filament and the inner surface of the shell. Next, you place the cable into a uniform external field $-E_1\hat{\mathbf{i}}$. What is the x component of the electric field at P then? (a) 0 (b) between 0 and E_1 (c) E_1 (d) greater than E_1 (e) between 0 and $-E_1$ (f) $-E_1$ (g) less than $-E_1$

13. A person is placed in a large, hollow, metallic sphere that is insulated from ground. If a large charge is placed on the sphere, will the person be harmed upon touching the inside of the sphere? Explain what will happen if the person also has an initial charge whose sign is opposite that of the charge on the sphere.

14. O A large, metallic, spherical shell has no net charge. It is supported on an insulating stand and has a small hole at the top. A small tack with charge Q is lowered on a silk thread through the hole into the interior of the shell. **(i)** What is the charge on the inner surface of the shell now? (a) Q (b) $Q/2$ (c) 0 (d) $-Q/2$ (e) $-Q$ Choose your answers to the following parts from the same possibilities. **(ii)** What is the charge on the outer surface of the shell? **(iii)** The tack is now allowed to touch the interior surface of the shell. After this contact, what is the charge on the tack? **(iv)** What is the charge on the inner surface of the shell now? **(v)** What is the charge on the outer surface of the shell now?

15. A common demonstration involves charging a rubber balloon, which is an insulator, by rubbing it on your hair and then touching the balloon to a ceiling or wall, which is also an insulator. Because of the electrical attraction between the charged balloon and the neutral wall, the balloon sticks to the wall. Imagine now that we have two infinitely large flat sheets of insulating material. One is charged, and the other is neutral. If these sheets are brought into contact, does an attractive force exist between them, as there was for the balloon and the wall?

Problems

WebAssign The Problems from this chapter may be assigned online in WebAssign.

ThomsonNOW Sign in at **www.thomsonedu.com** and go to ThomsonNOW to assess your understanding of this chapter's topics with additional quizzing and conceptual questions.

1, 2, 3 denotes straightforward, intermediate, challenging; ☐ denotes full solution available in *Student Solutions Manual/Study Guide;* ▲ denotes coached solution with hints available at **www.thomsonedu.com;** denotes developing symbolic reasoning; ● denotes asking for qualitative reasoning; denotes computer useful in solving problem

Section 24.1 Electric Flux

1. A 40.0-cm-diameter loop is rotated in a uniform electric field until the position of maximum electric flux is found. The flux in this position is 5.20×10^5 N $\cdot$ m^2/C. What is the magnitude of the electric field?

2. A vertical electric field of magnitude 2.00×10^4 N/C exists above the Earth's surface on a day when a thunderstorm is brewing. A car with a rectangular size of 6.00 m by 3.00 m is traveling along a dry gravel roadway sloping downward at 10.0°. Determine the electric flux through the bottom of the car.

3. A uniform electric field $a\hat{\mathbf{i}} + b\hat{\mathbf{j}}$ intersects a surface of area A. What is the flux through this area if the surface lies (a) in the yz plane, (b) in the xz plane, and (c) in the xy plane?

4. Consider a closed triangular box resting within a horizontal electric field of magnitude $E = 7.80 \times 10^4$ N/C as shown in Figure P24.4. Calculate the electric flux through (a) the vertical rectangular surface, (b) the slanted surface, and (c) the entire surface of the box.

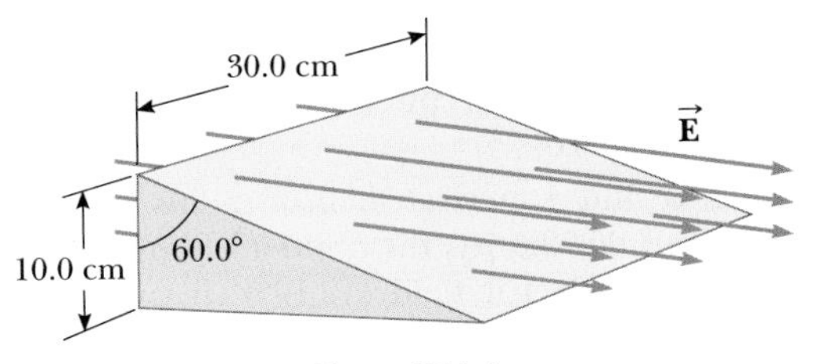

Figure P24.4

5. A pyramid with horizontal square base, 6.00 m on each side, and a height of 4.00 m is placed in a vertical electric field of 52.0 N/C. Calculate the total electric flux through the pyramid's four slanted surfaces.

Section 24.2 Gauss's Law

6. ● The electric field everywhere on the surface of a thin, spherical shell of radius 0.750 m is measured to be 890 N/C and points radially toward the center of the sphere. (a) What is the net charge within the sphere's surface? (b) What can you conclude about the nature and distribution of the charge inside the spherical shell?

7. The following charges are located inside a submarine: 5.00 μC, −9.00 μC, 27.0 μC, and −84.0 μC. (a) Calculate the net electric flux through the hull of the submarine. (b) Is the number of electric field lines leaving the submarine greater than, equal to, or less than the number entering it?

8. ● (a) A particle with charge q is located a distance d from an infinite plane. Determine the electric flux through the plane due to the charged particle. (b) **What If?** A particle with charge q is located a *very small* distance from the center of a *very large* square on the line perpendicular to the square and going through its center. Determine the approximate electric flux through the square due to the charged particle. (c) Explain why the answers to parts (a) and (b) are identical.

9. Four closed surfaces, S_1 through S_4, together with the charges $-2Q$, Q, and $-Q$ are sketched in Figure P24.9.

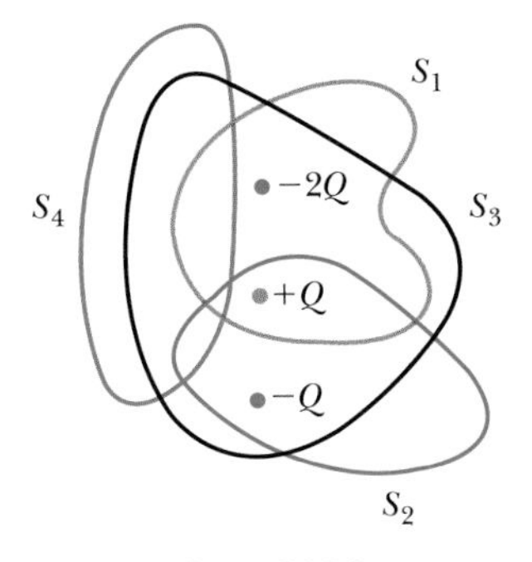

Figure P24.9

(The colored lines are the intersections of the surfaces with the page.) Find the electric flux through each surface.

10. ● A particle with charge of 12.0 μC is placed at the center of a spherical shell of radius 22.0 cm. What is the total electric flux through (a) the surface of the shell and (b) any hemispherical surface of the shell? (c) Do the results depend on the radius? Explain.

11. ▲ A particle with charge Q is located immediately above the center of the flat face of a hemisphere of radius R as shown in Figure P24.11. What is the electric flux (a) through the curved surface and (b) through the flat face?

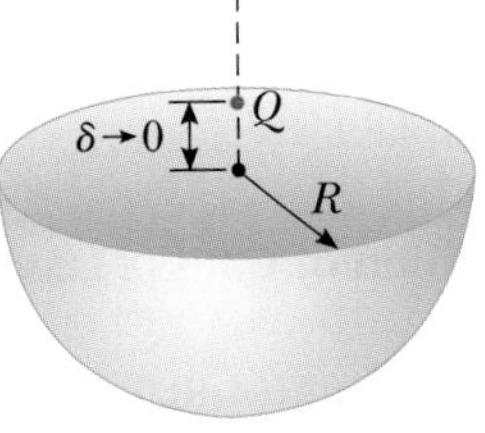

Figure P24.11

12. In the air over a particular region at an altitude of 500 m above the ground, the electric field is 120 N/C directed downward. At 600 m above the ground, the electric field is 100 N/C downward. What is the average volume charge density in the layer of air between these two elevations? Is it positive or negative?

13. A particle with charge $Q = 5.00$ μC is located at the center of a cube of edge $L = 0.100$ m. In addition, six other identical charged particles having $q = -1.00$ μC are positioned symmetrically around Q as shown in Figure P24.13. Determine the electric flux through one face of the cube.

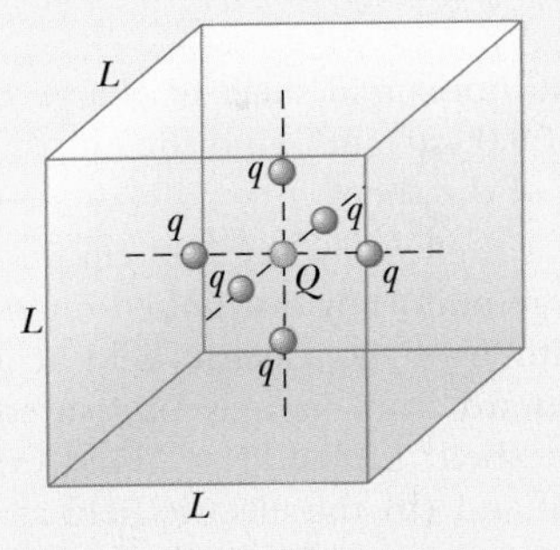

Figure P24.13 Problems 13 and 14.

14. A particle with charge Q is located at the center of a cube of edge L. In addition, six other identical negative charged particles $-q$ are positioned symmetrically around Q as shown in Figure P24.13. Determine the electric flux through one face of the cube.

15. An infinitely long line charge having a uniform charge per unit length λ lies a distance d from point O as shown in Figure P24.15. Determine the total electric flux

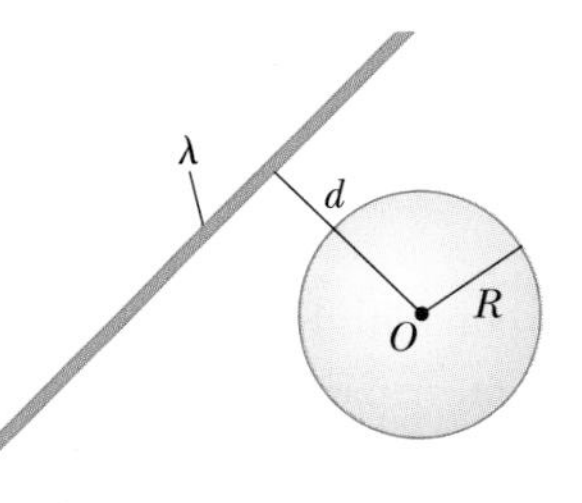

Figure P24.15

through the surface of a sphere of radius R centered at O resulting from this line charge. Consider both cases, where $R < d$ and $R > d$.

16. An uncharged nonconducting hollow sphere of radius 10.0 cm surrounds a 10.0-μC charge located at the origin of a cartesian coordinate system. A drill with a radius of 1.00 mm is aligned along the z axis, and a hole is drilled in the sphere. Calculate the electric flux through the hole.

17. ● A charge of 170 μC is at the center of a cube of edge 80.0 cm. No other charges are nearby. (a) Find the flux through each face of the cube. (b) Find the flux through the whole surface of the cube. (c) **What If?** Would your answers to parts (a) or (b) change if the charge were not at the center? Explain.

Section 24.3 Application of Gauss's Law to Various Charge Distributions

18. A solid sphere of radius 40.0 cm has a total positive charge of 26.0 μC uniformly distributed throughout its volume. Calculate the magnitude of the electric field (a) 0 cm, (b) 10.0 cm, (c) 40.0 cm, and (d) 60.0 cm from the center of the sphere.

19. Determine the magnitude of the electric field at the surface of a lead-208 nucleus, which contains 82 protons and 126 neutrons. Assume the lead nucleus has a volume 208 times that of one proton and consider a proton to be a sphere of radius 1.20×10^{-15} m.

20. The charge per unit length on a long, straight filament is -90.0 μC/m. Find the electric field (a) 10.0 cm, (b) 20.0 cm, and (c) 100 cm from the filament, where distances are measured perpendicular to the length of the filament.

21. A large, flat, horizontal sheet of charge has a charge per unit area of 9.00 μC/m^2. Find the electric field just above the middle of the sheet.

22. A cylindrical shell of radius 7.00 cm and length 240 cm has its charge uniformly distributed on its curved surface. The magnitude of the electric field at a point 19.0 cm radially outward from its axis (measured from the midpoint of the shell) is 36.0 kN/C. Find (a) the net charge on the shell and (b) the electric field at a point 4.00 cm from the axis, measured radially outward from the midpoint of the shell.

23. A 10.0-g piece of Styrofoam carries a net charge of -0.700 μC and floats above the center of a large, horizontal sheet of plastic that has a uniform charge density on its surface. What is the charge per unit area on the plastic sheet?

24. (a) Write a problem for which the following equation gives the solution. Include the required data in your problem statement and identify the one unknown.

$$2\pi(3\text{ cm})(8\text{ cm})E\cos 0° + 0 + 0 = \frac{\pi(2\text{ cm})^2(8\text{ cm})(5\times 10^{-6}\text{ C/m}^3)}{8.85\times 10^{-12}\text{ C}^2/\text{N}\cdot\text{m}^2}$$

(b) Solve the equation for the unknown.

25. **Review problem.** A particle with a charge of -60.0 nC is placed at the center of a nonconducting spherical shell of inner radius 20.0 cm and outer radius 25.0 cm. The spherical shell carries charge with a uniform density of -1.33 μC/m^3. A proton moves in a circular orbit just outside the spherical shell. Calculate the speed of the proton.

26. ● A nonconducting wall carries charge with a uniform density of 8.60 μC/cm^2. What is the electric field 7.00 cm in front of the wall? Explain whether your result changes as the distance from the wall is varied.

27. ▲ Consider a long, cylindrical charge distribution of radius R with a uniform charge density ρ. Find the electric field at distance r from the axis, where $r < R$.

28. In nuclear fission, a nucleus of uranium-238, containing 92 protons, can divide into two smaller spheres, each having 46 protons and a radius of 5.90×10^{-15} m. What is the magnitude of the repulsive electric force pushing the two spheres apart?

29. Consider a thin, spherical shell of radius 14.0 cm with a total charge of 32.0 μC distributed uniformly on its surface. Find the electric field (a) 10.0 cm and (b) 20.0 cm from the center of the charge distribution.

30. Fill two rubber balloons with air. Suspend both of them from the same point and let them hang down on strings of equal length. Rub each with wool or on your hair so that the balloons hang apart with a noticeable separation between them. Make order-of-magnitude estimates of (a) the force on each, (b) the charge on each, (c) the field each creates at the center of the other, and (d) the total flux of electric field created by each balloon. In your solution, state the quantities you take as data and the values you measure or estimate for them.

31. A uniformly charged, straight filament 7.00 m in length has a total positive charge of 2.00 μC. An uncharged cardboard cylinder 2.00 cm in length and 10.0 cm in radius surrounds the filament at its center, with the filament as the axis of the cylinder. Using reasonable approximations, find (a) the electric field at the surface of the cylinder and (b) the total electric flux through the cylinder.

Section 24.4 Conductors in Electrostatic Equilibrium

32. A very large, thin, flat plate of aluminum of area A has a total charge Q uniformly distributed over its surfaces. Assuming the same charge is spread uniformly over the *upper* surface of an otherwise identical glass plate, compare the electric fields just above the center of the upper surface of each plate.

33. A long, straight metal rod has a radius of 5.00 cm and a charge per unit length of 30.0 nC/m. Find the electric field (a) 3.00 cm, (b) 10.0 cm, and (c) 100 cm from the axis of the rod, where distances are measured perpendicular to the rod.

34. ● A solid copper sphere of radius 15.0 cm carries a charge of 40.0 nC. Find the electric field (a) 12.0 cm, (b) 17.0 cm, and (c) 75.0 cm from the center of the sphere. (d) **What If?** Explain how your answers would change if the sphere were hollow.

35. A square plate of copper with 50.0-cm sides has no net charge and is placed in a region of uniform electric field of 80.0 kN/C directed perpendicularly to the plate. Find (a) the charge density of each face of the plate and (b) the total charge on each face.

36. In a certain region of space, the electric field is $\vec{\mathbf{E}} = 6\,000x^2\hat{\mathbf{i}}$ N/C·m^2. Find the volume density of electric charge at $x = 0.300$ m. *Suggestion:* Apply Gauss's law to a box between $x = 0.300$ m and $x = 0.300$ m $+ dx$.

37. Two identical conducting spheres each having a radius of 0.500 cm are connected by a light 2.00-m-long conducting wire. A charge of 60.0 μC is placed on one of the conductors. Assume the surface distribution of charge on each sphere is uniform. Determine the tension in the wire.

38. ● A solid metallic sphere of radius a carries total charge Q. No other charges are nearby. The electric field just outside its surface is k_eQ/a^2 radially outward. Is the electric field here also given by σ/ϵ_0? By $\sigma/2\epsilon_0$? Explain whether you should expect it to be equal to either of these quantities.

39. A long, straight wire is surrounded by a hollow metal cylinder whose axis coincides with that of the wire. The wire has a charge per unit length of λ, and the cylinder has a net charge per unit length of 2λ. From this information, use Gauss's law to find (a) the charge per unit length on the inner and outer surfaces of the cylinder and (b) the electric field outside the cylinder, a distance r from the axis.

40. A positively charged particle is at a distance $R/2$ from the center of an uncharged thin, conducting, spherical shell of radius R. Sketch the electric field lines set up by this arrangement both inside and outside the shell.

41. ▲ A thin, square, conducting plate 50.0 cm on a side lies in the xy plane. A total charge of 4.00×10^{-8} C is placed on the plate. Find (a) the charge density on the plate, (b) the electric field just above the plate, and (c) the electric field just below the plate. You may assume the charge density is uniform.

Additional Problems

42. A nonuniform electric field is given by the expression

$$\vec{\mathbf{E}} = ay\hat{\mathbf{i}} + bz\hat{\mathbf{j}} + cx\hat{\mathbf{k}}$$

where a, b, and c are constants. Determine the electric flux through a rectangular surface in the xy plane, extending from $x = 0$ to $x = w$ and from $y = 0$ to $y = h$.

43. A sphere of radius R surrounds a particle with charge Q, located at its center. (a) Show that the electric flux through a circular cap of half-angle θ (Fig. P24.43) is

$$\Phi_E = \frac{Q}{2\epsilon_0}(1 - \cos\theta)$$

What is the flux for (b) $\theta = 90°$ and (c) $\theta = 180°$?

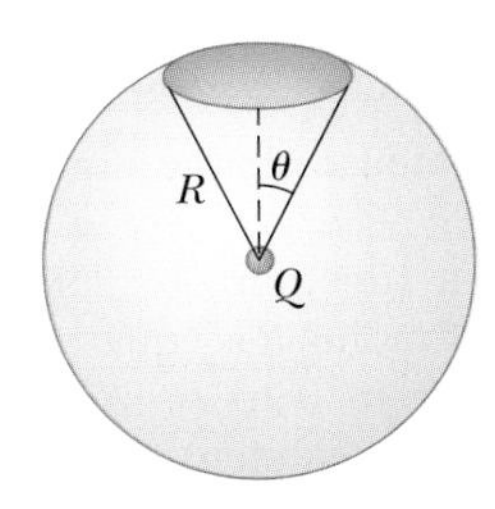

Figure P24.43

44. A solid insulating sphere of radius 5.00 cm carries a net positive charge of 3.00 μC, uniformly distributed throughout its volume. Concentric with this sphere is a conducting spherical shell with inner radius 10.0 cm and outer radius 15.0 cm, having net charge -1.00 μC, as shown in Figure Q24.11. (a) Consider a spherical gaussian surface of radius 16.0 cm and find the net charge enclosed by this surface. (b) What is the direction of the electric field at point D, to the right of the shell and at radius 16 cm? (c) Find the magnitude of the electric field at point D. (d) Find the vector electric field at point C, at radius 12.0 cm. (e) Consider a spherical gaussian surface through point C and find the net charge enclosed by this surface. (f) Consider a spherical gaussian surface of radius 8.00 cm and find the net charge enclosed by this surface. (g) Find the vector electric field at point B, at radius 8 cm. (h) Consider a spherical gaussian surface through point A, at radius 4.00 cm, and find the net charge enclosed by this surface. (i) Find the vector electric field at point A. (j) Determine the charge on the inner surface of the conducting shell. (k) Determine the charge on the outer surface of the conducting shell. (l) Sketch a graph of the magnitude of the electric field versus r.

45. ● A hollow, metallic, spherical shell has exterior radius 0.750 m, carries no net charge, and is supported on an insulating stand. The electric field everywhere just outside its surface is 890 N/C radially toward the center of the sphere. (a) Explain what you can conclude about the amount of charge on the exterior surface of the sphere and the distribution of this charge. (b) Explain what you can conclude about the amount of charge on the interior surface of the sphere and its distribution. (c) Explain what you can conclude about the amount of charge inside the shell and its distribution.

46. ● Consider two identical conducting spheres whose surfaces are separated by a small distance. One sphere is given a large net positive charge, and the other is given a small net positive charge. It is found that the force between the spheres is attractive even though they both have net charges of the same sign. Explain how this attraction is possible.

47. ▲ A solid, insulating sphere of radius a has a uniform charge density ρ and a total charge Q. Concentric with this sphere is an uncharged, conducting, hollow sphere whose inner and outer radii are b and c as shown in Figure P24.47. (a) Find the magnitude of the electric field in the regions $r < a$, $a < r < b$, $b < r < c$, and $r > c$. (b) Determine the induced charge per unit area on the inner and outer surfaces of the hollow sphere.

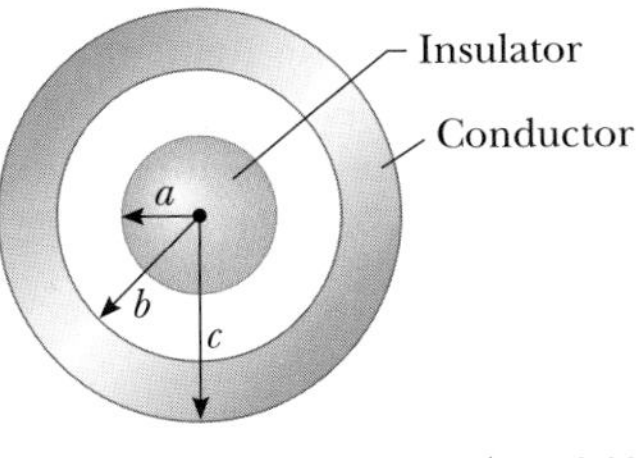

Figure P24.47 Problems 47 and 63.

48. **Review problem.** An early (incorrect) model of the hydrogen atom, suggested by J. J. Thomson, proposed that a positive cloud of charge $+e$ was uniformly distributed throughout the volume of a sphere of radius R, with the electron (an equal-magnitude negatively charged particle $-e$) at the center. (a) Using Gauss's law, show that the

electron would be in equilibrium at the center and, if displaced from the center a distance $r < R$, would experience a restoring force of the form $F = -Kr$, where K is a constant. (b) Show that $K = k_e e^2/R^3$. (c) Find an expression for the frequency f of simple harmonic oscillations that an electron of mass m_e would undergo if displaced a small distance ($< R$) from the center and released. (d) Calculate a numerical value for R that would result in a frequency of 2.47×10^{15} Hz, the frequency of the light radiated in the most intense line in the hydrogen spectrum.

49. A particle of mass m and charge q moves at high speed along the x axis. It is initially near $x = -\infty$, and it ends up near $x = +\infty$. A second charge Q is fixed at the point $x = 0$, $y = -d$. As the moving charge passes the stationary charge, its x component of velocity does not change appreciably, but it acquires a small velocity in the y direction. Determine the angle through which the moving charge is deflected. *Suggestion:* The integral you encounter in determining v_y can be evaluated by applying Gauss's law to a long cylinder of radius d, centered on the stationary charge.

50. Two infinite, nonconducting sheets of charge are parallel to each other as shown in Figure P24.50. The sheet on the left has a uniform surface charge density σ, and the one on the right has a uniform charge density $-\sigma$. Calculate the electric field at points (a) to the left of, (b) in between, and (c) to the right of the two sheets.

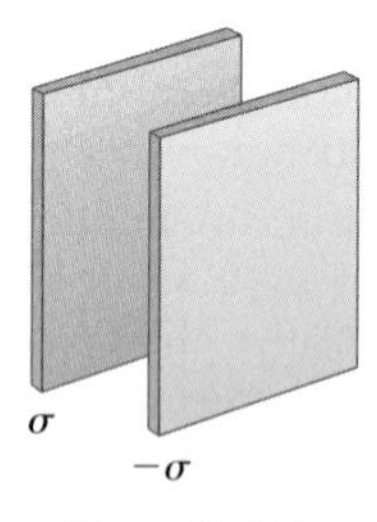

Figure P24.50

51. ▲ **What If?** Repeat the calculations for Problem 50 when both sheets have *positive* uniform surface charge densities of value σ.

52. A sphere of radius $2a$ is made of a nonconducting material that has a uniform volume charge density ρ. (Assume the material does not affect the electric field.) A spherical cavity of radius a is now removed from the sphere as shown in Figure P24.52. Show that the electric field within the cavity is uniform and is given by $E_x = 0$ and $E_y = \rho a/3\epsilon_0$. *Suggestion:* The field within the cavity is the superposition of the field due to the original uncut sphere plus the field due to a sphere the size of the cavity with a uniform negative charge density $-\rho$.

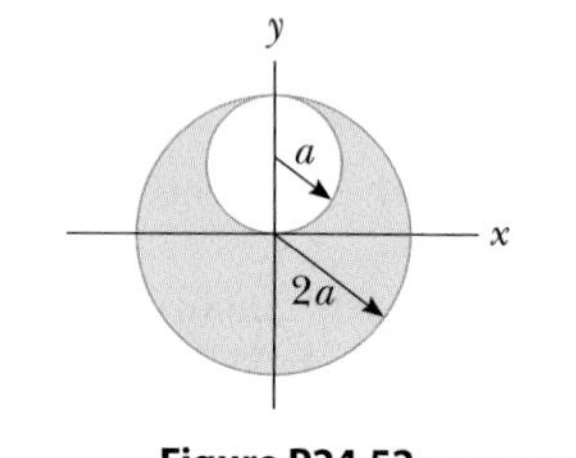

Figure P24.52

53. A uniformly charged spherical shell with surface charge density σ contains a circular hole in its surface. The radius of the hole is small compared with the radius of the sphere. What is the electric field at the center of the hole? *Suggestion:* This problem, like Problem 52, can be solved by using the idea of superposition.

54. A closed surface with dimensions $a = b = 0.400$ m and $c = 0.600$ m is located as shown in Figure P24.54. The left edge of the closed surface is located at position $x = a$. The electric field throughout the region is nonuniform and is given by $\vec{\mathbf{E}} = (3.0 + 2.0x^2)\hat{\mathbf{i}}$ N/C, where x is in meters. Calculate the net electric flux leaving the closed surface. What net charge is enclosed by the surface?

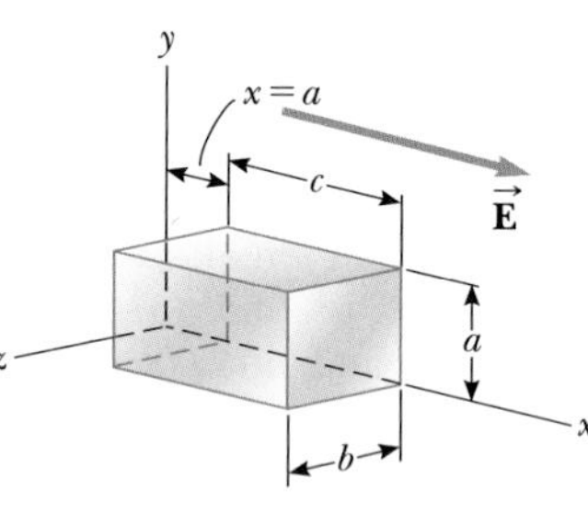

Figure P24.54

55. A solid insulating sphere of radius R has a nonuniform charge density that varies with r according to the expression $\rho = Ar^2$, where A is a constant and $r < R$ is measured from the center of the sphere. (a) Show that the magnitude of the electric field outside ($r > R$) the sphere is $E = AR^5/5\epsilon_0 r^2$. (b) Show that the magnitude of the electric field inside ($r < R$) the sphere is $E = Ar^3/5\epsilon_0$. *Suggestion:* The total charge Q on the sphere is equal to the integral of $\rho\, dV$, where r extends from 0 to R; also, the charge q within a radius $r < R$ is less than Q. To evaluate the integrals, note that the volume element dV for a spherical shell of radius r and thickness dr is equal to $4\pi r^2\, dr$.

56. A particle with charge Q is located on the axis of a disk of radius R at a distance b from the plane of the disk (Fig. P24.56). Show that if one fourth of the electric flux from the charge passes through the disk, then $R = \sqrt{3}b$.

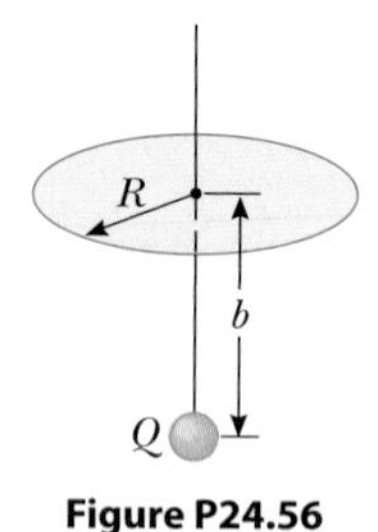

Figure P24.56

57. A spherically symmetric charge distribution has a charge density given by $\rho = a/r$, where a is constant. Find the electric field as a function of r. *Suggestion:* The charge within a sphere of radius R is equal to the integral of $\rho\, dV$, where r extends from 0 to R. To evaluate the integral, note that the volume element dV for a spherical shell of radius r and thickness dr is equal to $4\pi r^2\, dr$.

58. An infinitely long insulating cylinder of radius R has a volume charge density that varies with the radius as

$$\rho = \rho_0\left(a - \frac{r}{b}\right)$$

where ρ_0, a, and b are positive constants and r is the distance from the axis of the cylinder. Use Gauss's law to determine the magnitude of the electric field at radial distances (a) $r < R$ and (b) $r > R$.

59. **Review problem.** A slab of insulating material (infinite in two of its three dimensions) has a uniform positive charge density ρ. An edge view of the slab is shown in Figure P24.59. (a) Show that the magnitude of the electric field a distance x from its center and inside the slab is $E = \rho x/\epsilon_0$. (b) **What If?** Suppose an electron of charge $-e$ and mass m_e can move freely within the slab. It is released from rest at a distance x from the center. Show that the electron exhibits simple harmonic motion with a frequency

$$f = \frac{1}{2\pi}\sqrt{\frac{\rho e}{m_e \epsilon_0}}$$

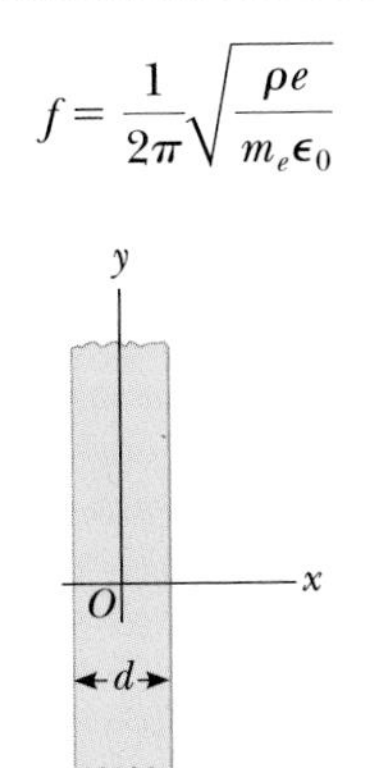

Figure P24.59 Problems 59 and 60.

60. A slab of insulating material has a nonuniform positive charge density $\rho = Cx^2$, where x is measured from the center of the slab as shown in Figure P24.59 and C is a constant. The slab is infinite in the y and z directions. Derive expressions for the electric field in (a) the exterior regions and (b) the interior region of the slab ($-d/2 < x < d/2$).

61. (a) Using the mathematical similarity between Coulomb's law and Newton's law of universal gravitation, show that Gauss's law for gravitation can be written as

$$\oint \vec{\mathbf{g}} \cdot d\vec{\mathbf{A}} = -4\pi G m_{\text{in}}$$

where m_{in} is the net mass inside the gaussian surface and $\vec{\mathbf{g}} = \vec{\mathbf{F}}_g/m$ represents the gravitational field at any point on the gaussian surface. (b) Determine the gravitational field at a distance r from the center of the Earth where $r < R_E$, assuming the Earth's mass density is uniform.

62. An insulating solid sphere of radius a has a uniform volume charge density and carries a total positive charge Q. A spherical gaussian surface of radius r, which shares a common center with the insulating sphere, is inflated starting from $r = 0$. (a) Find an expression for the electric flux passing through the surface of the gaussian sphere as a function of r for $r < a$. (b) Find an expression for the electric flux for $r > a$. (c) Plot the flux versus r.

63. For the configuration shown in Figure P24.47, suppose $a = 5.00$ cm, $b = 20.0$ cm, and $c = 25.0$ cm. Furthermore, suppose the electric field at a point 10.0 cm from the center is measured to be 3.60×10^3 N/C radially inward and the electric field at a point 50.0 cm from the center is 2.00×10^2 N/C radially outward. From this information, find (a) the charge on the insulating sphere, (b) the net charge on the hollow conducting sphere, and (c) the charges on the inner and outer surfaces of the hollow conducting sphere.

64. An infinitely long cylindrical insulating shell of inner radius a and outer radius b has a uniform volume charge density ρ. A line of uniform linear charge density λ is placed along the axis of the shell. Determine the electric field everywhere.

65. Consider an electric field that is uniform in direction throughout a certain volume. Can it be uniform in magnitude? Must it be uniform in magnitude? Answer these questions (a) assuming the volume is filled with an insulating material carrying charge described by a volume charge density and (b) assuming the volume is empty space. State reasoning to prove your answers.

Answers to Quick Quizzes

24.1 (e). The same number of field lines pass through a sphere of any size. Because points on the surface of the sphere are closer to the charge, the field is stronger.

24.2 (b) and (d). Statement (a) is not necessarily true because an equal number of positive and negative charges could be present inside the surface. Statement (c) is not necessarily true as can be seen from Figure 24.8: a nonzero electric field exists everywhere on the surface, but the charge is not enclosed within the surface and the net flux is therefore zero.

24.3 (a). Charges added to the metal cylinder by your brother will reside on the outer surface of the conducting cylinder. If you are on the inside, these charges cannot transfer to you from the inner surface. For this same reason, you are safe in a metal automobile during a lightning storm.

Processes occurring during thunderstorms cause large differences in electric potential between a thundercloud and the ground. The result of this potential difference is an electrical discharge that we call lightning, such as this display over Tucson, Arizona. (© Keith Kent/Photo Researchers, Inc.)

25 Electric Potential

The concept of potential energy was introduced in Chapter 7 in connection with such conservative forces as the gravitational force and the elastic force exerted by a spring. By using the law of conservation of energy when solving various problems in mechanics, we were able to avoid working directly with forces. The concept of potential energy is also of great value in the study of electricity. Because the electrostatic force is conservative, electrostatic phenomena can be conveniently described in terms of an electric potential energy. This idea enables us to define a quantity known as *electric potential.* Because the electric potential at any point in an electric field is a scalar quantity, we can use it to describe electrostatic phenomena more simply than if we were to rely only on the electric field and electric forces. The concept of electric potential is of great practical value in the operation of electric circuits and devices that we will study in later chapters.

25.1 Electric Potential and Potential Difference

When a test charge q_0 is placed in an electric field $\vec{\mathbf{E}}$ created by some source charge distribution, the electric force acting on the test charge is $q_0\vec{\mathbf{E}}$. The force $q_0\vec{\mathbf{E}}$ is conservative because the force between charges described by Coulomb's law is conservative. When the test charge is moved in the field by some external agent, the work done by the field on the charge is equal to the negative of the work done by the external agent causing the displacement. This situation is analogous to that of lifting an object with mass in a gravitational field: the work done by the external agent is mgh, and the work done by the gravitational force is $-mgh$.

When analyzing electric and magnetic fields, it is common practice to use the notation $d\vec{\mathbf{s}}$ to represent an infinitesimal displacement vector that is oriented tangent to a path through space. This path may be straight or curved, and an integral performed along this path is called either a *path integral* or a *line integral* (the two terms are synonymous).

For an infinitesimal displacement $d\vec{\mathbf{s}}$ of a point charge q_0 immersed in an electric field, the work done by the electric field on the charge is $\vec{\mathbf{F}} \cdot d\vec{\mathbf{s}} = q_0\vec{\mathbf{E}} \cdot d\vec{\mathbf{s}}$. As this amount of work is done by the field, the potential energy of the charge–field system is changed by an amount $dU = -q_0\vec{\mathbf{E}} \cdot d\vec{\mathbf{s}}$. For a finite displacement of the charge from point Ⓐ to point Ⓑ, the change in potential energy of the system $\Delta U = U_{Ⓑ} - U_{Ⓐ}$ is

$$\Delta U = -q_0 \int_{Ⓐ}^{Ⓑ} \vec{\mathbf{E}} \cdot d\vec{\mathbf{s}} \qquad (25.1)$$

◀ Change in electric potential energy of a system

The integration is performed along the path that q_0 follows as it moves from Ⓐ to Ⓑ. Because the force $q_0\vec{\mathbf{E}}$ is conservative, **this line integral does not depend on the path taken from Ⓐ to Ⓑ.**

For a given position of the test charge in the field, the charge–field system has a potential energy U relative to the configuration of the system that is defined as $U = 0$. Dividing the potential energy by the test charge gives a physical quantity that depends only on the source charge distribution and has a value at every point in an electric field. This quantity is called the **electric potential** (or simply the **potential**) V:

$$V = \frac{U}{q_0} \qquad (25.2)$$

Because potential energy is a scalar quantity, electric potential also is a scalar quantity.

As described by Equation 25.1, if the test charge is moved between two positions Ⓐ and Ⓑ in an electric field, the charge–field system experiences a change in potential energy. The **potential difference** $\Delta V = V_{Ⓑ} - V_{Ⓐ}$ between two points Ⓐ and Ⓑ in an electric field is defined as the change in potential energy of the system when a test charge q_0 is moved between the points divided by the test charge:

$$\Delta V \equiv \frac{\Delta U}{q_0} = -\int_{Ⓐ}^{Ⓑ} \vec{\mathbf{E}} \cdot d\vec{\mathbf{s}} \qquad (25.3)$$

◀ Potential difference between two points

PITFALL PREVENTION 25.1
Potential and Potential Energy

The *potential is characteristic of the field only,* independent of a charged test particle that may be placed in the field. *Potential energy is characteristic of the charge-field system* due to an interaction between the field and a charged particle placed in the field.

Just as with potential energy, only *differences* in electric potential are meaningful. We often take the value of the electric potential to be zero at some convenient point in an electric field.

Potential difference should not be confused with difference in potential energy. The potential difference between Ⓐ and Ⓑ depends only on the source charge distribution (consider points Ⓐ and Ⓑ *without* the presence of the test charge), whereas the difference in potential energy exists only if a test charge is moved between the points.

If an external agent moves a test charge from Ⓐ to Ⓑ without changing the kinetic energy of the test charge, the agent performs work that changes the potential energy of the system: $W = \Delta U$. Imagine an arbitrary charge q located in an electric field. From Equation 25.3, the work done by an external agent in moving a charge q through an electric field at constant velocity is

$$W = q\Delta V \qquad (25.4)$$

PITFALL PREVENTION 25.2
Voltage

A variety of phrases are used to describe the potential difference between two points, the most common being **voltage,** arising from the unit for potential. A voltage *applied* to a device, such as a television, or *across* a device is the same as the potential difference across the device.

PITFALL PREVENTION 25.3
The Electron Volt

The electron volt is a unit of *energy,* NOT of potential. The energy of any system may be expressed in eV, but this unit is most convenient for describing the emission and absorption of visible light from atoms. Energies of nuclear processes are often expressed in MeV.

Because electric potential is a measure of potential energy per unit charge, the SI unit of both electric potential and potential difference is joules per coulomb, which is defined as a **volt** (V):

$$1\ \text{V} \equiv 1\ \text{J/C}$$

That is, 1 J of work must be done to move a 1-C charge through a potential difference of 1 V.

Equation 25.3 shows that potential difference also has units of electric field times distance. It follows that the SI unit of electric field (N/C) can also be expressed in volts per meter:

$$1\ \text{N/C} = 1\ \text{V/m}$$

Therefore, **we can interpret the electric field as a measure of the rate of change with position of the electric potential.**

A unit of energy commonly used in atomic and nuclear physics is the **electron volt** (eV), which is defined as **the energy a charge–field system gains or loses when a charge of magnitude *e* (that is, an electron or a proton) is moved through a potential difference of 1 V.** Because 1 V = 1 J/C and the fundamental charge is 1.60×10^{-19} C, the electron volt is related to the joule as follows:

$$1\ \text{eV} = 1.60 \times 10^{-19}\ \text{C}\cdot\text{V} = 1.60 \times 10^{-19}\ \text{J} \quad \textbf{(25.5)}$$

For instance, an electron in the beam of a typical television picture tube may have a speed of 3.0×10^7 m/s. This speed corresponds to a kinetic energy equal to 4.1×10^{-16} J, which is equivalent to 2.6×10^3 eV. Such an electron has to be accelerated from rest through a potential difference of 2.6 kV to reach this speed.

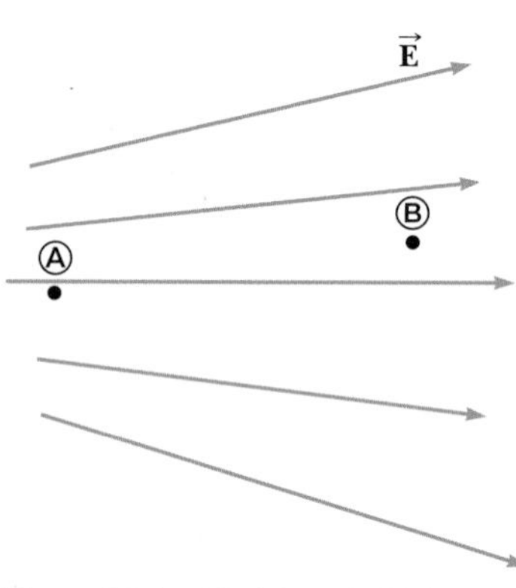

Figure 25.1 (Quick Quiz 25.1) Two points in an electric field.

Quick Quiz 25.1 In Figure 25.1, two points Ⓐ and Ⓑ are located within a region in which there is an electric field. **(i)** How would you describe the potential difference $\Delta V = V_{Ⓑ} - V_{Ⓐ}$? (a) It is positive. (b) It is negative. (c) It is zero. **(ii)** A negative charge is placed at Ⓐ and then moved to Ⓑ. How would you describe the change in potential energy of the charge-field system for this process? Choose from the same possibilities.

25.2 Potential Difference in a Uniform Electric Field

Equations 25.1 and 25.3 hold in all electric fields, whether uniform or varying, but they can be simplified for a uniform field. First, consider a uniform electric field directed along the negative *y* axis as shown in Active Figure 25.2a. Let's calculate the potential difference between two points Ⓐ and Ⓑ separated by a distance $|\vec{\mathbf{s}}| = d$, where $\vec{\mathbf{s}}$ is parallel to the field lines. Equation 25.3 gives

$$V_{Ⓑ} - V_{Ⓐ} = \Delta V = -\int_{Ⓐ}^{Ⓑ} \vec{\mathbf{E}} \cdot d\vec{\mathbf{s}} = -\int_{Ⓐ}^{Ⓑ} (E\cos 0°)\,ds = -\int_{Ⓐ}^{Ⓑ} E\,ds$$

Because E is constant, it can be removed from the integral sign, which gives

Potential difference between two points in a uniform electric field ▶

$$\Delta V = -E\int_{Ⓐ}^{Ⓑ} ds = -Ed \quad \textbf{(25.6)}$$

The negative sign indicates that the electric potential at point Ⓑ is lower than at point Ⓐ; that is, $V_{Ⓑ} < V_{Ⓐ}$. **Electric field lines always point in the direction of decreasing electric potential** as shown in Active Figure 25.2a.

Now suppose a test charge q_0 moves from Ⓐ to Ⓑ. We can calculate the change in the potential energy of the charge–field system from Equations 25.3 and 25.6:

$$\Delta U = q_0\,\Delta V = -q_0 Ed \quad \textbf{(25.7)}$$

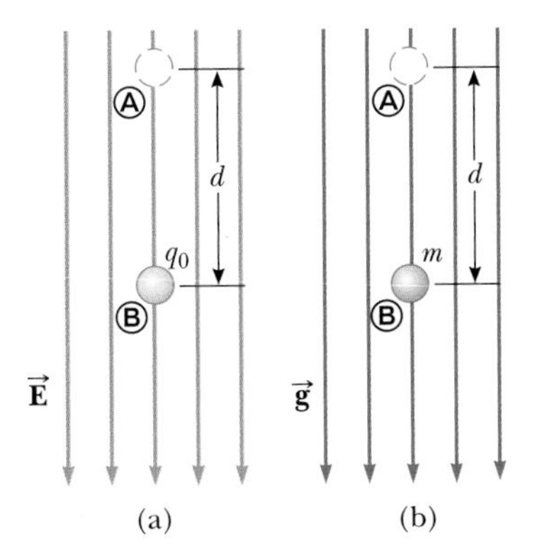

ACTIVE FIGURE 25.2

(a) When the electric field $\vec{E}$ is directed downward, point Ⓑ is at a lower electric potential than point Ⓐ. When a positive test charge moves from point Ⓐ to point Ⓑ, the electric potential energy of the charge–field system decreases. (b) When an object of mass m moves downward in the direction of the gravitational field $\vec{g}$, the gravitational potential energy of the object–field system decreases.

Sign in at www.thomsonedu.com and go to ThomsonNOW to observe and compare the motion of the charged object in an electric field and an object with mass in a gravitational field.

This result shows that if q_0 is positive, then U is negative. Therefore, **a system consisting of a positive charge and an electric field loses electric potential energy when the charge moves in the direction of the field.** Equivalently, an electric field does work on a positive charge when the charge moves in the direction of the electric field. (That is analogous to the work done by the gravitational field on a falling object as shown in Active Fig. 25.2b.) If a positive test charge is released from rest in this electric field, it experiences an electric force $q_0\vec{E}$ in the direction of $\vec{E}$ (downward in Active Fig. 25.2a). Therefore, it accelerates downward, gaining kinetic energy. **As the charged particle gains kinetic energy, the charge–field system loses an equal amount of potential energy.** This equivalence should not be surprising; it is simply conservation of mechanical energy in an isolated system as introduced in Chapter 8.

If q_0 is negative, then ΔU in Equation 25.7 is positive and the situation is reversed. **A system consisting of a negative charge and an electric field gains electric potential energy when the charge moves in the direction of the field.** If a negative charge is released from rest in an electric field, it accelerates in a direction opposite the direction of the field. For the negative charge to move in the direction of the field, an external agent must apply a force and do positive work on the charge.

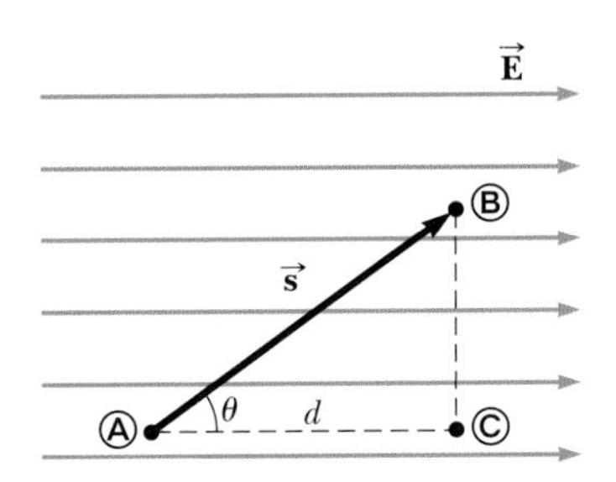

Figure 25.3 A uniform electric field directed along the positive x axis. Point Ⓑ is at a lower electric potential than point Ⓐ. Points Ⓑ and Ⓒ are at the *same* electric potential.

Now consider the more general case of a charged particle that moves between Ⓐ and Ⓑ in a uniform electric field such that the vector $\vec{s}$ is not parallel to the field lines as shown in Figure 25.3. In this case, Equation 25.3 gives

$$\Delta V = -\int_{Ⓐ}^{Ⓑ} \vec{E}\cdot d\vec{s} = -\vec{E}\cdot\int_{Ⓐ}^{Ⓑ} d\vec{s} = -\vec{E}\cdot\vec{s} \qquad (25.8)$$

◀ Change in potential energy when a charged particle is moved in a uniform electric field

where again $\vec{E}$ was removed from the integral because it is constant. The change in potential energy of the charge-field system is

$$\Delta U = q_0\,\Delta V = -q_0\vec{E}\cdot\vec{s} \qquad (25.9)$$

Finally, we conclude from Equation 25.8 that all points in a plane perpendicular to a uniform electric field are at the same electric potential. We can see that in Figure 25.3, where the potential difference $V_Ⓑ - V_Ⓐ$ is equal to the potential difference $V_Ⓒ - V_Ⓐ$. (Prove this fact to yourself by working out two dot products for $\vec{E}\cdot\vec{s}$: one for $\vec{s}_{Ⓐ\rightarrow Ⓑ}$, where the angle θ between $\vec{E}$ and $\vec{s}$ is arbitrary as shown in Figure 25.3, and one for $\vec{s}_{Ⓐ\rightarrow Ⓒ}$, where $\theta = 0$.) Therefore, $V_Ⓑ = V_Ⓒ$. **The name equipotential surface is given to any surface consisting of a continuous distribution of points having the same electric potential.**

The equipotential surfaces associated with a uniform electric field consist of a family of parallel planes that are all perpendicular to the field. Equipotential surfaces associated with fields having other symmetries are described in later sections.

Quick Quiz 25.2 The labeled points in Figure 25.4 are on a series of equipotential surfaces associated with an electric field. Rank (from greatest to least) the work done by the electric field on a positively charged particle that moves from Ⓐ to Ⓑ, from Ⓑ to Ⓒ, from Ⓒ to Ⓓ, and from Ⓓ to Ⓔ.

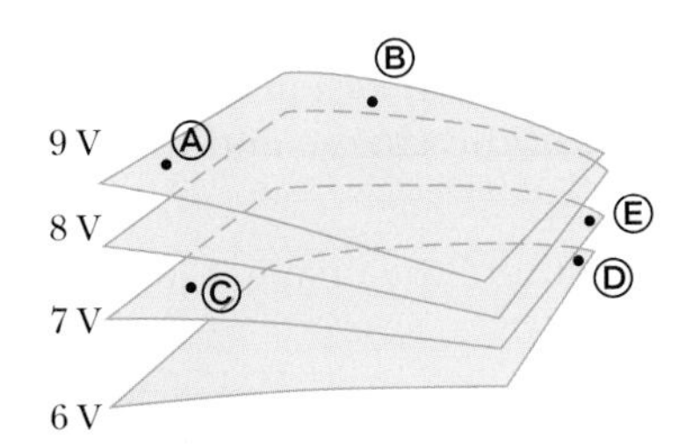

Figure 25.4 (Quick Quiz 25.2) Four equipotential surfaces.

EXAMPLE 25.1 The Electric Field Between Two Parallel Plates of Opposite Charge

A battery has a specified potential difference ΔV between its terminals and establishes that potential difference between conductors attached to the terminals. A 12-V battery is connected between two parallel plates as shown in Figure 25.5. The separation between the plates is $d = 0.30$ cm, and we assume the electric field between the plates to be uniform. (This assumption is reasonable if the plate separation is small relative to the plate dimensions and we do not consider locations near the plate edges.) Find the magnitude of the electric field between the plates.

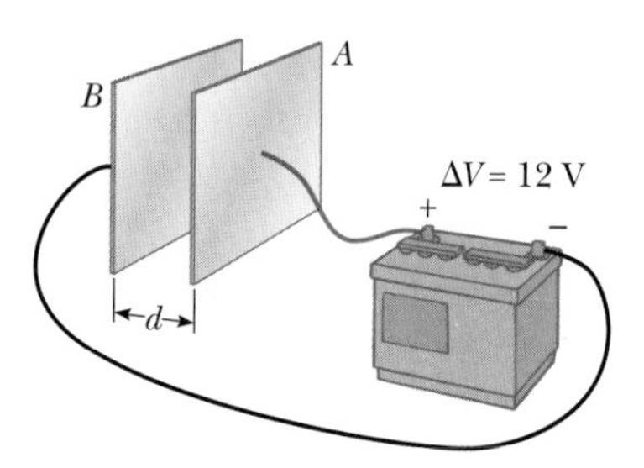

Figure 25.5 (Example 25.1) A 12-V battery connected to two parallel plates. The electric field between the plates has a magnitude given by the potential difference ΔV divided by the plate separation d.

SOLUTION

Conceptualize In earlier chapters, we investigated the uniform electric field between parallel plates. The new feature to this problem is that the electric field is related to the new concept of electric potential.

Categorize The electric field is evaluated from a relationship between field and potential given in this section, so we categorize this example as a substitution problem.

Use Equation 25.6 to evaluate the magnitude of the electric field between the plates:

$$E = \frac{|V_B - V_A|}{d} = \frac{12\ \text{V}}{0.30 \times 10^{-2}\ \text{m}} = 4.0 \times 10^3\ \text{V/m}$$

The configuration of plates in Figure 25.5 is called a *parallel-plate capacitor* and is examined in greater detail in Chapter 26.

EXAMPLE 25.2 Motion of a Proton in a Uniform Electric Field

A proton is released from rest at point Ⓐ in a uniform electric field that has a magnitude of 8.0×10^4 V/m (Fig. 25.6). The proton undergoes a displacement of 0.50 m to point Ⓑ in the direction of $\vec{\mathbf{E}}$. Find the speed of the proton after completing the 0.50 m displacement.

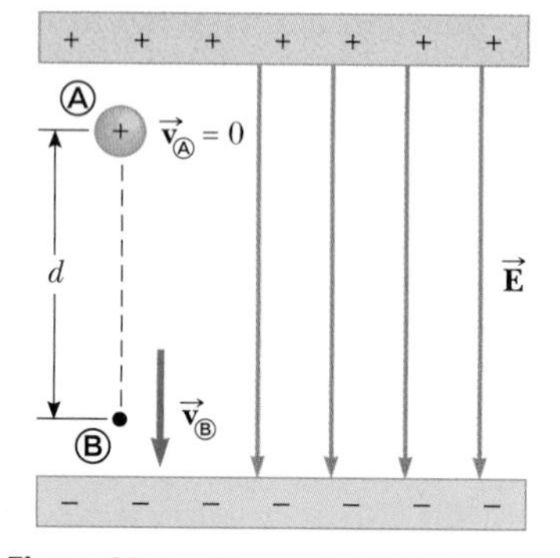

Figure 25.6 (Example 25.2) A proton accelerates from Ⓐ to Ⓑ in the direction of the electric field.

SOLUTION

Conceptualize Visualize the proton in Figure 25.6 moving downward through the potential difference. The situation is analogous to an object falling through a gravitational field.

Categorize The system of the proton and the two plates in Figure 25.6 does not interact with the environment, so we model it as an isolated system.

Analyze Use Equation 25.6 to find the potential difference between points Ⓐ and Ⓑ:

$$\Delta V = -Ed = -(8.0 \times 10^4\ \text{V/m})(0.50\ \text{m}) = -4.0 \times 10^4\ \text{V}$$

Write the appropriate reduction of Equation 8.2, the conservation of energy equation, for the isolated system of the charge and the electric field:

$$\Delta K + \Delta U = 0$$

Substitute the changes in energy for both terms:

$$(\tfrac{1}{2}mv^2 - 0) + e\,\Delta V = 0$$

Solve for the final speed of the proton:

$$v = \sqrt{\frac{-2e\,\Delta V}{m}}$$

Substitute numerical values:

$$v = \sqrt{\frac{-2(1.6 \times 10^{-19}\text{ C})(-4.0 \times 10^4\text{ V})}{1.67 \times 10^{-27}\text{ kg}}}$$

$$= 2.8 \times 10^6\text{ m/s}$$

Finalize Because ΔV is negative, ΔU is also negative. The negative value of ΔU means the potential energy of the system decreases as the proton moves in the direction of the electric field. As the proton accelerates in the direction of the field, it gains kinetic energy and the system loses electric potential energy at the same time.

Figure 25.6 is oriented so that the proton falls downward. The proton's motion is analogous to that of an object falling in a gravitational field. Although the gravitational field is always downward at the surface of the Earth, an electric field can be in any direction, depending on the orientation of the plates creating the field. Therefore, Figure 25.6 could be rotated 90° or 180° and the proton could fall horizontally or upward in the electric field!

25.3 Electric Potential and Potential Energy Due to Point Charges

As discussed in Section 23.4, an isolated positive point charge q produces an electric field directed radially outward from the charge. To find the electric potential at a point located a distance r from the charge, let's begin with the general expression for potential difference,

$$V_{Ⓑ} - V_{Ⓐ} = -\int_{Ⓐ}^{Ⓑ} \vec{\mathbf{E}} \cdot d\vec{\mathbf{s}}$$

where Ⓐ and Ⓑ are the two arbitrary points shown in Figure 25.7. At any point in space, the electric field due to the point charge is $\vec{\mathbf{E}} = (k_e q/r^2)\hat{\mathbf{r}}$ (Eq. 23.9), where $\hat{\mathbf{r}}$ is a unit vector directed from the charge toward the point. The quantity $\vec{\mathbf{E}} \cdot d\vec{\mathbf{s}}$ can be expressed as

$$\vec{\mathbf{E}} \cdot d\vec{\mathbf{s}} = k_e \frac{q}{r^2}\, \hat{\mathbf{r}} \cdot d\vec{\mathbf{s}}$$

Because the magnitude of $\hat{\mathbf{r}}$ is 1, the dot product $\hat{\mathbf{r}} \cdot d\vec{\mathbf{s}} = ds \cos\theta$, where θ is the angle between $\hat{\mathbf{r}}$ and $d\vec{\mathbf{s}}$. Furthermore, $ds \cos\theta$ is the projection of $d\vec{\mathbf{s}}$ onto $\vec{\mathbf{r}}$; therefore, $ds \cos\theta = dr$. That is, any displacement $d\vec{\mathbf{s}}$ along the path from point Ⓐ to point Ⓑ produces a change dr in the magnitude of $\vec{\mathbf{r}}$, the position vector of the point relative to the charge creating the field. Making these substitutions, we find that $\vec{\mathbf{E}} \cdot d\vec{\mathbf{s}} = (k_e q/r^2)dr$; hence, the expression for the potential difference becomes

$$V_{Ⓑ} - V_{Ⓐ} = -k_e q \int_{r_Ⓐ}^{r_Ⓑ} \frac{dr}{r^2} = k_e \frac{q}{r}\Bigg|_{r_Ⓐ}^{r_Ⓑ}$$

$$V_{Ⓑ} - V_{Ⓐ} = k_e q\left[\frac{1}{r_Ⓑ} - \frac{1}{r_Ⓐ}\right] \quad \textbf{(25.10)}$$

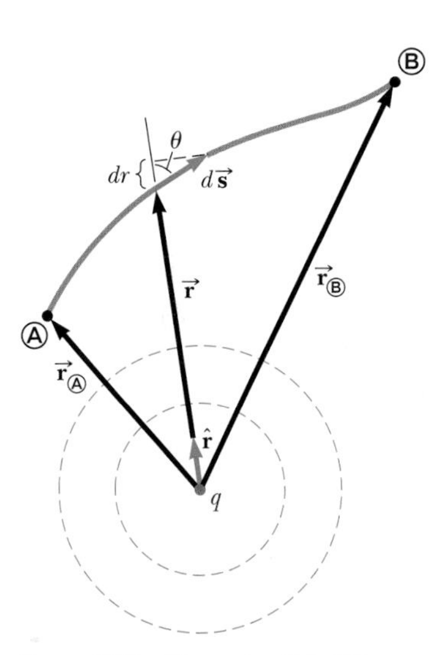

Figure 25.7 The potential difference between points Ⓐ and Ⓑ due to a point charge q depends *only* on the initial and final radial coordinates $r_Ⓐ$ and $r_Ⓑ$. The two dashed circles represent intersections of spherical equipotential surfaces with the page.

Equation 25.10 shows us that the integral of $\vec{\mathbf{E}} \cdot d\vec{\mathbf{s}}$ is *independent* of the path between points Ⓐ and Ⓑ. Multiplying by a charge q_0 that moves between points Ⓐ and Ⓑ, we see that the integral of $q_0\vec{\mathbf{E}} \cdot d\vec{\mathbf{s}}$ is also independent of path. This latter integral, which is the work done by the electric force, shows that the electric force is conservative (see Section 7.7). We define a field that is related to a conservative force as a **conservative field.** Therefore, Equation 25.10 tells us that the electric field of a fixed point charge is conservative. Furthermore, Equation 25.10 expresses the important result that the potential difference between any two

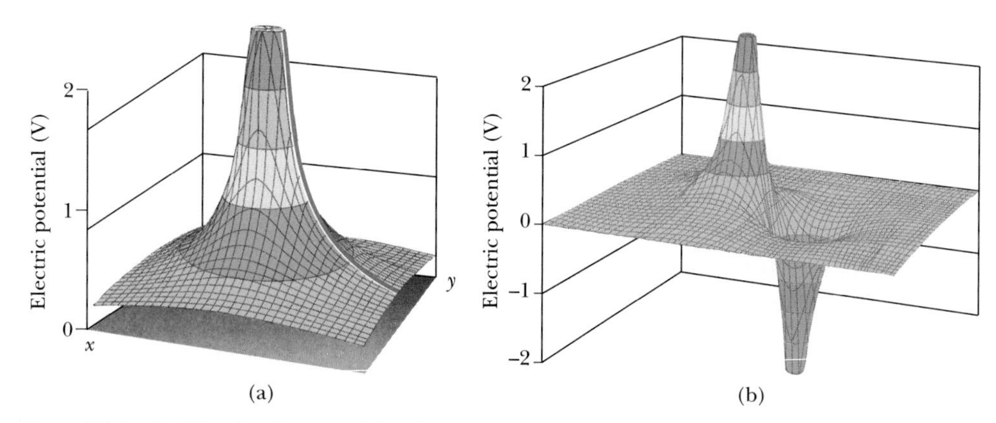

Figure 25.8 (a) The electric potential in the plane around a single positive charge is plotted on the vertical axis. (The electric potential function for a negative charge would look like a hole instead of a hill.) The red line shows the $1/r$ nature of the electric potential as given by Equation 25.11. (b) The electric potential in the plane containing a dipole.

PITFALL PREVENTION 25.4

Similar Equation Warning

Do not confuse Equation 25.11 for the electric potential of a point charge with Equation 23.9 for the electric field of a point charge. Potential is proportional to $1/r$, whereas the field is proportional to $1/r^2$. The effect of a charge on the space surrounding it can be described in two ways. The charge sets up a vector electric field $\vec{\mathbf{E}}$, which is related to the force experienced by a test charge placed in the field. It also sets up a scalar potential V, which is related to the potential energy of the two-charge system when a test charge is placed in the field.

points Ⓐ and Ⓑ in a field created by a point charge depends only on the radial coordinates $r_Ⓐ$ and $r_Ⓑ$. It is customary to choose the reference of electric potential for a point charge to be $V = 0$ at $r_Ⓐ = \infty$. With this reference choice, the electric potential created by a point charge at any distance r from the charge is

$$V = k_e \frac{q}{r} \quad (25.11)$$

Figure 25.8a shows a plot of the electric potential on the vertical axis for a positive charge located in the xy plane. Consider the following analogy to gravitational potential. Imagine trying to roll a marble toward the top of a hill shaped like the surface in Figure 25.8a. Pushing the marble up the hill is analogous to pushing one positively charged object toward another positively charged object. Similarly, the electric potential graph of the region surrounding a negative charge is analogous to a "hole" with respect to any approaching positively charged objects. A charged object must be infinitely distant from another charge before the surface in Figure 25.8a is "flat" and has an electric potential of zero.

We obtain the electric potential resulting from two or more point charges by applying the superposition principle. That is, the total electric potential at some point P due to several point charges is the sum of the potentials due to the individual charges. For a group of point charges, we can write the total electric potential at P as

Electric potential due to several point charges ▶

$$V = k_e \sum_i \frac{q_i}{r_i} \quad (25.12)$$

where the potential is again taken to be zero at infinity and r_i is the distance from the point P to the charge q_i. Notice that the sum in Equation 25.12 is an algebraic sum of scalars rather than a vector sum (which we use to calculate the electric field of a group of charges). Therefore, it is often much easier to evaluate V than $\vec{\mathbf{E}}$. The electric potential around a dipole is illustrated in Figure 25.8b. Notice the steep slope of the potential between the charges, representing a region of strong electric field.

Now consider the potential energy of a system of two charged particles. If V_2 is the electric potential at a point P due to charge q_2, the work an external agent must do to bring a second charge q_1 from infinity to P without acceleration is $q_1 V_2$. This work represents a transfer of energy into the system, and the energy appears in the system as potential energy U when the particles are separated by a distance

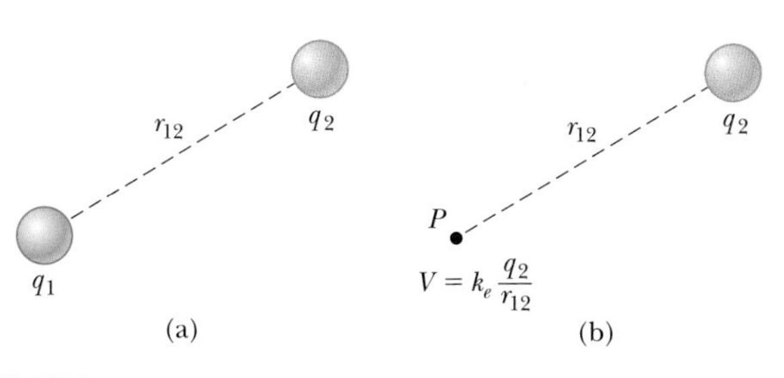

ACTIVE FIGURE 25.9

(a) If two point charges are separated by a distance r_{12}, the potential energy of the pair of charges is given by $k_e q_1 q_2 / r_{12}$. (b) If charge q_1 is removed, a potential $k_e q_2 / r_{12}$ exists at point P due to charge q_2.

Sign in at www.thomsonedu.com and go to ThomsonNOW to move charge q_1 or point P and see the result on the electric potential energy of the system for part (a) and the electric potential due to charge q_2 for part (b).

r_{12} (Active Fig. 25.9a). Therefore, the potential energy of the system can be expressed as[1]

$$U = k_e \frac{q_1 q_2}{r_{12}} \qquad (25.13)$$

If the charges are of the same sign, U is positive. Positive work must be done by an external agent on the system to bring the two charges near each other (because charges of the same sign repel). If the charges are of opposite sign, U is negative. Negative work is done by an external agent against the attractive force between the charges of opposite sign as they are brought near each other; a force must be applied opposite the displacement to prevent q_1 from accelerating toward q_2.

In Active Figure 25.9b, we have removed the charge q_1. At the position this charge previously occupied, point P, Equations 25.2 and 25.13 can be used to define a potential due to charge q_2 as $V = U/q_1 = k_e q_2 / r_{12}$. This expression is consistent with Equation 25.11.

If the system consists of more than two charged particles, we can obtain the total potential energy of the system by calculating U for every pair of charges and summing the terms algebraically. For example, the total potential energy of the system of three charges shown in Figure 25.10 is

$$U = k_e \left(\frac{q_1 q_2}{r_{12}} + \frac{q_1 q_3}{r_{13}} + \frac{q_2 q_3}{r_{23}} \right) \qquad (25.14)$$

Physically, this result can be interpreted as follows. Imagine q_1 is fixed at the position shown in Figure 25.10 but q_2 and q_3 are at infinity. The work an external agent must do to bring q_2 from infinity to its position near q_1 is $k_e q_1 q_2 / r_{12}$, which is the first term in Equation 25.14. The last two terms represent the work required to bring q_3 from infinity to its position near q_1 and q_2. (The result is independent of the order in which the charges are transported.)

PITFALL PREVENTION 25.5
Which Work?

There is a difference between work done *by one member of a system on another member* and work done *on a system by an external agent.* In the discussion related to Equation 25.14, we consider the group of charges to be the system; an external agent is doing work on the system to move the charges from an infinite separation to a small separation.

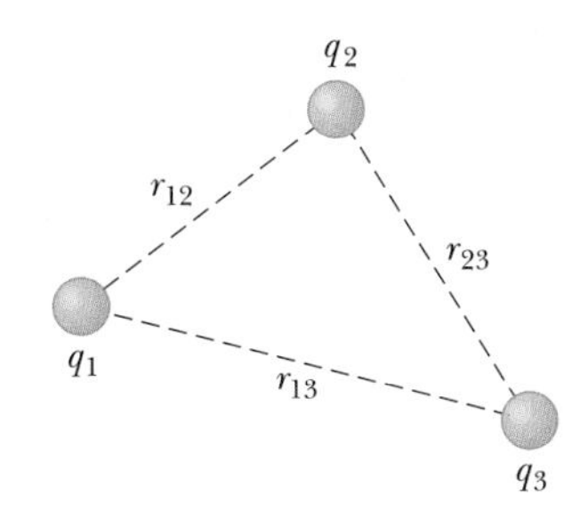

Figure 25.10 Three point charges are fixed at the positions shown. The potential energy of this system of charges is given by Equation 25.14.

Quick Quiz 25.3 In Active Figure 25.9a, take q_1 to be a negative source charge and q_2 to be the test charge. **(i)** If q_2 is initially positive and is changed to a charge of the same magnitude but negative, what happens to the potential at the position of q_2 due to q_1? (a) It increases. (b) It decreases. (c) It remains the same. **(ii)** When q_2 is changed from positive to negative, what happens to the potential energy of the two-charge system? Choose from the same possibilities.

---

[1] The expression for the electric potential energy of a system made up of two point charges, Equation 25.13, is of the *same* form as the equation for the gravitational potential energy of a system made up of two point masses, $-Gm_1 m_2 / r$ (see Chapter 13). The similarity is not surprising considering that both expressions are derived from an inverse-square force law.

EXAMPLE 25.3 The Electric Potential Due to Two Point Charges

As shown in Figure 25.11a, a charge $q_1 = 2.00\ \mu C$ is located at the origin and a charge $q_2 = -6.00\ \mu C$ is located at (0, 3.00) m.

(A) Find the total electric potential due to these charges at the point *P*, whose coordinates are (4.00, 0) m.

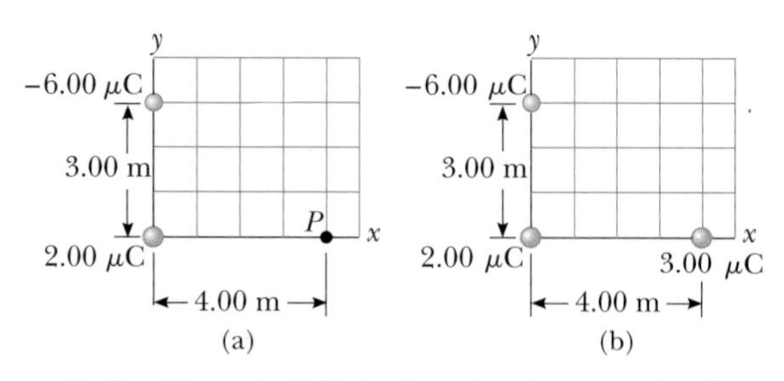

Figure 25.11 (Example 25.3) (a) The electric potential at *P* due to the two charges q_1 and q_2 is the algebraic sum of the potentials due to the individual charges. (b) A third charge $q_3 = 3.00\ \mu C$ is brought from infinity to point *P*.

SOLUTION

Conceptualize Recognize that the 2.00 μC and −6.00 μC charges are source charges and set up an electric field as well as a potential at all points in space, including point *P*.

Categorize The potential is evaluated using an equation developed in this chapter, so we categorize this example as a substitution problem.

Use Equation 25.12 for the system of two source charges:

$$V_P = k_e\left(\frac{q_1}{r_1} + \frac{q_2}{r_2}\right)$$

Substitute numerical values:

$$V_P = (8.99 \times 10^9\ \text{N}\cdot\text{m}^2/\text{C}^2)\left(\frac{2.00 \times 10^{-6}\ \text{C}}{4.00\ \text{m}} + \frac{-6.00 \times 10^{-6}\ \text{C}}{5.00\ \text{m}}\right)$$

$$= -6.29 \times 10^3\ \text{V}$$

(B) Find the change in potential energy of the system of two charges plus a third charge $q_3 = 3.00\ \mu C$ as the latter charge moves from infinity to point *P* (Fig. 25.11b).

SOLUTION

Assign $U_i = 0$ for the system to the configuration in which the charge q_3 is at infinity. Use Equation 25.2 to evaluate the potential energy for the configuration in which the charge is at *P*:

$$U_f = q_3 V_P$$

Substitute numerical values to evaluate ΔU:

$$\Delta U = U_f - U_i = q_3 V_P - 0 = (3.00 \times 10^{-6}\ \text{C})(-6.29 \times 10^3\ \text{V})$$

$$= -1.89 \times 10^{-2}\ \text{J}$$

Therefore, because the potential energy of the system has decreased, an external agent has to do positive work to remove the charge from point *P* back to infinity.

What If? You are working through this example with a classmate and she says, "Wait a minute! In part (B), we ignored the potential energy associated with the pair of charges q_1 and q_2!" How would you respond?

Answer Given the statement of the problem, it is not necessary to include this potential energy because part (B) asks for the *change* in potential energy of the system as q_3 is brought in from infinity. Because the configuration of charges q_1 and q_2 does not change in the process, there is no ΔU associated with these charges. Had part (B) asked to find the change in potential energy when *all three* charges start out infinitely far apart and are then brought to the positions in Figure 25.11b, however, you would have to calculate the change using Equation 25.14.

25.4 Obtaining the Value of the Electric Field from the Electric Potential

The electric field $\vec{\mathbf{E}}$ and the electric potential V are related as shown in Equation 25.3, which tells us how to find ΔV if the electric field $\vec{\mathbf{E}}$ is known. We now show how to calculate the value of the electric field if the electric potential is known in a certain region.

From Equation 25.3, we can express the potential difference dV between two points a distance ds apart as

$$dV = -\vec{\mathbf{E}} \cdot d\vec{\mathbf{s}} \qquad (25.15)$$

If the electric field has only one component E_x, then $\vec{\mathbf{E}} \cdot d\vec{\mathbf{s}} = E_x\, dx$. Therefore, Equation 25.15 becomes $dV = -E_x\, dx$, or

$$E_x = -\frac{dV}{dx} \qquad (25.16)$$

That is, the x component of the electric field is equal to the negative of the derivative of the electric potential with respect to x. Similar statements can be made about the y and z components. Equation 25.16 is the mathematical statement of the electric field being a measure of the rate of change with position of the electric potential as mentioned in Section 25.1.

Experimentally, electric potential and position can be measured easily with a voltmeter (see Section 28.5) and a meterstick. Consequently, an electric field can be determined by measuring the electric potential at several positions in the field and making a graph of the results. According to Equation 25.16, the slope of a graph of V versus x at a given point provides the magnitude of the electric field at that point.

When a test charge undergoes a displacement $d\vec{\mathbf{s}}$ along an equipotential surface, then $dV = 0$ because the potential is constant along an equipotential surface. From Equation 25.15, we see that $dV = -\vec{\mathbf{E}} \cdot d\vec{\mathbf{s}} = 0$; therefore, $\vec{\mathbf{E}}$ must be perpendicular to the displacement along the equipotential surface. This result shows that the **equipotential surfaces must always be perpendicular to the electric field lines passing through them.**

As mentioned at the end of Section 25.2, the equipotential surfaces associated with a uniform electric field consist of a family of planes perpendicular to the field lines. Figure 25.12a shows some representative equipotential surfaces for this situation.

If the charge distribution creating an electric field has spherical symmetry such that the volume charge density depends only on the radial distance r, the electric field is radial. In this case, $\vec{\mathbf{E}} \cdot d\vec{\mathbf{s}} = E_r\, dr$, and we can express dV as $dV = -E_r\, dr$. Therefore,

$$E_r = -\frac{dV}{dr} \qquad (25.17)$$

For example, the electric potential of a point charge is $V = k_e q/r$. Because V is a function of r only, the potential function has spherical symmetry. Applying Equation 25.17, we find that the electric field due to the point charge is $E_r = k_e q/r^2$, a familiar result. Notice that the potential changes only in the radial direction, not in any direction perpendicular to r. Therefore, V (like E_r) is a function only of r, which is again consistent with the idea that **equipotential surfaces are perpendicular to field lines.** In this case, the equipotential surfaces are a family of spheres concentric with the spherically symmetric charge distribution (Fig. 25.12b). The equipotential surfaces for an electric dipole are sketched in Figure 25.12c.

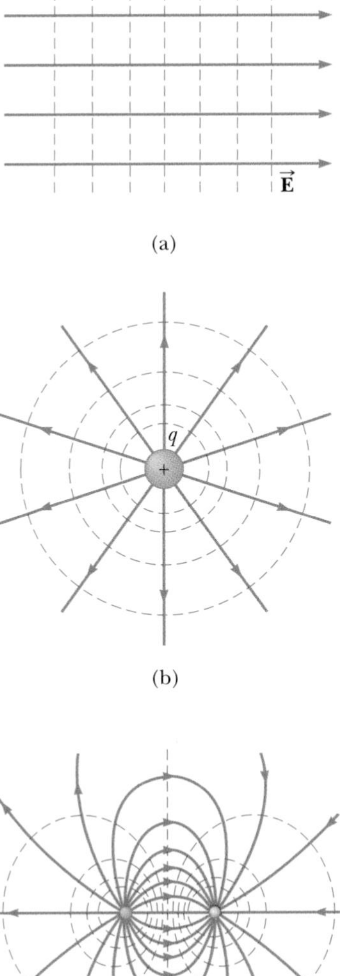

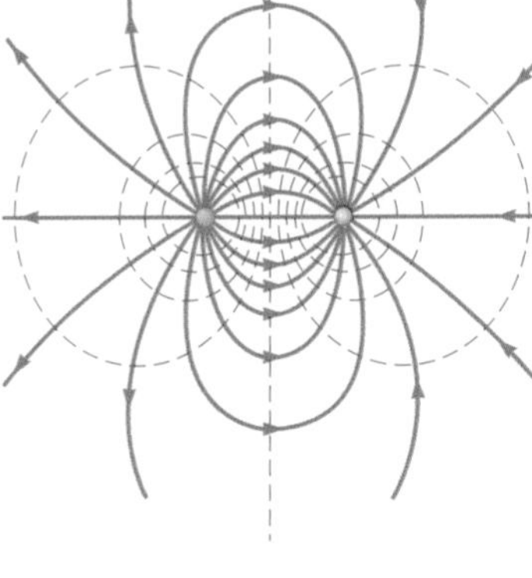

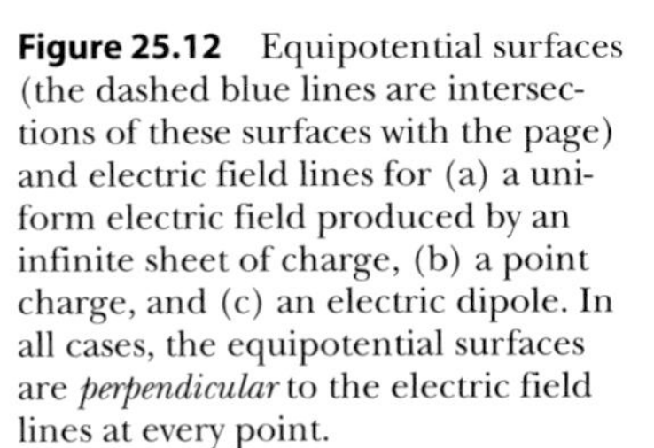

Figure 25.12 Equipotential surfaces (the dashed blue lines are intersections of these surfaces with the page) and electric field lines for (a) a uniform electric field produced by an infinite sheet of charge, (b) a point charge, and (c) an electric dipole. In all cases, the equipotential surfaces are *perpendicular* to the electric field lines at every point.

In general, the electric potential is a function of all three spatial coordinates. If $V(r)$ is given in terms of the Cartesian coordinates, the electric field components E_x, E_y, and E_z can readily be found from $V(x, y, z)$ as the partial derivatives[2]

Finding the electric field from the potential

$$E_x = -\frac{\partial V}{\partial x} \qquad E_y = -\frac{\partial V}{\partial y} \qquad E_z = -\frac{\partial V}{\partial z} \tag{25.18}$$

Quick Quiz 25.4 In a certain region of space, the electric potential is zero everywhere along the x axis. From this information, you can conclude that the x component of the electric field in this region is (a) zero, (b) in the $+x$ direction, or (c) in the $-x$ direction.

EXAMPLE 25.4 The Electric Potential Due to a Dipole

An electric dipole consists of two charges of equal magnitude and opposite sign separated by a distance $2a$ as shown in Figure 25.13. The dipole is along the x axis and is centered at the origin.

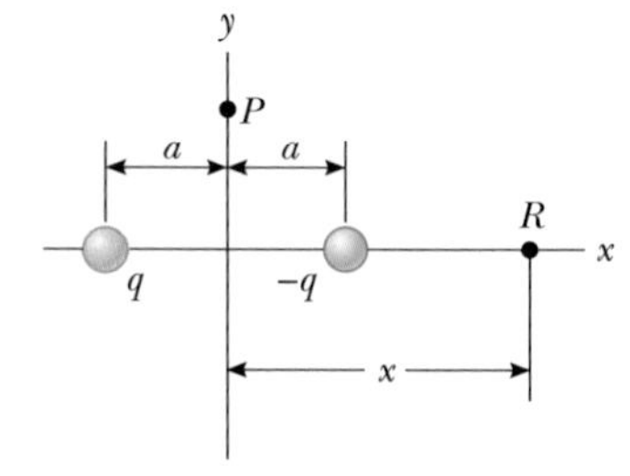

Figure 25.13 (Example 25.4) An electric dipole located on the x axis.

(A) Calculate the electric potential at point P on the y axis.

SOLUTION

Conceptualize Compare this situation to that in part (B) of Example 23.5. It is the same situation, but here we are seeking the electric potential rather than the electric field.

Categorize Because the dipole consists of only two source charges, the electric potential can be evaluated by summing the potentials due to the individual charges.

Analyze Use Equation 25.12 to find the electric potential at P due to the two charges:

$$V_P = k_e \sum_i \frac{q_i}{r_i} = k_e\left(\frac{q}{\sqrt{a^2 + y^2}} + \frac{-q}{\sqrt{a^2 + y^2}}\right) = 0$$

(B) Calculate the electric potential at point R on the $+x$ axis.

SOLUTION

Use Equation 25.12 to find the electric potential at R due to the two charges:

$$V_R = k_e \sum_i \frac{q_i}{r_i} = k_e\left(\frac{-q}{x - a} + \frac{q}{x + a}\right) = -\frac{2k_e qa}{x^2 - a^2}$$

(C) Calculate V and E_x at a point on the x axis far from the dipole.

SOLUTION

For point R far from the dipole such that $x \gg a$, neglect a^2 in the denominator of the answer to part (B) and write V in this limit:

$$V_R = \lim_{x \gg a}\left(-\frac{2k_e qa}{x^2 - a^2}\right) \approx -\frac{2k_e qa}{x^2} \quad (x \gg a)$$

[2] In vector notation, $\vec{\mathbf{E}}$ is often written in Cartesian coordinate systems as

$$\vec{\mathbf{E}} = -\nabla V = -\left(\hat{\mathbf{i}}\frac{\partial}{\partial x} + \hat{\mathbf{j}}\frac{\partial}{\partial y} + \hat{\mathbf{k}}\frac{\partial}{\partial z}\right)V$$

where ∇ is called the *gradient operator*.

Use Equation 25.16 and this result to calculate the x component of the electric field at a point on the x axis far from the dipole:

$$E_x = -\frac{dV}{dx} = -\frac{d}{dx}\left(-\frac{2k_e qa}{x^2}\right)$$

$$= 2k_e qa \frac{d}{dx}\left(\frac{1}{x^2}\right) = -\frac{4k_e qa}{x^3} \quad (x \gg a)$$

Finalize The potentials in parts (B) and (C) are negative because points on the $+x$ axis are closer to the negative charge than to the positive charge. For the same reason, the x component of the electric field is negative. Compare the result of part (C) to that of Problem 18 in Chapter 23, in which the electric field on the x axis due to a dipole was calculated directly.

What If? Suppose you want to find the electric field at a point P on the y axis. In part (A), the electric potential was found to be zero for all values of y. Is the electric field zero at all points on the y axis?

Answer No. That there is no change in the potential along the y axis tells us only that the y component of the electric field is zero. Look back at Figure 23.13 in Example 23.5. We showed there that the electric field of a dipole on the y axis has only an x component. We could not find the x component in the current example because we do not have an expression for the potential near the y axis as a function of x.

25.5 Electric Potential Due to Continuous Charge Distributions

The electric potential due to a continuous charge distribution can be calculated in two ways. If the charge distribution is known, we consider the potential due to a small charge element dq, treating this element as a point charge (Fig. 25.14). From Equation 25.11, the electric potential dV at some point P due to the charge element dq is

$$dV = k_e \frac{dq}{r} \tag{25.19}$$

where r is the distance from the charge element to point P. To obtain the total potential at point P, we integrate Equation 25.19 to include contributions from all elements of the charge distribution. Because each element is, in general, a different distance from point P and k_e is constant, we can express V as

$$V = k_e \int \frac{dq}{r} \tag{25.20}$$

◀ Electric potential due to a continuous charge distribution

In effect, we have replaced the sum in Equation 25.12 with an integral. In this expression for V, the electric potential is taken to be zero when point P is infinitely far from the charge distribution.

If the electric field is already known from other considerations such as Gauss's law, we can calculate the electric potential due to a continuous charge distribution using Equation 25.3. If the charge distribution has sufficient symmetry, we first evaluate $\vec{\mathbf{E}}$ using Gauss's law and then substitute the value obtained into Equation 25.3 to determine the potential difference ΔV between any two points. We then choose the electric potential V to be zero at some convenient point.

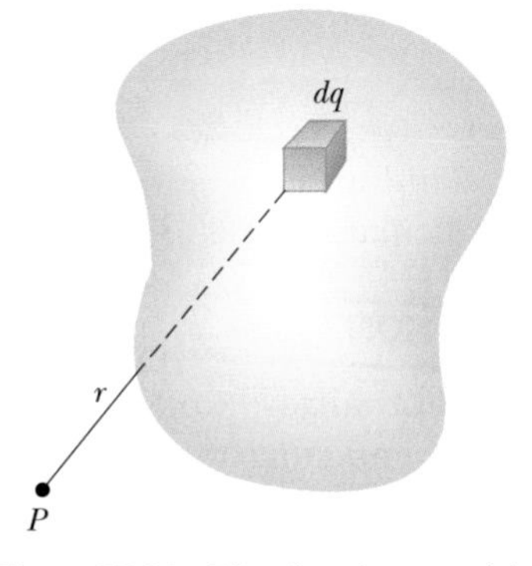

Figure 25.14 The electric potential at point P due to a continuous charge distribution can be calculated by dividing the charge distribution into elements of charge dq and summing the electric potential contributions over all elements.

PROBLEM-SOLVING STRATEGY Calculating Electric Potential

The following procedure is recommended for solving problems that involve the determination of an electric potential due to a charge distribution.

1. *Conceptualize.* Think carefully about the individual charges or the charge distribution you have in the problem and imagine what type of potential would be created. Appeal to any symmetry in the arrangement of charges to help you visualize the potential.

2. *Categorize.* Are you analyzing a group of individual charges or a continuous charge distribution? The answer to this question will tell you how to proceed in the *Analyze* step.

3. *Analyze.* When working problems involving electric potential, remember that it is a *scalar quantity,* so there are no components to consider. Therefore, when using the superposition principle to evaluate the electric potential at a point, simply take the algebraic sum of the potentials due to each charge. You must keep track of signs, however.

   As with potential energy in mechanics, only *changes* in electric potential are significant; hence, the point where the potential is set at zero is arbitrary. When dealing with point charges or a finite-sized charge distribution, we usually define $V = 0$ to be at a point infinitely far from the charges. If the charge distribution itself extends to infinity, however, some other nearby point must be selected as the reference point.

   (*a*) *If you are analyzing a group of individual charges:* Use the superposition principle, which states that when several point charges are present, the resultant potential at a point in space is the *algebraic sum* of the individual potentials due to the individual charges (Eq. 25.12). Example 25.4 demonstrated this procedure.

   (*b*) *If you are analyzing a continuous charge distribution:* Replace the sums for evaluating the total potential at some point P from individual charges by integrals (Eq. 25.20). The charge distribution is divided into infinitesimal elements of charge dq located at a distance r from the point P. An element is then treated as a point charge, so the potential at P due to the element is $dV = k_e\, dq/r$. The total potential at P is obtained by integrating over the entire charge distribution. For many problems, it is possible in performing the integration to express dq and r in terms of a single variable. To simplify the integration, give careful consideration to the geometry involved in the problem. Examples 25.5 through 25.7 demonstrate such a procedure.

   To obtain the potential from the electric field: Another method used to obtain the potential is to start with the definition of the potential difference given by Equation 25.3. If $\vec{\mathbf{E}}$ is known or can be obtained easily (such as from Gauss's law), the line integral of $\vec{\mathbf{E}} \cdot d\vec{\mathbf{s}}$ can be evaluated.

4. *Finalize.* Check to see if your expression for the potential is consistent with the mental representation and reflects any symmetry you noted previously. Imagine varying parameters such as the distance of the observation point from the charges or the radius of any circular objects to see if the mathematical result changes in a reasonable way.

EXAMPLE 25.5 Electric Potential Due to a Uniformly Charged Ring

(A) Find an expression for the electric potential at a point P located on the perpendicular central axis of a uniformly charged ring of radius a and total charge Q.

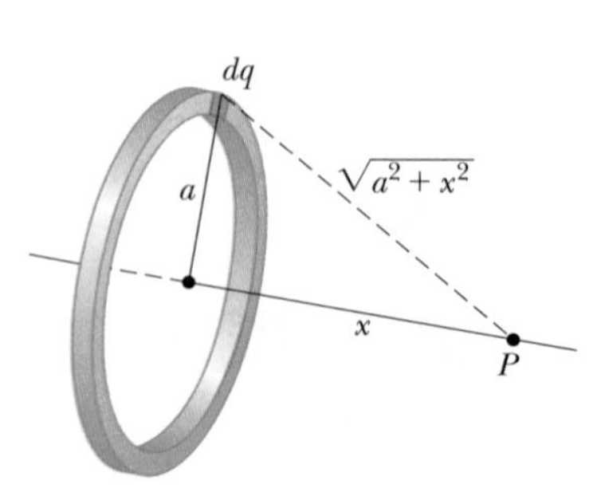

Figure 25.15 (Example 25.5) A uniformly charged ring of radius a lies in a plane perpendicular to the x axis. All elements dq of the ring are the same distance from a point P lying on the x axis.

SOLUTION

Conceptualize Study Figure 25.15, in which the ring is oriented so that its plane is perpendicular to the x axis and its center is at the origin.

Categorize Because the ring consists of a continuous distribution of charge rather than a set of discrete charges, we must use the integration technique represented by Equation 25.20 in this example.

Analyze We take point P to be at a distance x from the center of the ring as shown in Figure 25.15. Notice that all charge elements dq are at the same distance $\sqrt{a^2 + x^2}$ from point P.

Use Equation 25.20 to express V in terms of the geometry:

$$V = k_e \int \frac{dq}{r} = k_e \int \frac{dq}{\sqrt{a^2 + x^2}}$$

Noting that a and x are constants, bring $\sqrt{a^2 + x^2}$ in front of the integral sign and integrate over the ring:

$$V = \frac{k_e}{\sqrt{a^2 + x^2}} \int dq = \frac{k_e Q}{\sqrt{a^2 + x^2}} \quad (25.21)$$

(B) Find an expression for the magnitude of the electric field at point P.

SOLUTION

From symmetry, notice that along the x axis $\vec{\mathbf{E}}$ can have only an x component. Therefore, apply Equation 25.16 to Equation 25.21:

$$E_x = -\frac{dV}{dx} = -k_e Q \frac{d}{dx}(a^2 + x^2)^{-1/2}$$

$$= -k_e Q(-\tfrac{1}{2})(a^2 + x^2)^{-3/2}(2x)$$

$$E_x = \frac{k_e x}{(a^2 + x^2)^{3/2}} Q \quad (25.22)$$

Finalize The only variable in the expressions for V and E_x is x. That is not surprising because our calculation is valid only for points along the x axis, where y and z are both zero. This result for the electric field agrees with that obtained by direct integration (see Example 23.7).

EXAMPLE 25.6 Electric Potential Due to a Uniformly Charged Disk

A uniformly charged disk has radius R and surface charge density σ.

(A) Find the electric potential at a point P along the perpendicular central axis of the disk.

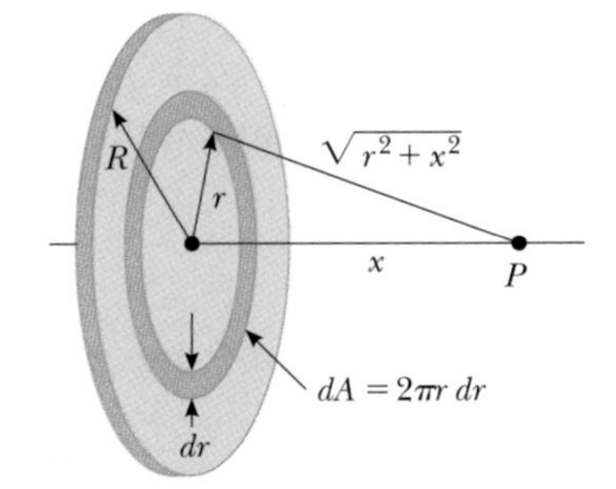

Figure 25.16 (Example 25.6) A uniformly charged disk of radius R lies in a plane perpendicular to the x axis. The calculation of the electric potential at any point P on the x axis is simplified by dividing the disk into many rings of radius r and width dr, with area $2\pi r\,dr$.

SOLUTION

Conceptualize If we consider the disk to be a set of concentric rings, we can use our result from Example 25.5—which gives the potential created by a ring of radius a—and sum the contributions of all rings making up the disk.

Categorize Because the disk is continuous, we evaluate the potential due to a continuous charge distribution rather than a group of individual charges.

Analyze Find the amount of charge dq on a ring of radius r and width dr as shown in Figure 25.16:

$$dq = \sigma\,dA = \sigma(2\pi r\,dr) = 2\pi\sigma r\,dr$$

Use this result in the equation given for V in Example 25.5 (with a replaced by r and Q replaced by dq) to find the potential due to the ring:

$$dV = \frac{k_e\,dq}{\sqrt{r^2 + x^2}} = \frac{k_e 2\pi\sigma r\,dr}{\sqrt{r^2 + x^2}}$$

To obtain the total potential at P, integrate this expression over the limits $r = 0$ to $r = R$, noting that x is a constant:

$$V = \pi k_e \sigma \int_0^R \frac{2r\,dr}{\sqrt{r^2 + x^2}} = \pi k_e \sigma \int_0^R (r^2 + x^2)^{-1/2}\,2r\,dr$$

This integral is of the common form $\int u^n\,du$ and has the value $u^{n+1}/(n+1)$, where $n = -\frac{1}{2}$ and $u = r^2 + x^2$. Use this result to evaluate the integral:

$$V = 2\pi k_e \sigma[(R^2 + x^2)^{1/2} - x] \quad (25.23)$$

(B) Find the x component of the electric field at a point P along the perpendicular central axis of the disk.

SOLUTION

As in Example 25.5, use Equation 25.16 to find the electric field at any axial point:

$$E_x = -\frac{dV}{dx} = 2\pi k_e\sigma\left[1 - \frac{x}{(R^2 + x^2)^{1/2}}\right] \quad (25.24)$$

Finalize Compare Equation 25.24 with the result of Example 23.8. The calculation of V and $\vec{\mathbf{E}}$ for an arbitrary point off the x axis is more difficult to perform, and we do not treat that situation in this book.

EXAMPLE 25.7 Electric Potential Due to a Finite Line of Charge

A rod of length ℓ located along the x axis has a total charge Q and a uniform linear charge density $\lambda = Q/\ell$. Find the electric potential at a point P located on the y axis a distance a from the origin (Fig. 25.17).

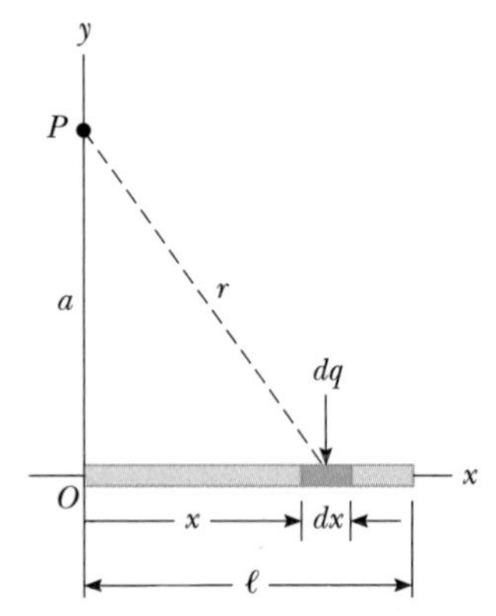

Figure 25.17 (Example 25.7) A uniform line charge of length ℓ located along the x axis. To calculate the electric potential at P, the line charge is divided into segments each of length dx and each carrying a charge $dq = \lambda\, dx$.

SOLUTION

Conceptualize The potential at P due to every segment of charge on the rod is positive because every segment carries a positive charge.

Categorize Because the rod is continuous, we evaluate the potential due to a continuous charge distribution rather than a group of individual charges.

Analyze In Figure 25.17, the rod lies along the x axis, dx is the length of one small segment, and dq is the charge on that segment. Because the rod has a charge per unit length λ, the charge dq on the small segment is $dq = \lambda\, dx$.

Find the potential at P due to one segment of the rod:

$$dV = k_e\frac{dq}{r} = k_e\frac{\lambda\, dx}{\sqrt{a^2 + x^2}}$$

Find the total potential at P by integrating this expression over the limits $x = 0$ to $x = \ell$:

$$V = \int_0^\ell k_e\frac{\lambda\, dx}{\sqrt{a^2 + x^2}}$$

Noting that k_e and $\lambda = Q/\ell$ are constants and can be removed from the integral, evaluate the integral with the help of Appendix B:

$$V = k_e\lambda\int_0^\ell \frac{dx}{\sqrt{a^2 + x^2}} = k_e\frac{Q}{\ell}\ln\left(x + \sqrt{a^2 + x^2}\right)\Big|_0^\ell$$

Evaluate the result between the limits:

$$V = k_e\frac{Q}{\ell}\left[\ln\left(\ell + \sqrt{a^2 + \ell^2}\right) - \ln a\right] = k_e\frac{Q}{\ell}\ln\left(\frac{\ell + \sqrt{a^2 + \ell^2}}{a}\right) \quad (25.25)$$

What If? What if you were asked to find the electric field at point P? Would that be a simple calculation?

Answer Calculating the electric field by means of Equation 23.11 would be a little messy. There is no symmetry to appeal to, and the integration over the line of charge would represent a vector addition of electric fields at point P. Using Equation 25.18, you could find E_y by replacing a with y in Equation 25.25 and performing the differentiation with respect to y. Because the charged rod in Figure 25.17 lies entirely to the right of $x = 0$, the electric field at point P would have an x component to the left if the rod is charged positively. You cannot use Equation 25.18 to find the x

component of the field, however, because the potential due to the rod was evaluated at a specific value of x ($x = 0$) rather than a general value of x. You would have to find the potential as a function of both x and y to be able to find the x and y components of the electric field using Equation 25.25.

25.6 Electric Potential Due to a Charged Conductor

In Section 24.4, we found that when a solid conductor in equilibrium carries a net charge, the charge resides on the conductor's outer surface. Furthermore, the electric field just outside the conductor is perpendicular to the surface and the field inside is zero.

We now show that **every point on the surface of a charged conductor in equilibrium is at the same electric potential.** Consider two points Ⓐ and Ⓑ on the surface of a charged conductor as shown in Figure 25.18. Along a surface path connecting these points, $\vec{\mathbf{E}}$ is always perpendicular to the displacement $d\vec{\mathbf{s}}$; therefore $\vec{\mathbf{E}} \cdot d\vec{\mathbf{s}} = 0$. Using this result and Equation 25.3, we conclude that the potential difference between Ⓐ and Ⓑ is necessarily zero:

$$V_{Ⓑ} - V_{Ⓐ} = -\int_{Ⓐ}^{Ⓑ} \vec{\mathbf{E}} \cdot d\vec{\mathbf{s}} = 0$$

This result applies to any two points on the surface. Therefore, V is constant everywhere on the surface of a charged conductor in equilibrium. That is,

> the surface of any charged conductor in electrostatic equilibrium is an equipotential surface. Furthermore, because the electric field is zero inside the conductor, the electric potential is constant everywhere inside the conductor and equal to its value at the surface.

PITFALL PREVENTION 25.6
Potential May Not Be Zero

The electric potential inside the conductor is not necessarily zero in Figure 25.18, even though the electric field is zero. Equation 25.15 shows that a zero value of the field results in no *change* in the potential from one point to another inside the conductor. Therefore, the potential everywhere inside the conductor, including the surface, has the same value, which may or may not be zero, depending on where the zero of potential is defined.

Because of the constant value of the potential, no work is required to move a test charge from the interior of a charged conductor to its surface.

Consider a solid metal conducting sphere of radius R and total positive charge Q as shown in Figure 25.19a. As determined in part (A) of Example 24.3, the electric field outside the sphere is k_eQ/r^2 and points radially outward. Because the field outside of a spherically symmetric charge distribution is identical to that of a point charge, we expect the potential to also be that of a point charge, k_eQ/r. At the surface of the conducting sphere in Figure 25.19a, the potential must be k_eQ/R. Because the entire sphere must be at the same potential, the potential at any point within the sphere must also be k_eQ/R. Figure 25.19b is a plot of the electric potential as a function of r, and Figure 25.19c shows how the electric field varies with r.

When a net charge is placed on a spherical conductor, the surface charge density is uniform as indicated in Figure 25.19a. If the conductor is nonspherical as in

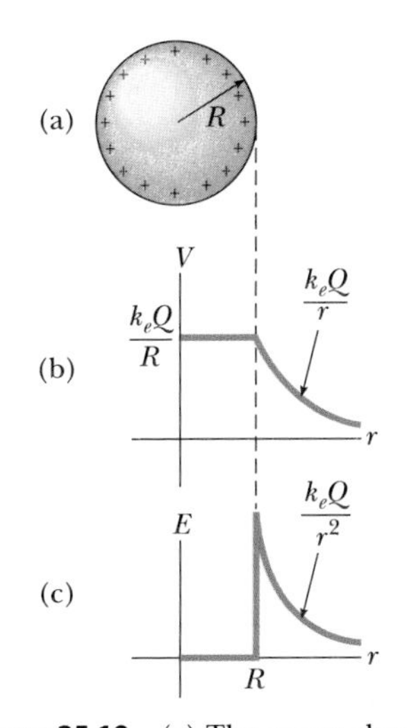

Figure 25.19 (a) The excess charge on a conducting sphere of radius R is uniformly distributed on its surface. (b) Electric potential versus distance r from the center of the charged conducting sphere. (c) Electric field magnitude versus distance r from the center of the charged conducting sphere.

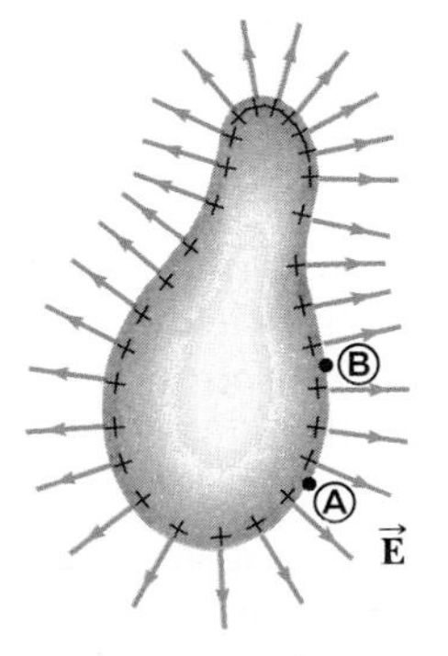

Figure 25.18 An arbitrarily shaped conductor carrying a positive charge. When the conductor is in electrostatic equilibrium, all the charge resides at the surface, $\vec{\mathbf{E}} = 0$ inside the conductor, and the direction of $\vec{\mathbf{E}}$ immediately outside the conductor is perpendicular to the surface. The electric potential is constant inside the conductor and is equal to the potential at the surface. Notice from the spacing of the positive signs that the surface charge density is nonuniform.

Figure 25.18, however, the surface charge density is high where the radius of curvature is small (as noted in Section 24.4) and low where the radius of curvature is large. Because the electric field immediately outside the conductor is proportional to the surface charge density, **the electric field is large near convex points having small radii of curvature and reaches very high values at sharp points.** In Example 25.8, the relationship between electric field and radius of curvature is explored mathematically.

EXAMPLE 25.8 Two Connected Charged Spheres

Two spherical conductors of radii r_1 and r_2 are separated by a distance much greater than the radius of either sphere. The spheres are connected by a conducting wire as shown in Figure 25.20. The charges on the spheres in equilibrium are q_1 and q_2, respectively, and they are uniformly charged. Find the ratio of the magnitudes of the electric fields at the surfaces of the spheres.

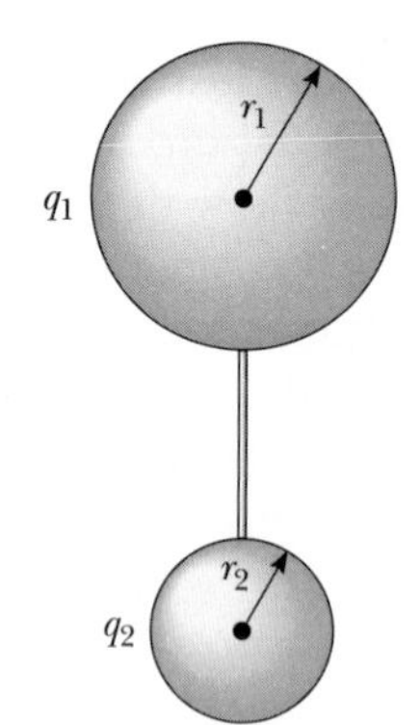

Figure 25.20 (Example 25.8) Two charged spherical conductors connected by a conducting wire. The spheres are at the *same* electric potential V.

SOLUTION

Conceptualize Imagine that the spheres are much farther apart than shown in Figure 25.20. Because they are so far apart, the field of one does not affect the charge distribution on the other. The conducting wire between them ensures that both spheres have the same electric potential.

Categorize Because the spheres are so far apart, we model the charge distribution on them as spherically symmetric, and we can model the field and potential outside the spheres to be that due to point charges.

Analyze Set the electric potentials at the surfaces of the spheres equal to each other:

$$V = k_e \frac{q_1}{r_1} = k_e \frac{q_2}{r_2}$$

Solve for the ratio of charges on the spheres:

$$(1) \quad \frac{q_1}{q_2} = \frac{r_1}{r_2}$$

Write expressions for the magnitudes of the electric fields at the surfaces of the spheres:

$$E_1 = k_e \frac{q_1}{r_1^2} \quad \text{and} \quad E_2 = k_e \frac{q_2}{r_2^2}$$

Evaluate the ratio of these two fields:

$$\frac{E_1}{E_2} = \frac{q_1}{q_2}\frac{r_2^2}{r_1^2}$$

Substitute for the ratio of charges from Equation (1):

$$(2) \quad \frac{E_1}{E_2} = \frac{r_1}{r_2}\frac{r_2^2}{r_1^2} = \frac{r_2}{r_1}$$

Finalize The field is stronger in the vicinity of the smaller sphere even though the electric potentials at the surfaces of both spheres are the same.

A Cavity Within a Conductor

Suppose a conductor of arbitrary shape contains a cavity as shown in Figure 25.21. Let's assume no charges are inside the cavity. **In this case, the electric field inside the cavity must be zero** regardless of the charge distribution on the outside surface of the conductor as we mentioned in Section 24.4. Furthermore, the field in the cavity is zero even if an electric field exists outside the conductor.

To prove this point, remember that every point on the conductor is at the same electric potential; therefore, any two points Ⓐ and Ⓑ on the cavity's surface must be at the same potential. Now imagine a field $\vec{\mathbf{E}}$ exists in the cavity and evaluate the potential difference $V_Ⓑ - V_Ⓐ$ defined by Equation 25.3:

$$V_Ⓑ - V_Ⓐ = -\int_Ⓐ^Ⓑ \vec{\mathbf{E}} \cdot d\vec{\mathbf{s}}$$

Because $V_Ⓑ - V_Ⓐ = 0$, the integral of $\vec{\mathbf{E}} \cdot d\vec{\mathbf{s}}$ must be zero for all paths between any two points Ⓐ and Ⓑ on the conductor. The only way that can be true for *all* paths is if $\vec{\mathbf{E}}$ is zero *everywhere* in the cavity. Therefore, **a cavity surrounded by conducting walls is a field-free region as long as no charges are inside the cavity.**

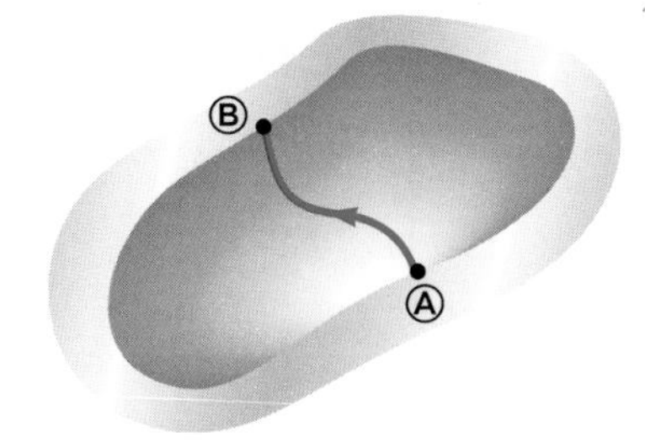

Figure 25.21 A conductor in electrostatic equilibrium containing a cavity. The electric field in the cavity is zero, regardless of the charge on the conductor.

Corona Discharge

A phenomenon known as **corona discharge** is often observed near a conductor such as a high-voltage power line. When the electric field in the vicinity of the conductor is sufficiently strong, electrons resulting from random ionizations of air molecules near the conductor accelerate away from their parent molecules. These rapidly moving electrons can ionize additional molecules near the conductor, creating more free electrons. The observed glow (or corona discharge) results from the recombination of these free electrons with the ionized air molecules. If a conductor has an irregular shape, the electric field can be very high near sharp points or edges of the conductor; consequently, the ionization process and corona discharge are most likely to occur around such points.

Corona discharge is used in the electrical transmission industry to locate broken or faulty components. For example, a broken insulator on a transmission tower has sharp edges where corona discharge is likely to occur. Similarly, corona discharge will occur at the sharp end of a broken conductor strand. Observation of these discharges is difficult because the visible radiation emitted is weak and most of the radiation is in the ultraviolet. (We will discuss ultraviolet radiation and other portions of the electromagnetic spectrum in Section 34.7.) Even use of traditional ultraviolet cameras is of little help because the radiation from the corona discharge is overwhelmed by ultraviolet radiation from the Sun. Newly developed dual-spectrum devices combine a narrow-band ultraviolet camera with a visible-light camera to show a daylight view of the corona discharge in the actual location on the transmission tower or cable. The ultraviolet part of the camera is designed to operate in a wavelength range in which radiation from the Sun is very weak.

25.7 The Millikan Oil-Drop Experiment

Robert Millikan performed a brilliant set of experiments from 1909 to 1913 in which he measured e, the magnitude of the elementary charge on an electron, and demonstrated the quantized nature of this charge. His apparatus, diagrammed in Active Figure 25.22, contains two parallel metallic plates. Oil droplets

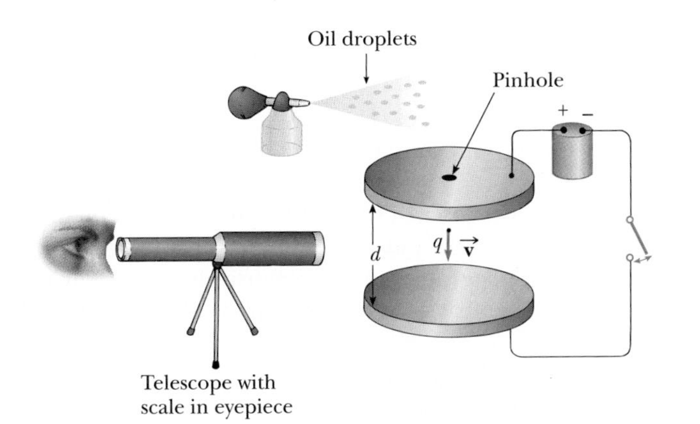

ACTIVE FIGURE 25.22

Schematic drawing of the Millikan oil-drop apparatus.

Sign in at www.thomsonedu.com and go to ThomsonNOW to perform a simplified version of the experiment yourself. You will be able to take data on a number of oil drops and determine the elementary charge from your data.

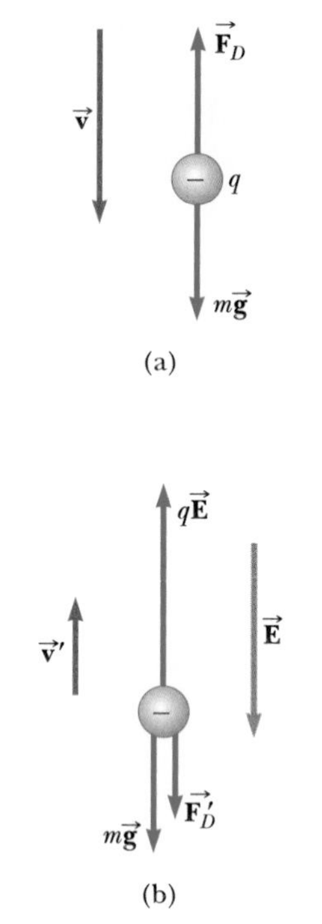

Figure 25.23 The forces acting on a negatively charged oil droplet in the Millikan experiment. (a) With the electric field off, the droplet falls at terminal velocity $\vec{v}$ under the influence of the gravitational and drag forces. (b) When the electric field is turned on, the droplet moves upward at terminal velocity $\vec{v}'$ under the influence of the electric, gravitational, and drag forces.

from an atomizer are allowed to pass through a small hole in the upper plate. Millikan used x-rays to ionize the air in the chamber so that freed electrons would adhere to the oil drops, giving them a negative charge. A horizontally directed light beam is used to illuminate the oil droplets, which are viewed through a telescope whose long axis is perpendicular to the light beam. When viewed in this manner, the droplets appear as shining stars against a dark background and the rate at which individual drops fall can be determined.

Let's assume a single drop having a mass m and carrying a charge q is being viewed and its charge is negative. If no electric field is present between the plates, the two forces acting on the charge are the gravitational force $m\vec{g}$ acting downward[3] and a viscous drag force $\vec{F}_D$ acting upward as indicated in Figure 25.23a. The drag force is proportional to the drop's speed as discussed in Section 6.4. When the drop reaches its terminal speed v, the two forces balance each other ($mg = F_D$).

Now suppose a battery connected to the plates sets up an electric field between the plates such that the upper plate is at the higher electric potential. In this case, a third force $q\vec{E}$ acts on the charged drop. Because q is negative and $\vec{E}$ is directed downward, this electric force is directed upward as shown in Figure 25.23b. If this upward force is strong enough, the drop moves upward and the drag force $\vec{F}'_D$ acts downward. When the upward electric force $q\vec{E}$ balances the sum of the gravitational force and the downward drag force $\vec{F}'_D$, the drop reaches a new terminal speed v' in the upward direction.

With the field turned on, a drop moves slowly upward, typically at rates of hundredths of a centimeter per second. The rate of fall in the absence of a field is comparable. Hence, one can follow a single droplet for hours, alternately rising and falling, by simply turning the electric field on and off.

After recording measurements on thousands of droplets, Millikan and his coworkers found that all droplets, to within about 1% precision, had a charge equal to some integer multiple of the elementary charge e:

$$q = ne \quad n = 0, -1, -2, -3, \ldots$$

where $e = 1.60 \times 10^{-19}$ C. Millikan's experiment yields conclusive evidence that charge is quantized. For this work, he was awarded the Nobel Prize in Physics in 1923.

25.8 Applications of Electrostatics

The practical application of electrostatics is represented by such devices as lightning rods and electrostatic precipitators and by such processes as xerography and the painting of automobiles. Scientific devices based on the principles of electrostatics include electrostatic generators, the field-ion microscope, and ion-drive rocket engines.

The Van de Graaff Generator

Experimental results show that when a charged conductor is placed in contact with the inside of a hollow conductor, all the charge on the charged conductor is transferred to the hollow conductor. In principle, the charge on the hollow conductor and its electric potential can be increased without limit by repetition of the process.

In 1929, Robert J. Van de Graaff (1901–1967) used this principle to design and build an electrostatic generator, and a schematic representation of it is given in Figure 25.24. This type of generator is used extensively in nuclear physics research. Charge is delivered continuously to a high-potential electrode by means of a mov-

[3] There is also a buoyant force on the oil drop due to the surrounding air. This force can be incorporated as a correction in the gravitational force $m\vec{g}$ on the drop, so we will not consider it in our analysis.

ing belt of insulating material. The high-voltage electrode is a hollow metal dome mounted on an insulating column. The belt is charged at point Ⓐ by means of a corona discharge between comb-like metallic needles and a grounded grid. The needles are maintained at a positive electric potential of typically 10^4 V. The positive charge on the moving belt is transferred to the dome by a second comb of needles at point Ⓑ. Because the electric field inside the dome is negligible, the positive charge on the belt is easily transferred to the conductor regardless of its potential. In practice, it is possible to increase the electric potential of the dome until electrical discharge occurs through the air. Because the "breakdown" electric field in air is about 3×10^6 V/m, a sphere 1 m in radius can be raised to a maximum potential of 3×10^6 V. The potential can be increased further by increasing the dome's radius and placing the entire system in a container filled with high-pressure gas.

Van de Graaff generators can produce potential differences as large as 20 million volts. Protons accelerated through such large potential differences receive enough energy to initiate nuclear reactions between themselves and various target nuclei. Smaller generators are often seen in science classrooms and museums. If a person insulated from the ground touches the sphere of a Van de Graaff generator, his or her body can be brought to a high electric potential. The person's hair acquires a net positive charge, and each strand is repelled by all the others as in the opening photograph of Chapter 23.

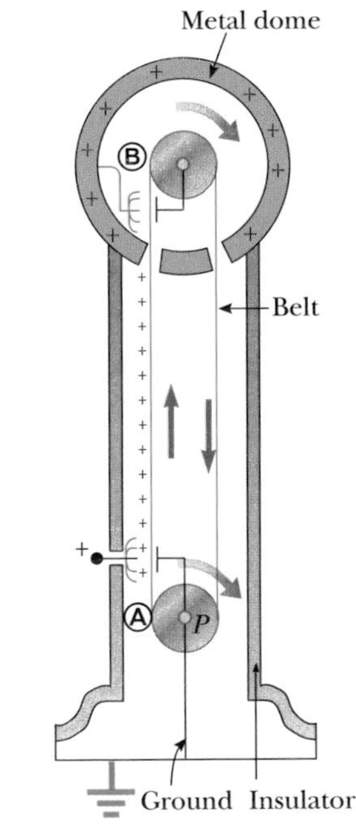

Figure 25.24 Schematic diagram of a Van de Graaff generator. Charge is transferred to the metal dome at the top by means of a moving belt. The charge is deposited on the belt at point Ⓐ and transferred to the hollow conductor at point Ⓑ.

The Electrostatic Precipitator

One important application of electrical discharge in gases is the *electrostatic precipitator.* This device removes particulate matter from combustion gases, thereby reducing air pollution. Precipitators are especially useful in coal-burning power plants and industrial operations that generate large quantities of smoke. Current systems are able to eliminate more than 99% of the ash from smoke.

Figure 25.25a shows a schematic diagram of an electrostatic precipitator. A high potential difference (typically 40 to 100 kV) is maintained between a wire running down the center of a duct and the walls of the duct, which are grounded. The wire is maintained at a negative electric potential with respect to the walls, so the electric field is directed toward the wire. The values of the field near the wire become high enough to cause a corona discharge around the wire; the air near the wire contains positive ions, electrons, and such negative ions as O_2^-. The air to be cleaned enters the duct and moves near the wire. As the electrons and negative

Figure 25.25 (a) Schematic diagram of an electrostatic precipitator. The high negative electric potential maintained on the central coiled wire creates a corona discharge in the vicinity of the wire. Compare the air pollution when the electrostatic precipitator is (b) operating and (c) turned off.

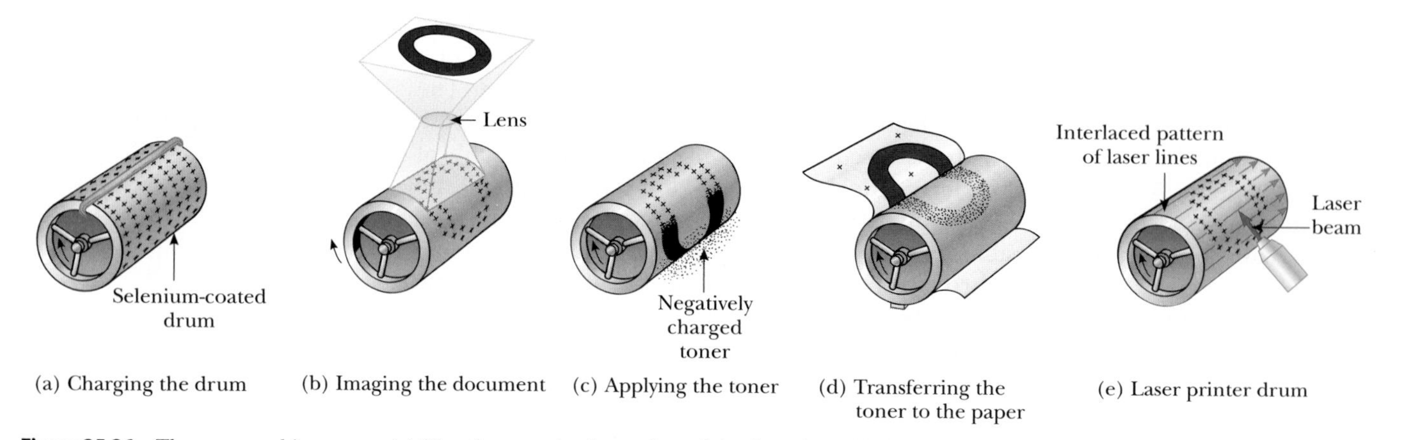

Figure 25.26 The xerographic process. (a) The photoconductive surface of the drum is positively charged. (b) Through the use of a light source and lens, an image is created on the surface in the form of positive charges. (c) The surface containing the image is covered with a negatively charged powder, which adheres only to the image area. (d) A piece of paper is placed over the surface and given a positive charge, which transfers the image to the paper as the negatively charged powder particles migrate to the paper. The paper is then thermally treated to "fix" the powder. (e) A laser printer operates similarly except that the image is produced by turning a laser beam on and off as it sweeps across the selenium-coated drum.

ions created by the discharge are accelerated toward the outer wall by the electric field, the dirt particles in the air become charged by collisions and ion capture. Because most of the charged dirt particles are negative, they too are drawn to the duct walls by the electric field. When the duct is periodically shaken, the particles break loose and are collected at the bottom.

In addition to reducing the level of particulate matter in the atmosphere (compare Figs. 25.25b and c), the electrostatic precipitator recovers valuable materials in the form of metal oxides.

Xerography and Laser Printers

The basic idea of xerography[4] was developed by Chester Carlson, who was granted a patent for the xerographic process in 1940. The unique feature of this process is the use of a photoconductive material to form an image. (A *photoconductor* is a material that is a poor electrical conductor in the dark but becomes a good electrical conductor when exposed to light.)

The xerographic process is illustrated in parts (a) through (d) of Figure 25.26. First, the surface of a plate or drum that has been coated with a thin film of photoconductive material (usually selenium or some compound of selenium) is given a positive electrostatic charge in the dark. An image of the page to be copied is then focused by a lens onto the charged surface. The photoconducting surface becomes conducting only in areas where light strikes it. In such areas, the light produces charge carriers in the photoconductor that move the positive charge off the drum. Positive charges, however, remain on those areas of the photoconductor not exposed to light, leaving a latent image of the object in the form of a positive surface charge distribution.

Next, a negatively charged powder called a *toner* is dusted onto the photoconducting surface. The charged powder adheres only to those areas of the surface that contain the positively charged image. The toner (and hence the image) is then transferred to the surface of a sheet of positively charged paper.

Finally, the toner is "fixed" to the surface of the paper as the toner melts while passing through high-temperature rollers. The result is a permanent copy of the original.

A laser printer (Fig. 25.26e) operates by the same principle, with the exception that a computer-directed laser beam is used to illuminate the photoconductor instead of a lens.

[4] The prefix *xero-* is from the Greek word meaning "dry." Note that liquid ink is not used in xerography.

Summary

ThomsonNOW™ Sign in at **www.thomsonedu.com** and go to ThomsonNOW to take a practice test for this chapter.

DEFINITIONS

The **potential difference** ΔV between points Ⓐ and Ⓑ in an electric field $\vec{\mathbf{E}}$ is defined as

$$\Delta V \equiv \frac{\Delta U}{q_0} = -\int_{Ⓐ}^{Ⓑ} \vec{\mathbf{E}} \cdot d\vec{\mathbf{s}} \qquad (25.3)$$

where ΔU is given by Equation 25.1 below. The **electric potential** $V = U/q_0$ is a scalar quantity and has the units of joules per coulomb, where $1\ \text{J/C} \equiv 1\ \text{V}$.

An **equipotential surface** is one on which all points are at the same electric potential. Equipotential surfaces are perpendicular to electric field lines.

CONCEPTS AND PRINCIPLES

When a positive test charge q_0 is moved between points Ⓐ and Ⓑ in an electric field $\vec{\mathbf{E}}$, the **change in the potential energy of the charge–field system** is

$$\Delta U = -q_0 \int_{Ⓐ}^{Ⓑ} \vec{\mathbf{E}} \cdot d\vec{\mathbf{s}} \qquad (25.1)$$

The potential difference between two points Ⓐ and Ⓑ separated by a distance d in a uniform electric field $\vec{\mathbf{E}}$, where $\vec{\mathbf{s}}$ is a vector that points from Ⓐ toward Ⓑ and is parallel to $\vec{\mathbf{E}}$, is

$$\Delta V = -E \int_{Ⓐ}^{Ⓑ} ds = -Ed \qquad (25.6)$$

If we define $V = 0$ at $r = \infty$, the electric potential due to a point charge at any distance r from the charge is

$$V = k_e \frac{q}{r} \qquad (25.11)$$

The electric potential associated with a group of point charges is obtained by summing the potentials due to the individual charges.

The **potential energy associated with a pair of point charges** separated by a distance r_{12} is

$$U = k_e \frac{q_1 q_2}{r_{12}} \qquad (25.13)$$

We obtain the potential energy of a distribution of point charges by summing terms like Equation 25.13 over all pairs of particles.

If the electric potential is known as a function of coordinates x, y, and z, we can obtain the components of the electric field by taking the negative derivative of the electric potential with respect to the coordinates. For example, the x component of the electric field is

$$E_x = -\frac{dV}{dx} \qquad (25.16)$$

The **electric potential due to a continuous charge distribution** is

$$V = k_e \int \frac{dq}{r} \qquad (25.20)$$

Every point on the surface of a charged conductor in electrostatic equilibrium is at the same electric potential. The potential is constant everywhere inside the conductor and equal to its value at the surface.

Questions

☐ denotes answer available in *Student Solutions Manual/Study Guide;* **O** denotes objective question

1. Distinguish between electric potential and electric potential energy.
2. **O** In a certain region of space, a uniform electric field is in the x direction. A particle with negative charge is carried from $x = 20$ cm to $x = 60$ cm. **(i)** Does the potential energy of the charge-field system (a) increase, (b) remain constant, (c) decrease, or (d) change unpredictably? **(ii)** Does the particle move to a position where the potential is (a) higher than before, (b) unchanged, (c) lower than before, or (d) unpredictable?
3. **O** Consider the equipotential surfaces shown in Figure 25.4. In this region of space, what is the approximate

direction of the electric field? (a) out of the page (b) into the page (c) toward the right (d) toward the left (e) toward the top of the page (f) toward the bottom of the page (g) the field is zero

4. **O** A particle with charge −40 nC is on the x axis at the point with coordinate $x = 0$. A second particle, with charge −20 nC, is on the x axis at $x = 500$ mm. **(i)** Is there a point at a finite distance where the electric field is zero? (a) Yes; it is to the left of $x = 0$. (b) Yes; it is between $x = 0$ and $x = 500$ mm. (c) Yes; it is to the right of $x = 500$ mm. (d) No. **(ii)** Is the electric potential zero at this point? (a) No; it is positive. (b) Yes. (c) No; it is negative. (d) No such point exists. **(iii)** Is there a point at a finite distance where the electric potential is zero? (a) Yes; it is to the left of $x = 0$. (b) Yes; it is between $x = 0$ and $x = 500$ mm. (c) Yes; it is to the right of $x = 500$ mm. (d) No. **(iv)** Is the electric field zero at this point? (a) No; it points to the right. (b) Yes. (c) No; it points to the left. (d) No such point exists.

5. The potential energy of a pair of charged particles with the same sign is positive, whereas the potential energy of a pair of charged particles with opposite signs is negative. Give a physical explanation of this statement.

6. Describe the equipotential surfaces for (a) an infinite line of charge and (b) a uniformly charged sphere.

7. **O** In a certain region of space, the electric field is zero. From this fact, what can you conclude about the electric potential in this region? (a) It is zero. (b) It is constant. (c) It is positive. (d) It is negative. (e) None of these answers is necessarily true.

8. **O** A filament running along the x axis from the origin to $x = 80$ cm carries electric charge with uniform density. At the point P with coordinates ($x = 80$ cm, $y = 80$ cm), this filament creates potential 100 V. Now we add another filament along the y axis, running from the origin to $y = 80$ cm, carrying the same amount of charge with the same uniform density. At the same point P, does the pair of filaments create potential (a) greater than 200 V, (b) 200 V, (c) between 141 V and 200 V, (d) 141 V, (e) between 100 V and 141 V, (f) 100 V, (g) between 0 and 100 V, or (h) 0?

9. **O** In different experimental trials, an electron, a proton, or a doubly charged oxygen atom (O^{--}) is fired within a vacuum tube. The particle's trajectory carries it through a point where the electric potential is 40 V and then through a point at a different potential. Rank each of the following cases according to the change in kinetic energy of the particle over this part of its flight, from the largest increase to the largest decrease in kinetic energy. (a) An electron moves from 40 V to 60 V. (b) An electron moves from 40 V to 20 V. (c) A proton moves from 40 V to 20 V. (d) A proton moves from 40 V to 10 V. (e) An O^{--} ion moves from 40 V to 50 V. (f) An O^{--} ion moves from 40 V to 60 V. For comparison, include also in your ranking (g) zero change and (h) +10 electron volts of change in kinetic energy. In your ranking, display any cases of equality.

10. What determines the maximum potential to which the dome of a Van de Graaff generator can be raised?

11. **O** **(i)** A metallic sphere A of radius 1 cm is several centimeters away from a metallic spherical shell B of radius 2 cm. Charge 450 nC is placed on A, with no charge on B or anywhere nearby. Next, the two objects are joined by a long, thin, metallic wire (as shown in Fig. 25.20), and finally the wire is removed. How is the charge shared between A and B? (a) 0 on A, 450 nC on B (b) 50 nC on A and 400 nC on B, with equal volume charge densities (c) 90 nC on A and 360 nC on B, with equal surface charge densities (d) 150 nC on A and 300 nC on B (e) 225 nC on A and 225 nC on B (f) 450 nC on A and 0 on B (g) in some other predictable way (h) in some unpredictable way **(ii)** A metallic sphere A of radius 1 cm with charge 450 nC hangs on an insulating thread inside an uncharged thin metallic spherical shell B of radius 2 cm. Next, A is made temporarily to touch the inner surface of B. How is the charge then shared between them? Choose from the same possibilities. Arnold Arons, the only physics teacher yet to have his picture on the cover of *Time* magazine, suggested the idea for this question.

12. Study Figure 23.3 and the accompanying text discussion of charging by induction. When the grounding wire is touched to the rightmost point on the sphere in Figure 23.3c, electrons are drained away from the sphere to leave the sphere positively charged. Suppose the grounding wire is touched to the leftmost point on the sphere instead. Will electrons still drain away, moving closer to the negatively charged rod as they do so? What kind of charge, if any, remains on the sphere?

Problems

WebAssign The Problems from this chapter may be assigned online in WebAssign.

ThomsonNOW Sign in at **www.thomsonedu.com** and go to ThomsonNOW to assess your understanding of this chapter's topics with additional quizzing and conceptual questions.

1, 2, 3 denotes straightforward, intermediate, challenging; ☐ denotes full solution available in *Student Solutions Manual/Study Guide;* ▲ denotes coached solution with hints available at **www.thomsonedu.com;** denotes developing symbolic reasoning; ● denotes asking for qualitative reasoning; denotes computer useful in solving problem

Section 25.1 Electric Potential and Potential Difference

1. (a) Calculate the speed of a proton that is accelerated from rest through a potential difference of 120 V. (b) Calculate the speed of an electron that is accelerated through the same potential difference.

2. How much work is done (by a battery, generator, or some other source of potential difference) in moving Avogadro's number of electrons from an initial point where the electric potential is 9.00 V to a point where the potential is -5.00 V? (The potential in each case is measured relative to a common reference point.)

Section 25.2 Potential Difference in a Uniform Electric Field

3. The difference in potential between the accelerating plates in the electron gun of a television picture tube is about 25 000 V. If the distance between these plates is 1.50 cm, what is the magnitude of the uniform electric field in this region?

4. A uniform electric field of magnitude 325 V/m is directed in the negative y direction in Figure P25.4. The coordinates of point A are $(-0.200, -0.300)$ m and those of point B are $(0.400, 0.500)$ m. Calculate the potential difference $V_B - V_A$, using the blue path.

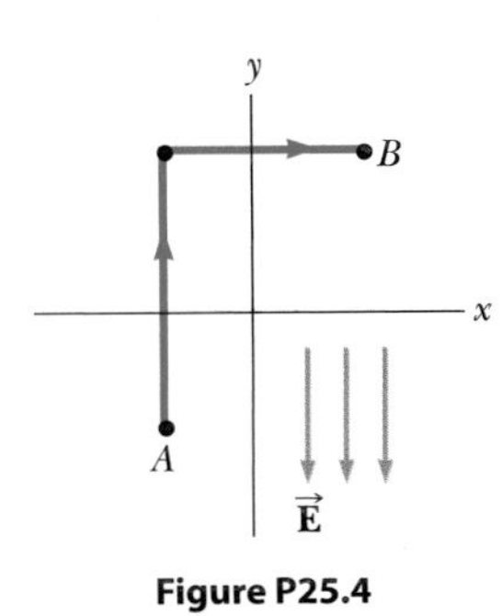

Figure P25.4

5. ▲ An electron moving parallel to the x axis has an initial speed of 3.70×10^6 m/s at the origin. Its speed is reduced to 1.40×10^5 m/s at the point $x = 2.00$ cm. Calculate the potential difference between the origin and that point. Which point is at the higher potential?

6. ● Starting with the definition of work, prove that at every point on an equipotential surface the surface must be perpendicular to the electric field there.

7. **Review problem.** A block having mass m and charge $+Q$ is connected to an insulating spring having constant k. The block lies on a frictionless, insulating horizontal track, and the system is immersed in a uniform electric field of magnitude E directed as shown in Figure P25.7. If the block is released from rest when the spring is unstretched (at $x = 0$), (a) by what maximum amount does the spring expand? (b) What is the equilibrium position of the block? (c) Show that the block's motion is simple harmonic and determine its period. (d) **What If?** Repeat part (a), assuming the coefficient of kinetic friction between block and surface is μ_k.

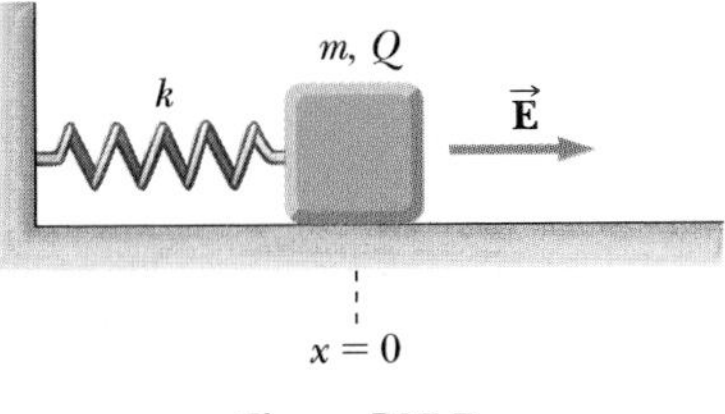

Figure P25.7

8. A particle having charge $q = +2.00$ μC and mass $m = 0.010\,0$ kg is connected to a string that is $L = 1.50$ m long and tied to the pivot point P in Figure P25.8. The particle, string, and pivot point all lie on a frictionless, horizontal table. The particle is released from rest when the string makes an angle $\theta = 60.0°$ with a uniform electric field of magnitude $E = 300$ V/m. Determine the speed of the particle when the string is parallel to the electric field (point a in Fig. P25.8).

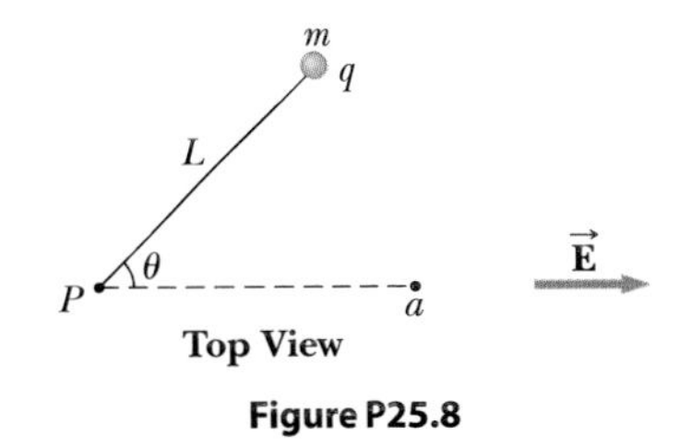

Figure P25.8

9. ● An insulating rod having linear charge density $\lambda = 40.0$ μC/m and linear mass density $\mu = 0.100$ kg/m is released from rest in a uniform electric field $E = 100$ V/m directed perpendicular to the rod (Fig. P25.9). (a) Determine the speed of the rod after it has traveled 2.00 m. (b) **What If?** How does your answer to part (a) change if the electric field is not perpendicular to the rod? Explain.

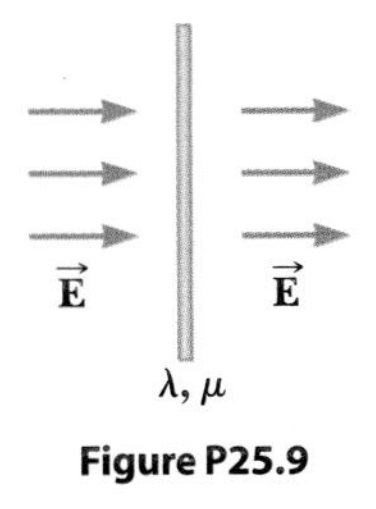

Figure P25.9

Section 25.3 Electric Potential and Potential Energy Due to Point Charges

Note: Unless stated otherwise, assume the reference level of potential is $V = 0$ at $r = \infty$.

10. Given two particles with 2.00-μC charges as shown in Figure P25.10 and a particle with charge $q = 1.28 \times 10^{-18}$ C at the origin, (a) what is the net force exerted by the two 2.00-μC charges on the test charge q? (b) What is the electric field at the origin due to the two 2.00-μC particles? (c) What is the electric potential at the origin due to the two 2.00-μC particles?

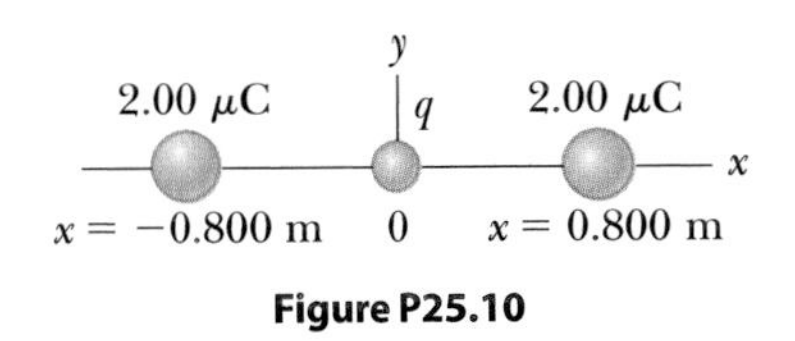

Figure P25.10

11. (a) Find the potential at a distance of 1.00 cm from a proton. (b) What is the potential difference between two points that are 1.00 cm and 2.00 cm from a proton? (c) **What If?** Repeat parts (a) and (b) for an electron.

12. A particle with charge $+q$ is at the origin. A particle with charge $-2q$ is at $x = 2.00$ m on the x axis. (a) For what finite value(s) of x is the electric field zero? (b) For what finite value(s) of x is the electric potential zero?

13. At a certain distance from a charged particle, the magnitude of the electric field is 500 V/m and the electric potential is −3.00 kV. (a) What is the distance to the particle? (b) What is the magnitude of the charge?

14. ● Two charged particles, $Q_1 = +5.00$ nC and $Q_2 = -3.00$ nC, are separated by 35.0 cm. (a) What is the potential energy of the pair? Explain the significance of the algebraic sign of your answer. (b) What is the electric potential at a point midway between the charged particles?

15. The three charged particles in Figure P25.15 are at the vertices of an isosceles triangle. Calculate the electric potential at the midpoint of the base, taking $q = 7.00\ \mu$C.

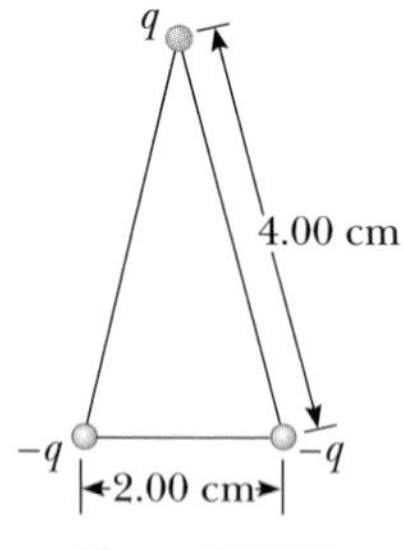

Figure P25.15

16. *Compare this problem with Problem 16 in Chapter 23.* Two charged particles each of magnitude 2.00 μC are located on the x axis. One is at $x = 1.00$ m, and the other is at $x = -1.00$ m. (a) Determine the electric potential on the y axis at $y = 0.500$ m. (b) Calculate the change in electric potential energy of the system as a third charged particle of −3.00 μC is brought from infinitely far away to a position on the y axis at $y = 0.500$ m.

17. *Compare this problem with Problem 47 in Chapter 23.* Four identical charged particles ($q = +10.0\ \mu$C) are located on the corners of a rectangle as shown in Figure P23.47. The dimensions of the rectangle are $L = 60.0$ cm and $W = 15.0$ cm. Calculate the change in electric potential energy of the system as the particle at the lower left corner in Figure P23.47 is brought to this position from infinitely far away. Assume the other three particles in Figure P23.47 remain fixed in position.

18. Two charged particles have effects at the origin, described by the expressions

$$8.99 \times 10^9\ \text{N}\cdot\text{m}^2/\text{C}^2\left[-\frac{7\times10^{-9}\ \text{C}}{(0.07\ \text{m})^2}\cos 70°\,\hat{\mathbf{i}} - \frac{7\times10^{-9}\ \text{C}}{(0.07\ \text{m})^2}\sin 70°\,\hat{\mathbf{j}} + \frac{8\times10^{-9}\ \text{C}}{(0.03\ \text{m})^2}\,\hat{\mathbf{j}}\right]$$

and

$$8.99 \times 10^9\ \text{N}\cdot\text{m}^2/\text{C}^2\left[\frac{7\times10^{-9}\ \text{C}}{0.07\ \text{m}} - \frac{8\times10^{-9}\ \text{C}}{0.03\ \text{m}}\right]$$

(a) Identify the locations of the particles and the charges on them. (b) Find the force on a particle with charge −16.0 nC placed at the origin. (c) Find the work required to move this third charged particle to the origin from a very distant point.

19. ▲ Show that the amount of work required to assemble four identical charged particles of magnitude Q at the corners of a square of side s is $5.41k_eQ^2/s$.

20. *Compare this problem with Problem 19 in Chapter 23.* Five equal negative charged particles $-q$ are placed symmetrically around a circle of radius R. Calculate the electric potential at the center of the circle.

21. *Compare this problem with Problem 35 in Chapter 23.* Three particles with equal positive charges q are at the corners of an equilateral triangle of side a as shown in Figure P23.35. (a) At what point, if any, in the plane of the particles is the electric potential zero? (b) What is the electric potential at the point P due to the two particles at the base of the triangle?

22. Two charged particles of equal magnitude are located along the y axis equal distances above and below the x axis as shown in Figure P25.22. (a) Plot a graph of the potential at points along the x axis over the interval $-3a < x < 3a$. You should plot the potential in units of k_eQ/a. (b) Let the charge of the particle located at $y = -a$ be negative. Plot the potential along the y axis over the interval $-4a < y < 4a$.

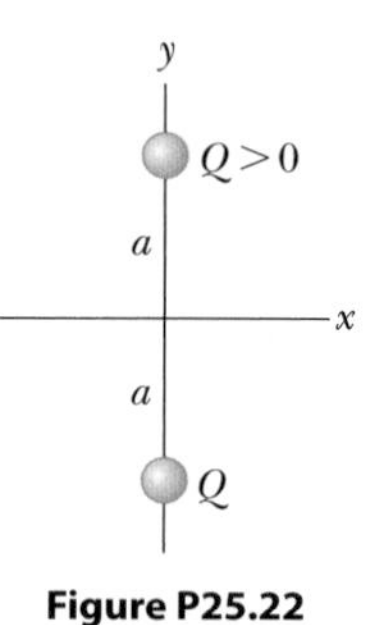

Figure P25.22

23. ● **Review problem.** Two insulating spheres have radii 0.300 cm and 0.500 cm, masses 0.100 kg and 0.700 kg, and uniformly distributed charges of −2.00 μC and 3.00 μC. They are released from rest when their centers are separated by 1.00 m. (a) How fast will each be moving when they collide? *Suggestion:* Consider conservation of energy and of linear momentum. (b) **What If?** If the spheres were conductors, would the speeds be greater or less than those calculated in part (a)? Explain.

24. ● **Review problem.** Two insulating spheres have radii r_1 and r_2, masses m_1 and m_2, and uniformly distributed charges $-q_1$ and q_2. They are released from rest when their centers are separated by a distance d. (a) How fast is each moving when they collide? *Suggestion:* Consider conservation of energy and conservation of linear momentum. (b) **What If?** If the spheres were conductors, would their speeds be greater or less than those calculated in part (a)? Explain.

25. **Review problem.** A light, unstressed spring has length d. Two identical particles, each with charge q, are connected to the opposite ends of the spring. The particles are held stationary a distance d apart and then released at the same moment. The system then oscillates on a horizontal, frictionless table. The spring has a bit of internal kinetic friction, so the oscillation is damped. The particles eventually stop vibrating when the distance between them is $3d$. Find the increase in internal energy that appears in the spring during the oscillations. Assume the system of the spring and two charged particles is isolated.

26. In 1911, Ernest Rutherford and his assistants Geiger and Marsden conducted an experiment in which they scattered alpha particles from thin sheets of gold. An alpha particle, having charge $+2e$ and mass 6.64×10^{-27} kg, is a product of certain radioactive decays. The results of the experiment led Rutherford to the idea that most of the mass of an atom is in a very small nucleus, with electrons in orbit around it, his planetary model of the atom. Assume an alpha particle, initially very far from a gold nucleus, is fired with a velocity of 2.00×10^7 m/s directly toward the nucleus (charge $+79e$). How close does the alpha particle get to the nucleus before turning around? Assume the gold nucleus remains stationary.

27. Four identical particles each have charge q and mass m. They are released from rest at the vertices of a square of side L. How fast is each particle moving when their distance from the center of the square doubles?

28. How much work is required to assemble eight identical charged particles, each of magnitude q, at the corners of a cube of side s?

Section 25.4 Obtaining the Value of the Electric Field from the Electric Potential

29. The potential in a region between $x = 0$ and $x = 6.00$ m is $V = a + bx$, where $a = 10.0$ V and $b = -7.00$ V/m. Determine (a) the potential at $x = 0$, 3.00 m, and 6.00 m and (b) the magnitude and direction of the electric field at $x = 0$, 3.00 m, and 6.00 m.

30. The electric potential inside a charged spherical conductor of radius R is given by $V = k_eQ/R$, and the potential outside is given by $V = k_eQ/r$. Using $E_r = -dV/dr$, derive the electric field (a) inside and (b) outside this charge distribution.

31. ▲ Over a certain region of space, the electric potential is $V = 5x - 3x^2y + 2yz^2$. Find the expressions for the x, y, and z components of the electric field over this region. What is the magnitude of the field at the point P that has coordinates $(1, 0, -2)$ m?

32. ● Figure P25.32 shows several equipotential lines, each labeled by its potential in volts. The distance between the lines of the square grid represents 1.00 cm. (a) Is the magnitude of the field larger at A or at B? Explain how you can tell. (b) Explain what you can determine about $\vec{\mathbf{E}}$ at B. (c) Represent what the field looks like by drawing at least eight field lines.

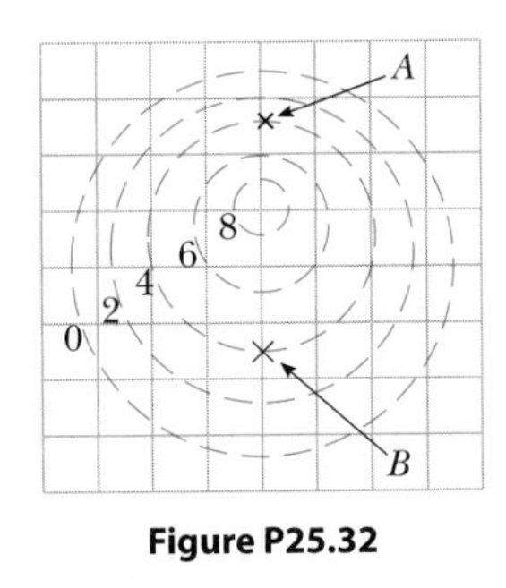

Figure P25.32

33. It is shown in Example 25.7 that the potential at a point P a distance a above one end of a uniformly charged rod of length ℓ lying along the x axis is

$$V = k_e \frac{Q}{\ell} \ln\left(\frac{\ell + \sqrt{a^2 + \ell^2}}{a}\right)$$

Use this result to derive an expression for the y component of the electric field at P. *Suggestion:* Replace a with y.

Section 25.5 Electric Potential Due to Continuous Charge Distributions

34. Consider a ring of radius R with the total charge Q spread uniformly over its perimeter. What is the potential difference between the point at the center of the ring and a point on its axis a distance $2R$ from the center?

35. A rod of length L (Fig. P25.35) lies along the x axis with its left end at the origin. It has a nonuniform charge density $\lambda = \alpha x$, where α is a positive constant. (a) What are the units of α? (b) Calculate the electric potential at A.

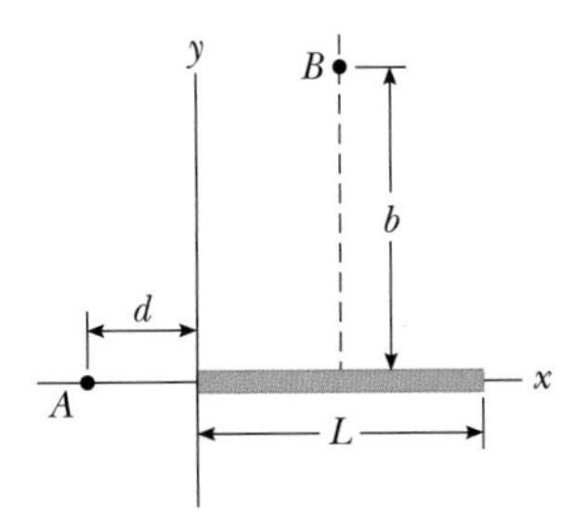

Figure P25.35 Problems 35 and 36.

36. For the arrangement described in Problem 35, calculate the electric potential at point B, which lies on the perpendicular bisector of the rod a distance b above the x axis.

37. *Compare this problem with Problem 27 in Chapter 23.* A uniformly charged insulating rod of length 14.0 cm is bent into the shape of a semicircle as shown in Figure P23.27. The rod has a total charge of -7.50 μC. Find the electric potential at O, the center of the semicircle.

38. A wire having a uniform linear charge density λ is bent into the shape shown in Figure P25.38. Find the electric potential at point O.

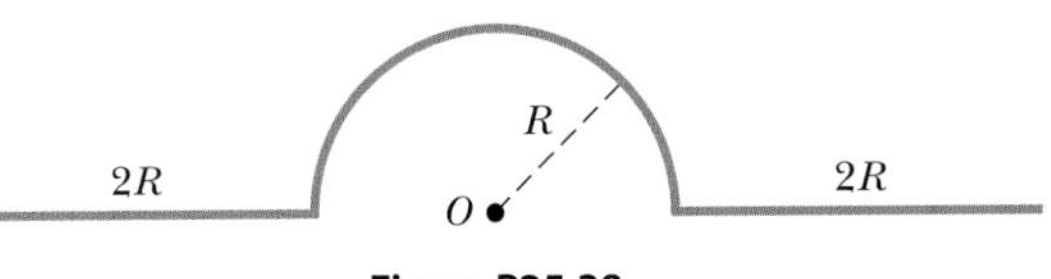

Figure P25.38

Section 25.6 Electric Potential Due to a Charged Conductor

39. ▲ A spherical conductor has a radius of 14.0 cm and charge of 26.0 μC. Calculate the electric field and the electric potential at (a) $r = 10.0$ cm, (b) $r = 20.0$ cm, and (c) $r = 14.0$ cm from the center.

40. How many electrons should be removed from an initially uncharged spherical conductor of radius 0.300 m to produce a potential of 7.50 kV at the surface?

41. The electric field on the surface of an irregularly shaped conductor varies from 56.0 kN/C to 28.0 kN/C. Calculate the local surface charge density at the point on the surface where the radius of curvature of the surface is (a) greatest and (b) smallest.

42. Electric charge can accumulate on an airplane in flight. You may have observed needle-shaped metal extensions on the wing tips and tail of an airplane. Their purpose is to allow charge to leak off before much of it accumulates. The electric field around the needle is much larger than the field around the body of the airplane and can become large enough to produce dielectric breakdown of the air, discharging the airplane. To model this process, assume two charged spherical conductors are connected by a long conducting wire and a charge of 1.20 μC is placed on the combination. One sphere, representing the body of the airplane, has a radius of 6.00 cm, and the other, representing the tip of the needle, has a radius of 2.00 cm. (a) What is the electric potential of each sphere? (b) What is the electric field at the surface of each sphere?

Section 25.8 Applications of Electrostatics

43. Lightning can be studied with a Van de Graaff generator, essentially consisting of a spherical dome on which charge is continuously deposited by a moving belt. Charge can be added until the electric field at the surface of the dome becomes equal to the dielectric strength of air. Any more charge leaks off in sparks as shown in Figure P25.43. Assume the dome has a diameter of 30.0 cm and is surrounded by dry air with dielectric strength 3.00×10^6 V/m. (a) What is the maximum potential of the dome? (b) What is the maximum charge on the dome?

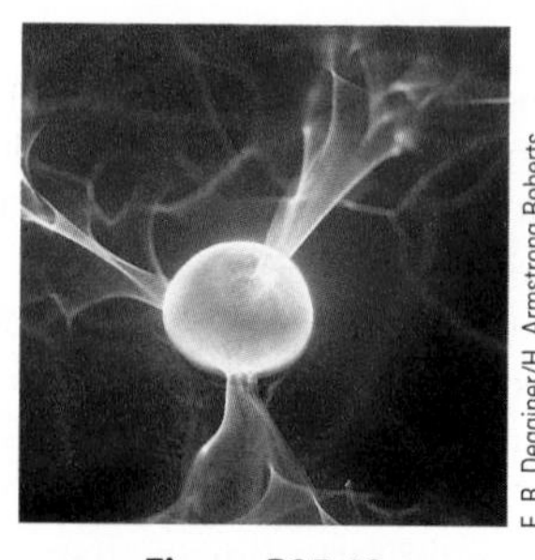
E. R. Degginer/H. Armstrong Roberts

Figure P25.43

44. A Geiger-Mueller tube is a radiation detector that consists of a closed, hollow, metal cylinder (the cathode) of inner radius r_a and a coaxial cylindrical wire (the anode) of radius r_b (Fig. P25.44). The charge per unit length on the anode is λ, and the charge per unit length on the cathode is $-\lambda$. A gas fills the space between the electrodes. When a high-energy elementary particle passes through this space, it can ionize an atom of the gas. The strong electric field makes the resulting ion and electron accelerate in opposite directions. They strike other molecules of the gas to ionize them, producing an avalanche of electrical discharge. The pulse of electric current between the wire and the cylinder is counted by an external circuit. (a) Show that the magnitude of the potential difference between the wire and the cylinder is

$$\Delta V = 2k_e\lambda \ln\left(\frac{r_a}{r_b}\right)$$

(b) Show that the magnitude of the electric field in the space between cathode and anode is

$$E = \frac{\Delta V}{\ln (r_a/r_b)}\left(\frac{1}{r}\right)$$

where r is the distance from the axis of the anode to the point where the field is to be calculated.

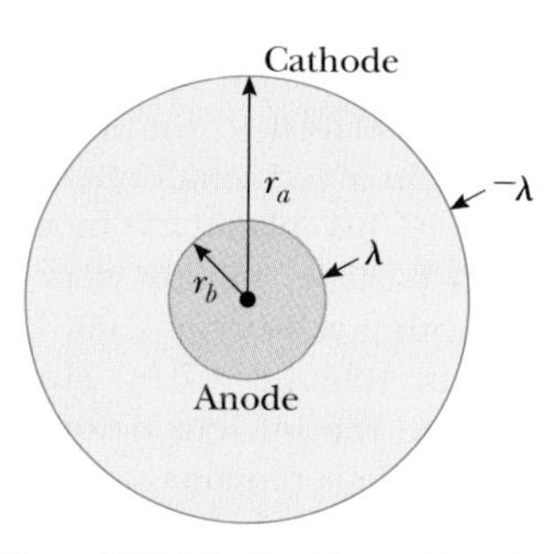

Figure P25.44 Problems 44 and 45.

45. The results of Problem 44 apply also to an electrostatic precipitator (Figs. 25.25 and P25.44). An applied potential difference $\Delta V = V_a - V_b = 50.0$ kV is to produce an electric field of magnitude 5.50 MV/m at the surface of the central wire. Assume the outer cylindrical wall has uniform radius $r_a = 0.850$ m. (a) What should be the radius r_b of the central wire? You will need to solve a transcendental equation. (b) What is the magnitude of the electric field at the outer wall?

Additional Problems

46. ● **Review problem.** From a large distance away, a particle of mass 2.00 g and charge 15.0 μC is fired at $21.0\hat{\mathbf{i}}$ m/s straight toward a second particle, originally stationary but free to move, with mass 5.00 g and charge 8.50 μC. (a) At the instant of closest approach, both particles will be moving at the same velocity. Explain why. (b) Find this velocity. (c) Find the distance of closest approach. (d) Find the velocities of both particles after they separate again.

47. The liquid-drop model of the atomic nucleus suggests high-energy oscillations of certain nuclei can split the nucleus into two unequal fragments plus a few neutrons. The fission products acquire kinetic energy from their mutual Coulomb repulsion. Calculate the electric potential energy (in electron volts) of two spherical fragments from a uranium nucleus having the following charges and radii: $38e$ and 5.50×10^{-15} m, $54e$ and 6.20×10^{-15} m. Assume the charge is distributed uniformly throughout the volume of each spherical fragment and, immediately before separating, each fragment is at rest and their surfaces are in contact. The electrons surrounding the nucleus can be ignored.

48. In fair weather, the electric field in the air at a particular location immediately above the Earth's surface is 120 N/C directed downward. (a) What is the surface charge density on the ground? Is it positive or negative? (b) Imagine the atmosphere is stripped off and the surface charge density is uniform over the planet. What then is the charge of the whole surface of the Earth? (c) What is the Earth's electric potential? (d) What is the difference in potential between the head and the feet of a person 1.75 m tall? (e) Imagine the Moon, with 27.3% of the radius of the Earth, had a charge 27.3% as large, with the same sign. Find the electric force that the Earth would then exert on the Moon. (f) State how the answer to part (e) compares with the gravitational force the Earth exerts on the Moon. (g) A

dust particle of mass 6.00 mg is in the air near the surface of the spherical Earth. What charge must the dust particle carry to be suspended in equilibrium between the electric and gravitational forces exerted on it? Ignore buoyancy. (h) The Earth is not perfectly spherical. It has an equatorial bulge due to its rotation, so the radius of curvature of the ground is slightly larger at the poles than at the equator. Would the dust particle in part (g) require more charge or less charge to be suspended at the equator compared with being suspended at one of the poles? Explain your answer with reference to variations in both the electric force and the gravitational force.

49. The Bohr model of the hydrogen atom states that the single electron can exist only in certain allowed orbits around the proton. The radius of each Bohr orbit is $r = n^2(0.052\ 9\ \text{nm})$, where $n = 1, 2, 3, \ldots$. Calculate the electric potential energy of a hydrogen atom when the electron (a) is in the first allowed orbit, with $n = 1$, (b) is in the second allowed orbit, with $n = 2$, and (c) has escaped from the atom, with $r = \infty$. Express your answers in electron volts.

50. On a dry winter day, you scuff your leather-soled shoes across a carpet and get a shock when you extend the tip of one finger toward a metal doorknob. In a dark room, you see a spark perhaps 5 mm long. Make order-of-magnitude estimates of (a) your electric potential and (b) the charge on your body before you touch the doorknob. Explain your reasoning.

51. The electric potential immediately outside a charged conducting sphere is 200 V, and 10.0 cm farther from the center of the sphere the potential is 150 V. (a) Is this information sufficient to determine the charge on the sphere and its radius? Explain. (b) The electric potential immediately outside another charged conducting sphere is 210 V, and 10.0 cm farther from the center the magnitude of the electric field is 400 V/m. Is this information sufficient to determine the charge on the sphere and its radius? Explain.

52. As shown in Figure P25.52, two large, parallel, vertical conducting plates separated by distance d are charged so that their potentials are $+V_0$ and $-V_0$. A small conducting ball of mass m and radius R (where $R \ll d$) is hung midway between the plates. The thread of length L supporting the ball is a conducting wire connected to ground, so the potential of the ball is fixed at $V = 0$. The ball hangs straight down in stable equilibrium when V_0 is sufficiently small. Show that the equilibrium of the ball is unstable if V_0 exceeds the critical value $k_e d^2 mg/(4RL)$. *Suggestion:* Consider the forces on the ball when it is displaced a distance $x \ll L$.

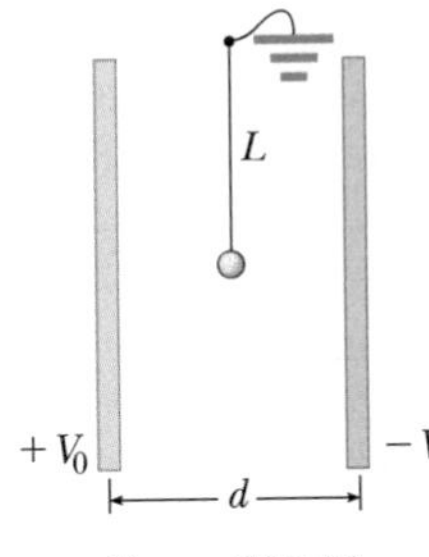

Figure P25.52

53. The electric potential everywhere on the xy plane is given by

$$V = \frac{36}{\sqrt{(x+1)^2 + y^2}} - \frac{45}{\sqrt{x^2 + (y-2)^2}}$$

where V is in volts and x and y are in meters. Determine the position and charge on each of the particles that create this potential.

54. *Compare this problem with Problem 28 in Chapter 23.* (a) A uniformly charged cylindrical shell has total charge Q, radius R, and height h. Determine the electric potential at a point a distance d from the right end of the cylinder as shown in Figure P25.54. *Suggestion:* Use the result of Example 25.5 by treating the cylinder as a collection of ring charges. (b) **What If?** Use the result of Example 25.6 to solve the same problem for a solid cylinder.

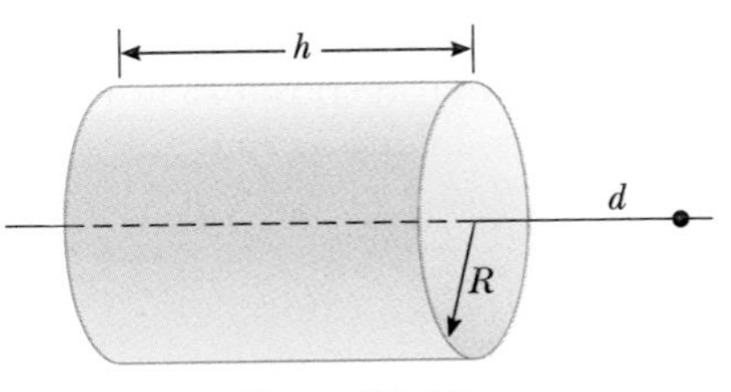

Figure P25.54

55. Calculate the work that must be done to charge a spherical shell of radius R to a total charge Q.

56. ● (a) Use the exact result from Example 25.4 to find the electric potential created by the dipole described at the point $(3a, 0)$. (b) Explain how this answer compares with the result of the approximate expression that is valid when x is much greater than a.

57. ▲ From Gauss's law, the electric field set up by a uniform line of charge is

$$\vec{\mathbf{E}} = \left(\frac{\lambda}{2\pi\epsilon_0 r}\right)\hat{\mathbf{r}}$$

where $\hat{\mathbf{r}}$ is a unit vector pointing radially away from the line and λ is the linear charge density along the line. Derive an expression for the potential difference between $r = r_1$ and $r = r_2$.

58. Four balls, each with mass m, are connected by four nonconducting strings to form a square with side a as shown in Figure P25.58. The assembly is placed on a horizontal, nonconducting, frictionless surface. Balls 1 and 2 each have charge q, and balls 3 and 4 are uncharged. Find the maximum speed of balls 3 and 4 after the string connecting balls 1 and 2 is cut.

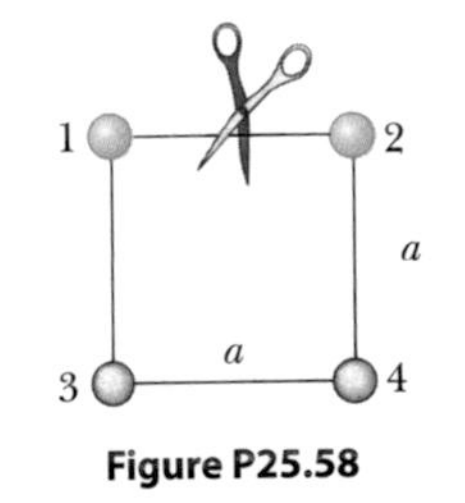

Figure P25.58

59. The x axis is the symmetry axis of a stationary, uniformly charged ring of radius R and charge Q (Fig. P25.59). A particle with charge Q and mass M is located initially at

the center of the ring. When it is displaced slightly, the particle accelerates along the x axis to infinity. Show that the ultimate speed of the particle is

$$v = \left(\frac{2k_eQ^2}{MR}\right)^{1/2}$$

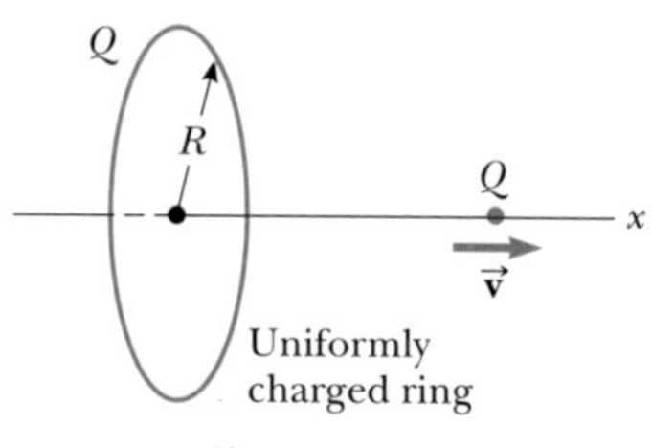

Figure P25.59

60. The thin, uniformly charged rod shown in Figure P25.60 has a linear charge density λ. Find an expression for the electric potential at P.

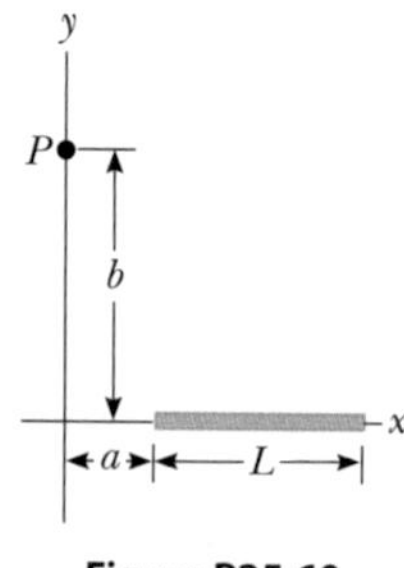

Figure P25.60

61. An electric dipole is located along the y axis as shown in Figure P25.61. The magnitude of its electric dipole moment is defined as $p = 2qa$. (a) At a point P, which is far from the dipole ($r \gg a$), show that the electric potential is

$$V = \frac{k_e p \cos\theta}{r^2}$$

(b) Calculate the radial component E_r and the perpendicular component E_θ of the associated electric field. Note that $E_\theta = -(1/r)(\partial V/\partial\theta)$. Do these results seem reasonable for $\theta = 90°$ and $0°$? For $r = 0$? (c) For the dipole arrangement shown, express V in terms of Cartesian coordinates using $r = (x^2 + y^2)^{1/2}$ and

$$\cos\theta = \frac{y}{(x^2 + y^2)^{1/2}}$$

Using these results and again taking $r \gg a$, calculate the field components E_x and E_y.

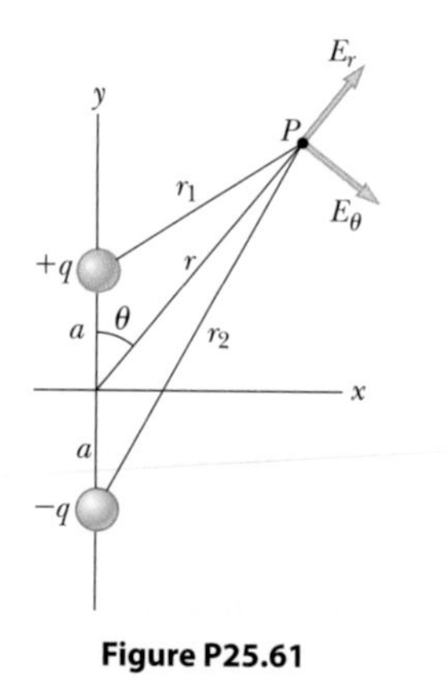

Figure P25.61

62. A solid sphere of radius R has a uniform charge density ρ and total charge Q. Derive an expression for its total electric potential energy. *Suggestion:* Imagine the sphere is constructed by adding successive layers of concentric shells of charge $dq = (4\pi r^2\,dr)\rho$ and use $dU = V\,dq$.

63. A disk of radius R (Fig. P25.63) has a nonuniform surface charge density $\sigma = Cr$, where C is a constant and r is measured from the center of the disk to a point on the surface of the disk. Find (by direct integration) the potential at P.

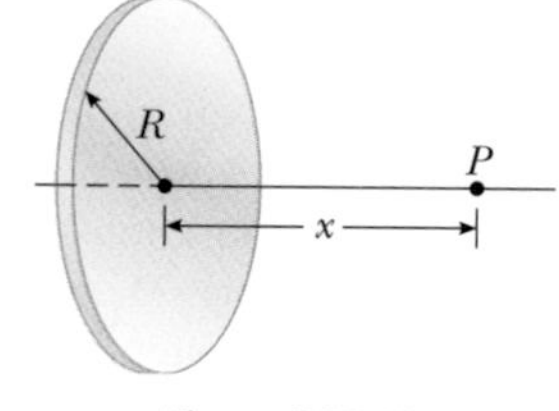

Figure P25.63

64. A uniformly charged filament lies along the x axis between $x = a = 1.00$ m and $x = a + \ell = 3.00$ m as shown in Figure 23.15. The total charge on the filament is 1.60 nC. Calculate successive approximations for the electric potential at the origin by modeling the filament as (a) a single charged particle at $x = 2.00$ m, (b) two 0.800-nC charged particles at $x = 1.5$ m and $x = 2.5$ m, and (c) four 0.400-nC charged particles at $x = 1.25$ m, $x = 1.75$ m, $x = 2.25$ m, and $x = 2.75$ m. Next, write and execute a computer program that will reproduce the results of parts (a), (b), and (c) and extend your calculation to (d) 32 and (e) 64 equally spaced charged particles. (f) Explain how the results compare with the potential given by the exact expression

$$V = \frac{k_eQ}{\ell}\ln\left(\frac{\ell + a}{a}\right)$$

65. Two parallel plates having charges of equal magnitude but opposite sign are separated by 12.0 cm. Each plate has a surface charge density of 36.0 nC/m^2. A proton is released from rest at the positive plate. Determine (a) the potential difference between the plates, (b) the kinetic energy of the proton when it reaches the negative plate, (c) the speed of the proton just before it strikes the negative plate, (d) the acceleration of the proton, and (e) the force on the proton. (f) From the force, find the magnitude of the electric field and show that it is equal to the electric field found from the charge densities on the plates.

66. A particle with charge q is located at $x = -R$, and a particle with charge $-2q$ is located at the origin. Prove that the equipotential surface that has zero potential is a sphere centered at $(-4R/3, 0, 0)$ and having a radius $r = 2R/3$.

67. When an uncharged conducting sphere of radius a is placed at the origin of an xyz coordinate system that lies in an initially uniform electric field $\vec{\mathbf{E}} = E_0\hat{\mathbf{k}}$, the resulting electric potential is $V(x, y, z) = V_0$ for points inside the sphere and

$$V(x, y, z) = V_0 - E_0 z + \frac{E_0 a^3 z}{(x^2 + y^2 + z^2)^{3/2}}$$

for points outside the sphere, where V_0 is the (constant) electric potential on the conductor. Use this equation to determine the x, y, and z components of the resulting electric field.

Answers to Quick Quizzes

25.1 **(i),** (b). When moving straight from Ⓐ to Ⓑ, $\vec{\mathbf{E}}$ and $d\vec{\mathbf{s}}$ both point toward the right. Therefore, the dot product $\vec{\mathbf{E}} \cdot d\vec{\mathbf{s}}$ in Equation 25.3 is positive and ΔV is negative. **(ii),** (a). From Equation 25.3, $\Delta U = q_0\, \Delta V$, so if a negative test charge is moved through a negative potential difference, the change in potential energy is positive. Work must be done to move the charge in the direction opposite to the electric force on it.

25.2 Ⓑ to Ⓒ, Ⓒ to Ⓓ, Ⓐ to Ⓑ, Ⓓ to Ⓔ. Moving from Ⓑ to Ⓒ decreases the electric potential by 2 V, so the electric field performs 2 J of work on each coulomb of positive charge that moves. Moving from Ⓒ to Ⓓ decreases the electric potential by 1 V, so 1 J of work is done by the field. It takes no work to move the charge from Ⓐ to Ⓑ because the electric potential does not change. Moving from Ⓓ to Ⓔ increases the electric potential by 1 V; therefore, the field does -1 J of work per unit of positive charge that moves.

25.3 **(i),** (c). The potential is established only by the source charge and is independent of the test charge. **(ii),** (a). The potential energy of the two-charge system is initially negative due to the product of charges of opposite sign in Equation 25.13. When the sign of q_2 is changed, both charges are negative and the potential energy of the system is positive.

25.4 (a). If the potential is constant (zero in this case), its derivative along this direction is zero.

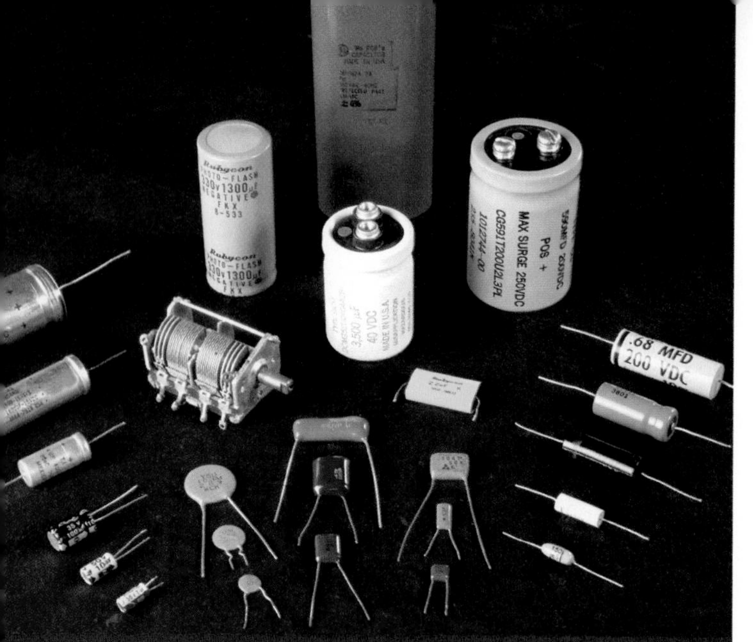

All these devices are capacitors, which store electric charge and energy. A capacitor is one type of circuit element that we can combine with others to make electric circuits. (Paul Silverman/Fundamental Photographs)

26 Capacitance and Dielectrics

In this chapter, we introduce the first of three simple *circuit elements* that can be connected with wires to form an electric circuit. Electric circuits are the basis for the vast majority of the devices used in our society. Here we shall discuss *capacitors,* devices that store electric charge. This discussion is followed by the study of *resistors* in Chapter 27 and *inductors* in Chapter 32. In later chapters, we will study more sophisticated circuit elements such as *diodes* and *transistors.*

Capacitors are commonly used in a variety of electric circuits. For instance, they are used to tune the frequency of radio receivers, as filters in power supplies, to eliminate sparking in automobile ignition systems, and as energy-storing devices in electronic flash units.

PITFALL PREVENTION 26.1
Capacitance Is a Capacity

To understand capacitance, think of similar notions that use a similar word. The *capacity* of a milk carton is the volume of milk it can store. The *heat capacity* of an object is the amount of energy an object can store per unit of temperature difference. The *capacitance* of a capacitor is the amount of charge the capacitor can store per unit of potential difference.

26.1 Definition of Capacitance

Consider two conductors as shown in Figure 26.1. Such a combination of two conductors is called a **capacitor.** The conductors are called *plates.* If the conductors carry charges of equal magnitude and opposite sign, a potential difference ΔV exists between them.

What determines how much charge is on the plates of a capacitor for a given voltage? Experiments show that the quantity of charge Q on a capacitor[1] is linearly pro-

[1] Although the total charge on the capacitor is zero (because there is as much excess positive charge on one conductor as there is excess negative charge on the other), it is common practice to refer to the magnitude of the charge on either conductor as "the charge on the capacitor."

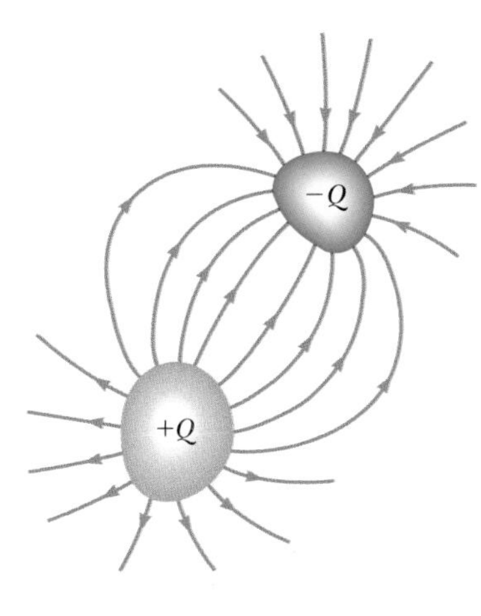

Figure 26.1 A capacitor consists of two conductors. When the capacitor is charged, the conductors carry charges of equal magnitude and opposite sign.

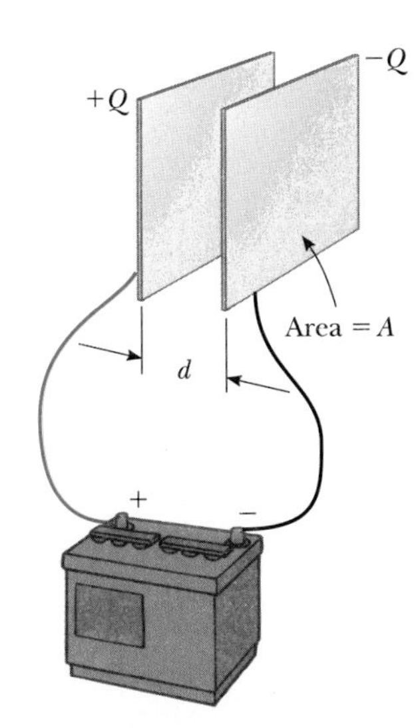

Figure 26.2 A parallel-plate capacitor consists of two parallel conducting plates, each of area A, separated by a distance d. When the capacitor is charged by connecting the plates to the terminals of a battery, the plates carry equal amounts of charge. One plate carries positive charge, and the other carries negative charge.

portional to the potential difference between the conductors; that is, $Q \propto \Delta V$. The proportionality constant depends on the shape and separation of the conductors.[2] This relationship can be written as $Q = C\,\Delta V$ if we define capacitance as follows:

The **capacitance** C of a capacitor is defined as the ratio of the magnitude of the charge on either conductor to the magnitude of the potential difference between the conductors:

$$C \equiv \frac{Q}{\Delta V} \qquad \textbf{(26.1)}$$

◀ Definition of capacitance

By definition *capacitance is always a positive quantity*. Furthermore, the charge Q and the potential difference ΔV are always expressed in Equation 26.1 as positive quantities.

From Equation 26.1, we see that capacitance has SI units of coulombs per volt. Named in honor of Michael Faraday, the SI unit of capacitance is the **farad** (F):

$$1\text{ F} = 1\text{ C/V}$$

The farad is a very large unit of capacitance. In practice, typical devices have capacitances ranging from microfarads (10^{-6} F) to picofarads (10^{-12} F). We shall use the symbol μF to represent microfarads. In practice, to avoid the use of Greek letters, physical capacitors are often labeled "mF" for microfarads and "mmF" for micromicrofarads or, equivalently, "pF" for picofarads.

Let's consider a capacitor formed from a pair of parallel plates as shown in Figure 26.2. Each plate is connected to one terminal of a battery, which acts as a source of potential difference. If the capacitor is initially uncharged, the battery establishes an electric field in the connecting wires when the connections are made. Let's focus on the plate connected to the negative terminal of the battery. The electric field in the wire applies a force on electrons in the wire immediately outside this plate; this force causes the electrons to move onto the plate. The movement continues until the plate, the wire, and the terminal are all at the same electric potential. Once this equilibrium situation is attained, a potential difference no longer exists between the terminal and the plate; as a result no electric field is present in the wire and the electrons stop moving. The plate now carries a negative charge. A similar process occurs at the other capacitor plate, where electrons move from the plate to the wire, leaving the plate positively charged. In this final configuration, the potential difference across the capacitor plates is the same as that between the terminals of the battery.

PITFALL PREVENTION 26.2
Potential Difference Is ΔV, Not V

We use the symbol ΔV for the potential difference across a circuit element or a device because this notation is consistent with our definition of potential difference and with the meaning of the delta sign. It is a common but confusing practice to use the symbol V without the delta sign for both a potential and a potential difference! Keep that in mind if you consult other texts.

PITFALL PREVENTION 26.3
Too Many Cs

Do not confuse an italic C for capacitance with a nonitalic C for the unit coulomb.

[2] The proportionality between ΔV and Q can be proven from Coulomb's law or by experiment.

Quick Quiz 26.1 A capacitor stores charge Q at a potential difference ΔV. What happens if the voltage applied to the capacitor by a battery is doubled to $2\Delta V$? (a) The capacitance falls to half its initial value, and the charge remains the same. (b) The capacitance and the charge both fall to half their initial values. (c) The capacitance and the charge both double. (d) The capacitance remains the same, and the charge doubles.

26.2 Calculating Capacitance

We can derive an expression for the capacitance of a pair of oppositely charged conductors having a charge of magnitude Q in the following manner. First we calculate the potential difference using the techniques described in Chapter 25. We then use the expression $C = Q/\Delta V$ to evaluate the capacitance. The calculation is relatively easy if the geometry of the capacitor is simple.

Although the most common situation is that of two conductors, a single conductor also has a capacitance. For example, imagine a spherical, charged conductor. The electric field lines around this conductor are exactly the same as if there were a conducting, spherical shell of infinite radius, concentric with the sphere and carrying a charge of the same magnitude but opposite sign. Therefore, we can identify the imaginary shell as the second conductor of a two-conductor capacitor. The electric potential of the sphere of radius a is simply k_eQ/a, and setting $V = 0$ for the infinitely large shell gives

Capacitance of an isolated charged sphere ▶

$$C = \frac{Q}{\Delta V} = \frac{Q}{k_eQ/a} = \frac{a}{k_e} = 4\pi\epsilon_0 a \qquad (26.2)$$

This expression shows that the capacitance of an isolated, charged sphere is proportional to its radius and is independent of both the charge on the sphere and the potential difference.

The capacitance of a pair of conductors is illustrated below with three familiar geometries, namely, parallel plates, concentric cylinders, and concentric spheres. In these calculations, we assume the charged conductors are separated by a vacuum.

Parallel-Plate Capacitors

Two parallel, metallic plates of equal area A are separated by a distance d as shown in Figure 26.2. One plate carries a charge $+Q$, and the other carries a charge $-Q$. The surface charge density on each plate is $\sigma = Q/A$. If the plates are very close together (in comparison with their length and width), we can assume the electric field is uniform between the plates and zero elsewhere. According to the **What If?** feature of Example 24.5, the value of the electric field between the plates is

$$E = \frac{\sigma}{\epsilon_0} = \frac{Q}{\epsilon_0 A}$$

Because the field between the plates is uniform, the magnitude of the potential difference between the plates equals Ed (see Eq. 25.6); therefore,

$$\Delta V = Ed = \frac{Qd}{\epsilon_0 A}$$

Substituting this result into Equation 26.1, we find that the capacitance is

$$C = \frac{Q}{\Delta V} = \frac{Q}{Qd/\epsilon_0 A}$$

Capacitance of parallel plates ▶

$$C = \frac{\epsilon_0 A}{d} \qquad (26.3)$$

That is, **the capacitance of a parallel-plate capacitor is proportional to the area of its plates and inversely proportional to the plate separation.**

Let's consider how the geometry of these conductors influences the capacity of the pair of plates to store charge. As a capacitor is being charged by a battery, electrons flow into the negative plate and out of the positive plate. If the capacitor plates are large, the accumulated charges are able to distribute themselves over a substantial area and the amount of charge that can be stored on a plate for a given potential difference increases as the plate area is increased. Therefore, it is reasonable that the capacitance is proportional to the plate area A as in Equation 26.3.

Now consider the region that separates the plates. Imagine moving the plates closer together. Consider the situation before any charges have had a chance to move in response to this change. Because no charges have moved, the electric field between the plates has the same value but extends over a shorter distance. Therefore, the magnitude of the potential difference between the plates $\Delta V = Ed$ (Eq. 25.6) is smaller. The difference between this new capacitor voltage and the terminal voltage of the battery appears as a potential difference across the wires connecting the battery to the capacitor, resulting in an electric field in the wires that drives more charge onto the plates and increases the potential difference between the plates. When the potential difference between the plates again matches that of the battery, the flow of charge stops. Therefore, moving the plates closer together causes the charge on the capacitor to increase. If d is increased, the charge decreases. As a result, the inverse relationship between C and d in Equation 26.3 is reasonable.

Quick Quiz 26.2 Many computer keyboard buttons are constructed of capacitors as shown in Figure 26.3. When a key is pushed down, the soft insulator between the movable plate and the fixed plate is compressed. When the key is pressed, what happens to the capacitance? (a) It increases. (b) It decreases. (c) It changes in a way you cannot determine because the electric circuit connected to the keyboard button may cause a change in ΔV.

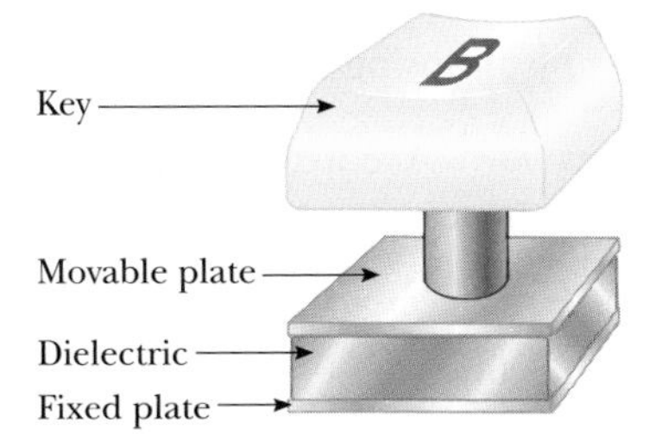

Figure 26.3 (Quick Quiz 26.2) One type of computer keyboard button.

EXAMPLE 26.1 The Cylindrical Capacitor

A solid, cylindrical conductor of radius a and charge Q is coaxial with a cylindrical shell of negligible thickness, radius $b > a$, and charge $-Q$ (Fig. 26.4a). Find the capacitance of this cylindrical capacitor if its length is ℓ.

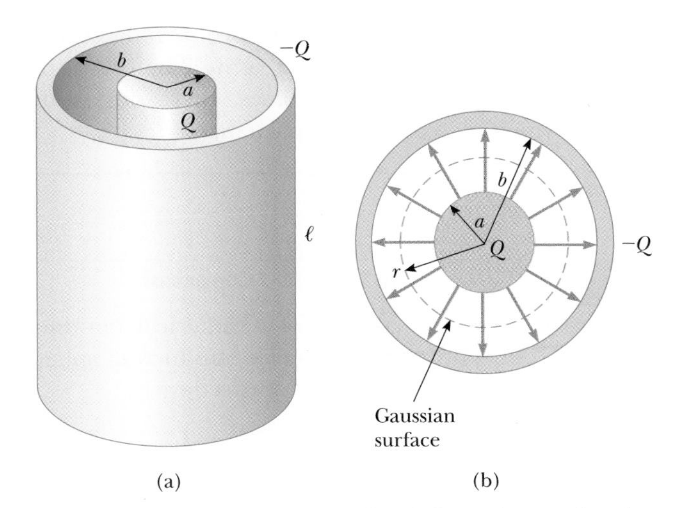

Figure 26.4 (Example 26.1) (a) A cylindrical capacitor consists of a solid cylindrical conductor of radius a and length ℓ surrounded by a coaxial cylindrical shell of radius b. (b) End view. The electric field lines are radial. The dashed line represents the end of the cylindrical gaussian surface of radius r and length ℓ.

SOLUTION

Conceptualize Recall that any pair of conductors qualifies as a capacitor, so the system described in this example therefore qualifies. Figure 26.4b helps visualize the electric field between the conductors.

Categorize Because of the cylindrical symmetry of the system, we can use results from previous studies of cylindrical systems to find the capacitance.

Analyze Assuming ℓ is much greater than a and b, we can neglect end effects. In this case, the electric field is perpendicular to the long axis of the cylinders and is confined to the region between them (Fig. 26.4b).

Write an expression for the potential difference between the two cylinders from Equation 25.3:

$$V_b - V_a = -\int_a^b \vec{\mathbf{E}} \cdot d\vec{\mathbf{s}}$$

Apply Equation 24.7 for the electric field outside a cylindrically symmetric charge distribution and notice from Figure 26.4b that $\vec{\mathbf{E}}$ is parallel to $d\vec{\mathbf{s}}$ along a radial line:

$$V_b - V_a = -\int_a^b E_r\,dr = -2k_e\lambda \int_a^b \frac{dr}{r} = -2k_e\lambda \ln\left(\frac{b}{a}\right)$$

Substitute the absolute value of ΔV into Equation 26.1 and use $\lambda = Q/\ell$:

$$C = \frac{Q}{\Delta V} = \frac{Q}{(2k_eQ/\ell)\ln(b/a)} = \frac{\ell}{2k_e \ln(b/a)} \tag{26.4}$$

Finalize The capacitance is proportional to the length of the cylinders. As you might expect, the capacitance also depends on the radii of the two cylindrical conductors. Equation 26.4 shows that the capacitance per unit length of a combination of concentric cylindrical conductors is

$$\frac{C}{\ell} = \frac{1}{2k_e \ln(b/a)} \tag{26.5}$$

An example of this type of geometric arrangement is a *coaxial cable*, which consists of two concentric cylindrical conductors separated by an insulator. You probably have a coaxial cable attached to your television set or VCR if you are a subscriber to cable television. The coaxial cable is especially useful for shielding electrical signals from any possible external influences.

What If? Suppose $b = 2.00a$ for the cylindrical capacitor. You would like to increase the capacitance, and you can do so by choosing to increase either ℓ by 10% or a by 10%. Which choice is more effective at increasing the capacitance?

Answer According to Equation 26.4, C is proportional to ℓ, so increasing ℓ by 10% results in a 10% increase in C. For the result of the change in a, let's use Equation 26.4 to set up a ratio of the capacitance C' for the enlarged cylinder radius a' to the original capacitance:

$$\frac{C'}{C} = \frac{\ell/2k_e \ln(b/a')}{\ell/2k_e \ln(b/a)} = \frac{\ln(b/a)}{\ln(b/a')}$$

We now substitute $b = 2.00a$ and $a' = 1.10a$, representing a 10% increase in a:

$$\frac{C'}{C} = \frac{\ln(2.00a/a)}{\ln(2.00a/1.10a)} = \frac{\ln 2.00}{\ln 1.82} = 1.16$$

which corresponds to a 16% increase in capacitance. Therefore, it is more effective to increase a than to increase ℓ.

Note two more extensions of this problem. First, it is advantageous to increase a only for a range of relationships between a and b. If $b > 2.85a$, increasing ℓ by 10% is more effective than increasing a (see Problem 66). Second, if b decreases, the capacitance increases. Increasing a or decreasing b has the effect of bringing the plates closer together, which increases the capacitance.

EXAMPLE 26.2 The Spherical Capacitor

A spherical capacitor consists of a spherical conducting shell of radius b and charge $-Q$ concentric with a smaller conducting sphere of radius a and charge Q (Fig. 26.5). Find the capacitance of this device.

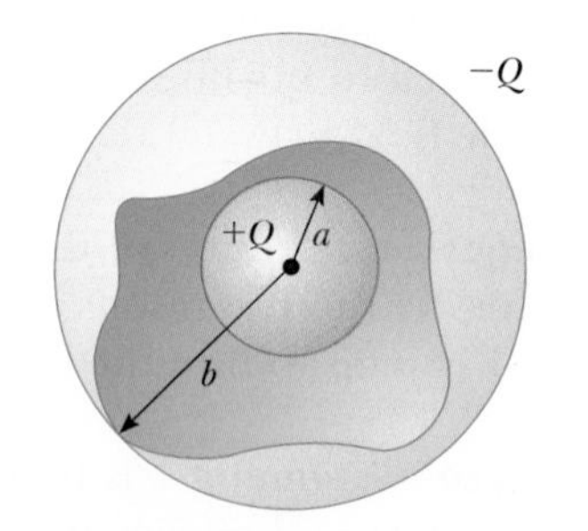

Figure 26.5 (Example 26.2) A spherical capacitor consists of an inner sphere of radius a surrounded by a concentric spherical shell of radius b. The electric field between the spheres is directed radially outward when the inner sphere is positively charged.

SOLUTION

Conceptualize As with Example 26.1, this system involves a pair of conductors and qualifies as a capacitor.

Categorize Because of the spherical symmetry of the system, we can use results from previous studies of spherical systems to find the capacitance.

Analyze As shown in Chapter 24, the magnitude of the electric field outside a spherically symmetric charge distribution is radial and given by the expression $E = k_eQ/r^2$. In this case, this result applies to the field *between* the spheres ($a < r < b$).

Write an expression for the potential difference between the two conductors from Equation 25.3:

$$V_b - V_a = -\int_a^b \vec{\mathbf{E}} \cdot d\vec{\mathbf{s}}$$

Apply the result of Example 24.3 for the electric field outside a spherically symmetric charge distribution and note that $\vec{\mathbf{E}}$ is parallel to $d\vec{\mathbf{s}}$ along a radial line:

$$V_b - V_a = -\int_a^b E_r\, dr = -k_e Q \int_a^b \frac{dr}{r^2} = k_e Q\left[\frac{1}{r}\right]_a^b$$

$$(1)\quad V_b - V_a = k_e Q\left(\frac{1}{b} - \frac{1}{a}\right) = k_e Q\frac{a-b}{ab}$$

Substitute the absolute value of ΔV into Equation 26.1:

$$C = \frac{Q}{\Delta V} = \frac{Q}{|V_b - V_a|} = \frac{ab}{k_e(b-a)} \qquad \textbf{(26.6)}$$

Finalize The potential difference between the spheres in Equation (1) is negative because of the choice of signs on the spheres. Therefore, in Equation 26.6, when we take the absolute value, we change $a - b$ to $b - a$. The result is a positive number because $b > a$.

What If? If the radius b of the outer sphere approaches infinity, what does the capacitance become?

Answer In Equation 26.6, we let $b \to \infty$:

$$C = \lim_{b\to\infty} \frac{ab}{k_e(b-a)} = \frac{ab}{k_e(b)} = \frac{a}{k_e} = 4\pi\epsilon_0 a$$

Notice that this expression is the same as Equation 26.2, the capacitance of an isolated spherical conductor.

26.3 Combinations of Capacitors

Two or more capacitors often are combined in electric circuits. We can calculate the equivalent capacitance of certain combinations using methods described in this section. Throughout this section, we assume the capacitors to be combined are initially uncharged.

In studying electric circuits, we use a simplified pictorial representation called a **circuit diagram.** Such a diagram uses **circuit symbols** to represent various circuit elements. The circuit symbols are connected by straight lines that represent the wires between the circuit elements. The circuit symbols for capacitors, batteries, and switches as well as the color codes used for them in this text are given in Figure 26.6. The symbol for the capacitor reflects the geometry of the most common model for a capacitor, a pair of parallel plates. The positive terminal of the battery is at the higher potential and is represented in the circuit symbol by the longer line.

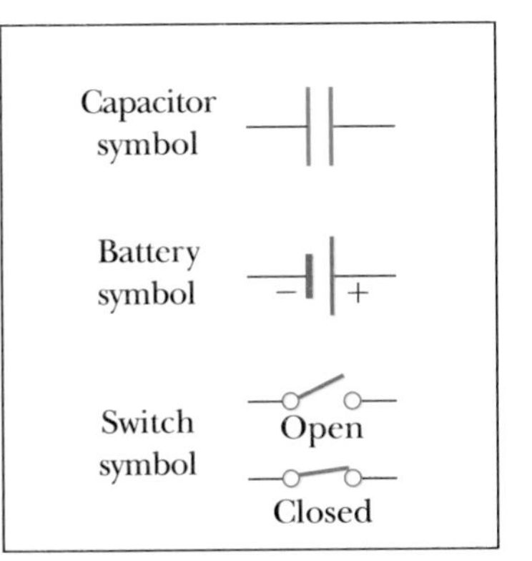

Figure 26.6 Circuit symbols for capacitors, batteries, and switches. Notice that capacitors are in blue and batteries and switches are in red. The closed switch can carry current, whereas the open one cannot.

Parallel Combination

Two capacitors connected as shown in Active Figure 26.7a (page 728) are known as a **parallel combination** of capacitors. Active Figure 26.7b shows a circuit diagram for this combination of capacitors. The left plates of the capacitors are connected to the positive terminal of the battery by a conducting wire and are therefore both at the same electric potential as the positive terminal. Likewise, the right plates are connected to the negative terminal and so are both at the same potential as the negative terminal. Therefore, **the individual potential differences across capacitors connected in parallel are the same and are equal to the potential difference applied across the combination.** That is,

$$\Delta V_1 = \Delta V_2 = \Delta V$$

where ΔV is the battery terminal voltage.

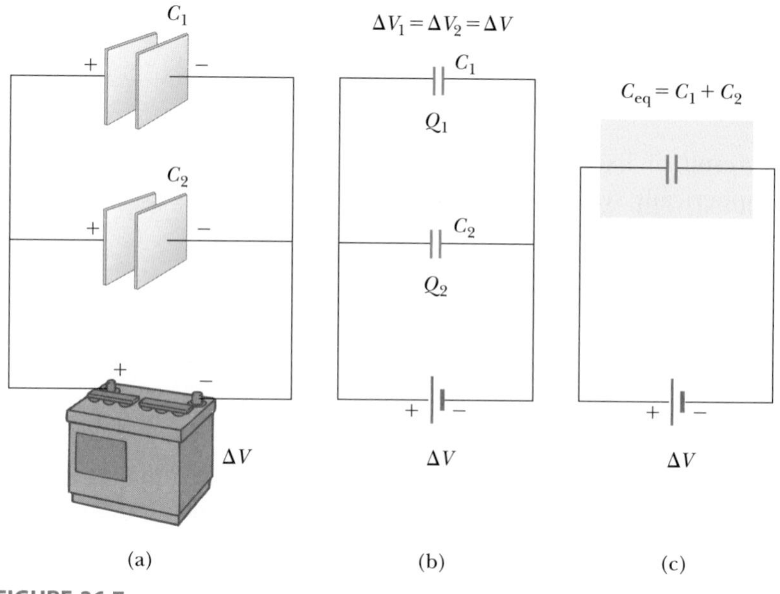

ACTIVE FIGURE 26.7

(a) A parallel combination of two capacitors in an electric circuit in which the potential difference across the battery terminals is ΔV. (b) The circuit diagram for the parallel combination. (c) The equivalent capacitance is given by Equation 26.8.

Sign in at www.thomsonedu.com and go to ThomsonNOW to adjust the battery voltage and the individual capacitances and see the resulting charges and voltages on the capacitors. You can combine up to four capacitors in parallel.

After the battery is attached to the circuit, the capacitors quickly reach their maximum charge. Let's call the maximum charges on the two capacitors Q_1 and Q_2. The *total charge* Q_{tot} stored by the two capacitors is

$$Q_{tot} = Q_1 + Q_2 \quad \textbf{(26.7)}$$

That is, **the total charge on capacitors connected in parallel is the sum of the charges on the individual capacitors.**

Suppose you wish to replace these two capacitors by one *equivalent capacitor* having a capacitance C_{eq} as in Active Figure 26.7c. The effect this equivalent capacitor has on the circuit must be exactly the same as the effect of the combination of the two individual capacitors. That is, the equivalent capacitor must store charge Q_{tot} when connected to the battery. Active Figure 26.7c shows that the voltage across the equivalent capacitor is ΔV because the equivalent capacitor is connected directly across the battery terminals. Therefore, for the equivalent capacitor,

$$Q_{tot} = C_{eq}\,\Delta V$$

Substituting for the charges in Equation 26.7 gives

$$C_{eq}\,\Delta V = C_1\,\Delta V_1 + C_2\,\Delta V_2$$

$$C_{eq} = C_1 + C_2 \quad \text{(parallel combination)}$$

where we have canceled the voltages because they are all the same. If this treatment is extended to three or more capacitors connected in parallel, the equivalent capacitance is found to be

Capacitors in parallel ▶

$$C_{eq} = C_1 + C_2 + C_3 + \cdots \quad \text{(parallel combination)} \quad \textbf{(26.8)}$$

Therefore, **the equivalent capacitance of a parallel combination of capacitors is (1) the algebraic sum of the individual capacitances and (2) greater than any of the individual capacitances.** Statement (2) makes sense because we are essentially combining the areas of all the capacitor plates when they are connected with conducting wire, and capacitance of parallel plates is proportional to area (Eq. 26.3).

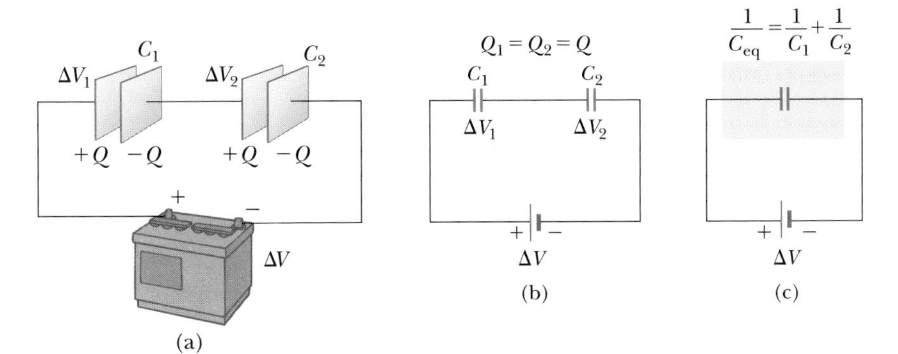

ACTIVE FIGURE 26.8

(a) A series combination of two capacitors. The charges on the two capacitors are the same. (b) The circuit diagram for the series combination. (c) The equivalent capacitance can be calculated from Equation 26.10.

Sign in at www.thomsonedu.com and go to ThomsonNOW to adjust the battery voltage and the individual capacitances and see the resulting charges and voltages on the capacitors. You can combine up to four capacitors in series.

Series Combination

Two capacitors connected as shown in Active Figure 26.8a and the equivalent circuit diagram in Active Figure 26.8b are known as a **series combination** of capacitors. The left plate of capacitor 1 and the right plate of capacitor 2 are connected to the terminals of a battery. The other two plates are connected to each other and to nothing else; hence, they form an isolated system that is initially uncharged and must continue to have zero net charge. To analyze this combination, let's first consider the uncharged capacitors and then follow what happens immediately after a battery is connected to the circuit. When the battery is connected, electrons are transferred out of the left plate of C_1 and into the right plate of C_2. As this negative charge accumulates on the right plate of C_2, an equivalent amount of negative charge is forced off the left plate of C_2, and this left plate therefore has an excess positive charge. The negative charge leaving the left plate of C_2 causes negative charges to accumulate on the right plate of C_1. As a result, all the right plates end up with a charge $-Q$ and all the left plates end up with a charge $+Q$. Therefore, **the charges on capacitors connected in series are the same:**

$$Q_1 = Q_2 = Q$$

where Q is the charge that moved between a wire and the connected outside plate of one of the capacitors.

Active Figure 26.8a shows that the total voltage ΔV_{tot} across the combination is split between the two capacitors:

$$\Delta V_{tot} = \Delta V_1 + \Delta V_2 \qquad \textbf{(26.9)}$$

where ΔV_1 and ΔV_2 are the potential differences across capacitors C_1 and C_2, respectively. In general, **the total potential difference across any number of capacitors connected in series is the sum of the potential differences across the individual capacitors.**

Suppose the equivalent single capacitor in Active Figure 26.8c has the same effect on the circuit as the series combination when it is connected to the battery. After it is fully charged, the equivalent capacitor must have a charge of $-Q$ on its right plate and a charge of $+Q$ on its left plate. Applying the definition of capacitance to the circuit in Active Figure 26.8c gives

$$\Delta V_{tot} = \frac{Q}{C_{eq}}$$

Substituting for the voltages in Equation 26.9, we have

$$\frac{Q}{C_{eq}} = \frac{Q_1}{C_1} + \frac{Q_2}{C_2}$$

Canceling the charges because they are all the same gives

$$\frac{1}{C_{eq}} = \frac{1}{C_1} + \frac{1}{C_2} \quad \text{(series combination)}$$

When this analysis is applied to three or more capacitors connected in series, the relationship for the equivalent capacitance is

Capacitors in series ▶

$$\frac{1}{C_{eq}} = \frac{1}{C_1} + \frac{1}{C_2} + \frac{1}{C_3} + \cdots \quad \text{(series combination)} \tag{26.10}$$

This expression shows that **(1) the inverse of the equivalent capacitance is the algebraic sum of the inverses of the individual capacitances and (2) the equivalent capacitance of a series combination is always less than any individual capacitance in the combination.**

Quick Quiz 26.3 Two capacitors are identical. They can be connected in series or in parallel. If you want the *smallest* equivalent capacitance for the combination, how should you connect them? (a) in series (b) in parallel (c) either way because both combinations have the same capacitance

EXAMPLE 26.3 Equivalent Capacitance

Find the equivalent capacitance between a and b for the combination of capacitors shown in Figure 26.9a. All capacitances are in microfarads.

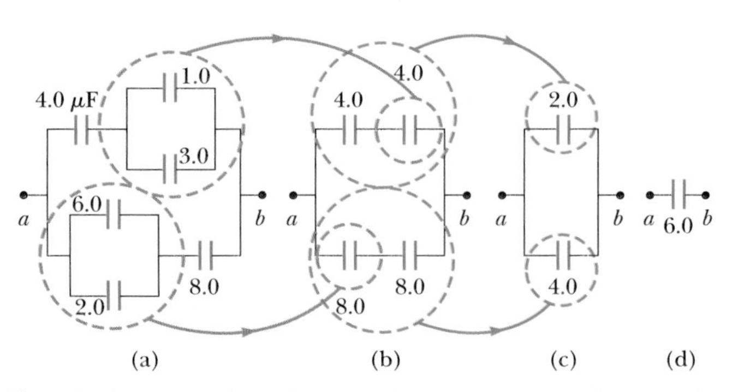

Figure 26.9 (Example 26.3) To find the equivalent capacitance of the capacitors in (a), we reduce the various combinations in steps as indicated in (b), (c), and (d), using the series and parallel rules described in the text.

SOLUTION

Conceptualize Study Figure 26.9a carefully and make sure you understand how the capacitors are connected.

Categorize Figure 26.9a shows that the circuit contains both series and parallel connections, so we use the rules for series and parallel combinations discussed in this section.

Analyze Using Equations 26.8 and 26.10, we reduce the combination step by step as indicated in the figure.

The 1.0-μF and 3.0-μF capacitors in Figure 26.9a are in parallel. Find the equivalent capacitance from Equation 26.8:

$$C_{eq} = C_1 + C_2 = 4.0\,\mu\text{F}$$

The 2.0-μF and 6.0-μF capacitors in Figure 26.9a are also in parallel:

$$C_{eq} = C_1 + C_2 = 8.0\,\mu\text{F}$$

The circuit now looks like Figure 26.9b. The two 4.0-μF capacitors in the upper branch are in series. Find the equivalent capacitance from Equation 26.10:

$$\frac{1}{C_{eq}} = \frac{1}{C_1} + \frac{1}{C_2} = \frac{1}{4.0\,\mu\text{F}} + \frac{1}{4.0\,\mu\text{F}} = \frac{1}{2.0\,\mu\text{F}}$$

$$C_{eq} = 2.0\,\mu\text{F}$$

The two 8.0-μF capacitors in the lower branch are also in series. Find the equivalent capacitance from Equation 26.10:

$$\frac{1}{C_{eq}} = \frac{1}{C_1} + \frac{1}{C_2} = \frac{1}{8.0\,\mu\text{F}} + \frac{1}{8.0\,\mu\text{F}} = \frac{1}{4.0\,\mu\text{F}}$$

$$C_{eq} = 4.0\,\mu\text{F}$$

The circuit now looks like Figure 26.9c. The 2.0-μF and 4.0-μF capacitors are in parallel:

$$C_{eq} = C_1 + C_2 = 6.0\ \mu\text{F}$$

Finalize This final value is that of the single equivalent capacitor shown in Figure 26.9d. For further practice in treating circuits with combinations of capacitors, imagine that a battery is connected between points a and b so that a potential difference ΔV is established across the combination. Can you find the voltage across and the charge on each capacitor?

26.4 Energy Stored in a Charged Capacitor

Because positive and negative charges are separated in the system of two conductors in a capacitor, electric potential energy is stored in the system. Many of those who work with electronic equipment have at some time verified that a capacitor can store energy. If the plates of a charged capacitor are connected by a conductor such as a wire, charge moves between each plate and its connecting wire until the capacitor is uncharged. The discharge can often be observed as a visible spark. If you accidentally touch the opposite plates of a charged capacitor, your fingers act as a pathway for discharge and the result is an electric shock. The degree of shock you receive depends on the capacitance and the voltage applied to the capacitor. Such a shock could be fatal if high voltages are present, as in the power supply of a television set. Because the charges can be stored in a capacitor even when the set is turned off, unplugging the television does not make it safe to open the case and touch the components inside.

Active Figure 26.10a shows a battery connected to a single parallel-plate capacitor with a switch in the circuit. Let us identify the circuit as a system. When the switch is closed (Active Fig. 26.10b), the battery establishes an electric field in the wires and charges flow between the wires and the capacitor. As that occurs, there is

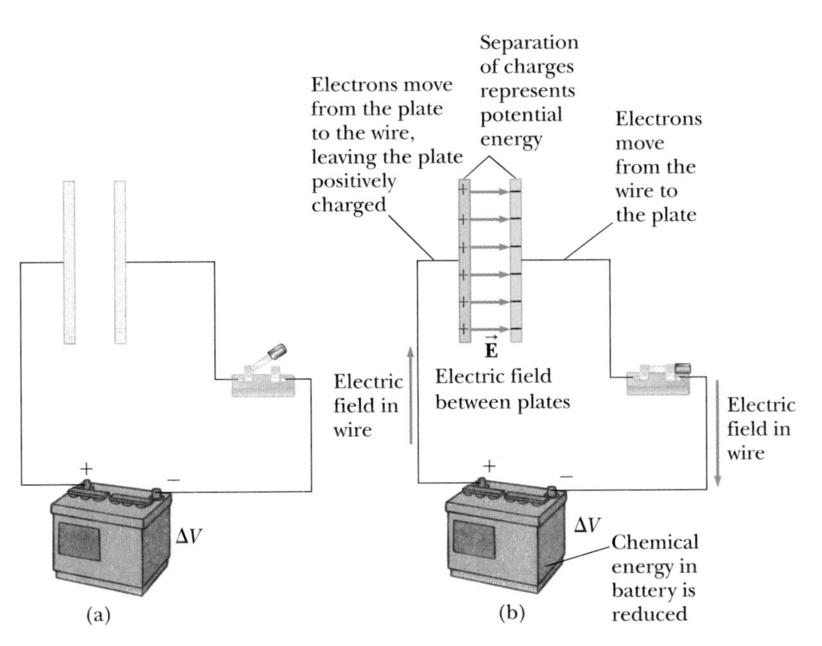

ACTIVE FIGURE 26.10

(a) A circuit consisting of a capacitor, a battery, and a switch. (b) When the switch is closed, the battery establishes an electric field in the wire that causes electrons to move from the left plate into the wire and into the right plate from the wire. As a result, a separation of charge exists on the plates, which represents an increase in electric potential energy of the system of the circuit. This energy in the system has been transformed from chemical energy in the battery.

Sign in at www.thomsonedu.com and go to ThomsonNOW to adjust the battery voltage and see the resulting charge on the plates and the electric field between the plates.

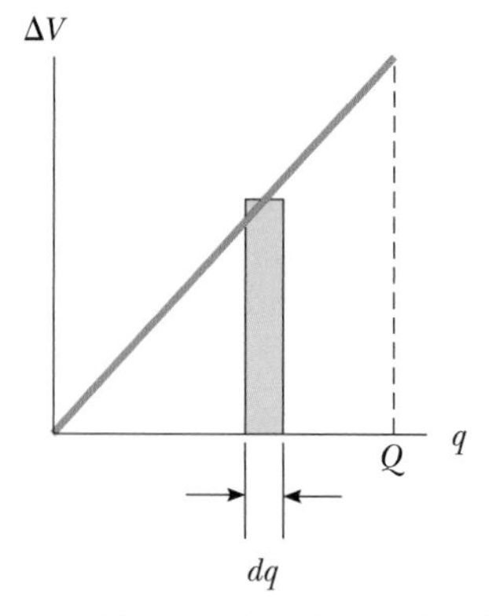

Figure 26.11 A plot of potential difference versus charge for a capacitor is a straight line having slope $1/C$. The work required to move charge dq through the potential difference ΔV existing at the time across the capacitor plates is given approximately by the area of the shaded rectangle. The total work required to charge the capacitor to a final charge Q is the triangular area under the straight line, $W = \frac{1}{2}Q\,\Delta V$. (Don't forget that 1 V = 1 J/C; hence, the unit for the triangular area is the joule.)

a transformation of energy within the system. Before the switch is closed, energy is stored as chemical energy in the battery. This energy is transformed during the chemical reaction that occurs within the battery when it is operating in an electric circuit. When the switch is closed, some of the chemical energy in the battery is converted to electric potential energy associated with the separation of positive and negative charges on the plates.

To calculate the energy stored in the capacitor, we shall assume a charging process that is different from the actual process described in Section 26.1 but that gives the same final result. This assumption is justified because the energy in the final configuration does not depend on the actual charge-transfer process.[3] Imagine that you transfer the charge mechanically through the space between the plates as follows. You grab a small amount of positive charge on the plate connected to the negative terminal and apply a force that causes this positive charge to move over to the plate connected to the positive terminal. Therefore, you do work on the charge as it is transferred from one plate to the other. At first, no work is required to transfer a small amount of charge dq from one plate to the other,[4] but once this charge has been transferred, a small potential difference exists between the plates. Therefore, work must be done to move additional charge through this potential difference. As more and more charge is transferred from one plate to the other, the potential difference increases in proportion and more work is required.

Suppose q is the charge on the capacitor at some instant during the charging process. At the same instant, the potential difference across the capacitor is $\Delta V = q/C$. From Section 25.1, we know that the work necessary to transfer an increment of charge dq from the plate carrying charge $-q$ to the plate carrying charge q (which is at the higher electric potential) is

$$dW = \Delta V\,dq = \frac{q}{C}\,dq$$

This situation is illustrated in Figure 26.11. The total work required to charge the capacitor from $q = 0$ to some final charge $q = Q$ is

$$W = \int_0^Q \frac{q}{C}\,dq = \frac{1}{C}\int_0^Q q\,dq = \frac{Q^2}{2C}$$

The work done in charging the capacitor appears as electric potential energy U stored in the capacitor. Using Equation 26.1, we can express the potential energy stored in a charged capacitor as

Energy stored in a charged capacitor ▶

$$U = \frac{Q^2}{2C} = \tfrac{1}{2}Q\,\Delta V = \tfrac{1}{2}C(\Delta V)^2 \qquad \textbf{(26.11)}$$

This result applies to any capacitor, regardless of its geometry. For a given capacitance, the stored energy increases as the charge and the potential difference increase. In practice, there is a limit to the maximum energy (or charge) that can be stored because, at a sufficiently large value of ΔV, discharge ultimately occurs between the plates. For this reason, capacitors are usually labeled with a maximum operating voltage.

We can consider the energy in a capacitor to be stored in the electric field created between the plates as the capacitor is charged. This description is reasonable because the electric field is proportional to the charge on the capacitor. For a parallel-plate capacitor, the potential difference is related to the electric field

[3] This discussion is similar to that of state variables in thermodynamics. The change in a state variable such as temperature is independent of the path followed between the initial and final states. The potential energy of a capacitor (or any system) is also a state variable, so it does not depend on the actual process followed to charge the capacitor.

[4] We shall use lowercase q for the time-varying charge on the capacitor while it is charging to distinguish it from uppercase Q, which is the total charge on the capacitor after it is completely charged.

through the relationship $\Delta V = Ed$. Furthermore, its capacitance is $C = \epsilon_0 A/d$ (Eq. 26.3). Substituting these expressions into Equation 26.11 gives

$$U = \frac{1}{2}\frac{\epsilon_0 A}{d}(E^2 d^2) = \frac{1}{2}(\epsilon_0 Ad)E^2 \quad (26.12)$$

Because the volume occupied by the electric field is Ad, the *energy per unit volume* $u_E = U/Ad$, known as the *energy density*, is

$$u_E = \frac{1}{2}\epsilon_0 E^2 \quad (26.13)$$

◀ Energy density in an electric field

Although Equation 26.13 was derived for a parallel-plate capacitor, the expression is generally valid regardless of the source of the electric field. That is, **the energy density in any electric field is proportional to the square of the magnitude of the electric field at a given point.**

PITFALL PREVENTION 26.4
Not a New Kind of Energy

The energy given by Equation 26.13 is not a new kind of energy. The equation describes familiar electric potential energy associated with a system of separated source charges. Equation 26.13 provides a new *interpretation*, or a new way of *modeling* the energy. Furthermore, the equation correctly describes the energy associated with *any* electric field, regardless of the source.

Quick Quiz 26.4 You have three capacitors and a battery. In which of the following combinations of the three capacitors is the maximum possible energy stored when the combination is attached to the battery? (a) series (b) parallel (c) no difference because both combinations store the same amount of energy

EXAMPLE 26.4 Rewiring Two Charged Capacitors

Two capacitors C_1 and C_2 (where $C_1 > C_2$) are charged to the same initial potential difference ΔV_i. The charged capacitors are removed from the battery, and their plates are connected with opposite polarity as in Figure 26.12a. The switches S_1 and S_2 are then closed as in Figure 26.12b.

(A) Find the final potential difference ΔV_f between a and b after the switches are closed.

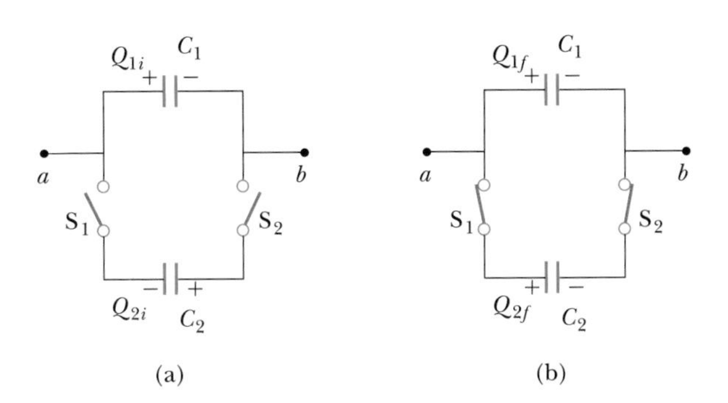

Figure 26.12 (Example 26.4) (a) Two capacitors are charged to the same initial potential difference and connected together with plates of opposite sign to be in contact when the switches are closed. (b) When the switches are closed, the charges redistribute.

SOLUTION

Conceptualize Figure 26.12 helps us understand the initial and final configurations of the system.

Categorize In Figure 26.12b, it might appear as if the capacitors are connected in parallel, but there is no battery in this circuit to apply a voltage across the combination. Therefore, we *cannot* categorize this problem as one in which capacitors are connected in parallel. We *can* categorize it as a problem involving an isolated system for electric charge. The left-hand plates of the capacitors form an isolated system because they are not connected to the right-hand plates by conductors.

Analyze Write an expression for the total charge on the left-hand plates of the system before the switches are closed, noting that a negative sign for Q_{2i} is necessary because the charge on the left plate of capacitor C_2 is negative:

$$(1)\quad Q_i = Q_{1i} + Q_{2i} = C_1\,\Delta V_i - C_2\,\Delta V_i = (C_1 - C_2)\Delta V_i$$

After the switches are closed, the charges on the individual capacitors change to new values Q_{1f} and Q_{2f} such that the potential difference is again the same across both capacitors, ΔV_f. Write an expression for the total charge on the left-hand plates of the system after the switches are closed:

$$(2)\quad Q_f = Q_{1f} + Q_{2f} = C_1\,\Delta V_f + C_2\,\Delta V_f = (C_1 + C_2)\,\Delta V_f$$

Because the system is isolated, the initial and final charges on the system must be the same. Use this condition and Equations (1) and (2) to solve for ΔV_f:

$$Q_f = Q_i \rightarrow (C_1 + C_2)\Delta V_f = (C_1 - C_2)\Delta V_i$$

$$(3)\quad \Delta V_f = \left(\frac{C_1 - C_2}{C_1 + C_2}\right)\Delta V_i$$

(B) Find the total energy stored in the capacitors before and after the switches are closed and determine the ratio of the final energy to the initial energy.

SOLUTION

Use Equation 26.11 to find an expression for the total energy stored in the capacitors before the switches are closed:

$$(4)\quad U_i = \tfrac{1}{2}C_1(\Delta V_i)^2 + \tfrac{1}{2}C_2(\Delta V_i)^2 = \tfrac{1}{2}(C_1 + C_2)(\Delta V_i)^2$$

Write an expression for the total energy stored in the capacitors after the switches are closed:

$$U_f = \tfrac{1}{2}C_1(\Delta V_f)^2 + \tfrac{1}{2}C_2(\Delta V_f)^2 = \tfrac{1}{2}(C_1 + C_2)(\Delta V_f)^2$$

Use the results of part (A) to rewrite this expression in terms of ΔV_i:

$$(5)\quad U_f = \tfrac{1}{2}(C_1 + C_2)\left[\left(\frac{C_1 - C_2}{C_1 + C_2}\right)\Delta V_i\right]^2 = \tfrac{1}{2}\frac{(C_1 - C_2)^2(\Delta V_i)^2}{(C_1 + C_2)}$$

Divide Equation (5) by Equation (4) to obtain the ratio of the energies stored in the system:

$$\frac{U_f}{U_i} = \frac{\tfrac{1}{2}(C_1 - C_2)^2(\Delta V_i)^2/(C_1 + C_2)}{\tfrac{1}{2}(C_1 + C_2)(\Delta V_i)^2}$$

$$(6)\quad \frac{U_f}{U_i} = \left(\frac{C_1 - C_2}{C_1 + C_2}\right)^2$$

Finalize The ratio of energies is *less* than unity, indicating that the final energy is *less* than the initial energy. At first, you might think the law of energy conservation has been violated, but that is not the case. The "missing" energy is transferred out of the system by the mechanism of electromagnetic waves (T_{ER} in Equation 8.2), as we shall see in Chapter 34.

What If? What if the two capacitors have the same capacitance? What would you expect to happen when the switches are closed?

Answer Because both capacitors have the same initial potential difference applied to them, the charges on the capacitors have the same magnitude. When the capacitors with opposite polarities are connected together, the equal-magnitude charges should cancel each other, leaving the capacitors uncharged.

Let's test our results to see if that is the case mathematically. In Equation (1), because the capacitances are equal, the initial charge Q_i on the system of left-hand plates is zero. Equation (3) shows that $\Delta V_f = 0$, which is consistent with uncharged capacitors. Finally, Equation (5) shows that $U_f = 0$, which is also consistent with uncharged capacitors.

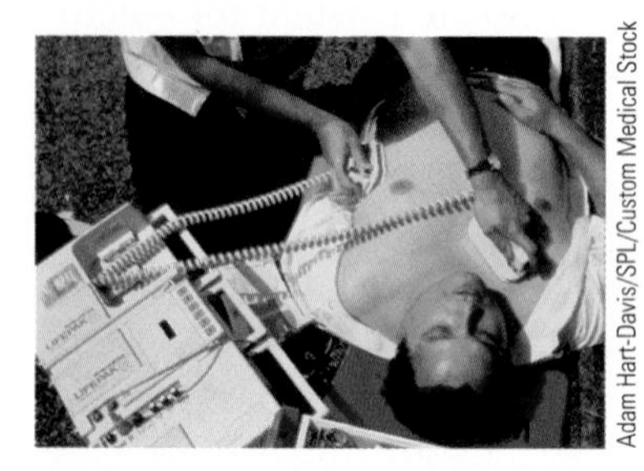

Adam Hart-Davis/SPL/Custom Medical Stock

Figure 26.13 In a hospital or at an emergency scene, you might see a patient being revived with a portable defibrillator. The defibrillator's paddles are applied to the patient's chest, and an electric shock is sent through the chest cavity. The aim of this technique is to restore the heart's normal rhythm pattern.

One device in which capacitors have an important role is the portable *defibrillator* (Fig. 26.13). When cardiac fibrillation (random contractions) occurs, the heart produces a rapid, irregular pattern of beats. A fast discharge of energy through the heart can return the organ to its normal beat pattern. Emergency medical teams use portable defibrillators that contain batteries capable of charging a capacitor to a high voltage. (The circuitry actually permits the capacitor to be charged to a much higher voltage than that of the battery.) Up to 360 J is stored in the electric field of a large capacitor in a defibrillator when it is fully charged. The stored energy is released through the heart by conducting electrodes, called paddles, which are placed on both sides of the victim's chest. The defibrillator can deliver the energy to a patient in about 2 ms (roughly equivalent to 3 000 times the power delivered to a 60-W lightbulb!). The paramedics must wait between applications of the energy because of the time necessary for the capacitors to become fully charged. In this application and others (e.g., camera flash units and lasers used for fusion experiments), capacitors serve as energy reservoirs that can be slowly charged and then quickly discharged to provide large amounts of energy in a short pulse.

26.5 Capacitors with Dielectrics

A **dielectric** is a nonconducting material such as rubber, glass, or waxed paper. We can perform the following experiment to illustrate the effect of a dielectric in a capacitor. Consider a parallel-plate capacitor that without a dielectric has a charge Q_0 and a capacitance C_0. The potential difference across the capacitor is $\Delta V_0 = Q_0/C_0$. Figure 26.14a illustrates this situation. The potential difference is measured by a *voltmeter,* a device discussed in greater detail in Chapter 28. Notice that no battery is shown in the figure; also, we must assume no charge can flow through an ideal voltmeter. Hence, there is no path by which charge can flow and alter the charge on the capacitor. If a dielectric is now inserted between the plates as in Figure 26.14b, the voltmeter indicates that the voltage between the plates decreases to a value ΔV. The voltages with and without the dielectric are related by a factor κ as follows:

$$\Delta V = \frac{\Delta V_0}{\kappa}$$

Because $\Delta V < \Delta V_0$, we see that $\kappa > 1$. The dimensionless factor κ is called the **dielectric constant** of the material. The dielectric constant varies from one material to another. In this section, we analyze this change in capacitance in terms of electrical parameters such as electric charge, electric field, and potential difference; Section 26.7 describes the microscopic origin of these changes.

Because the charge Q_0 on the capacitor does not change, the capacitance must change to the value

$$C = \frac{Q_0}{\Delta V} = \frac{Q_0}{\Delta V_0/\kappa} = \kappa\frac{Q_0}{\Delta V_0}$$

$$C = \kappa C_0 \qquad (26.14)$$

◀ Capacitance of a capacitor filled with a material of dielectric constant κ

That is, the capacitance *increases* by the factor κ when the dielectric completely fills the region between the plates.[5] Because $C_0 = \epsilon_0 A/d$ (Eq. 26.3) for a parallel-plate

PITFALL PREVENTION 26.5
Is the Capacitor Connected to a Battery?

For problems in which a capacitor is modified (by insertion of a dielectric, for example), you must note whether modifications to the capacitor are being made while the capacitor is connected to a battery or after it is disconnected. If the capacitor remains connected to the battery, the voltage across the capacitor necessarily remains the same. If you disconnect the capacitor from the battery before making any modifications to the capacitor, the capacitor is an isolated system and its charge remains the same.

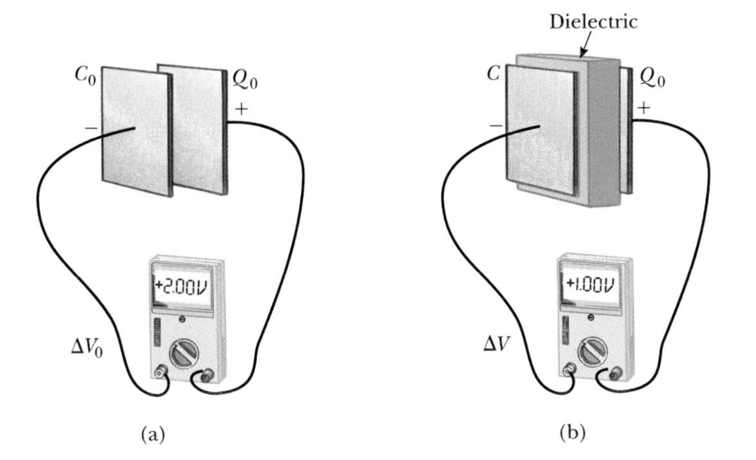

Figure 26.14 A charged capacitor (a) before and (b) after insertion of a dielectric between the plates. The charge on the plates remains unchanged, but the potential difference decreases from ΔV_0 to $\Delta V = \Delta V_0/\kappa$. Therefore, the capacitance increases from C_0 to κC_0.

[5] If the dielectric is introduced while the potential difference is held constant by a battery, the charge increases to a value $Q = \kappa Q_0$. The additional charge comes from the wires attached to the capacitor, and the capacitance again increases by the factor κ.

capacitor, we can express the capacitance of a parallel-plate capacitor filled with a dielectric as

$$C = \kappa \frac{\epsilon_0 A}{d} \tag{26.15}$$

From Equations 26.3 and 26.15, it would appear that the capacitance could be made very large by decreasing d, the distance between the plates. In practice, the lowest value of d is limited by the electric discharge that could occur through the dielectric medium separating the plates. For any given separation d, the maximum voltage that can be applied to a capacitor without causing a discharge depends on the **dielectric strength** (maximum electric field) of the dielectric. If the magnitude of the electric field in the dielectric exceeds the dielectric strength, the insulating properties break down and the dielectric begins to conduct.

Physical capacitors have a specification called by a variety of names, including *working voltage, breakdown voltage,* and *rated voltage.* This parameter represents the largest voltage that can be applied to the capacitor without exceeding the dielectric strength of the dielectric material in the capacitor. Consequently, when selecting a capacitor for a given application, you must consider its capacitance as well as the expected voltage across the capacitor in the circuit, making sure the expected voltage is smaller than the rated voltage of the capacitor. You can see the rated voltage on several of the capacitors in this chapter's opening photograph.

Insulating materials have values of κ greater than unity and dielectric strengths greater than that of air as Table 26.1 indicates. Therefore, a dielectric provides the following advantages:

- An increase in capacitance
- An increase in maximum operating voltage
- Possible mechanical support between the plates, which allows the plates to be close together without touching, thereby decreasing d and increasing C

TABLE 26.1

Approximate Dielectric Constants and Dielectric Strengths of Various Materials at Room Temperature

Material	Dielectric Constant κ	Dielectric Strength[a] (10^6 V/m)
Air (dry)	1.000 59	3
Bakelite	4.9	24
Fused quartz	3.78	8
Mylar	3.2	7
Neoprene rubber	6.7	12
Nylon	3.4	14
Paper	3.7	16
Paraffin-impregnated paper	3.5	11
Polystyrene	2.56	24
Polyvinyl chloride	3.4	40
Porcelain	6	12
Pyrex glass	5.6	14
Silicone oil	2.5	15
Strontium titanate	233	8
Teflon	2.1	60
Vacuum	1.000 00	—
Water	80	—

[a] The dielectric strength equals the maximum electric field that can exist in a dielectric without electrical breakdown. These values depend strongly on the presence of impurities and flaws in the materials.

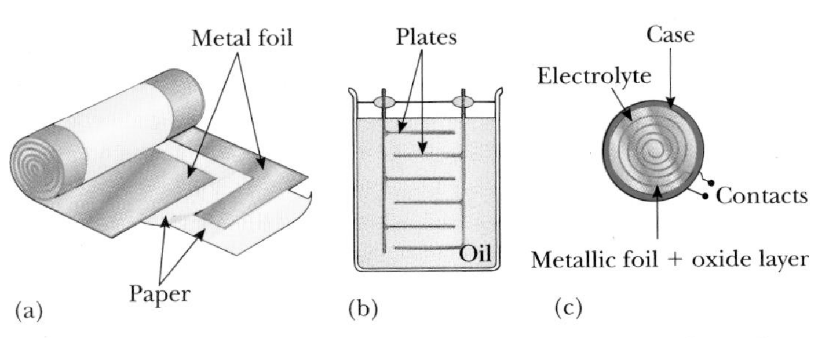

Figure 26.15 Three commercial capacitor designs. (a) A tubular capacitor, whose plates are separated by paper and then rolled into a cylinder. (b) A high-voltage capacitor consisting of many parallel plates separated by insulating oil. (c) An electrolytic capacitor.

Figure 26.16 A variable capacitor. When one set of metal plates is rotated so as to lie between a fixed set of plates, the capacitance of the device changes.

Types of Capacitors

Commercial capacitors are often made from metallic foil interlaced with thin sheets of either paraffin-impregnated paper or Mylar as the dielectric material. These alternate layers of metallic foil and dielectric are rolled into a cylinder to form a small package (Fig. 26.15a). High-voltage capacitors commonly consist of a number of interwoven metallic plates immersed in silicone oil (Fig. 26.15b). Small capacitors are often constructed from ceramic materials.

Often, an *electrolytic capacitor* is used to store large amounts of charge at relatively low voltages. This device, shown in Figure 26.15c, consists of a metallic foil in contact with an *electrolyte,* a solution that conducts electricity by virtue of the motion of ions contained in the solution. When a voltage is applied between the foil and the electrolyte, a thin layer of metal oxide (an insulator) is formed on the foil, and this layer serves as the dielectric. Very large values of capacitance can be obtained in an electrolytic capacitor because the dielectric layer is very thin and therefore the plate separation is very small.

Electrolytic capacitors are not reversible as are many other capacitors. They have a polarity, which is indicated by positive and negative signs marked on the device. When electrolytic capacitors are used in circuits, the polarity must be correct. If the polarity of the applied voltage is the opposite of what is intended, the oxide layer is removed and the capacitor conducts electricity instead of storing charge.

Variable capacitors (typically 10 to 500 pF) usually consist of two interwoven sets of metallic plates, one fixed and the other movable, and contain air as the dielectric (Fig. 26.16). These types of capacitors are often used in radio tuning circuits.

Quick Quiz 26.5 If you have ever tried to hang a picture or a mirror, you know it can be difficult to locate a wooden stud in which to anchor your nail or screw. A carpenter's stud finder is a capacitor with its plates arranged side by side instead of facing each other as shown in Figure 26.17. When the device is moved over a stud, does the capacitance (a) increase or (b) decrease?

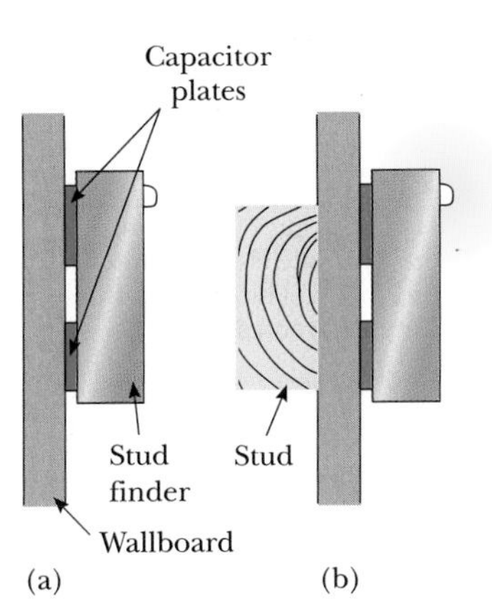

Figure 26.17 (Quick Quiz 26.5) A stud finder. (a) The materials between the plates of the capacitor are the wallboard and air. (b) When the capacitor moves across a stud in the wall, the materials between the plates are the wallboard and the wood. The change in the dielectric constant causes a signal light to illuminate.

EXAMPLE 26.5 Energy Stored Before and After

A parallel-plate capacitor is charged with a battery to a charge Q_0. The battery is then removed, and a slab of material that has a dielectric constant κ is inserted between the plates. Identify the system as the capacitor and the dielectric. Find the energy stored in the system before and after the dielectric is inserted.

SOLUTION

Conceptualize Think about what happens when the dielectric is inserted between the plates. Because the battery has been removed, the charge on the capacitor must remain the same. We know from our earlier discussion, however, that the capacitance must change. Therefore, we expect a change in the energy of the system.

Categorize Because we expect the energy of the system to change, we model it as a nonisolated system.

Analyze From Equation 26.11, find the energy stored in the absence of the dielectric:

$$U_0 = \frac{Q_0^2}{2C_0}$$

Find the energy stored in the capacitor after the dielectric is inserted between the plates:

$$U = \frac{Q_0^2}{2C}$$

Use Equation 26.14 to replace the capacitance C:

$$U = \frac{Q_0^2}{2\kappa C_0} = \frac{U_0}{\kappa}$$

Finalize Because $\kappa > 1$, the final energy is less than the initial energy. We can account for the "missing" energy by noting that the dielectric, when inserted, is pulled into the device. To keep the dielectric from accelerating, an external agent must do negative work (W in Eq. 8.2) on the dielectric, which is simply the difference $U - U_0$.

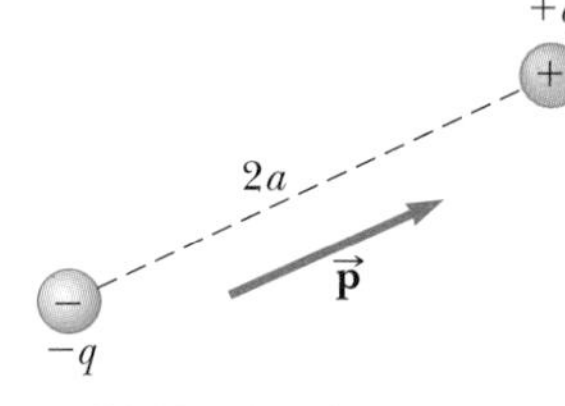

Figure 26.18 An electric dipole consists of two charges of equal magnitude and opposite sign separated by a distance of $2a$. The electric dipole moment $\vec{\mathbf{p}}$ is directed from $-q$ toward $+q$.

26.6 Electric Dipole in an Electric Field

We have discussed the effect on the capacitance of placing a dielectric between the plates of a capacitor. In Section 26.7, we shall describe the microscopic origin of this effect. Before we can do so, however, let's expand the discussion of the electric dipole introduced in Section 23.4 (see Example 23.5). The electric dipole consists of two charges of equal magnitude and opposite sign separated by a distance $2a$ as shown in Figure 26.18. The **electric dipole moment** of this configuration is defined as the vector $\vec{\mathbf{p}}$ directed from $-q$ toward $+q$ along the line joining the charges and having magnitude $2aq$:

$$p \equiv 2aq \qquad \textbf{(26.16)}$$

Now suppose an electric dipole is placed in a uniform electric field $\vec{\mathbf{E}}$ and makes an angle θ with the field as shown in Figure 26.19. We identify $\vec{\mathbf{E}}$ as the field *external* to the dipole, established by some other charge distribution, to distinguish it from the field *due to* the dipole, which we discussed in Section 23.4.

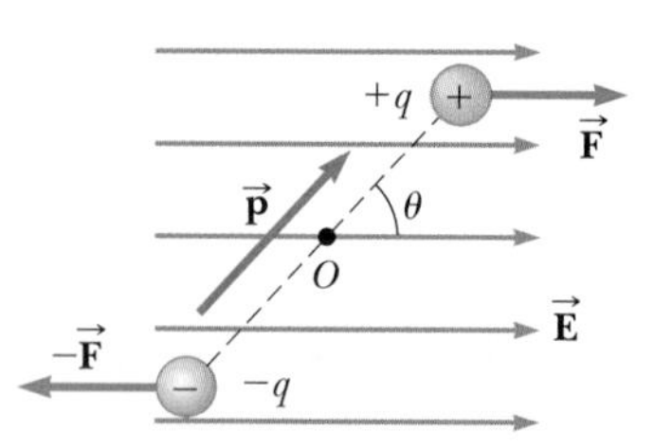

Figure 26.19 An electric dipole in a uniform external electric field. The dipole moment $\vec{\mathbf{p}}$ is at an angle θ to the field, causing the dipole to experience a torque.

The electric forces acting on the two charges are equal in magnitude ($F = qE$) and opposite in direction as shown in Figure 26.19. Therefore, the net force on the dipole is zero. The two forces produce a net torque on the dipole, however; as a result, the dipole rotates in the direction that brings the dipole moment vector into greater alignment with the field. The torque due to the force on the positive charge about an axis through O in Figure 26.19 has magnitude $Fa \sin \theta$, where $a \sin \theta$ is the moment arm of F about O. This force tends to produce a clockwise rotation. The torque about O on the negative charge is also of magnitude $Fa \sin \theta$; here again, the force tends to produce a clockwise rotation. Therefore, the magnitude of the net torque about O is

$$\tau = 2Fa \sin \theta$$

Because $F = qE$ and $p = 2aq$, we can express τ as

$$\tau = 2aqE \sin \theta = pE \sin \theta \qquad \textbf{(26.17)}$$

It is convenient to express the torque in vector form as the cross product of the vectors $\vec{\mathbf{p}}$ and $\vec{\mathbf{E}}$:

Torque on an electric dipole in an external electric field ▶

$$\vec{\boldsymbol{\tau}} = \vec{\mathbf{p}} \times \vec{\mathbf{E}} \qquad \textbf{(26.18)}$$

Let's determine the potential energy of the system of an electric dipole in an external electric field as a function of the dipole's orientation with respect to the field. To do so, recognize that work must be done by an external agent to rotate the dipole through an angle so as to cause the dipole moment vector to become less aligned with the field. The work done is then stored as potential energy in the system. The work dW required to rotate the dipole through an angle $d\theta$ is $dW = \tau d\theta$ (Eq. 10.22). Because $\tau = pE \sin\theta$ and the work results in an increase in the potential energy U, we find that for a rotation from θ_i to θ_f, the change in potential energy of the system is

$$U_f - U_i = \int_{\theta_i}^{\theta_f} \tau\, d\theta = \int_{\theta_i}^{\theta_f} pE \sin\theta\, d\theta = pE \int_{\theta_i}^{\theta_f} \sin\theta\, d\theta$$

$$= pE[-\cos\theta]_{\theta_i}^{\theta_f} = pE(\cos\theta_i - \cos\theta_f)$$

The term that contains $\cos\theta_i$ is a constant that depends on the initial orientation of the dipole. It is convenient to choose a reference angle of $\theta_i = 90°$ so that $\cos\theta_i = \cos 90° = 0$. Furthermore, let's choose $U_i = 0$ at $\theta_i = 90°$ as our reference of potential energy. Hence, we can express a general value of $U = U_f$ as

$$U = -pE\cos\theta \qquad \textbf{(26.19)}$$

We can write this expression for the potential energy of a dipole in an electric field as the dot product of the vectors $\vec{\mathbf{p}}$ and $\vec{\mathbf{E}}$:

$$U = -\vec{\mathbf{p}} \cdot \vec{\mathbf{E}} \qquad \textbf{(26.20)}$$

◀ Potential energy of the system of an electric dipole in an external electric field

To develop a conceptual understanding of Equation 26.19, compare it with the expression for the potential energy of the system of an object in the Earth's gravitational field, $U = mgy$ (see Chapter 7). This expression includes a parameter associated with the object placed in the gravitational field, its mass m. Likewise, Equation 26.19 includes a parameter of the object in the electric field, its dipole moment p. The gravitational expression includes the magnitude of the gravitational field g. Similarly, Equation 26.19 includes the magnitude of the electric field E. So far, these two contributions to the potential energy expressions appear analogous. The final contribution, however, is somewhat different in the two cases. In the gravitational expression, the potential energy depends on the vertical position of the object, measured by y. In Equation 26.19, the potential energy depends on the angle θ through which the dipole is rotated. In both cases, the configuration of the system is being changed. In the gravitational case, the change involves moving an object in a *translational* sense, whereas in the electrical case, the change involves moving an object in a *rotational* sense. In both cases, however, once the change is made, the system tends to return to the original configuration when the object is released: the object of mass m falls toward the ground, and the dipole begins to rotate back toward the configuration in which it is aligned with the field. Therefore, apart from the type of motion, the expressions for potential energy in these two cases are similar.

Molecules are said to be *polarized* when a separation exists between the average position of the negative charges and the average position of the positive charges in the molecule. In some molecules such as water, this condition is always present; such molecules are called **polar molecules.** Molecules that do not possess a permanent polarization are called **nonpolar molecules.**

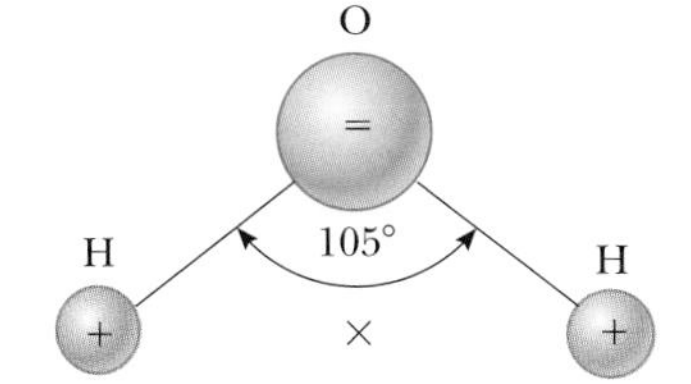

Figure 26.20 The water molecule, H_2O, has a permanent polarization resulting from its nonlinear geometry. The center of the positive charge distribution is at the point ×.

We can understand the permanent polarization of water by inspecting the geometry of the water molecule. The oxygen atom in the water molecule is bonded to the hydrogen atoms such that an angle of 105° is formed between the two bonds (Fig. 26.20). The center of the negative charge distribution is near the oxygen atom, and the center of the positive charge distribution lies at a point midway along the line joining the hydrogen atoms (the point labeled × in Fig. 26.20). We can model the water molecule and other polar molecules as dipoles because the average positions of the positive and negative charges act as point charges. As a result, we can apply our discussion of dipoles to the behavior of polar molecules.

Washing with soap and water is a household scenario in which the dipole structure of water is exploited. Grease and oil are made up of nonpolar molecules,

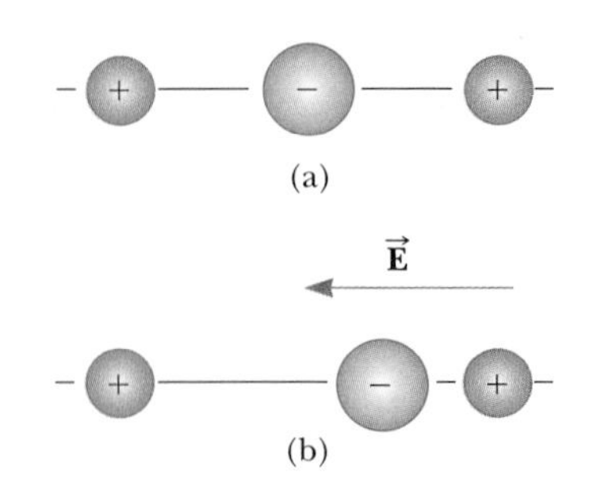

Figure 26.21 (a) A linear symmetric molecule has no permanent polarization. (b) An external electric field induces a polarization in the molecule.

which are generally not attracted to water. Plain water is not very useful for removing this type of grime. Soap contains long molecules called *surfactants.* In a long molecule, the polarity characteristics of one end of the molecule can be different from those at the other end. In a surfactant molecule, one end acts like a nonpolar molecule and the other acts like a polar molecule. The nonpolar end can attach to a grease or oil molecule, and the polar end can attach to a water molecule. Therefore, the soap serves as a chain, linking the dirt and water molecules together. When the water is rinsed away, the grease and oil go with it.

A symmetric molecule (Fig. 26.21a) has no permanent polarization, but polarization can be induced by placing the molecule in an electric field. A field directed to the left as in Figure 26.21b causes the center of the positive charge distribution to shift to the left from its initial position and the center of the negative charge distribution to shift to the right. This *induced polarization* is the effect that predominates in most materials used as dielectrics in capacitors.

EXAMPLE 26.6 The H_2O Molecule

The water (H_2O) molecule has an electric dipole moment of 6.3×10^{-30} C · m. A sample contains 10^{21} water molecules, with the dipole moments all oriented in the direction of an electric field of magnitude 2.5×10^5 N/C. How much work is required to rotate the dipoles from this orientation ($\theta = 0°$) to one in which all the moments are perpendicular to the field ($\theta = 90°$)?

SOLUTION

Conceptualize When all the dipoles are aligned with the electric field, the dipoles–electric field system has the minimum potential energy. This energy has a negative value given by the product of the right side of Equation 26.19, evaluated at 0°, and the number N of dipoles. Work must be done to rotate all the dipoles of the system by 90° because the system's potential energy is raised to a higher value of zero.

Categorize We use Equation 26.19 to evaluate the potential energy, so we categorize this example as a substitution problem.

Write the appropriate reduction of the conservation of energy equation, Equation 8.2, for this situation:

$$(1) \quad \Delta U = W$$

Use Equation 26.19 to evaluate the initial and final potential energies of the system and Equation (1) to calculate the work required to rotate the dipoles:

$$W = U_{90°} - U_{0°} = (-NpE\cos 90°) - (-NpE\cos 0°)$$

$$= NpE = (10^{21})(6.3 \times 10^{-30}\text{ C}\cdot\text{m})(2.5 \times 10^5\text{ N/C})$$

$$= 1.6 \times 10^{-3}\text{ J}$$

26.7 An Atomic Description of Dielectrics

In Section 26.5, we found that the potential difference ΔV_0 between the plates of a capacitor is reduced to $\Delta V_0/\kappa$ when a dielectric is introduced. The potential difference is reduced because the magnitude of the electric field decreases between the plates. In particular, if $\vec{\mathbf{E}}_0$ is the electric field without the dielectric, the field in the presence of a dielectric is

$$\vec{\mathbf{E}} = \frac{\vec{\mathbf{E}}_0}{\kappa} \qquad (26.21)$$

First consider a dielectric made up of polar molecules placed in the electric field between the plates of a capacitor. The dipoles (that is, the polar molecules making up the dielectric) are randomly oriented in the absence of an electric field

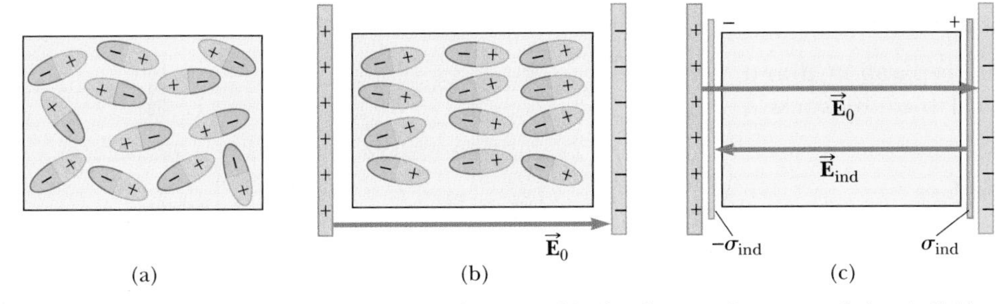

Figure 26.22 (a) Polar molecules are randomly oriented in the absence of an external electric field. (b) When an external electric field is applied, the molecules partially align with the field. (c) The charged edges of the dielectric can be modeled as an additional pair of parallel plates establishing an electric field $\vec{\mathbf{E}}_{ind}$ in the direction opposite that of $\vec{\mathbf{E}}_0$.

as shown in Figure 26.22a. When an external field $\vec{\mathbf{E}}_0$ due to charges on the capacitor plates is applied, a torque is exerted on the dipoles, causing them to partially align with the field as shown in Figure 26.22b. The dielectric is now polarized. The degree of alignment of the molecules with the electric field depends on temperature and the magnitude of the field. In general, the alignment increases with decreasing temperature and with increasing electric field.

If the molecules of the dielectric are nonpolar, the electric field due to the plates produces an induced polarization in the molecule. These induced dipole moments tend to align with the external field, and the dielectric is polarized. Therefore, a dielectric can be polarized by an external field regardless of whether the molecules in the dielectric are polar or nonpolar.

With these ideas in mind, consider a slab of dielectric material placed between the plates of a capacitor so that it is in a uniform electric field $\vec{\mathbf{E}}_0$ as shown in Figure 26.22b. The electric field due to the plates is directed to the right and polarizes the dielectric. The net effect on the dielectric is the formation of an *induced* positive surface charge density σ_{ind} on the right face and an equal-magnitude negative surface charge density $-\sigma_{ind}$ on the left face as shown in Figure 26.22c. Because we can model these surface charge distributions as being due to charged parallel plates, the induced surface charges on the dielectric give rise to an induced electric field $\vec{\mathbf{E}}_{ind}$ in the direction opposite the external field $\vec{\mathbf{E}}_0$. Therefore, the net electric field $\vec{\mathbf{E}}$ in the dielectric has a magnitude

$$E = E_0 - E_{ind} \tag{26.22}$$

In the parallel-plate capacitor shown in Figure 26.23, the external field E_0 is related to the charge density σ on the plates through the relationship $E_0 = \sigma/\epsilon_0$. The induced electric field in the dielectric is related to the induced charge density σ_{ind} through the relationship $E_{ind} = \sigma_{ind}/\epsilon_0$. Because $E = E_0/\kappa = \sigma/\kappa\epsilon_0$, substitution into Equation 26.22 gives

$$\frac{\sigma}{\kappa\epsilon_0} = \frac{\sigma}{\epsilon_0} - \frac{\sigma_{ind}}{\epsilon_0}$$

$$\sigma_{ind} = \left(\frac{\kappa - 1}{\kappa}\right)\sigma \tag{26.23}$$

Because $\kappa > 1$, this expression shows that the charge density σ_{ind} induced on the dielectric is less than the charge density σ on the plates. For instance, if $\kappa = 3$, the induced charge density is two-thirds the charge density on the plates. If no dielectric is present, then $\kappa = 1$ and $\sigma_{ind} = 0$ as expected. If the dielectric is replaced by an electrical conductor for which $E = 0$, however, Equation 26.22 indicates that $E_0 = E_{ind}$, which corresponds to $\sigma_{ind} = \sigma$. That is, the surface charge induced on the conductor is equal in magnitude but opposite in sign to that on the plates, resulting in a net electric field of zero in the conductor (see Fig. 24.14).

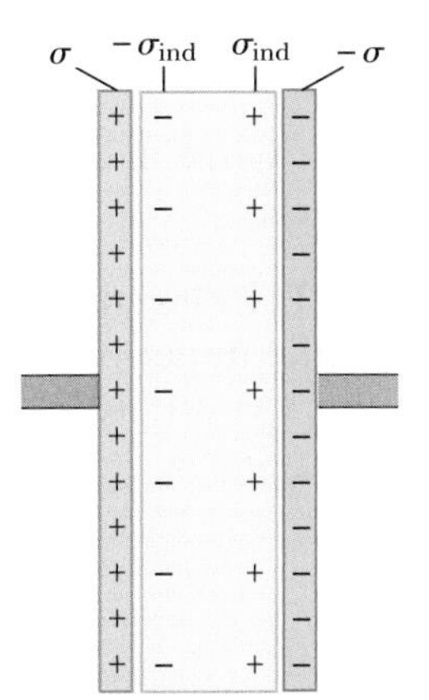

Figure 26.23 Induced charge on a dielectric placed between the plates of a charged capacitor. Notice that the induced charge density on the dielectric is *less* than the charge density on the plates.

EXAMPLE 26.7 Effect of a Metallic Slab

A parallel-plate capacitor has a plate separation d and plate area A. An uncharged metallic slab of thickness a is inserted midway between the plates.

(A) Find the capacitance of the device.

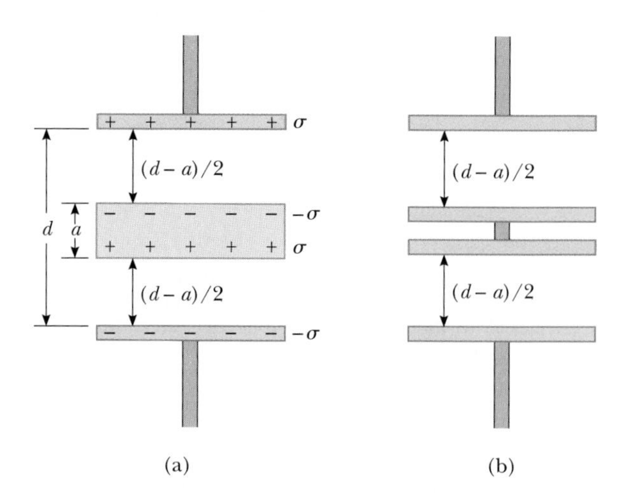

Figure 26.24 (Example 26.7) (a) A parallel-plate capacitor of plate separation d partially filled with a metallic slab of thickness a. (b) The equivalent circuit of the device in (a) consists of two capacitors in series, each having a plate separation $(d - a)/2$.

SOLUTION

Conceptualize Figure 26.24a shows the metallic slab between the plates of the capacitor. Any charge that appears on one plate of the capacitor must induce a charge of equal magnitude and opposite sign on the near side of the slab as shown in Figure 26.24a. Consequently, the net charge on the slab remains zero and the electric field inside the slab is zero.

Categorize The planes of charge on the metallic slab's upper and lower edges are identical to the distribution of charges on the plates of a capacitor. The metal between the slab's edges serves only to make an electrical connection between the edges. Therefore, we can model the edges of the slab as conducting planes and the bulk of the slab as a wire. As a result, the capacitor in Figure 26.24a is equivalent to two capacitors in series, each having a plate separation $(d - a)/2$ as shown in Figure 26.24b.

Analyze Use Equation 26.3 and the rule for adding two capacitors in series (Eq. 26.10) to find the equivalent capacitance in Figure 26.24b:

$$\frac{1}{C} = \frac{1}{C_1} + \frac{1}{C_2} = \frac{1}{\left[\dfrac{\epsilon_0 A}{(d-a)/2}\right]} + \frac{1}{\left[\dfrac{\epsilon_0 A}{(d-a)/2}\right]}$$

$$C = \frac{\epsilon_0 A}{d - a}$$

(B) Show that the capacitance of the original capacitor is unaffected by the insertion of the metallic slab if the slab is infinitesimally thin.

SOLUTION

In the result for part (A), let $a \to 0$:

$$C = \lim_{a \to 0}\left(\frac{\epsilon_0 A}{d - a}\right) = \frac{\epsilon_0 A}{d}$$

Finalize The result of part (B) is the original capacitance before the slab is inserted, which tells us that we can insert an infinitesimally thin metallic sheet between the plates of a capacitor without affecting the capacitance. We use this fact in the next example.

What If? What if the metallic slab in part (A) is not midway between the plates? How would that affect the capacitance?

Answer Let's imagine moving the slab in Figure 26.24a upward so that the distance between the upper edge of the slab and the upper plate is b. Then, the distance between the lower edge of the slab and the lower plate is $d - b - a$. As in part (A), we find the total capacitance of the series combination:

$$\frac{1}{C} = \frac{1}{C_1} + \frac{1}{C_2} = \frac{1}{\epsilon_0 A/b} + \frac{1}{\epsilon_0 A/(d - b - a)}$$

$$= \frac{b}{\epsilon_0 A} + \frac{d - b - a}{\epsilon_0 A} = \frac{d - a}{\epsilon_0 A} \quad \to \quad C = \frac{\epsilon_0 A}{d - a}$$

which is the same result as found in part (A). The capacitance is independent of the value of b, so it does not matter where the slab is located. In Figure 26.24b, when the central structure is moved up or down, the decrease in plate separation of one capacitor is compensated by the increase in plate separation for the other.

EXAMPLE 26.8 A Partially Filled Capacitor

A parallel-plate capacitor with a plate separation d has a capacitance C_0 in the absence of a dielectric. What is the capacitance when a slab of dielectric material of dielectric constant κ and thickness fd is inserted between the plates (Fig. 26.25a), where f is a fraction between 0 and 1?

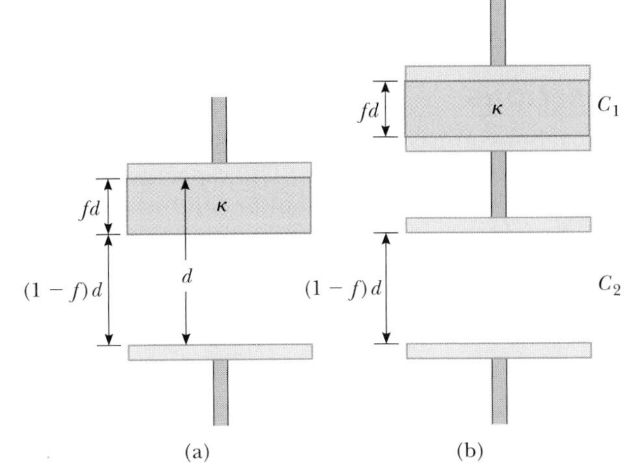

Figure 26.25 (Example 26.8) (a) A parallel-plate capacitor of plate separation d partially filled with a dielectric of thickness fd. (b) The equivalent circuit of the capacitor consists of two capacitors connected in series.

SOLUTION

Conceptualize In our previous discussions of dielectrics between the plates of a capacitor, the dielectric filled the volume between the plates. In this example, only part of the volume between the plates contains the dielectric material.

Categorize In Example 26.7, we found that an infinitesimally thin metallic sheet inserted between the plates of a capacitor does not affect the capacitance. Imagine sliding an infinitesimally thin metallic slab along the bottom face of the dielectric shown in Figure 26.25a. We can model this system as a series combination of two capacitors as shown in Figure 26.25b. One capacitor has a plate separation fd and is filled with a dielectric; the other has a plate separation $(1 - f)d$ and has air between its plates.

Analyze Evaluate the two capacitances in Figure 26.25b from Equation 26.15:

$$C_1 = \frac{\kappa\epsilon_0 A}{fd} \quad \text{and} \quad C_2 = \frac{\epsilon_0 A}{(1-f)d}$$

Find the equivalent capacitance C from Equation 26.10 for two capacitors combined in series:

$$\frac{1}{C} = \frac{1}{C_1} + \frac{1}{C_2} = \frac{fd}{\kappa\epsilon_0 A} + \frac{(1-f)d}{\epsilon_0 A}$$

$$\frac{1}{C} = \frac{fd}{\kappa\epsilon_0 A} + \frac{\kappa(1-f)d}{\kappa\epsilon_0 A} = \frac{f + \kappa(1-f)}{\kappa}\frac{d}{\epsilon_0 A}$$

Invert and substitute for the capacitance without the dielectric, $C_0 = \epsilon_0 A/d$:

$$C = \frac{\kappa}{f + \kappa(1-f)}\frac{\epsilon_0 A}{d} = \frac{\kappa}{f + \kappa(1-f)} C_0$$

Finalize Let's test this result for some known limits. If $f \to 0$, the dielectric should disappear. In this limit, $C \to C_0$, which is consistent with a capacitor with air between the plates. If $f \to 1$, the dielectric fills the volume between the plates. In this limit, $C \to \kappa C_0$, which is consistent with Equation 26.14.

Summary

ThomsonNOW™ Sign in at **www.thomsonedu.com** and go to ThomsonNOW to take a practice test for this chapter.

DEFINITIONS

A **capacitor** consists of two conductors carrying charges of equal magnitude and opposite sign. The **capacitance** C of any capacitor is the ratio of the charge Q on either conductor to the potential difference ΔV between them:

$$C \equiv \frac{Q}{\Delta V} \quad (26.1)$$

The capacitance depends only on the geometry of the conductors and not on an external source of charge or potential difference. The SI unit of capacitance is coulombs per volt, or the **farad** (F): 1 F = 1 C/V.

The **electric dipole moment** $\vec{\mathbf{p}}$ of an electric dipole has a magnitude

$$p \equiv 2aq \quad (26.16)$$

where $2a$ is the distance between the charges q and $-q$. The direction of the electric dipole moment vector is from the negative charge toward the positive charge.

CONCEPTS AND PRINCIPLES

If two or more capacitors are connected in parallel, the potential difference is the same across all capacitors. The equivalent capacitance of a **parallel combination** of capacitors is

$$C_{eq} = C_1 + C_2 + C_3 + \cdots \quad (26.8)$$

If two or more capacitors are connected in series, the charge is the same on all capacitors, and the equivalent capacitance of the **series combination** is given by

$$\frac{1}{C_{eq}} = \frac{1}{C_1} + \frac{1}{C_2} + \frac{1}{C_3} + \cdots \quad (26.10)$$

These two equations enable you to simplify many electric circuits by replacing multiple capacitors with a single equivalent capacitance.

Energy is stored in a capacitor because the charging process is equivalent to the transfer of charges from one conductor at a lower electric potential to another conductor at a higher potential. The energy stored in a capacitor with charge Q is

$$U = \frac{Q^2}{2C} = \tfrac{1}{2}Q\,\Delta V = \tfrac{1}{2}C(\Delta V)^2 \quad (26.11)$$

When a dielectric material is inserted between the plates of a capacitor, the capacitance increases by a dimensionless factor κ, called the **dielectric constant:**

$$C = \kappa C_0 \quad (26.14)$$

where C_0 is the capacitance in the absence of the dielectric.

The torque acting on an electric dipole in a uniform electric field $\vec{\mathbf{E}}$ is

$$\vec{\boldsymbol{\tau}} = \vec{\mathbf{p}} \times \vec{\mathbf{E}} \quad (26.18)$$

The potential energy of the system of an electric dipole in a uniform external electric field $\vec{\mathbf{E}}$ is

$$U = -\vec{\mathbf{p}} \cdot \vec{\mathbf{E}} \quad (26.20)$$

Questions

☐ denotes answer available in *Student Solutions Manual/Study Guide;* **O** denotes objective question

1. **O** True or False? (a) From the definition of capacitance $C = Q/\Delta V$, it follows that an uncharged capacitor has a capacitance of zero. (b) As described by the definition of capacitance, the potential difference across an uncharged capacitor is zero.
2. If you are given three different capacitors C_1, C_2, and C_3, how many different combinations of capacitance can you produce?
3. **O** By what factor is the capacitance of a metal sphere multiplied if its volume is tripled? (a) 9 (b) 3 (c) $3^{2/3}$ (d) $3^{1/3}$ (e) 1 (f) $3^{-1/3}$ (g) $3^{-2/3}$ (h) $\frac{1}{3}$
4. **O** A capacitor with very large capacitance is in series with another capacitor with very small capacitance. What is the equivalent capacitance of the combination? (a) slightly greater than the capacitance of the large capacitor (b) slightly less than the capacitance of the large capaci-

tor (c) slightly greater than the capacitance of the small capacitor (d) slightly less than the capacitance of the small capacitor.

5. **O (i)** Rank the following six capacitors in order from greatest to smallest capacitance, noting any cases of equality. (a) a 20-μF capacitor with a 4-V potential difference between its plates (b) a 30-μF capacitor with charges of magnitude 90 μC on each plate (c) a capacitor with charges of magnitude 80 μC on its plates, differing by 2 V in potential (d) a 10-μF capacitor storing 125 μJ (e) a capacitor storing energy 250 μJ with a 10-V potential difference (f) a capacitor storing charge 120 μC and energy 360 μJ **(ii)** Rank the same capacitors from largest to smallest according to the potential difference between the plates. **(iii)** Rank the capacitors in the order of the magnitudes of the charges on their plates. **(iv)** Rank the capacitors in the order of the energy they store.

6. The sum of the charges on both plates of a capacitor is zero. What does a capacitor store?

7. **O (i)** What happens to the magnitude of the charge on each plate of a capacitor if the potential difference between the conductors is doubled? (a) It becomes four times larger. (b) It becomes two times larger. (c) It is unchanged. (d) It becomes one-half as large. (e) It becomes one-fourth as large. **(ii)** If the potential difference across a capacitor is doubled, what happens to the energy stored? Choose from the same possibilities.

8. **O** A parallel-plate capacitor is charged and then is disconnected from the battery. By what factor does the stored energy change when the plate separation is then doubled? (a) It becomes four times larger. (b) It becomes two times larger. (c) It stays the same. (d) It becomes one-half as large (e) It becomes one-fourth as large.

9. **O** You charge a parallel-plate capacitor, remove it from the battery, and prevent the wires connected to the plates from touching each other. When you increase the plate separation, does each of the following quantities (a) increase, (b) decrease, or (c) stay the same? **(i)** C **(ii)** Q **(iii)** E between the plates **(iv)** ΔV **(v)** the energy stored in the capacitor

10. **O** Repeat Question 9, but this time answer for the situation in which the battery remains connected to the capacitor while you increase the plate separation.

11. Because the charges on the plates of a parallel-plate capacitor are opposite in sign, they attract each other. Hence, it would take positive work to increase the plate separation. What type of energy in the system changes due to the external work done in this process?

12. Explain why the work needed to move a particle with charge Q through a potential difference ΔV is $W = Q\,\Delta V$, whereas the energy stored in a charged capacitor is $U = \frac{1}{2}Q\,\Delta V$. Where does the $\frac{1}{2}$ factor come from?

13. **O** Assume a device is designed to obtain a large potential difference by first charging a bank of capacitors connected in parallel and then activating a switch arrangement that in effect disconnects the capacitors from the charging source and from each other and reconnects them all in a series arrangement. The group of charged capacitors is then discharged in series. What is the maximum potential difference that can be obtained in this manner by using ten capacitors each of 500 μF and a charging source of 800 V? (a) 80 kV (b) 8 kV (c) 2.5 kV (d) 800 V (e) 80 V (f) 8 V (g) 0

14. An air-filled capacitor is charged, then disconnected from the power supply, and finally connected to a voltmeter. Explain how and why the potential difference changes when a dielectric is inserted between the plates of the capacitor.

15. **O** A fully charged parallel-plate capacitor remains connected to a battery while you slide a dielectric between the plates. Do the following quantities (a) increase, (b) decrease, or (c) stay the same? **(i)** C **(ii)** Q **(iii)** E between the plates **(iv)** ΔV **(v)** the energy stored in the capacitor

16. Assume you want to increase the maximum operating voltage of a parallel-plate capacitor. Describe how you can do that with a fixed plate separation.

17. If you were asked to design a capacitor in which small size and large capacitance were required, what factors would be important in your design?

Problems

WebAssign The Problems from this chapter may be assigned online in WebAssign.

ThomsonNOW Sign in at **www.thomsonedu.com** and go to ThomsonNOW to assess your understanding of this chapter's topics with additional quizzing and conceptual questions.

1, 2, 3 denotes straightforward, intermediate, challenging; ☐ denotes full solution available in *Student Solutions Manual/Study Guide;* ▲ denotes coached solution with hints available at **www.thomsonedu.com;** denotes developing symbolic reasoning; ● denotes asking for qualitative reasoning; denotes computer useful in solving problem

Section 26.1 Definition of Capacitance

1. (a) How much charge is on each plate of a 4.00-μF capacitor when it is connected to a 12.0-V battery? (b) If this same capacitor is connected to a 1.50-V battery, what charge is stored?

2. Two conductors having net charges of $+10.0\ \mu$C and $-10.0\ \mu$C have a potential difference of 10.0 V between them. (a) Determine the capacitance of the system. (b) What is the potential difference between the two conductors if the charges on each are increased to $+100\ \mu$C and $-100\ \mu$C?

Section 26.2 Calculating Capacitance

3. An isolated, charged conducting sphere of radius 12.0 cm creates an electric field of 4.90×10^4 N/C at a distance 21.0 cm from its center. (a) What is its surface charge density? (b) What is its capacitance?

4. Regarding the Earth and a cloud layer 800 m above the Earth as the "plates" of a capacitor, calculate the capacitance of the Earth-cloud layer system. Assume the cloud layer has an area of 1.00 km^2 and the air between the cloud and the ground is pure and dry. Assume charge builds up on the cloud and on the ground until a uniform electric field of 3.00×10^6 N/C throughout the space between them makes the air break down and conduct electricity as a lightning bolt. What is the maximum charge the cloud can hold?

5. ▲ An air-filled capacitor consists of two parallel plates, each with an area of 7.60 cm^2, separated by a distance of 1.80 mm. A 20.0-V potential difference is applied to these plates. Calculate (a) the electric field between the plates, (b) the surface charge density, (c) the capacitance, and (d) the charge on each plate.

6. A variable air capacitor used in a radio tuning circuit is made of N semicircular plates each of radius R and positioned a distance d from its neighbors, to which it is electrically connected. As shown in Figures 26.16 and P26.6, a second identical set of plates is enmeshed with the first set. Each plate in the second set is halfway between two plates of the first set. The second set can rotate as a unit. Determine the capacitance as a function of the angle of rotation θ, where $\theta = 0$ corresponds to the maximum capacitance.

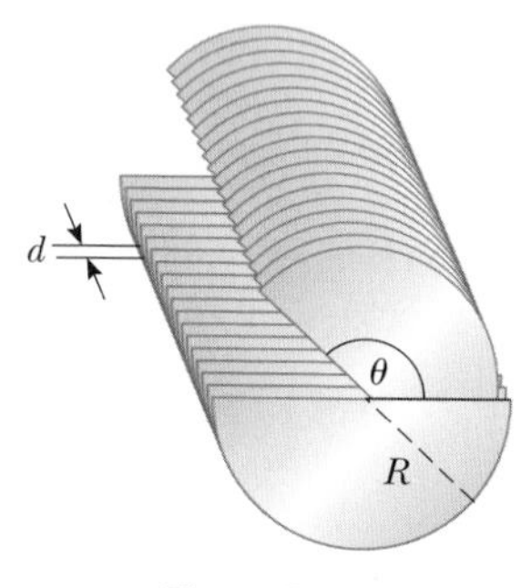

Figure P26.6

7. When a potential difference of 150 V is applied to the plates of a parallel-plate capacitor, the plates carry a surface charge density of 30.0 nC/cm^2. What is the spacing between the plates?

8. A small object of mass m carries a charge q and is suspended by a thread between the vertical plates of a parallel-plate capacitor. The plate separation is d. If the thread makes an angle θ with the vertical, what is the potential difference between the plates?

9. ▲ A 50.0-m length of coaxial cable has an inner conductor that has a diameter of 2.58 mm and carries a charge of 8.10 μC. The surrounding conductor has an inner diameter of 7.27 mm and a charge of -8.10 μC. (a) What is the capacitance of this cable? (b) What is the potential difference between the two conductors? Assume the region between the conductors is air.

10. ● A 10.0-μF capacitor has plates with vacuum between them. Each plate carries a charge of magnitude 1 000 μC. A particle with charge -3.00 μC and mass 2.00×10^{-16} kg is fired from the positive plate toward the negative plate with an initial speed of 2.00×10^6 m/s. Does the particle reach the negative plate? Explain how you can tell. If it does, what is its impact speed? If it does not, what fraction of the way across the capacitor does it travel?

11. An air-filled spherical capacitor is constructed with inner and outer shell radii of 7.00 and 14.0 cm, respectively. (a) Calculate the capacitance of the device. (b) What potential difference between the spheres results in a charge of 4.00 μC on the capacitor?

Section 26.3 Combinations of Capacitors

12. Two capacitors, $C_1 = 5.00$ μF and $C_2 = 12.0$ μF, are connected in parallel, and the resulting combination is connected to a 9.00-V battery. Find (a) the equivalent capacitance of the combination, (b) the potential difference across each capacitor, and (c) the charge stored on each capacitor.

13. **What If?** The two capacitors of Problem 12 are now connected in series and to a 9.00-V battery. Find (a) the equivalent capacitance of the combination, (b) the potential difference across each capacitor, and (c) the charge on each capacitor.

14. ● Three capacitors are connected to a battery as shown in Figure P26.14. Their capacitances are $C_1 = 3C$, $C_2 = C$, and $C_3 = 5C$. (a) What is the equivalent capacitance of this set of capacitors? (b) State the ranking of the capacitors according to the charge they store, from largest to smallest. (c) Rank the capacitors according to the potential differences across them, from largest to smallest. (d) **What If?** Assume C_3 is increased. Explain what happens to the charge stored by each of the capacitors.

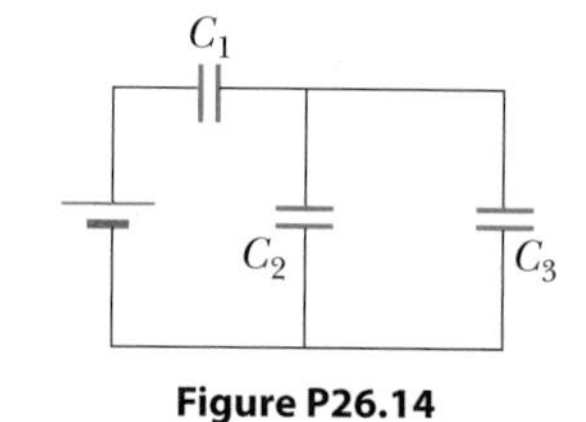

Figure P26.14

15. Two capacitors give an equivalent capacitance of 9.00 pF when connected in parallel and give an equivalent capacitance of 2.00 pF when connected in series. What is the capacitance of each capacitor?

16. Two capacitors give an equivalent capacitance of C_p when connected in parallel and an equivalent capacitance of C_s when connected in series. What is the capacitance of each capacitor?

17. ▲ Four capacitors are connected as shown in Figure P26.17. (a) Find the equivalent capacitance between

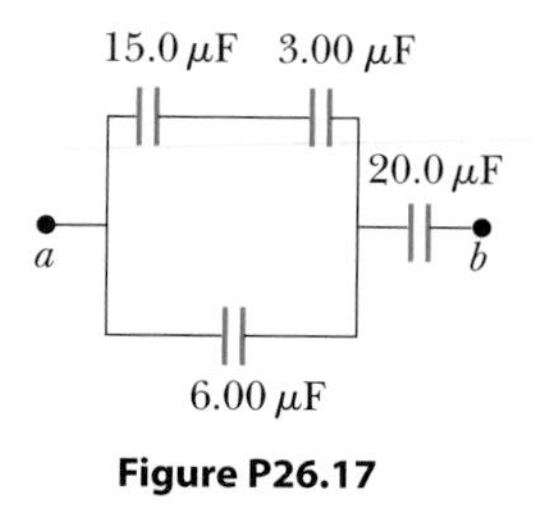

Figure P26.17

points a and b. (b) Calculate the charge on each capacitor, taking $\Delta V_{ab} = 15.0$ V.

18. According to its design specification, the timer circuit delaying the closing of an elevator door is to have a capacitance of 32.0 μF between two points A and B. (a) When one circuit is being constructed, the inexpensive but durable capacitor installed between these two points is found to have capacitance 34.8 μF. To meet the specification, one additional capacitor can be placed between the two points. Should it be in series or in parallel with the 34.8-μF capacitor? What should be its capacitance? (b) **What If?** The next circuit comes down the assembly line with capacitance 29.8 μF between A and B. To meet the specification, what additional capacitor should be installed in series or in parallel in that circuit?

19. Consider the circuit shown in Figure P26.19, where $C_1 = 6.00$ μF, $C_2 = 3.00$ μF, and $\Delta V = 20.0$ V. Capacitor C_1 is first charged by closing switch S_1. Switch S_1 is then opened, and the charged capacitor is connected to the uncharged capacitor by closing S_2. Calculate the initial charge acquired by C_1 and the final charge on each capacitor.

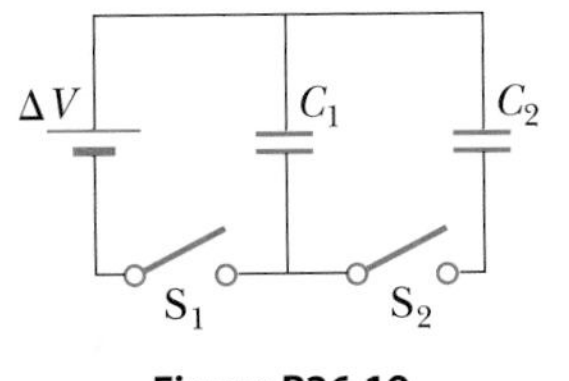

Figure P26.19

20. Consider three capacitors C_1, C_2, C_3, and a battery. If C_1 is connected to the battery, the charge on C_1 is 30.8 μC. Now C_1 is disconnected, discharged, and connected in series with C_2. When the series combination of C_2 and C_1 is connected across the battery, the charge on C_1 is 23.1 μC. The circuit is disconnected and the capacitors discharged. Capacitor C_3, capacitor C_1, and the battery are connected in series, resulting in a charge on C_1 of 25.2 μC. If, after being disconnected and discharged, C_1, C_2, and C_3 are connected in series with one another and with the battery, what is the charge on C_1?

21. A group of identical capacitors is connected first in series and then in parallel. The combined capacitance in parallel is 100 times larger than for the series connection. How many capacitors are in the group?

22. Some physical systems possessing capacitance continuously distributed over space can be modeled as an infinite array of discrete circuit elements. Examples are a microwave waveguide and the axon of a nerve cell. To practice analysis of an infinite array, determine the equivalent capacitance C between terminals X and Y of the infinite set of capacitors represented in Figure P26.22. Each capacitor has capacitance C_0. *Suggestion:* Imagine that the ladder is cut at the line AB and note that the equivalent capacitance of the infinite section to the right of AB is also C.

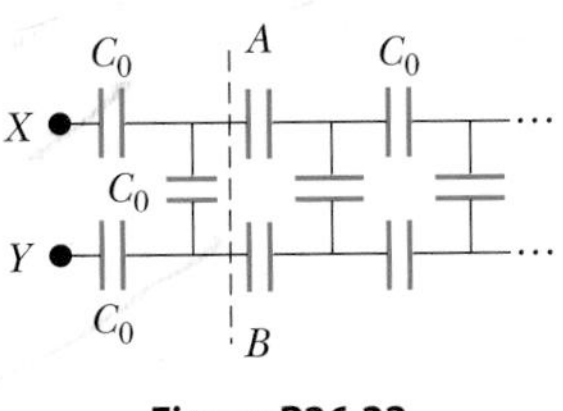

Figure P26.22

23. Find the equivalent capacitance between points a and b for the group of capacitors connected as shown in Figure P26.23. Take $C_1 = 5.00$ μF, $C_2 = 10.0$ μF, and $C_3 = 2.00$ μF.

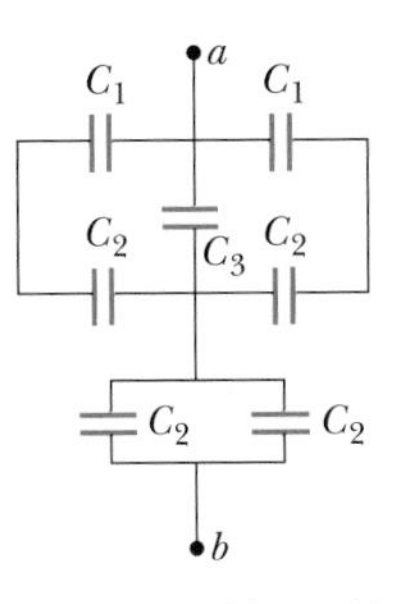

Figure P26.23 Problems 23 and 24.

24. For the network described in Problem 23, what charge is stored on C_3 if the potential difference between points a and b is 60.0 V?

25. Find the equivalent capacitance between points a and b in the combination of capacitors shown in Figure P26.25.

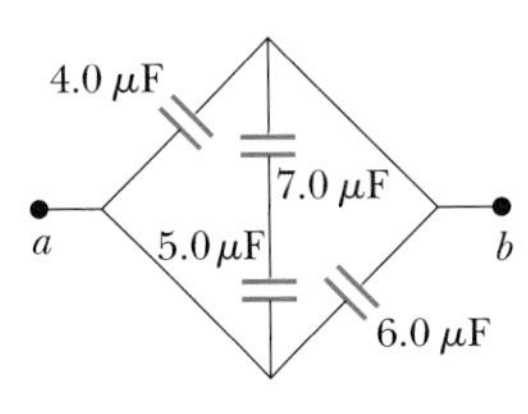

Figure P26.25

Section 26.4 Energy Stored in a Charged Capacitor

26. The immediate cause of many deaths is ventricular fibrillation, which is an uncoordinated quivering of the heart. An electric shock to the chest can cause momentary paralysis of the heart muscle, after which the heart sometimes resumes its proper beating. One type of *defibrillator* (Fig. 26.13) applies a strong electric shock to the chest over a time interval of a few milliseconds. This device contains a capacitor of several microfarads, charged to several thousand volts. Electrodes called paddles, about 8 cm across and coated with conducting paste, are held against the chest on both sides of the heart. Their handles are insulated to prevent injury to the operator, who calls "Clear!" and pushes a button on one paddle to discharge the capacitor through the patient's chest. Assume an energy of 300 J is to be delivered from a 30.0-μF capacitor. To what potential difference must it be charged?

27. (a) A 3.00-μF capacitor is connected to a 12.0-V battery. How much energy is stored in the capacitor? (b) Had the capacitor been connected to a 6.00-V battery, how much energy would have been stored?

28. Two capacitors, $C_1 = 25.0$ μF and $C_2 = 5.00$ μF, are connected in parallel and charged with a 100-V power supply. (a) Draw a circuit diagram and calculate the total energy stored in the two capacitors. (b) **What If?** What potential difference would be required across the same two capacitors connected in series for the combination to store the same amount of energy as in part (a)? Draw a circuit diagram of this circuit.

29. ▲ A parallel-plate capacitor has a charge Q and plates of area A. What force acts on one plate to attract it toward the other plate? Because the electric field between the plates is $E = Q/A\epsilon_0$, you might think the force is $F = QE = Q^2/A\epsilon_0$. This conclusion is wrong because the field E includes contributions from both plates and the field created by the positive plate cannot exert any force on the positive plate. Show that the force exerted on each plate is actually $F = Q^2/2\epsilon_0 A$. *Suggestion:* Let $C = \epsilon_0 A/x$ for an arbitrary plate separation x and note that the work done in separating the two charged plates is $W = \int F\,dx$.

30. The circuit in Figure P26.30 consists of two identical, parallel metal plates connected by identical metal springs to a 100-V battery. With the switch open, the plates are uncharged, are separated by a distance $d = 8.00$ mm, and have a capacitance $C = 2.00\ \mu$F. When the switch is closed, the distance between the plates decreases by a factor of 0.500. (a) How much charge collects on each plate? (b) What is the spring constant for each spring? *Suggestion:* Use the result of Problem 29.

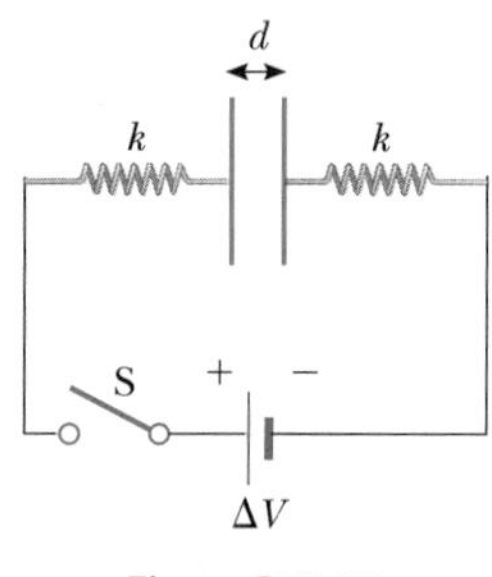

Figure P26.30

31. As a person moves about in a dry environment, electric charge accumulates on the person's body. Once it is at high voltage, either positive or negative, the body can discharge via sometimes noticeable sparks and shocks. Consider a human body isolated from ground, with the typical capacitance 150 pF. (a) What charge on the body will produce a potential of 10.0 kV? (b) Sensitive electronic devices can be destroyed by electrostatic discharge from a person. A particular device can be destroyed by a discharge releasing an energy of 250 μJ. To what voltage on the body does this situation correspond?

32. ● Two identical parallel-plate capacitors, each with capacitance C, are charged to potential difference ΔV and connected in parallel. Then the plate separation in one of the capacitors is doubled. (a) Find the total energy of the system of two capacitors *before* the plate separation is doubled. (b) Find the potential difference across each capacitor *after* the plate separation is doubled. (c) Find the total energy of the system *after* the plate separation is doubled. (d) Reconcile the difference in the answers to parts (a) and (c) with the law of conservation of energy.

33. Show that the energy associated with a conducting sphere of radius R and charge Q surrounded by a vacuum is $U = k_e Q^2/2R$.

34. Consider two conducting spheres with radii R_1 and R_2 separated by a distance much greater than either radius. A total charge Q is shared between the spheres, subject to the condition that the electric potential energy of the system has the smallest possible value. The total charge Q is equal to $q_1 + q_2$, where q_1 represents the charge on the first sphere and q_2 the charge on the second. Because the spheres are very far apart, you can assume the charge of each is uniformly distributed over its surface. You may use the result of Problem 33. (a) Determine the values of q_1 and q_2 in terms of Q, R_1, and R_2. (b) Show that the potential difference between the spheres is zero. (We saw in Chapter 25 that two conductors joined by a conducting wire are at the same potential in a static situation. This problem illustrates the general principle that charge on a conductor distributes itself so that the electric potential energy of the system is a minimum.)

35. **Review problem.** A certain storm cloud has a potential of 1.00×10^8 V relative to a tree. If, during a lightning storm, 50.0 C of charge is transferred through this potential difference and 1.00% of the energy is absorbed by the tree, how much sap in the tree can be boiled away? Model the sap as water initially at 30.0°C. Water has a specific heat of 4 186 J/kg · °C, a boiling point of 100°C, and a latent heat of vaporization of 2.26×10^6 J/kg.

Section 26.5 Capacitors with Dielectrics

36. (a) How much charge can be placed on a capacitor with air between the plates before it breaks down if the area of each of the plates is 5.00 cm^2? (b) **What If?** Find the maximum charge if polystyrene is used between the plates instead of air.

37. Determine (a) the capacitance and (b) the maximum potential difference that can be applied to a Teflon-filled parallel-plate capacitor having a plate area of 1.75 cm^2 and plate separation of 0.040 0 mm.

38. A supermarket sells rolls of aluminum foil, of plastic wrap, and of waxed paper. Describe a capacitor made from such materials. Compute order-of-magnitude estimates for its capacitance and its breakdown voltage.

39. A commercial capacitor is to be constructed as shown in Figure 26.15a. This particular capacitor is made from two strips of aluminum separated by a strip of paraffin-coated paper. Each strip of foil and paper is 7.00 cm wide. The foil is 0.004 00 mm thick, and the paper is 0.025 0 mm thick and has a dielectric constant of 3.70. What length should the strips have if a capacitance of 9.50×10^{-8} F is desired before the capacitor is rolled up? (Adding a second strip of paper and rolling the capacitor effectively doubles its capacitance by allowing charge storage on both sides of each strip of foil.)

40. A parallel-plate capacitor in air has a plate separation of 1.50 cm and a plate area of 25.0 cm^2. The plates are charged to a potential difference of 250 V and disconnected from the source. The capacitor is then immersed in distilled water. Determine (a) the charge on the plates before and after immersion, (b) the capacitance and potential difference after immersion, and (c) the change in energy of the capacitor. Assume the liquid is an insulator.

41. Each capacitor in the combination shown in Figure P26.41 has a breakdown voltage of 15.0 V. What is the breakdown voltage of the combination?

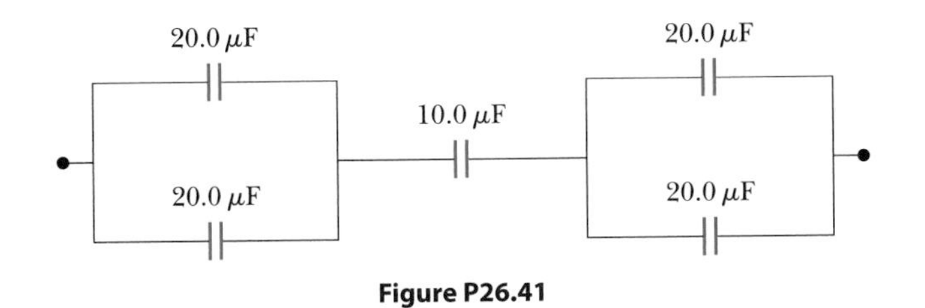

Figure P26.41

Section 26.6 Electric Dipole in an Electric Field

42. A small, rigid object carries positive and negative 3.50-nC charges. It is oriented so that the positive charge has coordinates (−1.20 mm, 1.10 mm) and the negative charge is at the point (1.40 mm, −1.30 mm). (a) Find the electric dipole moment of the object. The object is placed in an electric field $\vec{\mathbf{E}} = (7\,800\hat{\mathbf{i}} - 4\,900\hat{\mathbf{j}})$ N/C. (b) Find the torque acting on the object. (c) Find the potential energy of the object–field system when the object is in this orientation. (d) Assuming the orientation of the object can change, find the difference between the maximum and minimum potential energies of the system.

43. A small object with electric dipole moment $\vec{\mathbf{p}}$ is placed in a nonuniform electric field $\vec{\mathbf{E}} = E(x)\hat{\mathbf{i}}$. That is, the field is in the x direction and its magnitude depends on the coordinate x. Let θ represent the angle between the dipole moment and the x direction. (a) Prove that the net force on the dipole is

$$F = p\left(\frac{dE}{dx}\right)\cos\theta$$

acting in the direction of increasing field. (b) Consider a spherical balloon centered at the origin, with radius 15.0 cm and carrying charge 2.00 μC. Evaluate dE/dx at the point (16 cm, 0, 0). Assume a water droplet at this point has an induced dipole moment of $6.30\hat{\mathbf{i}}$ nC·m. Find the net force exerted on it.

Section 26.7 An Atomic Description of Dielectrics

44. The general form of Gauss's law describes how a charge creates an electric field in a material, as well as in vacuum:

$$\oint \vec{\mathbf{E}} \cdot d\vec{\mathbf{A}} = \frac{q_{\text{in}}}{\epsilon}$$

where $\epsilon = \kappa\epsilon_0$ is the permittivity of the material. (a) A sheet with charge Q uniformly distributed over its area A is surrounded by a dielectric. Show that the sheet creates a uniform electric field at nearby points, with magnitude $E = Q/2A\epsilon$. (b) Two large sheets of area A, carrying opposite charges of equal magnitude Q, are a small distance d apart. Show that they create uniform electric field in the space between them, with magnitude $E = Q/A\epsilon$. (c) Assume the negative plate is at zero potential. Show that the positive plate is at potential $Qd/A\epsilon$. (d) Show that the capacitance of the pair of plates is $A\epsilon/d = \kappa A\epsilon_0/d$.

45. The inner conductor of a coaxial cable has a radius of 0.800 mm, and the outer conductor's inside radius is 3.00 mm. The space between the conductors is filled with polyethylene, which has a dielectric constant of 2.30 and a dielectric strength of 18.0×10^6 V/m. What is the maximum potential difference that this cable can withstand?

Additional Problems

46. Two large, parallel metal plates each of area A are oriented horizontally and separated by a distance $3d$. A grounded conducting wire joins them, and initially each plate carries no charge. Now a third identical plate carrying charge Q is inserted between the two plates, parallel to them and located a distance d from the upper plate as shown in Figure P26.46. (a) What induced charge appears on each of the two original plates? (b) What potential difference appears between the middle plate and each of the other plates?

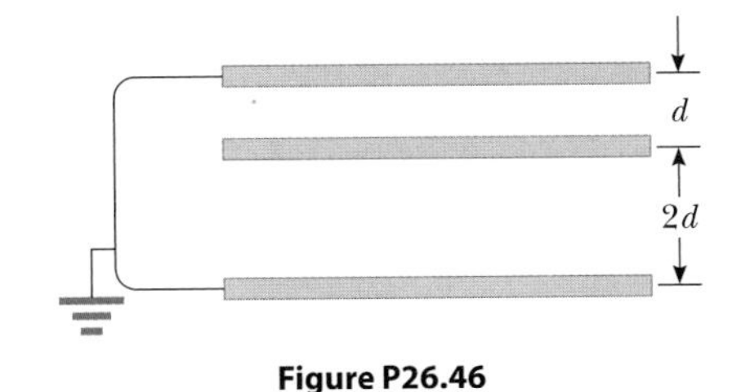

Figure P26.46

47. Four parallel metal plates P_1, P_2, P_3, and P_4, each of area 7.50 cm², are separated successively by a distance d = 1.19 mm as shown in Figure P26.47. P_1 is connected to the negative terminal of a battery, and P_2 is connected to the positive terminal. The battery maintains a potential difference of 12.0 V. (a) If P_3 is connected to the negative terminal, what is the capacitance of the three-plate system $P_1P_2P_3$? (b) What is the charge on P_2? (c) If P_4 is now connected to the positive terminal, what is the capacitance of the four-plate system $P_1P_2P_3P_4$? (d) What is the charge on P_4?

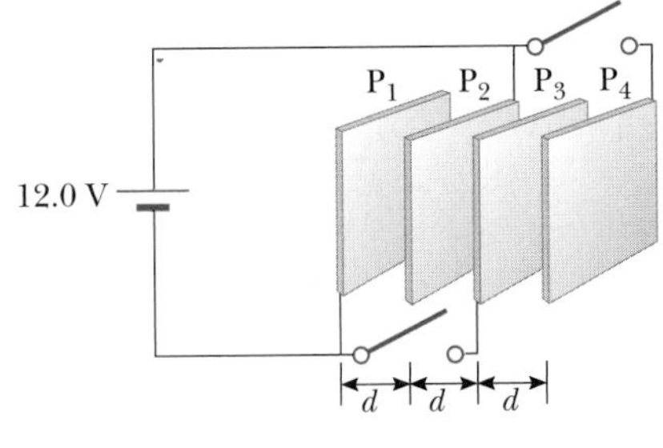

Figure P26.47

48. One conductor of an overhead electric transmission line is a long aluminum wire 2.40 cm in radius. Suppose it carries a charge per length of 1.40 μC/m at a particular moment and its potential is 345 kV. Find the potential 12.0 m below the wire. Ignore the other conductors of the transmission line and assume the electric field is radial everywhere.

49. A 2.00-nF parallel-plate capacitor is charged to an initial potential difference ΔV_i = 100 V and is then isolated. The dielectric material between the plates is mica, with a dielectric constant of 5.00. (a) How much work is required to withdraw the mica sheet? (b) What is the potential difference across the capacitor after the mica is withdrawn?

50. (a) Draw a circuit diagram showing four capacitors between two points a and b for which the following expression determines the equivalent capacitance:

$$\frac{1}{\dfrac{1}{30\ \mu\text{F}} + \dfrac{1}{20\ \mu\text{F} + C_1}} + 50\ \mu\text{F} = 70\ \mu\text{F}$$

(b) Find the value of C_1. (c) Assume a 6.00-V battery is connected between a and b. Find the potential difference across each of the individual capacitors and the charge on each.

51. ▲ A parallel-plate capacitor is constructed using a dielectric material whose dielectric constant is 3.00 and whose dielectric strength is 2.00×10^8 V/m. The desired capacitance is 0.250 μF, and the capacitor must withstand a maximum potential difference of 4.00 kV. Find the minimum area of the capacitor plates.

52. ● A horizontal, parallel-plate capacitor with vacuum between its plates has a capacitance of 25.0 μF. A nonconducting liquid with dielectric constant 6.50 is poured into the space between the plates, filling up a fraction f of its volume. (a) Find the new capacitance as a function of f. (b) What should you expect the capacitance to be when $f = 0$? Does your expression from part (a) agree with your answer? (c) What capacitance should you expect when $f = 1$? Does the expression from part (a) agree with your answer? (d) Charges of magnitude 300 μC are placed on the plates of the partially filled capacitor. What can you determine about the induced charge on the free upper surface of the liquid? How does this charge depend on f?

53. (a) Two spheres have radii a and b, and their centers are a distance d apart. Show that the capacitance of this system is

$$C = \frac{4\pi\epsilon_0}{\dfrac{1}{a} + \dfrac{1}{b} - \dfrac{2}{d}}$$

provided d is large compared with a and b. *Suggestion:* Because the spheres are far apart, assume the potential of each equals the sum of the potentials due to each sphere. When calculating those potentials, assume $V = k_eQ/r$ applies. (b) Show that as d approaches infinity, the above result reduces to that of two spherical capacitors in series.

54. A 10.0-μF capacitor is charged to 15.0 V. It is next connected in series with an uncharged 5.00-μF capacitor. The series combination is finally connected across a 50.0-V battery as diagrammed in Figure P26.54. Find the new potential differences across the 5.00-μF and 10.0-μF capacitors.

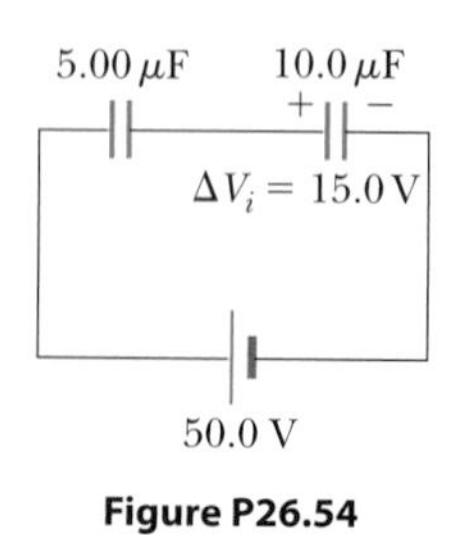

Figure P26.54

55. ● When considering the energy supply for an automobile, the energy per unit mass (in joules per kilogram) of the energy source is an important parameter. Using the following data, explain how the energy per unit mass compares among gasoline, lead-acid batteries, and capacitors. (The ampere A will be introduced in Chapter 27 as the SI unit of electric current. 1 A = 1 C/s.)

Gasoline: 126 000 Btu/gal; density = 670 kg/m^3.

Lead-acid battery: 12.0 V; 100 A·h; mass = 16.0 kg.

Capacitor: potential difference at full charge = 12.0 V; capacitance = 0.100 F; mass = 0.100 kg.

56. A capacitor is constructed from two square, metallic plates of sides ℓ and separation d. Charges $+Q$ and $-Q$ are placed on the plates, and the power supply is then removed. A material of dielectric constant κ is inserted a distance x into the capacitor as shown in Figure P26.56. Assume d is much smaller than x. (a) Find the equivalent capacitance of the device. (b) Calculate the energy stored in the capacitor. (c) Find the direction and magnitude of the force exerted by the plates on the dielectric. (d) Obtain a numerical value for the force when $x = \ell/2$, assuming $\ell = 5.00$ cm, $d = 2.00$ mm, the dielectric is glass ($\kappa = 4.50$), and the capacitor was charged to 2 000 V before the dielectric was inserted. *Suggestion:* The system can be considered as two capacitors connected in parallel.

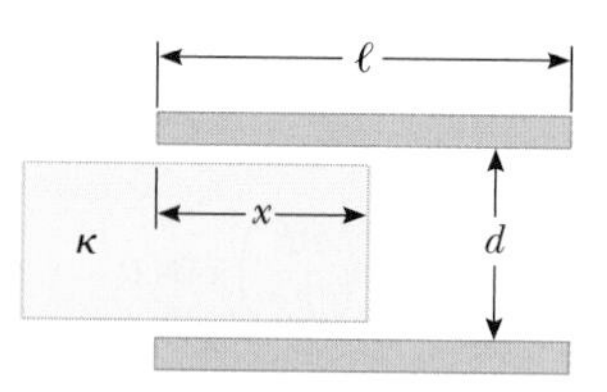

Figure P26.56 Problems 56 and 57.

57. ● Two square plates of sides ℓ are placed parallel to each other with separation d as suggested in Figure P26.56. You may assume d is much less than ℓ. The plates carry uniformly distributed static charges $+Q_0$ and $-Q_0$. A block of metal has width ℓ, length ℓ, and thickness slightly less than d. It is inserted a distance x into the space between the plates. The charges on the plates remain uniformly distributed as the block slides in. In a static situation, a metal prevents an electric field from penetrating inside it. The metal can be thought of as a perfect dielectric, with $\kappa \to \infty$. (a) Calculate the stored energy as a function of x. (b) Find the direction and magnitude of the force that acts on the metallic block. (c) The area of the advancing front face of the block is essentially equal to ℓd. Considering the force on the block as acting on this face, find the stress (force per area) on it. (d) Express the energy density in the electric field between the charged plates in terms of Q_0, ℓ, d, and ϵ_0. Explain how the answers to parts (c) and (d) compare with each other.

58. ● To repair a power supply for a stereo amplifier, an electronics technician needs a 100-μF capacitor capable of withstanding a potential difference of 90 V between the plates. The immediately available supply is a box of five 100-μF capacitors, each having a maximum voltage capability of 50 V. Can the technician use one of the capacitors from the box? Can she substitute a combination of these capacitors that has the proper electrical characteristics? Will the technician use all the capacitors in the box? Explain your answers. In a combination of capacitors,

what will be the maximum voltage across each of the capacitors used?

59. An isolated capacitor of unknown capacitance has been charged to a potential difference of 100 V. When the charged capacitor is then connected in parallel to an uncharged 10.0-μF capacitor, the potential difference across the combination is 30.0 V. Calculate the unknown capacitance.

60. A parallel-plate capacitor with plates of area LW and plate separation t has the region between its plates filled with wedges of two dielectric materials as shown in Figure P26.60. Assume t is much less than both L and W. (a) Determine its capacitance. (b) Should the capacitance be the same if the labels κ_1 and κ_2 are interchanged? Demonstrate that your expression does or does not have this property. (c) Show that if κ_1 and κ_2 approach equality to a common value κ, your result becomes the same as the capacitance of a capacitor containing a single dielectric: $C = \kappa\epsilon_0 LW/t$.

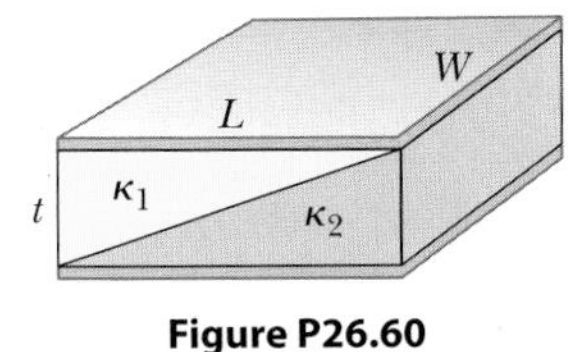

Figure P26.60

61. ● A parallel-plate capacitor of plate separation d is charged to a potential difference ΔV_0. A dielectric slab of thickness d and dielectric constant κ is introduced between the plates while the battery remains connected to the plates. (a) Show that the ratio of energy stored after the dielectric is introduced to the energy stored in the empty capacitor is $U/U_0 = \kappa$. Give a physical explanation for this increase in stored energy. (b) What happens to the charge on the capacitor? (Notice that this situation is not the same as in Example 26.5, in which the battery was removed from the circuit before the dielectric was introduced.)

62. Calculate the equivalent capacitance between points a and b in Figure P26.62. Notice that this system is not a simple series or parallel combination. *Suggestion:* Assume a potential difference ΔV between points a and b. Write expressions for ΔV_{ab} in terms of the charges and capacitances for the various possible pathways from a to b and require conservation of charge for those capacitor plates that are connected to each other.

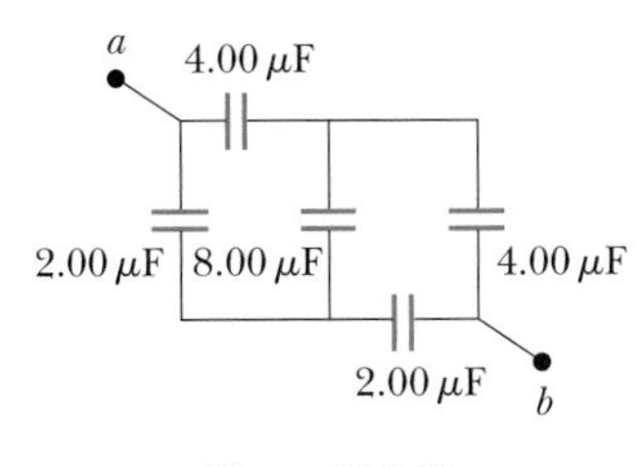

Figure P26.62

63. Capacitors $C_1 = 6.00\ \mu$F and $C_2 = 2.00\ \mu$F are charged as a parallel combination across a 250-V battery. The capacitors are disconnected from the battery and from each other. They are then connected positive plate to negative plate and negative plate to positive plate. Calculate the resulting charge on each capacitor.

64. Consider two long, parallel, and oppositely charged wires of radius r with their centers separated by a distance D that is much larger than r. Assuming the charge is distributed uniformly on the surface of each wire, show that the capacitance per unit length of this pair of wires is

$$\frac{C}{\ell} = \frac{\pi\epsilon_0}{\ln(D/r)}$$

65. Determine the equivalent capacitance of the combination shown in Figure P26.65. *Suggestion:* Consider the symmetry involved.

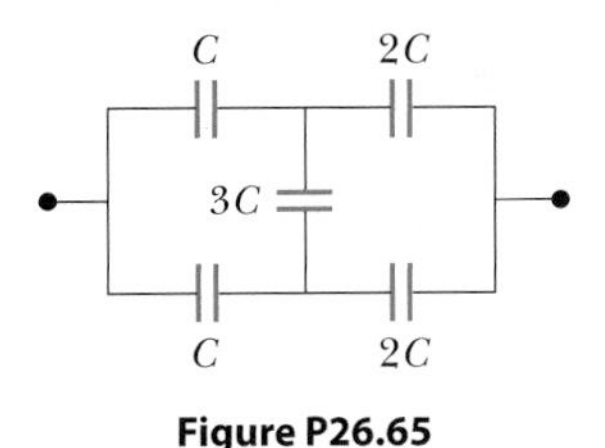

Figure P26.65

66. Example 26.1 explored a cylindrical capacitor of length ℓ with radii a and b for the two conductors. In the **What If?** section of that example, it was claimed that increasing ℓ by 10% is more effective in terms of increasing the capacitance than increasing a by 10% if $b > 2.85a$. Verify this claim mathematically.

Answers to Quick Quizzes

26.1 (d). The capacitance is a property of the physical system and does not vary with applied voltage. According to Equation 26.1, if the voltage is doubled, the charge is doubled.

26.2 (a). When the key is pressed, the plate separation is decreased and the capacitance increases. Capacitance depends only on how a capacitor is constructed and not on the external circuit.

26.3 (a). When connecting capacitors in series, the inverses of the capacitances add, resulting in a smaller overall equivalent capacitance.

26.4 (b). For a given voltage, the energy stored in a capacitor is proportional to C according to $U = C(\Delta V)^2/2$. Therefore, you want to maximize the equivalent capacitance. You do that by connecting the three capacitors in parallel so that the capacitances add.

26.5 (a). The dielectric constant of wood (and of all other insulating materials, for that matter) is greater than 1; therefore, the capacitance increases (Eq. 26.14). This increase is sensed by the stud finder's special circuitry, which causes an indicator on the device to light up.

These power lines transfer energy from the electric company to homes and businesses. The energy is transferred at a very high voltage, possibly hundreds of thousands of volts in some cases. Even though it makes power lines very dangerous, the high voltage results in less loss of energy due to resistance in the wires. (Telegraph Colour Library/FPG)

27 Current and Resistance

We now consider situations involving electric charges that are in motion through some region of space. We use the term *electric current,* or simply *current,* to describe the rate of flow of charge. Most practical applications of electricity deal with electric currents. For example, the battery in a flashlight produces a current in the filament of the bulb when the switch is turned on. A variety of home appliances operate on alternating current. In these common situations, current exists in a conductor such as a copper wire. Currents can also exist outside a conductor. For instance, a beam of electrons in a television picture tube constitutes a current.

This chapter begins with the definition of current. A microscopic description of current is given, and some factors that contribute to the opposition to the flow of charge in conductors are discussed. A classical model is used to describe electrical conduction in metals, and some limitations of this model are cited. We also define electrical resistance and introduce a new circuit element, the resistor. We conclude by discussing the rate at which energy is transferred to a device in an electric circuit.

27.1 Electric Current

In this section, we study the flow of electric charges through a piece of material. The amount of flow depends on both the material through which the charges are passing and the potential difference across the material. Whenever there is a net flow of charge through some region, an electric **current** is said to exist.

It is instructive to draw an analogy between water flow and current. In many localities, it is common practice to install low-flow showerheads in homes as a water-conservation measure. We quantify the flow of water from these and similar devices by specifying the amount of water that emerges during a given time interval, often measured in liters per minute. On a grander scale, we can characterize a river current by describing the rate at which the water flows past a particular location. For example, the flow over the brink at Niagara Falls is maintained at rates between 1 400 m^3/s and 2 800 m^3/s.

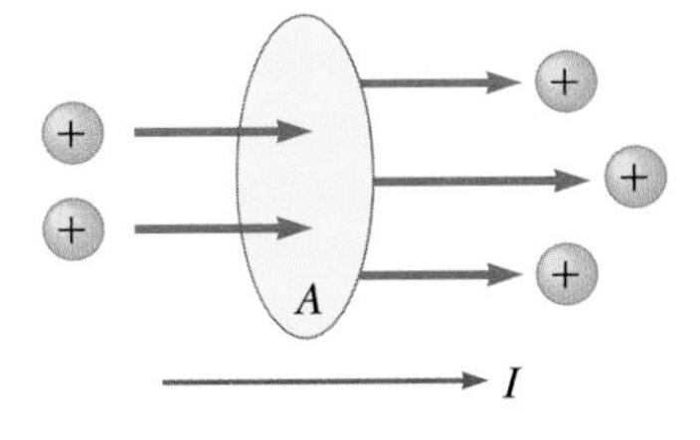

Figure 27.1 Charges in motion through an area A. The time rate at which charge flows through the area is defined as the current I. The direction of the current is the direction in which positive charges flow when free to do so.

There is also an analogy between thermal conduction and current. In Section 20.7, we discussed the flow of energy by heat through a sample of material. The rate of energy flow is determined by the material as well as the temperature difference across the material as described by Equation 20.15.

To define current more precisely, suppose charges are moving perpendicular to a surface of area A as shown in Figure 27.1. (This area could be the cross-sectional area of a wire, for example.) **The current is the rate at which charge flows through this surface.** If ΔQ is the amount of charge that passes through this surface in a time interval Δt, the **average current** I_{avg} is equal to the charge that passes through A per unit time:

$$I_{avg} = \frac{\Delta Q}{\Delta t} \tag{27.1}$$

If the rate at which charge flows varies in time, the current varies in time; we define the **instantaneous current** I as the differential limit of average current:

$$I \equiv \frac{dQ}{dt} \tag{27.2}$$

◀ Electric current

The SI unit of current is the **ampere** (A):

$$1 \text{ A} = 1 \text{ C/s} \tag{27.3}$$

That is, 1 A of current is equivalent to 1 C of charge passing through a surface in 1 s.

The charged particles passing through the surface in Figure 27.1 can be positive, negative, or both. **It is conventional to assign to the current the same direction as the flow of positive charge.** In electrical conductors such as copper or aluminum, the current results from the motion of negatively charged electrons. Therefore, in an ordinary conductor, **the direction of the current is opposite the direction of flow of electrons.** For a beam of positively charged protons in an accelerator, however, the current is in the direction of motion of the protons. In some cases—such as those involving gases and electrolytes, for instance—the current is the result of the flow of both positive and negative charges. It is common to refer to a moving charge (positive or negative) as a mobile **charge carrier.**

PITFALL PREVENTION 27.1
"Current Flow" Is Redundant

The phrase *current flow* is commonly used, although it is technically incorrect because current *is* a flow (of charge). This wording is similar to the phrase *heat transfer*, which is also redundant because heat *is* a transfer (of energy). We will avoid this phrase and speak of *flow of charge* or *charge flow*.

If the ends of a conducting wire are connected to form a loop, all points on the loop are at the same electric potential; hence, the electric field is zero within and at the surface of the conductor. Because the electric field is zero, there is no net transport of charge through the wire; therefore, there is no current. If the ends of the conducting wire are connected to a battery, however, all points on the loop are not at the same potential. The battery sets up a potential difference between the ends of the loop, creating an electric field within the wire. The electric field exerts forces on the conduction electrons in the wire, causing them to move in the wire and therefore creating a current.

PITFALL PREVENTION 27.2
Batteries Do Not Supply Electrons

A battery does not supply electrons to the circuit. It establishes the electric field that exerts a force on electrons already in the wires and elements of the circuit.

Microscopic Model of Current

We can relate current to the motion of the charge carriers by describing a microscopic model of conduction in a metal. Consider the current in a conductor of

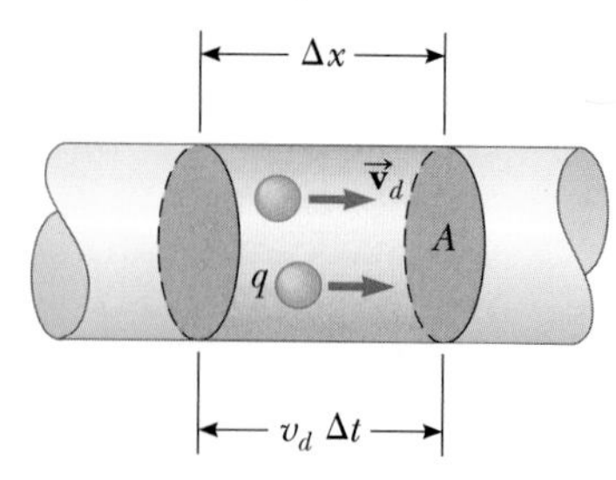

Figure 27.2 A section of a uniform conductor of cross-sectional area A. The mobile charge carriers move with a speed v_d, and the displacement they experience in the x direction in a time interval Δt is $\Delta x = v_d\,\Delta t$. If we choose Δt to be the time interval during which the charges are displaced, on average, by the length of the cylinder, the number of carriers in the section of length Δx is $nAv_d\,\Delta t$, where n is the number of carriers per unit volume.

cross-sectional area A (Fig. 27.2). The volume of a section of the conductor of length Δx (the gray region of the conductor shown in Fig. 27.2) is $A\,\Delta x$. If n represents the number of mobile charge carriers per unit volume (in other words, the charge carrier density), the number of carriers in the gray section is $nA\,\Delta x$. Therefore, the total charge ΔQ in this section is

$$\Delta Q = (nA\,\Delta x)q$$

where q is the charge on each carrier. If the carriers move with a speed v_d, the displacement they experience in the x direction in a time interval Δt is $\Delta x = v_d\,\Delta t$. Let Δt be the time interval required for the charge carriers in the cylinder to move through a displacement whose magnitude is equal to the length of the cylinder. This time interval is also the same as that required for all the charge carriers in the cylinder to pass through the circular area at one end. With this choice, we can write ΔQ as

$$\Delta Q = (nAv_d\,\Delta t)q$$

Dividing both sides of this equation by Δt, we find that the average current in the conductor is

Current in a conductor in terms of microscopic quantities ▶

$$I_{\text{avg}} = \frac{\Delta Q}{\Delta t} = nqv_dA \qquad \textbf{(27.4)}$$

The speed of the charge carriers v_d is an average speed called the **drift speed.** To understand the meaning of drift speed, consider a conductor in which the charge carriers are free electrons. If the conductor is isolated—that is, the potential difference across it is zero—these electrons undergo random motion that is analogous to the motion of gas molecules. The electrons collide repeatedly with the metal atoms, and their resultant motion is complicated and zigzagged as in Active Figure 27.3a. As discussed earlier, when a potential difference is applied across the conductor (for example, by means of a battery), an electric field is set up in the conductor; this field exerts an electric force on the electrons, producing a current. In addition to the zigzag motion due to the collisions with the metal atoms, the electrons move slowly along the conductor (in a direction opposite that of $\vec{\mathbf{E}}$) at the drift velocity $\vec{\mathbf{v}}_d$ as shown in Active Figure 27.3b.

You can think of the atom–electron collisions in a conductor as an effective internal friction (or drag force) similar to that experienced by a liquid's molecules flowing through a pipe stuffed with steel wool. The energy transferred from the electrons to the metal atoms during collisions causes an increase in the atom's vibrational energy and a corresponding increase in the conductor's temperature.

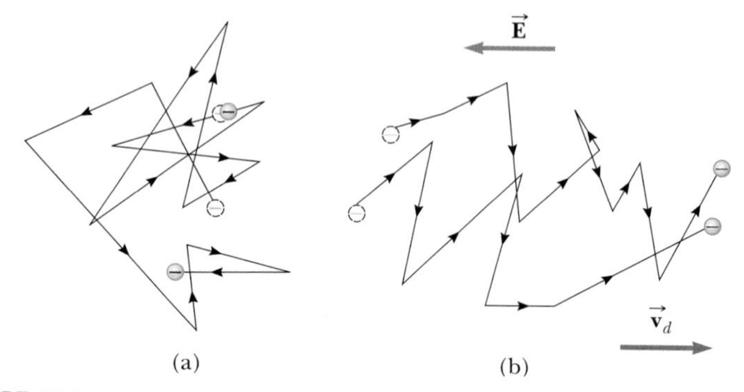

ACTIVE FIGURE 27.3

(a) A schematic diagram of the random motion of two charge carriers in a conductor in the absence of an electric field. The drift velocity is zero. (b) The motion of the charge carriers in a conductor in the presence of an electric field. Notice that the random motion is modified by the field and the charge carriers have a drift velocity opposite the direction of the electric field. Because of the acceleration of the charge carriers due to the electric force, the paths are actually parabolic. The drift speed, however, is much smaller than the average speed, so the parabolic shape is not visible on this scale.

Sign in at www.thomsonedu.com and go to ThomsonNOW to adjust the electric field and see the resulting effect on the motion of an electron.

Quick Quiz 27.1 Consider positive and negative charges moving horizontally through the four regions shown in Figure 27.4. Rank the current in these four regions from lowest to highest.

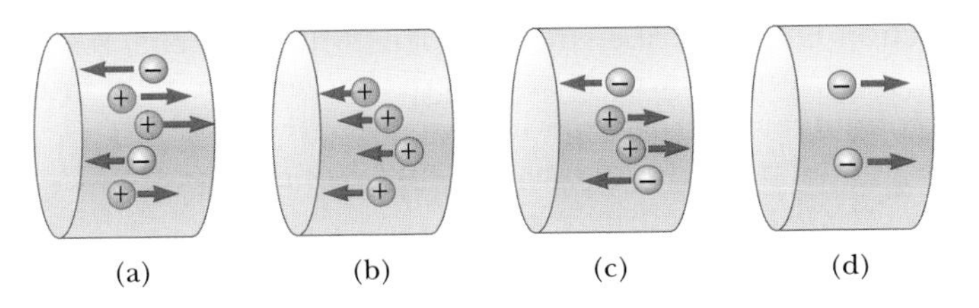

Figure 27.4 (Quick Quiz 27.1) Charges move through four regions.

EXAMPLE 27.1 Drift Speed in a Copper Wire

The 12-gauge copper wire in a typical residential building has a cross-sectional area of 3.31×10^{-6} m^2. It carries a constant current of 10.0 A. What is the drift speed of the electrons in the wire? Assume each copper atom contributes one free electron to the current. The density of copper is 8.92 g/cm^3.

SOLUTION

Conceptualize Imagine electrons following a zigzag motion such as that in Active Figure 27.3a, with a drift motion parallel to the wire superimposed on the motion as in Active Figure 27.3b. As mentioned earlier, the drift speed is small, and this example helps us quantify the speed.

Categorize We evaluate the drift speed using Equation 27.4. Because the current is constant, the average current during any time interval is the same as the constant current: $I_{\text{avg}} = I$.

Analyze The periodic table of the elements in Appendix C shows that the molar mass of copper is 63.5 g/mol. Recall that 1 mol of any substance contains Avogadro's number of atoms (6.02×10^{23}).

Use the molar mass and the density of copper to find the volume of 1 mole of copper:

$$V = \frac{m}{\rho} = \frac{63.5\text{ g}}{8.92\text{ g/cm}^3} = 7.12\text{ cm}^3$$

From the assumption that each copper atom contributes one free electron to the current, find the electron density in copper:

$$n = \frac{6.02 \times 10^{23}\text{ electrons}}{7.12\text{ cm}^3}\left(\frac{1.00 \times 10^6\text{ cm}^3}{1\text{ m}^3}\right)$$

$$= 8.46 \times 10^{28}\text{ electrons/m}^3$$

Solve Equation 27.4 for the drift speed:

$$v_d = \frac{I_{\text{avg}}}{nqA} = \frac{I}{nqA}$$

Substitute numerical values:

$$v_d = \frac{I}{neA} = \frac{10.0\text{ A}}{(8.46 \times 10^{28}\text{ m}^{-3})(1.60 \times 10^{-19}\text{ C})(3.31 \times 10^{-6}\text{ m}^2)}$$

$$= 2.23 \times 10^{-4}\text{ m/s}$$

Finalize This result shows that typical drift speeds are very small. For instance, electrons traveling with a speed of 2.23×10^{-4} m/s would take about 75 min to travel 1 m! You might therefore wonder why a light turns on almost instantaneously when its switch is thrown. In a conductor, changes in the electric field that drives the free electrons travel through the conductor with a speed close to that of light. So, when you flip on a light switch, electrons already in the filament of the lightbulb experience electric forces and begin moving after a time interval on the order of nanoseconds.

27.2 Resistance

In Chapter 24, we found that the electric field inside a conductor is zero. This statement is true, however, *only* if the conductor is in static equilibrium. The purpose of this section is to describe what happens when the charges in the conductor are not in equilibrium, in which case there is an electric field in the conductor.

Consider a conductor of cross-sectional area A carrying a current I. The **current density** J in the conductor is defined as the current per unit area. Because the current $I = nqv_dA$, the current density is

Current density ▶

$$J \equiv \frac{I}{A} = nqv_d \quad \textbf{(27.5)}$$

where J has SI units of amperes per meter squared. This expression is valid only if the current density is uniform and only if the surface of cross-sectional area A is perpendicular to the direction of the current.

A current density and an electric field are established in a conductor whenever a potential difference is maintained across the conductor. In some materials, the current density is proportional to the electric field:

$$J = \sigma E \quad \textbf{(27.6)}$$

where the constant of proportionality σ is called the **conductivity** of the conductor.[1] Materials that obey Equation 27.6 are said to follow **Ohm's law,** named after Georg Simon Ohm. More specifically, Ohm's law states the following:

GEORG SIMON OHM
German physicist (1789–1854)
Ohm, a high school teacher and later a professor at the University of Munich, formulated the concept of resistance and discovered the proportionalities expressed in Equations 27.6 and 27.7.

> For many materials (including most metals), the ratio of the current density to the electric field is a constant σ that is independent of the electric field producing the current.

Materials that obey Ohm's law and hence demonstrate this simple relationship between E and J are said to be *ohmic.* Experimentally, however, it is found that not all materials have this property. Materials and devices that do not obey Ohm's law are said to be *nonohmic.* Ohm's law is not a fundamental law of nature; rather, it is an empirical relationship valid only for certain materials.

We can obtain an equation useful in practical applications by considering a segment of straight wire of uniform cross-sectional area A and length ℓ as shown in Figure 27.5. A potential difference $\Delta V = V_b - V_a$ is maintained across the wire, creating in the wire an electric field and a current. If the field is assumed to be uniform, the potential difference is related to the field through the relationship[2]

$$\Delta V = E\ell$$

Therefore, we can express the current density in the wire as

$$J = \sigma E = \sigma \frac{\Delta V}{\ell}$$

Because $J = I/A$, the potential difference across the wire is

$$\Delta V = \frac{\ell}{\sigma} J = \left(\frac{\ell}{\sigma A}\right) I = RI$$

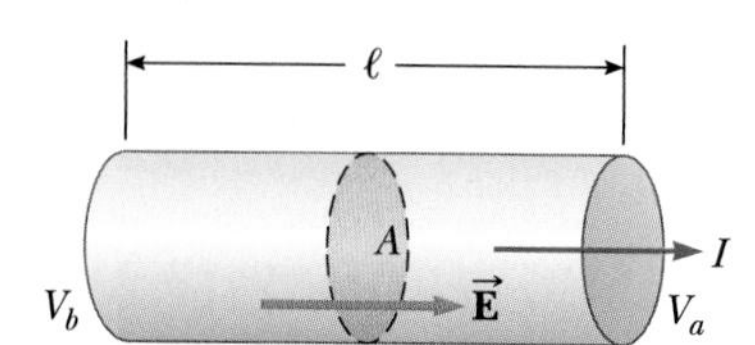

Figure 27.5 A uniform conductor of length ℓ and cross-sectional area A. A potential difference $\Delta V = V_b - V_a$ maintained across the conductor sets up an electric field $\vec{\mathbf{E}}$, and this field produces a current I that is proportional to the potential difference.

[1] Do not confuse conductivity σ with surface charge density, for which the same symbol is used.

[2] This result follows from the definition of potential difference:

$$V_b - V_a = -\int_a^b \vec{\mathbf{E}} \cdot d\vec{\mathbf{s}} = E\int_a^b dx = E\ell$$

The quantity $R = \ell/\sigma A$ is called the **resistance** of the conductor. We define the resistance as the ratio of the potential difference across a conductor to the current in the conductor:

$$R \equiv \frac{\Delta V}{I} \qquad (27.7)$$

We will use this equation again and again when studying electric circuits. This result shows that resistance has SI units of volts per ampere. One volt per ampere is defined to be one **ohm** (Ω):

$$1\ \Omega \equiv 1\ \text{V/A} \qquad (27.8)$$

This expression shows that if a potential difference of 1 V across a conductor causes a current of 1 A, the resistance of the conductor is 1 Ω. For example, if an electrical appliance connected to a 120-V source of potential difference carries a current of 6 A, its resistance is 20 Ω.

Most electric circuits use circuit elements called **resistors** to control the current in the various parts of the circuit. Two common types are the *composition resistor*, which contains carbon, and the *wire-wound resistor*, which consists of a coil of wire. Values of resistors in ohms are normally indicated by color coding as shown in Figure 27.6 and Table 27.1.

The inverse of conductivity is **resistivity**[3] ρ:

$$\rho = \frac{1}{\sigma} \qquad (27.9)$$

◀ Resistivity is the inverse of conductivity

where ρ has the units ohm meters ($\Omega \cdot \text{m}$). Because $R = \ell/\sigma A$, we can express the resistance of a uniform block of material along the length ℓ as

$$R = \rho \frac{\ell}{A} \qquad (27.10)$$

◀ Resistance of a uniform material along the length ℓ

Every ohmic material has a characteristic resistivity that depends on the properties of the material and on temperature. In addition, as you can see from Equation 27.10, the resistance of a sample depends on geometry as well as on resistivity. Table 27.2 (page 758) gives the resistivities of a variety of materials at 20°C. Notice the enormous range, from very low values for good conductors such as copper and silver to very high values for good insulators such as glass and rubber. An ideal conductor would have zero resistivity, and an ideal insulator would have infinite resistivity.

PITFALL PREVENTION 27.3
Equation 27.7 Is Not Ohm's Law

Many individuals call Equation 27.7 Ohm's law, but that is incorrect. This equation is simply the definition of resistance, and it provides an important relationship between voltage, current, and resistance. Ohm's law is related to a proportionality of J to E (Eq. 27.6) or, equivalently, of I to ΔV, which, from Equation 27.7, indicates that the resistance is constant, independent of the applied voltage.

TABLE 27.1

Color Coding for Resistors

Color	Number	Multiplier	Tolerance
Black	0	1	
Brown	1	10^1	
Red	2	10^2	
Orange	3	10^3	
Yellow	4	10^4	
Green	5	10^5	
Blue	6	10^6	
Violet	7	10^7	
Gray	8	10^8	
White	9	10^9	
Gold		10^{-1}	5%
Silver		10^{-2}	10%
Colorless			20%

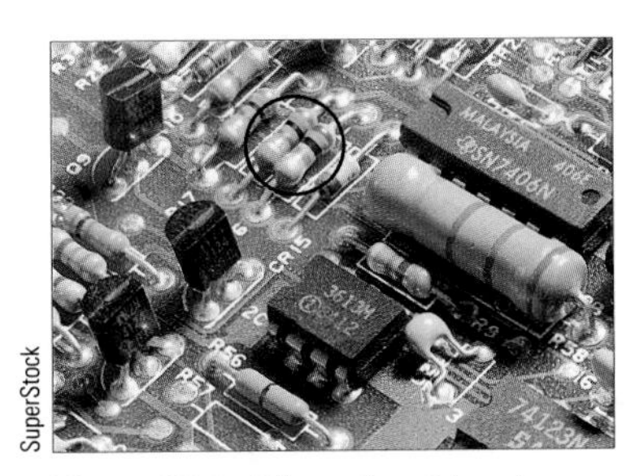

SuperStock

Figure 27.6 The colored bands on a resistor represent a code for determining resistance. The first two colors give the first two digits in the resistance value. The third color represents the power of 10 for the multiplier of the resistance value. The last color is the tolerance of the resistance value. As an example, the four colors on the circled resistors are red (= 2), black (= 0), orange (= 10^3), and gold (= 5%), and so the resistance value is $20 \times 10^3\ \Omega = 20\ \text{k}\Omega$ with a tolerance value of 5% = 1 kΩ. (The values for the colors are from Table 27.1.)

[3] Do not confuse resistivity ρ with mass density or charge density, for which the same symbol is used.

TABLE 27.2

Resistivities and Temperature Coefficients of Resistivity for Various Materials

Material	Resistivity[a] ($\Omega \cdot m$)	Temperature Coefficient[b] $\alpha[(°C)^{-1}]$
Silver	1.59×10^{-8}	3.8×10^{-3}
Copper	1.7×10^{-8}	3.9×10^{-3}
Gold	2.44×10^{-8}	3.4×10^{-3}
Aluminum	2.82×10^{-8}	3.9×10^{-3}
Tungsten	5.6×10^{-8}	4.5×10^{-3}
Iron	10×10^{-8}	5.0×10^{-3}
Platinum	11×10^{-8}	3.92×10^{-3}
Lead	22×10^{-8}	3.9×10^{-3}
Nichrome[c]	1.50×10^{-6}	0.4×10^{-3}
Carbon	3.5×10^{-5}	-0.5×10^{-3}
Germanium	0.46	-48×10^{-3}
Silicon[d]	2.3×10^{3}	-75×10^{-3}
Glass	10^{10} to 10^{14}	
Hard rubber	$\sim 10^{13}$	
Sulfur	10^{15}	
Quartz (fused)	75×10^{16}	

[a] All values at 20°C. All elements in this table are assumed to be free of impurities.

[b] See Section 27.4.

[c] A nickel–chromium alloy commonly used in heating elements.

[d] The resistivity of silicon is very sensitive to purity. The value can be changed by several orders of magnitude when it is doped with other atoms.

PITFALL PREVENTION 27.4
Resistance and Resistivity

Resistivity is a property of a *substance*, whereas resistance is a property of an *object*. We have seen similar pairs of variables before. For example, density is a property of a substance, whereas mass is a property of an object. Equation 27.10 relates resistance to resistivity and Equation 1.1 relates mass to density.

Equation 27.10 shows that the resistance of a given cylindrical conductor such as a wire is proportional to its length and inversely proportional to its cross-sectional area. If the length of a wire is doubled, its resistance doubles. If its cross-sectional area is doubled, its resistance decreases by one half. The situation is analogous to the flow of a liquid through a pipe. As the pipe's length is increased, the resistance to flow increases. As the pipe's cross-sectional area is increased, more liquid crosses a given cross section of the pipe per unit time interval. Therefore, more liquid flows for the same pressure differential applied to the pipe, and the resistance to flow decreases.

Ohmic materials and devices have a linear current–potential difference relationship over a broad range of applied potential differences (Fig. 27.7a). The slope of the I-versus-ΔV curve in the linear region yields a value for $1/R$. Nonohmic materials have a nonlinear current–potential difference relationship. One common semiconducting device with nonlinear I-versus-ΔV characteristics is the *junction diode* (Fig. 27.7b). The resistance of this device is low for currents in one direction (positive ΔV) and high for currents in the reverse direction (negative ΔV). In fact, most modern electronic devices, such as transistors, have nonlin-

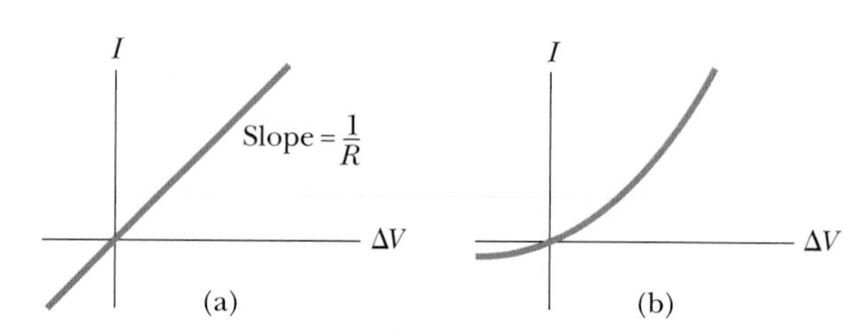

Figure 27.7 (a) The current–potential difference curve for an ohmic material. The curve is linear, and the slope is equal to the inverse of the resistance of the conductor. (b) A nonlinear current–potential difference curve for a junction diode. This device does not obey Ohm's law.

ear current–potential difference relationships; their proper operation depends on the particular way they violate Ohm's law.

Quick Quiz 27.2 A cylindrical wire has a radius r and length ℓ. If both r and ℓ are doubled, does the resistance of the wire (a) increase, (b) decrease, or (c) remain the same?

Quick Quiz 27.3 In Figure 27.7b, as the applied voltage increases, does the resistance of the diode (a) increase, (b) decrease, or (c) remain the same?

EXAMPLE 27.2 The Resistance of Nichrome Wire

The radius of 22-gauge Nichrome wire is 0.321 mm. **(A)** Calculate the resistance per unit length of this wire.

SOLUTION

Conceptualize Table 27.2 shows that Nichrome has a resistivity two orders of magnitude larger than the best conductors in the table. Therefore, we expect it to have some special practical applications that the best conductors may not have.

Categorize We model the wire as a cylinder so that a simple geometric analysis can be applied to find the resistance.

Analyze Use Equation 27.10 and the resistivity of Nichrome from Table 27.2 to find the resistance per unit length:

$$\frac{R}{\ell} = \frac{\rho}{A} = \frac{\rho}{\pi r^2} = \frac{1.5 \times 10^{-6}\ \Omega \cdot \text{m}}{\pi(0.321 \times 10^{-3}\ \text{m})^2} = 4.6\ \Omega/\text{m}$$

(B) If a potential difference of 10 V is maintained across a 1.0-m length of the Nichrome wire, what is the current in the wire?

SOLUTION

Analyze Use Equation 27.7 to find the current:

$$I = \frac{\Delta V}{R} = \frac{\Delta V}{(4.6\ \Omega/\text{m})\ell} = \frac{10\ \text{V}}{(4.6\ \Omega/\text{m})(1.0\ \text{m})} = 2.2\ \text{A}$$

Finalize A copper wire of the same radius would have a resistance per unit length of only 0.053 Ω/m. A 1.0-m length of copper wire of the same radius would carry the same current (2.2 A) with an applied potential difference of only 0.12 V.

Because of its high resistivity and resistance to oxidation, Nichrome is often used for heating elements in toasters, irons, and electric heaters.

EXAMPLE 27.3 The Radial Resistance of a Coaxial Cable

Coaxial cables are used extensively for cable television and other electronic applications. A coaxial cable consists of two concentric cylindrical conductors. The region between the conductors is completely filled with polyethylene plastic as shown in Figure 27.8a. Current leakage through the plastic, in the *radial* direction, is unwanted. (The cable is designed to conduct current along its length, but that is *not* the current being considered here.) The radius of the inner conductor is a = 0.500 cm, the radius of the outer conductor is b = 1.75 cm, and the length is L = 15.0 cm. The resistivity of the plastic is $1.0 \times 10^{13}\ \Omega \cdot \text{m}$. Calculate the resistance of the plastic between the two conductors.

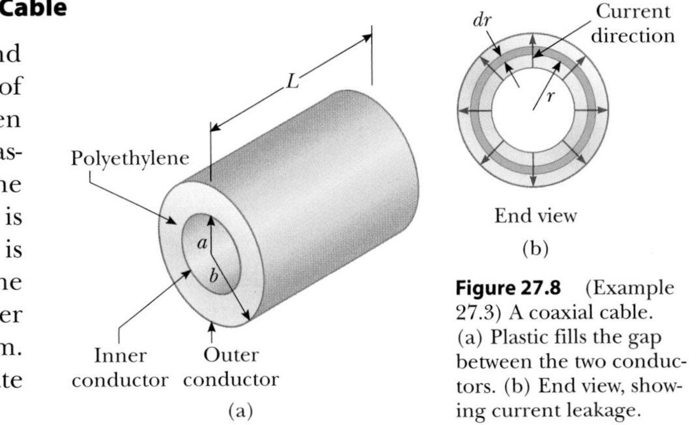

Figure 27.8 (Example 27.3) A coaxial cable. (a) Plastic fills the gap between the two conductors. (b) End view, showing current leakage.

SOLUTION

Conceptualize Imagine two currents as suggested in the text of the problem. The desired current is along the cable, carried within the conductors. The undesired current corresponds to charge leakage through the plastic, and its direction is radial.

Categorize Because the resistivity and the geometry of the plastic are known, we categorize this problem as one in which we find the resistance of the plastic from these parameters, using Equation 27.10. Because the area through which the charges pass depends on the radial position, we must use integral calculus to determine the answer.

Analyze We divide the plastic into concentric elements of infinitesimal thickness dr (Fig. 27.8b). Use the differential form of Equation 27.10, replacing ℓ with r for the distance variable: $dR = \rho\, dr/A$, where dR is the resistance of an element of plastic of thickness dr and surface area A. In this example, our representative element is a concentric hollow plastic cylinder of radius r, thickness dr, and length L as in Figure 27.8. Any charge passing from the inner to the outer conductor must move radially through this concentric element. The area through which this charge passes is $A = 2\pi rL$ (the curved surface area—circumference multiplied by length—of our hollow plastic cylinder of thickness dr).

Write an expression for the resistance of our hollow cylinder of plastic:

$$dR = \frac{\rho}{2\pi rL}\,dr$$

Integrate this expression from $r = a$ to $r = b$:

$$(1)\quad R = \int dR = \frac{\rho}{2\pi L}\int_a^b \frac{dr}{r} = \frac{\rho}{2\pi L}\ln\left(\frac{b}{a}\right)$$

Substitute the values given:

$$R = \frac{1.0 \times 10^{13}\ \Omega\cdot\text{m}}{2\pi(0.150\ \text{m})}\ln\left(\frac{1.75\ \text{cm}}{0.500\ \text{cm}}\right) = 1.33 \times 10^{13}\ \Omega$$

Finalize Let's compare this resistance to that of the inner copper conductor of the cable along the 15.0-cm length.

Use Equation 27.10 to find the resistance of the copper cylinder:

$$R = \rho\frac{\ell}{A} = (1.7 \times 10^{-8}\ \Omega\cdot\text{m})\left[\frac{0.150\ \text{m}}{\pi(5.00 \times 10^{-3}\ \text{m})^2}\right]$$

$$= 3.2 \times 10^{-5}\ \Omega$$

This resistance is 18 orders of magnitude smaller than the radial resistance. Therefore, almost all the current corresponds to charge moving along the length of the cable, with a very small fraction leaking in the radial direction.

What If? Suppose the coaxial cable is enlarged to twice the overall diameter with two possible choices: (1) the ratio b/a is held fixed or (2) the difference $b - a$ is held fixed. For which choice does the leakage current between the inner and outer conductors increase when the voltage is applied between them?

Answer For the current to increase, the resistance must decrease. For choice (1), in which b/a is held fixed, Equation (1) shows that the resistance is unaffected. For choice (2), we do not have an equation involving the difference $b - a$ to inspect. Looking at Figure 27.8b, however, we see that increasing b and a while holding the voltage constant results in charge flowing through the same thickness of plastic but through a larger area perpendicular to the flow. This larger area results in lower resistance and a higher current.

27.3 A Model for Electrical Conduction

In this section, we describe a classical model of electrical conduction in metals that was first proposed by Paul Drude (1863–1906) in 1900. This model leads to Ohm's law and shows that resistivity can be related to the motion of electrons in metals. Although the Drude model described here has limitations, it introduces concepts that are applied in more elaborate treatments.

Consider a conductor as a regular array of atoms plus a collection of free electrons, which are sometimes called *conduction* electrons. The conduction electrons, although bound to their respective atoms when the atoms are not part of a solid, become free when the atoms condense into a solid. In the absence of an electric field, the conduction electrons move in random directions through the conductor with average speeds on the order of 10^6 m/s (Active Fig. 27.3a). The situation is similar to the motion of gas molecules confined in a vessel. In fact, some scientists refer to conduction electrons in a metal as an *electron gas.*

When an electric field is applied, the free electrons drift slowly in a direction opposite that of the electric field (Active Fig. 27.3b), with an average drift speed v_d that is much smaller (typically 10^{-4} m/s) than their average speed between collisions (typically 10^6 m/s).

In our model, we make the following assumptions:

1. The electron's motion after a collision is independent of its motion before the collision.
2. The excess energy acquired by the electrons in the electric field is lost to the atoms of the conductor when the electrons and atoms collide.

With regard to assumption (2), the energy given up to the atoms increases their vibrational energy, which causes the temperature of the conductor to increase.

We are now in a position to derive an expression for the drift velocity. When a free electron of mass m_e and charge q $(= -e)$ is subjected to an electric field $\vec{\mathbf{E}}$, it experiences a force $\vec{\mathbf{F}} = q\vec{\mathbf{E}}$. The electron is a particle under a net force, and its acceleration can be found from Newton's second law, $\sum \vec{\mathbf{F}} = m\vec{\mathbf{a}}$:

$$\vec{\mathbf{a}} = \frac{\sum \vec{\mathbf{F}}}{m} = \frac{q\vec{\mathbf{E}}}{m_e} \tag{27.11}$$

Because the electric field is uniform, the electron's acceleration is constant, so the electron can be modeled as a particle under constant acceleration. If $\vec{\mathbf{v}}_i$ is the electron's initial velocity the instant after a collision (which occurs at a time defined as $t = 0$), the velocity of the electron at a very short time t later (immediately before the next collision occurs) is, from Equation 4.8,

$$\vec{\mathbf{v}}_f = \vec{\mathbf{v}}_i + \vec{\mathbf{a}}t = \vec{\mathbf{v}}_i + \frac{q\vec{\mathbf{E}}}{m_e}t \tag{27.12}$$

Let's now take the average value of $\vec{\mathbf{v}}_f$ for all the electrons in the wire over all possible collision times t and all possible values of $\vec{\mathbf{v}}_i$. Assuming the initial velocities are randomly distributed over all possible values, the average value of $\vec{\mathbf{v}}_i$ is zero. The average value of the second term of Equation 27.12 is $(q\vec{\mathbf{E}}/m_e)\tau$, where τ is the *average time interval between successive collisions.* Because the average value of $\vec{\mathbf{v}}_f$ is equal to the drift velocity,

$$\vec{\mathbf{v}}_{f,\text{avg}} = \vec{\mathbf{v}}_d = \frac{q\vec{\mathbf{E}}}{m_e}\tau \tag{27.13}$$

◀ Drift velocity in terms of microscopic quantities

The value of τ depends on the size of the metal atoms and the number of electrons per unit volume. We can relate this expression for drift velocity in Equation 27.13 to the current in the conductor. Substituting the magnitude of the velocity from Equation 27.13 into Equation 27.5, the current density becomes

$$J = nqv_d = \frac{nq^2E}{m_e}\tau \tag{27.14}$$

◀ Current density in terms of microscopic quantities

where n is the number of electrons per unit volume. Comparing this expression with Ohm's law, $J = \sigma E$, we obtain the following relationships for conductivity and resistivity of a conductor:

$$\sigma = \frac{nq^2\tau}{m_e} \tag{27.15}$$

◀ Conductivity in terms of microscopic quantities

Resistivity in terms of microscopic quantities ▶

$$\rho = \frac{1}{\sigma} = \frac{m_e}{nq^2\tau} \tag{27.16}$$

According to this classical model, conductivity and resistivity do not depend on the strength of the electric field. This feature is characteristic of a conductor obeying Ohm's law.

27.4 Resistance and Temperature

Over a limited temperature range, the resistivity of a conductor varies approximately linearly with temperature according to the expression

Variation of ρ with temperature ▶

$$\rho = \rho_0[1 + \alpha(T - T_0)] \tag{27.17}$$

where ρ is the resistivity at some temperature T (in degrees Celsius), ρ_0 is the resistivity at some reference temperature T_0 (usually taken to be 20°C), and α is the **temperature coefficient of resistivity.** From Equation 27.17, the temperature coefficient of resistivity can be expressed as

Temperature coefficient of resistivity ▶

$$\alpha = \frac{1}{\rho_0}\frac{\Delta\rho}{\Delta T} \tag{27.18}$$

where $\Delta\rho = \rho - \rho_0$ is the change in resistivity in the temperature interval $\Delta T = T - T_0$.

The temperature coefficients of resistivity for various materials are given in Table 27.2. Notice that the unit for α is degrees Celsius^{-1} [$(°\text{C})^{-1}$]. Because resistance is proportional to resistivity (Eq. 27.10), the variation of resistance of a sample is

$$R = R_0[1 + \alpha(T - T_0)] \tag{27.19}$$

where R_0 is the resistance at temperature T_0. Use of this property enables precise temperature measurements through careful monitoring of the resistance of a probe made from a particular material.

For some metals such as copper, resistivity is nearly proportional to temperature as shown in Figure 27.9. A nonlinear region always exists at very low temperatures, however, and the resistivity usually reaches some finite value as the temperature approaches absolute zero. This residual resistivity near absolute zero is caused primarily by the collision of electrons with impurities and imperfections in the metal. In contrast, high-temperature resistivity (the linear region) is predominantly characterized by collisions between electrons and metal atoms.

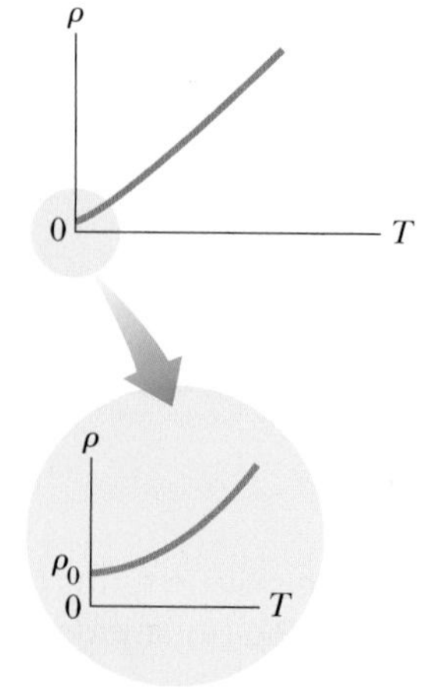

Figure 27.9 Resistivity versus temperature for a metal such as copper. The curve is linear over a wide range of temperatures, and ρ increases with increasing temperature. As T approaches absolute zero (inset), the resistivity approaches a finite value ρ_0.

Notice that three of the α values in Table 27.2 are negative, indicating that the resistivity of these materials decreases with increasing temperature. This behavior is indicative of a class of materials called *semiconductors*, first introduced in Section 23.2, and is due to an increase in the density of charge carriers at higher temperatures.

Because the charge carriers in a semiconductor are often associated with impurity atoms, the resistivity of these materials is very sensitive to the type and concentration of such impurities.

Quick Quiz 27.4 When does a lightbulb carry more current, (a) immediately after it is turned on and the glow of the metal filament is increasing or (b) after it has been on for a few milliseconds and the glow is steady?

27.5 Superconductors

There is a class of metals and compounds whose resistance decreases to zero when they are below a certain temperature T_c, known as the **critical temperature.** These materials are known as **superconductors.** The resistance–temperature graph for a superconductor follows that of a normal metal at temperatures above T_c (Fig. 27.10).

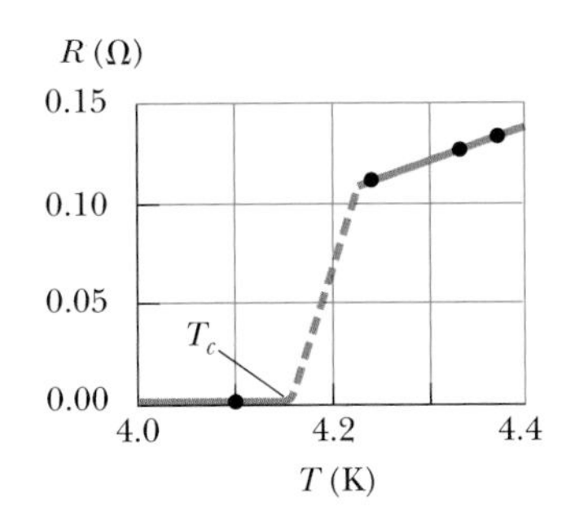

Figure 27.10 Resistance versus temperature for a sample of mercury (Hg). The graph follows that of a normal metal above the critical temperature T_c. The resistance drops to zero at T_c, which is 4.2 K for mercury.

TABLE 27.3

Critical Temperatures for Various Superconductors

Material	T_c (K)
$HgBa_2Ca_2Cu_3O_8$	134
Tl—Ba—Ca—Cu—O	125
Bi—Sr—Ca—Cu—O	105
$YBa_2Cu_3O_7$	92
Nb_3Ge	23.2
Nb_3Sn	18.05
Nb	9.46
Pb	7.18
Hg	4.15
Sn	3.72
Al	1.19
Zn	0.88

Courtesy of IBM Research Laboratory

A small permanent magnet levitated above a disk of the superconductor $YBa_2Cu_3O_7$, which is in liquid nitrogen at 77 K.

When the temperature is at or below T_c, the resistivity drops suddenly to zero. This phenomenon was discovered in 1911 by Dutch physicist Heike Kamerlingh-Onnes (1853–1926) as he worked with mercury, which is a superconductor below 4.2 K. Measurements have shown that the resistivities of superconductors below their T_c values are less than $4 \times 10^{-25}\ \Omega \cdot \text{m}$, or approximately 10^{17} times smaller than the resistivity of copper. In practice, these resistivities are considered to be zero.

Today, thousands of superconductors are known, and as Table 27.3 illustrates, the critical temperatures of recently discovered superconductors are substantially higher than initially thought possible. Two kinds of superconductors are recognized. The more recently identified ones are essentially ceramics with high critical temperatures, whereas superconducting materials such as those observed by Kamerlingh-Onnes are metals. If a room-temperature superconductor is ever identified, its effect on technology could be tremendous.

The value of T_c is sensitive to chemical composition, pressure, and molecular structure. Copper, silver, and gold, which are excellent conductors, do not exhibit superconductivity.

One truly remarkable feature of superconductors is that once a current is set up in them, it persists *without any applied potential difference* (because $R = 0$). Steady currents have been observed to persist in superconducting loops for several years with no apparent decay!

An important and useful application of superconductivity is in the development of superconducting magnets, in which the magnitudes of the magnetic field are approximately ten times greater than those produced by the best normal electromagnets. Such superconducting magnets are being considered as a means of storing energy. Superconducting magnets are currently used in medical magnetic resonance imaging, or MRI, units, which produce high-quality images of internal organs without the need for excessive exposure of patients to x-rays or other harmful radiation.

27.6 Electrical Power

In typical electric circuits, energy is transferred from a source such as a battery, to some device such as a lightbulb or a radio receiver. Let's determine an expression that will allow us to calculate the rate of this energy transfer. First, consider the simple circuit in Active Figure 27.11 (page 764), where energy is delivered to a resistor. (Resistors are designated by the circuit symbol —WW—.) Because

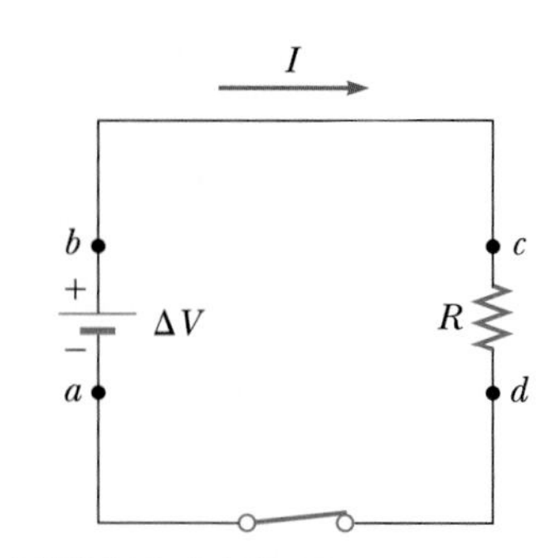

ACTIVE FIGURE 27.11

A circuit consisting of a resistor of resistance R and a battery having a potential difference ΔV across its terminals. Positive charge flows in the clockwise direction.

Sign in at www.thomsonedu.com and go to ThomsonNOW to adjust the battery voltage and the resistance and see the resulting current in the circuit and power delivered to the resistor.

PITFALL PREVENTION 27.5

Charges Do Not Move All the Way Around a Circuit in a Short Time

Because of the very small magnitude of the drift velocity, it might take *hours* for a single electron to make one complete trip around the circuit. In terms of understanding the energy transfer in a circuit, however, it is useful to *imagine* a charge moving all the way around the circuit.

PITFALL PREVENTION 27.6

Misconceptions About Current

Several common misconceptions are associated with current in a circuit like that in Active Figure 27.11. One is that current comes out of one terminal of the battery and is then "used up" as it passes through the resistor, leaving current in only one part of the circuit. The current is actually the same *everywhere* in the circuit. A related misconception has the current coming out of the resistor being smaller than that going in because some of the current is "used up." Yet another misconception has current coming out of both terminals of the battery, in opposite directions, and then "clashing" in the resistor, delivering the energy in this manner. That is not the case; charges flow in the same rotational sense at *all* points in the circuit.

the connecting wires also have resistance, some energy is delivered to the wires and some to the resistor. Unless noted otherwise, we shall assume the resistance of the wires is small compared with the resistance of the circuit element so that the energy delivered to the wires is negligible.

Imagine following a positive quantity of charge Q moving clockwise around the circuit in Active Figure 27.11 from point a through the battery and resistor back to point a. We identify the entire circuit as our system. As the charge moves from a to b through the battery, the electric potential energy of the system *increases* by an amount $Q\,\Delta V$ while the chemical potential energy in the battery *decreases* by the same amount. (Recall from Eq. 25.3 that $\Delta U = q\,\Delta V$.) As the charge moves from c to d through the resistor, however, the system *loses* this electric potential energy during collisions of electrons with atoms in the resistor. In this process, the energy is transformed to internal energy corresponding to increased vibrational motion of the atoms in the resistor. Because the resistance of the interconnecting wires is neglected, no energy transformation occurs for paths bc and da. When the charge returns to point a, the net result is that some of the chemical energy in the battery has been delivered to the resistor and resides in the resistor as internal energy associated with molecular vibration.

The resistor is normally in contact with air, so its increased temperature results in a transfer of energy by heat into the air. In addition, the resistor emits thermal radiation, representing another means of escape for the energy. After some time interval has passed, the resistor reaches a constant temperature. At this time, the input of energy from the battery is balanced by the output of energy from the resistor by heat and radiation. Some electrical devices include *heat sinks*[4] connected to parts of the circuit to prevent these parts from reaching dangerously high temperatures. Heat sinks are pieces of metal with many fins. Because the metal's high thermal conductivity provides a rapid transfer of energy by heat away from the hot component and the large number of fins provides a large surface area in contact with the air, energy can transfer by radiation and into the air by heat at a high rate.

Let's now investigate the rate at which the system loses electric potential energy as the charge Q passes through the resistor:

$$\frac{dU}{dt} = \frac{d}{dt}(Q\,\Delta V) = \frac{dQ}{dt}\Delta V = I\,\Delta V$$

where I is the current in the circuit. The system regains this potential energy when the charge passes through the battery, at the expense of chemical energy in the battery. The rate at which the system loses potential energy as the charge passes through the resistor is equal to the rate at which the system gains internal energy in the resistor. Therefore, the power $\mathcal{P}$, representing the rate at which energy is delivered to the resistor, is

$$\mathcal{P} = I\,\Delta V \qquad \textbf{(27.20)}$$

We derived this result by considering a battery delivering energy to a resistor. Equation 27.20, however, can be used to calculate the power delivered by a voltage source to *any* device carrying a current I and having a potential difference ΔV between its terminals.

Using Equation 27.20 and $\Delta V = IR$ for a resistor, we can express the power delivered to the resistor in the alternative forms

$$\mathcal{P} = I^2R = \frac{(\Delta V)^2}{R} \qquad \textbf{(27.21)}$$

[4] This usage is another misuse of the word *heat* that is ingrained in our common language.

When I is expressed in amperes, ΔV in volts, and R in ohms, the SI unit of power is the watt, as it was in Chapter 8 in our discussion of mechanical power. The process by which power is lost as internal energy in a conductor of resistance R is often called *joule heating*;[5] this transformation is also often referred to as an I^2R loss.

When transporting energy by electricity through power lines such as those shown in the opening photograph for this chapter, you should not assume that the lines have zero resistance. Real power lines do indeed have resistance, and power is delivered to the resistance of these wires. Utility companies seek to minimize the energy transformed to internal energy in the lines and maximize the energy delivered to the consumer. Because $\mathcal{P} = I\,\Delta V$, the same amount of energy can be transported either at high currents and low potential differences or at low currents and high potential differences. Utility companies choose to transport energy at low currents and high potential differences primarily for economic reasons. Copper wire is very expensive, so it is cheaper to use high-resistance wire (that is, wire having a small cross-sectional area; see Eq. 27.10). Therefore, in the expression for the power delivered to a resistor, $\mathcal{P} = I^2R$, the resistance of the wire is fixed at a relatively high value for economic considerations. The I^2R loss can be reduced by keeping the current I as low as possible, which means transferring the energy at a high voltage. In some instances, power is transported at potential differences as great as 765 kV. At the destination of the energy, the potential difference is usually reduced to 4 kV by a device called a *transformer.* Another transformer drops the potential difference to 240 V for use in your home. Of course, each time the potential difference decreases, the current increases by the same factor and the power remains the same. We shall discuss transformers in greater detail in Chapter 33.

PITFALL PREVENTION 27.7

Energy Is Not "Dissipated"

In some books, you may see Equation 27.21 described as the power "dissipated in" a resistor, suggesting that energy disappears. Instead, we say energy is "delivered to" a resistor. The notion of *dissipation* arises because a warm resistor expels energy by radiation and heat, so energy delivered by the battery leaves the circuit. (It does not disappear!)

Quick Quiz 27.5 For the two lightbulbs shown in Figure 27.12, rank the current values at points a through f from greatest to least.

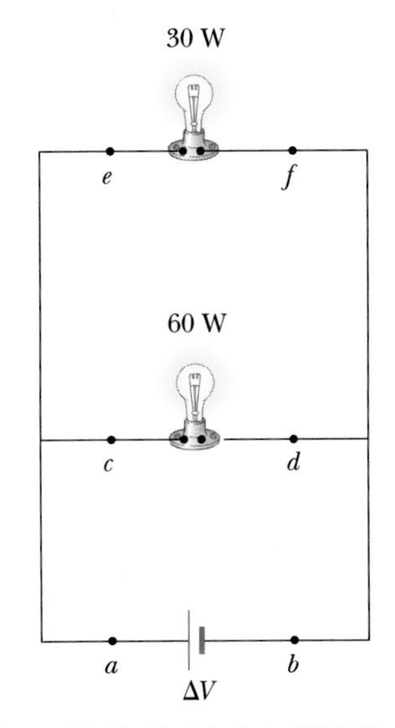

Figure 27.12 (Quick Quiz 27.5) Two lightbulbs connected across the same potential difference.

EXAMPLE 27.4 Power in an Electric Heater

An electric heater is constructed by applying a potential difference of 120 V across a Nichrome wire that has a total resistance of 8.00 Ω. Find the current carried by the wire and the power rating of the heater.

SOLUTION

Conceptualize As discussed in Example 27.2, Nichrome wire has high resistivity and is often used for heating elements in toasters, irons, and electric heaters. Therefore, we expect the power delivered to the wire to be relatively high.

Categorize We evaluate the power from Equation 27.21, so we categorize this example as a substitution problem.

Use Equation 27.7 to find the current in the wire:

$$I = \frac{\Delta V}{R} = \frac{120\ \text{V}}{8.00\ \Omega} = 15.0\ \text{A}$$

Find the power rating using the expression $\mathcal{P} = I^2R$ from Equation 27.21:

$$\mathcal{P} = I^2R = (15.0\ \text{A})^2(8.00\ \Omega) = 1.80 \times 10^3\ \text{W} = 1.80\ \text{kW}$$

What If? What if the heater were accidentally connected to a 240-V supply? (That is difficult to do because the shape and orientation of the metal contacts in 240-V plugs are different from those in 120-V plugs.) How would that affect the current carried by the heater and the power rating of the heater?

[5] It is commonly called *joule heating* even though the process of heat does not occur when energy delivered to a resistor appears as internal energy. This is another example of incorrect usage of the word *heat* that has become entrenched in our language.

Answer If the applied potential difference were doubled, Equation 27.7 shows that the current would double. According to Equation 27.21, $\mathcal{P} = (\Delta V)^2/R$, the power would be four times larger.

EXAMPLE 27.5 Linking Electricity and Thermodynamics

An immersion heater must increase the temperature of 1.50 kg of water from 10.0°C to 50.0°C in 10.0 min while operating at 110 V.

(A) What is the required resistance of the heater?

SOLUTION

Conceptualize An immersion heater is a resistor that is inserted into a container of water. As energy is delivered to the immersion heater, raising its temperature, energy leaves the surface of the resistor by heat, going into the water. When the immersion heater reaches a constant temperature, the rate of energy delivered to the resistance by electrical transmission is equal to the rate of energy delivered by heat to the water.

Categorize This example allows us to link our new understanding of power in electricity with our experience with specific heat in thermodynamics (Chapter 20). The water is a nonisolated system. Its internal energy is rising because of energy transferred into the water by heat from the resistor: $\Delta E_{\text{int}} = Q$. In our model, we assume the energy that enters the water from the heater remains in the water.

Analyze To simplify the analysis, let's ignore the initial period during which the temperature of the resistor increases and also ignore any variation of resistance with temperature. Therefore, we imagine a constant rate of energy transfer for the entire 10.0 min.

Set the rate of energy delivered to the resistor equal to the rate of energy Q entering the water by heat:

$$\mathcal{P} = \frac{(\Delta V)^2}{R} = \frac{Q}{\Delta t}$$

Use Equation 20.4, $Q = mc\,\Delta T$, to relate the energy input by heat to the resulting temperature change of the water and solve for the resistance:

$$\frac{(\Delta V)^2}{R} = \frac{mc\,\Delta T}{\Delta t} \quad \rightarrow \quad R = \frac{(\Delta V)^2 \Delta t}{mc\,\Delta T}$$

Substitute the values given in the statement of the problem:

$$R = \frac{(110\text{ V})^2(600\text{ s})}{(1.50\text{ kg})(4\,186\text{ J/kg}\cdot{}^\circ\text{C})(50.0^\circ\text{C} - 10.0^\circ\text{C})} = 28.9\ \Omega$$

(B) Estimate the cost of heating the water.

SOLUTION

Multiply the power by the time interval to find the amount of energy transferred:

$$\mathcal{P}\,\Delta t = \frac{(\Delta V)^2}{R}\Delta t = \frac{(110\text{ V})^2}{28.9\ \Omega}(10.0\text{ min})\left(\frac{1\text{ h}}{60.0\text{ min}}\right)$$

$$= 69.8\text{ Wh} = 0.069\,8\text{ kWh}$$

Find the cost knowing that energy is purchased at an estimated price of 10¢ per kilowatt-hour:

$$\text{Cost} = (0.069\,8\text{ kWh})(\$0.1/\text{kWh}) = \$0.007 = 0.7¢$$

Finalize The cost to heat the water is very low, less than one cent. In reality, the cost is higher because some energy is transferred from the water into the surroundings by heat and electromagnetic radiation while its temperature is increasing. If you have electrical devices in your home with power ratings on them, use this power rating and an approximate time interval of use to estimate the cost for one use of the device.

Summary

ThomsonNOW™ Sign in at **www.thomsonedu.com** and go to ThomsonNOW to take a practice test for this chapter.

DEFINITIONS

The electric **current** I in a conductor is defined as

$$I \equiv \frac{dQ}{dt} \qquad (27.2)$$

where dQ is the charge that passes through a cross section of the conductor in a time interval dt. The SI unit of current is the **ampere** (A), where 1 A = 1 C/s.

The **current density** J in a conductor is the current per unit area:

$$J \equiv \frac{I}{A} \qquad (27.5)$$

The **resistance** R of a conductor is defined as

$$R \equiv \frac{\Delta V}{I} \qquad (27.7)$$

where ΔV is the potential difference across it and I is the current it carries. The SI unit of resistance is volts per ampere, which is defined to be 1 **ohm** (Ω); that is, $1\ \Omega = 1\ \text{V/A}$.

CONCEPTS AND PRINCIPLES

The average current in a conductor is related to the motion of the charge carriers through the relationship

$$I_{\text{avg}} = nqv_dA \qquad (27.4)$$

where n is the density of charge carriers, q is the charge on each carrier, v_d is the drift speed, and A is the cross-sectional area of the conductor.

The current density in an ohmic conductor is proportional to the electric field according to the expression

$$J = \sigma E \qquad (27.6)$$

The proportionality constant σ is called the **conductivity** of the material of which the conductor is made. The inverse of σ is known as **resistivity** ρ (that is, $\rho = 1/\sigma$). Equation 27.6 is known as **Ohm's law,** and a material is said to obey this law if the ratio of its current density to its applied electric field is a constant that is independent of the applied field.

For a uniform block of material of cross-sectional area A and length ℓ, the resistance over the length ℓ is

$$R = \rho\frac{\ell}{A} \qquad (27.10)$$

where ρ is the resistivity of the material.

In a classical model of electrical conduction in metals, the electrons are treated as molecules of a gas. In the absence of an electric field, the average velocity of the electrons is zero. When an electric field is applied, the electrons move (on average) with a **drift velocity** $\vec{\mathbf{v}}_d$ that is opposite the electric field. The drift velocity is given by

$$\vec{\mathbf{v}}_d = \frac{q\vec{\mathbf{E}}}{m_e}\tau \qquad (27.13)$$

where q is the electron's charge, m_e is the mass of the electron, and τ is the average time interval between electron–atom collisions. According to this model, the resistivity of the metal is

$$\rho = \frac{m_e}{nq^2\tau} \qquad (27.16)$$

where n is the number of free electrons per unit volume.

The resistivity of a conductor varies approximately linearly with temperature according to the expression

$$\rho = \rho_0[1 + \alpha(T - T_0)] \qquad (27.17)$$

where ρ_0 is the resistivity at some reference temperature T_0 and α is the **temperature coefficient of resistivity.**

If a potential difference ΔV is maintained across a circuit element, the **power,** or rate at which energy is supplied to the element, is

$$\mathcal{P} = I\Delta V \qquad (27.20)$$

Because the potential difference across a resistor is given by $\Delta V = IR$, we can express the power delivered to a resistor as

$$\mathcal{P} = I^2R = \frac{(\Delta V)^2}{R} \qquad (27.21)$$

The energy delivered to a resistor by electrical transmission appears in the form of internal energy in the resistor.

Questions

☐ denotes answer available in *Student Solutions Manual/Study Guide;* **O** denotes objective question

1. Newspaper articles often contain a statement such as "10 000 volts of electricity surged through the victim's body." What is wrong with this statement?

2. What factors affect the resistance of a conductor?

3. **O** Two wires A and B with circular cross sections are made of the same metal and have equal lengths, but the resistance of wire A is three times greater than that of wire B. **(i)** What is the ratio of the cross-sectional area of A to that of B? (a) 9 (b) 3 (c) $\sqrt{3}$ (d) 1 (e) $1/\sqrt{3}$ (f) $\frac{1}{3}$ (g) $\frac{1}{9}$ (h) None of these answers is necessarily true. **(ii)** What is the ratio of the radius of A to that of B? Choose from the same possibilities.

4. **O** A metal wire of resistance R is cut into three equal pieces that are then braided together side by side to form a new cable with a length equal to one-third the original length. What is the resistance of this new wire? (a) $R/27$ (b) $R/9$ (c) $R/3$ (d) R (e) $3R$ (f) $9R$ (g) $27R$

5. When the potential difference across a certain conductor is doubled, the current is observed to increase by a factor of three. What can you conclude about the conductor?

6. Use the atomic theory of matter to explain why the resistance of a material should increase as its temperature increases.

7. **O** A current-carrying ohmic metal wire has a cross-sectional area that gradually becomes smaller from one end of the wire to the other. The current has the same value for each section of the wire, so charge does not accumulate at any one point. **(i)** How does the drift speed vary along the wire as the area becomes smaller? (a) It increases. (b) It decreases. (c) It remains constant. **(ii)** How does the resistance per unit length vary along the wire as the area becomes smaller? Choose from the same possibilities.

8. How does the resistance for copper and for silicon change with temperature? Why are the behaviors of these two materials different?

9. Over the time interval after a difference in potential is applied between the ends of a wire, what would happen to the drift velocity of the electrons in a wire and to the current in the wire if the electrons could move freely without resistance through the wire?

10. If charges flow very slowly through a metal, why does it not require several hours for a light to come on when you throw a switch?

11. **O** A cylindrical metal wire at room temperature is carrying electric current between its ends. One end is at potential $V_A = 50$ V, and the other end at potential $V_B = 0$ V. Rank the following actions in terms of the change that each one separately would produce in the current, from the greatest increase to the greatest decrease. In your ranking, note any cases of equality. (a) Make $V_A = 150$ V with $V_B = 0$ V. (b) Make $V_A = 150$ V with $V_B = 100$ V. (c) Adjust V_A to triple the power with which the wire converts electrically transmitted energy into internal energy. (d) Double the radius of the wire. (e) Double the length of the wire. (f) Double the Celsius temperature of the wire. (g) Change the material to an insulator.

12. **O** Two conductors made of the same material are connected across the same potential difference. Conductor A has twice the diameter and twice the length of conductor B. What is the ratio of the power delivered to A to the power delivered to B? (a) 32 (b) 16 (c) 8 (d) 4 (e) 2 (f) 1 (g) $\frac{1}{2}$ (h) $\frac{1}{4}$

13. **O** Two conducting wires A and B of the same length and radius are connected across the same potential difference. Conductor A has twice the resistivity of conductor B. What is the ratio of the power delivered to A to the power delivered to B? (a) 4 (b) 2 (c) $\sqrt{2}$ (d) 1 (e) $1/\sqrt{2}$ (f) $\frac{1}{2}$ (g) $\frac{1}{4}$ (h) None of these answers is necessarily correct.

14. **O** Two lightbulbs both operate from 120 V. One has a power of 25 W and the other 100 W. **(i)** Which lightbulb has higher resistance? (a) The dim 25-W lightbulb does. (b) The bright 100-W lightbulb does. (c) Both are the same. **(ii)** Which lightbulb carries more current? Choose from the same possibilities.

15. **O** Car batteries are often rated in ampere-hours. Does this information designate the amount of (a) current, (b) power, (c) energy, (d) charge, or (e) potential that the battery can supply?

16. If you were to design an electric heater using Nichrome wire as the heating element, what parameters of the wire could you vary to meet a specific power output such as 1 000 W?

Problems

WebAssign The Problems from this chapter may be assigned online in WebAssign.

ThomsonNOW Sign in at **www.thomsonedu.com** and go to ThomsonNOW to assess your understanding of this chapter's topics with additional quizzing and conceptual questions.

1, 2, 3 denotes straightforward, intermediate, challenging; ☐ denotes full solution available in *Student Solutions Manual/Study Guide;* ▲ denotes coached solution with hints available at **www.thomsonedu.com;** denotes developing symbolic reasoning; ● denotes asking for qualitative reasoning; denotes computer useful in solving problem

Section 27.1 Electric Current

1. In a particular cathode-ray tube, the measured beam current is 30.0 μA. How many electrons strike the tube screen every 40.0 s?

2. A teapot with a surface area of 700 cm^2 is to be plated with silver. It is attached to the negative electrode of an electrolytic cell containing silver nitrate ($Ag^+ NO_3^-$). The cell is powered by a 12.0-V battery and has a resistance of 1.80 Ω. Over what time interval does a 0.133-mm layer of silver build up on the teapot? (The density of silver is 10.5×10^3 kg/m^3.)

3. ▲ Suppose the current in a conductor decreases exponentially with time according to the equation $I(t) = I_0 e^{-t/\tau}$, where I_0 is the initial current (at $t = 0$) and τ is a constant having dimensions of time. Consider a fixed observation point within the conductor. (a) How much charge passes this point between $t = 0$ and $t = \tau$? (b) How much charge passes this point between $t = 0$ and $t = 10\tau$? (c) **What If?** How much charge passes this point between $t = 0$ and $t = \infty$?

4. A small sphere that carries a charge q is whirled in a circle at the end of an insulating string. The angular frequency of rotation is ω. What average current does this rotating charge represent?

5. The quantity of charge q (in coulombs) that has passed through a surface of area 2.00 cm^2 varies with time according to the equation $q = 4t^3 + 5t + 6$, where t is in seconds. (a) What is the instantaneous current through the surface at $t = 1.00$ s? (b) What is the value of the current density?

6. An electric current is given by the expression $I(t) = 100 \sin(120\pi t)$, where I is in amperes and t is in seconds. What is the total charge carried by the current from $t = 0$ to $t = \frac{1}{240}$ s?

7. The electron beam emerging from a certain high-energy electron accelerator has a circular cross section of radius 1.00 mm. (a) The beam current is 8.00 μA. Find the current density in the beam assuming it is uniform throughout. (b) The speed of the electrons is so close to the speed of light that their speed can be taken as 300 Mm/s with negligible error. Find the electron density in the beam. (c) Over what time interval does Avogadro's number of electrons emerge from the accelerator?

8. ● Figure P27.8 represents a section of a circular conductor of nonuniform diameter carrying a current of 5.00 A. The radius of cross-section A_1 is 0.400 cm. (a) What is the magnitude of the current density across A_1? (b) The radius at A_2 is larger than the radius at A_1. Is the current at A_2 larger, smaller, or the same? Is the current density larger, smaller, or the same? Assume one of these two quantities is different at A_2 by a factor of 4 from its value at A_1. Specify the current, current density, and radius at A_2.

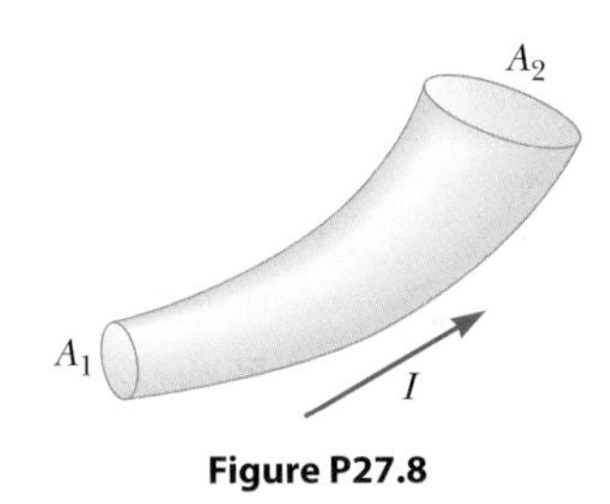

Figure P27.8

9. ● A Van de Graaff generator produces a beam of 2.00-MeV deuterons, which are heavy hydrogen nuclei containing a proton and a neutron. (a) If the beam current is 10.0 μA, how far apart are the deuterons? (b) Is the electrical force of repulsion among them a significant factor in beam stability? Explain.

10. An aluminum wire having a cross-sectional area of 4.00×10^{-6} m^2 carries a current of 5.00 A. Find the drift speed of the electrons in the wire. The density of aluminum is 2.70 g/cm^3. Assume each aluminum atom supplies one conduction electron.

Section 27.2 Resistance

11. ▲ A 0.900-V potential difference is maintained across a 1.50-m length of tungsten wire that has a cross-sectional area of 0.600 mm^2. What is the current in the wire?

12. A lightbulb has a resistance of 240 Ω when operating with a potential difference of 120 V across it. What is the current in the lightbulb?

13. Suppose you wish to fabricate a uniform wire from 1.00 g of copper. If the wire is to have a resistance of $R = 0.500$ Ω and all the copper is to be used, what must be (a) the length and (b) the diameter of this wire?

14. (a) Make an order-of-magnitude estimate of the resistance between the ends of a rubber band. (b) Make an order-of-magnitude estimate of the resistance between the "heads" and "tails" sides of a penny. In each case, state what quantities you take as data and the values you measure or estimate for them. (c) WARNING: Do not try this part at home! What is the order of magnitude of the current that each would carry if it were connected across a 120-V power supply?

15. A current density of 6.00×10^{-13} A/m^2 exists in the atmosphere at a location where the electric field is 100 V/m. Calculate the electrical conductivity of the Earth's atmosphere in this region.

Section 27.3 A Model for Electrical Conduction

16. ● If the current carried by a conductor is doubled, what happens to (a) the charge carrier density, (b) the current density, (c) the electron drift velocity, and (d) the average time interval between collisions? Explain your answers.

17. ▲ If the magnitude of the drift velocity of free electrons in a copper wire is 7.84×10^{-4} m/s, what is the electric field in the conductor?

Section 27.4 Resistance and Temperature

18. A certain lightbulb has a tungsten filament with a resistance of 19.0 Ω when cold and 140 Ω when hot. Assume the resistivity of tungsten varies linearly with temperature even over the large temperature range involved here. Find the temperature of the hot filament. Assume an initial temperature of 20.0°C.

19. An aluminum wire with a diameter of 0.100 mm has a uniform electric field of 0.200 V/m imposed along its entire length. The temperature of the wire is 50.0°C. Assume one free electron per atom. (a) Use the information in Table 27.2 and determine the resistivity. (b) What is the current density in the wire? (c) What is the total

current in the wire? (d) What is the drift speed of the conduction electrons? (e) What potential difference must exist between the ends of a 2.00-m length of the wire to produce the stated electric field?

20. An engineer needs a resistor with zero overall temperature coefficient of resistance at 20°C. She designs a pair of circular cylinders, one of carbon and one of Nichrome as shown in Figure P27.20. The device must have an overall resistance of $R_1 + R_2 = 10.0\ \Omega$ independent of temperature and a uniform radius of $r = 1.50$ mm. Can she meet the design goal with this method? If so, state what you can determine about the lengths ℓ_1 and ℓ_2 of each segment. You may ignore thermal expansion of the cylinders and assume both are always at the same temperature.

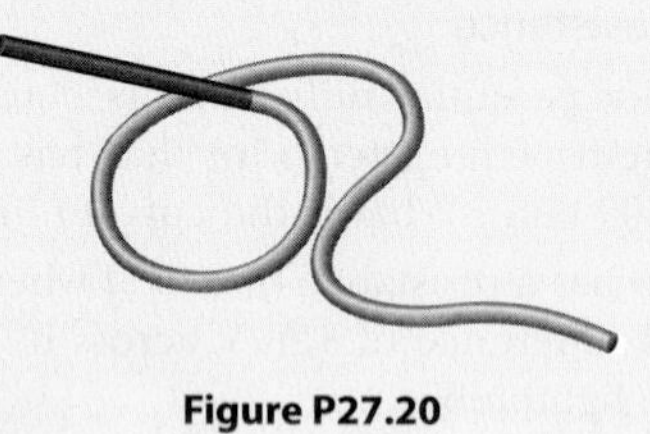

Figure P27.20

21. What is the fractional change in the resistance of an iron filament when its temperature changes from 25.0°C to 50.0°C?

22. **Review problem.** An aluminum rod has a resistance of 1.234 Ω at 20.0°C. Calculate the resistance of the rod at 120°C by accounting for the changes in both the resistivity and the dimensions of the rod.

Section 27.6 Electrical Power

23. A toaster is rated at 600 W when connected to a 120-V source. What current does the toaster carry and what is its resistance?

24. A Van de Graaff generator (see Fig. 25.24) is operating so that the potential difference between the high-potential electrode Ⓑ and the charging needles at Ⓐ is 15.0 kV. Calculate the power required to drive the belt against electrical forces at an instant when the effective current delivered to the high-potential electrode is 500 μA.

25. ▲ A well-insulated electric water heater warms 109 kg of water from 20.0°C to 49.0°C in 25.0 min. Find the resistance of its heating element, which is connected across a 220-V potential difference.

26. A 120-V motor has mechanical power output of 2.50 hp. It is 90.0% efficient in converting power that it takes in by electrical transmission into mechanical power. (a) Find the current in the motor. (b) Find the energy delivered to the motor by electrical transmission in 3.00 h of operation. (c) If the electric company charges \$0.160/kWh, what does it cost to run the motor for 3.00 h?

27. Suppose a voltage surge produces 140 V for a moment. By what percentage does the power output of a 120-V, 100-W lightbulb increase? Assume its resistance does not change.

28. One rechargeable battery of mass 15.0 g delivers an average current of 18.0 mA to a compact disc player at 1.60 V for 2.40 h before the battery needs to be recharged. The recharger maintains a potential difference of 2.30 V across the battery and delivers a charging current of 13.5 mA for 4.20 h. (a) What is the efficiency of the battery as an energy storage device? (b) How much internal energy is produced in the battery during one charge–discharge cycle? (b) If the battery is surrounded by ideal thermal insulation and has an overall effective specific heat of 975 J/kg · °C, by how much will its temperature increase during the cycle?

29. A 500-W heating coil designed to operate from 110 V is made of Nichrome wire 0.500 mm in diameter. (a) Assuming the resistivity of the Nichrome remains constant at its 20.0°C value, find the length of wire used. (b) **What If?** Now consider the variation of resistivity with temperature. What power is delivered to the coil of part (a) when it is warmed to 1 200°C?

30. A coil of Nichrome wire is 25.0 m long. The wire has a diameter of 0.400 mm and is at 20.0°C. If it carries a current of 0.500 A, what are (a) the magnitude of the electric field in the wire and (b) the power delivered to it? (c) **What If?** If the temperature is increased to 340°C and the potential difference across the wire remains constant, what is the power delivered?

31. Batteries are rated in terms of ampere-hours (A · h). For example, a battery that can produce a current of 2.00 A for 3.00 h is rated at 6.00 A · h. (a) What is the total energy, in kilowatt-hours, stored in a 12.0-V battery rated at 55.0 A · h? (b) At \$0.060 0 per kilowatt-hour, what is the value of the electricity produced by this battery?

32. ● Residential building codes typically require the use of 12-gauge copper wire (diameter 0.205 3 cm) for wiring receptacles. Such circuits carry currents as large as 20 A. If a wire of smaller diameter (with a higher gauge number) carried that much current, the wire could rise to a high temperature and cause a fire. (a) Calculate the rate at which internal energy is produced in 1.00 m of 12-gauge copper wire carrying 20.0 A. (b) **What If?** Repeat the calculation for an aluminum wire. Explain whether a 12-gauge aluminum wire would be as safe as a copper wire.

33. An 11.0-W energy-efficient fluorescent lamp is designed to produce the same illumination as a conventional 40.0-W incandescent lightbulb. How much money does the user of the energy-efficient lamp save during 100 h of use? Assume a cost of \$0.080 0/kWh for energy from the electric company.

34. We estimate that 270 million plug-in electric clocks are in the United States, approximately one clock for each person. The clocks convert energy at the average rate 2.50 W. To supply this energy, how many metric tons of coal are burned per hour in coal-fired power plants that are, on average, 25.0% efficient? The heat of combustion for coal is 33.0 MJ/kg.

35. Compute the cost per day of operating a lamp that draws a current of 1.70 A from a 110-V line. Assume the cost of energy from the electric company is \$0.060 0/kWh.

36. **Review problem.** The heating element of an electric coffee maker operates at 120 V and carries a current of 2.00 A. Assuming the water absorbs all the energy delivered to the resistor, calculate the time interval during which the temperature of 0.500 kg of water rises from room temperature (23.0°C) to the boiling point.

37. A certain toaster has a heating element made of Nichrome wire. When the toaster is first connected to a 120-V source (and the wire is at a temperature of 20.0°C),

the initial current is 1.80 A. The current decreases as the heating element warms up. When the toaster reaches its final operating temperature, the current is 1.53 A. (a) Find the power delivered to the toaster when it is at its operating temperature. (b) What is the final temperature of the heating element?

38. The cost of electricity varies widely through the United States; $0.120/kWh is one typical value. At this unit price, calculate the cost of (a) leaving a 40.0-W porch light on for two weeks while you are on vacation, (b) making a piece of dark toast in 3.00 min with a 970-W toaster, and (c) drying a load of clothes in 40.0 min in a 5 200-W dryer.

39. Make an order-of-magnitude estimate of the cost of one person's routine use of a handheld hair dryer for 1 yr. If you do not use a hair dryer yourself, observe or interview someone who does. State the quantities you estimate and their values.

Additional Problems

40. ● One lightbulb is marked "25 W 120 V," and another is marked "100 W 120 V." These labels mean that each lightbulb has its respective power delivered to it when it is connected to a constant 120-V source. (a) Find the resistance of each lightbulb. (b) During what time interval does 1.00 C pass into the dim lightbulb? Is this charge different upon its exit versus its entry into the lightbulb? Explain. (c) In what time interval does 1.00 J pass into the dim lightbulb? By what mechanisms does this energy enter and exit the lightbulb? Explain. (d) Find the cost of running the dim lightbulb continuously for 30.0 days, assuming the electric company sells its product at $0.070 0 per kWh. What product *does* the electric company sell? What is its price for one SI unit of this quantity?

41. An office worker uses an immersion heater to warm 250 g of water in a light, covered, insulated cup from 20°C to 100°C in 4.00 min. In electrical terms, the heater is a Nichrome resistance wire connected to a 120-V power supply. Specify a diameter and a length that the wire can have. Can it be made from less than 0.5 cm³ of Nichrome? You may assume the wire is at 100°C throughout the time interval.

42. A charge Q is placed on a capacitor of capacitance C. The capacitor is connected into the circuit shown in Figure P27.42, with an open switch, a resistor, and an initially uncharged capacitor of capacitance $3C$. The switch is then closed, and the circuit comes to equilibrium. In terms of Q and C, find (a) the final potential difference between the plates of each capacitor, (b) the charge on each capacitor, and (c) the final energy stored in each capacitor. (d) Find the internal energy appearing in the resistor.

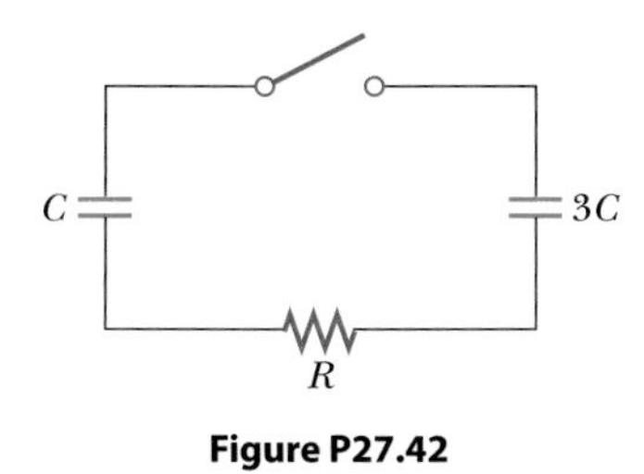

Figure P27.42

43. A more general definition of the temperature coefficient of resistivity is

$$\alpha = \frac{1}{\rho}\frac{d\rho}{dT}$$

where ρ is the resistivity at temperature T. (a) Assuming α is constant, show that

$$\rho = \rho_0 e^{\alpha(T-T_0)}$$

where ρ_0 is the resistivity at temperature T_0. (b) Using the series expansion $e^x \approx 1 + x$ for $x \ll 1$, show that the resistivity is given approximately by the expression $\rho = \rho_0[1 + \alpha(T - T_0)]$ for $\alpha(T - T_0) \ll 1$.

44. A high-voltage transmission line with a diameter of 2.00 cm and a length of 200 km carries a steady current of 1 000 A. If the conductor is copper wire with a free charge density of 8.46×10^{28} electrons/m³, over what time interval does one electron travel the full length of the line?

45. ▲ ● An experiment is conducted to measure the electrical resistivity of Nichrome in the form of wires with different lengths and cross-sectional areas. For one set of measurements, a student uses 30-gauge wire, which has a cross-sectional area of 7.30×10^{-8} m². The student measures the potential difference across the wire and the current in the wire with a voltmeter and an ammeter, respectively. For each set of measurements given in the table taken on wires of three different lengths, calculate the resistance of the wires and the corresponding values of the resistivity. What is the average value of the resistivity? Explain how this value compares with the value given in Table 27.2.

L (m)	ΔV (V)	I (A)	R (Ω)	ρ (Ω · m)
0.540	5.22	0.500		
1.028	5.82	0.276		
1.543	5.94	0.187		

46. An electric utility company supplies a customer's house from the main power lines (120 V) with two copper wires, each of which is 50.0 m long and has a resistance of 0.108 Ω per 300 m. (a) Find the potential difference at the customer's house for a load current of 110 A. For this load current, find (b) the power delivered to the customer and (c) the rate at which internal energy is produced in the copper wires.

47. A straight, cylindrical wire lying along the x axis has a length of 0.500 m and a diameter of 0.200 mm. It is made of a material described by Ohm's law with a resistivity of $\rho = 4.00 \times 10^{-8}$ Ω · m. Assume a potential of 4.00 V is maintained at $x = 0$. Also assume $V = 0$ at $x = 0.500$ m. Find (a) the electric field in the wire, (b) the resistance of the wire, (c) the electric current in the wire, and (d) the current density in the wire. State the direction of the electric field and of the current. (e) Show that $E = \rho J$.

48. A straight, cylindrical wire lying along the x axis has a length L and a diameter d. It is made of a material described by Ohm's law with a resistivity ρ. Assume potential V is maintained at $x = 0$. Also assume the potential is zero at $x = L$. In terms of L, d, V, ρ, and physical constants, derive expressions for (a) the electric field in the

wire, (b) the resistance of the wire, (c) the electric current in the wire, and (d) the current density in the wire. State the direction of the field and of the current. (e) Prove that $E = \rho J$.

49. An all-electric car (not a hybrid) is designed to run from a bank of 12.0-V batteries with total energy storage of 2.00×10^7 J. (a) If the electric motor draws 8.00 kW, what is the current delivered to the motor? (b) If the electric motor draws 8.00 kW as the car moves at a steady speed of 20.0 m/s, how far can the car travel before it is "out of juice"?

50. ● **Review problem.** When a straight wire is warmed, its resistance is given by $R = R_0\,[1 + \alpha\,(T - T_0)]$ according to Equation 27.19, where α is the temperature coefficient of resistivity. (a) Show that a more precise result, one that includes that the length and area of the wire change when it is warmed, is

$$R = \frac{R_0[1 + \alpha(T - T_0)][1 + \alpha'(T - T_0)]}{[1 + 2\alpha'(T - T_0)]}$$

where α' is the coefficient of linear expansion (see Chapter 19). (b) Explain how these two results compare for a 2.00-m-long copper wire of radius 0.100 mm, first at 20.0°C and then warmed to 100.0°C.

51. The temperature coefficients of resistivity in Table 27.2 were determined at a temperature of 20°C. What would they be at 0°C? Note that the temperature coefficient of resistivity at 20°C satisfies $\rho = \rho_0[1 + \alpha(T - T_0)]$, where ρ_0 is the resistivity of the material at $T_0 = 20$°C. The temperature coefficient of resistivity α' at 0°C must satisfy the expression $\rho = \rho'_0[1 + \alpha' T]$, where ρ'_0 is the resistivity of the material at 0°C.

52. An oceanographer is studying how the ion concentration in seawater depends on depth. She makes a measurement by lowering into the water a pair of concentric metallic cylinders (Fig. P27.52) at the end of a cable and taking data to determine the resistance between these electrodes as a function of depth. The water between the two cylinders forms a cylindrical shell of inner radius r_a, outer radius r_b, and length L much larger than r_b. The scientist applies a potential difference ΔV between the inner and outer surfaces, producing an outward radial current I. Let ρ represent the resistivity of the water. (a) Find the resistance of the water between the cylinders in terms of L, ρ, r_a, and r_b. (b) Express the resistivity of the water in terms of the measured quantities L, r_a, r_b, ΔV, and I.

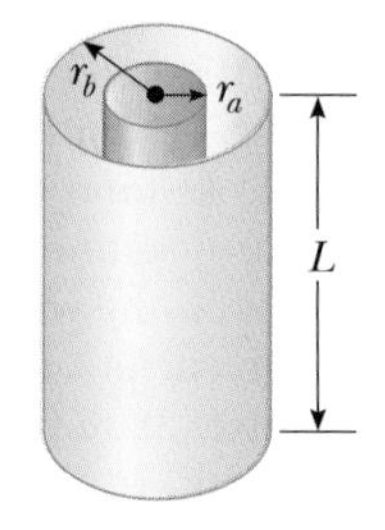

Figure P27.52

53. ● The strain in a wire can be monitored and computed by measuring the resistance of the wire. Let L_i represent the original length of the wire, A_i its original cross-sectional area, $R_i = \rho L_i/A_i$ the original resistance between its ends, and $\delta = \Delta L/L_i = (L - L_i)/L_i$ the strain resulting from the application of tension. Assume the resistivity and the volume of the wire do not change as the wire stretches. Show that the resistance between the ends of the wire under strain is given by $R = R_i(1 + 2\delta + \delta^2)$. If the assumptions are precisely true, is this result exact or approximate? Explain your answer.

54. ● In a certain stereo system, each speaker has a resistance of 4.00 Ω. The system is rated at 60.0 W in each channel, and each speaker circuit includes a fuse rated 4.00 A. Is this system adequately protected against overload? Explain your reasoning.

55. ● A close analogy exists between the flow of energy by heat because of a temperature difference (see Section 20.7) and the flow of electric charge because of a potential difference. In a metal, energy dQ and electrical charge dq are both transported by free electrons. Consequently, a good electrical conductor is usually a good thermal conductor as well. Consider a thin conducting slab of thickness dx, area A, and electrical conductivity σ, with a potential difference dV between opposite faces. (a) Show that the current $I = dq/dt$ is given by the equation on the left:

Charge conduction	Thermal conduction	
$\dfrac{dq}{dt} = \sigma A \left\lvert \dfrac{dV}{dx} \right\rvert$	$\dfrac{dQ}{dt} = kA \left\lvert \dfrac{dT}{dx} \right\rvert$	**(Eq. 20.15)**

In the analogous thermal conduction equation on the right, the rate of energy flow dQ/dt (in SI units of joules per second) is due to a temperature gradient dT/dx, in a material of thermal conductivity k. (b) State analogous rules relating the direction of the electric current to the change in potential and relating the direction of energy flow to the change in temperature.

56. A material of resistivity ρ is formed into the shape of a truncated cone of altitude h as shown in Figure P27.56. The bottom end has radius b, and the top end has radius a. Assume the current is distributed uniformly over any circular cross section of the cone so that the current density does not depend on radial position. (The current density does vary with position along the axis of the cone.) Show that the resistance between the two ends is

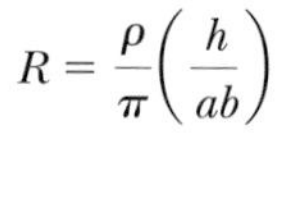

$$R = \frac{\rho}{\pi}\left(\frac{h}{ab}\right)$$

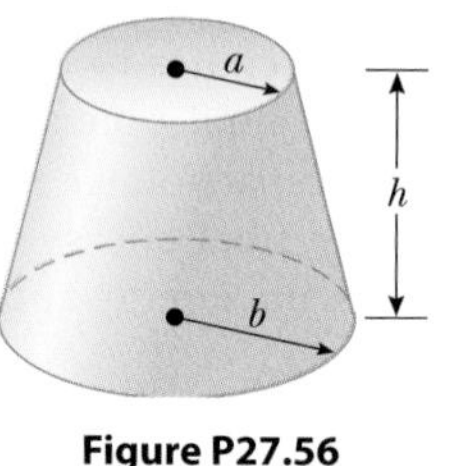

Figure P27.56

57. Material with uniform resistivity ρ is formed into a wedge as shown in Figure P27.57. Show that the resistance between face A and face B of this wedge is

$$R = \rho\,\frac{L}{w(y_2 - y_1)}\,\ln\left(\frac{y_2}{y_1}\right)$$

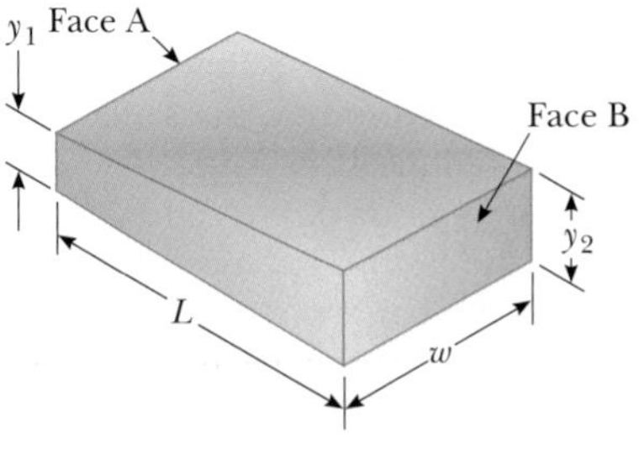

Figure P27.57

58. A spherical shell with inner radius r_a and outer radius r_b is formed from a material of resistivity ρ. It carries current radially, with uniform density in all directions. Show that its resistance is

$$R = \frac{\rho}{4\pi}\left(\frac{1}{r_a} - \frac{1}{r_b}\right)$$

59. ● Problems 56, 57, and 58 deal with calculating the resistance between specified surfaces of an oddly shaped resistor. To verify the results experimentally, a potential difference may be applied to the indicated surfaces and the resulting current measured. The resistance can then be calculated from its definition. Describe a method to ensure that the electric potential is uniform over the surface. Explain whether you can then be sure that the current is spread out over the whole surfaces where it enters and exits.

60. The dielectric material between the plates of a parallel-plate capacitor always has some nonzero conductivity σ. Let A represent the area of each plate and d the distance between them. Let κ represent the dielectric constant of the material. (a) Show that the resistance R and the capacitance C of the capacitor are related by

$$RC = \frac{\kappa \epsilon_0}{\sigma}$$

(b) Find the resistance between the plates of a 14.0-nF capacitor with a fused quartz dielectric.

61. **Review problem.** A parallel-plate capacitor consists of square plates of edge length ℓ that are separated by a distance d, where $d \ll \ell$. A potential difference ΔV is maintained between the plates. A material of dielectric constant κ fills half the space between the plates. The dielectric slab is withdrawn from the capacitor as shown in Figure P27.61. (a) Find the capacitance when the left edge of the dielectric is at a distance x from the center of the capacitor. (b) If the dielectric is removed at a constant speed v, what is the current in the circuit as the dielectric is being withdrawn?

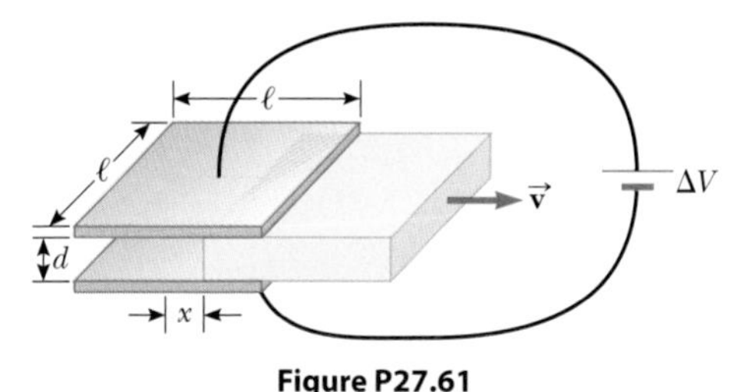

Figure P27.61

62. The current–voltage characteristic curve for a semiconductor diode as a function of temperature T is given by

$$I = I_0(e^{e\Delta V/k_B T} - 1)$$

Here the first symbol e represents Euler's number, the base of natural logarithms. The second e is the magnitude of the electron charge. The k_B stands for Boltzmann's constant, and T is the absolute temperature. Set up a spreadsheet to calculate I and $R = \Delta V/I$ for $\Delta V = 0.400$ V to 0.600 V in increments of 0.005 V. Assume $I_0 = 1.00$ nA. Plot R versus ΔV for $T = 280$ K, 300 K, and 320 K.

63. Gold is the most ductile of all metals. For example, one gram of gold can be drawn into a wire 2.40 km long. What is the resistance of such a wire at 20°C? You can find the necessary reference information in this textbook.

64. One wire in a high-voltage transmission line carries 1 000 A starting at 700 kV for a distance of 100 mi. If the resistance in the wire is 0.500 Ω/mi, what is the power loss due to the resistance of the wire?

65. The potential difference across the filament of a lamp is maintained at a constant value while equilibrium temperature is being reached. It is observed that the steady-state current in the lamp is only one tenth of the current drawn by the lamp when it is first turned on. If the temperature coefficient of resistivity for the lamp at 20.0°C is 0.004 50 $(°C)^{-1}$ and the resistance increases linearly with increasing temperature, what is the final operating temperature of the filament?

Answers to Quick Quizzes

27.1 (d), (b) = (c), (a). The current in part (d) is equivalent to two positive charges moving to the left. Parts (b) and (c) each represent four positive charges moving in the same direction because negative charges moving to the left are equivalent to positive charges moving to the right. The current in part (a) is equivalent to five positive charges moving to the right.

27.2 (b). The doubling of the radius causes the area A to be four times as large, so Equation 27.10 tells us that the resistance decreases.

27.3 (b). According to Equation 27.7, resistance is the ratio of voltage across a device to current in the device. In Figure 27.7b, a line drawn from the origin to a point on the curve will have a slope equal to $I/\Delta V$, which is the inverse of resistance. As ΔV increases, the slope of the line also increases, so the resistance decreases.

27.4 (a). When the filament is at room temperature, its resistance is low and the current is therefore relatively large. As the filament warms up, its resistance increases and the current decreases. Older lightbulbs often fail just as they are turned on because this large, initial current "spike" produces a rapid temperature increase and mechanical stress on the filament, causing it to break.

27.5 $I_a = I_b > I_c = I_d > I_e = I_f$. The current I_a leaves the positive terminal of the battery and then splits to flow through the two lightbulbs; therefore, $I_a = I_c + I_e$. Looking at Equation 27.21, we see that power rating is inversely related to resistance. Therefore, we know that the current in the 60-W lightbulb is greater than that in the 30-W lightbulb. Because charge does not build up in the lightbulbs, we know that the same amount of charge flowing into a lightbulb from the left must flow out on the right; consequently, $I_c = I_d$ and $I_e = I_f$. The two currents leaving the lightbulbs recombine to form the current back into the battery, $I_f + I_d = I_b$.

In our lives today, we use many items that are generally called "personal electronics," such as MP3 players, cell phones, and digital cameras. These items as well as dozens of others that we use contain electric circuits powered by batteries. In this chapter, we study simple types of circuits and learn how to analyze them. (© Thomson Learning/Charles D. Winters)

28 Direct Current Circuits

In this chapter, we analyze simple electric circuits that contain batteries, resistors, and capacitors in various combinations. Some circuits contain resistors that can be combined using simple rules. The analysis of more complicated circuits is simplified using *Kirchhoff's rules,* which follow from the laws of conservation of energy and conservation of electric charge for isolated systems. Most of the circuits analyzed are assumed to be in *steady state,* which means that currents in the circuit are constant in magnitude and direction. A current that is constant in direction is called a *direct current* (DC). We will study *alternating current* (AC), in which the current changes direction periodically, in Chapter 33. Finally, we describe electrical meters for measuring current and potential difference and then discuss electrical circuits in the home.

28.1 Electromotive Force

In Section 27.6, we discussed a circuit in which a battery produces a current. We will generally use a battery as a source of energy for circuits in our discussion. Because the potential difference at the battery terminals is constant in a particular circuit, the current in the circuit is constant in magnitude and direction and is called **direct current.** A battery is called either a *source of electromotive force* or, more commonly, a *source of emf.* (The phrase *electromotive force* is an unfortunate historical term, describing not a force, but rather a potential difference in volts.) **The emf $\mathcal{E}$**

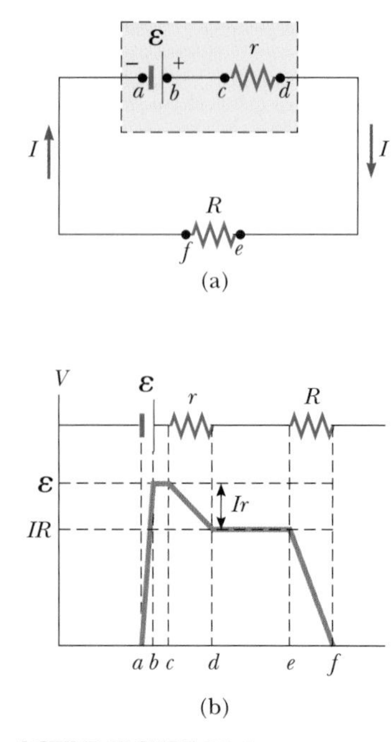

ACTIVE FIGURE 28.1

(a) Circuit diagram of a source of emf $\mathcal{E}$ (in this case, a battery), of internal resistance r, connected to an external resistor of resistance R. (b) Graphical representation showing how the electric potential changes as the circuit in (a) is traversed clockwise.

Sign in at www.thomsonedu.com and go to ThomsonNOW to adjust the emf and resistances r and R and see the effect on the current and on the graph in part (b).

of a battery is the maximum possible voltage the battery can provide between its terminals. You can think of a source of emf as a "charge pump." When an electric potential difference exists between two points, the source moves charges "uphill" from the lower potential to the higher.

We shall generally assume the connecting wires in a circuit have no resistance. The positive terminal of a battery is at a higher potential than the negative terminal. Because a real battery is made of matter, there is resistance to the flow of charge within the battery. This resistance is called **internal resistance** r. For an idealized battery with zero internal resistance, the potential difference across the battery (called its *terminal voltage*) equals its emf. For a real battery, however, the terminal voltage is *not* equal to the emf for a battery in a circuit in which there is a current. To understand why, consider the circuit diagram in Active Figure 28.1a. The battery in this diagram is represented by the dashed rectangle containing an ideal, resistance-free emf $\mathcal{E}$ in series with an internal resistance r. A resistor of resistance R is connected across the terminals of the battery. Now imagine moving through the battery from a to d and measuring the electric potential at various locations. Passing from the negative terminal to the positive terminal, the potential increases by an amount $\mathcal{E}$. As we move through the resistance r, however, the potential *decreases* by an amount Ir, where I is the current in the circuit. Therefore, the terminal voltage of the battery $\Delta V = V_d - V_a$ is

$$\Delta V = \mathcal{E} - Ir \tag{28.1}$$

From this expression, notice that $\mathcal{E}$ is equivalent to the **open-circuit voltage,** that is, the terminal voltage when the current is zero. The emf is the voltage labeled on a battery; for example, the emf of a D cell is 1.5 V. The actual potential difference between a battery's terminals depends on the current in the battery as described by Equation 28.1.

Active Figure 28.1b is a graphical representation of the changes in electric potential as the circuit is traversed in the clockwise direction. Active Figure 28.1a shows that the terminal voltage ΔV must equal the potential difference across the external resistance R, often called the **load resistance.** The load resistor might be a simple resistive circuit element as in Active Figure 28.1a, or it could be the resistance of some electrical device (such as a toaster, electric heater, or lightbulb) connected to the battery (or, in the case of household devices, to the wall outlet). The resistor represents a *load* on the battery because the battery must supply energy to operate the device containing the resistance. The potential difference across the load resistance is $\Delta V = IR$. Combining this expression with Equation 28.1, we see that

$$\mathcal{E} = IR + Ir \tag{28.2}$$

Solving for the current gives

$$I = \frac{\mathcal{E}}{R + r} \tag{28.3}$$

Equation 28.3 shows that the current in this simple circuit depends on both the load resistance R external to the battery and the internal resistance r. If R is much greater than r, as it is in many real-world circuits, we can neglect r.

Multiplying Equation 28.2 by the current I in the circuit gives

$$I\mathcal{E} = I^2R + I^2r \tag{28.4}$$

Equation 28.4 indicates that because power $\mathcal{P} = I\,\Delta V$ (see Eq. 27.20), the total power output $I\mathcal{E}$ of the battery is delivered to the external load resistance in the amount I^2R and to the internal resistance in the amount I^2r.

PITFALL PREVENTION 28.1

What Is Constant in a Battery?

It is a common misconception that a battery is a source of constant current. Equation 28.3 shows that is not true. The current in the circuit depends on the resistance R connected to the battery. It is also not true that a battery is a source of constant terminal voltage as shown by Equation 28.1. **A battery is a source of constant emf.**

Quick Quiz 28.1 To maximize the percentage of the power that is delivered from a battery to a device, what should the internal resistance of the battery be? (a) It should be as low as possible. (b) It should be as high as possible. (c) The percentage does not depend on the internal resistance.

EXAMPLE 28.1 Terminal Voltage of a Battery

A battery has an emf of 12.0 V and an internal resistance of 0.05 Ω. Its terminals are connected to a load resistance of 3.00 Ω.

(A) Find the current in the circuit and the terminal voltage of the battery.

SOLUTION

Conceptualize Study Active Figure 28.1a, which shows a circuit consistent with the problem statement. The battery delivers energy to the load resistor.

Categorize This example involves simple calculations from this section, so we categorize it as a substitution problem.

Use Equation 28.3 to find the current in the circuit:

$$I = \frac{\mathcal{E}}{R + r} = \frac{12.0\text{ V}}{(3.00\ \Omega + 0.05\ \Omega)} = \boxed{3.93\text{ A}}$$

Use Equation 28.1 to find the terminal voltage:

$$\Delta V = \mathcal{E} - Ir = 12.0\text{ V} - (3.93\text{ A})(0.05\ \Omega) = \boxed{11.8\text{ V}}$$

To check this result, calculate the voltage across the load resistance R:

$$\Delta V = IR = (3.93\text{ A})(3.00\ \Omega) = 11.8\text{ V}$$

(B) Calculate the power delivered to the load resistor, the power delivered to the internal resistance of the battery, and the power delivered by the battery.

SOLUTION

Use Equation 27.21 to find the power delivered to the load resistor:

$$\mathcal{P}_R = I^2R = (3.93\text{ A})^2(3.00\ \Omega) = \boxed{46.3\text{ W}}$$

Find the power delivered to the internal resistance:

$$\mathcal{P}_r = I^2r = (3.93\text{ A})^2(0.05\ \Omega) = \boxed{0.772\text{ W}}$$

Find the power delivered by the battery by adding these quantities:

$$\mathcal{P} = \mathcal{P}_R + \mathcal{P}_r = 46.3\text{ W} + 0.772\text{ W} = \boxed{47.1\text{ W}}$$

What If? As a battery ages, its internal resistance increases. Suppose the internal resistance of this battery rises to 2.00 Ω toward the end of its useful life. How does that alter the battery's ability to deliver energy?

Answer Let's connect the same 3.00-Ω load resistor to the battery.

Find the new current in the battery:

$$I = \frac{\mathcal{E}}{R + r} = \frac{12.0\text{ V}}{(3.00\ \Omega + 2.00\ \Omega)} = 2.40\text{ A}$$

Find the new terminal voltage:

$$\Delta V = \mathcal{E} - Ir = 12.0\text{ V} - (2.40\text{ A})(2.00\ \Omega) = 7.2\text{ V}$$

Find the new powers delivered to the load resistor and internal resistance:

$$\mathcal{P}_R = I^2R = (2.40\text{ A})^2(3.00\ \Omega) = 17.3\text{ W}$$

$$\mathcal{P}_r = I^2r = (2.40\text{ A})^2(2.00\ \Omega) = 11.5\text{ W}$$

The terminal voltage is only 60% of the emf. Notice that 40% of the power from the battery is delivered to the internal resistance when r is 2.00 Ω. When r is 0.05 Ω as in part (B), this percentage is only 1.6%. Consequently, even though the emf remains fixed, the increasing internal resistance of the battery significantly reduces the battery's ability to deliver energy.

EXAMPLE 28.2 Matching the Load

Find the load resistance R for which the maximum power is delivered to the load resistance in Active Figure 28.1a.

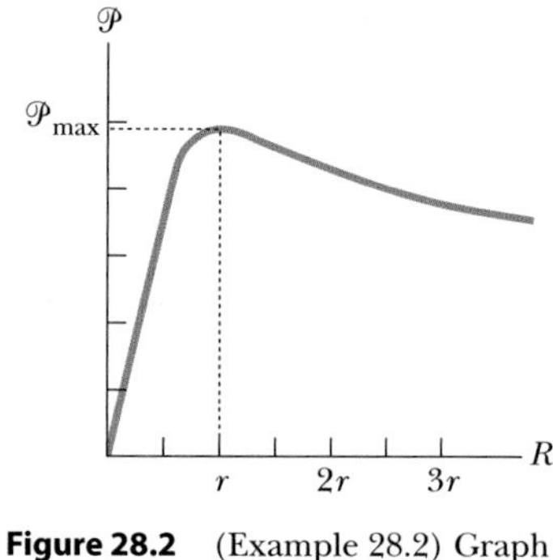

Figure 28.2 (Example 28.2) Graph of the power $\mathcal{P}$ delivered by a battery to a load resistor of resistance R as a function of R. The power delivered to the resistor is a maximum when the load resistance equals the internal resistance of the battery.

SOLUTION

Conceptualize Think about varying the load resistance in Active Figure 28.1a and the effect on the power delivered to the load resistance. When R is large, there is very little current, so the power I^2R delivered to the load resistor is small. When R is small, the current is large and there is significant loss of power I^2r as energy is delivered to the internal resistance. Therefore, the power delivered to the load resistor is small again. For some intermediate value of the resistance R, the power must maximize.

Categorize The circuit is the same as that in Example 28.1. The load resistance R in this case, however, is a variable.

Analyze Find the power delivered to the load resistance using Equation 27.21, with I given by Equation 28.3:

$$(1) \quad \mathcal{P} = I^2R = \frac{\mathcal{E}^2R}{(R+r)^2}$$

Differentiate the power with respect to the load resistance R and set the derivative equal to zero to maximize the power:

$$\frac{d\mathcal{P}}{dR} = \frac{d}{dR}\left[\frac{\mathcal{E}^2R}{(R+r)^2}\right] = \frac{d}{dR}\left[\mathcal{E}^2R(R+r)^{-2}\right] = 0$$

$$\left[\mathcal{E}^2(R+r)^{-2}\right] + \left[\mathcal{E}^2R(-2)(R+r)^{-3}\right] = 0$$

$$\frac{\mathcal{E}^2(R+r)}{(R+r)^3} - \frac{2\mathcal{E}^2R}{(R+r)^3} = \frac{\mathcal{E}^2(r-R)}{(R+r)^3} = 0$$

Solve for R:

$$R = r$$

Finalize To check this result, let's plot $\mathcal{P}$ versus R as in Figure 28.2. The graph shows that $\mathcal{P}$ reaches a maximum value at $R = r$. Equation (1) shows that this maximum value is $\mathcal{P}_{max} = \mathcal{E}^2/4r$.

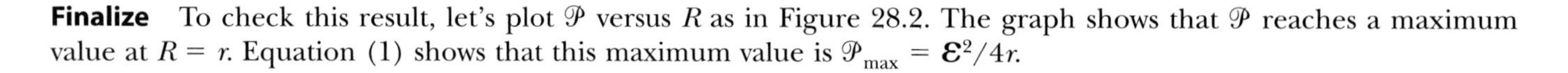

28.2 Resistors in Series and Parallel

When two or more resistors are connected together as are the lightbulbs in Active Figure 28.3a, they are said to be in a **series combination.** Active Figure 28.3b is the circuit diagram for the lightbulbs, shown as resistors, and the battery. In a series connection, if an amount of charge Q exits resistor R_1, charge Q must also enter the second resistor R_2. Otherwise, charge would accumulate on the wire between the resistors. Therefore, the same amount of charge passes through both resistors in a given time interval and the currents are the same in both resistors:

$$I = I_1 = I_2$$

where I is the current leaving the battery, I_1 is the current in resistor R_1, and I_2 is the current in resistor R_2.

The potential difference applied across the series combination of resistors divides between the resistors. In Active Figure 28.3b, because the voltage drop[1]

[1] The term *voltage drop* is synonymous with a decrease in electric potential across a resistor. It is often used by individuals working with electric circuits.

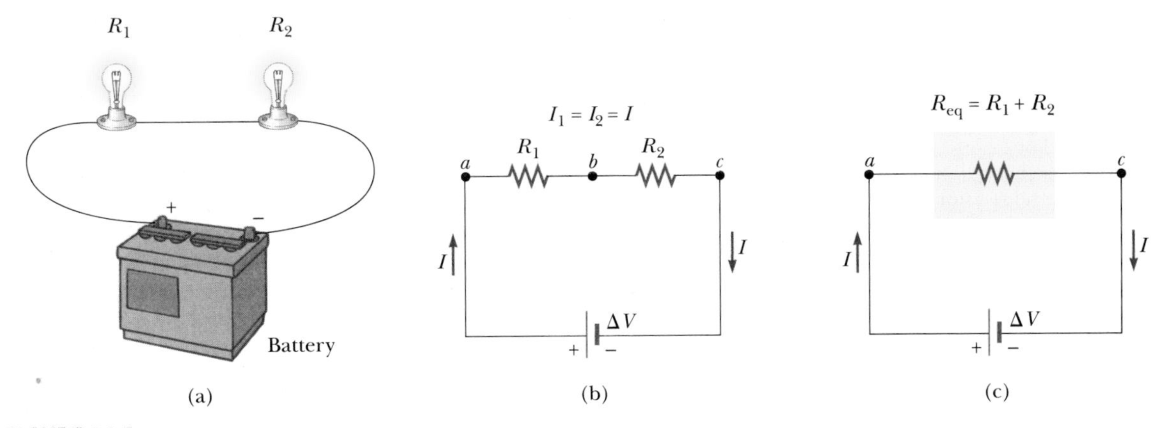

ACTIVE FIGURE 28.3

(a) A series combination of two lightbulbs with resistances R_1 and R_2. (b) Circuit diagram for the two-resistor circuit. The current in R_1 is the same as that in R_2. (c) The resistors replaced with a single resistor having an equivalent resistance $R_{eq} = R_1 + R_2$.

Sign in at www.thomsonedu.com and go to ThomsonNOW to adjust the battery voltage and resistances R_1 and R_2 and see the effect on the currents and voltages in the individual resistors.

from a to b equals I_1R_1 and the voltage drop from b to c equals I_2R_2, the voltage drop from a to c is

$$\Delta V = I_1R_1 + I_2R_2$$

The potential difference across the battery is also applied to the **equivalent resistance** R_{eq} in Active Figure 28.3c:

$$\Delta V = IR_{eq}$$

where the equivalent resistance has the same effect on the circuit as the series combination because it results in the same current I in the battery. Combining these equations for ΔV, we see that we can replace the two resistors in series with a single equivalent resistance whose value is the *sum* of the individual resistances:

$$\Delta V = IR_{eq} = I_1R_1 + I_2R_2 \quad \rightarrow \quad R_{eq} = R_1 + R_2 \qquad (28.5)$$

where we have canceled the currents I, I_1, and I_2 because they are all the same.

The equivalent resistance of three or more resistors connected in series is

$$R_{eq} = R_1 + R_2 + R_3 + \cdots \qquad (28.6)$$

◀ The equivalent resistance of a series combination of resistors

This relationship indicates that **the equivalent resistance of a series combination of resistors is the numerical sum of the individual resistances and is always greater than any individual resistance.**

Looking back at Equation 28.3, we see that the denominator is the simple algebraic sum of the external and internal resistances. That is consistent with the internal and external resistances being in series in Active Figure 28.1a.

If the filament of one lightbulb in Active Figure 28.3 were to fail, the circuit would no longer be complete (resulting in an open-circuit condition) and the second lightbulb would also go out. This fact is a general feature of a series circuit: if one device in the series creates an open circuit, all devices are inoperative.

PITFALL PREVENTION 28.2
Lightbulbs Don't Burn

We will describe the end of the life of a lightbulb by saying *the filament fails* rather than by saying the lightbulb "burns out." The word *burn* suggests a combustion process, which is not what occurs in a lightbulb. The failure of a lightbulb results from the slow sublimation of tungsten from the very hot filament over the life of the lightbulb. The filament eventually becomes very thin because of this process. The mechanical stress from a sudden temperature increase when the lightbulb is turned on causes the thin filament to break.

Quick Quiz 28.2 With the switch in the circuit of Figure 28.4a (page 780) closed, there is no current in R_2 because the current has an alternate zero-resistance path through the switch. There is current in R_1, and this current is measured with the ammeter (a device for measuring current) at the bottom of the circuit. If the switch is opened (Fig. 28.4b), there is current in R_2. What happens to the

PITFALL PREVENTION 28.3
Local and Global Changes

A local change in one part of a circuit may result in a global change throughout the circuit. For example, if a single resistor is changed in a circuit containing several resistors and batteries, the currents in all resistors and batteries, the terminal voltages of all batteries, and the voltages across all resistors may change as a result.

reading on the ammeter when the switch is opened? (a) The reading goes up. (b) The reading goes down. (c) The reading does not change.

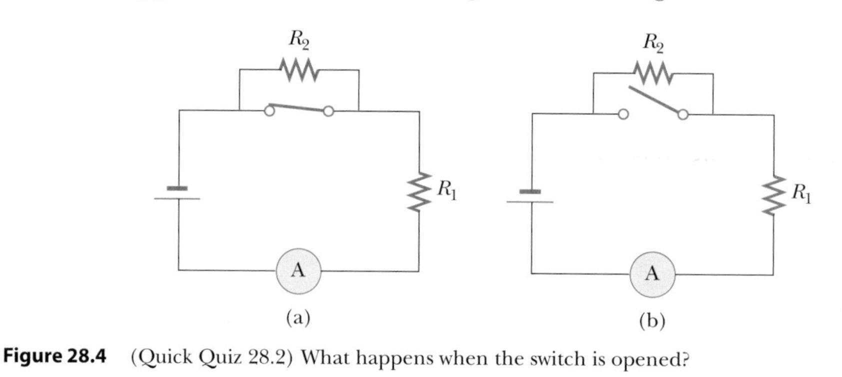

Figure 28.4 (Quick Quiz 28.2) What happens when the switch is opened?

PITFALL PREVENTION 28.4
Current Does Not Take the Path of Least Resistance

You may have heard the phrase "current takes the path of least resistance" (or similar wording) in reference to a parallel combination of current paths such that there are two or more paths for the current to take. Such wording is incorrect. The current takes *all* paths. Those paths with lower resistance have larger currents, but even very high resistance paths carry *some* of the current. In theory, if current has a choice between a zero-resistance path and a finite resistance path, all the current takes the path of zero-resistance; a path with zero resistance, however, is an idealization.

Now consider two resistors in a **parallel combination** as shown in Active Figure 28.5. Notice that both resistors are connected directly across the terminals of the battery. Therefore, the potential differences across the resistors are the same:

$$\Delta V = \Delta V_1 = \Delta V_2$$

where ΔV is the terminal voltage of the battery.

When charges reach point a in Active Figure 28.5b, they split into two parts, with some going toward R_1 and the rest going toward R_2. A **junction** is any such point in a circuit where a current can split. This split results in less current in each individual resistor than the current leaving the battery. Because electric charge is conserved, the current I that enters point a must equal the total current leaving that point:

$$I = I_1 + I_2$$

where I_1 is the current in R_1 and I_2 is the current in R_2.

The current in the **equivalent resistance** R_{eq} in Active Figure 28.5c is

$$I = \frac{\Delta V}{R_{eq}}$$

where the equivalent resistance has the same effect on the circuit as the two resistors in parallel; that is, the equivalent resistance draws the same current I from the

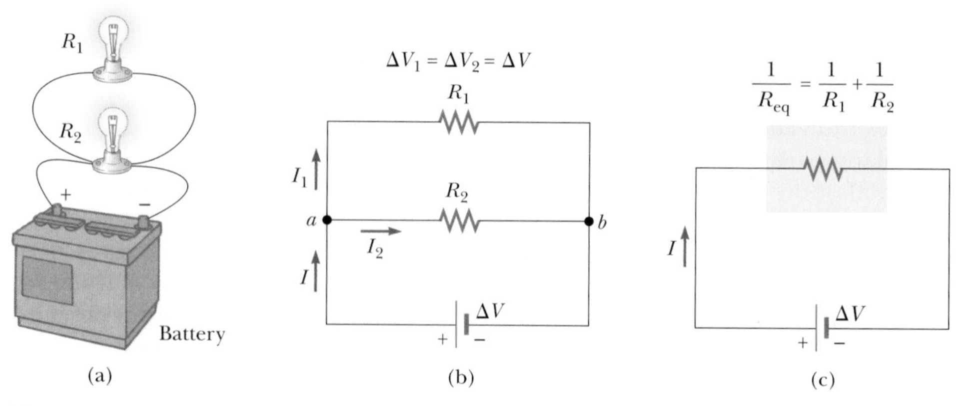

ACTIVE FIGURE 28.5

(a) A parallel combination of two lightbulbs with resistances R_1 and R_2. (b) Circuit diagram for the two-resistor circuit. The potential difference across R_1 is the same as that across R_2. (c) The resistors replaced with a single resistor having an equivalent resistance given by Equation 28.7.

Sign in at www.thomsonedu.com and go to ThomsonNOW to adjust the battery voltage and resistances R_1 and R_2 and see the effect on the currents and voltages in the individual resistors.

battery. Combining these equations for I, we see that the equivalent resistance of two resistors in parallel is given by

$$I = \frac{\Delta V}{R_{\text{eq}}} = \frac{\Delta V_1}{R_1} + \frac{\Delta V_2}{R_2} \rightarrow \frac{1}{R_{\text{eq}}} = \frac{1}{R_1} + \frac{1}{R_2} \tag{28.7}$$

where we have canceled ΔV, ΔV_1, and ΔV_2 because they are all the same.

An extension of this analysis to three or more resistors in parallel gives

$$\frac{1}{R_{\text{eq}}} = \frac{1}{R_1} + \frac{1}{R_2} + \frac{1}{R_3} + \cdots \tag{28.8}$$

◀ The equivalent resistance of a parallel combination of resistors

This expression shows that **the inverse of the equivalent resistance of two or more resistors in a parallel combination is equal to the sum of the inverses of the individual resistances. Furthermore, the equivalent resistance is always less than the smallest resistance in the group.**

Household circuits are always wired such that the appliances are connected in parallel. Each device operates independently of the others so that if one is switched off, the others remain on. In addition, in this type of connection, all the devices operate on the same voltage.

Let's consider two examples of practical applications of series and parallel circuits. Figure 28.6 illustrates how a three-way lightbulb is constructed to provide three levels of light intensity.[2] The socket of the lamp is equipped with a three-way switch for selecting different light intensities. The lightbulb contains two filaments. When the lamp is connected to a 120-V source, one filament receives 100 W of power and the other receives 75 W. The three light intensities are made possible by applying the 120 V to one filament alone, to the other filament alone, or to the two filaments in parallel. When switch S_1 is closed and switch S_2 is opened, current exists only in the 75-W filament. When switch S_1 is open and switch S_2 is closed, current exists only in the 100-W filament. When both switches are closed, current exists in both filaments and the total power is 175 W.

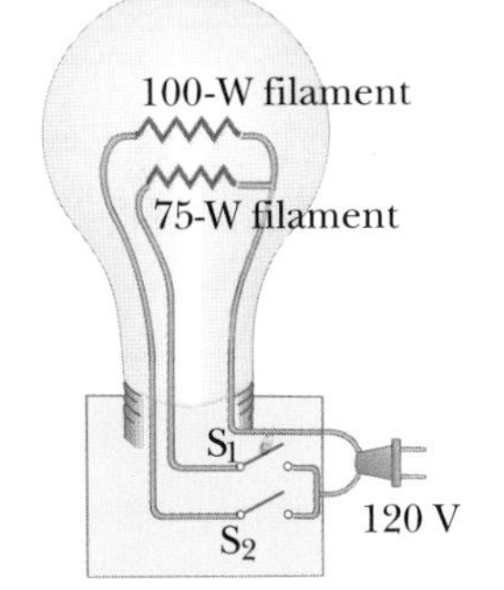

Figure 28.6 A three-way lightbulb.

If the filaments were connected in series and one of them were to break, no charges could pass through the lightbulb and it would not glow, regardless of the switch position. If, however, the filaments were connected in parallel and one of them (for example, the 75-W filament) were to break, the lightbulb would continue to glow in two of the switch positions because current exists in the other (100-W) filament.

As a second example, consider strings of lights that are used for many ornamental purposes such as decorating Christmas trees. Over the years, both parallel and series connections have been used for strings of lights. Because series-wired lightbulbs operate with less energy per bulb and at a lower temperature, they are safer than parallel-wired lightbulbs for indoor Christmas-tree use. If, however, the filament of a single lightbulb in a series-wired string were to fail (or if the lightbulb were removed from its socket), all the lights on the string would go out. The popularity of series-wired light strings diminished because troubleshooting a failed lightbulb is a tedious, time-consuming chore that involves trial-and-error substitution of a good lightbulb in each socket along the string until the defective one is found.

In a parallel-wired string, each lightbulb operates at 120 V. By design, the lightbulbs are brighter and hotter than those on a series-wired string. As a result, they are inherently more dangerous (more likely to start a fire, for instance), but if one lightbulb in a parallel-wired string fails or is removed, the rest of the lightbulbs continue to glow.

To prevent the failure of one lightbulb from causing the entire string to go out, a new design was developed for so-called miniature lights wired in series. When the filament breaks in one of these miniature lightbulbs, the break in the filament

[2] The three-way lightbulb and other household devices actually operate on alternating current (AC), to be introduced in Chapter 33.

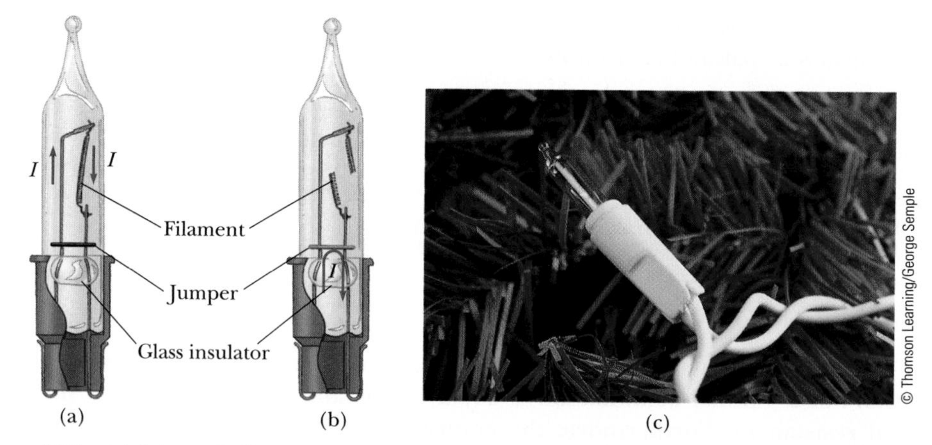

Figure 28.7 (a) Schematic diagram of a modern "miniature" holiday lightbulb, with a jumper connection to provide a current path if the filament breaks. When the filament is intact, charges flow in the filament. (b) A holiday lightbulb with a broken filament. In this case, charges flow in the jumper connection. (c) A Christmas-tree lightbulb.

represents the largest resistance in the series, much larger than that of the intact filaments. As a result, most of the applied 120 V appears across the lightbulb with the broken filament. Inside the lightbulb, a small jumper loop covered by an insulating material is wrapped around the filament leads. When the filament fails and 120 V appears across the lightbulb, an arc burns the insulation on the jumper and connects the filament leads. This connection now completes the circuit through the lightbulb even though its filament is no longer active (Fig. 28.7).

When a lightbulb fails, the resistance across its terminals is reduced to almost zero because of the alternate jumper connection mentioned in the preceding paragraph. All the other lightbulbs not only stay on, but they glow more brightly because the total resistance of the string is reduced and consequently the current in each lightbulb increases. Each lightbulb operates at a slightly higher temperature than before. As more lightbulbs fail, the current keeps rising, the filament of each lightbulb operates at a higher temperature, and the lifetime of the lightbulb is reduced. For this reason, you should check for failed (nonglowing) lightbulbs in such a series-wired string and replace them as soon as possible, thereby maximizing the lifetimes of all the lightbulbs.

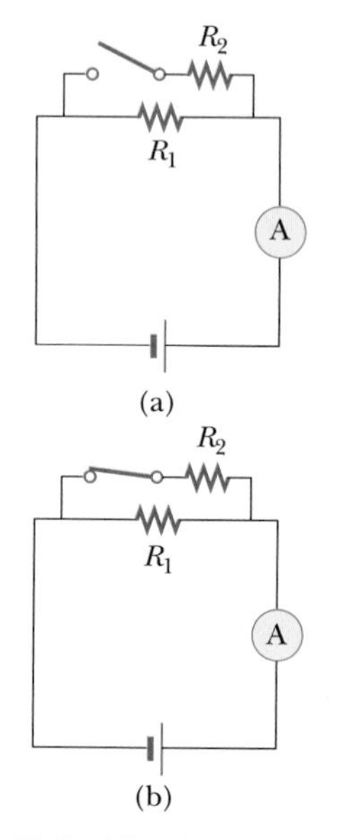

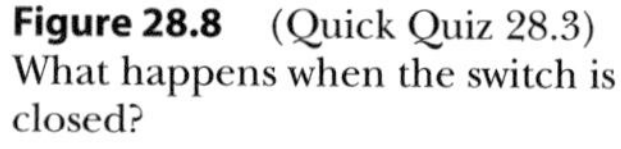

Figure 28.8 (Quick Quiz 28.3) What happens when the switch is closed?

Quick Quiz 28.3 With the switch in the circuit of Figure 28.8a open, there is no current in R_2. There is current in R_1, however, and it is measured with the ammeter at the right side of the circuit. If the switch is closed (Fig. 28.8b), there is current in R_2. What happens to the reading on the ammeter when the switch is closed? (a) The reading increases. (b) The reading decreases. (c) The reading does not change.

Quick Quiz 28.4 Consider the following choices: (a) increases, (b) decreases, (c) remains the same. From these choices, choose the best answer for the following situations. **(i)** In Active Figure 28.3, a third resistor is added in series with the first two. What happens to the current in the battery? **(ii)** What happens to the terminal voltage of the battery? **(iii)** In Active Figure 28.5, a third resistor is added in parallel with the first two. What happens to the current in the battery? **(iv)** What happens to the terminal voltage of the battery?

CONCEPTUAL EXAMPLE 28.3 Landscape Lights

A homeowner wishes to install low-voltage landscape lighting in his back yard. To save money, he purchases inexpensive 18-gauge cable, which has a relatively high resistance per unit length. This cable consists of two side-by-side wires separated by insulation, like the cord on an appliance. He runs a 200-foot length of this cable from the power supply to the farthest point at which he plans to position a light fixture. He attaches light fixtures across the two wires on the cable at 10-foot intervals so that the light fixtures are in parallel. Because of the cable's resistance, the brightness of the lightbulbs in the fixtures is not as desired. Which of the following problems does the homeowner have? (a) All the lightbulbs glow equally less brightly than they would if lower-resistance cable had been used. (b) The brightness of the lightbulbs decreases as you move farther from the power supply.

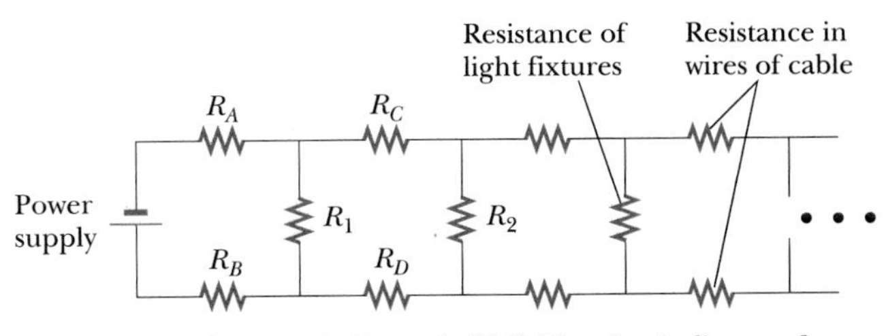

Figure 28.9 (Conceptual Example 28.3) The circuit diagram for a set of landscape light fixtures connected in parallel across the two wires of a two-wire cable. The horizontal resistors represent resistance in the wires of the cable. The vertical resistors represent the light fixtures.

SOLUTION

A circuit diagram for the system appears in Figure 28.9. The horizontal resistors with letter subscripts (such as R_A) represent the resistance of the wires in the cable between the light fixtures, and the vertical resistors with number subscripts (such as R_1) represent the resistance of the light fixtures themselves. Part of the terminal voltage of the power supply is dropped across resistors R_A and R_B. Therefore, the voltage across light fixture R_1 is less than the terminal voltage. There is a further voltage drop across resistors R_C and R_D. Consequently, the voltage across light fixture R_2 is smaller than that across R_1. This pattern continues down the line of light fixtures, so the correct choice is (b). Each successive light fixture has a smaller voltage across it and glows less brightly than the one before.

EXAMPLE 28.4 Find the Equivalent Resistance

Four resistors are connected as shown in Figure 28.10a.

(A) Find the equivalent resistance between points a and c.

SOLUTION

Conceptualize Imagine charges flowing into this combination from the left. All charges must pass through the first two resistors, but the charges split into two different paths when encountering the combination of the 6.0-Ω and the 3.0-Ω resistors.

Categorize Because of the simple nature of the combination of resistors in Figure 28.10, we categorize this example as one for which we can use the rules for series and parallel combinations of resistors.

Analyze The combination of resistors can be reduced in steps as shown in Figure 28.10.

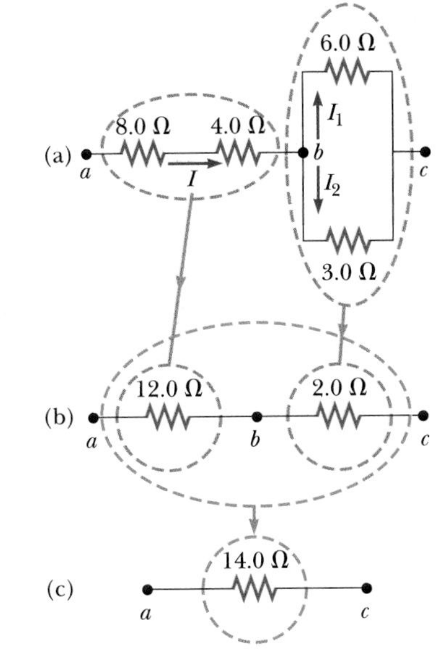

Figure 28.10 (Example 28.4) The original network of resistors is reduced to a single equivalent resistance.

Find the equivalent resistance between a and b of the 8.0-Ω and 4.0-Ω resistors, which are in series:

$$R_{eq} = 8.0\ \Omega + 4.0\ \Omega = 12.0\ \Omega$$

Find the equivalent resistance between b and c of the 6.0-Ω and 3.0-Ω resistors, which are in parallel:

$$\frac{1}{R_{eq}} = \frac{1}{6.0\ \Omega} + \frac{1}{3.0\ \Omega} = \frac{3}{6.0\ \Omega}$$

$$R_{eq} = \frac{6.0\ \Omega}{3} = 2.0\ \Omega$$

The circuit of equivalent resistances now looks like Figure 28.10b. Find the equivalent resistance from a to c:

$$R_{eq} = 12.0\ \Omega + 2.0\ \Omega = 14.0\ \Omega$$

This resistance is that of the single equivalent resistor in Figure 28.10c.

(B) What is the current in each resistor if a potential difference of 42 V is maintained between a and c?

SOLUTION

The currents in the 8.0-Ω and 4.0-Ω resistors are the same because they are in series. In addition, they carry the same current that would exist in the 14.0-Ω equivalent resistor subject to the 42-V potential difference.

Use Equation 27.7 ($R = \Delta V/I$) and the result from part (A) to find the current in the 8.0-Ω and 4.0-Ω resistors:

$$I = \frac{\Delta V_{ac}}{R_{eq}} = \frac{42\text{ V}}{14.0\ \Omega} = 3.0\text{ A}$$

Set the voltages across the resistors in parallel in Figure 28.10a equal to find a relationship between the currents:

$$\Delta V_1 = \Delta V_2 \rightarrow (6.0\ \Omega)I_1 = (3.0\ \Omega)I_2 \rightarrow I_2 = 2I_1$$

Use $I_1 + I_2 = 3.0$ A to find I_1:

$$I_1 + I_2 = 3.0\text{ A} \rightarrow I_1 + 2I_1 = 3.0\text{ A} \rightarrow I_1 = 1.0\text{ A}$$

Find I_2:

$$I_2 = 2I_1 = 2(1.0\text{ A}) = 2.0\text{ A}$$

Finalize As a final check of our results, note that $\Delta V_{bc} = (6.0\ \Omega)I_1 = (3.0\ \Omega)I_2 = 6.0$ V and $\Delta V_{ab} = (12.0\ \Omega)I = 36$ V; therefore, $\Delta V_{ac} = \Delta V_{ab} + \Delta V_{bc} = 42$ V, as it must.

EXAMPLE 28.5 Three Resistors in Parallel

Three resistors are connected in parallel as shown in Figure 28.11a. A potential difference of 18.0 V is maintained between points *a* and *b*.

(A) Calculate the equivalent resistance of the circuit.

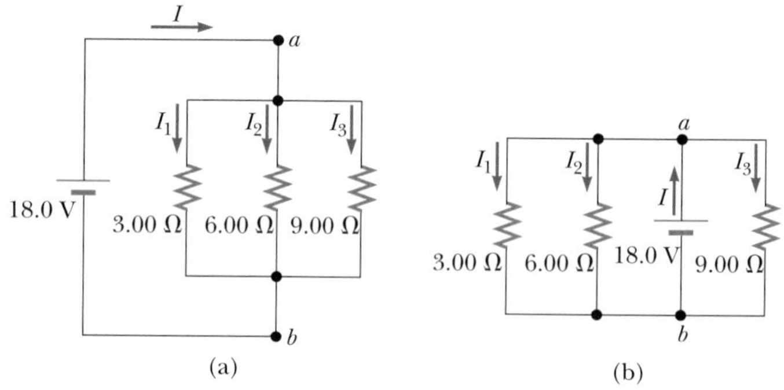

SOLUTION

Conceptualize Figure 28.11a shows that we are dealing with a simple parallel combination of three resistors.

Categorize Because the three resistors are connected in parallel, we can use Equation 28.8 to evaluate the equivalent resistance.

(a) (b)

Figure 28.11 (Example 28.5) (a) Three resistors connected in parallel. The voltage across each resistor is 18.0 V. (b) Another circuit with three resistors and a battery. Is it equivalent to the circuit in (a)?

Analyze Use Equation 28.8 to find R_{eq}:

$$\frac{1}{R_{eq}} = \frac{1}{3.00\ \Omega} + \frac{1}{6.00\ \Omega} + \frac{1}{9.00\ \Omega} = \frac{11.0}{18.0\ \Omega}$$

$$R_{eq} = \frac{18.0\ \Omega}{11.0} = 1.64\ \Omega$$

(B) Find the current in each resistor.

SOLUTION

The potential difference across each resistor is 18.0 V. Apply the relationship $\Delta V = IR$ to find the currents:

$$I_1 = \frac{\Delta V}{R_1} = \frac{18.0\text{ V}}{3.00\ \Omega} = 6.00\text{ A}$$

$$I_2 = \frac{\Delta V}{R_2} = \frac{18.0\text{ V}}{6.00\ \Omega} = 3.00\text{ A}$$

$$I_3 = \frac{\Delta V}{R_3} = \frac{18.0\text{ V}}{9.00\ \Omega} = 2.00\text{ A}$$

(C) Calculate the power delivered to each resistor and the total power delivered to the combination of resistors.

SOLUTION

Apply the relationship $\mathcal{P} = I^2R$ to each resistor using the currents calculated in part (B):

$$3.00\text{-}\Omega: \quad \mathcal{P}_1 = I_1{}^2R_1 = (6.00\text{ A})^2(3.00\ \Omega) = \boxed{108\text{ W}}$$

$$6.00\text{-}\Omega: \quad \mathcal{P}_2 = I_2{}^2R_2 = (3.00\text{ A})^2(6.00\ \Omega) = \boxed{54.0\text{ W}}$$

$$9.00\text{-}\Omega: \quad \mathcal{P}_3 = I_3{}^2R_3 = (2.00\text{ A})^2(9.00\ \Omega) = \boxed{36.0\text{ W}}$$

Finalize Part (C) shows that the smallest resistor receives the most power. Summing the three quantities gives a total power of 198 W. We could have calculated this final result from part (A) by considering the equivalent resistance as follows: $\mathcal{P} = (\Delta V)^2/R_{eq} = (18.0\text{ V})^2/\ 1.64\ \Omega = 198\text{ W}$.

What If? What if the circuit were as shown in Figure 28.11b instead of as in Figure 28.11a? How would that affect the calculation?

Answer There would be no effect on the calculation. The physical placement of the battery is not important. In Figure 28.11b, the battery still maintains a potential difference of 18.0 V between points a and b, so the two circuits in the figure are electrically identical.

28.3 Kirchhoff's Rules

As we saw in the preceding section, combinations of resistors can be simplified and analyzed using the expression $\Delta V = IR$ and the rules for series and parallel combinations of resistors. Very often, however, it is not possible to reduce a circuit to a single loop. The procedure for analyzing more complex circuits is made possible by using the two following principles, called **Kirchhoff's rules.**

1. **Junction rule.** At any junction, the sum of the currents must equal zero:

$$\sum_{\text{junction}} I = 0 \qquad \textbf{(28.9)}$$

2. **Loop rule.** The sum of the potential differences across all elements around any closed circuit loop must be zero:

$$\sum_{\text{closed loop}} \Delta V = 0 \qquad \textbf{(28.10)}$$

Kirchhoff's first rule is a statement of conservation of electric charge. All charges that enter a given point in a circuit must leave that point because charge cannot build up at a point. Currents directed into the junction are entered into the junction rule as $+I$, whereas currents directed out of a junction are entered as $-I$. Applying this rule to the junction in Figure 28.12a gives

$$I_1 - I_2 - I_3 = 0$$

Figure 28.12b represents a mechanical analog of this situation, in which water flows through a branched pipe having no leaks. Because water does not build up anywhere in the pipe, the flow rate into the pipe on the left equals the total flow rate out of the two branches on the right.

Kirchhoff's second rule follows from the law of conservation of energy. Let's imagine moving a charge around a closed loop of a circuit. When the charge returns to the starting point, the charge-circuit system must have the same total energy as it had before the charge was moved. The sum of the increases in energy

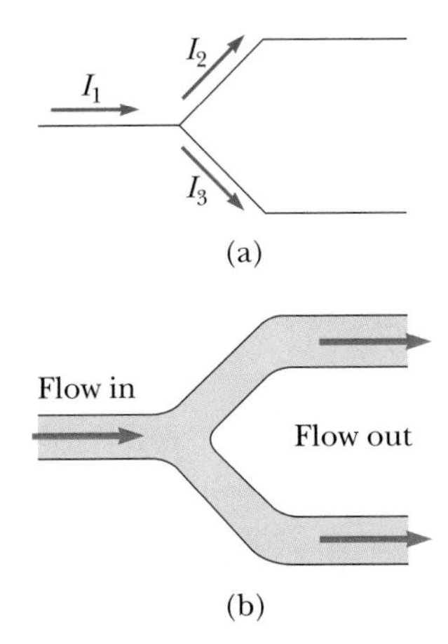

Figure 28.12 (a) Kirchhoff's junction rule. Conservation of charge requires that all charges entering a junction must leave that junction. Therefore, $I_1 - I_2 - I_3 = 0$. (b) A mechanical analog of the junction rule. The amount of water flowing out of the branches on the right must equal the amount flowing into the single branch on the left.

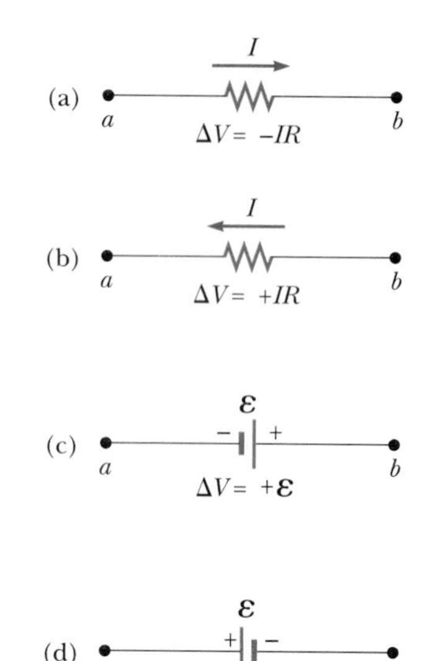

Figure 28.13 Rules for determining the potential differences across a resistor and a battery. (The battery is assumed to have no internal resistance.) Each circuit element is traversed from a to b, left to right.

as the charge passes through some circuit elements must equal the sum of the decreases in energy as it passes through other elements. The potential energy decreases whenever the charge moves through a potential drop $-IR$ across a resistor or whenever it moves in the reverse direction through a source of emf. The potential energy increases whenever the charge passes through a battery from the negative terminal to the positive terminal.

When applying Kirchhoff's second rule, imagine *traveling* around the loop and consider changes in *electric potential* rather than the changes in *potential energy* described in the preceding paragraph. Imagine traveling through the circuit elements in Figure 28.13 toward the right. The following sign conventions apply when using the second rule:

- Charges move from the high-potential end of a resistor toward the low-potential end, so if a resistor is traversed in the direction of the current, the potential difference ΔV across the resistor is $-IR$ (Fig. 28.13a).
- If a resistor is traversed in the direction *opposite* the current, the potential difference ΔV across the resistor is $+IR$ (Fig. 28.13b).
- If a source of emf (assumed to have zero internal resistance) is traversed in the direction of the emf (from negative to positive), the potential difference ΔV is $+\mathcal{E}$ (Fig. 28.13c).
- If a source of emf (assumed to have zero internal resistance) is traversed in the direction opposite the emf (from positive to negative), the potential difference ΔV is $-\mathcal{E}$ (Fig. 28.13d).

There are limits on the numbers of times you can usefully apply Kirchhoff's rules in analyzing a circuit. You can use the junction rule as often as you need as long as you include in it a current that has not been used in a preceding junction-rule equation. In general, the number of times you can use the junction rule is one fewer than the number of junction points in the circuit. You can apply the loop rule as often as needed as long as a new circuit element (resistor or battery) or a new current appears in each new equation. In general, **to solve a particular circuit problem, the number of independent equations you need to obtain from the two rules equals the number of unknown currents.**

Complex networks containing many loops and junctions generate great numbers of independent linear equations and a correspondingly great number of unknowns. Such situations can be handled formally through the use of matrix algebra. Computer software can also be used to solve for the unknowns.

The following examples illustrate how to use Kirchhoff's rules. In all cases, it is assumed the circuits have reached steady-state conditions; in other words, the currents in the various branches are constant. **Any capacitor acts as an open branch in a circuit;** that is, the current in the branch containing the capacitor is zero under steady-state conditions.

GUSTAV KIRCHHOFF
German Physicist (1824–1887)
Kirchhoff, a professor at Heidelberg, and Robert Bunsen invented the spectroscope and founded the science of spectroscopy, which we shall study in Chapter 42. They discovered the elements cesium and rubidium and invented astronomical spectroscopy.

PROBLEM-SOLVING STRATEGY Kirchhoff's Rules

The following procedure is recommended for solving problems that involve circuits that cannot be reduced by the rules for combining resistors in series or parallel.

1. *Conceptualize.* Study the circuit diagram and make sure you recognize all elements in the circuit. Identify the polarity of each battery and try to imagine the directions in which the current would exist in the batteries.

2. *Categorize.* Determine whether the circuit can be reduced by means of combining series and parallel resistors. If so, use the techniques of Section 28.2. If not, apply Kirchhoff's rules according to the *Analyze* step below.

3. *Analyze.* Assign labels to all known quantities and symbols to all unknown quantities. You must assign *directions* to the currents in each part of the circuit.

Although the assignment of current directions is arbitrary, you must adhere *rigorously* to the directions you assign when you apply Kirchhoff's rules.

Apply the junction rule (Kirchhoff's first rule) to all junctions in the circuit except one. Now apply the loop rule (Kirchhoff's second rule) to as many loops in the circuit as are needed to obtain, in combination with the equations from the junction rule, as many equations as there are unknowns. To apply this rule, you must choose a direction in which to travel around the loop (either clockwise or counterclockwise) and correctly identify the change in potential as you cross each element. Be careful with signs!

Solve the equations simultaneously for the unknown quantities.

4. *Finalize.* Check your numerical answers for consistency. Do not be alarmed if any of the resulting currents have a negative value. That only means you have guessed the direction of that current incorrectly, but *its magnitude will be correct.*

EXAMPLE 28.6 A Single-Loop Circuit

A single-loop circuit contains two resistors and two batteries as shown in Figure 28.14. (Neglect the internal resistances of the batteries.) Find the current in the circuit.

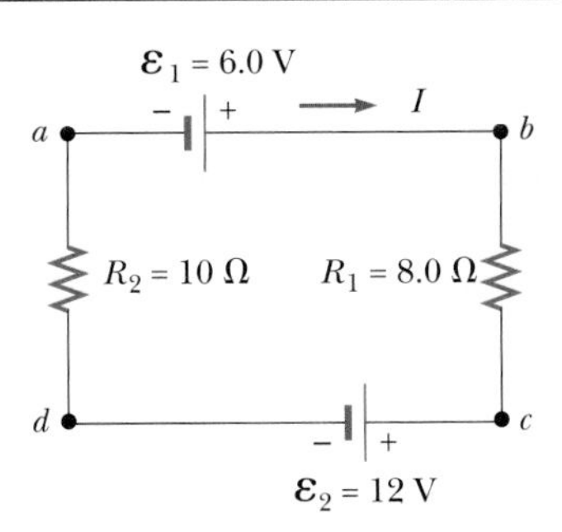

Figure 28.14 (Example 28.6) A series circuit containing two batteries and two resistors, where the polarities of the batteries are in opposition.

SOLUTION

Conceptualize Figure 28.14 shows the polarities of the batteries and a guess at the direction of the current.

Categorize We do not need Kirchhoff's rules to analyze this simple circuit, but let's use them anyway simply to see how they are applied. There are no junctions in this single-loop circuit; therefore, the current is the same in all elements.

Analyze Let's assume the current is clockwise as shown in Figure 28.14. Traversing the circuit in the clockwise direction, starting at a, we see that $a \rightarrow b$ represents a potential difference of $+\mathcal{E}_1$, $b \rightarrow c$ represents a potential difference of $-IR_1$, $c \rightarrow d$ represents a potential difference of $-\mathcal{E}_2$, and $d \rightarrow a$ represents a potential difference of $-IR_2$.

Apply Kirchhoff's loop rule to the single loop in the circuit:

$$\sum \Delta V = 0 \quad \rightarrow \quad \mathcal{E}_1 - IR_1 - \mathcal{E}_2 - IR_2 = 0$$

Solve for I and use the values given in Figure 28.14:

$$(1) \quad I = \frac{\mathcal{E}_1 - \mathcal{E}_2}{R_1 + R_2} = \frac{6.0\text{ V} - 12\text{ V}}{8.0\ \Omega + 10\ \Omega} = -0.33\text{ A}$$

Finalize The negative sign for I indicates that the direction of the current is opposite the assumed direction. The emfs in the numerator subtract because the batteries in Figure 28.14 have opposite polarities. The resistances in the denominator add because the two resistors are in series.

What If? What if the polarity of the 12.0-V battery were reversed? How would that affect the circuit?

Answer Although we could repeat the Kirchhoff's rules calculation, let's instead examine Equation (1) and modify it accordingly. Because the polarities of the two batteries are now in the same direction, the signs of $\mathcal{E}_1$ and $\mathcal{E}_2$ are the same and Equation (1) becomes

$$I = \frac{\mathcal{E}_1 + \mathcal{E}_2}{R_1 + R_2} = \frac{6.0\text{ V} + 12\text{ V}}{8.0\ \Omega + 10\ \Omega} = 1.0\text{ A}$$

EXAMPLE 28.7 A Multiloop Circuit

Find the currents I_1, I_2, and I_3 in the circuit shown in Figure 28.15.

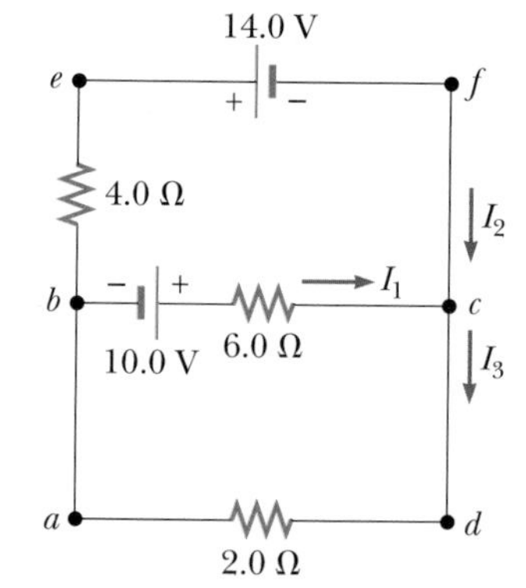

Figure 28.15 (Example 28.7) A circuit containing different branches.

SOLUTION

Conceptualize We cannot simplify the circuit by the rules associated with combining resistances in series and in parallel. (If the 10.0-V battery were not present, we could reduce the remaining circuit with series and parallel combinations.)

Categorize Because the circuit is not a simple series and parallel combination of resistances, this problem is one in which we must use Kirchhoff's rules.

Analyze We arbitrarily choose the directions of the currents as labeled in Figure 28.15.

Apply Kirchhoff's junction rule to junction c:

$$(1) \quad I_1 + I_2 - I_3 = 0$$

We now have one equation with three unknowns: I_1, I_2, and I_3. There are three loops in the circuit: *abcda, befcb,* and *aefda.* We need only two loop equations to determine the unknown currents. (The third loop equation would give no new information.) Let's choose to traverse these loops in the clockwise direction. Apply Kirchhoff's loop rule to loops *abcda* and *befcb*:

$$abcda: \quad (2) \quad 10.0\text{ V} - (6.0\ \Omega)I_1 - (2.0\ \Omega)I_3 = 0$$

$$befcb: \quad -(4.0\ \Omega)I_2 - 14.0\text{ V} + (6.0\ \Omega)I_1 - 10.0\text{ V} = 0$$

$$(3) \quad -24.0\text{ V} + (6.0\ \Omega)I_1 - (4.0\ \Omega)I_2 = 0$$

Solve Equation (1) for I_3 and substitute into Equation (2):

$$10.0\text{ V} - (6.0\ \Omega)I_1 - (2.0\ \Omega)(I_1 + I_2) = 0$$

$$(4) \quad 10.0\text{ V} - (8.0\ \Omega)I_1 - (2.0\ \Omega)I_2 = 0$$

Multiply each term in Equation (3) by 4 and each term in Equation (4) by 3:

$$(5) \quad -96.0\text{ V} + (24.0\ \Omega)I_1 - (16.0\ \Omega)I_2 = 0$$

$$(6) \quad 30.0\text{ V} - (24.0\ \Omega)I_1 - (6.0\ \Omega)I_2 = 0$$

Add Equation (6) to Equation (5) to eliminate I_1 and find I_2:

$$-66.0\text{ V} - (22.0\ \Omega)I_2 = 0$$

$$I_2 = -3.0\text{ A}$$

Use this value of I_2 in Equation (3) to find I_1:

$$-24.0\text{ V} + (6.0\ \Omega)I_1 - (4.0\ \Omega)(-3.0\text{ A}) = 0$$

$$-24.0\text{ V} + (6.0\ \Omega)I_1 + 12.0\text{ V} = 0$$

$$I_1 = 2.0\text{ A}$$

Use Equation (1) to find I_3:

$$I_3 = I_1 + I_2 = 2.0\text{ A} - 3.0\text{ A} = -1.0\text{ A}$$

Finalize Because our values for I_2 and I_3 are negative, the directions of these currents are opposite those indicated in Figure 28.15. The numerical values for the currents are correct. Despite the incorrect direction, we *must* continue to use these negative values in subsequent calculations because our equations were established with our original choice of direction. What would have happened had we left the current directions as labeled in Figure 28.15 but traversed the loops in the opposite direction?

28.4 *RC* Circuits

So far, we have analyzed direct current circuits in which the current is constant. In DC circuits containing capacitors, the current is always in the same direction but may vary in time. A circuit containing a series combination of a resistor and a capacitor is called an ***RC* circuit.**

Charging a Capacitor

Active Figure 28.16 shows a simple series *RC* circuit. Let's assume the capacitor in this circuit is initially uncharged. There is no current while the switch is open (Active Fig. 28.16a). If the switch is thrown to position *a* at $t = 0$ (Active Fig. 28.16b), however, charge begins to flow, setting up a current in the circuit, and the capacitor begins to charge.[3] Notice that during charging, charges do not jump across the capacitor plates because the gap between the plates represents an open circuit. Instead, charge is transferred between each plate and its connecting wires due to the electric field established in the wires by the battery until the capacitor is fully charged. As the plates are being charged, the potential difference across the capacitor increases. The value of the maximum charge on the plates depends on the voltage of the battery. Once the maximum charge is reached, the current in the circuit is zero because the potential difference across the capacitor matches that supplied by the battery.

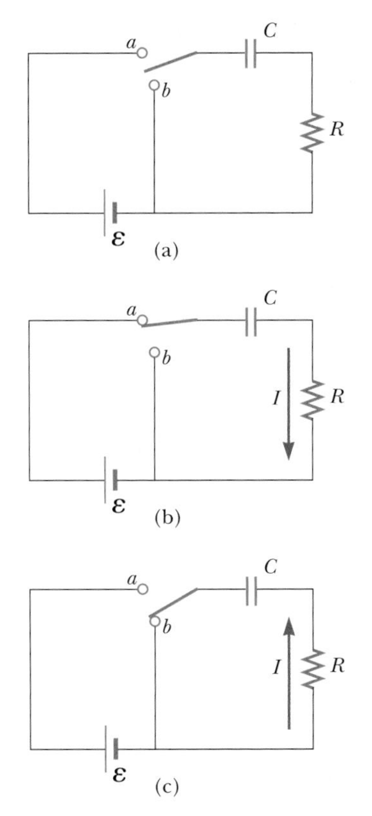

ACTIVE FIGURE 28.16

(a) A capacitor in series with a resistor, switch, and battery. (b) When the switch is thrown to position *a*, the capacitor begins to charge up. (c) When the switch is thrown to position *b*, the capacitor discharges.

Sign in at www.thomsonedu.com and go to ThomsonNOW to adjust the values of *R* and *C* and see the effect on the charging and discharging of the capacitor.

To analyze this circuit quantitatively, let's apply Kirchhoff's loop rule to the circuit after the switch is thrown to position *a*. Traversing the loop in Active Figure 28.16b clockwise gives

$$\mathcal{E} - \frac{q}{C} - IR = 0 \qquad \textbf{(28.11)}$$

where q/C is the potential difference across the capacitor and IR is the potential difference across the resistor. We have used the sign conventions discussed earlier for the signs on $\mathcal{E}$ and IR. The capacitor is traversed in the direction from the positive plate to the negative plate, which represents a decrease in potential. Therefore, we use a negative sign for this potential difference in Equation 28.11. Note that q and I are *instantaneous* values that depend on time (as opposed to steady-state values) as the capacitor is being charged.

We can use Equation 28.11 to find the initial current in the circuit and the maximum charge on the capacitor. At the instant the switch is thrown to position *a* ($t = 0$), the charge on the capacitor is zero. Equation 28.11 shows that the initial current I_i in the circuit is a maximum and is given by

$$I_i = \frac{\mathcal{E}}{R} \quad \text{(current at } t = 0) \qquad \textbf{(28.12)}$$

At this time, the potential difference from the battery terminals appears entirely across the resistor. Later, when the capacitor is charged to its maximum value Q, charges cease to flow, the current in the circuit is zero, and the potential difference from the battery terminals appears entirely across the capacitor. Substituting $I = 0$ into Equation 28.11 gives the maximum charge on the capacitor:

$$Q = C\mathcal{E} \quad \text{(maximum charge)} \qquad \textbf{(28.13)}$$

To determine analytical expressions for the time dependence of the charge and current, we must solve Equation 28.11, a single equation containing two variables q and I. The current in all parts of the series circuit must be the same. Therefore, the current in the resistance R must be the same as the current between each capacitor plate and the wire connected to it. This current is equal to the time rate of change of the charge on the capacitor plates. Therefore, we substitute $I = dq/dt$ into Equation 28.11 and rearrange the equation:

$$\frac{dq}{dt} = \frac{\mathcal{E}}{R} - \frac{q}{RC}$$

[3] In previous discussions of capacitors, we assumed a steady-state situation, in which no current was present in any branch of the circuit containing a capacitor. Now we are considering the case *before* the steady-state condition is realized; in this situation, charges are moving and a current exists in the wires connected to the capacitor.

To find an expression for q, we solve this separable differential equation as follows. First combine the terms on the right-hand side:

$$\frac{dq}{dt} = \frac{C\mathcal{E}}{RC} - \frac{q}{RC} = -\frac{q - C\mathcal{E}}{RC}$$

Multiply this equation by dt and divide by $q - C\mathcal{E}$:

$$\frac{dq}{q - C\mathcal{E}} = -\frac{1}{RC}\,dt$$

Integrate this expression, using $q = 0$ at $t = 0$:

$$\int_0^q \frac{dq}{q - C\mathcal{E}} = -\frac{1}{RC}\int_0^t dt$$

$$\ln\left(\frac{q - C\mathcal{E}}{-C\mathcal{E}}\right) = -\frac{t}{RC}$$

From the definition of the natural logarithm, we can write this expression as

Charge as a function of time for a capacitor being charged ▶

$$q(t) = C\mathcal{E}(1 - e^{-t/RC}) = Q(1 - e^{-t/RC}) \quad \textbf{(28.14)}$$

where e is the base of the natural logarithm and we have made the substitution from Equation 28.13.

We can find an expression for the charging current by differentiating Equation 28.14 with respect to time. Using $I = dq/dt$, we find that

Current as a function of time for a capacitor being charged ▶

$$I(t) = \frac{\mathcal{E}}{R}e^{-t/RC} \quad \textbf{(28.15)}$$

Plots of capacitor charge and circuit current versus time are shown in Figure 28.17. Notice that the charge is zero at $t = 0$ and approaches the maximum value $C\mathcal{E}$ as $t \to \infty$. The current has its maximum value $I_i = \mathcal{E}/R$ at $t = 0$ and decays exponentially to zero as $t \to \infty$. The quantity RC, which appears in the exponents of Equations 28.14 and 28.15, is called the **time constant** τ of the circuit:

$$\tau = RC \quad \textbf{(28.16)}$$

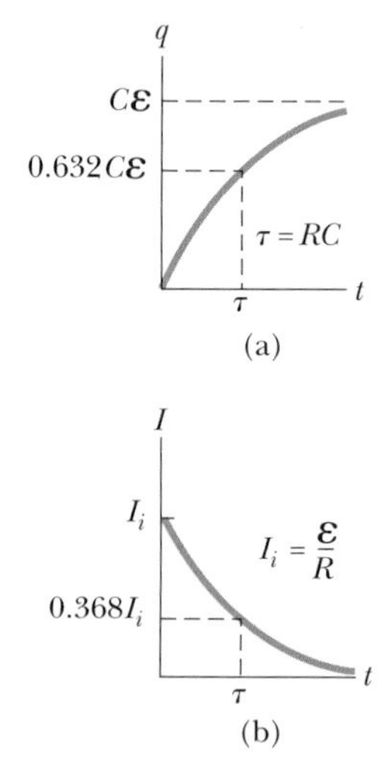

Figure 28.17 (a) Plot of capacitor charge versus time for the circuit shown in Active Figure 28.16. After a time interval equal to one time constant τ has passed, the charge is 63.2% of the maximum value $C\mathcal{E}$. The charge approaches its maximum value as t approaches infinity. (b) Plot of current versus time for the circuit shown in Active Figure 28.16. The current has its maximum value $I_i = \mathcal{E}/R$ at $t = 0$ and decays to zero exponentially as t approaches infinity. After a time interval equal to one time constant τ has passed, the current is 36.8% of its initial value.

The time constant represents the time interval during which the current decreases to $1/e$ of its initial value; that is, after a time interval τ, the current decreases to $I = e^{-1}I_i = 0.368I_i$. After a time interval 2τ, the current decreases to $I = e^{-2}I_i = 0.135I_i$, and so forth. Likewise, in a time interval τ, the charge increases from zero to $C\mathcal{E}[1 - e^{-1}] = 0.632C\mathcal{E}$.

The following dimensional analysis shows that τ has units of time:

$$[\tau] = [RC] = \left[\left(\frac{\Delta V}{I}\right)\left(\frac{Q}{\Delta V}\right)\right] = \left[\frac{Q}{Q/\Delta t}\right] = [\Delta t] = \mathrm{T}$$

Because $\tau = RC$ has units of time, the combination t/RC is dimensionless, as it must be to be an exponent of e in Equations 28.14 and 28.15.

The energy output of the battery as the capacitor is fully charged is $Q\mathcal{E} = C\mathcal{E}^2$. After the capacitor is fully charged, the energy stored in the capacitor is $\frac{1}{2}Q\mathcal{E} = \frac{1}{2}C\mathcal{E}^2$, which is only half the energy output of the battery. It is left as a problem (Problem 52) to show that the remaining half of the energy supplied by the battery appears as internal energy in the resistor.

Discharging a Capacitor

Imagine that the capacitor in Active Figure 28.16b is completely charged. A potential difference Q/C exists across the capacitor and there is zero potential difference across the resistor because $I = 0$. If the switch is now thrown to position b at $t = 0$ (Active Fig. 28.16c), the capacitor begins to discharge through the resistor.

At some time t during the discharge, the current in the circuit is I and the charge on the capacitor is q. The circuit in Active Figure 28.16c is the same as the circuit in Active Figure 28.16b except for the absence of the battery. Therefore, we eliminate the emf $\mathcal{E}$ from Equation 28.11 to obtain the appropriate loop equation for the circuit in Active Figure 28.16c:

$$-\frac{q}{C} - IR = 0 \qquad (28.17)$$

When we substitute $I = dq/dt$ into this expression, it becomes

$$-R\frac{dq}{dt} = \frac{q}{C}$$

$$\frac{dq}{q} = -\frac{1}{RC}\,dt$$

Integrating this expression using $q = Q$ at $t = 0$ gives

$$\int_Q^q \frac{dq}{q} = -\frac{1}{RC}\int_0^t dt$$

$$\ln\left(\frac{q}{Q}\right) = -\frac{t}{RC}$$

$$q(t) = Qe^{-t/RC} \qquad (28.18)$$

◀ Charge as a function of time for a discharging capacitor

Differentiating Equation 28.18 with respect to time gives the instantaneous current as a function of time:

$$I(t) = -\frac{Q}{RC}e^{-t/RC} \qquad (28.19)$$

◀ Current as a function of time for a discharging capacitor

where $Q/RC = I_i$ is the initial current. The negative sign indicates that as the capacitor discharges, the current direction is opposite its direction when the capacitor was being charged. (Compare the current directions in Figs. 28.16b and 28.16c.) Both the charge on the capacitor and the current decay exponentially at a rate characterized by the time constant $\tau = RC$.

Quick Quiz 28.5 Consider the circuit in Figure 28.18 and assume the battery has no internal resistance. **(i)** Just after the switch is closed, what is the current in the battery? (a) 0 (b) $\mathcal{E}/2R$ (c) $2\mathcal{E}/R$ (d) $\mathcal{E}/R$ (e) impossible to determine **(ii)** After a very long time, what is the current in the battery? Choose from the same choices.

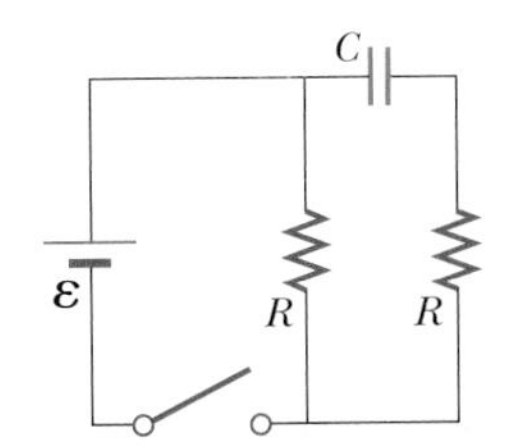

Figure 28.18 (Quick Quiz 28.5) How does the current vary after the switch is closed?

CONCEPTUAL EXAMPLE 28.8 Intermittent Windshield Wipers

Many automobiles are equipped with windshield wipers that can operate intermittently during a light rainfall. How does the operation of such wipers depend on the charging and discharging of a capacitor?

SOLUTION

The wipers are part of an RC circuit whose time constant can be varied by selecting different values of R through a multiposition switch. As the voltage across the capacitor increases, the capacitor reaches a point at which it discharges and triggers the wipers. The circuit then begins another charging cycle. The time interval between the individual sweeps of the wipers is determined by the value of the time constant.

EXAMPLE 28.9 Charging a Capacitor in an *RC* Circuit

An uncharged capacitor and a resistor are connected in series to a battery as shown in Active Figure 28.16, where $\mathcal{E} = 12.0$ V, $C = 5.00\ \mu$F, and $R = 8.00 \times 10^5\ \Omega$. The switch is thrown to position *a*. Find the time constant of the circuit, the maximum charge on the capacitor, the maximum current in the circuit, and the charge and current as functions of time.

SOLUTION

Conceptualize Study Active Figure 28.16 and imagine throwing the switch to position *a* as shown in Active Figure 28.16b. Upon doing so, the capacitor begins to charge.

Categorize We evaluate our results using equations developed in this section, so we categorize this example as a substitution problem.

Evaluate the time constant of the circuit from Equation 28.16:

$$\tau = RC = (8.00 \times 10^5\ \Omega)(5.00 \times 10^{-6}\ \text{F}) = 4.00\ \text{s}$$

Evaluate the maximum charge on the capacitor from Equation 28.13:

$$Q = C\mathcal{E} = (5.00\ \mu\text{F})(12.0\ \text{V}) = 60.0\ \mu\text{C}$$

Evaluate the maximum current in the circuit from Equation 28.12:

$$I_i = \frac{\mathcal{E}}{R} = \frac{12.0\ \text{V}}{8.00 \times 10^5\ \Omega} = 15.0\ \mu\text{A}$$

Use these values in Equations 28.14 and 28.15 to find the charge and current as functions of time:

$$q(t) = (60.0\ \mu\text{C})(1 - e^{-t/4.00\ \text{s}})$$

$$I(t) = (15.0\ \mu\text{A})e^{-t/4.00\ \text{s}}$$

EXAMPLE 28.10 Discharging a Capacitor in an *RC* Circuit

Consider a capacitor of capacitance C that is being discharged through a resistor of resistance R as shown in Active Figure 28.16c.

(A) After how many time constants is the charge on the capacitor one-fourth its initial value?

SOLUTION

Conceptualize Study Active Figure 28.16 and imagine throwing the switch to position *b* as shown in Active Figure 28.16c. Upon doing so, the capacitor begins to discharge.

Categorize We categorize the example as one involving a discharging capacitor and use the appropriate equations.

Analyze Substitute $q(t) = Q/4$ into Equation 28.18:

$$\frac{Q}{4} = Qe^{-t/RC}$$

$$\tfrac{1}{4} = e^{-t/RC}$$

Take the logarithm of both sides of the equation and solve for t:

$$-\ln 4 = -\frac{t}{RC}$$

$$t = RC \ln 4 = 1.39RC = 1.39\tau$$

(B) The energy stored in the capacitor decreases with time as the capacitor discharges. After how many time constants is this stored energy one-fourth its initial value?

SOLUTION

Use Equations 26.11 and 28.18 to express the energy stored in the capacitor at any time t:

$$(1)\quad U(t) = \frac{q^2}{2C} = \frac{Q^2}{2C}e^{-2t/RC}$$

Substitute $U(t) = \frac{1}{4}(Q^2/2C)$ into Equation (1):

$$\frac{1}{4}\frac{Q^2}{2C} = \frac{Q^2}{2C}e^{-2t/RC}$$

$$\frac{1}{4} = e^{-2t/RC}$$

Take the logarithm of both sides of the equation and solve for t:

$$-\ln 4 = -\frac{2t}{RC}$$

$$t = \frac{1}{2}RC\ln 4 = 0.693RC = 0.693\tau$$

Finalize Notice that because the energy depends on the square of the charge, the energy in the capacitor drops more rapidly than the charge on the capacitor.

What If? What if you want to describe the circuit in terms of the time interval required for the charge to fall to one-half its original value rather than by the time constant τ? That would give a parameter for the circuit called its *half-life* $t_{1/2}$. How is the half-life related to the time constant?

Answer In one half-life, the charge falls from Q to $Q/2$. Therefore, from Equation 28.18,

$$\frac{Q}{2} = Qe^{-t_{1/2}/RC} \rightarrow \frac{1}{2} = e^{-t_{1/2}/RC}$$

which leads to

$$t_{1/2} = 0.693\tau$$

The concept of half-life will be important to us when we study nuclear decay in Chapter 44. The radioactive decay of an unstable sample behaves in a mathematically similar manner to a discharging capacitor in an *RC* circuit.

EXAMPLE 28.11 Energy Delivered to a Resistor

A 5.00-μF capacitor is charged to a potential difference of 800 V and then discharged through a resistor. How much energy is delivered to the resistor in the time interval required to fully discharge the capacitor?

SOLUTION

Conceptualize In Example 28.10, we considered the energy decrease in a discharging capacitor to a value of one-fourth of the initial energy. In this example, the capacitor fully discharges.

Categorize We solve this example using two approaches. The first approach is to model the circuit as an isolated system. Because energy in an isolated system is conserved, the initial electric potential energy U_C stored in the capacitor is transformed into internal energy $E_{\text{int}} = E_R$ in the resistor. The second approach is to model the resistor as a nonisolated system. Energy enters the resistor by electrical transmission from the capacitor, causing an increase in the resistor's internal energy.

Analyze We begin with the isolated system approach.

Write the appropriate reduction of the conservation of energy equation, Equation 8.2:

$$\Delta U + \Delta E_{\text{int}} = 0$$

Substitute the initial and final values of the energies:

$$(0 - U_C) + (E_{\text{int}} - 0) = 0 \rightarrow E_R = U_C$$

Use Equation 26.11 for the electric potential energy in the capacitor:

$$E_R = \tfrac{1}{2}C\mathcal{E}^2$$

Substitute numerical values:

$$E_R = \tfrac{1}{2}(5.00 \times 10^{-6}\ \text{F})(800\ \text{V})^2 = \boxed{1.60\ \text{J}}$$

The second approach, which is more difficult but perhaps more instructive, is to note that as the capacitor discharges through the resistor, the rate at which energy is delivered to the resistor by electrical transmission is I^2R, where I is the instantaneous current given by Equation 28.19.

Evaluate the energy delivered to the resistor by integrating the power over all time because it takes an infinite time interval for the capacitor to completely discharge:

$$\mathcal{P} = \frac{dE}{dt} \rightarrow E_R = \int_0^\infty \mathcal{P}\,dt$$

Substitute for the power delivered to the resistor:

$$E_R = \int_0^\infty I^2R\,dt$$

Substitute for the current from Equation 28.19:

$$E_R = \int_0^\infty \left(-\frac{Q}{RC}e^{-t/RC}\right)^2 R\,dt = \frac{Q^2}{RC^2}\int_0^\infty e^{-2t/RC}\,dt = \frac{\mathcal{E}^2}{R}\int_0^\infty e^{-2t/RC}\,dt$$

Substitute the value of the integral, which is $RC/2$ (see Problem 30):

$$E_R = \frac{\mathcal{E}^2}{R}\left(\frac{RC}{2}\right) = \tfrac{1}{2}C\mathcal{E}^2$$

Finalize This result agrees with that obtained using the isolated system approach, as it must. We can use this second approach to find the total energy delivered to the resistor at *any* time after the switch is closed by simply replacing the upper limit in the integral with that specific value of t.

28.5 Electrical Meters

In this section, we discuss various electrical meters that are used in the electrical and electronics industries to make electrical measurements.

The Galvanometer

The **galvanometer** is the main component in analog meters for measuring current and voltage. (Many analog meters are still in use, although digital meters, which operate on a different principle, are currently more common.) One type, called the *D'Arsonval galvanometer,* consists of a coil of wire mounted so that it is free to rotate on a pivot in a magnetic field provided by a permanent magnet. The deflection of a needle attached to the coil is proportional to the current in the galvanometer. Once the instrument is properly calibrated, it can be used in conjunction with other circuit elements to measure either currents or potential differences.

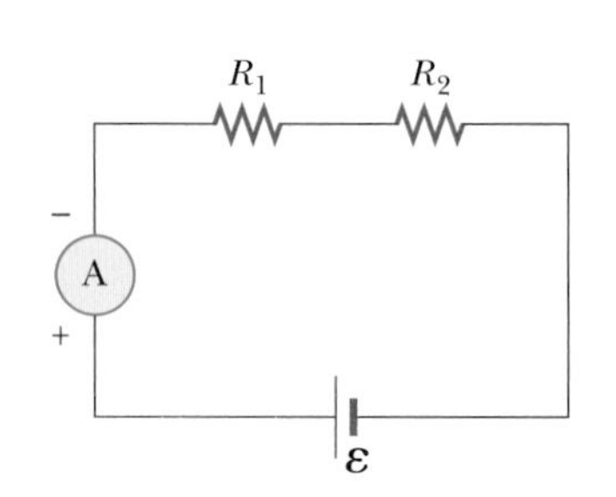

Figure 28.19 Current can be measured with an ammeter connected in series with the elements in which the measurement of a current is desired. An ideal ammeter has zero resistance.

The Ammeter

A device that measures current is called an **ammeter.** Because the charges constituting the current to be measured must pass directly through the ammeter, the ammeter must be connected in series with other elements in the circuit as shown in Figure 28.19. When using an ammeter to measure direct currents, you must connect it so that charges enter the instrument at the positive terminal and exit at the negative terminal.

Ideally, an ammeter should have zero resistance so that the current being measured is not altered. In the circuit shown in Figure 28.19, this condition requires that the resistance of the ammeter be much less than $R_1 + R_2$. Because any ammeter always has some internal resistance, the presence of the ammeter in the circuit slightly reduces the current from the value it would have in the meter's absence.

A typical off-the-shelf galvanometer is often not suitable for use as an ammeter primarily because it has a resistance of about 60 Ω. An ammeter resistance this great considerably alters the current in a circuit. Consider the following example. The current in a simple series circuit containing a 3-V battery and a 3-Ω resistor is 1 A. If you insert a 60-Ω galvanometer in this circuit to measure the current, the total resistance becomes 63 Ω and the current is reduced to 0.048 A!

A second factor that limits the use of a galvanometer as an ammeter is that a typical galvanometer gives a full-scale deflection for currents on the order of 1 mA or less. Consequently, such a galvanometer cannot be used directly to measure currents greater than this value. It can, however, be converted to a useful ammeter by placing a shunt resistor R_p in parallel with the galvanometer as shown in Active Figure 28.20. The value of R_p must be much less than the galvanometer resistance so that most of the current to be measured is directed to the shunt resistor.

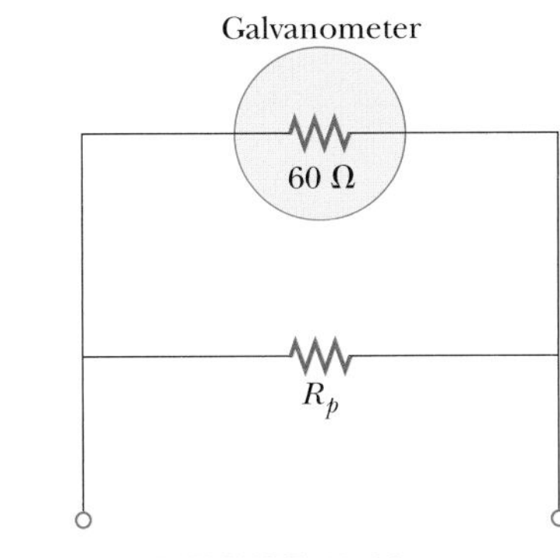

ACTIVE FIGURE 28.20

A galvanometer is represented here by its internal resistance of 60 Ω. When a galvanometer is to be used as an ammeter, a shunt resistor R_p is connected in parallel with the galvanometer.

Sign in at www.thomsonedu.com and go to ThomsonNOW to predict the value of R_p needed to cause full-scale deflection in the circuit of Figure 28.19 and test your result.

The Voltmeter

A device that measures potential difference is called a **voltmeter.** The potential difference between any two points in a circuit can be measured by attaching the terminals of the voltmeter between these points without breaking the circuit as shown in Figure 28.21. The potential difference across resistor R_2 is measured by connecting the voltmeter in parallel with R_2. Again, it is necessary to observe the instrument's polarity. The voltmeter's positive terminal must be connected to the end of the resistor that is at the higher potential, and its negative terminal must be connected to the end of the resistor at the lower potential.

An ideal voltmeter has infinite resistance so that no current exists in it. In Figure 28.21, this condition requires that the voltmeter have a resistance much greater than R_2. In practice, corrections should be made for the known resistance of the voltmeter if this condition is not met.

A galvanometer can also be used as a voltmeter by adding an external resistor R_s in series with it as shown in Active Figure 28.22. In this case, the external resistor must have a value much greater than the resistance of the galvanometer to ensure that the galvanometer does not significantly alter the voltage being measured.

A digital multimeter is used to measure a voltage across a circuit element.

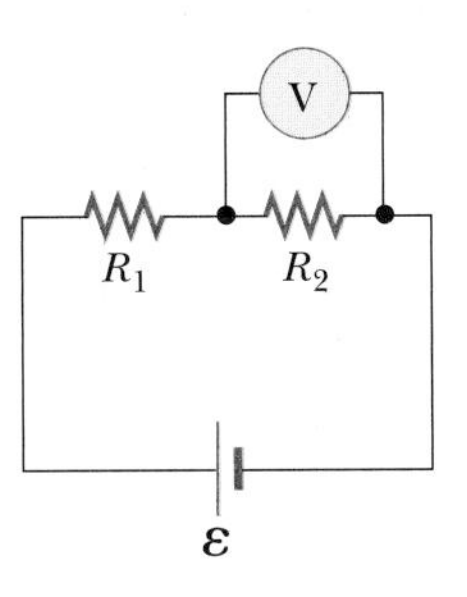

Figure 28.21 The potential difference across a resistor can be measured with a voltmeter connected in parallel with the resistor. An ideal voltmeter has infinite resistance.

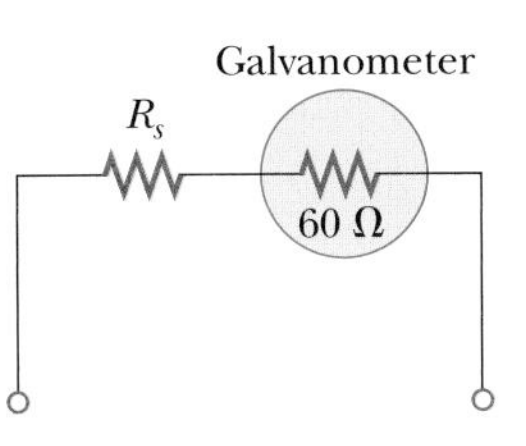

ACTIVE FIGURE 28.22

When the galvanometer is used as a voltmeter, a resistor R_s is connected in series with the galvanometer.

Sign in at www.thomsonedu.com and go to ThomsonNOW to predict the value of R_s needed to cause full-scale deflection in the circuit of Figure 28.21 and test your result.

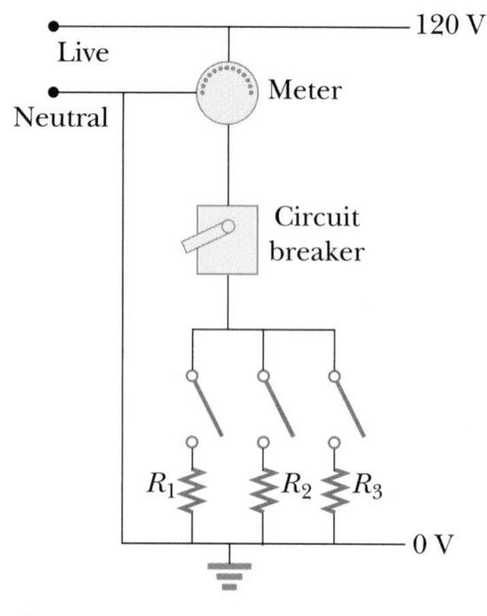

Figure 28.23 Wiring diagram for a household circuit. The resistances represent appliances or other electrical devices that operate with an applied voltage of 120 V.

28.6 Household Wiring and Electrical Safety

Many considerations are important in the design of an electrical system of a home that will provide adequate electrical service for the occupants while maximizing their safety. We discuss some aspects of a home electrical system in this section.

Household Wiring

Household circuits represent a practical application of some of the ideas presented in this chapter. In our world of electrical appliances, it is useful to understand the power requirements and limitations of conventional electrical systems and the safety measures that prevent accidents.

In a conventional installation, the utility company distributes electric power to individual homes by means of a pair of wires, with each home connected in parallel to these wires. One wire is called the *live wire*[4] as illustrated in Figure 28.23, and the other is called the *neutral wire*. The neutral wire is grounded; that is, its electric potential is taken to be zero. The potential difference between the live and neutral wires is approximately 120 V. This voltage alternates in time, and the potential of the live wire oscillates relative to ground. Much of what we have learned so far for the constant-emf situation (direct current) can also be applied to the alternating current that power companies supply to businesses and households. (Alternating voltage and current are discussed in Chapter 33.)

To record a household's energy consumption, a meter is connected in series with the live wire entering the house. After the meter, the wire splits so that there are several separate circuits in parallel distributed throughout the house. Each circuit contains a circuit breaker (or, in older installations, a fuse). The wire and circuit breaker for each circuit are carefully selected to meet the current requirements for that circuit. If a circuit is to carry currents as large as 30 A, a heavy wire and an appropriate circuit breaker must be selected to handle this current. A circuit used to power only lamps and small appliances often requires only 20 A. Each circuit has its own circuit breaker to provide protection for that part of the entire electrical system of the house.

As an example, consider a circuit in which a toaster oven, a microwave oven, and a coffee maker are connected (corresponding to R_1, R_2, and R_3 in Fig. 28.23). We can calculate the current in each appliance by using the expression $\mathcal{P} = I\,\Delta V$. The toaster oven, rated at 1 000 W, draws a current of 1 000 W/120 V = 8.33 A. The microwave oven, rated at 1 300 W, draws 10.8 A, and the coffee maker, rated at 800 W, draws 6.67 A. When the three appliances are operated simultaneously, they draw a total current of 25.8 A. Therefore, the circuit must be wired to handle at least this much current. If the rating of the circuit breaker protecting the circuit is too small—say, 20 A—the breaker will be tripped when the third appliance is turned on, preventing all three appliances from operating. To avoid this situation, the toaster oven and coffee maker can be operated on one 20-A circuit and the microwave oven on a separate 20-A circuit.

Many heavy-duty appliances such as electric ranges and clothes dryers require 240 V for their operation. The power company supplies this voltage by providing a third wire that is 120 V below ground potential (Fig. 28.24). The potential difference between this live wire and the other live wire (which is 120 V above ground potential) is 240 V. An appliance that operates from a 240-V line requires half as much current compared with operating it at 120 V; therefore, smaller wires can be used in the higher-voltage circuit without overheating.

(a)

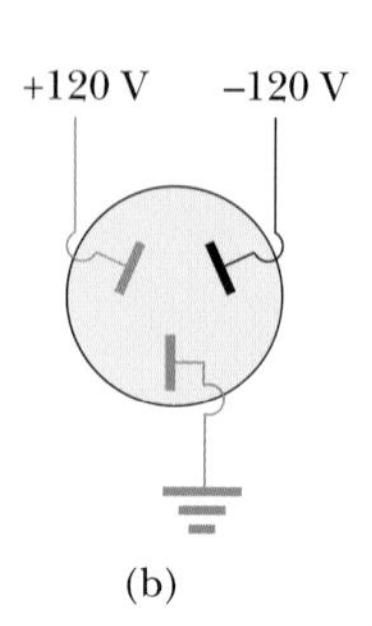

(b)

Figure 28.24 (a) An outlet for connection to a 240-V supply. (b) The connections for each of the openings in a 240-V outlet.

Electrical Safety

When the live wire of an electrical outlet is connected directly to ground, the circuit is completed and a *short-circuit condition* exists. A short circuit occurs when

[4] *Live wire* is a common expression for a conductor whose electric potential is above or below ground potential.

almost zero resistance exists between two points at different potentials, and the result is a very large current. When that happens accidentally, a properly operating circuit breaker opens the circuit and no damage is done. A person in contact with ground, however, can be electrocuted by touching the live wire of a frayed cord or other exposed conductor. An exceptionally effective (and dangerous!) ground contact is made when the person either touches a water pipe (normally at ground potential) or stands on the ground with wet feet. The latter situation represents effective ground contact because normal, nondistilled water is a conductor due to the large number of ions associated with impurities. This situation should be avoided at all cost.

Electric shock can result in fatal burns or can cause the muscles of vital organs such as the heart to malfunction. The degree of damage to the body depends on the magnitude of the current, the length of time it acts, the part of the body touched by the live wire, and the part of the body in which the current exists. Currents of 5 mA or less cause a sensation of shock, but ordinarily do little or no damage. If the current is larger than about 10 mA, the muscles contract and the person may be unable to release the live wire. If the body carries a current of about 100 mA for only a few seconds, the result can be fatal. Such a large current paralyzes the respiratory muscles and prevents breathing. In some cases, currents of approximately 1 A can produce serious (and sometimes fatal) burns. In practice, no contact with live wires is regarded as safe whenever the voltage is greater than 24 V.

Many 120-V outlets are designed to accept a three-pronged power cord. (This feature is required in all new electrical installations.) One of these prongs is the live wire at a nominal potential of 120 V. The second is the neutral wire, nominally at 0 V, which carries current to ground. Figure 28.25a shows a connection to an electric drill with only these two wires. If the live wire accidentally makes contact with the casing of the electric drill (which can occur if the wire insulation wears off), current can be carried to ground by way of the person, resulting in an electric shock. The third wire in a three-pronged power cord, the round prong, is a

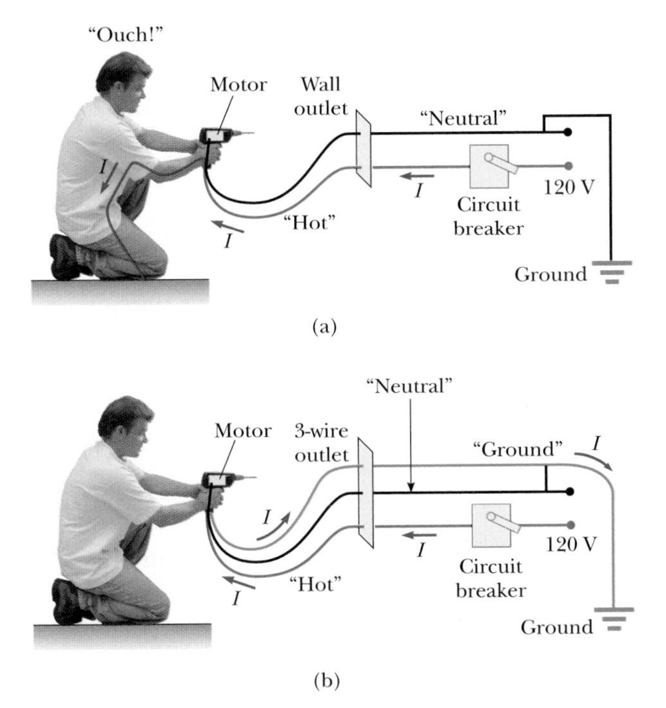

Figure 28.25 (a) A diagram of the circuit for an electric drill with only two connecting wires. The normal current path is from the live wire through the motor connections and back to ground through the neutral wire. In the situation shown, the live wire has come into contact with the drill case. As a result, the person holding the drill acts as a current path to ground and receives an electric shock. (b) This shock can be avoided by connecting the drill case to ground through a third ground wire. In this situation, the drill case remains at ground potential and no current exists in the person.

safety ground wire that normally carries no current. It is both grounded and connected directly to the casing of the appliance. If the live wire is accidentally shorted to the casing in this situation, most of the current takes the low-resistance path through the appliance to ground as shown in Figure 28.25b.

Special power outlets called *ground-fault interrupters,* or GFIs, are used in kitchens, bathrooms, basements, exterior outlets, and other hazardous areas of homes. These devices are designed to protect persons from electric shock by sensing small currents (< 5 mA) leaking to ground. (The principle of their operation is described in Chapter 31.) When an excessive leakage current is detected, the current is shut off in less than 1 ms.

Summary

ThomsonNOW™ Sign in at **www.thomsonedu.com** and go to ThomsonNOW to take a practice test for this chapter.

DEFINITIONS

The **emf** of a battery is equal to the voltage across its terminals when the current is zero. That is, the emf is equivalent to the **open-circuit voltage** of the battery.

CONCEPTS AND PRINCIPLES

The **equivalent resistance** of a set of resistors connected in a **series combination** is

$$R_{eq} = R_1 + R_2 + R_3 + \cdots \qquad (28.6)$$

The **equivalent resistance** of a set of resistors connected in a **parallel combination** is found from the relationship

$$\frac{1}{R_{eq}} = \frac{1}{R_1} + \frac{1}{R_2} + \frac{1}{R_3} + \cdots \qquad (28.8)$$

Circuits involving more than one loop are conveniently analyzed with the use of **Kirchhoff's rules:**

1. **Junction rule.** At any junction, the sum of the currents must equal zero:

$$\sum_{\text{junction}} I = 0 \qquad (28.9)$$

2. **Loop rule.** The sum of the potential differences across all elements around any circuit loop must be zero:

$$\sum_{\text{closed loop}} \Delta V = 0 \qquad (28.10)$$

When a resistor is traversed in the direction of the current, the potential difference ΔV across the resistor is $-IR$. When a resistor is traversed in the direction opposite the current, $\Delta V = +IR$. When a source of emf is traversed in the direction of the emf (negative terminal to positive terminal), the potential difference is $+\mathcal{E}$. When a source of emf is traversed opposite the emf (positive to negative), the potential difference is $-\mathcal{E}$.

If a capacitor is charged with a battery through a resistor of resistance R, the charge on the capacitor and the current in the circuit vary in time according to the expressions

$$q(t) = Q(1 - e^{-t/RC}) \qquad (28.14)$$

$$I(t) = \frac{\mathcal{E}}{R} e^{-t/RC} \qquad (28.15)$$

where $Q = C\mathcal{E}$ is the maximum charge on the capacitor. The product RC is called the **time constant** τ of the circuit.

If a charged capacitor is discharged through a resistor of resistance R, the charge and current decrease exponentially in time according to the expressions

$$q(t) = Qe^{-t/RC} \qquad (28.18)$$

$$I(t) = -I_i e^{-t/RC} \qquad (28.19)$$

where Q is the initial charge on the capacitor and $I_i = Q/RC$ is the initial current in the circuit.

Questions

☐ denotes answer available in *Student Solutions Manual/Study Guide;* **O** denotes objective question

1. Is the direction of current in a battery always from the negative terminal to the positive terminal? Explain.

2. **O** A certain battery has some internal resistance. **(i)** Can the potential difference across the terminals of a battery be equal to its emf? (a) No. (b) Yes, if the battery is absorbing energy by electrical transmission. (c) Yes, if more than one wire is connected to each terminal. (d) Yes, if the current in the battery is zero. (e) Yes; no special condition is required. **(ii)** Can the terminal voltage exceed the emf? Choose your answer from the same possibilities.

3. Given three lightbulbs and a battery, sketch as many different electric circuits as you can.

4. **O** When resistors with different resistances are connected in series, which of the following must be the same for each resistor? Choose all correct answers. (a) potential difference (b) current (c) power delivered (d) charge entering (e) none of these answers

5. **O** When resistors with different resistances are connected in parallel, which of the following must be the same for each resistor? Choose all correct answers. (a) potential difference (b) current (c) power delivered (d) charge entering (e) none of these answers

6. Why is it possible for a bird to sit on a high-voltage wire without being electrocuted?

7. **O** Are the two headlights of a car wired (a) in series with each other, (b) in parallel, (c) neither in series or in parallel, or (d) is it impossible to tell?

8. A student claims that the second of two lightbulbs in series is less bright than the first, because the first lightbulb uses up some of the current. How would you respond to this statement?

9. **O** Is a circuit breaker wired (a) in series with the device it is protecting, (b) in parallel, (c) neither in series or in parallel, or (d) is it impossible to tell?

10. **O** In the circuit shown in Figure Q28.10, each battery is delivering energy to the circuit by electrical transmission. All the resistors have equal resistance. **(i)** Rank the electric potentials at points *a, b, c, d, e, f, g,* and *h* from highest to lowest, noting any cases of equality in the ranking. **(ii)** Rank the magnitudes of the currents at the same points from greatest to least, noting any cases of equality.

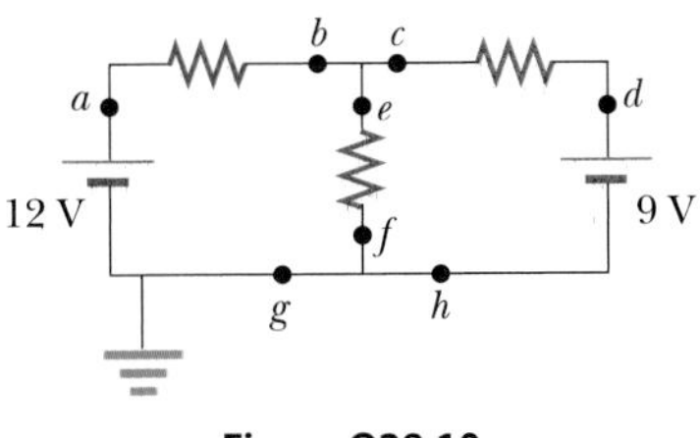

Figure Q28.10

11. **O** A series circuit consists of three identical lamps connected to a battery as shown in Figure Q28.11. The switch S, originally open, is closed. **(i)** What then happens to the brightness of lamp B? (a) It increases. (b) It decreases somewhat. (c) It does not change. (d) It drops to zero. **(ii)** What happens to the brightness of lamp C? Choose from the same possibilities. **(iii)** What happens to the current in the battery? Choose from the same possibilities. **(iv)** What happens to the potential difference across lamp A? **(v)** What happens to the potential difference across lamp C? **(vi)** What happens to the total power delivered to the lamps by the battery? Choose in each case from the same possibilities (a) through (d).

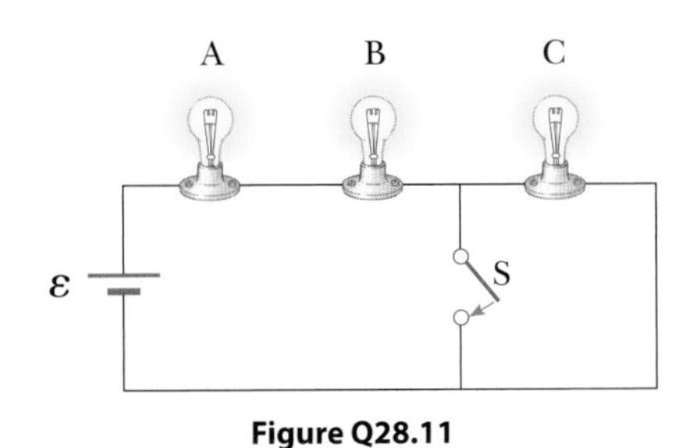

Figure Q28.11

12. **O** A circuit consists of three identical lamps connected to a battery having some internal resistance as in Figure Q28.12. The switch S, originally open, is closed. **(i)** What then happens to the brightness of lamp B? (a) It increases. (b) It decreases somewhat. (c) It does not change. (d) It drops to zero. **(ii)** What happens to the brightness of lamp C? Choose from the same possibilities. **(iii)** What happens to the current in the battery? Choose from the same possibilities. **(iv)** What happens to the potential difference across lamp A? **(v)** What happens to the potential difference across lamp C? **(vi)** What happens to the total power delivered to the lamps by the battery? Choose in each case from the same possibilities (a) through (d).

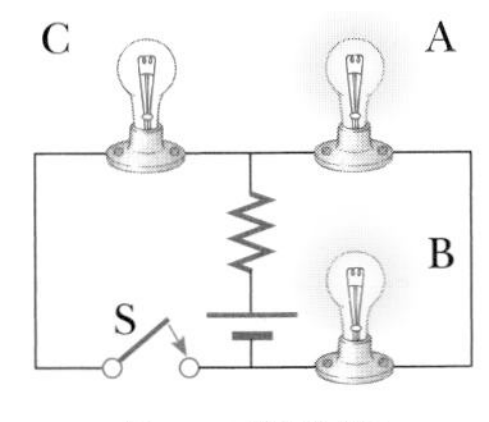

Figure Q28.12

13. A ski resort consists of a few chairlifts and several interconnected downhill runs on the side of a mountain, with a lodge at the bottom. The chairlifts are analogous to batteries, and the runs are analogous to resistors. Describe how two runs can be in series. Describe how three runs can be in parallel. Sketch a junction between one chairlift and two runs. State Kirchhoff's junction rule for ski resorts. One of the skiers happens to be carrying a skydiver's altimeter. She never takes the same set of chairlifts and runs twice, but keeps passing you at the fixed location where you are working. State Kirchhoff's loop rule for ski resorts.

14. Referring to Figure Q28.14, describe what happens to the lightbulb after the switch is closed. Assume the capacitor has a large capacitance and is initially uncharged and assume the light illuminates when connected directly across the battery terminals.

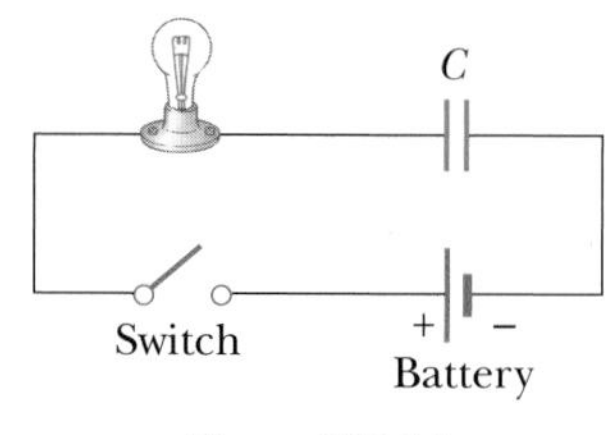

Figure Q28.14

15. So that your grandmother can listen to *A Prairie Home Companion,* you take her bedside radio to the hospital where she is staying. You are required to have a maintenance worker test the radio for electrical safety. Finding that it develops 120 V on one of its knobs, he does not let you take it up to your grandmother's room. She complains that she has had the radio for many years and nobody has ever gotten a shock from it. You end up having to buy a new plastic radio. Is that fair? Will the old radio be safe back in her bedroom?

16. What advantage does 120-V operation offer over 240 V? What disadvantages does it have?

Problems

WebAssign The Problems from this chapter may be assigned online in WebAssign.

ThomsonNOW™ Sign in at **www.thomsonedu.com** and go to ThomsonNOW to assess your understanding of this chapter's topics with additional quizzing and conceptual questions.

1, 2, 3 denotes straightforward, intermediate, challenging; ☐ denotes full solution available in *Student Solutions Manual/Study Guide;* ▲ denotes coached solution with hints available at **www.thomsonedu.com;** ☐ denotes developing symbolic reasoning; ● denotes asking for qualitative reasoning; denotes computer useful in solving problem

Section 28.1 Electromotive Force

1. ▲ A battery has an emf of 15.0 V. The terminal voltage of the battery is 11.6 V when it is delivering 20.0 W of power to an external load resistor R. (a) What is the value of R? (b) What is the internal resistance of the battery?

2. Two 1.50-V batteries—with their positive terminals in the same direction—are inserted in series into the barrel of a flashlight. One battery has an internal resistance of 0.255 Ω, the other an internal resistance of 0.153 Ω. When the switch is closed, a current of 600 mA occurs in the lamp. (a) What is the lamp's resistance? (b) What fraction of the chemical energy transformed appears as internal energy in the batteries?

3. An automobile battery has an emf of 12.6 V and an internal resistance of 0.080 0 Ω. The headlights together have an equivalent resistance of 5.00 Ω (assumed constant). What is the potential difference across the headlight bulbs (a) when they are the only load on the battery and (b) when the starter motor is operated, requiring an additional 35.0 A from the battery?

4. ● As in Example 28.2, consider a power supply with fixed emf $\mathcal{E}$ and internal resistance r causing current in a load resistance R. In this problem, R is fixed and r is a variable. The efficiency is defined as the energy delivered to the load divided by the energy delivered by the emf. (a) When the internal resistance is adjusted for maximum power transfer, what is the efficiency? (b) What should be the internal resistance for maximum possible efficiency? (c) When the electric company sells energy to a customer, does it have a goal of high efficiency or of maximum power transfer? Explain. (d) When a student connects a loudspeaker to an amplifier, does she most want high efficiency or high power transfer? Explain.

Section 28.2 Resistors in Series and Parallel

5. (a) Find the equivalent resistance between points a and b in Figure P28.5. (b) A potential difference of 34.0 V is applied between points a and b. Calculate the current in each resistor.

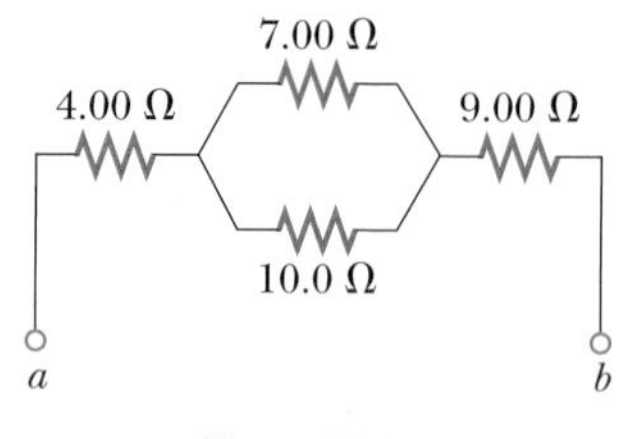

Figure P28.5

6. ● A lightbulb marked "75 W [at] 120 V" is screwed into a socket at one end of a long extension cord, in which each of the two conductors has resistance 0.800 Ω. The other end of the extension cord is plugged into a 120-V outlet. (a) Explain why the actual power delivered to the lightbulb cannot be 75 W in this situation. (b) What can you reasonably model as constant about the lightbulb? Draw a circuit diagram and find the actual power delivered to the lightbulb in this circuit.

7. ▲ Consider the circuit shown in Figure P28.7. Find (a) the current in the 20.0-Ω resistor and (b) the potential difference between points a and b.

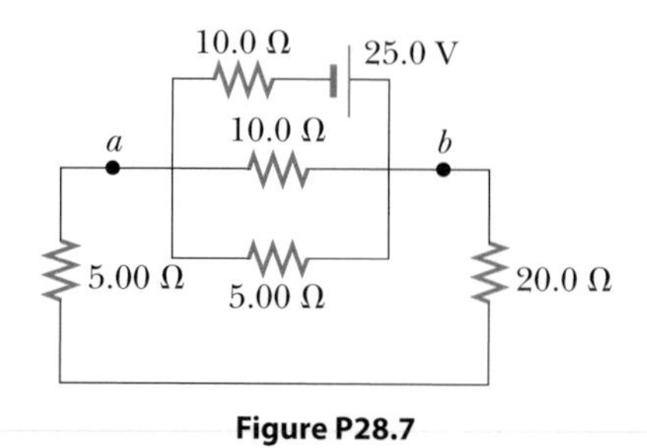

Figure P28.7

8. For the purpose of measuring the electric resistance of shoes through the body of the wearer to a metal ground

plate, the American National Standards Institute (ANSI) specifies the circuit shown in Figure P28.8. The potential difference ΔV across the 1.00-MΩ resistor is measured with a high-resistance voltmeter. (a) Show that the resistance of the footwear is

$$R_{\text{shoes}} = 1.00\ \text{M}\Omega\left(\frac{50.0\ \text{V} - \Delta V}{\Delta V}\right)$$

(b) In a medical test, a current through the human body should not exceed 150 μA. Can the current delivered by the ANSI-specified circuit exceed 150 μA? To decide, consider a person standing barefoot on the ground plate.

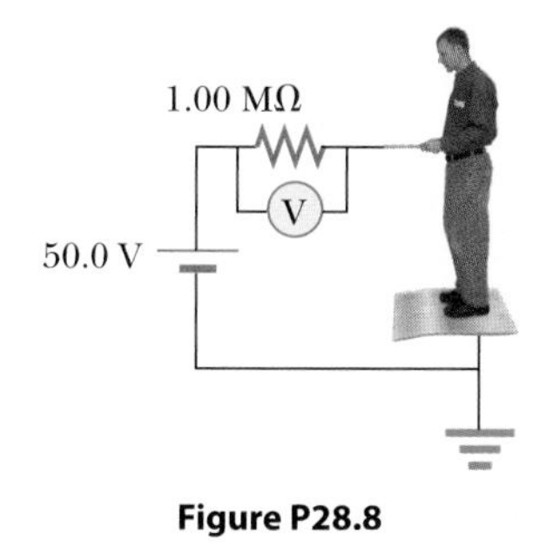

Figure P28.8

9. Three 100-Ω resistors are connected as shown in Figure P28.9. The maximum power that can safely be delivered to any one resistor is 25.0 W. (a) What is the maximum potential difference that can be applied to the terminals a and b? (b) For the voltage determined in part (a), what is the power delivered to each resistor? What is the total power delivered?

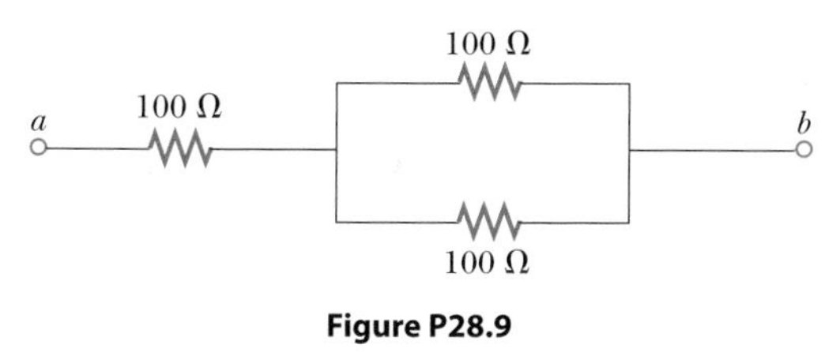

Figure P28.9

10. Using only three resistors—2.00 Ω, 3.00 Ω, and 4.00 Ω—find 17 resistance values that may be obtained by various combinations of one or more resistors. Tabulate the combinations in order of increasing resistance.

11. A 6.00-V battery supplies current to the circuit shown in Figure P28.11. When the double-throw switch S is open as shown in the figure, the current in the battery is 1.00 mA. When the switch is closed in position a, the current in the battery is 1.20 mA. When the switch is closed in position b, the current in the battery is 2.00 mA. Find the resistances R_1, R_2, and R_3.

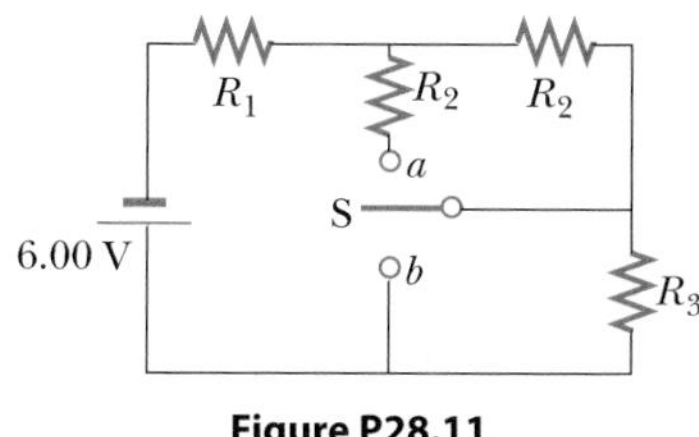

Figure P28.11

12. Two resistors connected in series have an equivalent resistance of 690 Ω. When they are connected in parallel, their equivalent resistance is 150 Ω. Find the resistance of each resistor.

13. ● When the switch S in the circuit of Figure P28.13 is closed, will the equivalent resistance between points a and b increase or decrease? State your reasoning. Assume the equivalent resistance changes by a factor of 2. Determine the value of R.

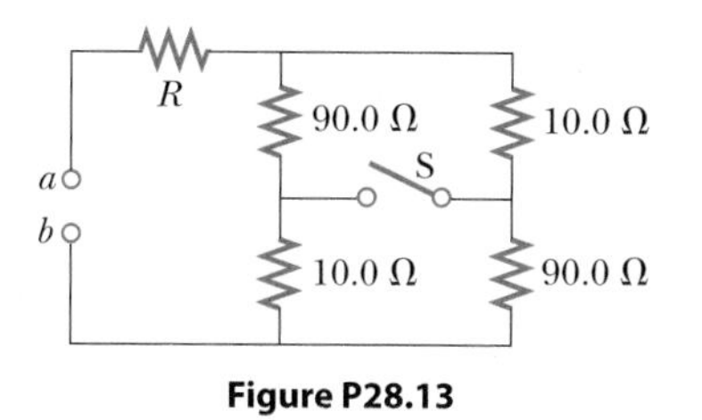

Figure P28.13

14. ● Four resistors are connected to a battery as shown in Figure P28.14. The current in the battery is I; the battery emf is $\mathcal{E}$; and the resistor values are $R_1 = R$, $R_2 = 2R$, $R_3 = 4R$, and $R_4 = 3R$. (a) Rank the resistors according to the potential difference across them from largest to smallest. Note any cases of equal potential differences. (b) Determine the potential difference across each resistor in terms of $\mathcal{E}$. (c) Rank the resistors according to the current in them from largest to smallest. Note any cases of equal currents. (d) Determine the current in each resistor in terms of I. (e) **What If?** If R_3 is increased, explain what happens to the current in each of the resistors. (f) In the limit that $R_3 \to \infty$, what are the new values of the current in each resistor in terms of I, the original current in the battery?

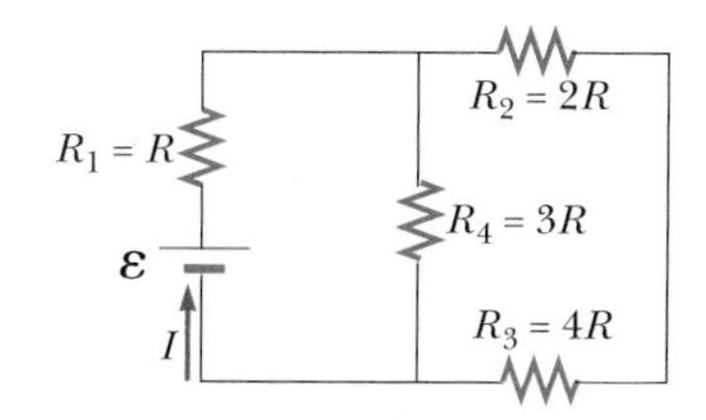

Figure P28.14

15. Calculate the power delivered to each resistor in the circuit shown in Figure P28.15.

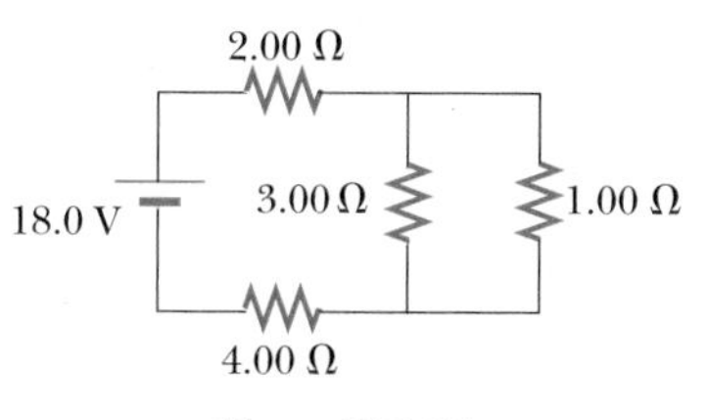

Figure P28.15

Section 28.3 Kirchhoff's Rules

16. The ammeter shown in Figure P28.16 reads 2.00 A. Find I_1, I_2, and $\mathcal{E}$.

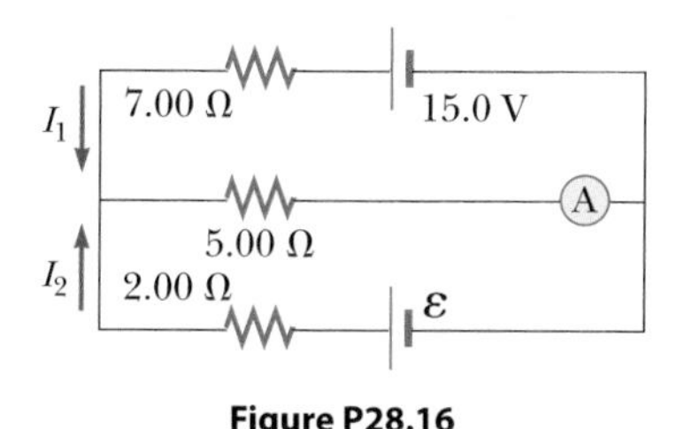

Figure P28.16

17. ▲ Determine the current in each branch of the circuit shown in Figure P28.17.

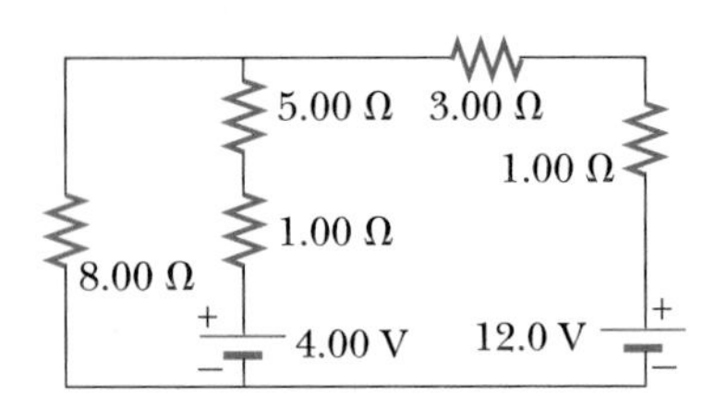

Figure P28.17 Problems 17, 18, and 19.

18. In Figure P28.17, show how to add only enough ammeters to measure every different current. Show how to add only enough voltmeters to measure the potential difference across each resistor and across each battery.

19. ● The circuit considered in Problem 17 and shown in Figure P28.17 is connected for 2.00 min. (a) Find the energy delivered by each battery. (b) Find the energy delivered to each resistor. (c) Identify the net energy transformation that occurs in the operation of the circuit. Find the total amount of energy transformed.

20. The following equations describe an electric circuit:

$$-I_1(220\ \Omega) + 5.80\ \text{V} - I_2(370\ \Omega) = 0$$

$$I_2(370\ \Omega) + I_3(150\ \Omega) - 3.10\ \text{V} = 0$$

$$I_1 + I_3 - I_2 = 0$$

(a) Draw a diagram of the circuit. (b) Calculate the unknowns and identify the physical meaning of each unknown.

21. Consider the circuit shown in Figure P28.21. What are the expected readings of the ideal ammeter and ideal voltmeter?

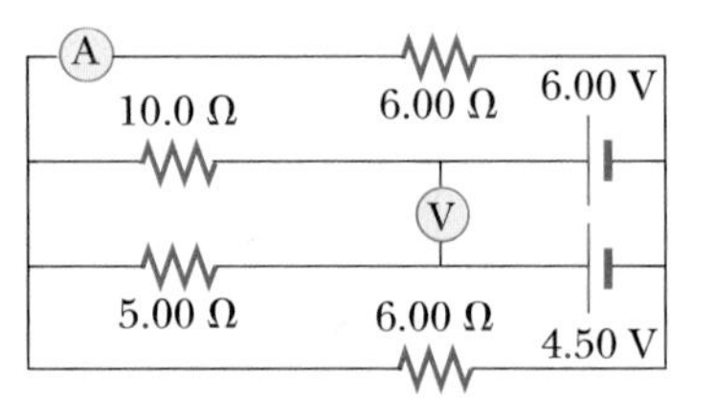

Figure P28.21

22. Taking $R = 1.00$ kΩ and $\mathcal{E} = 250$ V in Figure P28.22, determine the direction and magnitude of the current in the horizontal wire between a and e.

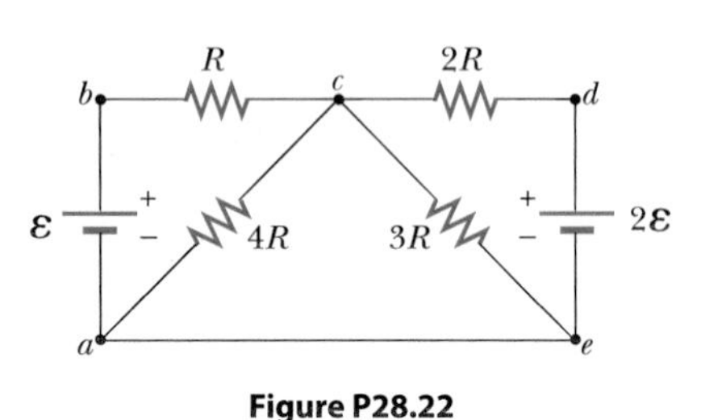

Figure P28.22

23. In the circuit of Figure P28.23, determine the current in each resistor and the potential difference across the 200-Ω resistor.

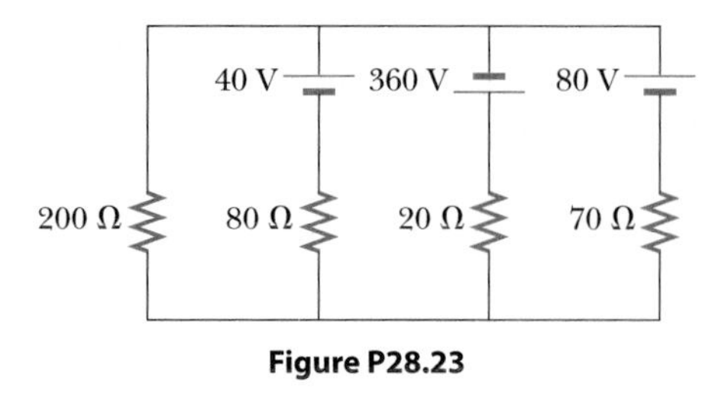

Figure P28.23

24. A dead battery is charged by connecting it to the live battery of another car with jumper cables (Fig. P28.24). Determine the current in the starter and in the dead battery.

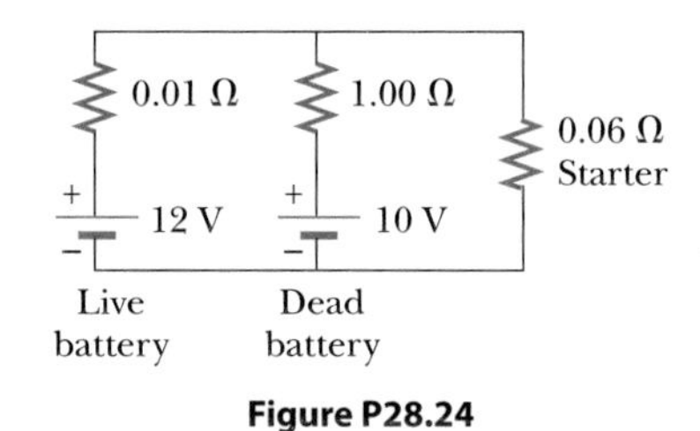

Figure P28.24

25. For the circuit shown in Figure P28.25, calculate (a) the current in the 2.00-Ω resistor and (b) the potential difference between points a and b.

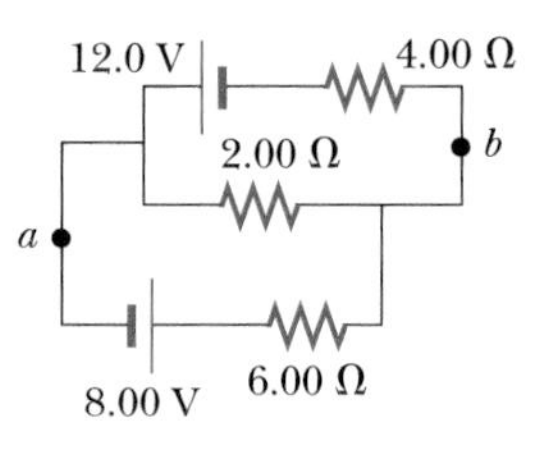

Figure P28.25

26. For the network shown in Figure P28.26, show that the resistance $R_{ab} = \frac{27}{17}$ Ω.

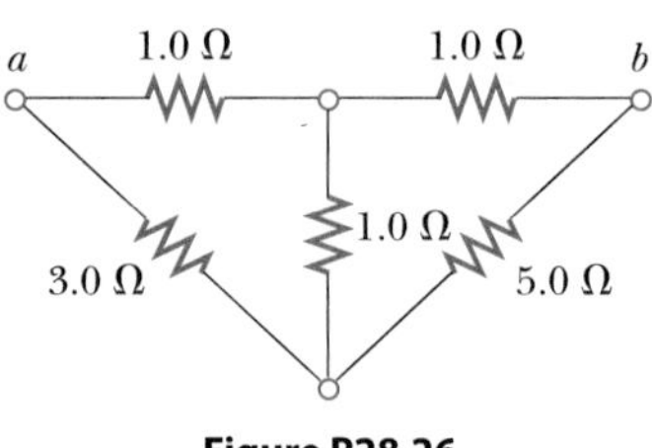

Figure P28.26

Section 28.4 *RC* Circuits

27. ▲ Consider a series *RC* circuit (see Active Fig. 28.16) for which $R = 1.00$ MΩ, $C = 5.00\ \mu$F, and $\mathcal{E} = 30.0$ V. Find (a) the time constant of the circuit and (b) the maximum charge on the capacitor after the switch is thrown to a, connecting the capacitor to the battery. (c) Find the current in the resistor 10.0 s after the switch is thrown to a.

28. A 10.0-μF capacitor is charged by a 10.0-V battery through a resistance R. The capacitor reaches a potential difference of 4.00 V in a time interval of 3.00 s after charging begins. Find R.

29. A 2.00-nF capacitor with an initial charge of 5.10 μC is discharged through a 1.30-kΩ resistor. (a) Calculate the current in the resistor 9.00 μs after the resistor is con-

nected across the terminals of the capacitor. (b) What charge remains on the capacitor after 8.00 μs? (c) What is the maximum current in the resistor?

30. Show that the integral $\int_0^\infty e^{-2t/RC}dt$ in Example 28.11 has the value $RC/2$.

31. The circuit in Figure P28.31 has been connected for a long time. (a) What is the potential difference across the capacitor? (b) If the battery is disconnected from the circuit, over what time interval does the capacitor discharge to one-tenth of its initial voltage?

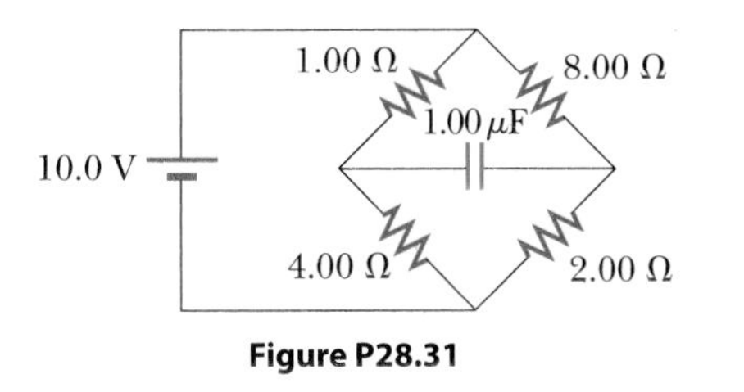

Figure P28.31

32. In the circuit of Figure P28.32, the switch S has been open for a long time. It is then suddenly closed. Determine the time constant (a) before the switch is closed and (b) after the switch is closed. (c) Let the switch be closed at $t = 0$. Determine the current in the switch as a function of time.

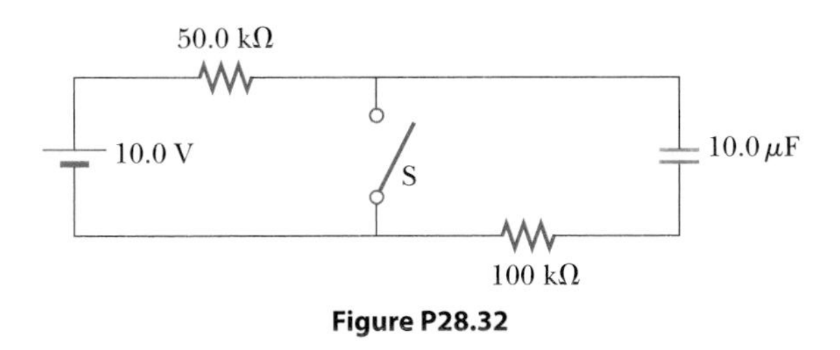

Figure P28.32

Section 28.5 Electrical Meters

33. Assume a galvanometer has an internal resistance of 60.0 Ω and requires a current of 0.500 mA to produce full-scale deflection. What resistance must be connected in parallel with the galvanometer if the combination is to serve as an ammeter that has a full-scale deflection for a current of 0.100 A?

34. A particular galvanometer serves as a 2.00-V full-scale voltmeter when a 2 500-Ω resistor is connected in series with it. It serves as a 0.500-A full-scale ammeter when a 0.220-Ω resistor is connected in parallel with it. Determine the internal resistance of the galvanometer and the current required to produce full-scale deflection.

35. A particular galvanometer requires a current of 1.50 mA for full-scale deflection and has a resistance of 75.0 Ω. It can be used to measure voltages by wiring a large resistor in series with the galvanometer as suggested in Active Figure 28.22. The effect is to limit the current in the galvanometer when large voltages are applied. Calculate the value of the resistor that allows the galvanometer to measure an applied voltage of 25.0 V at full-scale deflection.

36. ● *Meter loading.* Work this problem to five-digit precision. Refer to Figure P28.36. (a) When a 180.00-Ω resistor is connected across a battery of emf 6.000 0 V and internal resistance 20.000 Ω, what is the current in the resistor? What is the potential difference across it? (b) Suppose now an ammeter of resistance 0.500 00 Ω and a voltmeter of resistance 20 000 Ω are added to the circuit as shown in Figure P28.36b. Find the reading of each. (c) **What If?** Now one terminal of one wire is moved as shown in Figure P28.36c. Find the new meter readings. (d) Explain whether one of the voltmeter–ammeter connections is significantly better for taking data to determine the resistance of the resistor.

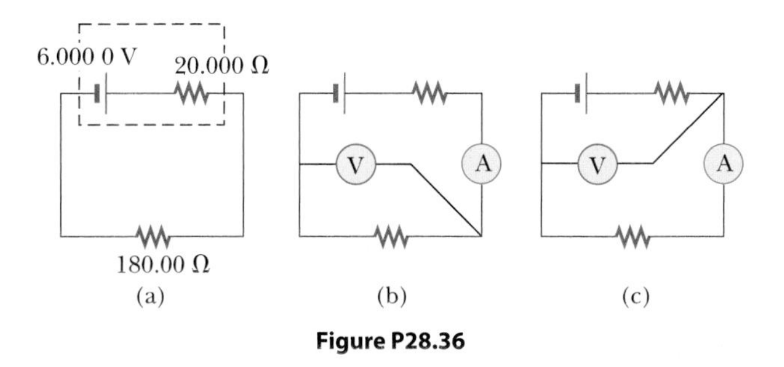

Figure P28.36

Section 28.6 Household Wiring and Electrical Safety

37. ● ▲ An electric heater is rated at 1 500 W, a toaster at 750 W, and an electric grill at 1 000 W. The three appliances are connected to a common 120-V household circuit. (a) How much current does each draw? (b) Is a circuit with a 25.0-A circuit breaker sufficient in this situation? Explain your answer.

38. Turn on your desk lamp. Pick up the cord, with your thumb and index finger spanning the width of the cord. (a) Compute an order-of-magnitude estimate for the current in your hand. Assume the conductor inside the lamp cord next to your thumb is at potential ~ 10^2 V at a typical instant and the conductor next to your index finger is at ground potential (0 V). The resistance of your hand depends strongly on the thickness and the moisture content of the outer layers of your skin. Assume the resistance of your hand between fingertip and thumb tip is ~10^4 Ω. You may model the cord as having rubber insulation. State the other quantities you measure or estimate and their values. Explain your reasoning. (b) Suppose your body is isolated from any other charges or currents. In order-of-magnitude terms, describe the potential of your thumb where it contacts the cord and the potential of your finger where it touches the cord.

Additional Problems

39. The circuit in Figure P28.39 has been connected for several seconds. Find the current (a) in the 4.00-V battery,

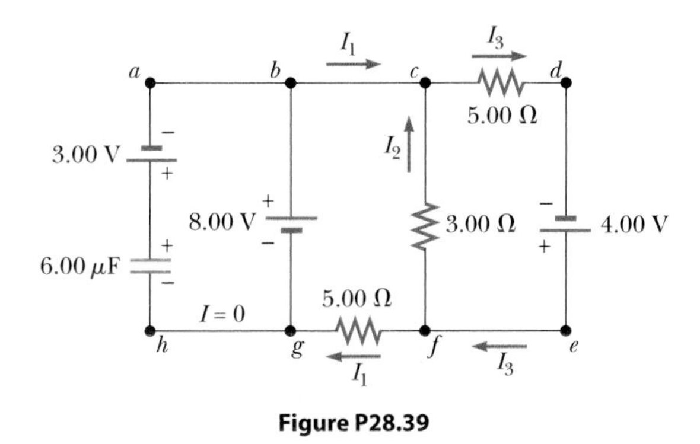

Figure P28.39

(b) in the 3.00-Ω resistor, (c) in the 8.00-V battery, and (d) in the 3.00-V battery. Find (e) the charge on the capacitor.

40. ● The circuit in Figure P28.40a consists of three resistors and one battery with no internal resistance. (a) Find the current in the 5.00-Ω resistor. (b) Find the power delivered to the 5.00-Ω resistor. (c) In each of the circuits in Figures P28.40b, P28.40c, and P28.40d, an additional 15.0-V battery has been inserted into the circuit. Which diagram or diagrams represent a circuit that requires the use of Kirchhoff's rules to find the currents? Explain why. In which of these three circuits is the smallest amount of power delivered to the 10.0-Ω resistor? You need not calculate the power in each circuit if you explain your answer.

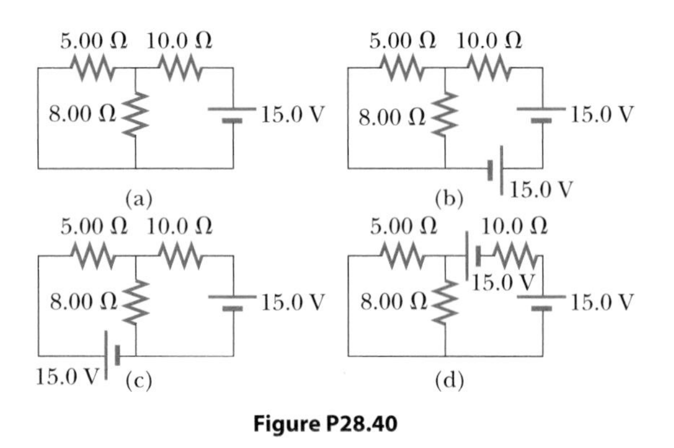

Figure P28.40

41. Four 1.50-V AA batteries in series are used to power a transistor radio. If the batteries can move a charge of 240 C, how long will they last if the radio has a resistance of 200 Ω?

42. ● A battery has an emf of 9.20 V and an internal resistance of 1.20 Ω. (a) What resistance across the battery will extract from it a power of 12.8 W? (b) A power of 21.2 W? Explain your answers.

43. Calculate the potential difference between points a and b in Figure P28.43 and identify which point is at the higher potential.

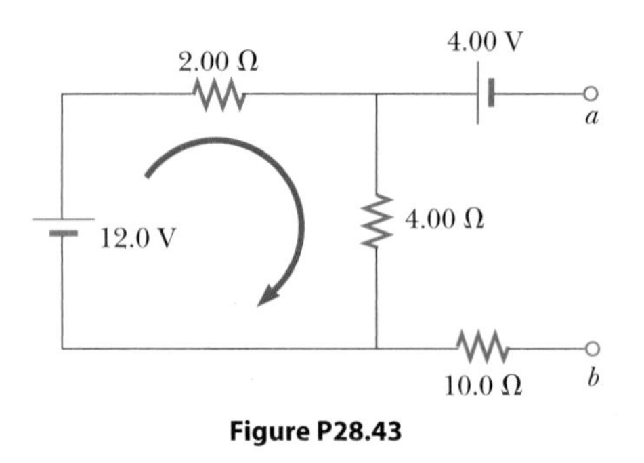

Figure P28.43

44. Assume you have a battery of emf $\mathcal{E}$ and three identical lightbulbs, each having constant resistance R. What is the total power delivered by the battery if the lightbulbs are connected (a) in series? (b) In parallel? (c) For which connection will the lightbulbs shine the brightest?

45. A rechargeable battery has a constant emf of 13.2 V and an internal resistance of 0.850 Ω. It is charged by a 14.7-V power supply for a time interval of 1.80 h. After charging, the battery returns to its original state as it delivers a constant current to a load resistor over 7.30 h. Find the efficiency of the battery as an energy storage device. (The efficiency here is defined as the energy delivered to the load during discharge divided by the energy delivered by the 14.7-V power supply during the charging process.)

46. A power supply has an open-circuit voltage of 40.0 V and an internal resistance of 2.00 Ω. It is used to charge two storage batteries connected in series, each having an emf of 6.00 V and internal resistance of 0.300 Ω. If the charging current is to be 4.00 A, (a) what additional resistance should be added in series? (b) At what rate does the internal energy increase in the supply, in the batteries, and in the added series resistance? (c) At what rate does the chemical energy increase in the batteries?

47. When two unknown resistors are connected in series with a battery, the battery delivers 225 W and carries a total current of 5.00 A. For the same total current, 50.0 W is delivered when the resistors are connected in parallel. Determine the value of each resistor.

48. When two unknown resistors are connected in series with a battery, the battery delivers total power $\mathcal{P}_s$ and carries a total current of I. For the same total current, a total power $\mathcal{P}_p$ is delivered when the resistors are connected in parallel. Determine the value of each resistor.

49. Two resistors R_1 and R_2 are in parallel with each other. Together they carry total current I. (a) Determine the current in each resistor. (b) Prove that this division of the total current I between the two resistors results in less power delivered to the combination than any other division. It is a general principle that *current in a direct current circuit distributes itself so that the total power delivered to the circuit is a minimum.*

50. ● (a) Determine the equilibrium charge on the capacitor in the circuit of Figure P28.50 as a function of R. (b) Evaluate the charge when R = 10.0 Ω. (c) Can the charge on the capacitor be zero? If so, for what value of R? (d) What is the maximum possible magnitude of the charge on the capacitor? For what value of R is it achieved? (e) Is it experimentally meaningful to take $R = \infty$? Explain your answer. If so, what charge magnitude does it imply? *Suggestion:* You may do part (b) before part (a), as practice for it.

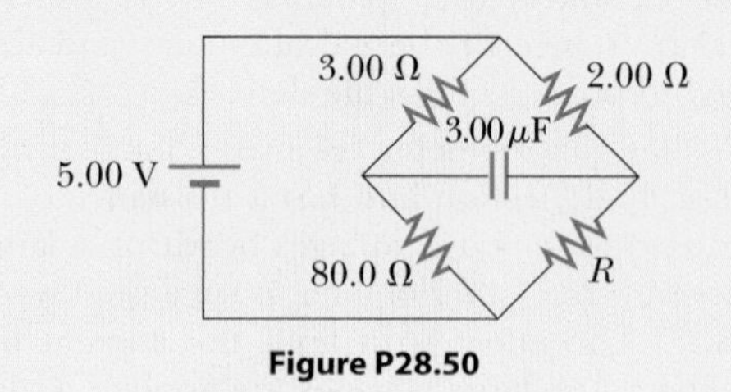

Figure P28.50

51. The value of a resistor R is to be determined using the ammeter–voltmeter setup shown in Figure P28.51. The ammeter has a resistance of 0.500 Ω, and the voltmeter has a resistance of 20.0 kΩ. Within what range of actual values of R will the measured values be correct to within

2 = intermediate; 3 = challenging; □ = SSM/SG; ▲ = ThomsonNOW; ▒ = symbolic reasoning; ● = qualitative reasoning

5.00% if the measurement is made using the circuit shown in (a) Figure P28.51a and (b) Figure P28.51b?

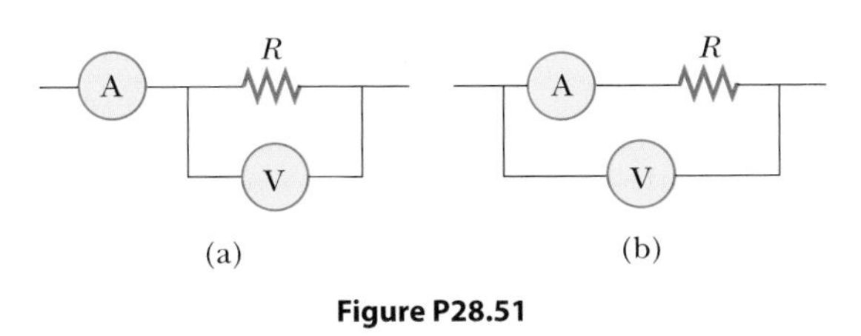

Figure P28.51

52. A battery is used to charge a capacitor through a resistor as shown in Active Figure 28.16b. Show that half the energy supplied by the battery appears as internal energy in the resistor and half is stored in the capacitor.

53. The values of the components in a simple series RC circuit containing a switch (Active Fig. 28.16b) are $C = 1.00\ \mu\text{F}$, $R = 2.00 \times 10^6\ \Omega$, and $\mathcal{E} = 10.0$ V. At the instant 10.0 s after the switch is thrown to a, calculate (a) the charge on the capacitor, (b) the current in the resistor, (c) the rate at which energy is being stored in the capacitor, and (d) the rate at which energy is being delivered by the battery.

54. A young man owns a canister vacuum cleaner marked 535 W at 120 V and a Volkswagen Beetle, which he wishes to clean. He parks the car in his apartment parking lot and uses an inexpensive extension cord 15.0 m long to plug in the vacuum cleaner. You may assume the cleaner has constant resistance. (a) If the resistance of each of the two conductors in the extension cord is 0.900 Ω, what is the actual power delivered to the cleaner? (b) If instead the power is to be at least 525 W, what must be the diameter of each of two identical copper conductors in the cord he buys? (c) Repeat part (b) assuming the power is to be at least 532 W. *Suggestion:* A symbolic solution can simplify the calculations.

55. Three 60.0-W, 120-V lightbulbs are connected across a 120-V power source as shown in Figure P28.55. Find (a) the total power delivered to the three lightbulbs and (b) the potential difference across each. Assume the resistance of each lightbulb is constant (even though in reality the resistance might increase markedly with current).

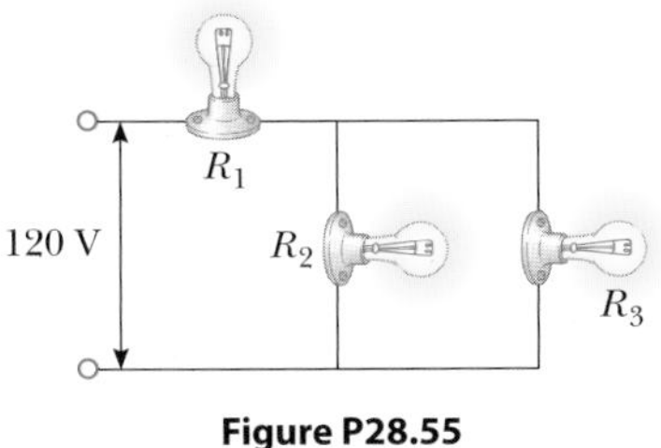

Figure P28.55

56. Switch S shown in Figure P28.56 has been closed for a long time and the electric circuit carries a constant current. Take $C_1 = 3.00\ \mu\text{F}$, $C_2 = 6.00\ \mu\text{F}$, $R_1 = 4.00$ kΩ, and $R_2 = 7.00$ kΩ. The power delivered to R_2 is 2.40 W. (a) Find the charge on C_1. (b) Now the switch is opened. After many milliseconds, by how much has the charge on C_2 changed?

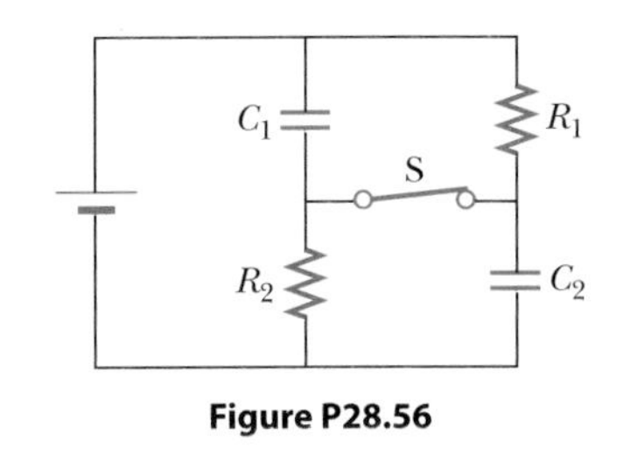

Figure P28.56

57. ● An ideal voltmeter connected across a certain fresh battery reads 9.30 V, and an ideal ammeter briefly connected across the same battery reads 3.70 A. We say that the battery has an open-circuit voltage of 9.30 V and a short-circuit current of 3.70 A. (a) Model the battery as a source of emf $\mathcal{E}$ in series with an internal resistance r. Determine both $\mathcal{E}$ and r. (b) An irresponsible experimenter connects 20 of these identical batteries together as suggested in Figure P28.57. Do not try this experiment yourself! Find the open-circuit voltage and the short-circuit current of the set of connected batteries. (c) Assume the resistance between the palms of the experimenter's two hands is 120 Ω. Find the current in his body that would result if his palms touched the two exposed terminals of the set of connected batteries. (d) Find the power that would be delivered to his body in this situation. (e) Thinking it is safe to do so, the experimenter threads a copper wire inside his shirt between his hands, like a mitten string. To reduce the current in his body to 5.00 mA when he presses the ends of the wire against the battery poles, what should the resistance of the copper wire be? (f) Find the power delivered to his body in this situation. (g) Find the power delivered to the copper wire. (h) Explain why the sum of the two powers in parts (f) and (g) is much less than the power calculated in part (d). Is it meaningful to ask where the rest of the power is going?

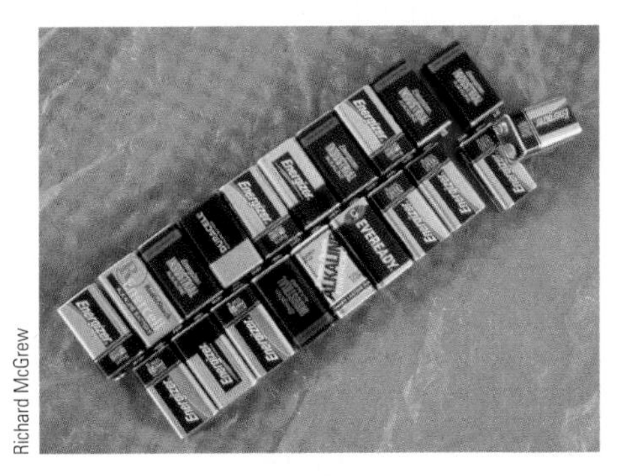

Figure P28.57

58. ● Four resistors are connected in parallel across a 9.20-V battery. They carry currents of 150 mA, 45.0 mA, 14.0 mA, and 4.00 mA. (a) If the resistor with the largest resistance is replaced with one having twice the resistance, what is the ratio of the new current in the battery to the original current? (b) **What If?** If instead the resistor with the smallest resistance is replaced with one having twice the resistance, what is the ratio of the new total current to the original current? (c) On a February night, energy leaves a

house by several energy leaks, including the following: 1 500 W by conduction through the ceiling, 450 W by infiltration (airflow) around the windows, 140 W by conduction through the basement wall above the foundation sill, and 40.0 W by conduction through the plywood door to the attic. To produce the biggest saving in heating bills, which one of these energy transfers should be reduced first? Explain how you decide. Clifford Swartz suggested the idea for this problem.

59. Figure P28.59 shows a circuit model for the transmission of an electrical signal such as cable TV to a large number of subscribers. Each subscriber connects a load resistance R_L between the transmission line and the ground. The ground is assumed to be at zero potential and able to carry any current between any ground connections with negligible resistance. The resistance of the transmission line between the connection points of different subscribers is modeled as the constant resistance R_T. Show that the equivalent resistance across the signal source is

$$R_{eq} = \tfrac{1}{2}[(4R_TR_L + R_T^2)^{1/2} + R_T]$$

Suggestion: Because the number of subscribers is large, the equivalent resistance would not change noticeably if the first subscriber canceled the service. Consequently, the equivalent resistance of the section of the circuit to the right of the first load resistor is nearly equal to R_{eq}.

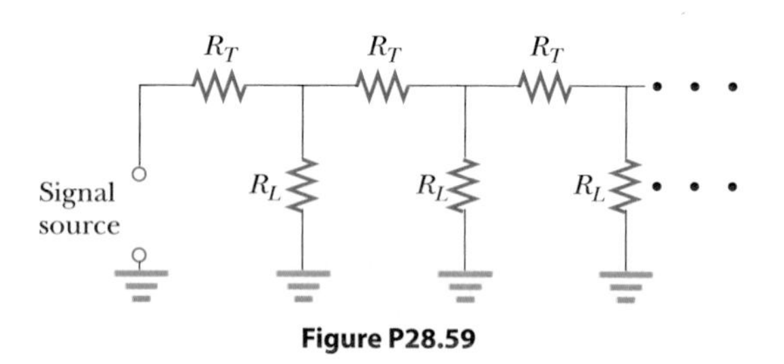

Figure P28.59

60. A regular tetrahedron is a pyramid with a triangular base. Six 10.0-Ω resistors are placed along its six edges, with junctions at its four vertices. A 12.0-V battery is connected to any two of the vertices. Find (a) the equivalent resistance of the tetrahedron between these vertices and (b) the current in the battery.

61. In Figure P28.61, suppose the switch has been closed for a time interval sufficiently long for the capacitor to become fully charged. Find (a) the steady-state current in each resistor and (b) the charge Q on the capacitor. (c) The switch is now opened at $t = 0$. Write an equation for the current I_{R_2} in R_2 as a function of time and (d) find the time interval required for the charge on the capacitor to fall to one-fifth its initial value.

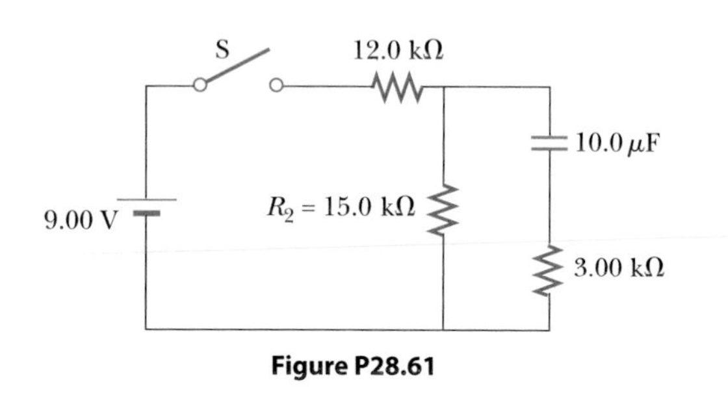

Figure P28.61

62. The circuit shown in Figure P28.62 is set up in the laboratory to measure an unknown capacitance C with the use of a voltmeter of resistance R = 10.0 MΩ and a battery whose emf is 6.19 V. The data given in the table are the measured voltages across the capacitor as a function of time, where $t = 0$ represents the instant at which the switch is opened. (a) Construct a graph of $\ln(\mathcal{E}/\Delta V)$ versus t and perform a linear least-squares fit to the data. (b) From the slope of your graph, obtain a value for the time constant of the circuit and a value for the capacitance.

ΔV (V)	t (s)	$\ln(\mathcal{E}/\Delta V)$
6.19	0	
5.55	4.87	
4.93	11.1	
4.34	19.4	
3.72	30.8	
3.09	46.6	
2.47	67.3	
1.83	102.2	

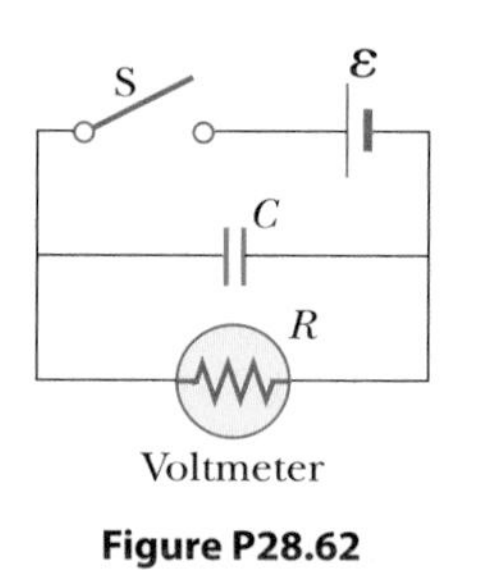

Figure P28.62

63. The student engineer of a campus radio station wishes to verify the effectiveness of the lightning rod on the antenna mast (Fig. P28.63). The unknown resistance R_x is between points C and E. Point E is a true ground, but it is inaccessible for direct measurement because this stratum is several meters below the Earth's surface. Two identical rods are driven into the ground at A and B, introducing an unknown resistance R_y. The procedure is as follows. Measure resistance R_1 between points A and B, then connect A and B with a heavy conducting wire and measure resistance R_2 between points A and C. (a) Derive an equation for R_x in terms of the observable resistances, R_1 and R_2. (b) A satisfactory ground resistance would be $R_x <$ 2.00 Ω. Is the grounding of the station adequate if measurements give R_1 = 13.0 Ω and R_2 = 6.00 Ω?

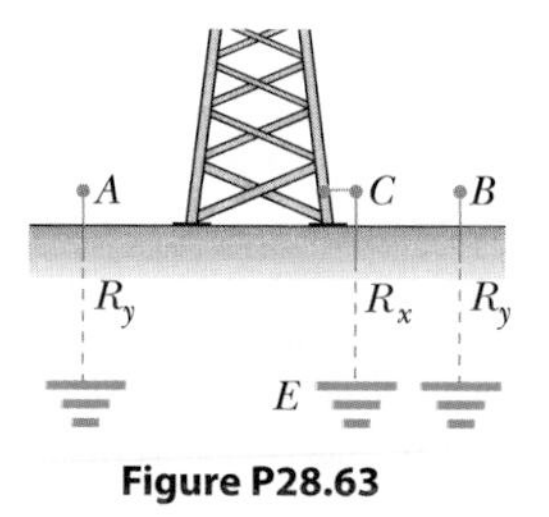

Figure P28.63

64. The switch in Figure P28.64a closes when $\Delta V_c > 2\Delta V/3$ and opens when $\Delta V_c < \Delta V/3$. The voltmeter reads a

potential difference as plotted in Figure P28.64b. What is the period T of the waveform in terms of R_1, R_2, and C?

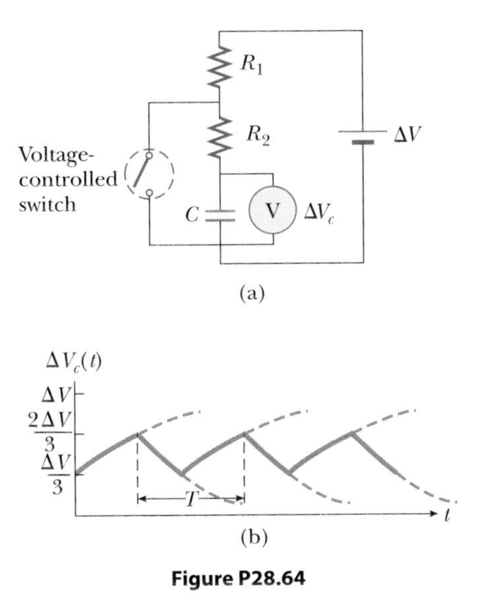

Figure P28.64

65. An electric teakettle has a multiposition switch and two heating coils. When only one coil is switched on, the well-insulated kettle brings a full pot of water to a boil over the time interval Δt. When only the other coil is switched on, it takes a time interval of $2\Delta t$ to boil the same amount of water. Find the time interval required to boil the same amount of water if both coils are switched on (a) in a parallel connection and (b) in a series connection.

66. In places such as hospital operating rooms or factories for electronic circuit boards, electric sparks must be avoided. A person standing on a grounded floor and touching nothing else can typically have a body capacitance of 150 pF, in parallel with a foot capacitance of 80.0 pF produced by the dielectric soles of his or her shoes. The person acquires static electric charge from interactions with furniture, clothing, equipment, packaging materials, and essentially everything else. The static charge flows to ground through the equivalent resistance of the two shoe soles in parallel with each other. A pair of rubber-soled street shoes can present an equivalent resistance of 5 000 MΩ. A pair of shoes with special static-dissipative soles can have an equivalent resistance of 1.00 MΩ. Consider the person's body and shoes as forming an RC circuit with the ground. (a) How long does it take the rubber-soled shoes to reduce a person's potential from 3 000 V to 100 V? (b) How long does it take the static-dissipative shoes to do the same thing?

Answers to Quick Quizzes

28.1 (a). Power is delivered to the internal resistance of a battery, so decreasing the internal resistance decreases this "lost" power and increase the percentage of the power delivered to the device.

28.2 (b). When the switch is opened, resistors R_1 and R_2 are in series, so the total circuit resistance is larger than when the switch was closed. As a result, the current decreases.

28.3 (a). When the switch is closed, resistors R_1 and R_2 are in parallel, so the total circuit resistance is smaller than when the switch was open. As a result, the current increases.

28.4 **(i),** (b). Adding another series resistor increases the total resistance of the circuit and therefore reduces the current in the circuit. **(ii),** (a). The potential difference across the battery terminals increases because the reduced current results in a smaller voltage decrease across the internal resistance. **(iii),** (a). If a third resistor were connected in parallel, the total resistance of the circuit would decrease and the current in the battery would increase. **(iv),** (b). The potential difference across the terminals would decrease because the increased current results in a greater voltage drop across the internal resistance.

28.5 **(i),** (c). Just after the switch is closed, there is no charge on the capacitor. Current exists in both branches of the circuit as the capacitor begins to charge, so the right half of the circuit is equivalent to two resistances R in parallel for an equivalent resistance of $\frac{1}{2}R$. **(ii),** (d). After a long time, the capacitor is fully charged and the current in the right-hand branch drops to zero. Now, current exists only in a resistance R across the battery.

Magnetic fingerprinting allows fingerprints to be seen on surfaces that otherwise would not allow prints to be lifted. The powder spread on the surface is coated with an organic material that adheres to the greasy residue in a fingerprint. A magnetic "brush" removes the excess powder and makes the fingerprint visible. (James King-Holmes/Photo Researchers, Inc.)

29 Magnetic Fields

Many historians of science believe that the compass, which uses a magnetic needle, was used in China as early as the 13th century BC, its invention being of Arabic or Indian origin. The early Greeks knew about magnetism as early as 800 BC. They discovered that the stone magnetite (Fe_3O_4) attracts pieces of iron. Legend ascribes the name *magnetite* to the shepherd Magnes, the nails of whose shoes and the tip of whose staff stuck fast to chunks of magnetite while he pastured his flocks.

In 1269, Pierre de Maricourt of France found that the directions of a needle near a spherical natural magnet formed lines that encircled the sphere and passed through two points diametrically opposite each other, which he called the *poles* of the magnet. Subsequent experiments showed that every magnet, regardless of its shape, has two poles, called *north* (N) and *south* (S) poles, that exert forces on other magnetic poles similar to the way electric charges exert forces on one another. That is, like poles (N–N or S–S) repel each other, and opposite poles (N–S) attract each other.

The poles received their names because of the way a magnet, such as that in a compass, behaves in the presence of the Earth's magnetic field. If a bar magnet is suspended from its midpoint and can swing freely in a horizontal plane, it will rotate until its north pole points to the Earth's geographic North Pole and its south pole points to the Earth's geographic South Pole.[1]

In 1600, William Gilbert (1540–1603) extended de Maricourt's experiments to a variety of materials. He knew that a compass needle orients in preferred directions, so he suggested that the Earth itself is a large, permanent magnet. In 1750, experimenters used a torsion balance to show that magnetic poles exert attractive or repulsive forces on each other and that these forces vary as the inverse square of the distance between interacting poles. Although the force between two magnetic poles is otherwise similar to the force between two electric charges, electric charges can be isolated (witness the electron and proton), whereas **a single magnetic pole has never been isolated.** That is, **magnetic poles are always found in pairs.** All attempts thus far to detect an isolated magnetic pole have been unsuccessful. No matter how many times a permanent magnet is cut in two, each piece always has a north and a south pole.[2]

The relationship between magnetism and electricity was discovered in 1819 when, during a lecture demonstration, Hans Christian Oersted found that an electric current in a wire deflected a nearby compass needle.[3] In the 1820s, further connections between electricity and magnetism were demonstrated independently by Faraday and Joseph Henry (1797–1878). They showed that an electric current can be produced in a circuit either by moving a magnet near the circuit or by changing the current in a nearby circuit. These observations demonstrate that a changing magnetic field creates an electric field. Years later, theoretical work by Maxwell showed that the reverse is also true: a changing electric field creates a magnetic field.

This chapter examines the forces that act on moving charges and on current-carrying wires in the presence of a magnetic field. The source of the magnetic field is described in Chapter 30.

HANS CHRISTIAN OERSTED
Danish Physicist and Chemist (1777–1851)
Oersted is best known for observing that a compass needle deflects when placed near a wire carrying a current. This important discovery was the first evidence of the connection between electric and magnetic phenomena. Oersted was also the first to prepare pure aluminum.

29.1 Magnetic Fields and Forces

In our study of electricity, we described the interactions between charged objects in terms of electric fields. Recall that an electric field surrounds any electric charge. In addition to containing an electric field, the region of space surrounding any *moving* electric charge also contains a magnetic field. A magnetic field also surrounds a magnetic substance making up a permanent magnet.

Historically, the symbol $\vec{\mathbf{B}}$ has been used to represent a magnetic field, and we use this notation in this book. The direction of the magnetic field $\vec{\mathbf{B}}$ at any location is the direction in which a compass needle points at that location. As with the electric field, we can represent the magnetic field by means of drawings with *magnetic field lines.*

Active Figure 29.1 shows how the magnetic field lines of a bar magnet can be traced with the aid of a compass. Notice that the magnetic field lines outside the

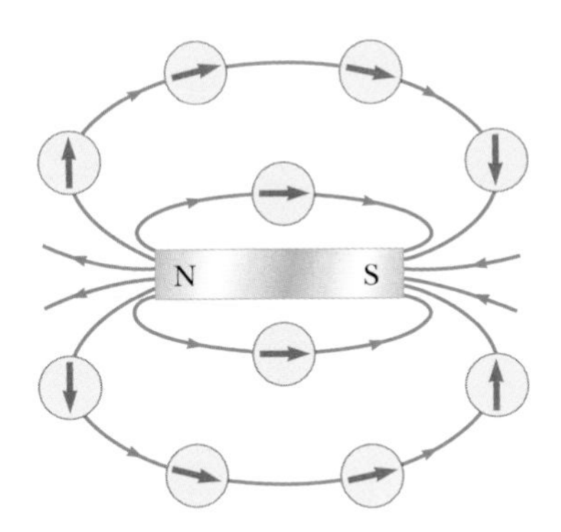

ACTIVE FIGURE 29.1

Compass needles can be used to trace the magnetic field lines in the region outside a bar magnet.

Sign in at www.thomsonedu.com and go to ThomsonNOW to move the compass around and trace the magnetic field lines for yourself.

[1] The Earth's geographic North Pole is magnetically a south pole, whereas the Earth's geographic South Pole is magnetically a north pole. Because *opposite* magnetic poles attract each other, the pole on a magnet that is attracted to the Earth's geographic North Pole is the magnet's *north* pole and the pole attracted to the Earth's geographic South Pole is the magnet's *south* pole.

[2] There is some theoretical basis for speculating that magnetic *monopoles*—isolated north or south poles—may exist in nature, and attempts to detect them are an active experimental field of investigation.

[3] The same discovery was reported in 1802 by an Italian jurist, Gian Domenico Romagnosi, but was overlooked, probably because it was published in an obscure journal.

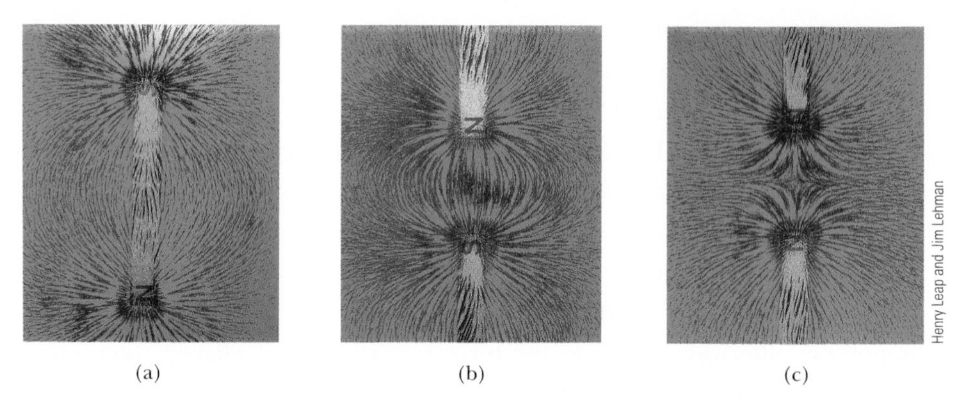

Figure 29.2 (a) Magnetic field pattern surrounding a bar magnet as displayed with iron filings. (b) Magnetic field pattern between *opposite* poles (N–S) of two bar magnets. (c) Magnetic field pattern between *like* poles (N–N) of two bar magnets.

magnet point away from the north pole and toward the south pole. One can display magnetic field patterns of a bar magnet using small iron filings as shown in Figure 29.2.

We can define a magnetic field $\vec{\mathbf{B}}$ at some point in space in terms of the magnetic force $\vec{\mathbf{F}}_B$ that the field exerts on a charged particle moving with a velocity $\vec{\mathbf{v}}$, which we call the test object. For the time being, let's assume no electric or gravitational fields are present at the location of the test object. Experiments on various charged particles moving in a magnetic field give the following results:

Properties of the magnetic force on a charge moving in a magnetic field ▶

- The magnitude F_B of the magnetic force exerted on the particle is proportional to the charge q and to the speed v of the particle.
- When a charged particle moves parallel to the magnetic field vector, the magnetic force acting on the particle is zero.
- When the particle's velocity vector makes any angle $\theta \neq 0$ with the magnetic field, the magnetic force acts in a direction perpendicular to both $\vec{\mathbf{v}}$ and $\vec{\mathbf{B}}$; that is, $\vec{\mathbf{F}}_B$ is perpendicular to the plane formed by $\vec{\mathbf{v}}$ and $\vec{\mathbf{B}}$ (Fig. 29.3a).
- The magnetic force exerted on a positive charge is in the direction opposite the direction of the magnetic force exerted on a negative charge moving in the same direction (Fig. 29.3b).
- The magnitude of the magnetic force exerted on the moving particle is proportional to $\sin\theta$, where θ is the angle the particle's velocity vector makes with the direction of $\vec{\mathbf{B}}$.

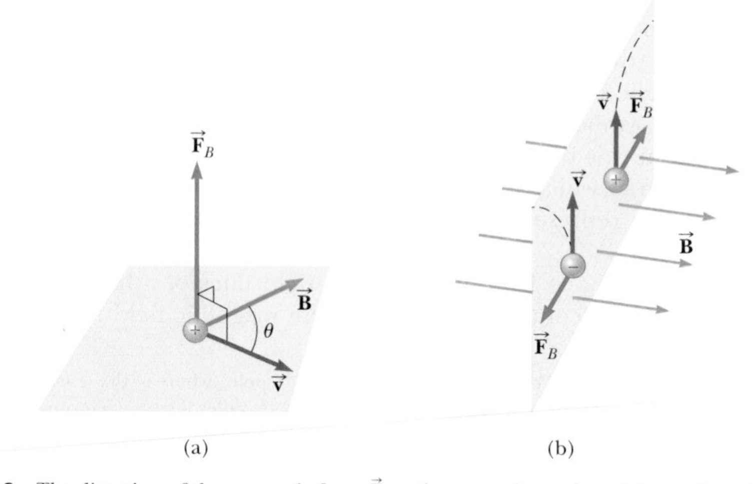

Figure 29.3 The direction of the magnetic force $\vec{\mathbf{F}}_B$ acting on a charged particle moving with a velocity $\vec{\mathbf{v}}$ in the presence of a magnetic field $\vec{\mathbf{B}}$. (a) The magnetic force is perpendicular to both $\vec{\mathbf{v}}$ and $\vec{\mathbf{B}}$. (b) Oppositely directed magnetic forces $\vec{\mathbf{F}}_B$ are exerted on two oppositely charged particles moving at the same velocity in a magnetic field. The dashed lines show the paths of the particles, which are investigated in Section 29.2.

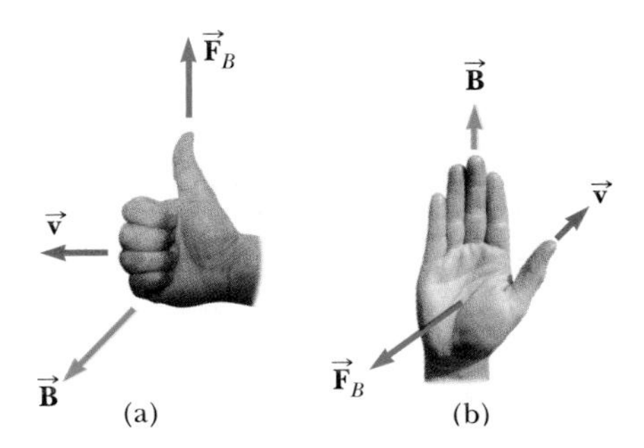

Figure 29.4 Two right-hand rules for determining the direction of the magnetic force $\vec{F}_B = q\vec{v} \times \vec{B}$ acting on a particle with charge q moving with a velocity $\vec{v}$ in a magnetic field $\vec{B}$. (a) In this rule, your fingers point in the direction of $\vec{v}$, with $\vec{B}$ coming out of your palm, so that you can curl your fingers in the direction of $\vec{B}$. The direction of $\vec{v} \times \vec{B}$, and the force on a positive charge, is the direction in which your thumb points. (b) In this rule, the vector $\vec{v}$ is in the direction of your thumb and $\vec{B}$ in the direction of your fingers. The force $\vec{F}_B$ on a positive charge is in the direction of your palm, as if you are pushing the particle with your hand.

We can summarize these observations by writing the magnetic force in the form

$$\vec{F}_B = q\vec{v} \times \vec{B} \tag{29.1}$$

◀ Vector expression for the magnetic force on a charged particle moving in a magnetic field

which by definition of the cross product (see Section 11.1) is perpendicular to both $\vec{v}$ and $\vec{B}$. We can regard this equation as an operational definition of the magnetic field at some point in space. That is, the magnetic field is defined in terms of the force acting on a moving charged particle.

Figure 29.4 reviews two right-hand rules for determining the direction of the cross product $\vec{v} \times \vec{B}$ and determining the direction of $\vec{F}_B$. The rule in Figure 29.4a depends on our right-hand rule for the cross product in Figure 11.2. Point the four fingers of your right hand along the direction of $\vec{v}$ with the palm facing $\vec{B}$ and curl them toward $\vec{B}$. Your extended thumb, which is at a right angle to your fingers, points in the direction of $\vec{v} \times \vec{B}$. Because $\vec{F}_B = q\vec{v} \times \vec{B}$, $\vec{F}_B$ is in the direction of your thumb if q is positive and is opposite the direction of your thumb if q is negative. (If you need more help understanding the cross product, you should review Section 11.1, including Fig. 11.2.)

An alternative rule is shown in Figure 29.4b. Here the thumb points in the direction of $\vec{v}$ and the extended fingers in the direction of $\vec{B}$. Now, the force $\vec{F}_B$ on a positive charge extends outward from the palm. The advantage of this rule is that the force on the charge is in the direction that you would push on something with your hand: outward from your palm. The force on a negative charge is in the opposite direction. You can use either of these two right-hand rules.

The magnitude of the magnetic force on a charged particle is

$$F_B = |q|vB\sin\theta \tag{29.2}$$

◀ Magnitude of the magnetic force on a charged particle moving in a magnetic field

where θ is the smaller angle between $\vec{v}$ and $\vec{B}$. From this expression, we see that F_B is zero when $\vec{v}$ is parallel or antiparallel to $\vec{B}$ ($\theta = 0$ or $180°$) and maximum when $\vec{v}$ is perpendicular to $\vec{B}$ ($\theta = 90°$).

Electric and magnetic forces have several important differences:

- The electric force vector is along the direction of the electric field, whereas the magnetic force vector is perpendicular to the magnetic field.
- The electric force acts on a charged particle regardless of whether the particle is moving, whereas the magnetic force acts on a charged particle only when the particle is in motion.
- The electric force does work in displacing a charged particle, whereas the magnetic force associated with a steady magnetic field does no work when a particle is displaced because the force is perpendicular to the displacement.

From the last statement and on the basis of the work–kinetic energy theorem, we conclude that the kinetic energy of a charged particle moving through a magnetic field cannot be altered by the magnetic field alone. The field can alter the

TABLE 29.1
Some Approximate Magnetic Field Magnitudes

Source of Field	Field Magnitude (T)
Strong superconducting laboratory magnet	30
Strong conventional laboratory magnet	2
Medical MRI unit	1.5
Bar magnet	10^{-2}
Surface of the Sun	10^{-2}
Surface of the Earth	0.5×10^{-4}
Inside human brain (due to nerve impulses)	10^{-13}

direction of the velocity vector, but it cannot change the speed or kinetic energy of the particle.

From Equation 29.2, we see that the SI unit of magnetic field is the newton per coulomb-meter per second, which is called the **tesla** (T):

The tesla ▶

$$1 \text{ T} = 1 \frac{\text{N}}{\text{C} \cdot \text{m/s}}$$

Because a coulomb per second is defined to be an ampere,

$$1 \text{ T} = 1 \frac{\text{N}}{\text{A} \cdot \text{m}}$$

A non-SI magnetic-field unit in common use, called the *gauss* (G), is related to the tesla through the conversion $1 \text{ T} = 10^4 \text{ G}$. Table 29.1 shows some typical values of magnetic fields.

Quick Quiz 29.1 An electron moves in the plane of this paper toward the top of the page. A magnetic field is also in the plane of the page and directed toward the right. What is the direction of the magnetic force on the electron? (a) toward the top of the page (b) toward the bottom of the page (c) toward the left edge of the page (d) toward the right edge of the page (e) upward out of the page (f) downward into the page

EXAMPLE 29.1 An Electron Moving in a Magnetic Field

An electron in a television picture tube moves toward the front of the tube with a speed of 8.0×10^6 m/s along the x axis (Fig. 29.5). Surrounding the neck of the tube are coils of wire that create a magnetic field of magnitude 0.025 T, directed at an angle of 60° to the x axis and lying in the xy plane. Calculate the magnetic force on the electron.

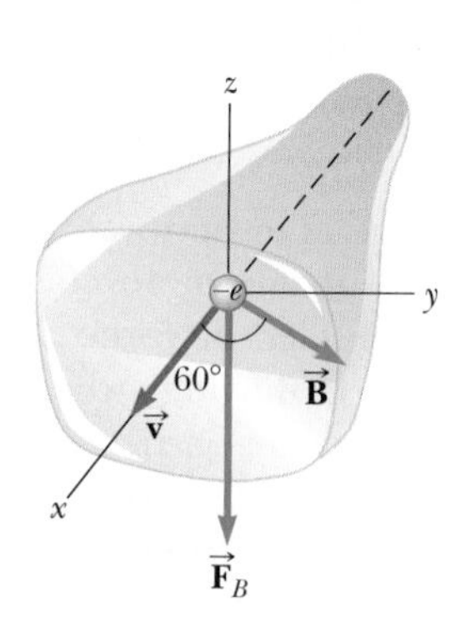

Figure 29.5 (Example 29.1) The magnetic force $\vec{\mathbf{F}}_B$ acting on the electron is in the negative z direction when $\vec{\mathbf{v}}$ and $\vec{\mathbf{B}}$ lie in the xy plane.

SOLUTION

Conceptualize Recall that the magnetic force on a charged particle is perpendicular to the plane formed by the velocity and magnetic field vectors. Use the right-hand rule in Figure 29.4 to convince yourself that the direction of the force on the electron is downward in Figure 29.5.

Categorize We evaluate the magnetic force using an equation developed in this section, so we categorize this example as a substitution problem.

Use Equation 29.2 to find the magnitude of the magnetic force:

$$F_B = |q|vB\sin\theta$$
$$= (1.6 \times 10^{-19}\ \text{C})(8.0 \times 10^{6}\ \text{m/s})(0.025\ \text{T})(\sin 60^\circ)$$
$$= 2.8 \times 10^{-14}\ \text{N}$$

For practice using the vector product, evaluate this force in vector notation using Equation 29.1.

29.2 Motion of a Charged Particle in a Uniform Magnetic Field

Before we continue our discussion, some explanation of the notation used in this book is in order. To indicate the direction of $\vec{\mathbf{B}}$ in illustrations, we sometimes present perspective views such as those in Figure 29.5. If $\vec{\mathbf{B}}$ lies in the plane of the page or is present in a perspective drawing, we use green vectors or green field lines with arrowheads. In nonperspective illustrations, we depict a magnetic field perpendicular to and directed out of the page with a series of green dots, which represent the tips of arrows coming toward you (see Fig. 29.6a). In this case, the field is labeled $\vec{\mathbf{B}}_{\text{out}}$. If $\vec{\mathbf{B}}$ is directed perpendicularly into the page, we use green crosses, which represent the feathered tails of arrows fired away from you, as in Figure 29.6b. In this case, the field is labeled $\vec{\mathbf{B}}_{\text{in}}$, where the subscript "in" indicates "into the page." The same notation with crosses and dots is also used for other quantities that might be perpendicular to the page such as forces and current directions.

$\vec{\mathbf{B}}$ out of page:

(a)

$\vec{\mathbf{B}}$ into page:

(b)

Figure 29.6 (a) Magnetic field lines coming out of the paper are indicated by dots, representing the tips of arrows coming outward. (b) Magnetic field lines going into the paper are indicated by crosses, representing the feathers of arrows going inward.

In Section 29.1, we found that the magnetic force acting on a charged particle moving in a magnetic field is perpendicular to the particle's velocity and consequently the work done by the magnetic force on the particle is zero. Now consider the special case of a positively charged particle moving in a uniform magnetic field with the initial velocity vector of the particle perpendicular to the field. Let's assume that the direction of the magnetic field is into the page as in Active Figure 29.7. As the particle changes the direction of its velocity in response to the magnetic force, the magnetic force remains perpendicular to the velocity. As we found in Section 6.1, if the force is always perpendicular to the velocity, the path of the particle is a circle! Active Figure 29.7 shows the particle moving in a circle in a plane perpendicular to the magnetic field.

The particle moves in a circle because the magnetic force $\vec{\mathbf{F}}_B$ is perpendicular to $\vec{\mathbf{v}}$ and $\vec{\mathbf{B}}$ and has a constant magnitude qvB. As Active Figure 29.7 illustrates, the rotation is counterclockwise for a positive charge in a magnetic field directed into the page. If q were negative, the rotation would be clockwise. We use the particle under a net force model to write Newton's second law for the particle:

$$\sum F = F_B = ma$$

Because the particle moves in a circle, we also model it as a particle in uniform circular motion and we replace the acceleration with centripetal acceleration:

$$F_B = qvB = \frac{mv^2}{r}$$

This expression leads to the following equation for the radius of the circular path:

$$r = \frac{mv}{qB} \tag{29.3}$$

That is, the radius of the path is proportional to the linear momentum mv of the particle and inversely proportional to the magnitude of the charge on the particle and to the magnitude of the magnetic field. The angular speed of the particle (from Eq. 10.10) is

$$\omega = \frac{v}{r} = \frac{qB}{m} \tag{29.4}$$

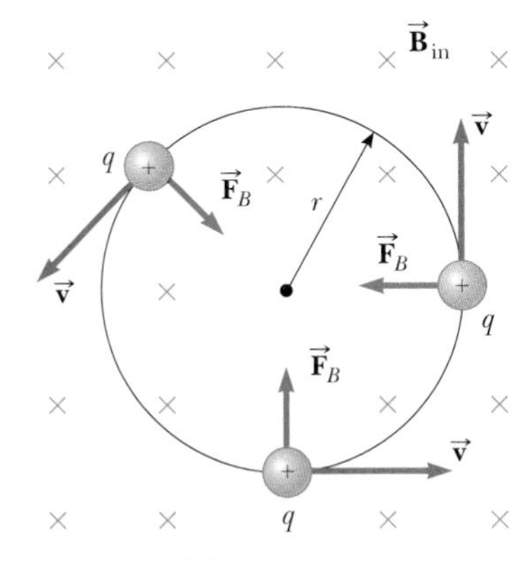

ACTIVE FIGURE 29.7

When the velocity of a charged particle is perpendicular to a uniform magnetic field, the particle moves in a circular path in a plane perpendicular to $\vec{\mathbf{B}}$. The magnetic force $\vec{\mathbf{F}}_B$ acting on the charge is always directed toward the center of the circle.

Sign in at www.thomsonedu.com and go to ThomsonNOW to adjust the mass, speed, and charge of the particle and the magnitude of the magnetic field and observe the resulting circular motion.

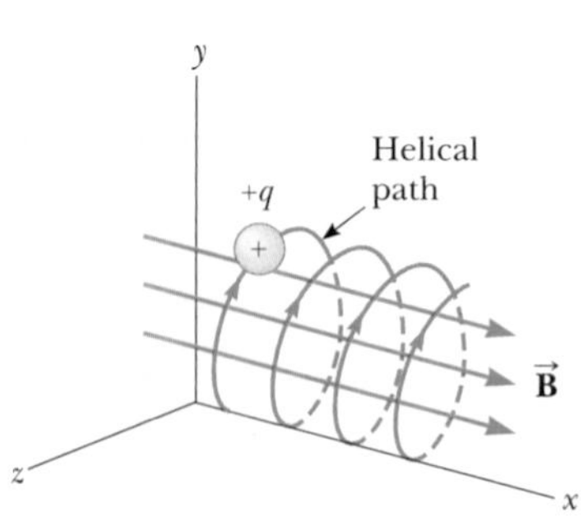

ACTIVE FIGURE 29.8

A charged particle having a velocity vector that has a component parallel to a uniform magnetic field moves in a helical path.

Sign in at www.thomsonedu.com and go to ThomsonNOW to adjust the x component of the velocity of the particle and observe the resulting helical motion.

The period of the motion (the time interval the particle requires to complete one revolution) is equal to the circumference of the circle divided by the speed of the particle:

$$T = \frac{2\pi r}{v} = \frac{2\pi}{\omega} = \frac{2\pi m}{qB} \qquad \textbf{(29.5)}$$

These results show that the angular speed of the particle and the period of the circular motion do not depend on the speed of the particle or on the radius of the orbit. The angular speed ω is often referred to as the **cyclotron frequency** because charged particles circulate at this angular frequency in the type of accelerator called a *cyclotron*, which is discussed in Section 29.3.

If a charged particle moves in a uniform magnetic field with its velocity at some arbitrary angle with respect to $\vec{\mathbf{B}}$, its path is a helix. For example, if the field is directed in the x direction as shown in Active Figure 29.8, there is no component of force in the x direction. As a result, $a_x = 0$, and the x component of velocity remains constant. The magnetic force $q\vec{\mathbf{v}} \times \vec{\mathbf{B}}$ causes the components v_y and v_z to change in time, however, and the resulting motion is a helix whose axis is parallel to the magnetic field. The projection of the path onto the yz plane (viewed along the x axis) is a circle. (The projections of the path onto the xy and xz planes are sinusoids!) Equations 29.3 to 29.5 still apply provided v is replaced by $v_\perp = \sqrt{v_y^2 + v_z^2}$.

Quick Quiz 29.2 A charged particle is moving perpendicular to a magnetic field in a circle with a radius r. **(i)** An identical particle enters the field, with $\vec{\mathbf{v}}$ perpendicular to $\vec{\mathbf{B}}$, but with a higher speed than the first particle. Compared with the radius of the circle for the first particle, is the radius of the circular path for the second particle (a) smaller, (b) larger, or (c) equal in size? **(ii)** The magnitude of the magnetic field is increased. From the same choices, compare the radius of the new circular path of the first particle with the radius of its initial path.

EXAMPLE 29.2 A Proton Moving Perpendicular to a Uniform Magnetic Field

A proton is moving in a circular orbit of radius 14 cm in a uniform 0.35-T magnetic field perpendicular to the velocity of the proton. Find the speed of the proton.

SOLUTION

Conceptualize From our discussion in this section, we know that the proton follows a circular path when moving in a uniform magnetic field.

Categorize We evaluate the speed of the proton using an equation developed in this section, so we categorize this example as a substitution problem.

Solve Equation 29.3 for the speed of the particle:

$$v = \frac{qBr}{m_p}$$

Substitute numerical values:

$$v = \frac{(1.60 \times 10^{-19}\ \text{C})(0.35\ \text{T})(0.14\ \text{m})}{1.67 \times 10^{-27}\ \text{kg}}$$

$$= 4.7 \times 10^{6}\ \text{m/s}$$

What If? What if an electron, rather than a proton, moves in a direction perpendicular to the same magnetic field with this same speed? Will the radius of its orbit be different?

Answer An electron has a much smaller mass than a proton, so the magnetic force should be able to change its velocity much more easily than that for the proton. Therefore, we expect the radius to be smaller. Equation 29.3 shows that r is proportional to m with q, B, and v the same for the electron as for the proton. Consequently, the radius will be smaller by the same factor as the ratio of masses m_e/m_p.

EXAMPLE 29.3 Bending an Electron Beam

In an experiment designed to measure the magnitude of a uniform magnetic field, electrons are accelerated from rest through a potential difference of 350 V and then enter a uniform magnetic field that is perpendicular to the velocity vector of the electrons. The electrons travel along a curved path because of the magnetic force exerted on them, and the radius of the path is measured to be 7.5 cm. (Such a curved beam of electrons is shown in Fig. 29.9.)

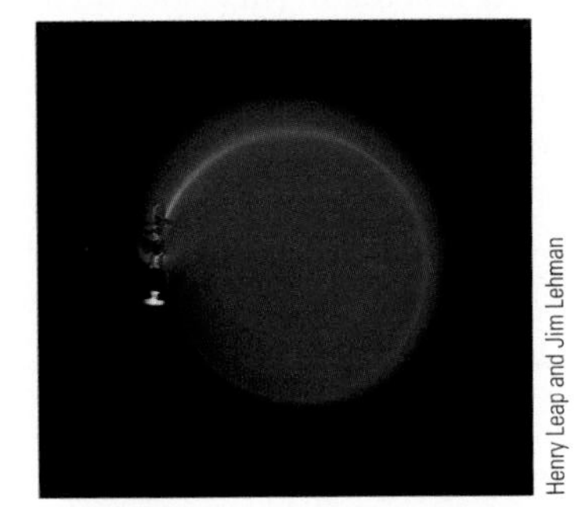
Henry Leap and Jim Lehman

Figure 29.9 (Example 29.3) The bending of an electron beam in a magnetic field.

(A) What is the magnitude of the magnetic field?

SOLUTION

Conceptualize With the help of Figures 29.7 and 29.9, visualize the circular motion of the electrons.

Categorize This example involves electrons accelerating from rest due to an electric force and then moving in a circular path due to a magnetic force. Equation 29.3 shows that we need the speed v of the electron to find the magnetic field magnitude, and v is not given. Consequently, we must find the speed of the electron based on the potential difference through which it is accelerated. To do so, we categorize the first part of the problem by modeling an electron and the electric field as an isolated system. Once the electron enters the magnetic field, we categorize the second part of the problem as one similar to those we have studied in this section.

Analyze Write the appropriate reduction of the conservation of energy equation, Equation 8.2, for the electron–electric field system:

$$\Delta K + \Delta U = 0$$

Substitute the appropriate initial and final energies:

$$\left(\tfrac{1}{2}m_e v^2 - 0\right) + (q\Delta V) = 0$$

Solve for the speed of the electron:

$$v = \sqrt{\frac{-2q\,\Delta V}{m_e}}$$

Substitute numerical values:

$$v = \sqrt{\frac{-2(-1.60 \times 10^{-19}\ \text{C})(350\ \text{V})}{9.11 \times 10^{-31}\ \text{kg}}} = 1.11 \times 10^7\ \text{m/s}$$

Now imagine the electron entering the magnetic field with this speed. Solve Equation 29.3 for the magnitude of the magnetic field:

$$B = \frac{m_e v}{er}$$

Substitute numerical values:

$$B = \frac{(9.11 \times 10^{-31}\ \text{kg})(1.11 \times 10^7\ \text{m/s})}{(1.60 \times 10^{-19}\ \text{C})(0.075\ \text{m})} = 8.4 \times 10^{-4}\ \text{T}$$

(B) What is the angular speed of the electrons?

SOLUTION

Use Equation 10.10:

$$\omega = \frac{v}{r} = \frac{1.11 \times 10^7\ \text{m/s}}{0.075\ \text{m}} = 1.5 \times 10^8\ \text{rad/s}$$

Finalize The angular speed can be represented as $\omega = (1.5 \times 10^8 \text{ rad/s})(1 \text{ rev}/2\pi \text{ rad}) = 2.4 \times 10^7 \text{ rev/s}$. The electrons travel around the circle 24 million times per second! This answer is consistent with the very high speed found in part (A).

What If? What if a sudden voltage surge causes the accelerating voltage to increase to 400 V? How does that affect the angular speed of the electrons, assuming the magnetic field remains constant?

Answer The increase in accelerating voltage ΔV causes the electrons to enter the magnetic field with a higher speed v. This higher speed causes them to travel in a circle with a larger radius r. The angular speed is the ratio of v to r. Both v and r increase by the same factor, so the effects cancel and the angular speed remains the same. Equation 29.4 is an expression for the cyclotron frequency, which is the same as the angular speed of the electrons. The cyclotron frequency depends only on the charge q, the magnetic field B, and the mass m_e, none of which have changed. Therefore, the voltage surge has no effect on the angular speed. (In reality, however, the voltage surge may also increase the magnetic field if the magnetic field is powered by the same source as the accelerating voltage. In that case, the angular speed increases according to Equation 29.4.)

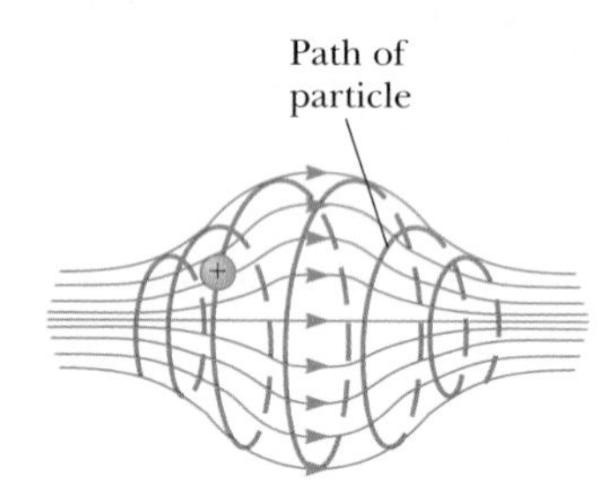

Figure 29.10 A charged particle moving in a nonuniform magnetic field (a magnetic bottle) spirals about the field and oscillates between the endpoints. The magnetic force exerted on the particle near either end of the bottle has a component that causes the particle to spiral back toward the center.

When charged particles move in a nonuniform magnetic field, the motion is complex. For example, in a magnetic field that is strong at the ends and weak in the middle such as that shown in Figure 29.10, the particles can oscillate between two positions. A charged particle starting at one end spirals along the field lines until it reaches the other end, where it reverses its path and spirals back. This configuration is known as a *magnetic bottle* because charged particles can be trapped within it. The magnetic bottle has been used to confine a *plasma,* a gas consisting of ions and electrons. Such a plasma-confinement scheme could fulfill a crucial role in the control of nuclear fusion, a process that could supply us in the future with an almost endless source of energy. Unfortunately, the magnetic bottle has its problems. If a large number of particles are trapped, collisions between them cause the particles to eventually leak from the system.

The Van Allen radiation belts consist of charged particles (mostly electrons and protons) surrounding the Earth in doughnut-shaped regions (Fig. 29.11). The particles, trapped by the Earth's nonuniform magnetic field, spiral around the field lines from pole to pole, covering the distance in only a few seconds. These particles originate mainly from the Sun, but some come from stars and other heavenly objects. For this reason, the particles are called *cosmic rays.* Most cosmic rays are deflected by the Earth's magnetic field and never reach the atmosphere. Some of the particles become trapped, however, and it is these particles that make up the Van Allen belts. When the particles are located over the poles, they sometimes collide with atoms in the atmosphere, causing the atoms to emit visible light. Such collisions are the origin of the beautiful Aurora Borealis, or Northern Lights, in the northern hemisphere and the Aurora Australis in the southern hemisphere. Auroras are usually confined to the polar regions because the Van Allen belts are nearest the Earth's surface there. Occasionally, though, solar activity causes larger numbers of charged particles to enter the belts and significantly distort the normal magnetic field lines associated with the Earth. In these situations, an aurora can sometimes be seen at lower latitudes.

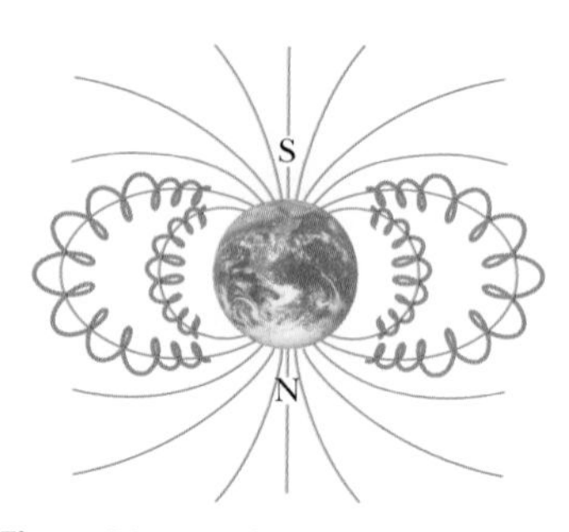

Figure 29.11 The Van Allen belts are made up of charged particles trapped by the Earth's nonuniform magnetic field. The magnetic field lines are in green, and the particle paths are in brown.

29.3 Applications Involving Charged Particles Moving in a Magnetic Field

A charge moving with a velocity $\vec{\mathbf{v}}$ in the presence of both an electric field $\vec{\mathbf{E}}$ and a magnetic field $\vec{\mathbf{B}}$ experiences both an electric force $q\vec{\mathbf{E}}$ and a magnetic force $q\vec{\mathbf{v}} \times \vec{\mathbf{B}}$. The total force (called the Lorentz force) acting on the charge is

Lorentz force ▶

$$\vec{\mathbf{F}} = q\vec{\mathbf{E}} + q\vec{\mathbf{v}} \times \vec{\mathbf{B}} \qquad (29.6)$$

Velocity Selector

In many experiments involving moving charged particles, it is important that all particles move with essentially the same velocity, which can be achieved by applying a combination of an electric field and a magnetic field oriented as shown in Active Figure 29.12. A uniform electric field is directed to the right (in the plane of the page in Active Fig. 29.12), and a uniform magnetic field is applied in the direction perpendicular to the electric field (into the page in Active Fig. 29.12). If q is positive and the velocity $\vec{\mathbf{v}}$ is upward, the magnetic force $q\vec{\mathbf{v}} \times \vec{\mathbf{B}}$ is to the left and the electric force $q\vec{\mathbf{E}}$ is to the right. When the magnitudes of the two fields are chosen so that $qE = qvB$, the charged particle is modeled as a particle in equilibrium and moves in a straight vertical line through the region of the fields. From the expression $qE = qvB$, we find that

$$v = \frac{E}{B} \quad \textbf{(29.7)}$$

Only those particles having this speed pass undeflected through the mutually perpendicular electric and magnetic fields. The magnetic force exerted on particles moving at speeds greater than that is stronger than the electric force, and the particles are deflected to the left. Those moving at slower speeds are deflected to the right.

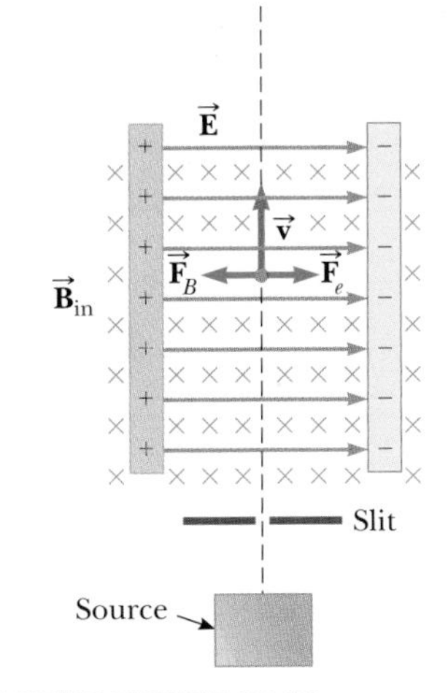

ACTIVE FIGURE 29.12

A velocity selector. When a positively charged particle is moving with velocity $\vec{\mathbf{v}}$ in the presence of a magnetic field directed into the page and an electric field directed to the right, it experiences an electric force $q\vec{\mathbf{E}}$ to the right and a magnetic force $q\vec{\mathbf{v}} \times \vec{\mathbf{B}}$ to the left.

Sign in at www.thomsonedu.com and go to ThomsonNOW to adjust the electric and magnetic fields and try to achieve straight-line motion for the charge.

The Mass Spectrometer

A **mass spectrometer** separates ions according to their mass-to-charge ratio. In one version of this device, known as the *Bainbridge mass spectrometer,* a beam of ions first passes through a velocity selector and then enters a second uniform magnetic field $\vec{\mathbf{B}}_0$ that has the same direction as the magnetic field in the selector (Active Fig. 29.13). Upon entering the second magnetic field, the ions move in a semicircle of radius r before striking a detector array at P. If the ions are positively charged, the beam deflects to the left as Active Figure 29.13 shows. If the ions are negatively charged, the beam deflects to the right. From Equation 29.3, we can express the ratio m/q as

$$\frac{m}{q} = \frac{rB_0}{v}$$

Using Equation 29.7 gives

$$\frac{m}{q} = \frac{rB_0B}{E} \quad \textbf{(29.8)}$$

Therefore, we can determine m/q by measuring the radius of curvature and knowing the field magnitudes B, B_0, and E. In practice, one usually measures the masses of various isotopes of a given ion, with the ions all carrying the same charge q. In this way, the mass ratios can be determined even if q is unknown.

A variation of this technique was used by J. J. Thomson (1856–1940) in 1897 to measure the ratio e/m_e for electrons. Figure 29.14a (page 818) shows the basic apparatus he used. Electrons are accelerated from the cathode and pass through two slits. They then drift into a region of perpendicular electric and magnetic fields. The magnitudes of the two fields are first adjusted to produce an undeflected beam. When the magnetic field is turned off, the electric field produces a measurable beam deflection that is recorded on the fluorescent screen. From the size of the deflection and the measured values of E and B, the charge-to-mass ratio can be determined. The results of this crucial experiment represent the discovery of the electron as a fundamental particle of nature.

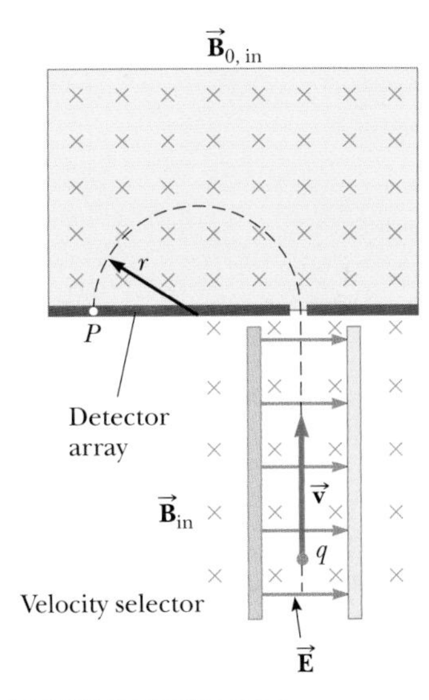

ACTIVE FIGURE 29.13

A mass spectrometer. Positively charged particles are sent first through a velocity selector and then into a region where the magnetic field $\vec{\mathbf{B}}_0$ causes the particles to move in a semicircular path and strike a detector array at P.

Sign in at www.thomsonedu.com and go to ThomsonNOW to predict where particles will strike the detector array.

The Cyclotron

A **cyclotron** is a device that can accelerate charged particles to very high speeds. The energetic particles produced are used to bombard atomic nuclei and thereby

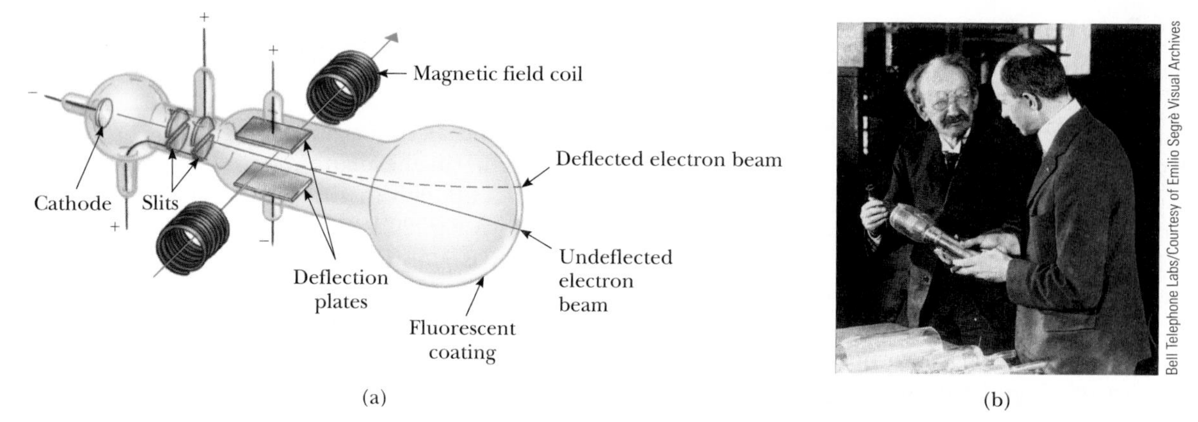

Figure 29.14 (a) Thomson's apparatus for measuring e/m_e. Electrons are accelerated from the cathode, pass through two slits, and are deflected by both an electric field and a magnetic field (directed perpendicular to the electric field). The beam of electrons then strikes a fluorescent screen. (b) J. J. Thomson *(left)* in the Cavendish Laboratory, University of Cambridge. The man on the right, Frank Baldwin Jewett, is a distant relative of John W. Jewett, Jr., coauthor of this text.

PITFALL PREVENTION 29.1

The Cyclotron Is Not State-of-the-Art Technology

The cyclotron is important historically because it was the first particle accelerator to produce particles with very high speeds. Cyclotrons are still in use in medical applications, but most accelerators currently in research use are not cyclotrons. Research accelerators work on a different principle and are generally called *synchrotrons.*

produce nuclear reactions of interest to researchers. A number of hospitals use cyclotron facilities to produce radioactive substances for diagnosis and treatment.

Both electric and magnetic forces play a key role in the operation of a cyclotron, a schematic drawing of which is shown in Figure 29.15a. The charges move inside two semicircular containers D_1 and D_2, referred to as *dees* because of their shape like the letter D. A high-frequency alternating potential difference is applied to the dees, and a uniform magnetic field is directed perpendicular to them. A positive ion released at P near the center of the magnet in one dee moves in a semicircular path (indicated by the dashed brown line in the drawing) and arrives back at the gap in a time interval $T/2$, where T is the time interval needed to make one complete trip around the two dees, given by Equation 29.5. The frequency of the applied potential difference is adjusted so that the polarity of the dees is reversed in the same time interval during which the ion travels around one dee. If the applied potential difference is adjusted such that D_2 is at a lower electric potential than D_1 by an amount ΔV, the ion accelerates across the gap to D_2 and its kinetic energy increases by an amount $q\,\Delta V$. It then moves around D_2 in a semicircular path of greater radius (because its speed has increased). After a time interval $T/2$, it again arrives at the gap between the dees. By this time, the polarity across the dees has again been reversed and the ion is given another "kick" across

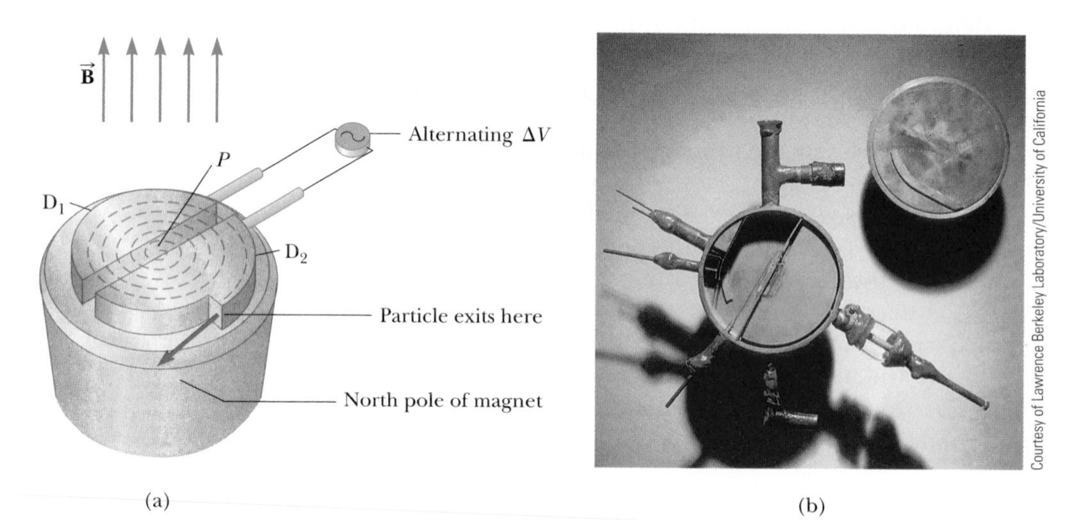

Figure 29.15 (a) A cyclotron consists of an ion source at P, two dees D_1 and D_2 across which an alternating potential difference is applied, and a uniform magnetic field. (The south pole of the magnet is not shown.) The brown, dashed, curved lines represent the path of the particles. (b) The first cyclotron, invented by E. O. Lawrence and M. S. Livingston in 1934.

the gap. The motion continues so that for each half-circle trip around one dee, the ion gains additional kinetic energy equal to $q\,\Delta V$. When the radius of its path is nearly that of the dees, the energetic ion leaves the system through the exit slit. The cyclotron's operation depends on T being independent of the speed of the ion and of the radius of the circular path (Eq. 29.5).

We can obtain an expression for the kinetic energy of the ion when it exits the cyclotron in terms of the radius R of the dees. From Equation 29.3 we know that $v = qBR/m$. Hence, the kinetic energy is

$$K = \tfrac{1}{2}mv^2 = \frac{q^2B^2R^2}{2m} \qquad \textbf{(29.9)}$$

When the energy of the ions in a cyclotron exceeds about 20 MeV, relativistic effects come into play. (Such effects are discussed in Chapter 39.) Observations show that T increases and the moving ions do not remain in phase with the applied potential difference. Some accelerators overcome this problem by modifying the period of the applied potential difference so that it remains in phase with the moving ions.

29.4 Magnetic Force Acting on a Current-Carrying Conductor

If a magnetic force is exerted on a single charged particle when the particle moves through a magnetic field, it should not surprise you that a current-carrying wire also experiences a force when placed in a magnetic field. The current is a collection of many charged particles in motion; hence, the resultant force exerted by the field on the wire is the vector sum of the individual forces exerted on all the charged particles making up the current. The force exerted on the particles is transmitted to the wire when the particles collide with the atoms making up the wire.

One can demonstrate the magnetic force acting on a current-carrying conductor by hanging a wire between the poles of a magnet as shown in Figure 29.16a. For ease in visualization, part of the horseshoe magnet in part (a) is removed to show the end face of the south pole in parts (b), (c), and (d) of Figure 29.16. The magnetic field is directed into the page and covers the region within the shaded squares. When the current in the wire is zero, the wire remains vertical as in Figure 29.16b. When the wire carries a current directed upward as in Figure 29.16c, however, the wire deflects to the left. If the current is reversed as in Figure 29.16d, the wire deflects to the right.

Let's quantify this discussion by considering a straight segment of wire of length L and cross-sectional area A carrying a current I in a uniform magnetic field $\vec{\mathbf{B}}$ as in

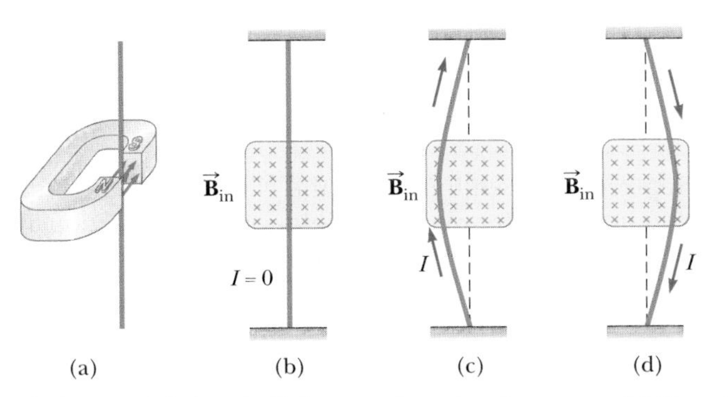

Figure 29.16 (a) A wire suspended vertically between the poles of a magnet. (b) The setup shown in (a) as seen looking at the south pole of the magnet so that the magnetic field (green crosses) is directed into the page. When there is no current in the wire, the wire remains vertical. (c) When the current is upward, the wire deflects to the left. (d) When the current is downward, the wire deflects to the right.

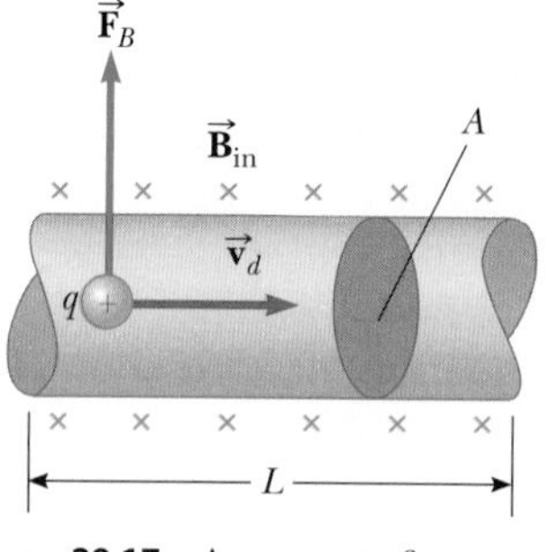

Figure 29.17 A segment of a current-carrying wire in a magnetic field $\vec{B}$. The magnetic force exerted on each charge making up the current is $q\vec{v}_d \times \vec{B}$, and the net force on the segment of length L is $I\vec{L} \times \vec{B}$.

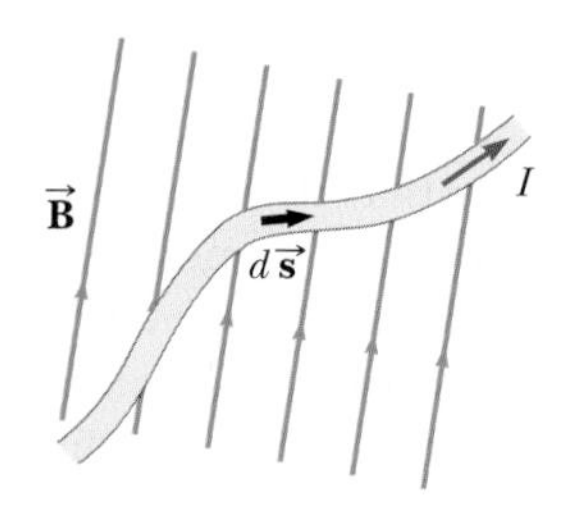

Figure 29.18 A wire segment of arbitrary shape carrying a current I in a magnetic field $\vec{B}$ experiences a magnetic force. The magnetic force on any segment $d\vec{s}$ is $I\,d\vec{s} \times \vec{B}$ and is directed out of the page. You should use the right-hand rule to confirm this force direction.

Figure 29.17. The magnetic force exerted on a charge q moving with a drift velocity $\vec{v}_d$ is $q\vec{v}_d \times \vec{B}$. To find the total force acting on the wire, we multiply the force $q\vec{v}_d \times \vec{B}$ exerted on one charge by the number of charges in the segment. Because the volume of the segment is AL, the number of charges in the segment is nAL, where n is the number of charges per unit volume. Hence, the total magnetic force on the wire of length L is

$$\vec{F}_B = (q\vec{v}_d \times \vec{B})nAL$$

We can write this expression in a more convenient form by noting that, from Equation 27.4, the current in the wire is $I = nqv_dA$. Therefore,

Force on a segment of current-carrying wire in a uniform magnetic field ▶

$$\vec{F}_B = I\vec{L} \times \vec{B} \quad (29.10)$$

where $\vec{L}$ is a vector that points in the direction of the current I and has a magnitude equal to the length L of the segment. This expression applies only to a straight segment of wire in a uniform magnetic field.

Now consider an arbitrarily shaped wire segment of uniform cross section in a magnetic field as shown in Figure 29.18. It follows from Equation 29.10 that the magnetic force exerted on a small segment of vector length $d\vec{s}$ in the presence of a field $\vec{B}$ is

$$d\vec{F}_B = I\,d\vec{s} \times \vec{B} \quad (29.11)$$

where $d\vec{F}_B$ is directed out of the page for the directions of $\vec{B}$ and $d\vec{s}$ in Figure 29.18. Equation 29.11 can be considered as an alternative definition of $\vec{B}$. That is, we can define the magnetic field $\vec{B}$ in terms of a measurable force exerted on a current element, where the force is a maximum when $\vec{B}$ is perpendicular to the element and zero when $\vec{B}$ is parallel to the element.

To calculate the total force $\vec{F}_B$ acting on the wire shown in Figure 29.18, we integrate Equation 29.11 over the length of the wire:

$$\vec{F}_B = I\int_a^b d\vec{s} \times \vec{B} \quad (29.12)$$

where a and b represent the endpoints of the wire. When this integration is carried out, the magnitude of the magnetic field and the direction the field makes with the vector $d\vec{s}$ may differ at different points.

Quick Quiz 29.3 A wire carries current in the plane of this paper toward the top of the page. The wire experiences a magnetic force toward the right edge of the page. Is the direction of the magnetic field causing this force (a) in the plane of the page and toward the left edge, (b) in the plane of the page and toward the bottom edge, (c) upward out of the page, or (d) downward into the page?

EXAMPLE 29.4 **Force on a Semicircular Conductor**

A wire bent into a semicircle of radius R forms a closed circuit and carries a current I. The wire lies in the xy plane, and a uniform magnetic field is directed along the positive y axis as in Figure 29.19. Find the magnitude and direction of the magnetic force acting on the straight portion of the wire and on the curved portion.

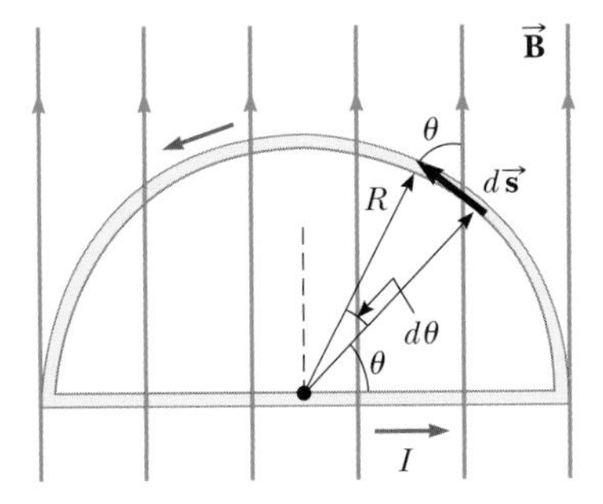

Figure 29.19 (Example 29.4) The magnetic force on the straight portion of the loop is directed out of the page, and the magnetic force on the curved portion is directed into the page.

SOLUTION

Conceptualize Using the right-hand rule for cross products, we see that the force $\vec{F}_1$ on the straight portion of the wire is out of the page and the force $\vec{F}_2$ on the curved portion is into the page. Is $\vec{F}_2$ larger in magnitude than $\vec{F}_1$ because the length of the curved portion is longer than that of the straight portion?

Categorize Because we are dealing with a current-carrying wire in a magnetic field rather than a single charged particle, we must use Equation 29.12 to find the total force on each portion of the wire.

Analyze Note that $d\vec{s}$ is perpendicular to $\vec{B}$ everywhere on the straight portion of the wire. Use Equation 29.12 to find the force on this portion:

$$\vec{F}_1 = I\int_a^b d\vec{s} \times \vec{B} = I\int_0^{2R} B\,ds\,\hat{k} = 2IRB\hat{k}$$

To find the magnetic force on the curved part, first write an expression for the magnetic force $d\vec{F}_2$ on the element $d\vec{s}$ in Figure 29.19:

$$(1)\quad d\vec{F}_2 = I d\vec{s} \times \vec{B} = -IB\sin\theta\,ds\,\hat{k}$$

From the geometry in Figure 29.19, write an expression for ds:

$$(2)\quad ds = R\,d\theta$$

Substitute Equation (2) into Equation (1) and integrate over the angle θ from 0 to π:

$$\vec{F}_2 = -\int_0^{\pi} IRB\sin\theta\,d\theta\,\hat{k} = -IRB\int_0^{\pi}\sin\theta\,d\theta\,\hat{k} = -IRB[-\cos\theta]_0^{\pi}\,\hat{k}$$

$$= IRB(\cos\pi - \cos 0)\hat{k} = IRB(-1-1)\hat{k} = -2IRB\hat{k}$$

Finalize Two very important general statements follow from this example. First, the force on the curved portion is the same in magnitude as the force on a straight wire between the same two points. In general, **the magnetic force on a curved current-carrying wire in a uniform magnetic field is equal to that on a straight wire connecting the endpoints and carrying the same current.** Furthermore, $\vec{F}_1 + \vec{F}_2 = 0$ is also a general result: **the net magnetic force acting on any closed current loop in a uniform magnetic field is zero.**

29.5 Torque on a Current Loop in a Uniform Magnetic Field

In Section 29.4, we showed how a magnetic force is exerted on a current-carrying conductor placed in a magnetic field. With that as a starting point, we now show that a torque is exerted on a current loop placed in a magnetic field.

Consider a rectangular loop carrying a current I in the presence of a uniform magnetic field directed parallel to the plane of the loop as shown in Figure 29.20a (page 822). No magnetic forces act on sides ① and ③ because these wires are parallel to the field; hence, $\vec{L} \times \vec{B} = 0$ for these sides. Magnetic forces do, however, act on sides ② and ④ because these sides are oriented perpendicular to the field. The magnitude of these forces is, from Equation 29.10,

$$F_2 = F_4 = IaB$$

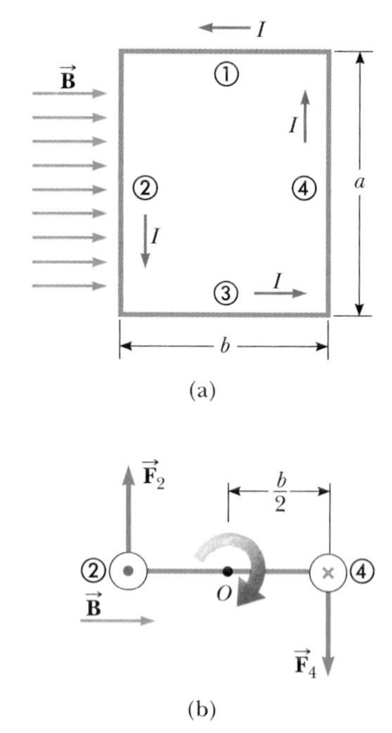

Figure 29.20 (a) Overhead view of a rectangular current loop in a uniform magnetic field. No magnetic forces are acting on sides ① and ③ because these sides are parallel to $\vec{\mathbf{B}}$. Forces are acting on sides ② and ④, however. (b) Edge view of the loop sighting down sides ② and ④ shows that the magnetic forces $\vec{\mathbf{F}}_2$ and $\vec{\mathbf{F}}_4$ exerted on these sides create a torque that tends to twist the loop clockwise. The purple dot in the left circle represents current in wire ② coming toward you; the purple cross in the right circle represents current in wire ④ moving away from you.

The direction of $\vec{\mathbf{F}}_2$, the magnetic force exerted on wire ②, is out of the page in the view shown in Figure 29.20a and that of $\vec{\mathbf{F}}_4$, the magnetic force exerted on wire ④, is into the page in the same view. If we view the loop from side ③ and sight along sides ② and ④, we see the view shown in Figure 29.20b, and the two magnetic forces $\vec{\mathbf{F}}_2$ and $\vec{\mathbf{F}}_4$ are directed as shown. Notice that the two forces point in opposite directions but are *not* directed along the same line of action. If the loop is pivoted so that it can rotate about point O, these two forces produce about O a torque that rotates the loop clockwise. The magnitude of this torque τ_{max} is

$$\tau_{max} = F_2 \frac{b}{2} + F_4 \frac{b}{2} = (IaB)\frac{b}{2} + (IaB)\frac{b}{2} = IabB$$

where the moment arm about O is $b/2$ for each force. Because the area enclosed by the loop is $A = ab$, we can express the maximum torque as

$$\tau_{max} = IAB \tag{29.13}$$

This maximum-torque result is valid only when the magnetic field is parallel to the plane of the loop. The sense of the rotation is clockwise when viewed from side ③ as indicated in Figure 29.20b. If the current direction were reversed, the force directions would also reverse and the rotational tendency would be counterclockwise.

Now suppose the uniform magnetic field makes an angle $\theta < 90°$ with a line perpendicular to the plane of the loop as in Active Figure 29.21. For convenience, let's assume $\vec{\mathbf{B}}$ is perpendicular to sides ② and ④. In this case, the magnetic forces $\vec{\mathbf{F}}_1$ and $\vec{\mathbf{F}}_3$ exerted on sides ① and ③ cancel each other and produce no torque because they pass through a common origin. The magnetic forces $\vec{\mathbf{F}}_2$ and $\vec{\mathbf{F}}_4$ acting on sides ② and ④, however, produce a torque about *any point.* Referring to the end view shown in Active Figure 29.21, we see that the moment arm of $\vec{\mathbf{F}}_2$ about the point O is equal to $(b/2)\sin\theta$. Likewise, the moment arm of $\vec{\mathbf{F}}_4$ about O is also $(b/2)\sin\theta$. Because $F_2 = F_4 = IaB$, the magnitude of the net torque about O is

$$\begin{aligned}\tau &= F_2 \frac{b}{2}\sin\theta + F_4\frac{b}{2}\sin\theta \\ &= IaB\left(\frac{b}{2}\sin\theta\right) + IaB\left(\frac{b}{2}\sin\theta\right) = IabB\sin\theta \\ &= IAB\sin\theta\end{aligned}$$

where $A = ab$ is the area of the loop. This result shows that the torque has its maximum value IAB when the field is perpendicular to the normal to the plane of the loop ($\theta = 90°$) as discussed with regard to Figure 29.20 and is zero when the field is parallel to the normal to the plane of the loop ($\theta = 0$).

A convenient expression for the torque exerted on a loop placed in a uniform magnetic field $\vec{\mathbf{B}}$ is

Torque on a current loop in a magnetic field ▶

$$\vec{\boldsymbol{\tau}} = I\vec{\mathbf{A}} \times \vec{\mathbf{B}} \tag{29.14}$$

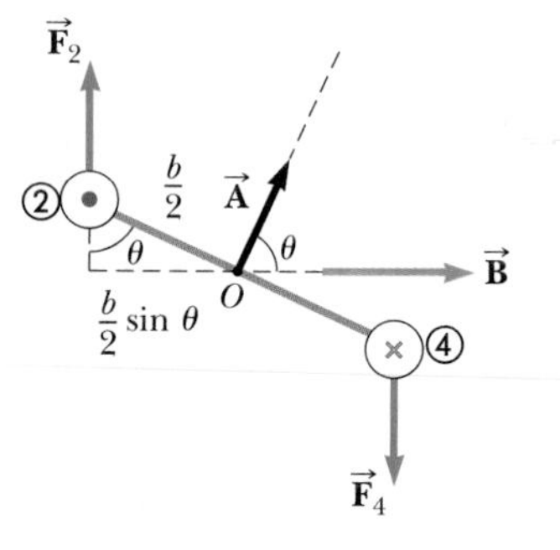

ACTIVE FIGURE 29.21

An end view of the loop in Figure 29.20b rotated through an angle with respect to the magnetic field. If $\vec{\mathbf{B}}$ is at an angle θ with respect to vector $\vec{\mathbf{A}}$, which is perpendicular to the plane of the loop, the torque is $IAB\sin\theta$ where the magnitude of $\vec{\mathbf{A}}$ is A, the area of the loop.

Sign in at www.thomsonedu.com and go to ThomsonNOW to choose the current in the loop, the magnetic field, and the initial orientation of the loop and observe the subsequent motion.

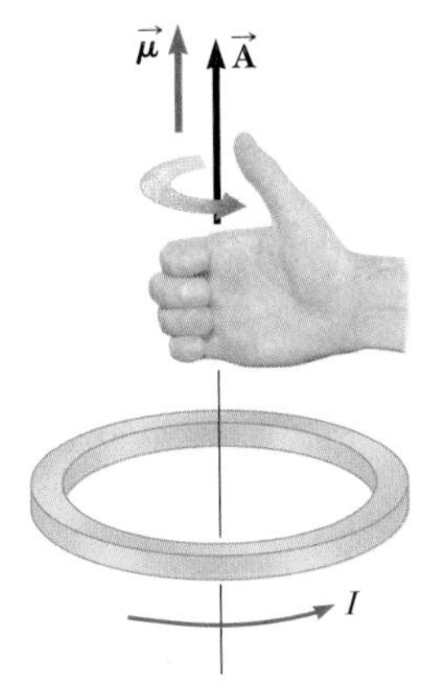

Figure 29.22 Right-hand rule for determining the direction of the vector $\vec{\mathbf{A}}$. The direction of the magnetic moment $\vec{\boldsymbol{\mu}}$ is the same as the direction of $\vec{\mathbf{A}}$.

where $\vec{\mathbf{A}}$, the vector shown in Active Figure 29.21, is perpendicular to the plane of the loop and has a magnitude equal to the area of the loop. To determine the direction of $\vec{\mathbf{A}}$, use the right-hand rule described in Figure 29.22. When you curl the fingers of your right hand in the direction of the current in the loop, your thumb points in the direction of $\vec{\mathbf{A}}$. Active Figure 29.21 shows that the loop tends to rotate in the direction of decreasing values of θ (that is, such that the area vector $\vec{\mathbf{A}}$ rotates toward the direction of the magnetic field).

The product $I\vec{\mathbf{A}}$ is defined to be the **magnetic dipole moment** $\vec{\boldsymbol{\mu}}$ (often simply called the "magnetic moment") of the loop:

$$\vec{\boldsymbol{\mu}} \equiv I\vec{\mathbf{A}} \qquad \textbf{(29.15)}$$

◀ Magnetic dipole moment of a current loop

The SI unit of magnetic dipole moment is the ampere-meter^2 ($\text{A} \cdot \text{m}^2$). If a coil of wire contains N loops of the same area, the magnetic moment of the coil is

$$\vec{\boldsymbol{\mu}}_{\text{coil}} = NI\vec{\mathbf{A}} \qquad \textbf{(29.16)}$$

Using Equation 29.15, we can express the torque exerted on a current-carrying loop in a magnetic field $\vec{\mathbf{B}}$ as

$$\vec{\boldsymbol{\tau}} = \vec{\boldsymbol{\mu}} \times \vec{\mathbf{B}} \qquad \textbf{(29.17)}$$

◀ Torque on a magnetic moment in a magnetic field

This result is analogous to Equation 26.18, $\vec{\boldsymbol{\tau}} = \vec{\mathbf{p}} \times \vec{\mathbf{E}}$, for the torque exerted on an electric dipole in the presence of an electric field $\vec{\mathbf{E}}$, where $\vec{\mathbf{p}}$ is the electric dipole moment.

Although we obtained the torque for a particular orientation of $\vec{\mathbf{B}}$ with respect to the loop, the equation $\vec{\boldsymbol{\tau}} = \vec{\boldsymbol{\mu}} \times \vec{\mathbf{B}}$ is valid for any orientation. Furthermore, although we derived the torque expression for a rectangular loop, the result is valid for a loop of any shape. The torque on an N-turn coil is given by Equation 29.17 by using Equation 29.16 for the magnetic moment.

In Section 26.6, we found that the potential energy of a system of an electric dipole in an electric field is given by $U = -\vec{\mathbf{p}} \cdot \vec{\mathbf{E}}$. This energy depends on the orientation of the dipole in the electric field. Likewise, the potential energy of a system of a magnetic dipole in a magnetic field depends on the orientation of the dipole in the magnetic field and is given by

$$U = -\vec{\boldsymbol{\mu}} \cdot \vec{\mathbf{B}} \qquad \textbf{(29.18)}$$

◀ Potential energy of a system of a magnetic moment in a magnetic field

This expression shows that the system has its lowest energy $U_{\text{min}} = -\mu B$ when $\vec{\boldsymbol{\mu}}$ points in the same direction as $\vec{\mathbf{B}}$. The system has its highest energy $U_{\text{max}} = +\mu B$ when $\vec{\boldsymbol{\mu}}$ points in the direction opposite $\vec{\mathbf{B}}$.

The torque on a current loop causes the loop to rotate; this effect is exploited practically in a **motor.** Energy enters the motor by electrical transmission, and the rotating coil can do work on some device external to the motor. For example, the motor in an car's electrical window system does work on the windows, applying a force on them and moving them up or down through some displacement. We will discuss motors in more detail in Section 31.5.

Quick Quiz 29.4 **(i)** Rank the magnitudes of the torques acting on the rectangular loops (a), (b), and (c) shown edge-on in Figure 29.23 from highest to lowest. All loops are identical and carry the same current. **(ii)** Rank the magnitudes of the net forces acting on the rectangular loops shown in Figure 29.23 from highest to lowest.

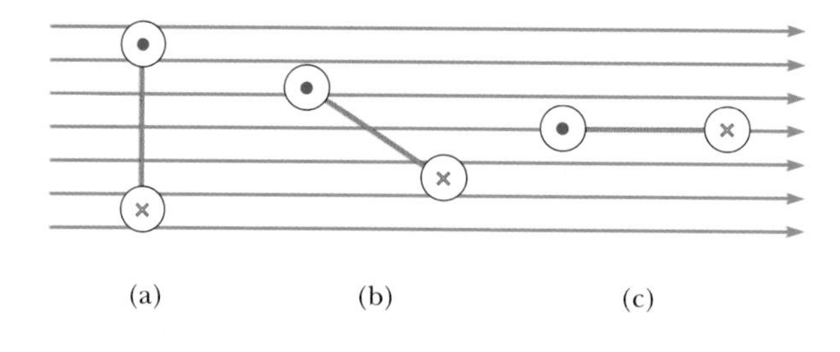

Figure 29.23 (Quick Quiz 29.4) Which current loop (seen edge-on) experiences the greatest torque, (a), (b), or (c)? Which experiences the greatest net force?

EXAMPLE 29.5 The Magnetic Dipole Moment of a Coil

A rectangular coil of dimensions 5.40 cm × 8.50 cm consists of 25 turns of wire and carries a current of 15.0 mA. A 0.350-T magnetic field is applied parallel to the plane of the coil.

(A) Calculate the magnitude of the magnetic dipole moment of the coil.

SOLUTION

Conceptualize The magnetic moment of the coil is independent of any magnetic field in which the loop resides, so it depends only on the geometry of the loop and the current it carries.

Categorize We evaluate quantities based on equations developed in this section, so we categorize this example as a substitution problem.

Use Equation 29.16 to calculate the magnetic moment:

$$\mu_{\text{coil}} = NIA = (25)(15.0 \times 10^{-3}\ \text{A})(0.054\ 0\ \text{m})(0.085\ 0\ \text{m})$$
$$= 1.72 \times 10^{-3}\ \text{A} \cdot \text{m}^2$$

(B) What is the magnitude of the torque acting on the loop?

SOLUTION

Use Equation 29.17, noting that $\vec{\mathbf{B}}$ is perpendicular to $\vec{\boldsymbol{\mu}}_{\text{coil}}$:

$$\tau = \mu_{\text{coil}}B = (1.72 \times 10^{-3}\ \text{A} \cdot \text{m}^2)(0.350\ \text{T})$$
$$= 6.02 \times 10^{-4}\ \text{N} \cdot \text{m}$$

EXAMPLE 29.6 Rotating a Coil

Consider the loop of wire in Figure 29.24a. Imagine it is pivoted along side ④, which is parallel to the z axis and fastened so that side ④ remains fixed and the rest of the loop hangs vertically but can rotate around side ④ (Fig. 29.24b). The mass of the loop is 50.0 g, and the sides are of lengths $a = 0.200$ m and $b = 0.100$ m. The loop carries a current of 3.50 A and is immersed in a vertical uniform magnetic field of magnitude 0.010 0 T in the $+y$ direction (Fig. 29.24c). What angle does the plane of the loop make with the vertical?

SOLUTION

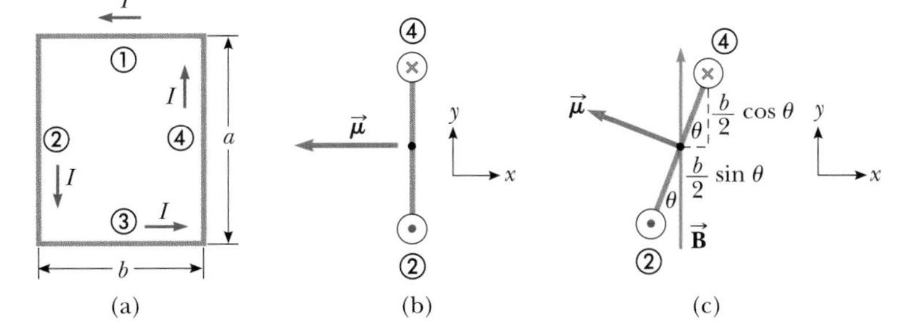

Figure 29.24 (Example 29.6) (a) Overhead view of a rectangular current loop in a uniform magnetic field. This figure is similar to the situations in Figure 29.20 and 29.21. (b) Edge view of the loop sighting down sides ② and ④. The loop hangs vertically and is pivoted so that it can rotate around side ④. (c) An end view of the loop in (b) rotated through an angle with respect to the horizontal when it is placed in a magnetic field. The magnetic torque causes the loop to rotate in a clockwise direction around side ④, whereas the gravitational torque causes a counterclockwise rotation.

Conceptualize In the side view of Figure 29.24b, notice that the magnetic moment of the loop is to the left. Therefore, when the loop is in the magnetic field, the magnetic torque on the loop causes it to rotate in a clockwise direction around side ④, which we choose as the rotation axis. Imagine the loop making this clockwise rotation so that the plane of the loop is at some angle θ to the vertical as in Figure 29.24c. The gravitational force on the loop exerts a torque that would cause a rotation in the counterclockwise direction if the magnetic field were turned off.

Categorize At some angle of the loop, the two torques described in the *Conceptualize* step are equal in magnitude and the loop is at rest. We therefore model the loop as a rigid object in equilibrium.

Analyze Evaluate the magnetic torque on the loop from Equation 29.17:

$$\vec{\boldsymbol{\tau}}_B = \vec{\boldsymbol{\mu}} \times \vec{\mathbf{B}} = -\mu B \sin(90° - \theta)\hat{\mathbf{k}} = -IAB\cos\theta\,\hat{\mathbf{k}} = -IabB\cos\theta\,\hat{\mathbf{k}}$$

Evaluate the gravitational torque on the loop, noting that the gravitational force can be modeled to act at the center of the loop:

$$\vec{\boldsymbol{\tau}}_g = \vec{\mathbf{r}} \times m\vec{\mathbf{g}} = mg\frac{b}{2}\sin\theta\,\hat{\mathbf{k}}$$

From the rigid body in equilibrium model, add the torques and set the net torque equal to zero:

$$\sum \vec{\boldsymbol{\tau}} = -IabB\cos\theta\,\hat{\mathbf{k}} + mg\frac{b}{2}\sin\theta\,\hat{\mathbf{k}} = 0$$

Solve for $\tan\theta$:

$$IabB\cos\theta = mg\frac{b}{2}\sin\theta \quad\to\quad \tan\theta = \frac{2IaB}{mg}$$

Substitute numerical values:

$$\theta = \tan^{-1}\left(\frac{2IaB}{mg}\right)$$

$$= \tan^{-1}\left[\frac{2(3.50\text{ A})(0.200\text{ m})(0.010\,0\text{ T})}{(0.050\,0\text{ kg})(9.80\text{ m/s}^2)}\right] = 1.64°$$

Finalize The angle is relatively small, so the loop still hangs almost vertically. If the current I or the magnetic field B is increased, however, the angle increases as the magnetic torque becomes stronger.

29.6 The Hall Effect

When a current-carrying conductor is placed in a magnetic field, a potential difference is generated in a direction perpendicular to both the current and the magnetic field. This phenomenon, first observed by Edwin Hall (1855–1938) in 1879, is known as the *Hall effect.* The arrangement for observing the Hall effect consists of a flat conductor carrying a current I in the x direction as shown in Figure 29.25 (page 826). A uniform magnetic field $\vec{\mathbf{B}}$ is applied in the y direction. If the charge

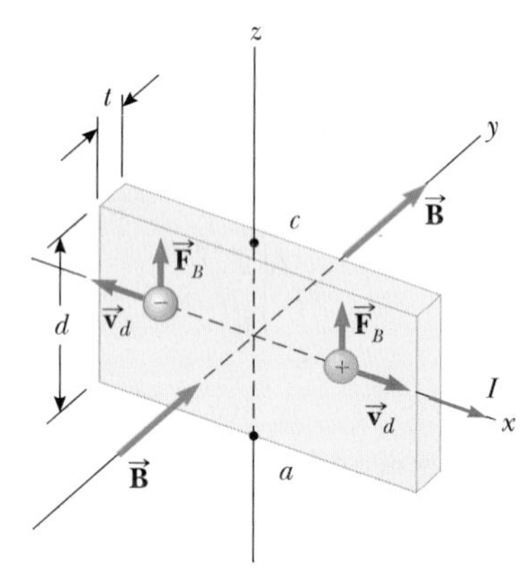

Figure 29.25 To observe the Hall effect, a magnetic field is applied to a current-carrying conductor. When I is in the x direction and $\vec{B}$ in the y direction, both positive and negative charge carriers are deflected upward in the magnetic field. The Hall voltage is measured between points a and c.

carriers are electrons moving in the negative x direction with a drift velocity $\vec{v}_d$, they experience an upward magnetic force $\vec{F}_B = q\vec{v}_d \times \vec{B}$, are deflected upward, and accumulate at the upper edge of the flat conductor, leaving an excess of positive charge at the lower edge (Fig. 29.26a). This accumulation of charge at the edges establishes an electric field in the conductor and increases until the electric force on carriers remaining in the bulk of the conductor balances the magnetic force acting on the carriers. When this equilibrium condition is reached, the electrons are no longer deflected upward. A sensitive voltmeter connected across the sample as shown in Figure 29.26 can measure the potential difference, known as the **Hall voltage** ΔV_H, generated across the conductor.

If the charge carriers are positive and hence move in the positive x direction (for rightward current) as shown in Figures 29.25 and 29.26b, they also experience an upward magnetic force $q\vec{v}_d \times \vec{B}$, which produces a buildup of positive charge on the upper edge and leaves an excess of negative charge on the lower edge. Hence, the sign of the Hall voltage generated in the sample is opposite the sign of the Hall voltage resulting from the deflection of electrons. The sign of the charge carriers can therefore be determined from measuring the polarity of the Hall voltage.

In deriving an expression for the Hall voltage, first note that the magnetic force exerted on the carriers has magnitude qv_dB. In equilibrium, this force is balanced by the electric force qE_H, where E_H is the magnitude of the electric field due to the charge separation (sometimes referred to as the *Hall field*). Therefore,

$$qv_dB = qE_H$$

$$E_H = v_dB$$

If d is the width of the conductor, the Hall voltage is

$$\Delta V_H = E_H d = v_d B d \quad \textbf{(29.19)}$$

Therefore, the measured Hall voltage gives a value for the drift speed of the charge carriers if d and B are known.

We can obtain the charge carrier density n by measuring the current in the sample. From Equation 27.4, we can express the drift speed as

$$v_d = \frac{I}{nqA} \quad \textbf{(29.20)}$$

where A is the cross-sectional area of the conductor. Substituting Equation 29.20 into Equation 29.19 gives

$$\Delta V_H = \frac{IBd}{nqA} \quad \textbf{(29.21)}$$

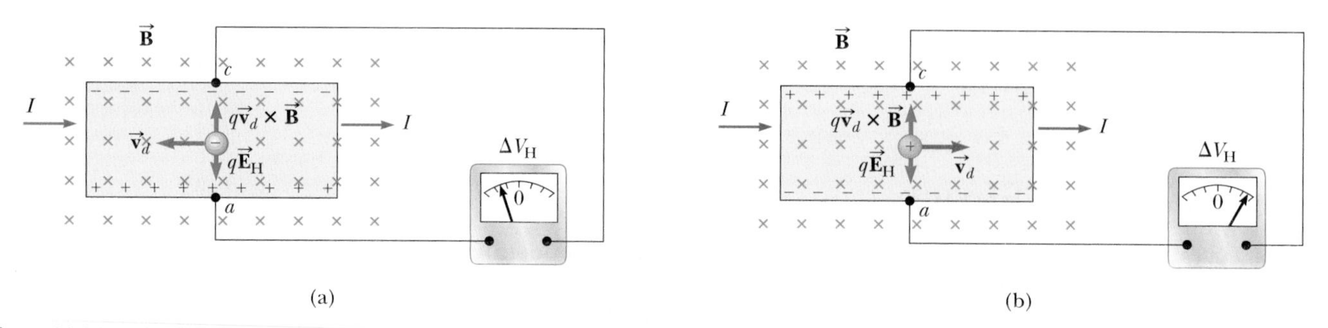

Figure 29.26 (a) When the charge carriers in a Hall-effect apparatus are negative, the upper edge of the conductor becomes negatively charged and c is at a lower electric potential than a. (b) When the charge carriers are positive, the upper edge becomes positively charged and c is at a higher potential than a. In either case, the charge carriers are no longer deflected when the edges become sufficiently charged that there is a balance on the charge carriers between the electrostatic force qE_H and the magnetic deflection force qvB.

Because $A = td$, where t is the thickness of the conductor, we can also express Equation 29.21 as

$$\Delta V_H = \frac{IB}{nqt} = \frac{R_H IB}{t} \qquad (29.22)$$

◀ The Hall voltage

where $R_H = 1/nq$ is the **Hall coefficient.** This relationship shows that a properly calibrated conductor can be used to measure the magnitude of an unknown magnetic field.

Because all quantities in Equation 29.23 other than nq can be measured, a value for the Hall coefficient is readily obtainable. The sign and magnitude of R_H give the sign of the charge carriers and their number density. In most metals, the charge carriers are electrons and the charge-carrier density determined from Hall-effect measurements is in good agreement with calculated values for such metals as lithium (Li), sodium (Na), copper (Cu), and silver (Ag), whose atoms each give up one electron to act as a current carrier. In this case, n is approximately equal to the number of conducting electrons per unit volume. This classical model, however, is not valid for metals such as iron (Fe), bismuth (Bi), and cadmium (Cd) or for semiconductors. These discrepancies can be explained only by using a model based on the quantum nature of solids.

EXAMPLE 29.7 The Hall Effect for Copper

A rectangular copper strip 1.5 cm wide and 0.10 cm thick carries a current of 5.0 A. Find the Hall voltage for a 1.2-T magnetic field applied in a direction perpendicular to the strip.

SOLUTION

Conceptualize Study Figures 29.25 and 29.26 carefully and make sure you understand that a Hall voltage is developed between the top and bottom edges of the strip.

Categorize We evaluate the Hall voltage using an equation developed in this section, so we categorize this example as a substitution problem.

Assuming that one electron per atom is available for conduction, we can take the charge carrier density to be 8.46×10^{28} electrons/m^3 (see Example 27.1). Substitute this value and the given data into Equation 29.22:

$$\Delta V_H = \frac{IB}{nqt}$$

$$= \frac{(5.0\text{ A})(1.2\text{ T})}{(8.46 \times 10^{28}\text{ m}^{-3})(1.6 \times 10^{-19}\text{ C})(0.001\,0\text{ m})}$$

$$\Delta V_H = 0.44\ \mu\text{V}$$

Such an extremely small Hall voltage is expected in good conductors. (Notice that the width of the conductor is not needed in this calculation.)

What If? What if the strip has the same dimensions but is made of a semiconductor? Will the Hall voltage be smaller or larger?

Answer In semiconductors, n is much smaller than it is in metals that contribute one electron per atom to the current; hence, the Hall voltage is usually larger because it varies as the inverse of n. Currents on the order of 0.1 mA are generally used for such materials. Consider a piece of silicon that has the same dimensions as the copper strip in this example and whose value for n is 1.0×10^{20} electrons/m^3. Taking $B = 1.2$ T and $I = 0.10$ mA, we find that $\Delta V_H = 7.5$ mV. A potential difference of this magnitude is readily measured.

Summary

ThomsonNOW™ Sign in at **www.thomsonedu.com** and go to ThomsonNOW to take a practice test for this chapter.

DEFINITION

The **magnetic dipole moment** $\vec{\mu}$ of a loop carrying a current I is

$$\vec{\mu} \equiv I\vec{\mathbf{A}} \quad (29.5)$$

where the area vector $\vec{\mathbf{A}}$ is perpendicular to the plane of the loop and $|\vec{\mathbf{A}}|$ is equal to the area of the loop. The SI unit of $\vec{\mu}$ is $A \cdot m^2$.

CONCEPTS AND PRINCIPLES

The magnetic force that acts on a charge q moving with a velocity $\vec{\mathbf{v}}$ in a magnetic field $\vec{\mathbf{B}}$ is

$$\vec{\mathbf{F}}_B = q\vec{\mathbf{v}} \times \vec{\mathbf{B}} \quad (29.1)$$

The direction of this magnetic force is perpendicular both to the velocity of the particle and to the magnetic field. The magnitude of this force is

$$F_B = |q| vB \sin\theta \quad (29.2)$$

where θ is the smaller angle between $\vec{\mathbf{v}}$ and $\vec{\mathbf{B}}$. The SI unit of $\vec{\mathbf{B}}$ is the **tesla** (T), where $1\ T = 1\ N/A \cdot m$.

If a charged particle moves in a uniform magnetic field so that its initial velocity is perpendicular to the field, the particle moves in a circle, the plane of which is perpendicular to the magnetic field. The radius of the circular path is

$$r = \frac{mv}{qB} \quad (29.3)$$

where m is the mass of the particle and q is its charge. The angular speed of the charged particle is

$$\omega = \frac{qB}{m} \quad (29.4)$$

If a straight conductor of length L carries a current I, the force exerted on that conductor when it is placed in a uniform magnetic field $\vec{\mathbf{B}}$ is

$$\vec{\mathbf{F}}_B = I\vec{\mathbf{L}} \times \vec{\mathbf{B}} \quad (29.10)$$

where the direction of $\vec{\mathbf{L}}$ is in the direction of the current and $|\vec{\mathbf{L}}| = L$.

If an arbitrarily shaped wire carrying a current I is placed in a magnetic field, the magnetic force exerted on a very small segment $d\vec{\mathbf{s}}$ is

$$d\vec{\mathbf{F}}_B = I\, d\vec{\mathbf{s}} \times \vec{\mathbf{B}} \quad (29.11)$$

To determine the total magnetic force on the wire, one must integrate Equation 29.11 over the wire, keeping in mind that both $\vec{\mathbf{B}}$ and $d\vec{\mathbf{s}}$ may vary at each point.

The torque $\vec{\tau}$ on a current loop placed in a uniform magnetic field $\vec{\mathbf{B}}$ is

$$\vec{\tau} = \vec{\mu} \times \vec{\mathbf{B}} \quad (29.17)$$

The potential energy of the system of a magnetic dipole in a magnetic field is

$$U = -\vec{\mu} \cdot \vec{\mathbf{B}} \quad (29.18)$$

Questions

☐ denotes answer available in *Student Solutions Manual/Study Guide;* **O** denotes objective question

Questions 2, 3, and 4 in Chapter 11 can be assigned with this chapter.

1. O Answer each question yes or no. Assume the motions and currents mentioned are along the x axis and fields are in the y direction. (a) Does an electric field exert a force on a stationary charged object? (b) Does a magnetic field do so? (c) Does an electric field exert a force on a moving charged object? (d) Does a magnetic field do so? (e) Does an electric field exert a force on a straight current-carrying wire? (f) Does a magnetic field do so? (g) Does an electric field exert a force on a beam of electrons? (h) Does a magnetic field do so?

2. O Electron A is fired horizontally with speed 1 Mm/s into a region where a vertical magnetic field exists. Electron B is fired along the same path with speed 2 Mm/s. **(i)** Which electron has a larger magnetic force exerted on it? (a) A does. (b) B does. (c) The forces have the same nonzero magnitude. (d) The forces are both zero. **(ii)** Which electron has a path that curves more sharply? (a) A does. (b) B does. (c) The particles follow the same curved path. (d) The particles continue to go straight.

3. O Classify each of the following as a characteristic (a) of electric forces only, (b) of magnetic forces only, (c) of both electric and magnetic forces, or (d) of neither electric nor magnetic forces. **(i)** The force is proportional to the magnitude of the field exerting it. **(ii)** The force is proportional to the magnitude of the charge of the object on which the force is exerted. **(iii)** The force exerted on a negatively charged object is opposite in direction to the force on a positive charge. **(iv)** The force exerted on a stationary charged object is zero. **(v)** The force exerted on a moving charged object is zero. **(vi)** The force exerted on a charged object is proportional to its speed. **(vii)** The force exerted on a charged object cannot alter the object's speed. **(viii)** The magnitude of the force depends on the charged object's direction of motion.

4. O Rank the magnitudes of the forces exerted on the following particles from the largest to the smallest. In your ranking, display any cases of equality. (a) An electron moving at 1 Mm/s perpendicular to a 1-mT magnetic field. (b) An electron moving at 1 Mm/s parallel to a 1-mT magnetic field. (c) An electron moving at 2 Mm/s perpendicular to a 1-mT magnetic field. (d) An electron moving at 1 Mm/s perpendicular to a 2-mT magnetic field. (e) A proton moving at 1 Mm/s perpendicular to a 1-mT magnetic field. (f) A proton moving at 1 Mm/s at a 45° angle to a 1-mT magnetic field.

5. O At a certain instant, a proton is moving in the positive x direction through a magnetic field in the negative z direction. What is the direction of the magnetic force exerted on the proton? (a) x (b) $-x$ (c) y (d) $-y$ (e) z (f) $-z$ (g) halfway between the x and $-z$ axes, at 45° to both (h) The force is zero.

6. O A particle with electric charge is fired into a region of space where the electric field is zero. It moves in a straight line. Can you conclude that the magnetic field in that region is zero? (a) Yes. (b) No; the field might be perpendicular to the particle's velocity. (c) No; the field might be parallel to the particle's velocity. (d) No; the particle might need to have charge of the opposite sign to have a force exerted on it. (e) No; an observation of an object with *electric* charge gives no information about a *magnetic* field.

7. ☐ Two charged particles are projected in the same direction into a magnetic field perpendicular to their velocities. If the particles are deflected in opposite directions, what can you say about them?

8. How can the motion of a moving charged particle be used to distinguish between a magnetic field and an electric field? Give a specific example to justify your argument.

9. O In the velocity selector shown in Active Figure 29.12, electrons with speed $v = E/B$ follow a straight path. Electrons moving significantly faster than this speed through the same selector will move along what kind of path? (a) a circle (b) a parabola (c) a straight line (d) a more complicated trajectory

10. ☐ Is it possible to orient a current loop in a uniform magnetic field such that the loop does not tend to rotate? Explain.

11. Explain why it is not possible to determine the charge and the mass of a charged particle separately by measuring accelerations produced by electric and magnetic forces on the particle.

12. ☐ How can a current loop be used to determine the presence of a magnetic field in a given region of space?

13. Charged particles from outer space, called cosmic rays, strike the Earth more frequently near the poles than near the equator. Why?

14. Can a constant magnetic field set into motion an electron initially at rest? Explain your answer.

Problems

WebAssign The Problems from this chapter may be assigned online in WebAssign.

ThomsonNOW Sign in at **www.thomsonedu.com** and go to ThomsonNOW to assess your understanding of this chapter's topics with additional quizzing and conceptual questions.

1, 2, 3 denotes straightforward, intermediate, challenging; □ denotes full solution available in *Student Solutions Manual/Study Guide;* ▲ denotes coached solution with hints available at **www.thomsonedu.com;** ▒ denotes developing symbolic reasoning; ● denotes asking for qualitative reasoning; ▪ denotes computer useful in solving problem

Section 29.1 Magnetic Fields and Forces

Problems 1, 2, 3, 4, 6, 7, and 10 in Chapter 11 can be assigned with this section.

1. ▲ Determine the initial direction of the deflection of charged particles as they enter the magnetic fields shown in Figure P29.1.

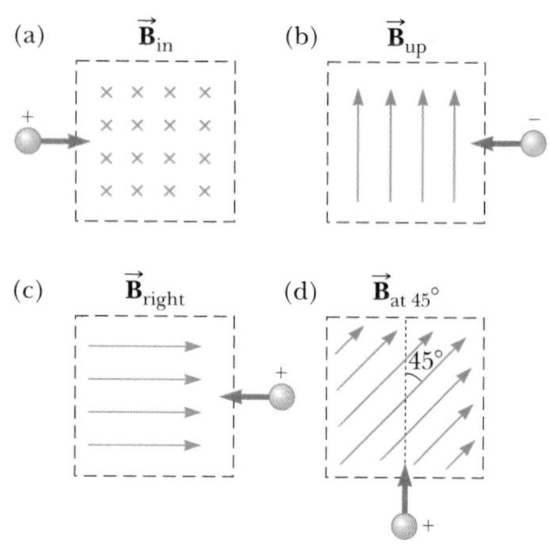

Figure P29.1

2. Consider an electron near the Earth's equator. In which direction does it tend to deflect if its velocity is (a) directed downward? (b) Directed northward? (c) Directed westward? (d) Directed southeastward?

3. A proton moves perpendicular to a uniform magnetic field $\vec{B}$ at a speed of 1.00×10^7 m/s and experiences an acceleration of 2.00×10^{13} m/s² in the $+x$ direction when its velocity is in the $+z$ direction. Determine the magnitude and direction of the field.

4. A proton travels with a speed of 3.00×10^6 m/s at an angle of 37.0° with the direction of a magnetic field of 0.300 T in the $+y$ direction. What are (a) the magnitude of the magnetic force on the proton and (b) its acceleration?

5. A proton moving at 4.00×10^6 m/s through a magnetic field of magnitude 1.70 T experiences a magnetic force of magnitude 8.20×10^{-13} N. What is the angle between the proton's velocity and the field?

6. An electron is accelerated through 2 400 V from rest and then enters a uniform 1.70-T magnetic field. What are (a) the maximum and (b) the minimum values of the magnetic force this particle can experience?

7. A proton moves with a velocity of $\vec{v} = (2\hat{i} - 4\hat{j} + \hat{k})$ m/s in a region in which the magnetic field is $\vec{B} = (\hat{i} + 2\hat{j} - 3\hat{k})$ T. What is the magnitude of the magnetic force this particle experiences?

8. ● An electron in a uniform electric and magnetic field has a velocity of 1.20×10^4 m/s (in the positive x direction) and an acceleration of 2.00×10^{12} m/s² (in the positive z direction). If the electric field has a magnitude of 20.0 N/C (in the positive z direction), what can you determine about the magnetic field in the region? What can you not determine?

Section 29.2 Motion of a Charged Particle in a Uniform Magnetic Field

9. The magnetic field of the Earth at a certain location is directed vertically downward and has a magnitude of 50.0 μT. A proton is moving horizontally toward the west in this field with a speed of 6.20×10^6 m/s. (a) What are the direction and magnitude of the magnetic force the field exerts on this particle? (b) What is the radius of the circular arc followed by this proton?

10. ● An accelerating voltage of 2 500 V is applied to an electron gun, producing a beam of electrons originally traveling horizontally north in vacuum toward the center of a viewing screen 35.0 cm away. (a) What are the magnitude and direction of the deflection on the screen caused by the Earth's gravitational field? (b) What are the magnitude and direction of the deflection on the screen caused by the vertical component of the Earth's magnetic field, taken as 20.0 μT down? Does an electron in this vertical magnetic field move as a projectile, with constant vector acceleration perpendicular to a constant northward component of velocity? Is it a good approximation to assume it has this projectile motion? Explain.

11. A proton (charge $+e$, mass m_p), a deuteron (charge $+e$, mass $2m_p$), and an alpha particle (charge $+2e$, mass $4m_p$) are accelerated through a common potential difference ΔV. Each of the particles enters a uniform magnetic field $\vec{B}$, with its velocity in a direction perpendicular to $\vec{B}$. The proton moves in a circular path of radius r_p. Determine the radii of the circular orbits for the deuteron, r_d, and the alpha particle, r_α, in terms of r_p.

12. **Review problem.** One electron collides elastically with a second electron initially at rest. After the collision, the radii of their trajectories are 1.00 cm and 2.40 cm. The trajectories are perpendicular to a uniform magnetic field of magnitude 0.044 0 T. Determine the energy (in keV) of the incident electron.

13. **Review problem.** An electron moves in a circular path perpendicular to a constant magnetic field of magnitude 1.00 mT. The angular momentum of the electron about the center of the circle is 4.00×10^{-25} kg · m²/s. Determine (a) the radius of the circular path and (b) the speed of the electron.

14. A singly charged ion of mass m is accelerated from rest by a potential difference ΔV. It is then deflected by a uniform magnetic field (perpendicular to the ion's velocity) into a semicircle of radius R. Now a doubly charged ion of mass m' is accelerated through the same potential difference and deflected by the same magnetic field into a semicircle of radius $R' = 2R$. What is the ratio of the masses of the ions?

15. A cosmic-ray proton in interstellar space has an energy of 10.0 MeV and executes a circular orbit having a radius equal to that of Mercury's orbit around the Sun (5.80×10^{10} m). What is the magnetic field in that region of space?

16. Assume the region to the right of a certain vertical plane contains a vertical magnetic field of magnitude 1.00 mT and the field is zero in the region to the left of the plane. An electron, originally traveling perpendicular to the boundary plane, passes into the region of the field. (a) Determine the time interval required for the electron to leave the "field-filled" region, noting that its path is a semicircle. (b) Find the kinetic energy of the electron, assuming the maximum depth of penetration into the field is 2.00 cm.

Section 29.3 Applications Involving Charged Particles Moving in a Magnetic Field

17. A velocity selector consists of electric and magnetic fields described by the expressions $\vec{\mathbf{E}} = E\hat{\mathbf{k}}$ and $\vec{\mathbf{B}} = B\hat{\mathbf{j}}$, with $B = 15.0$ mT. Find the value of E such that a 750-eV electron moving along the positive x axis is undeflected.

18. ● Singly charged uranium-238 ions are accelerated through a potential difference of 2.00 kV and enter a uniform magnetic field of 1.20 T directed perpendicular to their velocities. (a) Determine the radius of their circular path. (b) Repeat for uranium-235 ions. **What If?** How does the ratio of these path radii depend on the accelerating voltage? On the magnitude of the magnetic field?

19. Consider the mass spectrometer shown schematically in Active Figure 29.13. The magnitude of the electric field between the plates of the velocity selector is 2 500 V/m, and the magnetic field in both the velocity selector and the deflection chamber has a magnitude of 0.035 0 T. Calculate the radius of the path for a singly charged ion having a mass $m = 2.18 \times 10^{-26}$ kg.

20. A cyclotron designed to accelerate protons has an outer radius of 0.350 m. The protons are emitted nearly at rest from a source at the center and are accelerated through 600 V each time they cross the gap between the dees. The dees are between the poles of an electromagnet where the field is 0.800 T. (a) Find the cyclotron frequency for the protons in this cyclotron. (b) Find the speed at which protons exit the cyclotron and (c) their maximum kinetic energy. (d) How many revolutions does a proton make in the cyclotron? (e) For what time interval does one proton accelerate?

21. A cyclotron designed to accelerate protons has a magnetic field of magnitude 0.450 T over a region of radius 1.20 m. What are (a) the cyclotron frequency and (b) the maximum speed acquired by the protons?

22. ● A particle in the cyclotron shown in Figure 29.15a gains energy $q\,\Delta V$ from the alternating power supply each time it passes from one dee to the other. The time interval for each full orbit is

$$T = \frac{2\pi}{\omega} = \frac{2\pi m}{qB}$$

so the particle's average rate of increase in energy is

$$\frac{2q\,\Delta V}{T} = \frac{q^2 B\,\Delta V}{\pi m}$$

Note that this power input is constant in time. (a) Show that the rate of increase in the radius r of its path is not constant, but is given by

$$\frac{dr}{dt} = \frac{1}{r}\frac{\Delta V}{\pi B}$$

(b) Describe how the path of the particles in Figure 29.15a could be drawn more realistically. (c) At what rate is the radial position of the protons in Problem 20 increasing immediately before the protons leave the cyclotron? (d) By how much does the radius of the protons' path increase during their last full revolution?

23. ▲ The picture tube in a television uses magnetic deflection coils rather than electric deflection plates. Suppose an electron beam is accelerated through a 50.0-kV potential difference and then through a region of uniform magnetic field 1.00 cm wide. The screen is located 10.0 cm from the center of the coils and is 50.0 cm wide. When the field is turned off, the electron beam hits the center of the screen. What field magnitude is necessary to deflect the beam to the side of the screen? Ignore relativistic corrections.

24. ● In his "discovery of the electron," J. J. Thomson showed that the same beam deflections resulted with tubes having cathodes made of *different* materials and containing *various* gases before evacuation. (a) Are these observations important? Explain your answer. (b) When he applied various potential differences to the deflection plates and turned on the magnetic coils, alone or in combination with the deflection plates, Thomson observed that the fluorescent screen continued to show a *single small* glowing patch. Argue whether his observation is important. (c) Do calculations to show that the charge-to-mass ratio Thomson obtained was huge compared to that of any macroscopic object or of any ionized atom or molecule. How can one make sense of that fact? (d) Could Thomson observe any deflection of the beam due to gravitation? Do a calculation to argue for your answer. (To obtain a visibly glowing patch on the fluorescent screen, the potential difference between the slits and the cathode must be 100 V or more.)

Section 29.4 Magnetic Force Acting on a Current-Carrying Conductor

25. ▲ A wire having a mass per unit length of 0.500 g/cm carries a 2.00-A current horizontally to the south. What are the direction and magnitude of the minimum magnetic field needed to lift this wire vertically upward?

26. A wire carries a steady current of 2.40 A. A straight section of the wire is 0.750 m long and lies along the x axis

within a uniform magnetic field, $\vec{\mathbf{B}} = 1.60\hat{\mathbf{k}}$ T. If the current is in the $+x$ direction, what is the magnetic force on the section of wire?

27. A wire 2.80 m in length carries a current of 5.00 A in a region where a uniform magnetic field has a magnitude of 0.390 T. Calculate the magnitude of the magnetic force on the wire assuming the angle between the magnetic field and the current is (a) 60.0°, (b) 90.0°, and (c) 120°.

28. Imagine a wire with linear mass density 2.40 g/m encircling the Earth at its magnetic equator, where the field is modeled as having the uniform value 28.0 μT horizontally north. What magnitude and direction of the current in the wire will keep the wire levitated immediately above the ground?

29. Review problem. A rod of mass 0.720 kg and radius 6.00 cm rests on two parallel rails (Fig. P29.29) that are $d = 12.0$ cm apart and $L = 45.0$ cm long. The rod carries a current of $I = 48.0$ A in the direction shown and rolls along the rails without slipping. A uniform magnetic field of magnitude 0.240 T is directed perpendicular to the rod and the rails. If it starts from rest, what is the speed of the rod as it leaves the rails?

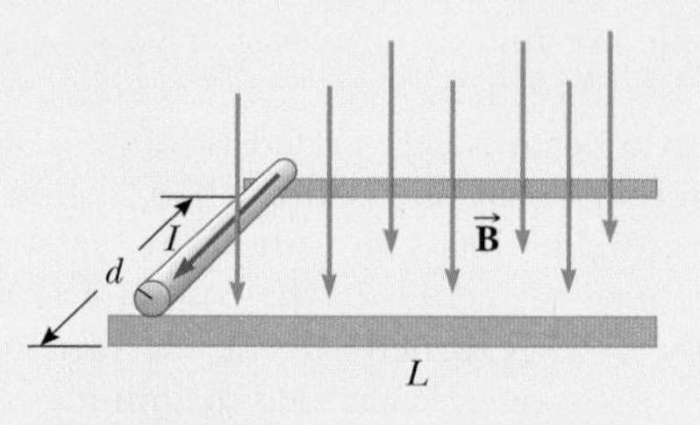

Figure P29.29 Problems 29 and 30.

30. Review problem. A rod of mass m and radius R rests on two parallel rails (Fig. P29.29) that are a distance d apart and have a length L. The rod carries a current I in the direction shown and rolls along the rails without slipping. A uniform magnetic field B is directed perpendicular to the rod and the rails. If it starts from rest, what is the speed of the rod as it leaves the rails?

31. ▲ *A nonuniform magnetic field exerts a net force on a magnetic dipole.* A strong magnet is placed under a horizontal conducting ring of radius r that carries current I as shown in Figure P29.31. If the magnetic field $\vec{\mathbf{B}}$ makes an angle θ with the vertical at the ring's location, what are the magnitude and direction of the resultant magnetic force on the ring?

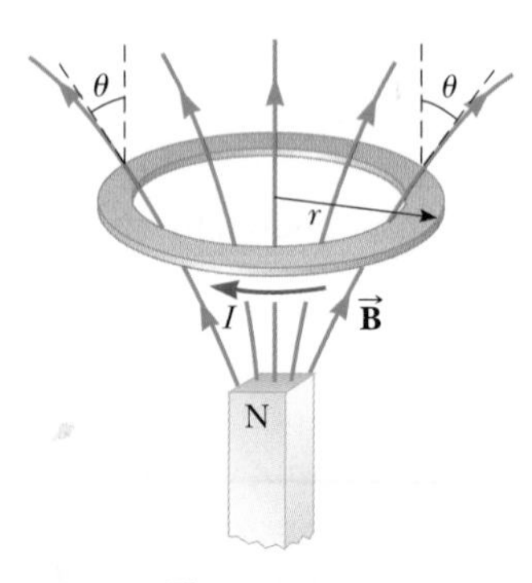

Figure P29.31

32. ● In Figure P29.32, the cube is 40.0 cm on each edge. Four straight segments of wire—*ab*, *bc*, *cd*, and *da*—form a closed loop that carries a current $I = 5.00$ A in the direction shown. A uniform magnetic field of magnitude $B = 0.020\,0$ T is in the positive y direction. (a) Determine the magnitude and direction of the magnetic force on each segment. (b) Explain how you could find the force exerted on the fourth of these segments from the forces on the other three, without further calculation involving the magnetic field.

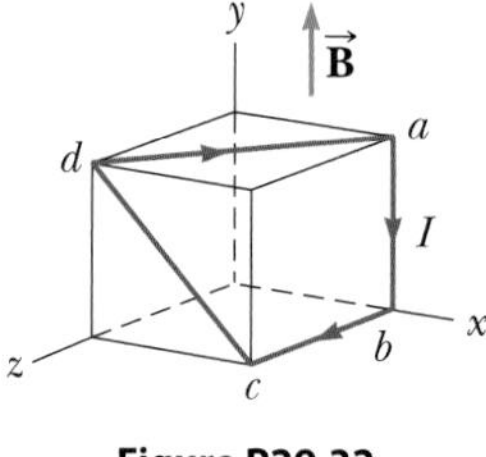

Figure P29.32

33. Assume the Earth's magnetic field is 52.0 μT northward at 60.0° below the horizontal in Atlanta, Georgia. A tube in a neon sign—situated between two diagonally opposite corners of a shop window, which lies in a north–south vertical plane—carries current 35.0 mA. The current enters the tube at the bottom south corner of the shop's window. It exits at the opposite corner, which is 1.40 m farther north and 0.850 m higher up. Between these two points, the glowing tube spells out DONUTS. Determine the total vector magnetic force on the tube. You may use the first "important statement" presented in the *Finalize* section of Example 29.4.

Section 29.5 Torque on a Current Loop in a Uniform Magnetic Field

34. A current of 17.0 mA is maintained in a single circular loop of 2.00 m circumference. A magnetic field of 0.800 T is directed parallel to the plane of the loop. (a) Calculate the magnetic moment of the loop. (b) What is the magnitude of the torque exerted by the magnetic field on the loop?

35. ▲ A rectangular coil consists of $N = 100$ closely wrapped turns and has dimensions $a = 0.400$ m and $b = 0.300$ m. The coil is hinged along the y axis, and its plane makes an angle $\theta = 30.0°$ with the x axis (Fig. P29.35). What is the magnitude of the torque exerted on the coil by a uniform magnetic field $B = 0.800$ T directed along the x axis when the current is $I = 1.20$ A in the direction shown? What is the expected direction of rotation of the coil?

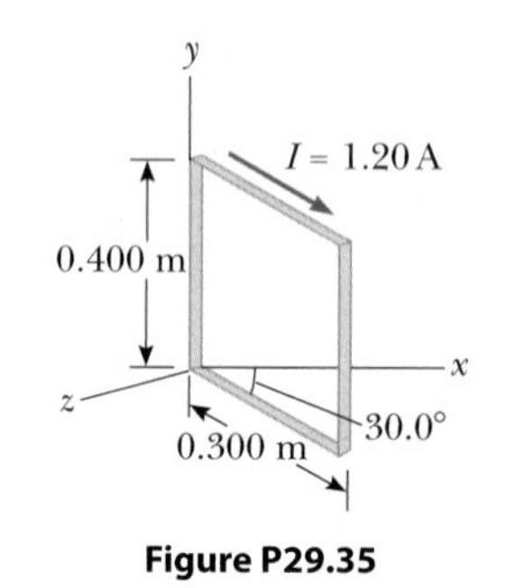

Figure P29.35

36. A current loop with magnetic dipole moment $\vec{\mu}$ is placed in a uniform magnetic field $\vec{\mathbf{B}}$, with its moment making angle θ with the field. With the arbitrary choice of $U = 0$ for $\theta = 90°$, prove that the potential energy of the dipole–field system is $U = -\vec{\mu} \cdot \vec{\mathbf{B}}$. You may imitate the discussion in Chapter 26 of the potential energy of an electric dipole in an electric field.

37. ● The needle of a magnetic compass has magnetic moment 9.70 mA · m². At its location, the Earth's magnetic field is 55.0 μT north at 48.0° below the horizontal. (a) Identify the orientations of the compass needle that represent minimum potential energy and maximum potential energy of the needle–field system. (b) How much work must be done on the needle to move it from the former to the latter orientation?

38. A wire is formed into a circle having a diameter of 10.0 cm and placed in a uniform magnetic field of 3.00 mT. The wire carries a current of 5.00 A. Find (a) the maximum torque on the wire and (b) the range of potential energies of the wire–field system for different orientations of the circle.

39. ● A wire 1.50 m long carries a current of 30.0 mA when it is connected to a battery. The whole wire can be arranged as a single loop with the shape of a circle, a square, or an equilateral triangle. The whole wire can be made into a flat, compact, circular coil with N turns. Explain how its magnetic moment compares in all these cases. In particular, can its magnetic moment go to infinity? To zero? Does its magnetic moment have a well-defined maximum value? If so, identify it. Does it have minimum value? If so, identify it.

40. The rotor in a certain electric motor is a flat, rectangular coil with 80 turns of wire and dimensions 2.50 cm by 4.00 cm. The rotor rotates in a uniform magnetic field of 0.800 T. When the plane of the rotor is perpendicular to the direction of the magnetic field, it carries a current of 10.0 mA. In this orientation, the magnetic moment of the rotor is directed opposite the magnetic field. The rotor then turns through one-half revolution. This process is repeated to cause the rotor to turn steadily at 3 600 rev/min. (a) Find the maximum torque acting on the rotor. (b) Find the peak power output of the motor. (c) Determine the amount of work performed by the magnetic field on the rotor in every full revolution. (d) What is the average power of the motor?

Section 29.6 The Hall Effect

41. In an experiment designed to measure the Earth's magnetic field using the Hall effect, a copper bar 0.500 cm thick is positioned along an east–west direction. If a current of 8.00 A in the conductor results in a Hall voltage of 5.10×10^{-12} V, what is the magnitude of the Earth's magnetic field? (Assume $n = 8.46 \times 10^{28}$ electrons/m³ and the plane of the bar is rotated to be perpendicular to the direction of $\vec{\mathbf{B}}$.)

42. A Hall-effect probe operates with a 120-mA current. When the probe is placed in a uniform magnetic field of magnitude 0.080 0 T, it produces a Hall voltage of 0.700 μV. (a) When it is used to measure an unknown magnetic field, the Hall voltage is 0.330 μV. What is the magnitude of the unknown field? (b) The thickness of the probe in the direction of $\vec{\mathbf{B}}$ is 2.00 mm. Find the density of the charge carriers, each of which has charge of magnitude e.

Additional Problems

43. ● Heart-lung machines and artificial kidney machines employ blood pumps. A mechanical pump can mangle blood cells. Figure P29.43 represents an electromagnetic pump. The blood is confined to an electrically insulating tube, cylindrical in practice but represented as a rectangle of width w and height h. The simplicity of design makes the pump dependable. The blood is easily kept uncontaminated; the tube is simple to clean or inexpensive to replace. Two electrodes fit into the top and the bottom of the tube. The potential difference between them establishes an electric current through the blood, with current density J over a section of length L. A perpendicular magnetic field exists in the same region. (a) Explain why this arrangement produces on the liquid a force that is directed along the length of the pipe. (b) Show that the section of liquid in the magnetic field experiences a pressure increase JLB. (c) After the blood leaves the pump, is it charged? Is it current carrying? Is it magnetized? The same magnetic pump can be used for any fluid that conducts electricity, such as liquid sodium in a nuclear reactor.

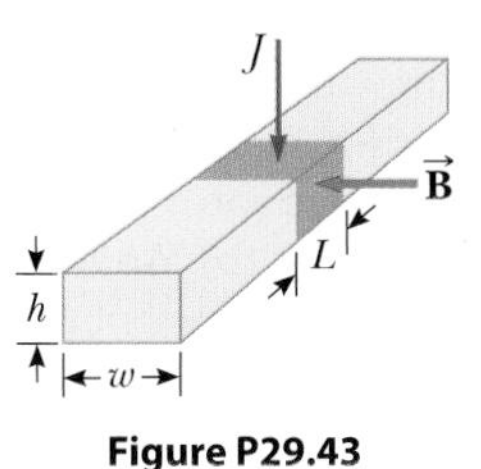

Figure P29.43

44. ● Figure 29.10 shows a charged particle traveling in a nonuniform magnetic field forming a magnetic bottle. (a) Explain why the positively charged particle in the figure must be moving clockwise. The particle travels along a helix whose radius decreases and whose pitch decreases as the particle moves into a stronger magnetic field. If the particle is moving to the right along the x axis, its velocity in this direction will be reduced to zero and it will be reflected from the right-hand side of the bottle, acting as a "magnetic mirror." The particle ends up bouncing back and forth between the ends of the bottle. (b) Explain qualitatively why the axial velocity is reduced to zero as the particle moves into the region of strong magnetic field at the end of the bottle. (c) Explain why the tangential velocity increases as the particle approaches the end of the bottle. (d) Explain why the orbiting particle has a magnetic dipole moment. (e) Sketch the magnetic moment and use the result of Problem 31 to explain again how the nonuniform magnetic field exerts a force on the orbiting particle along the x axis.

45. ● Assume in the plane of the Earth's magnetic equator the planet's field is uniform with the value 25.0 μT northward perpendicular to this plane, everywhere inside a radius of 100 Mm. Also assume the Earth's field is zero outside this circle. A cosmic-ray proton traveling at one tenth of the speed of light is heading directly toward the center of the Earth in the plane of the magnetic equator. Find the radius of curvature of the path it follows when it

enters the region of the planet's assumed field. Explain whether the proton will hit the Earth.

46. A 0.200-kg metal rod carrying a current of 10.0 A glides on two horizontal rails 0.500 m apart. What vertical magnetic field is required to keep the rod moving at a constant speed if the coefficient of kinetic friction between the rod and rails is 0.100?

47. Protons having a kinetic energy of 5.00 MeV are moving in the positive x direction and enter a magnetic field $\vec{\mathbf{B}} = 0.050\,0\hat{\mathbf{k}}$ T directed out of the plane of the page and extending from $x = 0$ to $x = 1.00$ m as shown in Figure P29.47. (a) Calculate the y component of the protons' momentum as they leave the magnetic field. (b) Find the angle α between the initial velocity vector of the proton beam and the velocity vector after the beam emerges from the field. Ignore relativistic effects and note that 1 eV $= 1.60 \times 10^{-19}$ J.

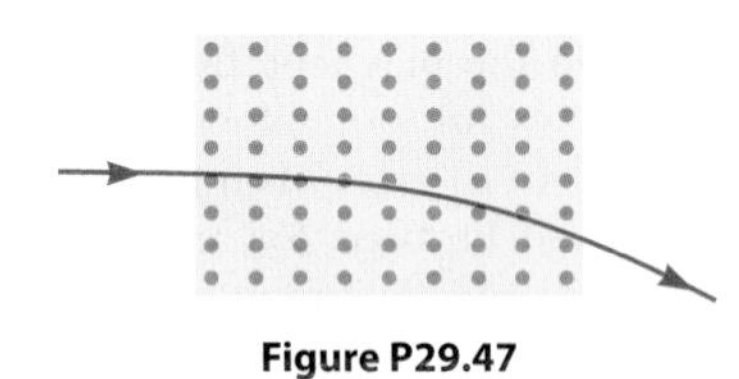

Figure P29.47

48. ● (a) A proton moving in the $+x$ direction with velocity $\vec{\mathbf{v}} = v_i\hat{\mathbf{i}}$ experiences a magnetic force $\vec{\mathbf{F}} = F_i\hat{\mathbf{j}}$ in the $+y$ direction. Explain what you can and cannot infer about $\vec{\mathbf{B}}$ from this information. (b) **What If?** In terms of F_i, what would be the force on a proton in the same field moving with velocity $\vec{\mathbf{v}} = -v_i\hat{\mathbf{i}}$? (c) What would be the force on an electron in the same field moving with velocity $\vec{\mathbf{v}} = -v_i\hat{\mathbf{i}}$?

49. A particle with positive charge $q = 3.20 \times 10^{-19}$ C moves with a velocity $\vec{\mathbf{v}} = (2\hat{\mathbf{i}} + 3\hat{\mathbf{j}} - \hat{\mathbf{k}})$ m/s through a region where both a uniform magnetic field and a uniform electric field exist. (a) Calculate the total force on the moving particle (in unit–vector notation), taking $\vec{\mathbf{B}} = (2\hat{\mathbf{i}} + 4\hat{\mathbf{j}} + \hat{\mathbf{k}})$ T and $\vec{\mathbf{E}} = (4\hat{\mathbf{i}} - \hat{\mathbf{j}} - 2\hat{\mathbf{k}})$ V/m. (b) What angle does the force vector make with the positive x axis?

50. A proton having an initial velocity of $20.0\hat{\mathbf{i}}$ Mm/s enters a uniform magnetic field of magnitude 0.300 T with a direction perpendicular to the proton's velocity. It leaves the field-filled region with velocity $-20.0\hat{\mathbf{j}}$ Mm/s. Determine (a) the direction of the magnetic field, (b) the radius of curvature of the proton's path while in the field, (c) the distance the proton traveled in the field, and (d) the time interval for which the proton is in the field.

51. **Review problem.** A wire having a linear mass density of 1.00 g/cm is placed on a horizontal surface that has a coefficient of kinetic friction of 0.200. The wire carries a current of 1.50 A toward the east and slides horizontally to the north. What are the magnitude and direction of the smallest magnetic field that enables the wire to move in this fashion?

52. **Review problem.** A proton is at rest at the plane vertical boundary of a region containing a uniform vertical magnetic field B. An alpha particle moving horizontally makes a head-on elastic collision with the proton. Immediately after the collision, both particles enter the magnetic field, moving perpendicular to the direction of the field. The radius of the proton's trajectory is R. Find the radius of the alpha particle's trajectory. The mass of the alpha particle is four times that of the proton, and its charge is twice that of the proton.

53. The circuit in Figure P29.53 consists of wires at the top and bottom and identical metal springs in the left and right sides. The upper portion of the circuit is fixed. The wire at the bottom has a mass of 10.0 g and is 5.00 cm long. The springs stretch 0.500 cm under the weight of the wire, and the circuit has a total resistance of 12.0 Ω. When a magnetic field is turned on, directed out of the page, the springs stretch an additional 0.300 cm. What is the magnitude of the magnetic field?

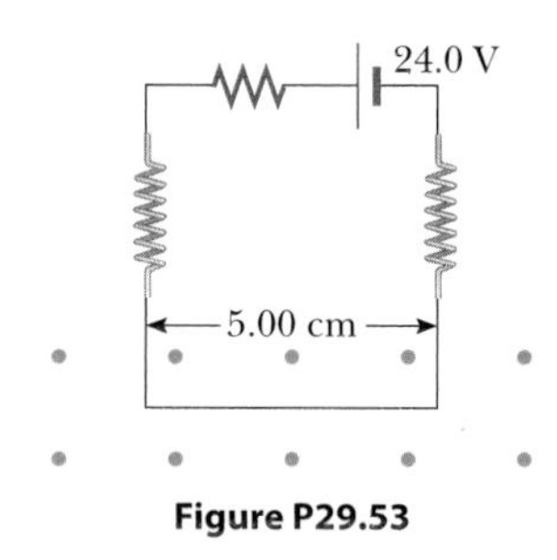

Figure P29.53

54. A handheld electric mixer contains an electric motor. Model the motor as a single flat, compact, circular coil carrying electric current in a region where a magnetic field is produced by an external permanent magnet. You need consider only one instant in the operation of the motor. (We will consider motors again in Chapter 31.) The coil moves because the magnetic field exerts torque on the coil as described in Section 29.5. Make order-of-magnitude estimates of the magnetic field, the torque on the coil, the current in it, its area, and the number of turns in the coil so that they are related according to Equation 29.17. Note that the input power to the motor is electric, given by $\mathcal{P} = I\,\Delta V$, and the useful output power is mechanical, $\mathcal{P} = \tau\omega$.

55. A nonconducting sphere has mass 80.0 g and radius 20.0 cm. A flat, compact coil of wire with five turns is wrapped tightly around it, with each turn concentric with the sphere. As shown in Figure P29.55, the sphere is placed on an inclined plane that slopes downward to the left, making an angle θ with the horizontal so that the coil is parallel to the inclined plane. A uniform magnetic field of 0.350 T vertically upward exists in the region of the sphere. What current in the coil will enable the sphere to rest in equilibrium on the inclined plane? Show that the result does not depend on the value of θ.

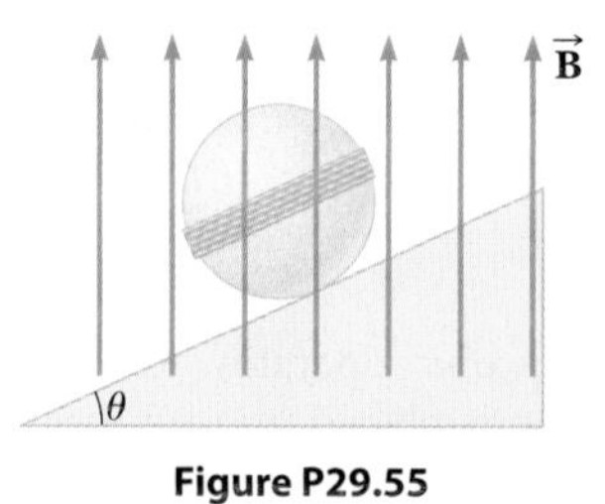

Figure P29.55

56. A metal rod having a mass per unit length λ carries a current I. The rod hangs from two vertical wires in a uniform vertical magnetic field as shown in Figure P29.56. The

wires make an angle θ with the vertical when in equilibrium. Determine the magnitude of the magnetic field.

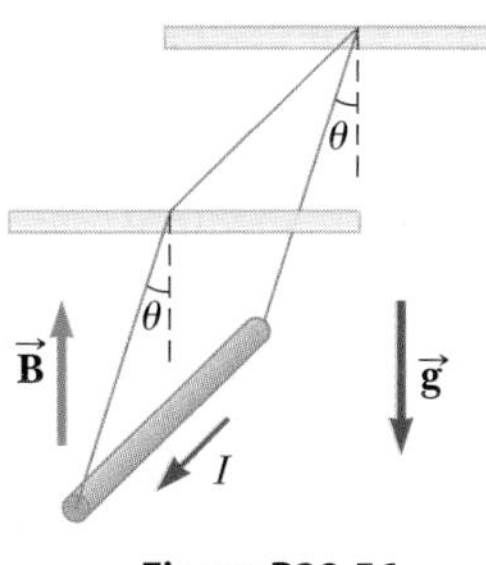

Figure P29.56

57. A cyclotron is sometimes used for carbon dating as will be described in Chapter 44. Carbon-14 and carbon-12 ions are obtained from a sample of the material to be dated and accelerated in the cyclotron. If the cyclotron has a magnetic field of magnitude 2.40 T, what is the difference in cyclotron frequencies for the two ions?

58. A uniform magnetic field of magnitude 0.150 T is directed along the positive x axis. A positron moving at 5.00×10^6 m/s enters the field along a direction that makes an angle of 85.0° with the x axis (Fig. P29.58). The motion of the particle is expected to be a helix as described in Section 29.2. Calculate (a) the pitch p and (b) the radius r of the trajectory.

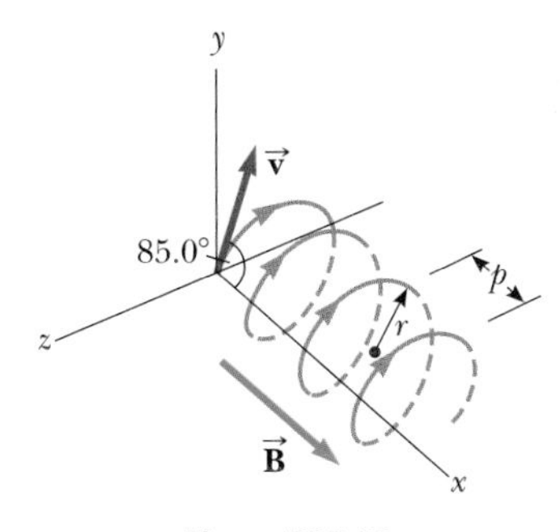

Figure P29.58

59. Consider an electron orbiting a proton and maintained in a fixed circular path of radius $R = 5.29 \times 10^{-11}$ m by the Coulomb force. Treat the orbiting particle as a current loop and calculate the resulting torque when the system is in a magnetic field of 0.400 T directed perpendicular to the magnetic moment of the electron.

60. A proton moving in the plane of the page has a kinetic energy of 6.00 MeV. A magnetic field of magnitude B = 1.00 T is directed into the page. The proton enters the magnetic field with its velocity vector at an angle θ = 45.0° to the linear boundary of the field as shown in Figure P29.60. (a) Find x, the distance from the point of entry to where the proton will leave the field. (b) Determine θ', the angle between the boundary and the proton's velocity vector as it leaves the field.

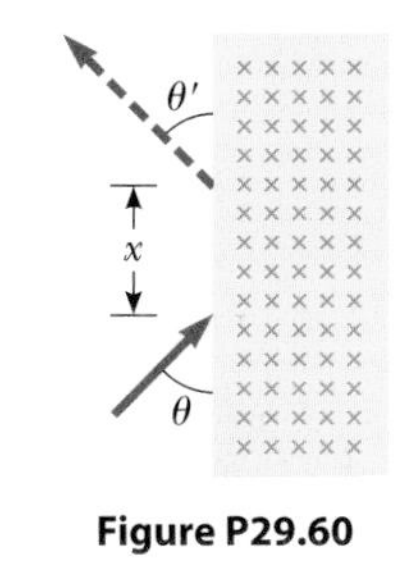

Figure P29.60

61. ● A heart surgeon monitors the flow rate of blood through an artery using an electromagnetic flowmeter (Fig. P29.61). Electrodes A and B make contact with the outer surface of the blood vessel, which has interior diameter 3.00 mm. (a) For a magnetic field magnitude of 0.040 0 T, an emf of 160 μV appears between the electrodes. Calculate the speed of the blood. (b) Verify that electrode A is positive as shown. Does the sign of the emf depend on whether the mobile ions in the blood are predominantly positively or negatively charged? Explain.

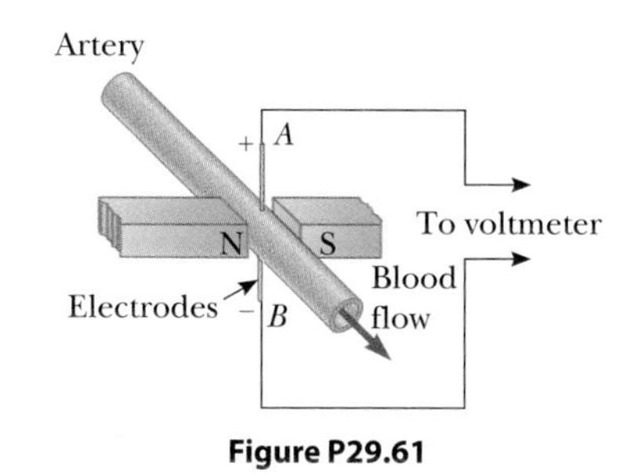

Figure P29.61

62. The following table shows measurements of a Hall voltage and corresponding magnetic field for a probe used to measure magnetic fields. (a) Plot these data and deduce a relationship between the two variables. (b) If the measurements were taken with a current of 0.200 A and the sample is made from a material having a charge-carrier density of 1.00×10^{26} kg/m³, what is the thickness of the sample?

ΔV_H (μV)	B (T)
0	0.00
11	0.10
19	0.20
28	0.30
42	0.40
50	0.50
61	0.60
68	0.70
79	0.80
90	0.90
102	1.00

63. ● As shown in Figure P29.63, a particle of mass m having positive charge q is initially traveling with velocity $v\hat{\mathbf{j}}$. At the origin of coordinates it enters a region between $y = 0$ and $y = h$ containing a uniform magnetic field $B\hat{\mathbf{k}}$

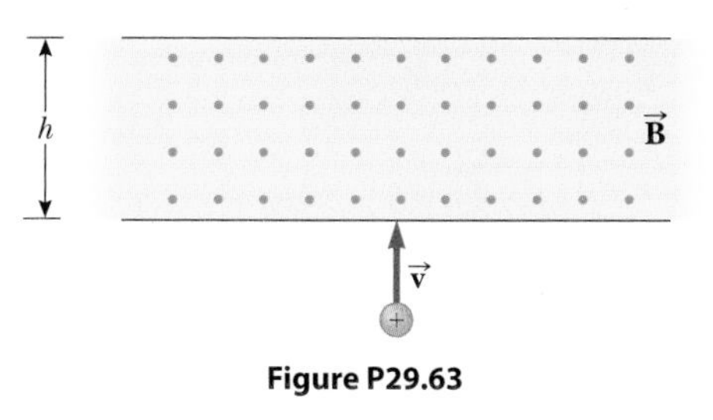

Figure P29.63

directed perpendicularly out of the page. (a) What is the critical value of v such that the particle just reaches $y = h$? Describe the path of the particle under this condition and predict its final velocity. (b) Specify the path the particle takes and its final velocity if v is less than the critical value. (c) **What If?** Specify the path the particle takes and its final velocity if v is greater than the critical value.

64. In Niels Bohr's 1913 model of the hydrogen atom, the single electron is in a circular orbit of radius 5.29×10^{-11} m and its speed is 2.19×10^{6} m/s. (a) What is the magnitude of the magnetic moment due to the electron's motion? (b) If the electron moves in a horizontal circle, counterclockwise as seen from above, what is the direction of this magnetic moment vector?

65. ● **Review problem.** Review Section 15.5 on torsional pendulums. (a) Show that a magnetic dipole in a uniform magnetic field, displaced from its equilibrium orientation and released, can oscillate as a torsional pendulum in simple harmonic motion. Is this statement true for all angular displacements, for all displacements less than 180°, or only for small angular displacements? Explain. (b) Assume the dipole is a compass needle—a light bar magnet—with a magnetic moment of magnitude μ. It has moment of inertia I about its center, where it is mounted on a frictionless vertical axle, and it is placed in a horizontal magnetic field of magnitude B. Evaluate its frequency of oscillation. (c) Explain how the compass needle can be conveniently used as an indicator of the magnitude of the external magnetic field. If its frequency is 0.680 Hz in the Earth's local field, with a horizontal component of 39.2 μT, what is the magnitude of a field in which its frequency of oscillation is 4.90 Hz?

Answers to Quick Quizzes

29.1 (e). The right-hand rule gives the direction. Be sure to account for the negative charge on the electron.

29.2 **(i),** (b). The magnetic force on the particle increases in proportion to v, but the centripetal acceleration increases according to the square of v. The result is a larger radius, as you can see from Equation 29.3. **(ii),** (a). The magnetic force on the particle increases in proportion to B. The result is a smaller radius as you can see from Equation 29.3.

29.3 (c). Use the right-hand rule to determine the direction of the magnetic field.

29.4 **(i),** (c), (b), (a). Because all loops enclose the same area and carry the same current, the magnitude of $\vec{\mu}$ is the same for all. For (c), $\vec{\mu}$ points upward and is perpendicular to the magnetic field and $\tau = \mu B$, the maximum torque possible. For the loop in (a), $\vec{\mu}$ points along the direction of $\vec{\mathbf{B}}$ and the torque is zero. For (b), the torque is intermediate between zero and the maximum value. **(ii),** (a) = (b) = (c). Because the magnetic field is uniform, there is zero net force on all three loops.

A proposed method for launching future payloads into space is the use of *rail guns*, in which projectiles are accelerated by means of magnetic forces. This photo shows the firing of a projectile at a speed of over 3 km/s from an experimental rail gun at Sandia National Research Laboratories, Albuquerque, New Mexico. (Defense Threat Reduction Agency [DTRA])

30 Sources of the Magnetic Field

In Chapter 29, we discussed the magnetic force exerted on a charged particle moving in a magnetic field. To complete the description of the magnetic interaction, this chapter explores the origin of the magnetic field, moving charges. We begin by showing how to use the law of Biot and Savart to calculate the magnetic field produced at some point in space by a small current element. This formalism is then used to calculate the total magnetic field due to various current distributions. Next, we show how to determine the force between two current-carrying conductors, leading to the definition of the ampere. We also introduce Ampère's law, which is useful in calculating the magnetic field of a highly symmetric configuration carrying a steady current.

This chapter is also concerned with the complex processes that occur in magnetic materials. All magnetic effects in matter can be explained on the basis of atomic magnetic moments, which arise both from the orbital motion of electrons and from an intrinsic property of electrons known as spin.

30.1 The Biot–Savart Law

Shortly after Oersted's discovery in 1819 that a compass needle is deflected by a current-carrying conductor, Jean-Baptiste Biot (1774–1862) and Félix Savart

PITFALL PREVENTION 30.1

The Biot–Savart Law

The magnetic field described by the Biot–Savart law is the field *due to* a given current-carrying conductor. Do not confuse this field with any *external* field that may be applied to the conductor from some other source.

(1791–1841) performed quantitative experiments on the force exerted by an electric current on a nearby magnet. From their experimental results, Biot and Savart arrived at a mathematical expression that gives the magnetic field at some point in space in terms of the current that produces the field. That expression is based on the following experimental observations for the magnetic field $d\vec{\mathbf{B}}$ at a point P associated with a length element $d\vec{\mathbf{s}}$ of a wire carrying a steady current I (Fig. 30.1):

- The vector $d\vec{\mathbf{B}}$ is perpendicular both to $d\vec{\mathbf{s}}$ (which points in the direction of the current) and to the unit vector $\hat{\mathbf{r}}$ directed from $d\vec{\mathbf{s}}$ toward P.
- The magnitude of $d\vec{\mathbf{B}}$ is inversely proportional to r^2, where r is the distance from $d\vec{\mathbf{s}}$ to P.
- The magnitude of $d\vec{\mathbf{B}}$ is proportional to the current and to the magnitude ds of the length element $d\vec{\mathbf{s}}$.
- The magnitude of $d\vec{\mathbf{B}}$ is proportional to $\sin\theta$, where θ is the angle between the vectors $d\vec{\mathbf{s}}$ and $\hat{\mathbf{r}}$.

These observations are summarized in the mathematical expression known today as the **Biot–Savart law:**

Biot–Savart law ▶

$$d\vec{\mathbf{B}} = \frac{\mu_0}{4\pi}\frac{I\,d\vec{\mathbf{s}} \times \hat{\mathbf{r}}}{r^2} \tag{30.1}$$

where μ_0 is a constant called the **permeability of free space:**

Permeability of free space ▶

$$\mu_0 = 4\pi \times 10^{-7}\ \mathrm{T \cdot m/A} \tag{30.2}$$

Notice that the field $d\vec{\mathbf{B}}$ in Equation 30.1 is the field created at a point by the current in only a small length element $d\vec{\mathbf{s}}$ of the conductor. To find the *total* magnetic field $\vec{\mathbf{B}}$ created at some point by a current of finite size, we must sum up contributions from all current elements $I\,d\vec{\mathbf{s}}$ that make up the current. That is, we must evaluate $\vec{\mathbf{B}}$ by integrating Equation 30.1:

$$\vec{\mathbf{B}} = \frac{\mu_0 I}{4\pi}\int \frac{d\vec{\mathbf{s}} \times \hat{\mathbf{r}}}{r^2} \tag{30.3}$$

where the integral is taken over the entire current distribution. This expression must be handled with special care because the integrand is a cross product and therefore a vector quantity. We shall see one case of such an integration in Example 30.1.

Although the Biot–Savart law was discussed for a current-carrying wire, it is also valid for a current consisting of charges flowing through space such as the electron beam in a television picture tube. In that case, $d\vec{\mathbf{s}}$ represents the length of a small segment of space in which the charges flow.

Interesting similarities exist between Equation 30.1 for the magnetic field due to a current element and Equation 23.9 for the electric field due to a point charge. The magnitude of the magnetic field varies as the inverse square of the distance from the source, as does the electric field due to a point charge. The directions of the two fields are quite different, however. The electric field created by a point charge is radial, but the magnetic field created by a current element is perpendicular to both the length element $d\vec{\mathbf{s}}$ and the unit vector $\hat{\mathbf{r}}$ as described by the cross product in Equation 30.1. Hence, if the conductor lies in the plane of the page as shown in Figure 30.1, $d\vec{\mathbf{B}}$ points out of the page at P and into the page at P'.

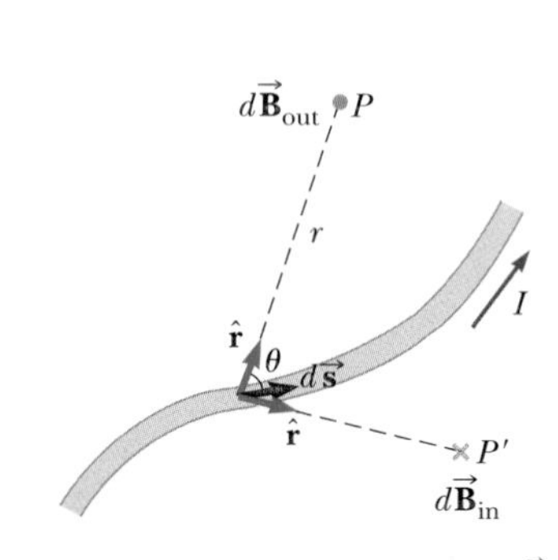

Figure 30.1 The magnetic field $d\vec{\mathbf{B}}$ at a point due to the current I through a length element $d\vec{\mathbf{s}}$ is given by the Biot–Savart law. The direction of the field is out of the page at P and into the page at P'.

Another difference between electric and magnetic fields is related to the source of the field. An electric field is established by an isolated electric charge. The Biot–Savart law gives the magnetic field of an isolated current element at some point, but such an isolated current element cannot exist the way an isolated electric charge can. A current element *must* be part of an extended current distribution because a complete circuit is needed for charges to flow. Therefore, the Biot–Savart law (Eq. 30.1) is only the first step in a calculation of a magnetic field; it must be followed by an integration over the current distribution as in Equation 30.3.

Quick Quiz 30.1 Consider the magnetic field due to the current in the length of wire shown in Figure 30.2. Rank the points A, B, and C in terms of magnitude of the magnetic field that is due to the current in just the length element $d\vec{\mathbf{s}}$ shown from greatest to least.

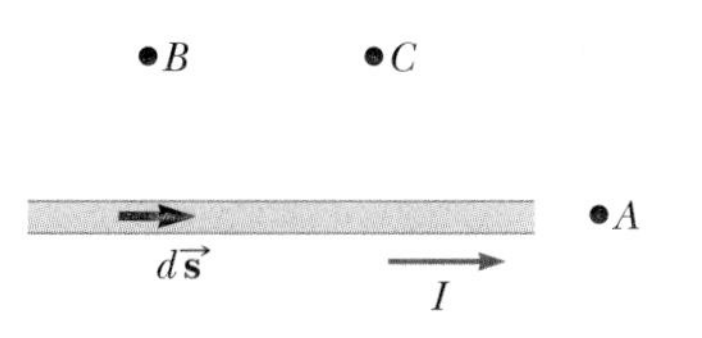

Figure 30.2 (Quick Quiz 30.1) Where is the magnetic field the greatest?

EXAMPLE 30.1 Magnetic Field Surrounding a Thin, Straight Conductor

Consider a thin, straight wire carrying a constant current I and placed along the x axis as shown in Figure 30.3. Determine the magnitude and direction of the magnetic field at point P due to this current.

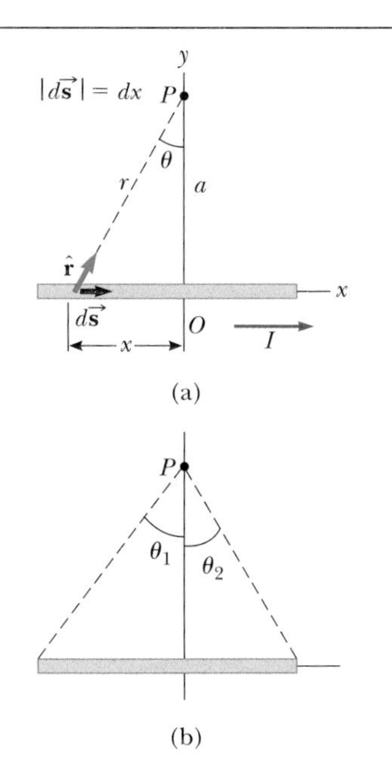

Figure 30.3 (Example 30.1) (a) A thin, straight wire carrying a current I. The magnetic field at point P due to the current in each element $d\vec{\mathbf{s}}$ of the wire is out of the page, so the net field at point P is also out of the page. (b) The angles θ_1 and θ_2 used for determining the net field.

SOLUTION

Conceptualize From the Biot–Savart law, we expect that the magnitude of the field is proportional to the current in the wire and decreases as the distance a from the wire to point P increases.

Categorize We are asked to find the magnetic field due to a simple current distribution, so this example is a typical problem for which the Biot–Savart law is appropriate.

Analyze Let's start by considering a length element $d\vec{\mathbf{s}}$ located a distance r from P. The direction of the magnetic field at point P due to the current in this element is out of the page because $d\vec{\mathbf{s}} \times \hat{\mathbf{r}}$ is out of the page. In fact, because *all* the current elements $I\,d\vec{\mathbf{s}}$ lie in the plane of the page, they all produce a magnetic field directed out of the page at point P. Therefore, the direction of the magnetic field at point P is out of the page and we need only find the magnitude of the field. We place the origin at O and let point P be along the positive y axis, with $\hat{\mathbf{k}}$ being a unit vector pointing out of the page.

Evaluate the cross product in the Biot–Savart law:

$$d\vec{\mathbf{s}} \times \hat{\mathbf{r}} = |d\vec{\mathbf{s}} \times \hat{\mathbf{r}}|\hat{\mathbf{k}} = \left[dx \sin\left(\frac{\pi}{2} - \theta\right)\right]\hat{\mathbf{k}} = (dx\cos\theta)\hat{\mathbf{k}}$$

Substitute into Equation 30.1:

$$(1)\quad d\vec{\mathbf{B}} = (dB)\hat{\mathbf{k}} = \frac{\mu_0 I}{4\pi}\frac{dx\cos\theta}{r^2}\hat{\mathbf{k}}$$

From the geometry in Figure 30.3a, express r in terms of θ:

$$(2)\quad r = \frac{a}{\cos\theta}$$

Notice that $\tan\theta = -x/a$ from the right triangle in Figure 30.3a (the negative sign is necessary because $d\vec{\mathbf{s}}$ is located at a negative value of x) and solve for x:

$$x = -a\tan\theta$$

Find the differential dx:

$$(3)\quad dx = -a\sec^2\theta\, d\theta = -\frac{a\,d\theta}{\cos^2\theta}$$

Substitute Equations (2) and (3) into the magnitude of the field from Equation (1):

$$(4)\quad dB = -\frac{\mu_0 I}{4\pi}\frac{(a\,d\theta)\cos\theta\cos^2\theta}{a^2\cos^2\theta} = -\frac{\mu_0 I}{4\pi a}\cos\theta\, d\theta$$

Integrate Equation (4) over all length elements on the wire, where the subtending angles range from θ_1 to θ_2 as defined in Figure 30.3b:

$$B = -\frac{\mu_0 I}{4\pi a}\int_{\theta_1}^{\theta_2} \cos\theta\, d\theta = \frac{\mu_0 I}{4\pi a}(\sin\theta_1 - \sin\theta_2) \qquad \textbf{(30.4)}$$

Finalize We can use this result to find the magnetic field of *any* straight current-carrying wire if we know the geometry and hence the angles θ_1 and θ_2. Consider the special case of an infinitely long, straight wire. If the wire in Figure 30.3b becomes infinitely long, we see that $\theta_1 = \pi/2$ and $\theta_2 = -\pi/2$ for length elements ranging between positions $x = -\infty$ and $x = +\infty$. Because $(\sin\theta_1 - \sin\theta_2) = (\sin\pi/2 - \sin(-\pi/2)) = 2$, Equation 30.4 becomes

$$B = \frac{\mu_0 I}{2\pi a} \qquad \textbf{(30.5)}$$

Equations 30.4 and 30.5 both show that the magnitude of the magnetic field is proportional to the current and decreases with increasing distance from the wire, as expected. Equation 30.5 has the same mathematical form as the expression for the magnitude of the electric field due to a long charged wire (see Eq. 24.7).

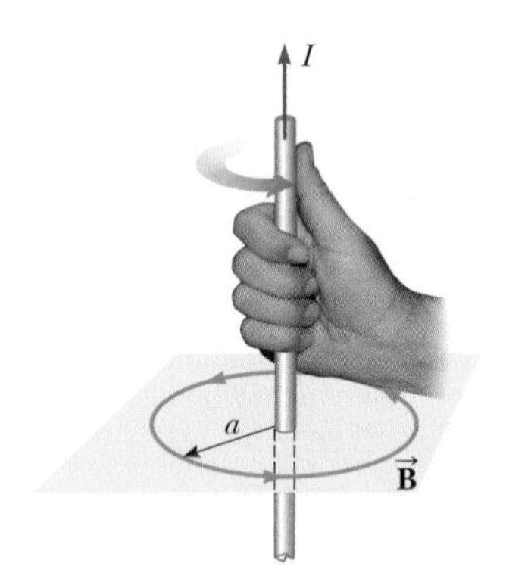

Figure 30.4 The right-hand rule for determining the direction of the magnetic field surrounding a long, straight wire carrying a current. Notice that the magnetic field lines form circles around the wire.

The result of Example 30.1 is important because a current in the form of a long, straight wire occurs often. Figure 30.4 is a perspective view of the magnetic field surrounding a long, straight, current-carrying wire. Because of the wire's symmetry, the magnetic field lines are circles concentric with the wire and lie in planes perpendicular to the wire. The magnitude of $\vec{\mathbf{B}}$ is constant on any circle of radius a and is given by Equation 30.5. A convenient rule for determining the direction of $\vec{\mathbf{B}}$ is to grasp the wire with the right hand, positioning the thumb along the direction of the current. The four fingers wrap in the direction of the magnetic field.

Figure 30.4 also shows that the magnetic field line has no beginning and no end. Rather, it forms a closed loop. That is a major difference between magnetic field lines and electric field lines, which begin on positive charges and end on negative charges. We will explore this feature of magnetic field lines further in Section 30.5.

EXAMPLE 30.2 Magnetic Field Due to a Curved Wire Segment

Calculate the magnetic field at point O for the current-carrying wire segment shown in Figure 30.5. The wire consists of two straight portions and a circular arc of radius a, which subtends an angle θ.

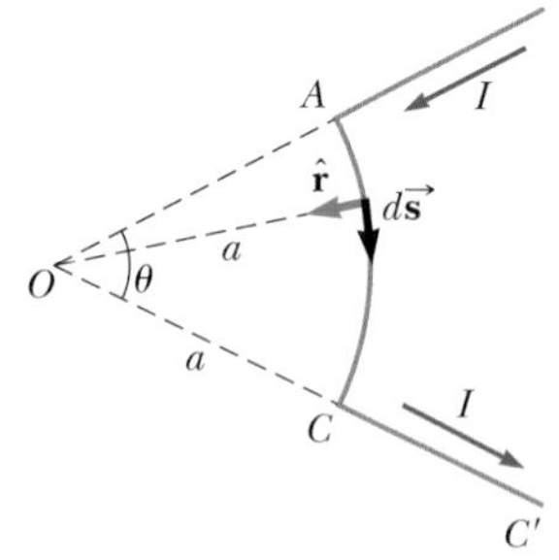

Figure 30.5 (Example 30.2) The magnetic field at O due to the current in the curved segment AC is into the page. The contribution to the field at O due to the current in the two straight segments is zero. The length of the curved segment AC is s.

SOLUTION

Conceptualize The magnetic field at O due to the current in the straight segments AA' and CC' is zero because $d\vec{\mathbf{s}}$ is parallel to $\hat{\mathbf{r}}$ along these paths, which means that $d\vec{\mathbf{s}} \times \hat{\mathbf{r}} = 0$ for these paths.

Categorize Because we can ignore segments AA' and CC', this example is categorized as an application of the Biot–Savart law to the curved wire segment AC.

Analyze Each length element $d\vec{\mathbf{s}}$ along path AC is at the same distance a from O, and the current in each contributes a field element $d\vec{\mathbf{B}}$ directed into the page at O. Furthermore, at every point on AC, $d\vec{\mathbf{s}}$ is perpendicular to $\hat{\mathbf{r}}$; hence, $|d\vec{\mathbf{s}} \times \hat{\mathbf{r}}| = ds$.

From Equation 30.1, find the magnitude of the field at O due to the current in an element of length ds:

$$dB = \frac{\mu_0}{4\pi}\frac{I\,ds}{a^2}$$

Integrate this expression over the curved path *AC*, noting that *I* and *a* are constants:

$$B = \frac{\mu_0 I}{4\pi a^2}\int ds = \frac{\mu_0 I}{4\pi a^2}s$$

From the geometry, note that $s = a\theta$ and substitute:

$$B = \frac{\mu_0 I}{4\pi a^2}(a\theta) = \frac{\mu_0 I}{4\pi a}\theta \qquad \textbf{(30.6)}$$

Finalize Equation 30.6 gives the magnitude of the magnetic field at *O*. The direction of $\vec{\mathbf{B}}$ is into the page at *O* because $d\vec{\mathbf{s}} \times \hat{\mathbf{r}}$ is into the page for every length element.

What If? What if you were asked to find the magnetic field at the center of a circular wire loop of radius *R* that carries a current *I*? Can this question be answered at this point in our understanding of the source of magnetic fields?

Answer Yes, it can. The straight wires in Figure 30.5 do not contribute to the magnetic field. The only contribution is from the curved segment. As the angle θ increases, the curved segment becomes a full circle when $\theta = 2\pi$. Therefore, you can find the magnetic field at the center of a wire loop by letting $\theta = 2\pi$ in Equation 30.6:

$$B = \frac{\mu_0 I}{4\pi a}2\pi = \frac{\mu_0 I}{2a}$$

This result is a limiting case of a more general result discussed in Example 30.3.

EXAMPLE 30.3 Magnetic Field on the Axis of a Circular Current Loop

Consider a circular wire loop of radius *a* located in the *yz* plane and carrying a steady current *I* as in Figure 30.6. Calculate the magnetic field at an axial point *P* a distance *x* from the center of the loop.

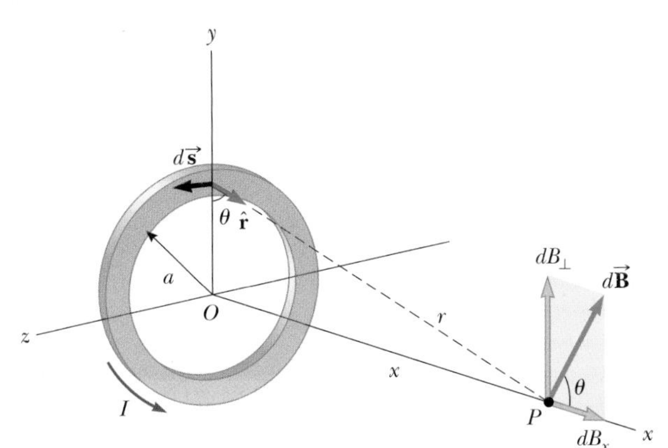

Figure 30.6 (Example 30.3) Geometry for calculating the magnetic field at a point *P* lying on the axis of a current loop. By symmetry, the total field $\vec{\mathbf{B}}$ is along this axis.

SOLUTION

Conceptualize Figure 30.6 shows the magnetic field contribution $d\vec{\mathbf{B}}$ at *P* due to a single current element at the top of the ring. This field vector can be resolved into components dB_x parallel to the axis of the ring and $dB_\perp$ perpendicular to the axis. Think about the magnetic field contributions from a current element at the bottom of the loop. Because of the symmetry of the situation, the perpendicular components of the field due to elements at the top and bottom of the ring cancel. This cancellation occurs for all pairs of segments around the ring, so we can ignore the perpendicular component of the field and focus solely on the parallel components, which simply add.

Categorize We are asked to find the magnetic field due to a simple current distribution, so this example is a typical problem for which the Biot–Savart law is appropriate.

Analyze In this situation, every length element $d\vec{\mathbf{s}}$ is perpendicular to the vector $\hat{\mathbf{r}}$ at the location of the element. Therefore, for any element, $|d\vec{\mathbf{s}} \times \hat{\mathbf{r}}| = (ds)(1)\sin 90° = ds$. Furthermore, all length elements around the loop are at the same distance *r* from *P*, where $r^2 = a^2 + x^2$.

Use Equation 30.1 to find the magnitude of $d\vec{\mathbf{B}}$ due to the current in any length element $d\vec{\mathbf{s}}$:

$$dB = \frac{\mu_0 I}{4\pi}\frac{|d\vec{\mathbf{s}} \times \hat{\mathbf{r}}|}{r^2} = \frac{\mu_0 I}{4\pi}\frac{ds}{(a^2 + x^2)}$$

Find the *x* component of the field element:

$$dB_x = \frac{\mu_0 I}{4\pi}\frac{ds}{(a^2 + x^2)}\cos\theta$$

Integrate over the entire loop:

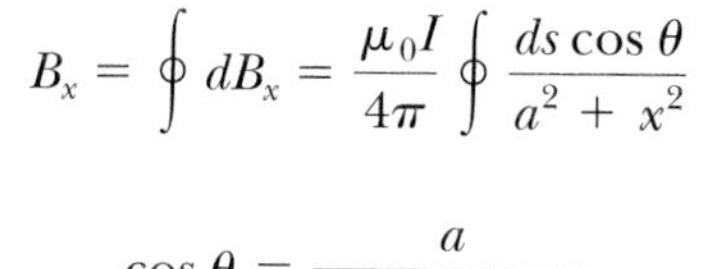

$$B_x = \oint dB_x = \frac{\mu_0 I}{4\pi} \oint \frac{ds \cos\theta}{a^2 + x^2}$$

From the geometry, evaluate $\cos\theta$:

$$\cos\theta = \frac{a}{(a^2 + x^2)^{1/2}}$$

Substitute this expression for $\cos\theta$ into the integral and note that x, a, and θ are all constant:

$$B_x = \frac{\mu_0 I}{4\pi} \oint \frac{ds}{a^2 + x^2} \frac{a}{(a^2 + x^2)^{1/2}} = \frac{\mu_0 I}{4\pi} \frac{a}{(a^2 + x^2)^{3/2}} \oint ds$$

Integrate around the loop:

$$B_x = \frac{\mu_0 I}{4\pi} \frac{a}{(a^2 + x^2)^{3/2}} (2\pi a) = \frac{\mu_0 I a^2}{2(a^2 + x^2)^{3/2}} \quad \textbf{(30.7)}$$

Finalize To find the magnetic field at the center of the loop, set $x = 0$ in Equation 30.7. At this special point,

$$B = \frac{\mu_0 I}{2a} \quad (\text{at } x = 0) \quad \textbf{(30.8)}$$

which is consistent with the result of the **What If?** feature of Example 30.2.

The pattern of magnetic field lines for a circular current loop is shown in Figure 30.7a. For clarity, the lines are drawn for only the plane that contains the axis of the loop. The field-line pattern is axially symmetric and looks like the pattern around a bar magnet, which is shown in Figure 30.7c.

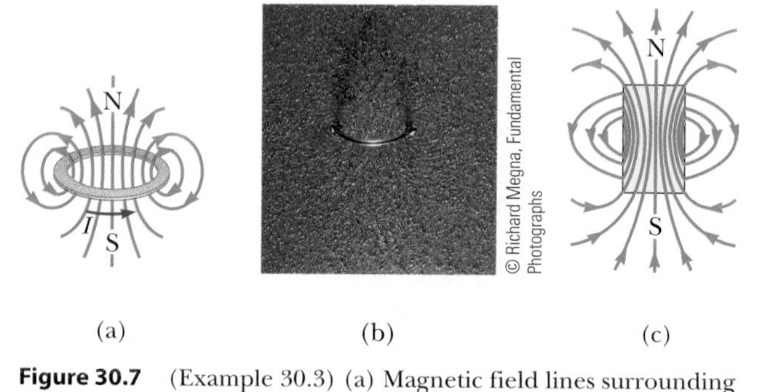

Figure 30.7 (Example 30.3) (a) Magnetic field lines surrounding a current loop. (b) Magnetic field lines surrounding a current loop, displayed with iron filings. (c) Magnetic field lines surrounding a bar magnet. Notice the similarity between this line pattern and that of a current loop.

What If? What if we consider points on the x axis very far from the loop? How does the magnetic field behave at these distant points?

Answer In this case, in which $x \gg a$, we can neglect the term a^2 in the denominator of Equation 30.7 and obtain

$$B \approx \frac{\mu_0 I a^2}{2x^3} \quad (\text{for } x \gg a) \quad \textbf{(30.9)}$$

The magnitude of the magnetic moment μ of the loop is defined as the product of current and loop area (see Eq. 29.15): $\mu = I(\pi a^2)$ for our circular loop. We can express Equation 30.9 as

$$B \approx \frac{\mu_0}{2\pi} \frac{\mu}{x^3} \quad \textbf{(30.10)}$$

This result is similar in form to the expression for the electric field due to an electric dipole, $E = k_e(p/y^3)$ (see Example 23.5), where $p = 2qa$ is the electric dipole moment as defined in Equation 26.16.

30.2 The Magnetic Force Between Two Parallel Conductors

In Chapter 29, we described the magnetic force that acts on a current-carrying conductor placed in an external magnetic field. Because a current in a conductor sets up its own magnetic field, it is easy to understand that two current-carrying conductors exert magnetic forces on each other. Such forces can be used as the basis for defining the ampere and the coulomb.

Consider two long, straight, parallel wires separated by a distance a and carrying currents I_1 and I_2 in the same direction as in Active Figure 30.8. Let's determine the force exerted on one wire due to the magnetic field set up by the other

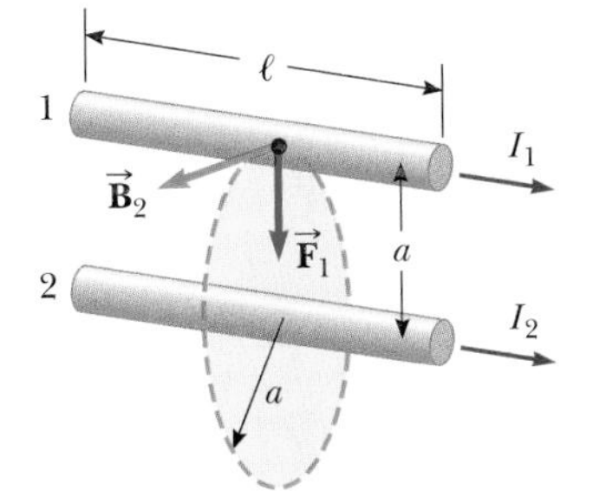

ACTIVE FIGURE 30.8

Two parallel wires that each carry a steady current exert a magnetic force on each other. The field $\vec{B}_2$ due to the current in wire 2 exerts a magnetic force of magnitude $F_1 = I_1 \ell B_2$ on wire 1. The force is attractive if the currents are parallel (as shown) and repulsive if the currents are antiparallel.

Sign in at www.thomsonedu.com and go to ThomsonNOW to adjust the currents in the wires and the distance between them to see the effect on the force.

wire. Wire 2, which carries a current I_2 and is identified arbitrarily as the source wire, creates a magnetic field $\vec{B}_2$ at the location of wire 1, the test wire. The direction of $\vec{B}_2$ is perpendicular to wire 1 as shown in Active Figure 30.8. According to Equation 29.10, the magnetic force on a length ℓ of wire 1 is $\vec{F}_1 = I_1 \vec{\ell} \times \vec{B}_2$. Because $\vec{\ell}$ is perpendicular to $\vec{B}_2$ in this situation, the magnitude of $\vec{F}_1$ is $F_1 = I_1 \ell B_2$. Because the magnitude of $\vec{B}_2$ is given by Equation 30.5,

$$F_1 = I_1 \ell B_2 = I_1 \ell \left(\frac{\mu_0 I_2}{2\pi a} \right) = \frac{\mu_0 I_1 I_2}{2\pi a} \ell \qquad \textbf{(30.11)}$$

The direction of $\vec{F}_1$ is toward wire 2 because $\vec{\ell} \times \vec{B}_2$ is in that direction. When the field set up at wire 2 by wire 1 is calculated, the force $\vec{F}_2$ acting on wire 2 is found to be equal in magnitude and opposite in direction to $\vec{F}_1$, which is what we expect because Newton's third law must be obeyed. When the currents are in opposite directions (that is, when one of the currents is reversed in Active Fig. 30.8), the forces are reversed and the wires repel each other. Hence, **parallel conductors carrying currents in the same direction attract each other, and parallel conductors carrying currents in opposite directions repel each other**.

Because the magnitudes of the forces are the same on both wires, we denote the magnitude of the magnetic force between the wires as simply F_B. We can rewrite this magnitude in terms of the force per unit length:

$$\frac{F_B}{\ell} = \frac{\mu_0 I_1 I_2}{2\pi a} \qquad \textbf{(30.12)}$$

The force between two parallel wires is used to define the **ampere** as follows:

◀ Definition of the ampere

When the magnitude of the force per unit length between two long, parallel wires that carry identical currents and are separated by 1 m is 2×10^{-7} N/m, the current in each wire is defined to be 1 A.

The value 2×10^{-7} N/m is obtained from Equation 30.12 with $I_1 = I_2 = 1$ A and $a = 1$ m. Because this definition is based on a force, a mechanical measurement can be used to standardize the ampere. For instance, the National Institute of Standards and Technology uses an instrument called a *current balance* for primary current measurements. The results are then used to standardize other, more conventional instruments such as ammeters.

The SI unit of charge, the **coulomb**, is defined in terms of the ampere: When a conductor carries a steady current of 1 A, the quantity of charge that flows through a cross section of the conductor in 1 s is 1 C.

In deriving Equations 30.11 and 30.12, we assumed that both wires are long compared with their separation distance. In fact, only one wire needs to be long. The equations accurately describe the forces exerted on each other by a long wire and a straight, parallel wire of limited length ℓ.

Quick Quiz 30.2 A loose spiral spring carrying no current is hung from a ceiling. When a switch is thrown so that a current exists in the spring, do the coils (a) move closer together, (b) move farther apart, or (c) not move at all?

EXAMPLE 30.4 Suspending a Wire

Two infinitely long, parallel wires are lying on the ground 1.00 cm apart as shown in Figure 30.9a. A third wire, of length 10.0 m and mass 400 g, carries a current of $I_1 = 100$ A and is levitated above the first two wires, at a horizontal position midway between them. The infinitely long wires carry equal currents I_2 in the same direction, but in the direction opposite to that in the levitated wire. What current must the infinitely long wires carry so that the three wires form an equilateral triangle?

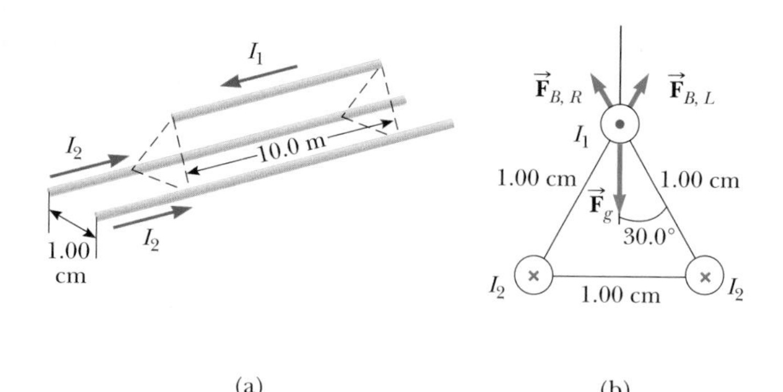

Figure 30.9 (Example 30.4) (a) Two current-carrying wires lie on the ground and suspend a third wire in the air by magnetic forces. (b) End view. In the situation described in the example, the three wires form an equilateral triangle. The two magnetic forces on the levitated wire are $\vec{F}_{B,L}$, the force due to the left-hand wire on the ground, and $\vec{F}_{B,R}$, the force due to the right-hand wire. The gravitational force $\vec{F}_g$ on the levitated wire is also shown.

SOLUTION

Conceptualize Because the current in the short wire is opposite those in the long wires, the short wire is repelled from both of the others. Imagine the currents in the long wires are increased. The repulsive force becomes stronger, and the levitated wire rises to the point at which the weight of the wire is once again levitated in equilibrium. Figure 30.9b shows the desired situation with the three wires forming an equilateral triangle.

Categorize We model the levitated wire as a particle in equilibrium.

Analyze The horizontal components of the magnetic forces on the levitated wire cancel. The vertical components are both positive and add together.

Find the total magnetic force in the upward direction on the levitated wire:

$$\vec{F}_B = 2\left(\frac{\mu_0 I_1 I_2}{2\pi a}\ell\right)\cos 30.0°\,\hat{k} = 0.866\,\frac{\mu_0 I_1 I_2}{\pi a}\ell\hat{k}$$

Find the gravitational force on the levitated wire:

$$\vec{F}_g = -mg\hat{k}$$

Apply the particle in equilibrium model by adding the forces and setting the net force equal to zero:

$$\sum \vec{F} = \vec{F}_B + \vec{F}_g = 0.866\,\frac{\mu_0 I_1 I_2}{\pi a}\ell\hat{k} - mg\hat{k} = 0$$

Solve for the current in the wires on the ground:

$$I_2 = \frac{mg\pi a}{0.866\mu_0 I_1 \ell}$$

Substitute numerical values:

$$I_2 = \frac{(0.400\text{ kg})(9.80\text{ m/s}^2)\pi(0.010\,0\text{ m})}{0.866(4\pi \times 10^{-7}\text{ T}\cdot\text{m/A})(100\text{ A})(10.0\text{ m})}$$

$$= 113\text{ A}$$

Finalize The currents in all wires are on the order of 10^2 A. Such large currents would require specialized equipment. Therefore, this situation would be difficult to establish in practice.

30.3 Ampère's Law

Oersted's 1819 discovery about deflected compass needles demonstrates that a current-carrying conductor produces a magnetic field. Active Figure 30.10a shows how this effect can be demonstrated in the classroom. Several compass needles are placed in a horizontal plane near a long, vertical wire. When no current is present in the wire, all the needles point in the same direction (that of the Earth's magnetic field) as expected. When the wire carries a strong, steady current, the needles all deflect in a direction tangent to the circle as in Active Figure 30.10b. These observations demonstrate that the direction of the magnetic field produced by the current in the wire is consistent with the right-hand rule described in Figure 30.4. When the current is reversed, the needles in Active Figure 30.10b also reverse.

Because the compass needles point in the direction of $\vec{\mathbf{B}}$, we conclude that the lines of $\vec{\mathbf{B}}$ form circles around the wire as discussed in Section 30.1. By symmetry, the magnitude of $\vec{\mathbf{B}}$ is the same everywhere on a circular path centered on the wire and lying in a plane perpendicular to the wire. By varying the current and distance from the wire, we find that B is proportional to the current and inversely proportional to the distance from the wire as described by Equation 30.5.

Now let's evaluate the product $\vec{\mathbf{B}} \cdot d\vec{\mathbf{s}}$ for a small length element $d\vec{\mathbf{s}}$ on the circular path defined by the compass needles and sum the products for all elements over the closed circular path.[1] Along this path, the vectors $d\vec{\mathbf{s}}$ and $\vec{\mathbf{B}}$ are parallel at each point (see Active Fig. 30.10b), so $\vec{\mathbf{B}} \cdot d\vec{\mathbf{s}} = B\,ds$. Furthermore, the magnitude of $\vec{\mathbf{B}}$ is constant on this circle and is given by Equation 30.5. Therefore, the sum of the products $B\,ds$ over the closed path, which is equivalent to the line integral of $\vec{\mathbf{B}} \cdot d\vec{\mathbf{s}}$, is

$$\oint \vec{\mathbf{B}} \cdot d\vec{\mathbf{s}} = B \oint ds = \frac{\mu_0 I}{2\pi r}(2\pi r) = \mu_0 I$$

where $\oint ds = 2\pi r$ is the circumference of the circular path. Although this result was calculated for the special case of a circular path surrounding a wire, it holds for a closed path of *any* shape (an *amperian loop*) surrounding a current that exists in an unbroken circuit. The general case, known as **Ampère's law**, can be stated as follows:

The line integral of $\vec{\mathbf{B}} \cdot d\vec{\mathbf{s}}$ around any closed path equals $\mu_0 I$, where I is the total steady current passing through any surface bounded by the closed path:

$$\oint \vec{\mathbf{B}} \cdot d\vec{\mathbf{s}} = \mu_0 I \qquad \textbf{(30.13)}$$

◀ Ampère's law

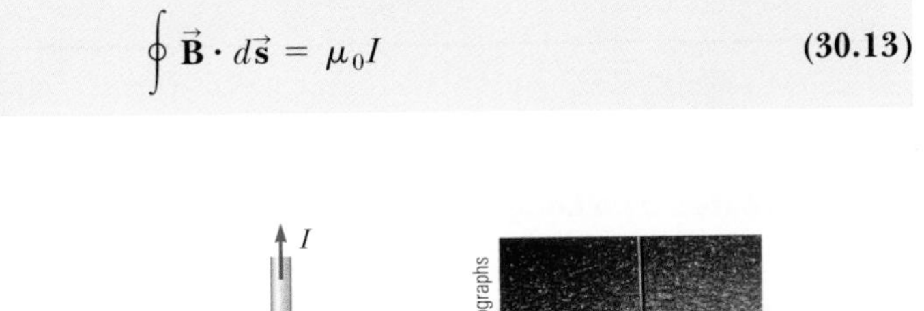

ACTIVE FIGURE 30.10

(a) When no current is present in the wire, all compass needles point in the same direction (toward the Earth's north pole). (b) When the wire carries a strong current, the compass needles deflect in a direction tangent to the circle, which is the direction of the magnetic field created by the current. (c) Circular magnetic field lines surrounding a current-carrying conductor, displayed with iron filings.

Sign in at www.thomsonedu.com and go to ThomsonNOW to change the value of the current and see the effect on the compasses.

ANDRE-MARIE AMPÈRE
French Physicist (1775–1836)

Ampère is credited with the discovery of electromagnetism, which is the relationship between electric currents and magnetic fields. Ampère's genius, particularly in mathematics, became evident by the time he was 12 years old; his personal life, however, was filled with tragedy. His father, a wealthy city official, was guillotined during the French Revolution, and his wife died young, in 1803. Ampère died at the age of 61 of pneumonia. His judgment of his life is clear from the epitaph he chose for his gravestone: *Tandem Felix* (Happy at Last).

PITFALL PREVENTION 30.2
Avoiding Problems with Signs

When using Ampère's law, apply the following right-hand rule. Point your thumb in the direction of the current through the amperian loop. Your curled fingers then point in the direction that you should integrate when traversing the loop to avoid having to define the current as negative.

[1] You may wonder why we would choose to evaluate this scalar product. The origin of Ampère's law is in 19th-century science, in which a "magnetic charge" (the supposed analog to an isolated electric charge) was imagined to be moved around a circular field line. The work done on the charge was related to $\vec{\mathbf{B}} \cdot d\vec{\mathbf{s}}$, just as the work done moving an electric charge in an electric field is related to $\vec{\mathbf{E}} \cdot d\vec{\mathbf{s}}$. Therefore, Ampère's law, a valid and useful principle, arose from an erroneous and abandoned work calculation!

Ampère's law describes the creation of magnetic fields by all continuous current configurations, but at our mathematical level it is useful only for calculating the magnetic field of current configurations having a high degree of symmetry. Its use is similar to that of Gauss's law in calculating electric fields for highly symmetric charge distributions.

Quick Quiz 30.3 Rank the magnitudes of $\oint \vec{\mathbf{B}} \cdot d\vec{\mathbf{s}}$ for the closed paths a through d in Figure 30.11 from least to greatest.

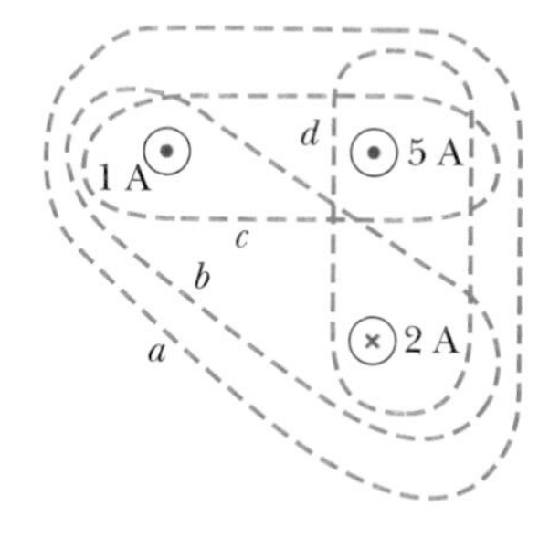

Figure 30.11 (Quick Quiz 30.3) Four closed paths around three current-carrying wires.

Quick Quiz 30.4 Rank the magnitudes of $\oint \vec{\mathbf{B}} \cdot d\vec{\mathbf{s}}$ for the closed paths a through d in Figure 30.12 from least to greatest.

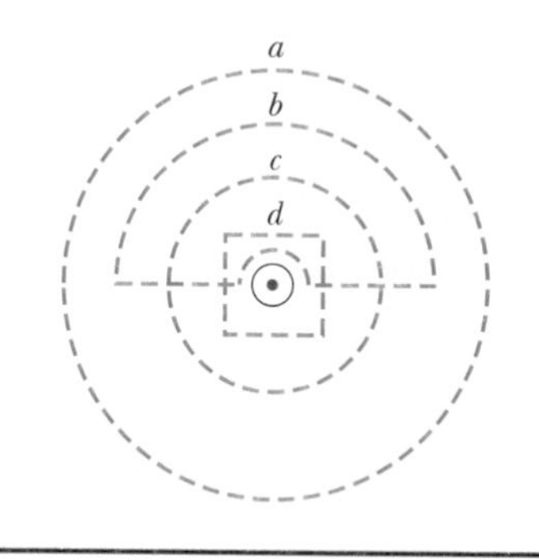

Figure 30.12 (Quick Quiz 30.4) Several closed paths near a single current-carrying wire.

EXAMPLE 30.5 The Magnetic Field Created by a Long Current-Carrying Wire

A long, straight wire of radius R carries a steady current I that is uniformly distributed through the cross section of the wire (Fig. 30.13). Calculate the magnetic field a distance r from the center of the wire in the regions $r \geq R$ and $r < R$.

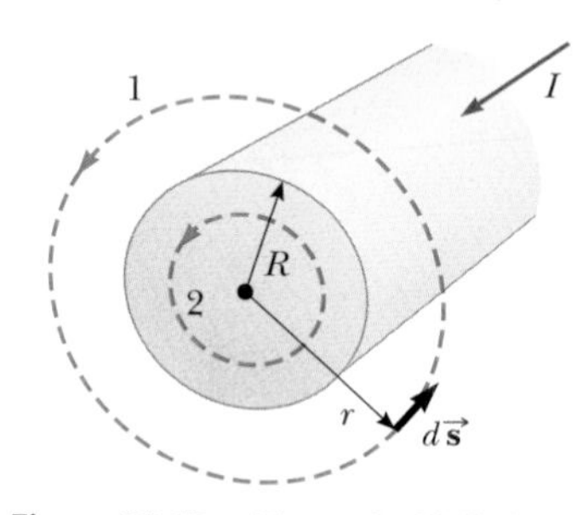

Figure 30.13 (Example 30.5) A long, straight wire of radius R carrying a steady current I uniformly distributed across the cross section of the wire. The magnetic field at any point can be calculated from Ampère's law using a circular path of radius r, concentric with the wire.

SOLUTION

Conceptualize Study Figure 30.13 to understand the structure of the wire and the current in the wire. The current creates magnetic fields everywhere, both inside and outside the wire.

Categorize Because the wire has a high degree of symmetry, we categorize this example as an Ampère's law problem. For the $r \geq R$ case, we should arrive at the same result as was obtained in Example 30.1, where we applied the Biot–Savart law to the same situation.

Analyze For the magnetic field exterior to the wire, let us choose for our path of integration circle 1 in Figure 30.13. From symmetry, $\vec{\mathbf{B}}$ must be constant in magnitude and parallel to $d\vec{\mathbf{s}}$ at every point on this circle.

Note that the total current passing through the plane of the circle is I and apply Ampère's law:

$$\oint \vec{\mathbf{B}} \cdot d\vec{\mathbf{s}} = B \oint ds = B(2\pi r) = \mu_0 I$$

Solve for B:

$$B = \frac{\mu_0 I}{2\pi r} \quad (\text{for } r \geq R) \tag{30.14}$$

Now consider the interior of the wire, where $r < R$. Here the current I' passing through the plane of circle 2 is less than the total current I.

Set the ratio of the current I' enclosed by circle 2 to the entire current I equal to the ratio of the area πr^2 enclosed by circle 2 to the cross-sectional area πR^2 of the wire:

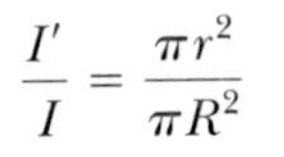

$$\frac{I'}{I} = \frac{\pi r^2}{\pi R^2}$$

Solve for I':

$$I' = \frac{r^2}{R^2} I$$

Apply Ampère's law to circle 2:

$$\oint \vec{\mathbf{B}} \cdot d\vec{\mathbf{s}} = B(2\pi r) = \mu_0 I' = \mu_0\left(\frac{r^2}{R^2} I\right)$$

Solve for B:

$$B = \left(\frac{\mu_0 I}{2\pi R^2}\right) r \quad (\text{for } r < R) \tag{30.15}$$

Finalize The magnetic field exterior to the wire is identical in form to Equation 30.5. As is often the case in highly symmetric situations, it is much easier to use Ampère's law than the Biot–Savart law (Example 30.1). The magnetic field interior to the wire is similar in form to the expression for the electric field inside a uniformly charged sphere (see Example 24.3). The magnitude of the magnetic field versus r for this configuration is plotted in Figure 30.14. Inside the wire, $B \rightarrow 0$ as $r \rightarrow 0$. Furthermore, Equations 30.14 and 30.15 give the same value of the magnetic field at $r = R$, demonstrating that the magnetic field is continuous at the surface of the wire.

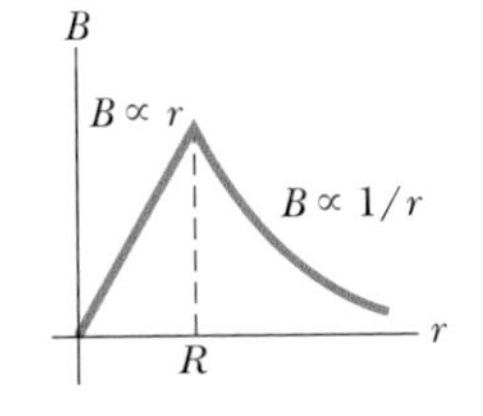

Figure 30.14 (Example 30.5) Magnitude of the magnetic field versus r for the wire shown in Figure 30.13. The field is proportional to r inside the wire and varies as $1/r$ outside the wire.

EXAMPLE 30.6 The Magnetic Field Created by a Toroid

A device called a *toroid* (Fig. 30.15) is often used to create an almost uniform magnetic field in some enclosed area. The device consists of a conducting wire wrapped around a ring (a *torus*) made of a nonconducting material. For a toroid having N closely spaced turns of wire, calculate the magnetic field in the region occupied by the torus, a distance r from the center.

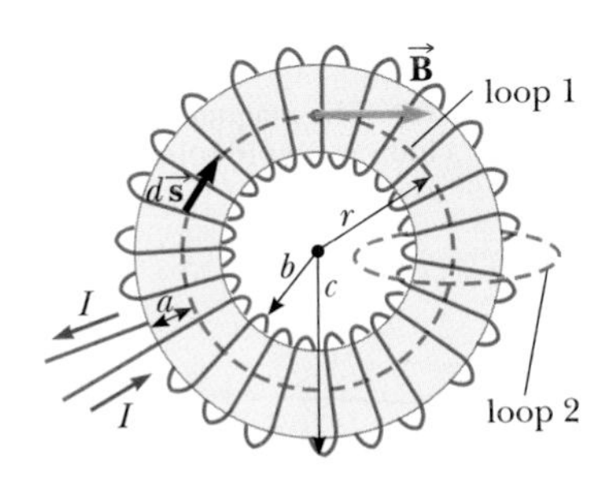

Figure 30.15 (Example 30.6) A toroid consisting of many turns of wire. If the turns are closely spaced, the magnetic field in the interior of the torus (the gold-shaded region) is tangent to the dashed circle (loop 1) and varies as $1/r$. The dimension a is the cross-sectional radius of the torus. The field outside the toroid is very small and can be described by using the amperian loop (loop 2) at the right side, perpendicular to the page.

SOLUTION

Conceptualize Study Figure 30.15 carefully to understand how the wire is wrapped around the torus. The torus could be a solid material or it could be air, with a stiff wire wrapped into the shape shown in Figure 30.15 to form an empty toroid.

Categorize Because the toroid has a high degree of symmetry, we categorize this example as an Ampère's law problem.

Analyze Consider the circular amperian loop (loop 1) of radius r in the plane of Figure 30.15. By symmetry, the magnitude of the field is constant on this circle and tangent to it, so $\vec{\mathbf{B}} \cdot d\vec{\mathbf{s}} = B\,ds$. Furthermore, the wire passes through the loop N times, so the total current through the loop is NI.

Apply Ampère's law to loop 1:

$$\oint \vec{\mathbf{B}} \cdot d\vec{\mathbf{s}} = B \oint ds = B(2\pi r) = \mu_0 NI$$

Solve for B:

$$B = \frac{\mu_0 NI}{2\pi r} \quad \textbf{(30.16)}$$

Finalize This result shows that B varies as $1/r$ and hence is *nonuniform* in the region occupied by the torus. If, however, r is very large compared with the cross-sectional radius a of the torus, the field is approximately uniform inside the torus.

For an ideal toroid, in which the turns are closely spaced, the external magnetic field is close to zero, but it is not exactly zero. In Figure 30.15, imagine the radius r of the amperian loop to be either smaller than b or larger than c. In either case, the loop encloses zero net current, so $\oint \vec{\mathbf{B}} \cdot d\vec{\mathbf{s}} = 0$. You might think that this result proves that $\vec{\mathbf{B}} = 0$, but it does not. Consider the amperian loop (loop 2) on the right side of the toroid in Figure 30.15. The plane of this loop is perpendicular to the page, and the toroid passes through the loop. As charges enter the toroid as indicated by the current directions in Figure 30.15, they work their way counterclockwise around the toroid. Therefore, a current passes through the perpendicular amperian loop! This current is small, but not zero. As a result, the toroid acts as a current loop and produces a weak external field of the form shown in Figure 30.7. The reason $\oint \vec{\mathbf{B}} \cdot d\vec{\mathbf{s}} = 0$ for the amperian loops of radius $r < b$ and $r > c$ in the plane of the page is that the field lines are perpendicular to $d\vec{\mathbf{s}}$, *not* because $\vec{\mathbf{B}} = 0$.

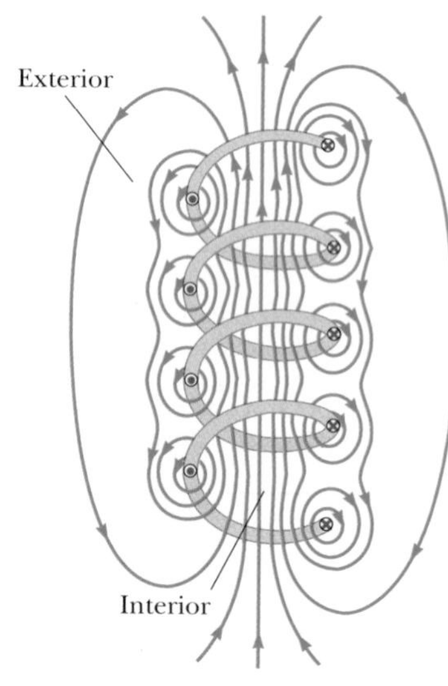

Figure 30.16 The magnetic field lines for a loosely wound solenoid.

30.4 The Magnetic Field of a Solenoid

A **solenoid** is a long wire wound in the form of a helix. With this configuration, a reasonably uniform magnetic field can be produced in the space surrounded by the turns of wire—which we shall call the *interior* of the solenoid—when the solenoid carries a current. When the turns are closely spaced, each can be approximated as a circular loop; the net magnetic field is the vector sum of the fields resulting from all the turns.

Figure 30.16 shows the magnetic field lines surrounding a loosely wound solenoid. The field lines in the interior are nearly parallel to one another, are uniformly distributed, and are close together, indicating that the field in this space is strong and almost uniform.

If the turns are closely spaced and the solenoid is of finite length, the magnetic field lines are as shown in Figure 30.17a. This field line distribution is similar to that surrounding a bar magnet (Fig. 30.17b). Hence, one end of the solenoid behaves like the north pole of a magnet and the opposite end behaves like the south pole. As the length of the solenoid increases, the interior field becomes more uniform and the exterior field becomes weaker. An *ideal solenoid* is

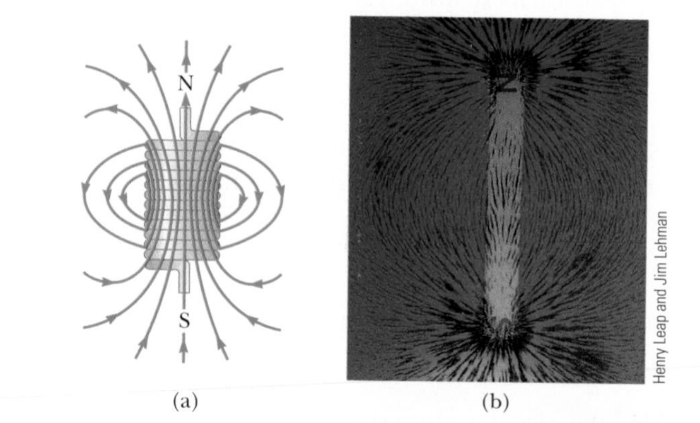

Figure 30.17 (a) Magnetic field lines for a tightly wound solenoid of finite length, carrying a steady current. The field in the interior space is strong and nearly uniform. Notice that the field lines resemble those of a bar magnet, meaning that the solenoid effectively has north and south poles. (b) The magnetic field pattern of a bar magnet, displayed with small iron filings on a sheet of paper.

approached when the turns are closely spaced and the length is much greater than the radius of the turns. Figure 30.18 shows a longitudinal cross section of part of such a solenoid carrying a current I. In this case, the external field is close to zero and the interior field is uniform over a great volume.

Consider the amperian loop (loop 1) perpendicular to the page in Figure 30.18, surrounding the ideal solenoid. This loop encloses a small current as the charges in the wire move coil by coil along the length of the solenoid. Therefore, there is a nonzero magnetic field outside the solenoid. It is a weak field, with circular field lines, like those due to a line of current as in Figure 30.4. For an ideal solenoid, this weak field is the only field external to the solenoid. We could eliminate this field in Figure 30.18 by adding a second layer of turns of wire outside the first layer, with the current carried along the axis of the solenoid in the opposite direction compared with the first layer. Then the net current along the axis is zero.

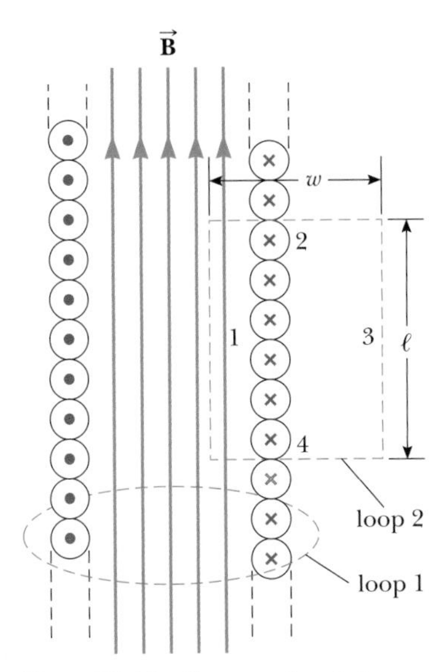

Figure 30.18 Cross-sectional view of an ideal solenoid, where the interior magnetic field is uniform and the exterior field is close to zero. Ampère's law applied to the circular path near the bottom whose plane is perpendicular to the page can be used to show that there is a weak field outside the solenoid. Ampère's law applied to the rectangular dashed path in the plane of the page can be used to calculate the magnitude of the interior field.

We can use Ampère's law to obtain a quantitative expression for the interior magnetic field in an ideal solenoid. Because the solenoid is ideal, $\vec{\mathbf{B}}$ in the interior space is uniform and parallel to the axis and the magnetic field lines in the exterior space form circles around the solenoid. The planes of these circles are perpendicular to the page. Consider the rectangular path (loop 2) of length ℓ and width w shown in Figure 30.18. Let's apply Ampère's law to this path by evaluating the integral of $\vec{\mathbf{B}} \cdot d\vec{\mathbf{s}}$ over each side of the rectangle. The contribution along side 3 is zero because the magnetic field lines are perpendicular to the path in this region. The contributions from sides 2 and 4 are both zero, again because $\vec{\mathbf{B}}$ is perpendicular to $d\vec{\mathbf{s}}$ along these paths, both inside and outside the solenoid. Side 1 gives a contribution to the integral because along this path $\vec{\mathbf{B}}$ is uniform and parallel to $d\vec{\mathbf{s}}$. The integral over the closed rectangular path is therefore

$$\oint \vec{\mathbf{B}} \cdot d\vec{\mathbf{s}} = \int_{\text{path 1}} \vec{\mathbf{B}} \cdot d\vec{\mathbf{s}} = B \int_{\text{path 1}} ds = B\ell$$

The right side of Ampère's law involves the total current I through the area bounded by the path of integration. In this case, the total current through the rectangular path equals the current through each turn multiplied by the number of turns. If N is the number of turns in the length ℓ, the total current through the rectangle is NI. Therefore, Ampère's law applied to this path gives

$$\oint \vec{\mathbf{B}} \cdot d\vec{\mathbf{s}} = B\ell = \mu_0 NI$$

$$B = \mu_0 \frac{N}{\ell} I = \mu_0 nI \quad \textbf{(30.17)}$$

◀ Magnetic field inside a solenoid

where $n = N/\ell$ is the number of turns per unit length.

We also could obtain this result by reconsidering the magnetic field of a toroid (see Example 30.6). If the radius r of the torus in Figure 30.15 containing N turns is much greater than the toroid's cross-sectional radius a, a short section of the toroid approximates a solenoid for which $n = N/2\pi r$. In this limit, Equation 30.16 agrees with Equation 30.17.

Equation 30.17 is valid only for points near the center (that is, far from the ends) of a very long solenoid. As you might expect, the field near each end is smaller than the value given by Equation 30.17. At the very end of a long solenoid, the magnitude of the field is half the magnitude at the center (see Problem 36).

Quick Quiz 30.5 Consider a solenoid that is very long compared with its radius. Of the following choices, what is the most effective way to increase the magnetic field in the interior of the solenoid? (a) double its length, keeping the number of turns per unit length constant (b) reduce its radius by half, keeping the number of turns per unit length constant (c) overwrap the entire solenoid with an additional layer of current-carrying wire

---

30.5 Gauss's Law in Magnetism

The flux associated with a magnetic field is defined in a manner similar to that used to define electric flux (see Eq. 24.3). Consider an element of area dA on an arbitrarily shaped surface as shown in Figure 30.19. If the magnetic field at this element is $\vec{\mathbf{B}}$, the magnetic flux through the element is $\vec{\mathbf{B}} \cdot d\vec{\mathbf{A}}$, where $d\vec{\mathbf{A}}$ is a vector that is perpendicular to the surface and has a magnitude equal to the area dA. Therefore, the total magnetic flux Φ_B through the surface is

Definition of magnetic flux ▶

$$\Phi_B \equiv \int \vec{\mathbf{B}} \cdot d\vec{\mathbf{A}} \qquad (30.18)$$

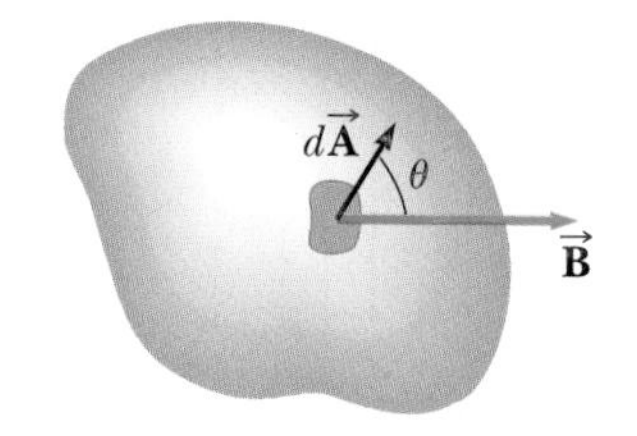

Figure 30.19 The magnetic flux through an area element dA is $\vec{\mathbf{B}} \cdot d\vec{\mathbf{A}} = B\,dA\cos\theta$, where $d\vec{\mathbf{A}}$ is a vector perpendicular to the surface.

Consider the special case of a plane of area A in a uniform field $\vec{\mathbf{B}}$ that makes an angle θ with $d\vec{\mathbf{A}}$. The magnetic flux through the plane in this case is

$$\Phi_B = BA\cos\theta \qquad (30.19)$$

If the magnetic field is parallel to the plane as in Active Figure 30.20a, then $\theta = 90°$ and the flux through the plane is zero. If the field is perpendicular to the plane as in Active Figure 30.20b, then $\theta = 0$ and the flux through the plane is BA (the maximum value).

The unit of magnetic flux is $\mathrm{T \cdot m^2}$, which is defined as a *weber* (Wb); $1\ \mathrm{Wb} = 1\ \mathrm{T \cdot m^2}$.

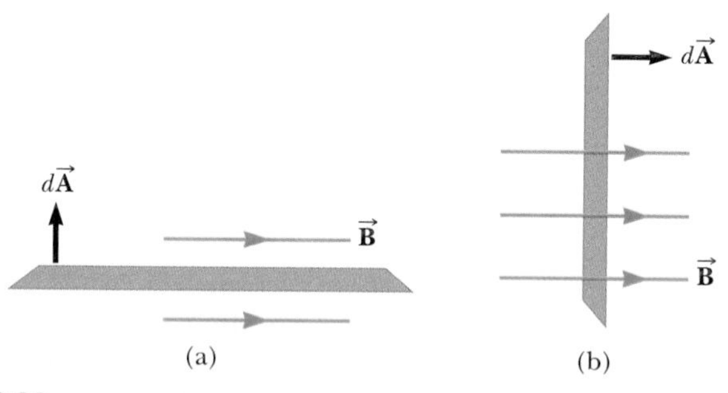

ACTIVE FIGURE 30.20

Magnetic flux through a plane lying in a magnetic field. (a) The flux through the plane is zero when the magnetic field is parallel to the plane surface. (b) The flux through the plane is a maximum when the magnetic field is perpendicular to the plane.

Sign in at www.thomsonedu.com and go to ThomsonNOW to rotate the plane and change the value of the field to see the effect on the flux.

EXAMPLE 30.7 Magnetic Flux Through a Rectangular Loop

A rectangular loop of width a and length b is located near a long wire carrying a current I (Fig. 30.21). The distance between the wire and the closest side of the loop is c. The wire is parallel to the long side of the loop. Find the total magnetic flux through the loop due to the current in the wire.

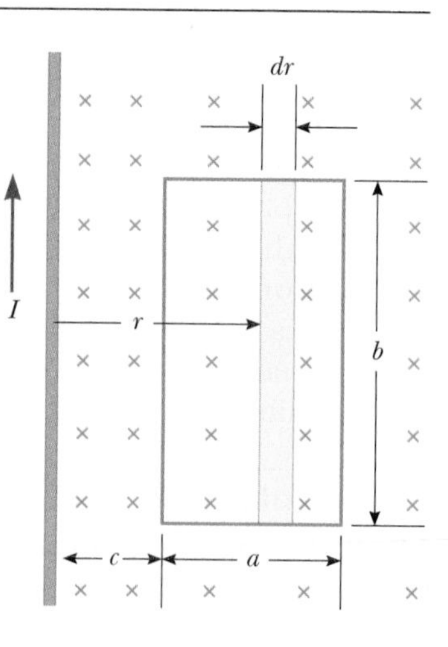

Figure 30.21 (Example 30.7) The magnetic field due to the wire carrying a current I is not uniform over the rectangular loop.

SOLUTION

Conceptualize We know that the magnetic field is a function of distance r from a long wire. Therefore, the magnetic field varies over the area of the rectangular loop.

Categorize Because the magnetic field varies over the area of the loop, we must integrate over this area to find the total flux.

Analyze Noting that $\vec{\mathbf{B}}$ is parallel to $d\vec{\mathbf{A}}$ at any point within the loop, find the magnetic flux through the rectangular area using Equation 30.18 and incorporate Equation 30.14 for the magnetic field:

$$\Phi_B = \int \vec{\mathbf{B}} \cdot d\vec{\mathbf{A}} = \int B\, dA = \int \frac{\mu_0 I}{2\pi r}\, dA$$

Express the area element (the tan strip in Fig. 30.21) as $dA = b\,dr$ and substitute:

$$\Phi_B = \int \frac{\mu_0 I}{2\pi r}\, b\, dr = \frac{\mu_0 I b}{2\pi} \int \frac{dr}{r}$$

Integrate from $r = c$ to $r = a + c$:

$$\Phi_B = \frac{\mu_0 I b}{2\pi} \int_c^{a+c} \frac{dr}{r} = \frac{\mu_0 I b}{2\pi} \ln r \Big|_c^{a+c}$$

$$= \frac{\mu_0 I b}{2\pi} \ln\left(\frac{a+c}{c}\right) = \frac{\mu_0 I b}{2\pi} \ln\left(1 + \frac{a}{c}\right)$$

Finalize Notice how the flux depends on the size of the loop. Increasing either a or b increases the flux as expected. If c becomes large such that the loop is very far from the wire, the flux approaches zero, also as expected. If c goes to zero, the flux becomes infinite. In principle, this infinite value occurs because the field becomes infinite at $r = 0$ (assuming an infinitesimally thin wire). That will not happen in reality because the thickness of the wire prevents the left edge of the loop from reaching $r = 0$.

In Chapter 24, we found that the electric flux through a closed surface surrounding a net charge is proportional to that charge (Gauss's law). In other words, the number of electric field lines leaving the surface depends only on the net charge within it. This behavior exists because electric field lines originate and terminate on electric charges.

The situation is quite different for magnetic fields, which are continuous and form closed loops. In other words, as illustrated by the magnetic field lines of a current in Figure 30.4 and of a bar magnet in Figure 30.22, magnetic field lines do not begin or end at any point. For any closed surface such as the one outlined by the dashed line in Figure 30.22, the number of lines entering the surface equals the number leaving the surface; therefore, the net magnetic flux is zero. In contrast, for a closed surface surrounding one charge of an electric dipole (Fig. 30.23), the net electric flux is not zero.

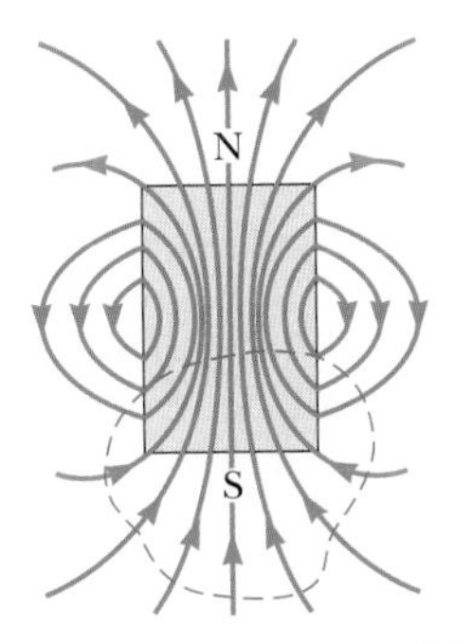

Figure 30.22 The magnetic field lines of a bar magnet form closed loops. Notice that the net magnetic flux through a closed surface surrounding one of the poles (or any other closed surface) is zero. (The dashed line represents the intersection of the surface with the page.)

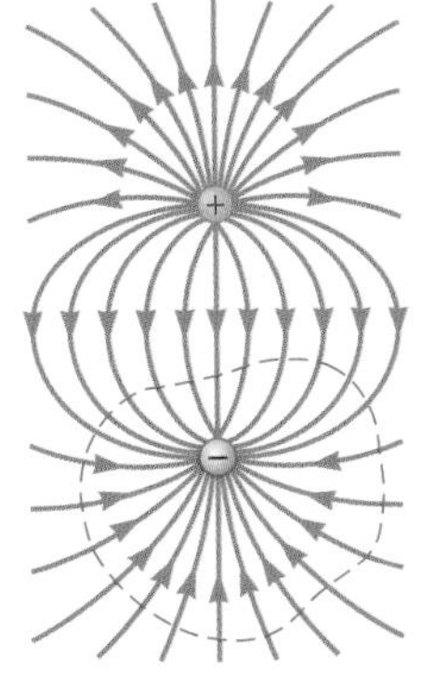

Figure 30.23 The electric field lines surrounding an electric dipole begin on the positive charge and terminate on the negative charge. The electric flux through a closed surface surrounding one of the charges is not zero.

Gauss's law in magnetism states that

Gauss's law in magnetism ▶

the net magnetic flux through any closed surface is always zero:

$$\oint \vec{\mathbf{B}} \cdot d\vec{\mathbf{A}} = 0 \qquad \textbf{(30.20)}$$

This statement represents that isolated magnetic poles (monopoles) have never been detected and perhaps do not exist. Nonetheless, scientists continue the search because certain theories that are otherwise successful in explaining fundamental physical behavior suggest the possible existence of magnetic monopoles.

30.6 Magnetism in Matter

The magnetic field produced by a current in a coil of wire gives us a hint as to what causes certain materials to exhibit strong magnetic properties. Earlier we found that a coil like the one shown in Figure 30.17a has a north pole and a south pole. In general, *any* current loop has a magnetic field and therefore has a magnetic dipole moment, including the atomic-level current loops described in some models of the atom.

The Magnetic Moments of Atoms

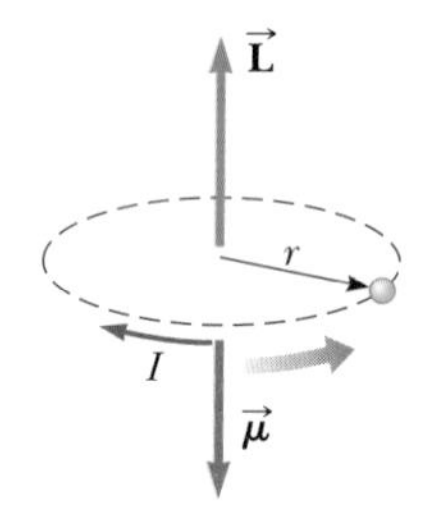

Figure 30.24 An electron moving in the direction of the gray arrow in a circular orbit of radius r has an angular momentum $\vec{\mathbf{L}}$ in one direction and a magnetic moment $\vec{\boldsymbol{\mu}}$ in the opposite direction. Because the electron carries a negative charge, the direction of the current due to its motion about the nucleus is opposite the direction of that motion.

Let's begin our discussion with a classical model of the atom in which electrons move in circular orbits around the much more massive nucleus. In this model, an orbiting electron constitutes a tiny current loop (because it is a moving charge) and the magnetic moment of the electron is associated with this orbital motion. Although this model has many deficiencies, some of its predictions are in good agreement with the correct theory, which is expressed in terms of quantum physics.

In our classical model, we assume an electron moves with constant speed v in a circular orbit of radius r about the nucleus as in Figure 30.24. The current I associated with this orbiting electron is its charge e divided by its period T. Using $T = 2\pi/\omega$ and $\omega = v/r$ gives

$$I = \frac{e}{T} = \frac{e\omega}{2\pi} = \frac{ev}{2\pi r}$$

The magnitude of the magnetic moment associated with this current loop is given by $\mu = IA$, where $A = \pi r^2$ is the area enclosed by the orbit. Therefore,

$$\mu = IA = \left(\frac{ev}{2\pi r}\right)\pi r^2 = \tfrac{1}{2}evr \qquad \textbf{(30.21)}$$

Because the magnitude of the orbital angular momentum of the electron is given by $L = m_e vr$ (Eq. 11.12 with $\phi = 90°$), the magnetic moment can be written as

Orbital magnetic moment ▶

$$\mu = \left(\frac{e}{2m_e}\right)L \qquad \textbf{(30.22)}$$

This result demonstrates that **the magnetic moment of the electron is proportional to its orbital angular momentum**. Because the electron is negatively charged, the vectors $\vec{\boldsymbol{\mu}}$ and $\vec{\mathbf{L}}$ point in *opposite* directions. Both vectors are perpendicular to the plane of the orbit as indicated in Figure 30.24.

A fundamental outcome of quantum physics is that orbital angular momentum is quantized and is equal to multiples of $\hbar = h/2\pi = 1.05 \times 10^{-34}$ J·s, where h is

Planck's constant (see Chapter 40). The smallest nonzero value of the electron's magnetic moment resulting from its orbital motion is

$$\mu = \sqrt{2}\,\frac{e}{2m_e}\,\hbar \qquad (30.23)$$

We shall see in Chapter 42 how expressions such as Equation 30.23 arise.

Because all substances contain electrons, you may wonder why most substances are not magnetic. The main reason is that, in most substances, the magnetic moment of one electron in an atom is canceled by that of another electron orbiting in the opposite direction. The net result is that, for most materials, **the magnetic effect produced by the orbital motion of the electrons is either zero or very small.**

In addition to its orbital magnetic moment, an electron (as well as protons, neutrons, and other particles) has an intrinsic property called **spin** that also contributes to its magnetic moment. Classically, the electron might be viewed as spinning about its axis as shown in Figure 30.25, but you should be very careful with the classical interpretation. The magnitude of the angular momentum $\vec{\mathbf{S}}$ associated with spin is on the same order of magnitude as the magnitude of the angular momentum $\vec{\mathbf{L}}$ due to the orbital motion. The magnitude of the spin angular momentum of an electron predicted by quantum theory is

$$S = \frac{\sqrt{3}}{2}\,\hbar$$

The magnetic moment characteristically associated with the spin of an electron has the value

$$\mu_{\text{spin}} = \frac{e\hbar}{2m_e} \qquad (30.24)$$

This combination of constants is called the **Bohr magneton μ_B:**

$$\mu_B = \frac{e\hbar}{2m_e} = 9.27 \times 10^{-24}\ \text{J/T} \qquad (30.25)$$

Therefore, atomic magnetic moments can be expressed as multiples of the Bohr magneton. (Note that $1\ \text{J/T} = 1\ \text{A} \cdot \text{m}^2$.)

In atoms containing many electrons, the electrons usually pair up with their spins opposite each other; therefore, the spin magnetic moments cancel. Atoms containing an odd number of electrons, however, must have at least one unpaired electron and therefore some spin magnetic moment. The total magnetic moment of an atom is the vector sum of the orbital and spin magnetic moments, and a few examples are given in Table 30.1. Notice that helium and neon have zero moments because their individual spin and orbital moments cancel.

The nucleus of an atom also has a magnetic moment associated with its constituent protons and neutrons. The magnetic moment of a proton or neutron, however, is much smaller than that of an electron and can usually be neglected. We can understand this smaller value by inspecting Equation 30.25 and replacing the mass of the electron with the mass of a proton or a neutron. Because the masses of the proton and neutron are much greater than that of the electron, their magnetic moments are on the order of 10^3 times smaller than that of the electron.

Ferromagnetism

A small number of crystalline substances exhibit strong magnetic effects called **ferromagnetism**. Some examples of ferromagnetic substances are iron, cobalt, nickel, gadolinium, and dysprosium. These substances contain permanent atomic magnetic moments that tend to align parallel to each other even in a weak external magnetic field. Once the moments are aligned, the substance remains magnetized

PITFALL PREVENTION 30.3
The Electron Does Not Spin

The electron is *not* physically spinning. It has an intrinsic angular momentum *as if it were spinning*, but the notion of rotation for a point particle is meaningless. Rotation applies only to a *rigid object*, with an extent in space, as in Chapter 10. Spin angular momentum is actually a relativistic effect.

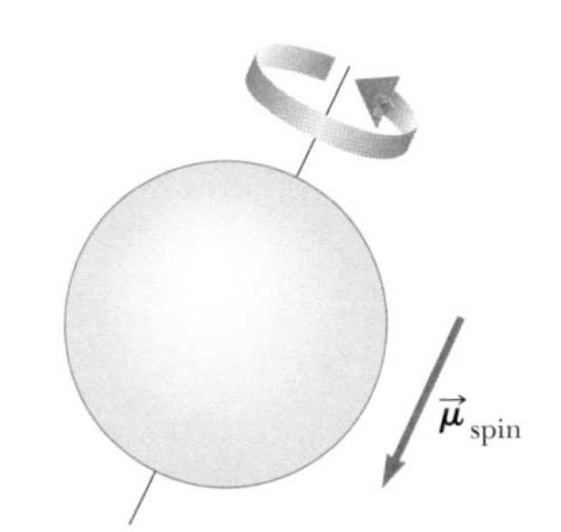

Figure 30.25 Classical model of a spinning electron. We can adopt this model to remind ourselves that electrons have an intrinsic angular momentum. The model should not be pushed too far, however; it gives an incorrect magnitude for the magnetic moment, incorrect quantum numbers, and too many degrees of freedom.

TABLE 30.1
Magnetic Moments of Some Atoms and Ions

Atom or Ion	Magnetic Moment (10^{-24} J/T)
H	9.27
He	0
Ne	0
Ce^{3+}	19.8
Yb^{3+}	37.1

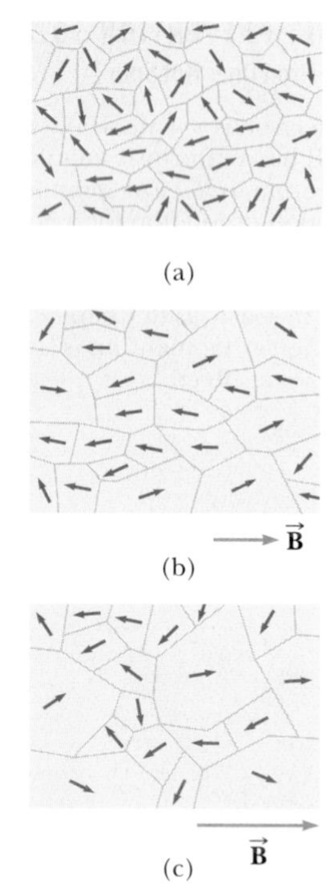

Figure 30.26 (a) Random orientation of atomic magnetic dipoles in the domains of an unmagnetized substance. (b) When an external field $\vec{B}$ is applied, the domains with components of magnetic moment in the same direction as $\vec{B}$ grow larger, giving the sample a net magnetization. (c) As the field is made even stronger, the domains with magnetic moment vectors not aligned with the external field become very small.

after the external field is removed. This permanent alignment is due to a strong coupling between neighboring moments, a coupling that can be understood only in quantum-mechanical terms.

All ferromagnetic materials are made up of microscopic regions called **domains**, regions within which all magnetic moments are aligned. These domains have volumes of about 10^{-12} to 10^{-8} m^3 and contain 10^{17} to 10^{21} atoms. The boundaries between the various domains having different orientations are called **domain walls.** In an unmagnetized sample, the magnetic moments in the domains are randomly oriented so that the net magnetic moment is zero as in Figure 30.26a. When the sample is placed in an external magnetic field $\vec{B}$, the size of those domains with magnetic moments aligned with the field grows, which results in a magnetized sample as in Figure 30.26b. As the external field becomes very strong as in Figure 30.26c, the domains in which the magnetic moments are not aligned with the field become very small. When the external field is removed, the sample may retain a net magnetization in the direction of the original field. At ordinary temperatures, thermal agitation is not sufficient to disrupt this preferred orientation of magnetic moments.

Magnetic computer disks store information by alternating the direction of $\vec{B}$ for portions of a thin layer of ferromagnetic material. Floppy disks have the layer on a circular sheet of plastic. Hard disks have several rigid platters with magnetic coatings on each side. Audio tapes and videotapes work the same way as floppy disks except that the ferromagnetic material is on a very long strip of plastic. Tiny coils of wire in a recording head are placed close to the magnetic material (which is moving rapidly past the head). Varying the current in the coils creates a magnetic field that magnetizes the recording material. To retrieve the information, the magnetized material is moved past a playback coil. The changing magnetism of the material induces a current in the coil as discussed in Chapter 31. This current is then amplified by audio or video equipment, or it is processed by computer circuitry.

When the temperature of a ferromagnetic substance reaches or exceeds a critical temperature called the **Curie temperature**, the substance loses its residual magnetization. Below the Curie temperature, the magnetic moments are aligned and the substance is ferromagnetic. Above the Curie temperature, the thermal agitation is great enough to cause a random orientation of the moments and the substance becomes paramagnetic. Curie temperatures for several ferromagnetic substances are given in Table 30.2.

TABLE 30.2

Curie Temperatures for Several Ferromagnetic Substances

Substance	T_{Curie} (K)
Iron	1 043
Cobalt	1 394
Nickel	631
Gadolinium	317
Fe_2O_3	893

Paramagnetism

Paramagnetic substances have a small but positive magnetism resulting from the presence of atoms (or ions) that have permanent magnetic moments. These moments interact only weakly with one another and are randomly oriented in the absence of an external magnetic field. When a paramagnetic substance is placed in an external magnetic field, its atomic moments tend to line up with the field. This alignment process, however, must compete with thermal motion, which tends to randomize the magnetic moment orientations.

Diamagnetism

When an external magnetic field is applied to a diamagnetic substance, a weak magnetic moment is induced in the direction opposite the applied field, causing diamagnetic substances to be weakly repelled by a magnet. Although diamagnetism is present in all matter, its effects are much smaller than those of paramagnetism or ferromagnetism and are evident only when those other effects do not exist.

We can attain some understanding of diamagnetism by considering a classical model of two atomic electrons orbiting the nucleus in opposite directions but with the same speed. The electrons remain in their circular orbits because of the attractive electrostatic force exerted by the positively charged nucleus. Because the magnetic moments of the two electrons are equal in magnitude and opposite in direc-

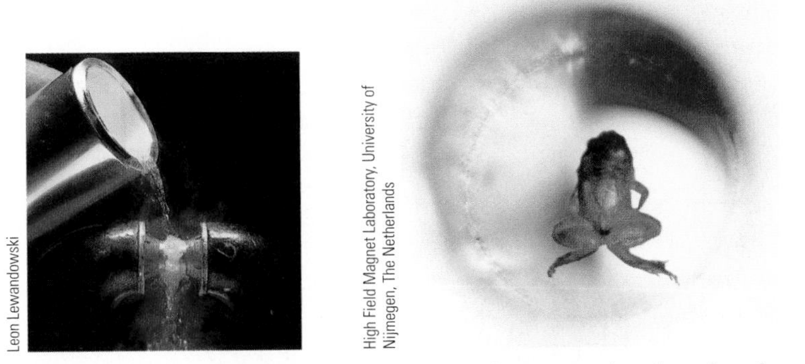

(*Left*) Paramagnetism: liquid oxygen, a paramagnetic material, is attracted to the poles of a magnet. (*Right*) Diamagnetism: a frog is levitated in a 16-T magnetic field at the Nijmegen High Field Magnet Laboratory in the Netherlands. The levitation force is exerted on the diamagnetic water molecules in the frog's body. The frog suffered no ill effects from the levitation experience.

Figure 30.27 An illustration of the Meissner effect, shown by this magnet suspended above a cooled ceramic superconductor disk, has become our most visual image of high-temperature superconductivity. Superconductivity is the loss of all resistance to electrical current and is a key to more-efficient energy use. In the Meissner effect, the magnet induces superconducting currents in the disk, which is cooled to $-321°F$ (77 K). The currents create a magnetic force that repels and levitates the disk.

tion, they cancel each other and the magnetic moment of the atom is zero. When an external magnetic field is applied, the electrons experience an additional magnetic force $q\vec{\mathbf{v}} \times \vec{\mathbf{B}}$. This added magnetic force combines with the electrostatic force to increase the orbital speed of the electron whose magnetic moment is antiparallel to the field and to decrease the speed of the electron whose magnetic moment is parallel to the field. As a result, the two magnetic moments of the electrons no longer cancel and the substance acquires a net magnetic moment that is opposite the applied field.

As you recall from Chapter 27, a superconductor is a substance in which the electrical resistance is zero below some critical temperature. Certain types of superconductors also exhibit perfect diamagnetism in the superconducting state. As a result, an applied magnetic field is expelled by the superconductor so that the field is zero in its interior. This phenomenon is known as the **Meissner effect**. If a permanent magnet is brought near a superconductor, the two objects repel each other. This repulsion is illustrated in Figure 30.27, which shows a small permanent magnet levitated above a superconductor maintained at 77 K.

30.7 The Magnetic Field of the Earth

When we speak of a compass magnet having a north pole and a south pole, it is more proper to say that it has a "north-seeking" pole and a "south-seeking" pole. This wording means that one pole of the magnet seeks, or points to, the north geographic pole of the Earth. Because the north pole of a magnet is attracted toward the north geographic pole of the Earth, **the Earth's south magnetic pole is located near the north geographic pole and the Earth's north magnetic pole is located near the south geographic pole**. In fact, the configuration of the Earth's magnetic field, pictured in Figure 30.28 (page 856), is very much like the one that would be achieved by burying a gigantic bar magnet deep in the interior of the Earth.

If a compass needle is suspended in bearings that allow it to rotate in the vertical plane as well as in the horizontal plane, the needle is horizontal with respect to the Earth's surface only near the equator. As the compass is moved northward, the needle rotates so that it points more and more toward the surface of the Earth. Finally, at a point near Hudson Bay in Canada, the north pole of the needle points directly downward. This site, first found in 1832, is considered to be the location of the south magnetic pole of the Earth. It is approximately 1 300 mi from the Earth's geographic North Pole, and its exact position varies slowly with time. Similarly, the north magnetic pole of the Earth is about 1 200 mi away from the Earth's geographic South Pole.

Because of this distance between the north geographic and south magnetic poles, it is only approximately correct to say that a compass needle points north.

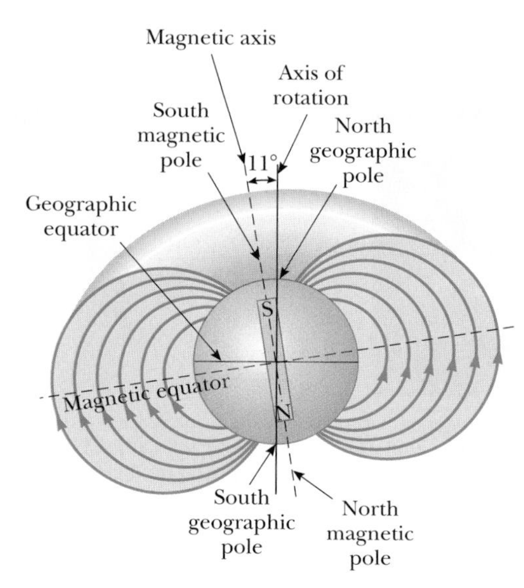

Figure 30.28 The Earth's magnetic field lines. Notice that a south magnetic pole is near the north geographic pole and a north magnetic pole is near the south geographic pole.

The difference between true north, defined as the geographic North Pole, and north indicated by a compass varies from point to point on the Earth. This difference is referred to as *magnetic declination.* For example, along a line through Florida and the Great Lakes, a compass indicates true north, whereas in the state of Washington, it aligns 25° east of true north. Figure 30.29 shows some representative values of the magnetic declination for the contiguous United States.

Although the Earth's magnetic field pattern is similar to the one that would be set up by a bar magnet deep within the Earth, it is easy to understand why the source of this magnetic field cannot be large masses of permanently magnetized material. The Earth does have large deposits of iron ore deep beneath its surface, but the high temperatures in the Earth's core prevent the iron from retaining any permanent magnetization. Scientists consider it more likely that the source of the Earth's magnetic field is convection currents in the Earth's core. Charged ions or electrons circulating in the liquid interior could produce a magnetic field just as a current loop does. There is also strong evidence that the magnitude of a planet's magnetic field is related to the planet's rate of rotation. For example, Jupiter rotates faster than the Earth, and space probes indicate that Jupiter's magnetic field is stronger than the Earth's. Venus, on the other hand, rotates more slowly than the Earth, and its magnetic field is found to be weaker. Investigation into the cause of the Earth's magnetism is ongoing.

It is interesting to point out that that the direction of the Earth's magnetic field has reversed several times during the last million years. Evidence for this reversal is provided by basalt, a type of rock that contains iron and that forms from material spewed forth by volcanic activity on the ocean floor. As the lava cools, it solidifies and retains a picture of the Earth's magnetic field direction. The rocks are dated by other means to provide a timeline for these periodic reversals of the magnetic field.

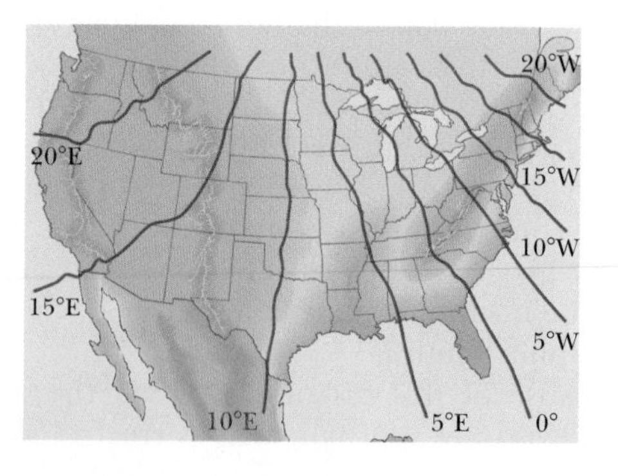

Figure 30.29 A map of the contiguous United States showing several lines of constant magnetic declination.

Summary

ThomsonNOW™ Sign in at **www.thomsonedu.com** and go to ThomsonNOW to take a practice test for this chapter.

DEFINITION

The **magnetic flux** Φ_B through a surface is defined by the surface integral

$$\Phi_B \equiv \int \vec{\mathbf{B}} \cdot d\vec{\mathbf{A}} \qquad \textbf{(30.18)}$$

CONCEPTS AND PRINCIPLES

The **Biot–Savart law** says that the magnetic field $d\vec{\mathbf{B}}$ at a point P due to a length element $d\vec{\mathbf{s}}$ that carries a steady current I is

$$d\vec{\mathbf{B}} = \frac{\mu_0}{4\pi} \frac{I\, d\vec{\mathbf{s}} \times \hat{\mathbf{r}}}{r^2} \qquad \textbf{(30.1)}$$

where μ_0 is the **permeability of free space**, r is the distance from the element to the point P, and $\hat{\mathbf{r}}$ is a unit vector pointing from $d\vec{\mathbf{s}}$ toward point P. We find the total field at P by integrating this expression over the entire current distribution.

The magnetic force per unit length between two parallel wires separated by a distance a and carrying currents I_1 and I_2 has a magnitude

$$\frac{F_B}{\ell} = \frac{\mu_0 I_1 I_2}{2\pi a} \qquad \textbf{(30.12)}$$

The force is attractive if the currents are in the same direction and repulsive if they are in opposite directions.

Ampère's law says that the line integral of $\vec{\mathbf{B}} \cdot d\vec{\mathbf{s}}$ around any closed path equals $\mu_0 I$, where I is the total steady current through any surface bounded by the closed path:

$$\oint \vec{\mathbf{B}} \cdot d\vec{\mathbf{s}} = \mu_0 I \qquad \textbf{(30.13)}$$

The magnitude of the magnetic field at a distance r from a long, straight wire carrying an electric current I is

$$B = \frac{\mu_0 I}{2\pi r} \qquad \textbf{(30.14)}$$

The field lines are circles concentric with the wire.

The magnitudes of the fields inside a toroid and solenoid are

$$B = \frac{\mu_0 N I}{2\pi r} \quad \text{(toroid)} \qquad \textbf{(30.16)}$$

$$B = \mu_0 \frac{N}{\ell} I = \mu_0 n I \quad \text{(solenoid)} \qquad \textbf{(30.17)}$$

where N is the total number of turns.

Gauss's law of magnetism states that the net magnetic flux through any closed surface is zero.

Substances can be classified into one of three categories that describe their magnetic behavior. **Diamagnetic** substances are those in which the magnetic moment is weak and opposite the applied magnetic field. **Paramagnetic** substances are those in which the magnetic moment is weak and in the same direction as the applied magnetic field. In **ferromagnetic** substances, interactions between atoms cause magnetic moments to align and create a strong magnetization that remains after the external field is removed.

Questions

☐ denotes answer available in *Student Solutions Manual/Study Guide;* **O** denotes objective question

1. O What creates a magnetic field? Choose every correct answer. (a) a stationary object with electric charge (b) a moving object with electric charge (c) a stationary conductor carrying electric current (d) a difference in electric potential (e) an electric resistor. *Note:* In Chapter 34, we will see that a changing electric field also creates a magnetic field.

2. O A long, vertical, metallic wire carries downward electric current. **(i)** What is the direction of the magnetic field it creates at a point 2 cm horizontally east of the center of the wire? (a) north (b) south (c) east (d) west (e) up (f) down **(ii)** What would be the direction of the field if the current consisted of positive charges moving downward, instead of electrons moving upward? Choose from the same possibilities.

3. O Suppose you are facing a tall makeup mirror on a vertical wall. Fluorescent tubes framing the mirror carry a clockwise electric current. **(i)** What is the direction of the magnetic field created by that current at a point slightly to the right of the center of the mirror? (a) up (b) down (c) left (d) right (e) horizontally toward you (f) away from you **(ii)** What is the direction of the field the current creates at a point on the wall outside the frame to the right? Choose from the same possibilities.

4. Explain why two parallel wires carrying currents in opposite directions repel each other.

5. O In Active Figure 30.8, assume $I_1 = 2$ A and $I_2 = 6$ A. What is the relationship between the magnitude F_1 of the force exerted on wire 1 and the magnitude F_2 of the force exerted on wire 2? (a) $F_1 = 6F_2$ (b) $F_1 = 3F_2$ (c) $F_1 = F_2$ (d) $F_1 = F_2/3$ (e) $F_1 = F_2/6$

6. O Answer each question yes or no. (a) Is it possible for each of three stationary charged particles to exert a force of attraction on the other two? (b) Is it possible for each of three stationary charged particles to repel both of the other particles? (c) Is it possible for each of three current-carrying metal wires to attract the other two? (d) Is it possible for each of three current-carrying metal wires to repel both of the other wires? André-Marie Ampère's experiments on electromagnetism are models of logical precision and included observation of the phenomena referred to in this question.

7. Is Ampère's law valid for all closed paths surrounding a conductor? Why is it not useful for calculating $\vec{\mathbf{B}}$ for all such paths?

8. Compare Ampère's law with the Biot–Savart law. Which is more generally useful for calculating $\vec{\mathbf{B}}$ for a current-carrying conductor?

9. A hollow copper tube carries a current along its length. Why is $\vec{\mathbf{B}} = 0$ inside the tube? Is $\vec{\mathbf{B}}$ nonzero outside the tube?

10. O (i) What happens to the magnitude of the magnetic field inside a long solenoid if the current is doubled? (a) It becomes 4 times larger. (b) It becomes twice as large. (c) It is unchanged. (d) It becomes one-half as large. (e) It becomes one-fourth as large. **(ii)** What happens to the field if instead the length of the solenoid is doubled, with the number of turns remaining the same? Choose from the same possibilities. **(iii)** What happens to the field if the number of turns is doubled, with the length remaining the same? Choose from the same possibilities. **(iv)** What happens to the field if the radius is doubled? Choose from the same possibilities.

11. O A long solenoid with closely spaced turns carries electric current. Does each turn of wire exert (a) an attractive force on the next adjacent turn, (b) a repulsive force on the next adjacent turn, (c) zero force on the next adjacent turn, or (d) either an attractive or a repulsive force on the next turn, depending on the direction of current in the solenoid?

12. O A uniform magnetic field is directed along the x axis. For what orientation of a flat, rectangular coil is the flux through the rectangle a maximum? (a) It is a maximum in the xy plane. (b) It is a maximum in the xz plane. (c) It is a maximum in the yz plane. (d) The flux has the same nonzero value for all these orientations. (e) The flux is zero in all cases.

13. The quantity $\oint \vec{\mathbf{B}} \cdot d\vec{\mathbf{s}}$ in Ampère's law is called *magnetic circulation.* Active Figure 30.10 and Figure 30.13 show paths around which the magnetic circulation was evaluated. Each of these paths encloses an area. What is the magnetic flux through each area? Explain your answer.

14. O (a) Two stationary charged particles exert forces of attraction on each other. One of the particles has negative charge. Is the other positive or negative? (b) Is the net electric field at a point halfway between the particles larger, smaller, or the same in magnitude as the field due to one charge by itself? (c) Two straight, vertical, current-carrying wires exert forces of attraction on each other. One of them carries downward current. Does the other wire carry upward or downward current? (d) Is the net magnetic field at a point halfway between the wires larger, smaller, or the same in magnitude as the field due to one wire by itself?

15. O Rank the magnitudes of the following magnetic fields from the largest to the smallest, noting any cases of equality. (a) the field 2 cm away from a long, straight wire carrying a current of 3 A (b) the field at the center of a flat, compact, circular coil, 2 cm in radius, with 10 turns, carrying a current of 0.3 A (c) the field at the center of a solenoid 2 cm in radius and 200 cm long, with 1 000 turns, carrying a current of 0.3 A (d) the field at the center of a long, straight metal bar, 2 cm in radius, carrying a current of 300 A (e) a field of 1 mT

16. One pole of a magnet attracts a nail. Will the other pole of the magnet attract the nail? Explain. Explain how a magnet sticks to a refrigerator door.

17. A magnet attracts a piece of iron. The iron can then attract another piece of iron. On the basis of domain alignment, explain what happens in each piece of iron.

18. Why does hitting a magnet with a hammer cause the magnetism to be reduced?

19. Which way would a compass point if you were at the north magnetic pole of the Earth?

20. Figure Q30.20 shows four permanent magnets, each having a hole through its center. Notice that the blue and yellow magnets are levitated above the red ones. (a) How does this levitation occur? (b) What purpose do the rods serve? (c) What can you say about the poles of the magnets from this observation? (d) If the upper magnet were inverted, what do you suppose would happen?

Figure Q30.20

Problems

WebAssign The Problems from this chapter may be assigned online in WebAssign.

ThomsonNOW Sign in at **www.thomsonedu.com** and go to ThomsonNOW to assess your understanding of this chapter's topics with additional quizzing and conceptual questions.

1, 2, 3 denotes straightforward, intermediate, challenging; □ denotes full solution available in *Student Solutions Manual/Study Guide;* ▲ denotes coached solution with hints available at **www.thomsonedu.com;** ▭ denotes developing symbolic reasoning; ● denotes asking for qualitative reasoning; ▭ denotes computer useful in solving problem

Section 30.1 The Biot–Savart Law

1. In Niels Bohr's 1913 model of the hydrogen atom, an electron circles the proton at a distance of 5.29×10^{-11} m with a speed of 2.19×10^{6} m/s. Compute the magnitude of the magnetic field this motion produces at the location of the proton.

2. Calculate the magnitude of the magnetic field at a point 100 cm from a long, thin conductor carrying a current of 1.00 A.

3. (a) A conductor in the shape of a square loop of edge length $\ell = 0.400$ m carries a current $I = 10.0$ A as shown in Figure P30.3. Calculate the magnitude and direction of the magnetic field at the center of the square. (b) **What If?** If this conductor is formed into a single circular turn and carries the same current, what is the value of the magnetic field at the center?

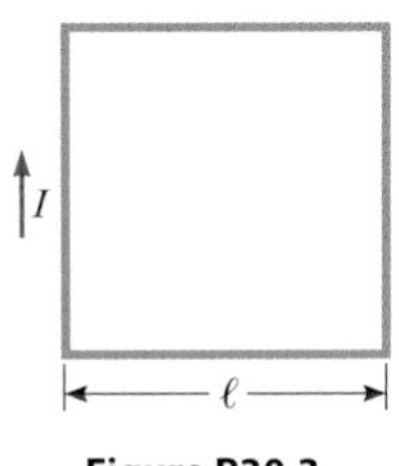

Figure P30.3

4. A conductor consists of a circular loop of radius R and two straight, long sections as shown in Figure P30.4. The wire lies in the plane of the paper and carries a current I. Find an expression for the vector magnetic field at the center of the loop.

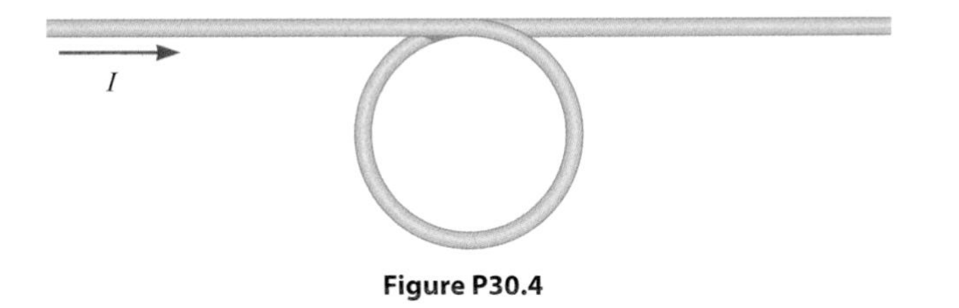

Figure P30.4

5. ▲ Determine the magnetic field at a point P located a distance x from the corner of an infinitely long wire bent at a right angle as shown in Figure P30.5. The wire carries a steady current I.

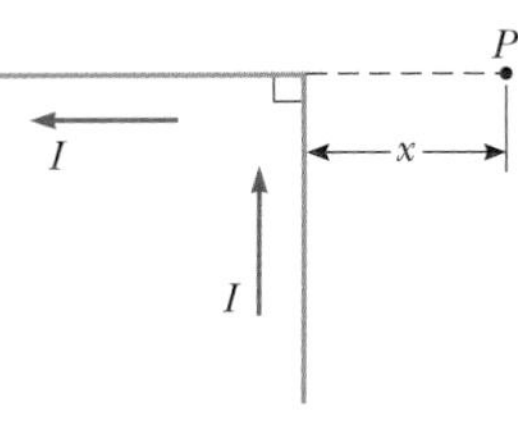

Figure P30.5

6. Consider a flat, circular current loop of radius R carrying current I. Choose the x axis to be along the axis of the loop, with the origin at the center of the loop. Plot a graph of the ratio of the magnitude of the magnetic field at coordinate x to that at the origin, for $x = 0$ to $x = 5R$. It may be useful to use a programmable calculator or a computer to solve this problem.

7. Two long, straight, parallel wires carry currents that are directed perpendicular to the page as shown in Figure P30.7. Wire 1 carries a current I_1 into the page (in the $-z$ direction) and passes through the x axis at $x = +a$. Wire 2 passes through the x axis at $x = -2a$ and carries an unknown current I_2. The total magnetic field at the origin due to the current-carrying wires has the magnitude $2\mu_0 I_1/(2\pi a)$. The current I_2 can have either of two possible values. (a) Find the value of I_2 with the smaller magnitude, stating it in terms of I_1 and giving its direction. (b) Find the other possible value of I_2.

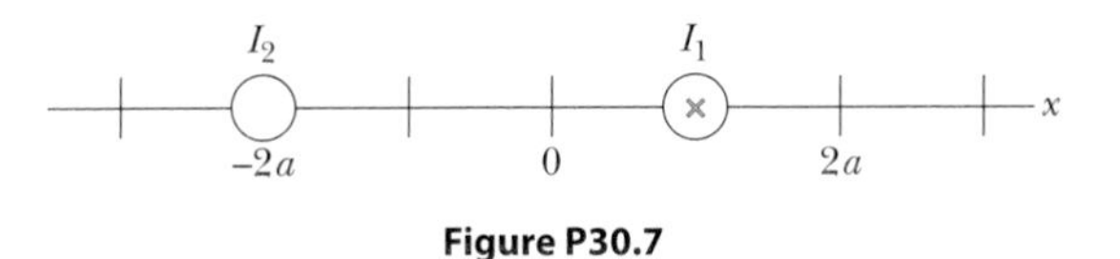

Figure P30.7

8. A long, straight wire carries current I. A right-angle bend is made in the middle of the wire. The bend forms an arc

of a circle of radius r as shown in Figure P30.8. Determine the magnetic field at the center of the arc.

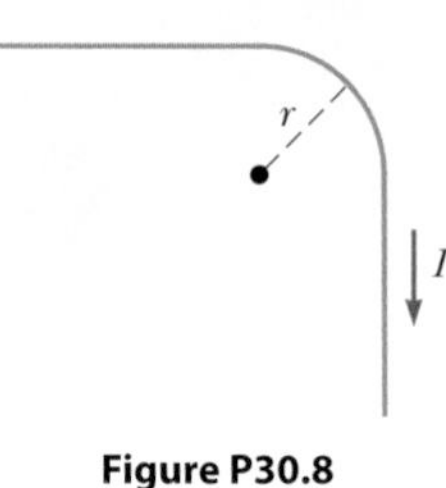

Figure P30.8

9. One long wire carries current 30.0 A to the left along the x axis. A second long wire carries current 50.0 A to the right along the line (y = 0.280 m, z = 0). (a) Where in the plane of the two wires is the total magnetic field equal to zero? (b) A particle with a charge of -2.00 μC is moving with a velocity of $150\hat{\mathbf{i}}$ Mm/s along the line (y = 0.100 m, z = 0). Calculate the vector magnetic force acting on the particle. (c) **What If?** A uniform electric field is applied to allow this particle to pass through this region undeflected. Calculate the required vector electric field.

10. A current path shaped as shown in Figure P30.10 produces a magnetic field at P, the center of the arc. If the arc subtends an angle of 30.0° and the radius of the arc is 0.600 m, what are the magnitude and direction of the field produced at P if the current is 3.00 A?

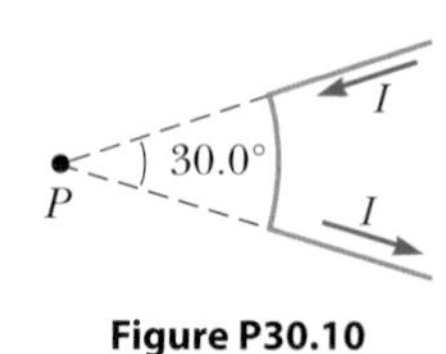

Figure P30.10

11. Three long, parallel conductors carry currents of I = 2.00 A. Figure P30.11 is an end view of the conductors, with each current coming out of the page. Taking a = 1.00 cm, determine the magnitude and direction of the magnetic field at points A, B, and C.

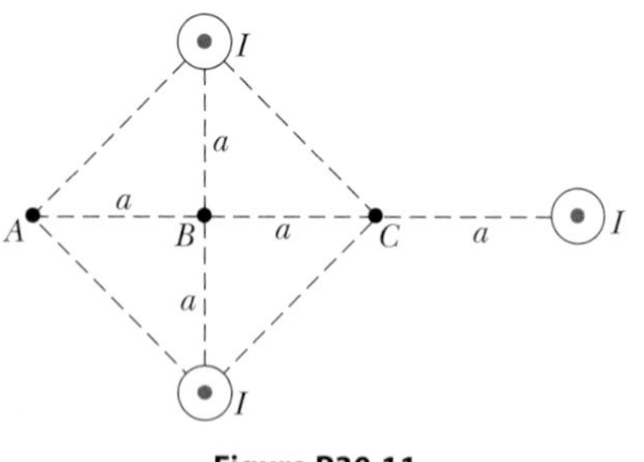

Figure P30.11

12. ● In a long, straight, vertical lightning stroke, electrons move downward and positive ions move upward, to constitute a current of magnitude 20.0 kA. At a location 50.0 m east of the middle of the stroke, a free electron drifts through the air toward the west with a speed of 300 m/s. (a) Find the vector force the lightning stroke exerts on the electron. Make a sketch showing the various vectors involved. Ignore the effect of the Earth's magnetic field. (b) Find the radius of the electron's path. Is it a good approximation to model the electron as moving in a uniform field? Explain your answer. (c) If it does not collide with any obstacles, how many revolutions will the electron complete during the 60.0-μs duration of the lightning stroke?

13. ● A wire carrying a current I is bent into the shape of an equilateral triangle of side L. (a) Find the magnitude of the magnetic field at the center of the triangle. (b) At a point halfway between the center and any vertex, is the field stronger or weaker than at the center? Give a qualitative argument for your answer.

14. Determine the magnetic field (in terms of I, a, and d) at the origin due to the current loop in Figure P30.14.

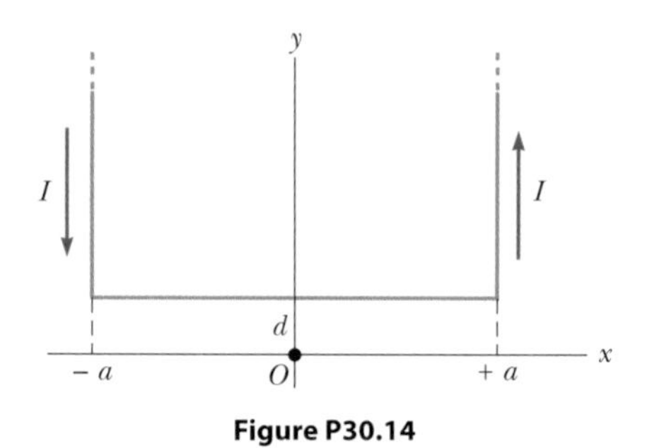

Figure P30.14

15. Two long, parallel conductors carry currents I_1 = 3.00 A and I_2 = 3.00 A, both directed into the page in Figure P30.15. Determine the magnitude and direction of the resultant magnetic field at P.

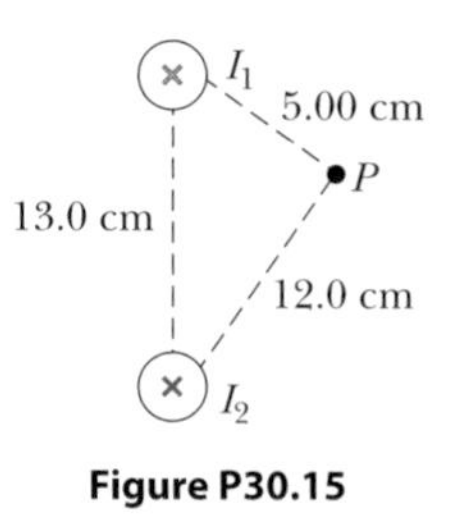

Figure P30.15

16. The idea that a magnetic field can have therapeutic value has been around for centuries. A rare-earth magnet sold to relieve joint pain is a disk 1.20 mm thick and 3.50 mm in diameter. Its circular flat faces are its north and south poles. Assume it is accurately modeled as a magnetic dipole. Also assume Equation 30.10 describes the magnetic field it produces at all points along its axis. The field is strongest, with the value 40.0 mT, at the center of each flat face. At what distance from the surface is the magnitude of the magnetic field like that of the Earth, with a value of 50.0 μT?

Section 30.2 The Magnetic Force Between Two Parallel Conductors

17. In Figure P30.17, the current in the long, straight wire is I_1 = 5.00 A and the wire lies in the plane of the rectangular loop, which carries the current I_2 = 10.0 A. The dimensions are c = 0.100 m, a = 0.150 m, and ℓ = 0.450 m. Find the magnitude and direction of the net force exerted on the loop by the magnetic field created by the wire.

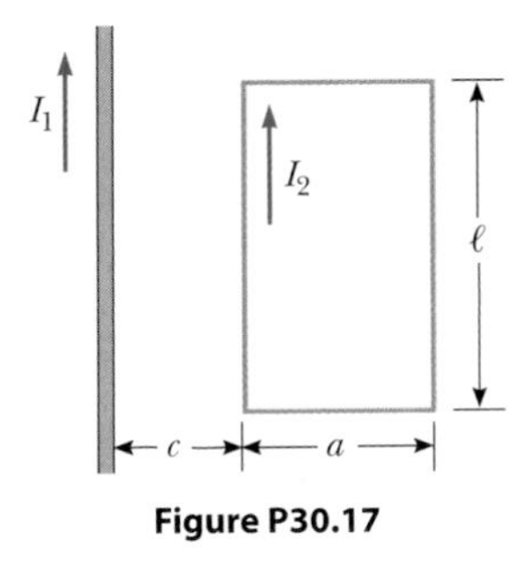

Figure P30.17

18. Two long, parallel conductors, separated by 10.0 cm, carry currents in the same direction. The first wire carries current $I_1 = 5.00$ A, and the second carries $I_2 = 8.00$ A. (a) What is the magnitude of the magnetic field created by I_1 at the location of I_2? (b) What is the force per unit length exerted by I_1 on I_2? (c) What is the magnitude of the magnetic field created by I_2 at the location of I_1? (d) What is the force per length exerted by I_2 on I_1?

19. Two long, parallel wires are attracted to each other by a force per unit length of 320 μN/m when they are separated by a vertical distance of 0.500 m. The current in the upper wire is 20.0 A to the right. Determine the location of the line in the plane of the two wires along which the total magnetic field is zero.

20. ● Three long wires (wire 1, wire 2, and wire 3) hang vertically. The distance between wire 1 and wire 2 is 20.0 cm. On the left, wire 1 carries an upward current of 1.50 A. To the right, wire 2 carries a downward current of 4.00 A. Wire 3 is to be located such that when it carries a certain current, each wire experiences no net force. (a) Is this situation possible? Is it possible in more than one way? Describe (b) the position of wire 3 and (c) the magnitude and direction of the current in wire 3.

21. ● The unit of magnetic flux is named for Wilhelm Weber. A practical-size unit of magnetic field is named for Johann Karl Friedrich Gauss. Both were scientists at Göttingen, Germany. Along with their individual accomplishments, together they built a telegraph in 1833. It consisted of a battery and switch, at one end of a transmission line 3 km long, operating an electromagnet at the other end. (André Ampère suggested electrical signaling in 1821; Samuel Morse built a telegraph line between Baltimore and Washington, D.C., in 1844.) Suppose Weber and Gauss's transmission line was as diagrammed in Figure P30.21. Two long, parallel wires, each having a mass per unit length of 40.0 g/m, are supported in a horizontal plane by strings 6.00 cm long. When both wires carry the same current I, the wires repel each other so that the angle θ between the supporting strings is 16.0°. (a) Are the currents in the same direction or in opposite directions? (b) Find the magnitude of the current. (c) If this apparatus were taken to Mars, would the current required to separate the wires by 16° be larger or smaller than on Earth? Why?

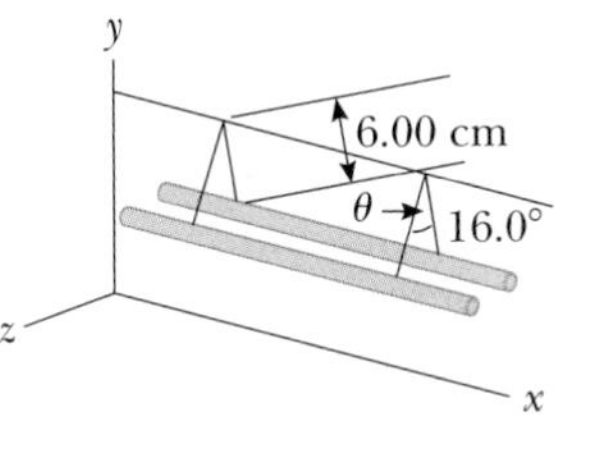

Figure P30.21

22. ● Two parallel copper conductors are each 0.500 m long. They carry 10.0-A currents in opposite directions. (a) What center-to-center separation must the conductors have if they are to repel each other with a force of 1.00 N? (b) Is this situation physically possible? Explain.

Section 30.3 Ampère's Law

23. ▲ Four long, parallel conductors carry equal currents of $I = 5.00$ A. Figure P30.23 is an end view of the conductors. The current direction is into the page at points A and B (indicated by the crosses) and out of the page at C and D (indicated by the dots). Calculate the magnitude and direction of the magnetic field at point P, located at the center of the square of edge length 0.200 m.

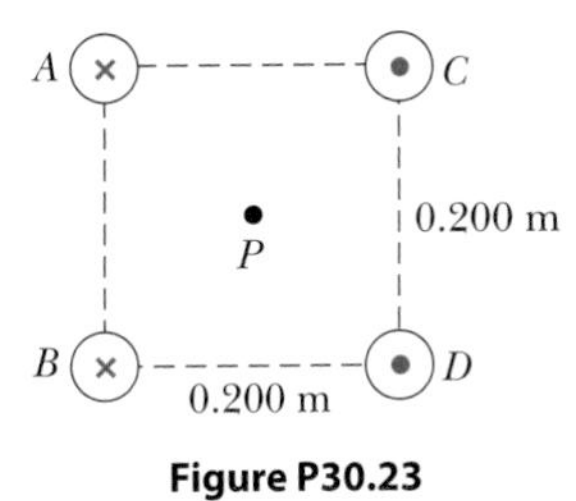

Figure P30.23

24. A long, straight wire lies on a horizontal table and carries a current of 1.20 μA. In a vacuum, a proton moves parallel to the wire (opposite the current) with a constant speed of 2.30×10^4 m/s at a distance d above the wire. Determine the value of d. You may ignore the magnetic field due to the Earth.

25. Figure P30.25 is a cross-sectional view of a coaxial cable. The center conductor is surrounded by a rubber layer, which is surrounded by an outer conductor, which is surrounded by another rubber layer. In a particular application, the current in the inner conductor is 1.00 A out of the page and the current in the outer conductor is 3.00 A into the page. Determine the magnitude and direction of the magnetic field at points a and b.

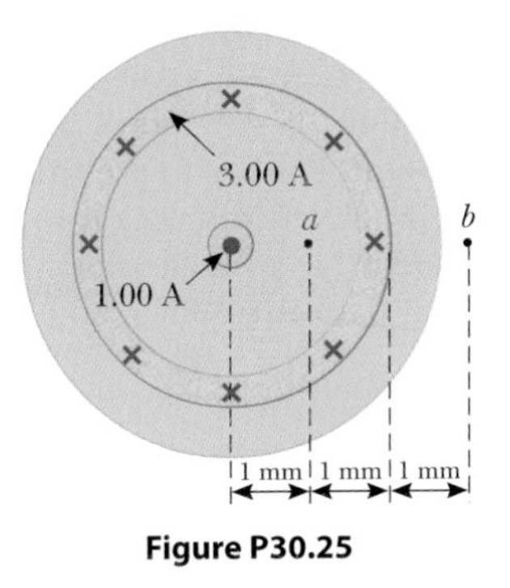

Figure P30.25

26. The magnetic field 40.0 cm away from a long,straight wire carrying current 2.00 A is 1.00 μT. (a) At what distance is it 0.100 μT? (b) **What If?** At one instant, the two conductors in a long household extension cord carry equal 2.00-A currents in opposite directions. The two wires are 3.00 mm apart. Find the magnetic field 40.0 cm away

from the middle of the straight cord, in the plane of the two wires. (c) At what distance is it one-tenth as large? (d) The center wire in a coaxial cable carries current 2.00 A in one direction, and the sheath around it carries current 2.00 A in the opposite direction. What magnetic field does the cable create at points outside?

27. ● ▲ A packed bundle of 100 long, straight, insulated wires forms a cylinder of radius $R = 0.500$ cm. (a) If each wire carries 2.00 A, what are the magnitude and direction of the magnetic force per unit length acting on a wire located 0.200 cm from the center of the bundle? (b) **What If?** Would a wire on the outer edge of the bundle experience a force greater or smaller than the value calculated in part (a)? Give a qualitative argument for your answer.

28. The magnetic coils of a tokamak fusion reactor are in the shape of a toroid having an inner radius of 0.700 m and an outer radius of 1.30 m. The toroid has 900 turns of large-diameter wire, each of which carries a current of 14.0 kA. Find the magnitude of the magnetic field inside the toroid along (a) the inner radius and (b) the outer radius.

29. Consider a column of electric current passing through plasma (ionized gas). Filaments of current within the column are magnetically attracted to one another. They can crowd together to yield a very great current density and a very strong magnetic field in a small region. Sometimes the current can be cut off momentarily by this *pinch effect*. (In a metallic wire, a pinch effect is not important because the current-carrying electrons repel one another with electric forces.) The pinch effect can be demonstrated by making an empty aluminum can carry a large current parallel to its axis. Let R represent the radius of the can and I the upward current, uniformly distributed over its curved wall. Determine the magnetic field (a) just inside the wall and (b) just outside. (c) Determine the pressure on the wall.

30. Niobium metal becomes a superconductor when cooled below 9 K. Its superconductivity is destroyed when the surface magnetic field exceeds 0.100 T. Determine the maximum current a 2.00-mm-diameter niobium wire can carry and remain superconducting, in the absence of any external magnetic field.

31. A long, cylindrical conductor of radius R carries a current I as shown in Figure P30.31. The current density J, however, is not uniform over the cross section of the conductor but is a function of the radius according to $J = br$, where b is a constant. Find an expression for the magnetic field magnitude B (a) at a distance $r_1 < R$ and (b) at a distance $r_2 > R$, measured from the axis.

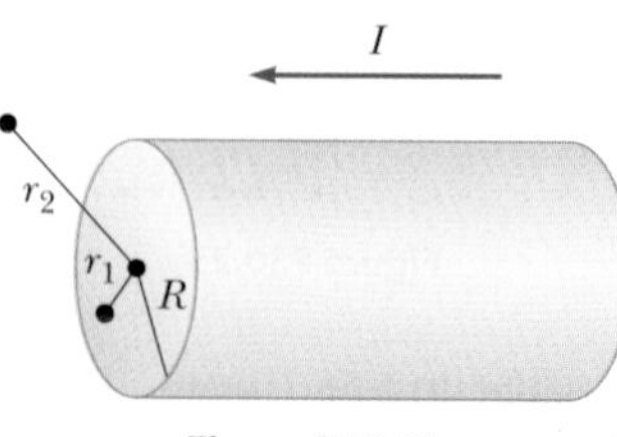

Figure P30.31

32. In Figure P30.32, both currents in the infinitely long wires are 8.00 A in the negative x direction. The wires are separated by the distance $2a = 6.00$ cm. (a) Sketch the magnetic field pattern in the yz plane. (b) What is the value of the magnetic field at the origin? At ($y = 0$, $z \to \infty$)? (c) Find the magnetic field at points along the z axis as a function of z. (d) At what distance d along the positive z axis is the magnetic field a maximum? (e) What is this maximum value?

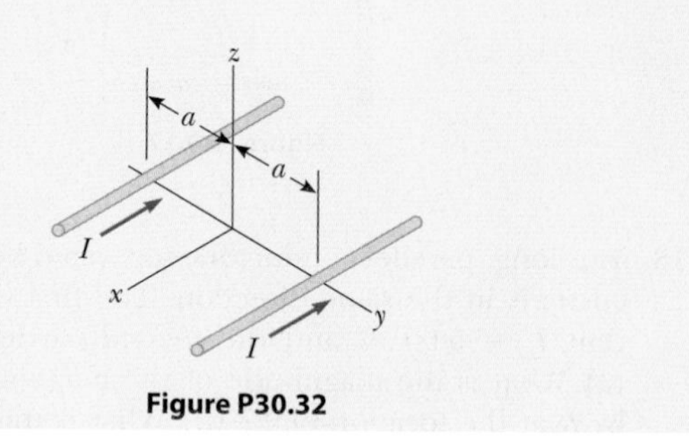

Figure P30.32

33. An infinite sheet of current lying in the yz plane carries a surface current of linear density J_s. The current is in the y direction, and J_s represents the current per unit length measured along the z axis. Figure P30.33 is an edge view of the sheet. Prove that the magnetic field near the sheet is parallel to the sheet and perpendicular to the current direction, with magnitude $\mu_0 J_s/2$. *Suggestion:* Use Ampère's law and evaluate the line integral for a rectangular path around the sheet, represented by the dashed line in Figure P30.33.

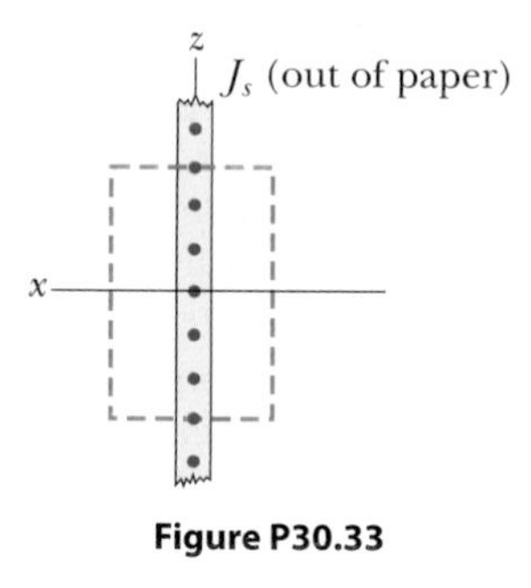

Figure P30.33

Section 30.4 The Magnetic Field of a Solenoid

34. ● You are given a certain volume of copper from which you can make copper wire. To insulate the wire, you can have as much enamel as you like. You will use the wire to make a tightly wound solenoid 20 cm long having the greatest possible magnetic field at the center and using a power supply that can deliver a current of 5 A. The solenoid can be wrapped with wire in one or more layers. (a) Should you make the wire long and thin or shorter and thick? Explain. (b) Should you make the solenoid radius small or large? Explain.

35. ▲ What current is required in the windings of a long solenoid that has 1 000 turns uniformly distributed over a length of 0.400 m to produce at the center of the solenoid a magnetic field of magnitude 1.00×10^{-4} T?

36. Consider a solenoid of length ℓ and radius R, containing N closely spaced turns and carrying a steady current I. (a) In terms of these parameters, find the magnetic field at a point along the axis as a function of distance a from the end of the solenoid. (b) Show that as ℓ becomes very long, B approaches $\mu_0 NI/2\ell$ at each end of the solenoid.

37. A single-turn square loop of wire, 2.00 cm on each edge, carries a clockwise current of 0.200 A. The loop is inside a solenoid, with the plane of the loop perpendicular to the magnetic field of the solenoid. The solenoid has 30 turns/cm and carries a clockwise current of 15.0 A. Find the force on each side of the loop and the torque acting on the loop.

38. A solenoid 10.0 cm in diameter and 75.0 cm long is made from copper wire of diameter 0.100 cm, with very thin insulation. The wire is wound onto a cardboard tube in a single layer, with adjacent turns touching each other. What power must be delivered to the solenoid if it is to produce a field of 8.00 mT at its center?

Section 30.5 Gauss's Law in Magnetism

39. A cube of edge length $\ell = 2.50$ cm is positioned as shown in Figure P30.39. A uniform magnetic field given by $\vec{\mathbf{B}} = (5\hat{\mathbf{i}} + 4\hat{\mathbf{j}} + 3\hat{\mathbf{k}})$ T exists throughout the region. (a) Calculate the magnetic flux through the shaded face. (b) What is the total flux through the six faces?

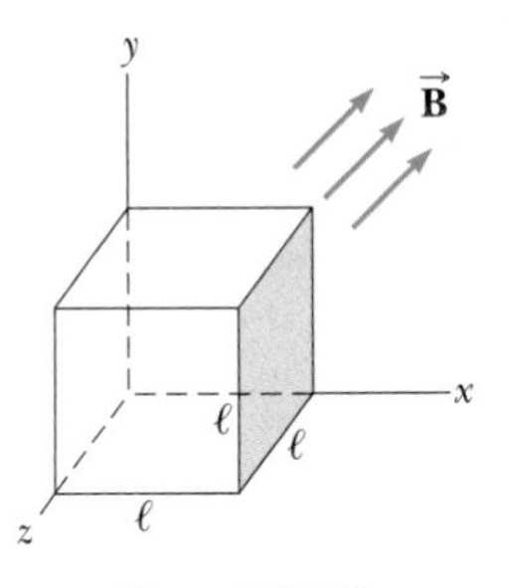

Figure P30.39

40. Consider the hemispherical closed surface in Figure P30.40. The hemisphere is in a uniform magnetic field that makes an angle θ with the vertical. Calculate the magnetic flux through (a) the flat surface S_1 and (b) the hemispherical surface S_2.

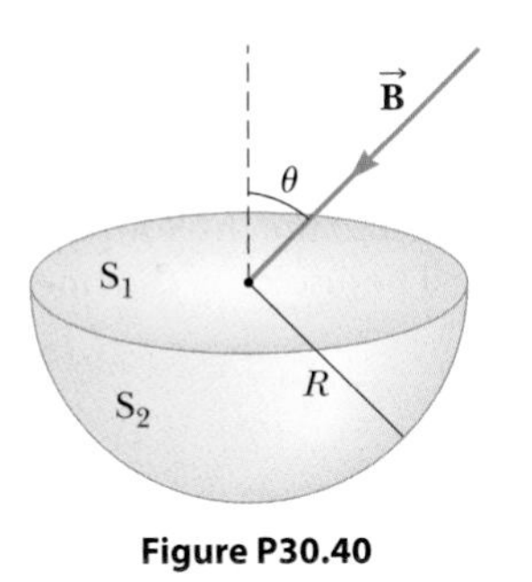

Figure P30.40

41. A solenoid 2.50 cm in diameter and 30.0 cm long has 300 turns and carries 12.0 A. (a) Calculate the flux through the surface of a disk of radius 5.00 cm that is positioned perpendicular to and centered on the axis of the solenoid, as shown in Figure P30.41a. (b) Figure P30.41b shows an enlarged end view of the same solenoid. Calculate the flux through the blue area, which is an annulus with an inner radius of 0.400 cm and an outer radius of 0.800 cm.

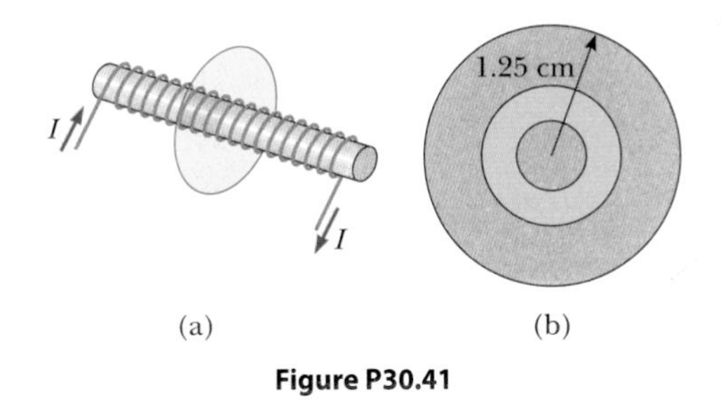

Figure P30.41

42. *Compare this problem with Problem 65 in Chapter 24.* Consider a magnetic field that is uniform in direction throughout a certain volume. Can it be uniform in magnitude? Must it be uniform in magnitude? Give evidence for your answers.

Section 30.6 Magnetism in Matter

43. At *saturation,* when nearly all the atoms have their magnetic moments aligned, the magnetic field in a sample of iron can be 2.00 T. If each electron contributes a magnetic moment of 9.27×10^{-24} A · m² (one Bohr magneton), how many electrons per atom contribute to the saturated field of iron? The number density of atoms in iron is approximately 8.50×10^{28} atoms/m³.

Section 30.7 The Magnetic Field of the Earth

44. A circular coil of 5 turns and a diameter of 30.0 cm is oriented in a vertical plane with its axis perpendicular to the horizontal component of the Earth's magnetic field. A horizontal compass placed at the center of the coil is made to deflect 45.0° from magnetic north by a current of 0.600 A in the coil. (a) What is the horizontal component of the Earth's magnetic field? (b) The current in the coil is switched off. A "dip needle" is a magnetic compass mounted so that it can rotate in a vertical north–south plane. At this location, a dip needle makes an angle of 13.0° from the vertical. What is the total magnitude of the Earth's magnetic field at this location?

45. The magnetic moment of the Earth is approximately 8.00×10^{22} A · m². (a) Imagine that the planetary magnetic field were caused by the complete magnetization of a huge iron deposit. How many unpaired electrons would participate? (b) At two unpaired electrons per iron atom, how many kilograms of iron would compose the deposit? Iron has a density of 7 900 kg/m³ and approximately 8.50×10^{28} iron atoms/m³.

46. ● A particular location on the Earth's surface is characterized by a value of gravitational field, a value of magnetic field, and a value of atmospheric pressure. (a) Which of these quantities are vectors and which are scalars? (b) Determine a value for each quantity at your current location. Include the direction of each vector quantity. State your sources. (c) Which of the quantities have separate causes from which of the others?

Additional Problems

47. A very long, thin strip of metal of width w carries a current I along its length as shown in Figure P30.47. Find the magnetic field at the point P in the diagram. The point P is in the plane of the strip at distance b away from it.

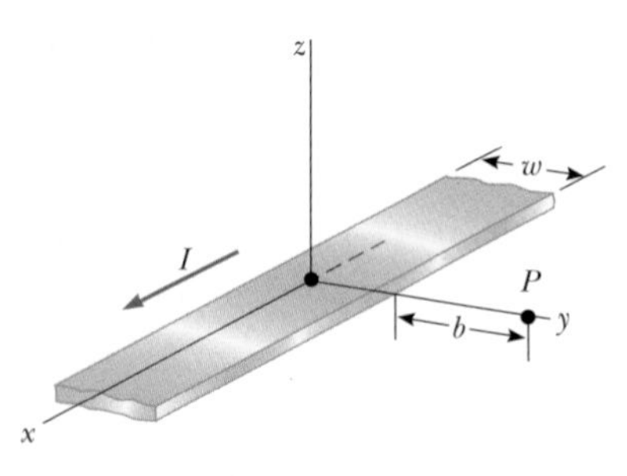

Figure P30.47

48. The magnitude of the Earth's magnetic field at either pole is approximately 7.00×10^{-5} T. Suppose the field fades away, before its next reversal. Scouts, sailors, and conservative politicians around the world join together in a program to replace the field. One plan is to use a current loop around the equator, without relying on magnetization of any materials inside the Earth. Determine the current that would generate such a field if this plan were carried out. Take the radius of the Earth as $R_E = 6.37 \times 10^6$ m.

49. A thin copper bar of length $\ell = 10.0$ cm is supported horizontally by two (nonmagnetic) contacts. The bar carries current $I_1 = 100$ A in the $-x$ direction as shown in Figure P30.49. At a distance $h = 0.500$ cm below one end of the bar, a long, straight wire carries a current $I_2 = 200$ A in the z direction. Determine the magnetic force exerted on the bar.

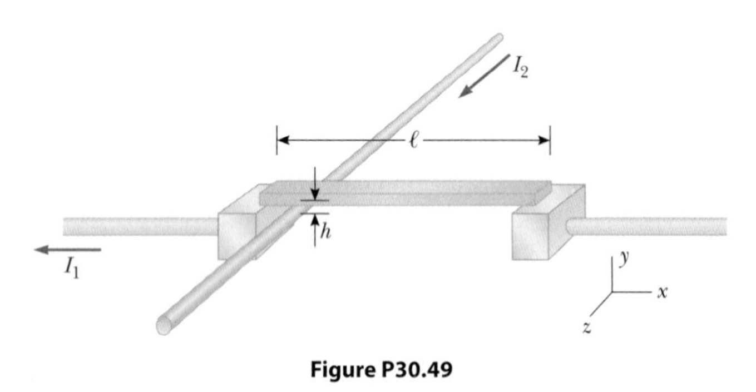

Figure P30.49

50. Suppose you install a compass on the center of the dashboard of a car. Compute an order-of-magnitude estimate for the magnetic field at this location produced by the current when you switch on the headlights. How does this estimate compare with the Earth's magnetic field? You may suppose the dashboard is made mostly of plastic.

51. ▲ A nonconducting ring of radius 10.0 cm is uniformly charged with a total positive charge 10.0 μC. The ring rotates at a constant angular speed 20.0 rad/s about an axis through its center, perpendicular to the plane of the ring. What is the magnitude of the magnetic field on the axis of the ring 5.00 cm from its center?

52. A nonconducting ring of radius R is uniformly charged with a total positive charge q. The ring rotates at a constant angular speed ω about an axis through its center, perpendicular to the plane of the ring. What is the magnitude of the magnetic field on the axis of the ring a distance $R/2$ from its center?

53. Two circular coils of radius R, each with N turns, are perpendicular to a common axis. The coil centers are a distance R apart. Each coil carries a steady current I in the same direction as shown in Figure P30.53. (a) Show that the magnetic field on the axis at a distance x from the center of one coil is

$$B = \frac{N\mu_0 IR^2}{2}\left[\frac{1}{(R^2 + x^2)^{3/2}} + \frac{1}{(2R^2 + x^2 - 2Rx)^{3/2}}\right]$$

(b) Show that dB/dx and d^2B/dx^2 are both zero at the point midway between the coils. We may then conclude that the magnetic field in the region midway between the coils is uniform. Coils in this configuration are called *Helmholtz coils.*

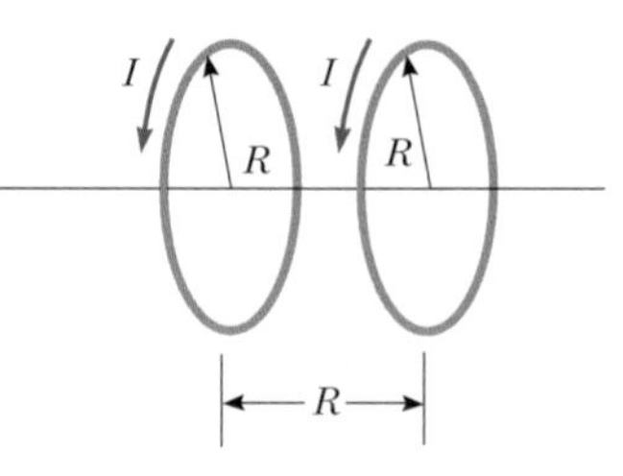

Figure P30.53 Problems 53 and 54.

54. Two identical, flat, circular coils of wire each have 100 turns and a radius of 0.500 m. The coils are arranged as a set of Helmholtz coils (see Fig. P30.53), parallel and with separation 0.500 m. Each coil carries a current of 10.0 A. Determine the magnitude of the magnetic field at a point on the common axis of the coils and halfway between them.

55. We have seen that a long solenoid produces a uniform magnetic field directed along the axis of a cylindrical region. To produce a uniform magnetic field directed parallel to a *diameter* of a cylindrical region, however, one can use the *saddle coils* illustrated in Figure P30.55. The loops are wrapped over a somewhat flattened tube. Assume the straight sections of wire are very long. The end view of the tube shows how the windings are applied. The overall current distribution is the superposition of two overlapping, circular cylinders of uniformly distributed current, one toward you and one away from you. The current density J is the same for each cylinder. The position of the axis of one cylinder is described by a position vector $\vec{\mathbf{a}}$ relative to the other cylinder. Prove that the magnetic field inside the hollow tube is $\mu_0 Ja/2$ downward. *Suggestion:* The use of vector methods simplifies the calculation.

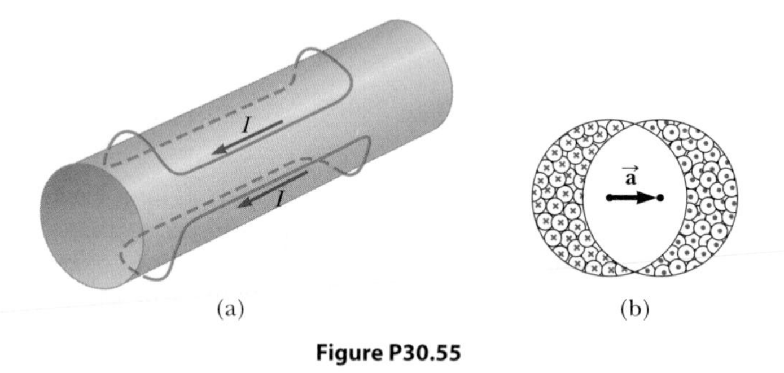

Figure P30.55

56. *You may use the result of Problem 33 in solving this problem.* A very large parallel-plate capacitor carries charge with uniform charge per unit area $+\sigma$ on the upper plate and $-\sigma$ on the lower plate. The plates are horizontal and both move horizontally with speed v to the right. (a) What is the magnetic field between the plates? (b) What is the magnetic field close to the plates but outside of the capacitor? (c) What is the magnitude and direction of the magnetic force per unit area on the upper plate? (d) At what extrapolated speed v will the magnetic force on a plate balance the electric force on the plate? Calculate this speed numerically.

57. ● Two circular loops are parallel, coaxial, and almost in contact, 1.00 mm apart (Fig. P30.57). Each loop is 10.0 cm in radius. The top loop carries a clockwise current of 140 A. The bottom loop carries a counterclockwise current of 140 A. (a) Calculate the magnetic force exerted by the bottom loop on the top loop. (b) Suppose a student thinks the first step in solving part (a) is to use Equation 30.7 to find the magnetic field created by one of the loops. How would you argue for or against this idea? *Suggestion:* Think about how one loop looks to a bug perched on the other loop. (c) The upper loop has a mass of 0.021 0 kg. Calculate its acceleration, assuming the only forces acting on it are the force in part (a) and the gravitational force.

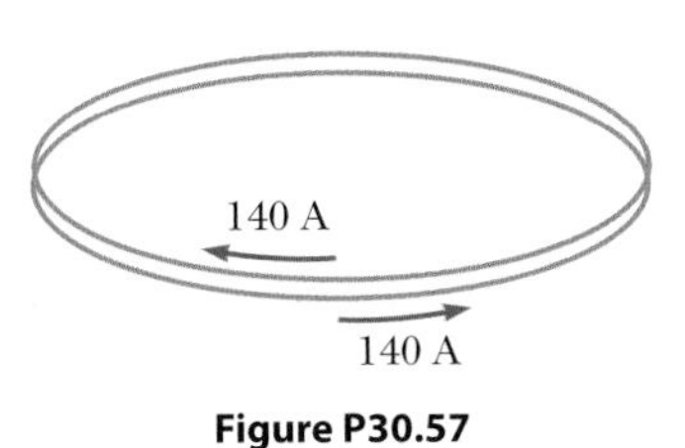

Figure P30.57

58. What objects experience a force in an electric field? Chapter 23 gives the answer: any object with electric charge, stationary or moving, other than the charged object that created the field. What creates an electric field? Any object with electric charge, stationary or moving, as you studied in Chapter 23. What objects experience a force in a magnetic field? An electric current or a moving electric charge, other than the current or charge that created the field, as discussed in Chapter 29. What creates a magnetic field? An electric current, as you studied in Section 30.1, or a moving electric charge, as shown in this problem. (a) To understand how a moving charge creates a magnetic field, consider a particle with charge q moving with velocity $\vec{\mathbf{v}}$. Define the position vector $\vec{\mathbf{r}} = r\hat{\mathbf{r}}$ leading from the particle to some location. Show that the magnetic field at that location is

$$\vec{\mathbf{B}} = \frac{\mu_0}{4\pi}\frac{q\vec{\mathbf{v}} \times \hat{\mathbf{r}}}{r^2}$$

(b) Find the magnitude of the magnetic field 1.00 mm to the side of a proton moving at 2.00×10^7 m/s. (c) Find the magnetic force on a second proton at this point, moving with the same speed in the opposite direction. (d) Find the electric force on the second proton.

59. The chapter-opening photograph shows a rail gun. Rail guns have been suggested for launching projectiles into space without chemical rockets and for ground-to-air antimissile weapons of war. A tabletop model rail gun (Fig. P30.59) consists of two long, parallel, horizontal rails 3.50 cm apart, bridged by a bar *BD* of mass 3.00 g. The bar is originally at rest at the midpoint of the rails and is free to slide without friction. When the switch is closed, electric current is quickly established in the circuit *ABCDEA*. The rails and bar have low electric resistance, and the current is limited to a constant 24.0 A by the power supply. (a) Find the magnitude of the magnetic field 1.75 cm from a single very long, straight wire carrying current 24.0 A. (b) Find the magnitude and direction of the magnetic field at point *C* in the diagram, the midpoint of the bar, immediately after the switch is closed. *Suggestion:* Consider what conclusions you can draw from the Biot–Savart law. (c) At other points along the bar *BD*, the field is in the same direction as at point *C*, but is larger in magnitude. Assume the average effective magnetic field along *BD* is five times larger than the field at *C*. With this assumption, find the magnitude and direction of the force on the bar. (d) Find the acceleration of the bar when it is in motion. (e) Does the bar move with constant acceleration? (f) Find the velocity of the bar after it has traveled 130 cm to the end of the rails.

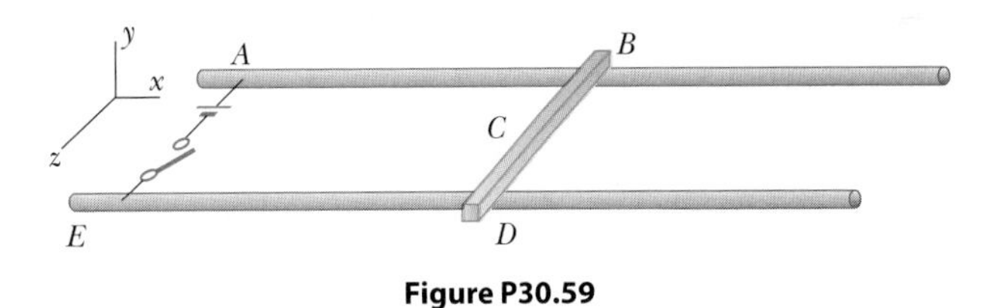

Figure P30.59

60. Fifty turns of insulated wire 0.100 cm in diameter are tightly wound to form a flat spiral. The spiral fills a disk surrounding a circle of radius 5.00 cm and extending to a radius 10.00 cm at the outer edge. Assume the wire carries current I at the center of its cross section. Approximate each turn of wire as a circle. Then a loop of current exists at radius 5.05 cm, another at 5.15 cm, and so on. Numerically calculate the magnetic field at the center of the coil.

61. An infinitely long, straight wire carrying a current I_1 is partially surrounded by a loop as shown in Figure P30.61. The loop has a length L and radius R, and it carries a current I_2. The axis of the loop coincides with the wire. Calculate the force exerted on the loop.

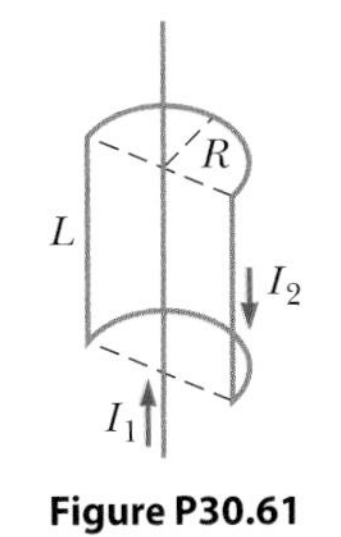

Figure P30.61

62. The magnitude of the force on a magnetic dipole $\vec{\boldsymbol{\mu}}$ aligned with a nonuniform magnetic field in the x direction is $F_x = |\vec{\boldsymbol{\mu}}|\, dB/dx$. Suppose two flat loops of wire each have radius R and carry current I. (a) The loops are arranged coaxially and separated by a variable distance x, large compared with R. Show that the magnetic force

between them varies as $1/x^4$. (b) Evaluate the magnitude of this force, taking $I = 10.0$ A, $R = 0.500$ cm, and $x = 5.00$ cm.

63. A wire is formed into the shape of a square of edge length L (Fig. P30.63). Show that when the current in the loop is I, the magnetic field at point P, a distance x from the center of the square along its axis is

$$B = \frac{\mu_0 I L^2}{2\pi(x^2 + L^2/4)\sqrt{x^2 + L^2/2}}$$

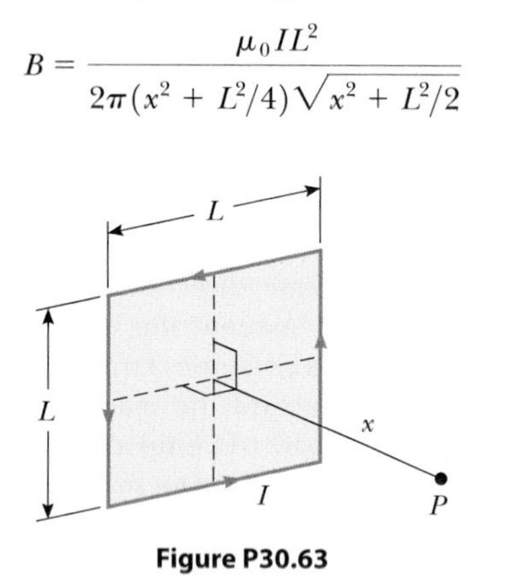

Figure P30.63

64. A wire carrying a current I is bent into the shape of an exponential spiral, $r = e^{\theta}$, from $\theta = 0$ to $\theta = 2\pi$ as suggested in Figure P30.64. To complete a loop, the ends of the spiral are connected by a straight wire along the x axis. Find the magnitude and direction of $\vec{\mathbf{B}}$ at the origin. *Suggestions:* Use the Biot–Savart law. The angle β between a radial line and its tangent line at any point on the curve $r = f(\theta)$ is related to the function as follows:

$$\tan \beta = \frac{r}{dr/d\theta}$$

Therefore, in this case $r = e^{\theta}$, $\tan \beta = 1$, and $\beta = \pi/4$, and the angle between $d\vec{\mathbf{s}}$ and $\hat{\mathbf{r}}$ is $\pi - \beta = 3\pi/4$. Also,

$$ds = \frac{dr}{\sin(\pi/4)} = \sqrt{2}\, dr$$

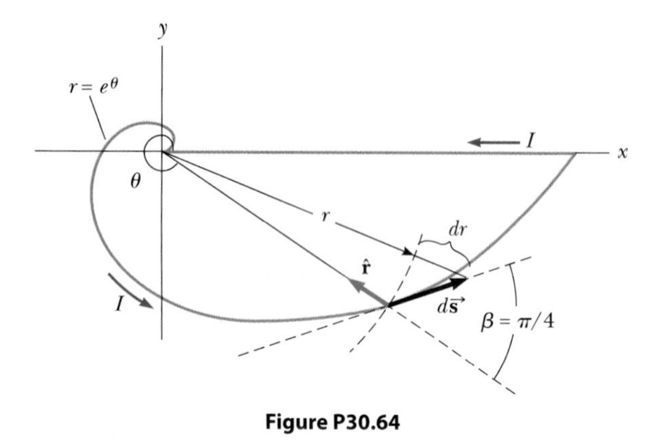

Figure P30.64

65. A sphere of radius R has a uniform volume charge density ρ. Determine the magnetic field at the center of the sphere when it rotates as a rigid object with angular speed ω about an axis through its center (Fig. P30.65).

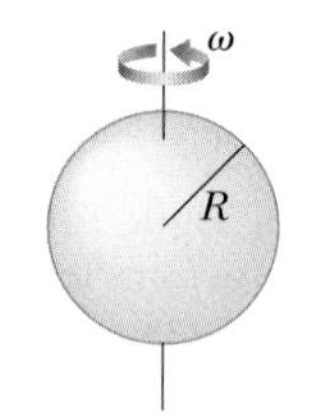

Figure P30.65 Problems 65 and 66.

66. A sphere of radius R has a uniform volume charge density ρ. Determine the magnetic dipole moment of the sphere when it rotates as a rigid body with angular speed ω about an axis through its center (Fig. P30.65).

67. A long, cylindrical conductor of radius a has two cylindrical cavities of diameter a through its entire length as shown in Figure P30.67. A current I is directed out of the page and is uniform through a cross section of the conductor. Find the magnitude and direction of the magnetic field in terms of μ_0, I, r, and a at (a) point P_1 and (b) point P_2.

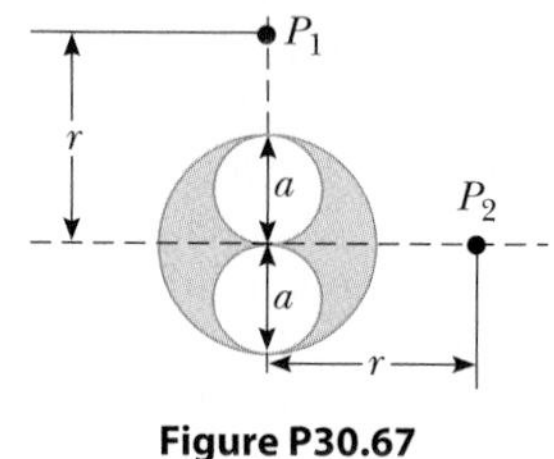

Figure P30.67

Answers to Quick Quizzes

30.1 *B, C, A*. Point *B* is closest to the current element. Point *C* is farther away, and the field is further reduced by the $\sin\theta$ factor in the cross product $d\vec{\mathbf{s}} \times \hat{\mathbf{r}}$. The field at *A* is zero because $\theta = 0$.

30.2 (a). The coils act like wires carrying parallel currents in the same direction and hence attract one another.

30.3 *b, d, a, c*. Equation 30.13 indicates that the value of the line integral depends only on the net current through each closed path. Path *b* encloses 1 A, path *d* encloses 3 A, path *a* encloses 4 A, and path *c* encloses 6 A.

30.4 *b*, then $a = c = d$. Paths *a*, *c*, and *d* all give the same nonzero value $\mu_0 I$ because the size and shape of the paths do not matter. Path *b* does not enclose the current; hence, its line integral is zero.

30.5 (c). The magnetic field in a very long solenoid is independent of its length or radius. Overwrapping with an additional layer of wire increases the number of turns per unit length.

In a commercial electric power plant, large generators transform energy that is then transferred out of the plant by electrical transmission. These generators use magnetic induction to generate a potential difference when coils of wire in the generator are rotated in a magnetic field. The source of energy to rotate the coils might be falling water, burning fossil fuels, or a nuclear reaction. (Michael Melford/Getty Images)

31 Faraday's Law

So far, our studies in electricity and magnetism have focused on the electric fields produced by stationary charges and the magnetic fields produced by moving charges. This chapter explores the effects produced by magnetic fields that vary in time.

Experiments conducted by Michael Faraday in England in 1831 and independently by Joseph Henry in the United States that same year showed that an emf can be induced in a circuit by a changing magnetic field. The results of these experiments led to a very basic and important law of electromagnetism known as *Faraday's law of induction.* An emf (and therefore a current as well) can be induced in various processes that involve a change in a magnetic flux.

MICHAEL FARADAY

British Physicist and Chemist (1791–1867)

Faraday is often regarded as the greatest experimental scientist of the 1800s. His many contributions to the study of electricity include the invention of the electric motor, electric generator, and transformer as well as the discovery of electromagnetic induction and the laws of electrolysis. Greatly influenced by religion, he refused to work on the development of poison gas for the British military.

31.1 Faraday's Law of Induction

To see how an emf can be induced by a changing magnetic field, consider the experimental results obtained when a loop of wire is connected to a sensitive ammeter as illustrated in Active Figure 31.1 (page 868). When a magnet is moved toward the loop, the reading on the ammeter changes from zero in one direction, arbitrarily shown as negative in Active Figure 31.1a. When the magnet is brought to rest and held stationary relative to the loop (Active Fig. 31.1b), a reading of

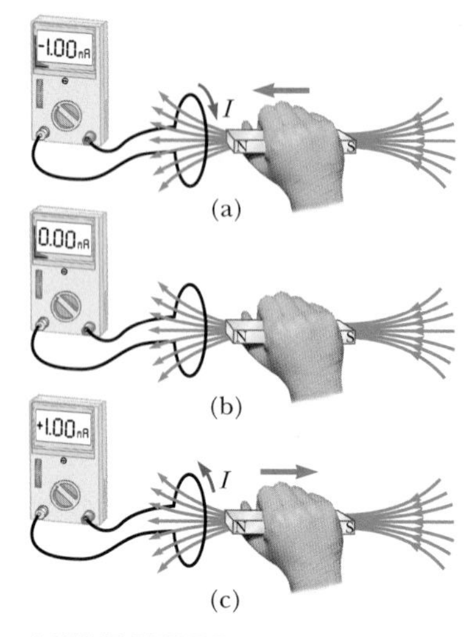

ACTIVE FIGURE 31.1

(a) When a magnet is moved toward a loop of wire connected to a sensitive ammeter, the ammeter reading changes from zero, indicating that a current is induced in the loop. (b) When the magnet is held stationary, there is no induced current in the loop, even when the magnet is inside the loop. (c) When the magnet is moved away from the loop, the ammeter reading changes in the opposite direction, indicating that the induced current is opposite that shown in (a). Changing the direction of the magnet's motion changes the direction of the current induced by that motion.

Sign in at www.thomsonedu.com and go to ThomsonNOW to move the magnet and observe the current in the ammeter.

zero is observed. When the magnet is moved away from the loop, the reading on the ammeter changes in the opposite direction as shown in Active Figure 31.1c. Finally, when the magnet is held stationary and the loop is moved either toward or away from it, the reading changes from zero. From these observations, we conclude that the loop detects that the magnet is moving relative to it and we relate this detection to a change in magnetic field. Therefore, it seems that a relationship exists between current and changing magnetic field.

These results are quite remarkable because **a current is set up even though no batteries are present in the circuit!** We call such a current an *induced current* and say that it is produced by an *induced emf.*

Now let's describe an experiment conducted by Faraday and illustrated in Active Figure 31.2. A primary coil is wrapped around an iron ring and connected to a switch and a battery. A current in the coil produces a magnetic field when the switch is closed. A secondary coil also is wrapped around the ring and is connected to a sensitive ammeter. No battery is present in the secondary circuit, and the secondary coil is not electrically connected to the primary coil. Any current detected in the secondary circuit must be induced by some external agent.

Initially, you might guess that no current is ever detected in the secondary circuit. Something quite amazing happens when the switch in the primary circuit is either opened or thrown closed, however. At the instant the switch is closed, the ammeter reading changes from zero in one direction and then returns to zero. At the instant the switch is opened, the ammeter changes in the opposite direction and again returns to zero. Finally, the ammeter reads zero when there is either a steady current or no current in the primary circuit. To understand what happens in this experiment, note that when the switch is closed, the current in the primary circuit produces a magnetic field that penetrates the secondary circuit. Furthermore, when the switch is closed, the magnetic field produced by the current in the primary circuit changes from zero to some value over some finite time, and this changing field induces a current in the secondary circuit.

As a result of these observations, Faraday concluded that **an electric current can be induced in a loop by a changing magnetic field.** The induced current exists only while the magnetic field through the loop is changing. Once the magnetic field reaches a steady value, the current in the loop disappears. In effect, the loop behaves as though a source of emf were connected to it for a short time. It is customary to say that **an induced emf is produced in the loop by the changing magnetic field.**

The experiments shown in Active Figures 31.1 and 31.2 have one thing in common: in each case, an emf is induced in a loop when the magnetic flux through the loop changes with time. In general, this emf is directly proportional to the

PITFALL PREVENTION 31.1

Induced emf Requires a Change

The *existence* of a magnetic flux through an area is not sufficient to create an induced emf. The magnetic flux must *change* to induce an emf.

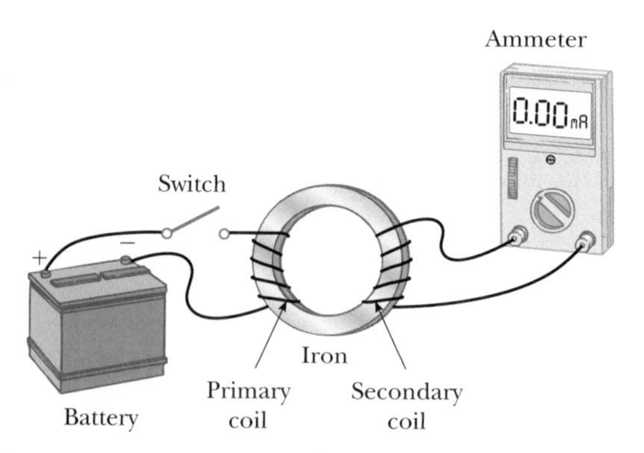

ACTIVE FIGURE 31.2

Faraday's experiment. When the switch in the primary circuit is closed, the ammeter reading in the secondary circuit changes momentarily. The emf induced in the secondary circuit is caused by the changing magnetic field through the secondary coil.

Sign in at www.thomsonedu.com and go to ThomsonNOW to open and close the switch and observe the current in the ammeter.

time rate of change of the magnetic flux through the loop. This statement can be written mathematically as **Faraday's law of induction:**

$$\mathcal{E} = -\frac{d\Phi_B}{dt} \tag{31.1}$$

◀ Faraday's law

where $\Phi_B = \oint \vec{\mathbf{B}} \cdot d\vec{\mathbf{A}}$ is the magnetic flux through the loop. (See Section 30.5.)

If a coil consists of N loops with the same area and Φ_B is the magnetic flux through one loop, an emf is induced in every loop. The loops are in series, so their emfs add; therefore, the total induced emf in the coil is given by

$$\mathcal{E} = -N\frac{d\Phi_B}{dt} \tag{31.2}$$

The negative sign in Equations 31.1 and 31.2 is of important physical significance as discussed in Section 31.3.

Suppose a loop enclosing an area A lies in a uniform magnetic field $\vec{\mathbf{B}}$ as in Figure 31.3. The magnetic flux through the loop is equal to $BA \cos \theta$; hence, the induced emf can be expressed as

$$\mathcal{E} = -\frac{d}{dt}(BA \cos \theta) \tag{31.3}$$

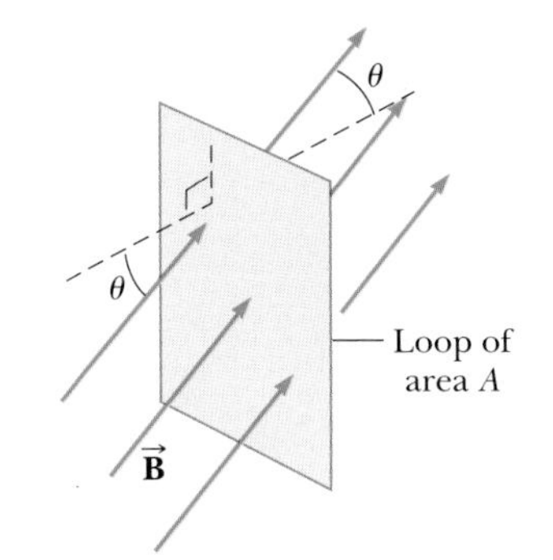

Figure 31.3 A conducting loop that encloses an area A in the presence of a uniform magnetic field $\vec{\mathbf{B}}$. The angle between $\vec{\mathbf{B}}$ and the normal to the loop is θ.

From this expression, we see that an emf can be induced in the circuit in several ways:

- The magnitude of $\vec{\mathbf{B}}$ can change with time.
- The area enclosed by the loop can change with time.
- The angle θ between $\vec{\mathbf{B}}$ and the normal to the loop can change with time.
- Any combination of the above can occur.

Quick Quiz 31.1 A circular loop of wire is held in a uniform magnetic field, with the plane of the loop perpendicular to the field lines. Which of the following will *not* cause a current to be induced in the loop? (a) crushing the loop (b) rotating the loop about an axis perpendicular to the field lines (c) keeping the orientation of the loop fixed and moving it along the field lines (d) pulling the loop out of the field

Some Applications of Faraday's Law

The ground fault interrupter (GFI) is an interesting safety device that protects users of electrical appliances against electric shock. Its operation makes use of Faraday's law. In the GFI shown in Figure 31.4, wire 1 leads from the wall outlet to the appliance to be protected and wire 2 leads from the appliance back to the wall outlet. An iron ring surrounds the two wires, and a sensing coil is wrapped around part of the ring. Because the currents in the wires are in opposite directions and of equal magnitude, there is no magnetic field surrounding the wires and the net magnetic flux through the sensing coil is zero. If the return current in wire 2 changes so that the two currents are not equal, however, circular magnetic field lines exist around the pair of wires. (This can happen if, for example, the appliance becomes wet, enabling current to leak to ground.) Therefore, the net magnetic flux through the sensing coil is no longer zero. Because household current is alternating (meaning that its direction keeps reversing), the magnetic flux through the sensing coil changes with time, inducing an emf in the coil. This induced emf is used to trigger a circuit breaker, which stops the current before it is able to reach a harmful level.

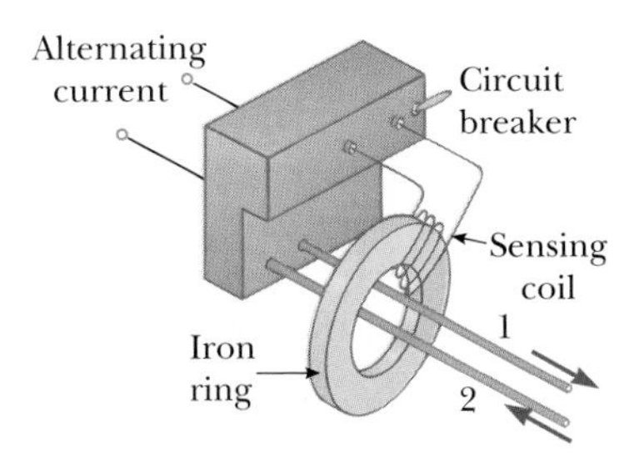

Figure 31.4 Essential components of a ground fault interrupter.

Another interesting application of Faraday's law is the production of sound in an electric guitar. The coil in this case, called the *pickup coil*, is placed near the

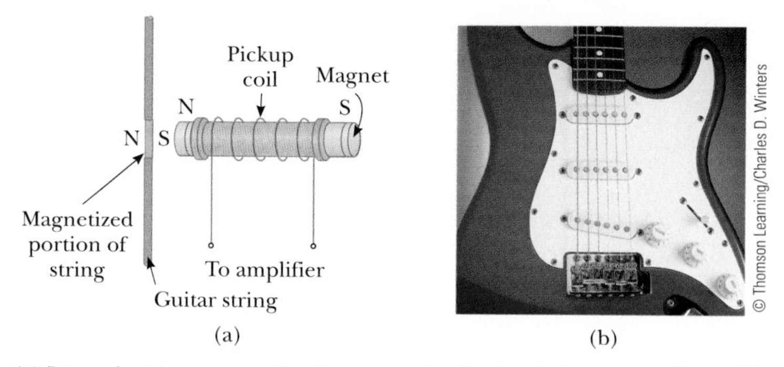

Figure 31.5 (a) In an electric guitar, a vibrating magnetized string induces an emf in a pickup coil. (b) The pickups (the circles beneath the metallic strings) of this electric guitar detect the vibrations of the strings and send this information through an amplifier and into speakers. (A switch on the guitar allows the musician to select which set of six pickups is used.)

vibrating guitar string, which is made of a metal that can be magnetized. A permanent magnet inside the coil magnetizes the portion of the string nearest the coil (Fig. 31.5a). When the string vibrates at some frequency, its magnetized segment produces a changing magnetic flux through the coil. The changing flux induces an emf in the coil that is fed to an amplifier. The output of the amplifier is sent to the loudspeakers, which produce the sound waves we hear.

EXAMPLE 31.1 Inducing an emf in a Coil

A coil consists of 200 turns of wire. Each turn is a square of side $d = 18$ cm, and a uniform magnetic field directed perpendicular to the plane of the coil is turned on. If the field changes linearly from 0 to 0.50 T in 0.80 s, what is the magnitude of the induced emf in the coil while the field is changing?

SOLUTION

Conceptualize From the description in the problem, imagine magnetic field lines passing through the coil. Because the magnetic field is changing in magnitude, an emf is induced in the coil.

Categorize We will evaluate the emf using Faraday's law from this section, so we categorize this example as a substitution problem.

Evaluate Equation 31.2 for the situation described here, noting that the magnetic field changes linearly with time:

$$|\mathcal{E}| = N\frac{\Delta\Phi_B}{\Delta t} = N\frac{\Delta(BA)}{\Delta t} = NA\frac{\Delta B}{\Delta t} = Nd^2\frac{B_f - B_i}{\Delta t}$$

Substitute numerical values:

$$|\mathcal{E}| = (200)(0.18\text{ m})^2\frac{(0.50\text{ T} - 0)}{0.80\text{ s}} = 4.0\text{ V}$$

What If? What if you were asked to find the magnitude of the induced current in the coil while the field is changing? Can you answer that question?

Answer If the ends of the coil are not connected to a circuit, the answer to this question is easy: the current is zero! (Charges move within the wire of the coil, but they cannot move into or out of the ends of the coil.) For a steady current to exist, the ends of the coil must be connected to an external circuit. Let's assume the coil is connected to a circuit and the total resistance of the coil and the circuit is 2.0 Ω. Then, the current in the coil is

$$I = \frac{\mathcal{E}}{R} = \frac{4.0\text{ V}}{2.0\ \Omega} = 2.0\text{ A}$$

EXAMPLE 31.2 **An Exponentially Decaying B Field**

A loop of wire enclosing an area A is placed in a region where the magnetic field is perpendicular to the plane of the loop. The magnitude of $\vec{\mathbf{B}}$ varies in time according to the expression $B = B_{max}e^{-at}$, where a is some constant. That is, at $t = 0$, the field is B_{max}, and for $t > 0$, the field decreases exponentially (Fig. 31.6). Find the induced emf in the loop as a function of time.

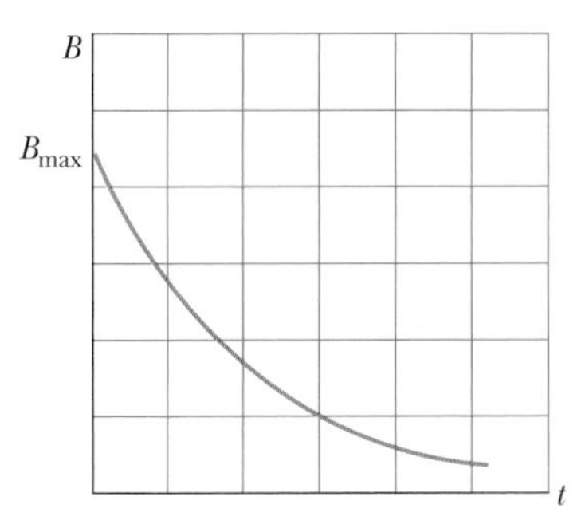

Figure 31.6 (Example 31.2) Exponential decrease in the magnitude of the magnetic field with time. The induced emf and induced current vary with time in the same way.

SOLUTION

Conceptualize The physical situation is similar to that in Example 31.1 except for two things: there is only one loop, and the field varies exponentially with time rather than linearly.

Categorize We will evaluate the emf using Faraday's law from this section, so we categorize this example as a substitution problem.

Evaluate Equation 31.1 for the situation described here:

$$\mathcal{E} = -\frac{d\Phi_B}{dt} = -\frac{d}{dt}(AB_{max}e^{-at}) = -AB_{max}\frac{d}{dt}e^{-at} = aAB_{max}e^{-at}$$

This expression indicates that the induced emf decays exponentially in time. The maximum emf occurs at $t = 0$, where $\mathcal{E}_{max} = aAB_{max}$. The plot of $\mathcal{E}$ versus t is similar to the B-versus-t curve shown in Figure 31.6.

31.2 Motional emf

In Examples 31.1 and 31.2, we considered cases in which an emf is induced in a stationary circuit placed in a magnetic field when the field changes with time. In this section, we describe **motional emf,** the emf induced in a conductor moving through a constant magnetic field.

The straight conductor of length ℓ shown in Figure 31.7 is moving through a uniform magnetic field directed into the page. For simplicity, let's assume the conductor is moving in a direction perpendicular to the field with constant velocity under the influence of some external agent. The electrons in the conductor experience a force $\vec{\mathbf{F}}_B = q\vec{\mathbf{v}} \times \vec{\mathbf{B}}$ that is directed along the length ℓ, perpendicular to both $\vec{\mathbf{v}}$ and $\vec{\mathbf{B}}$ (Eq. 29.1). Under the influence of this force, the electrons move to the lower end of the conductor and accumulate there, leaving a net positive charge at the upper end. As a result of this charge separation, an electric field $\vec{\mathbf{E}}$ is produced inside the conductor. The charges accumulate at both ends until the downward magnetic force qvB on charges remaining in the conductor is balanced by the upward electric force qE. The condition for equilibrium requires that the forces on the electrons balance:

$$qE = qvB \quad \text{or} \quad E = vB$$

The electric field produced in the conductor is related to the potential difference across the ends of the conductor according to the relationship $\Delta V = E\ell$ (Eq. 25.6). Therefore, for the equilibrium condition,

$$\Delta V = E\ell = B\ell v \tag{31.4}$$

where the upper end of the conductor in Figure 31.7 is at a higher electric potential than the lower end. Therefore, **a potential difference is maintained between the ends of the conductor as long as the conductor continues to move through the uniform magnetic field.** If the direction of the motion is reversed, the polarity of the potential difference is also reversed.

A more interesting situation occurs when the moving conductor is part of a closed conducting path. This situation is particularly useful for illustrating how a

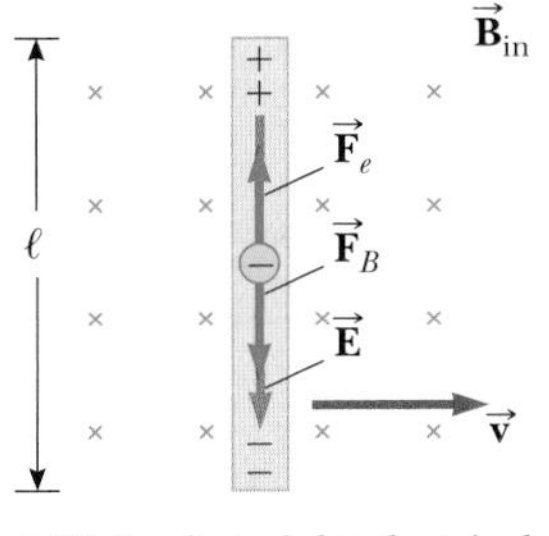

Figure 31.7 A straight electrical conductor of length ℓ moving with a velocity $\vec{\mathbf{v}}$ through a uniform magnetic field $\vec{\mathbf{B}}$ directed perpendicular to $\vec{\mathbf{v}}$. Due to the magnetic force on electrons, the ends of the conductor become oppositely charged, which establishes an electric field in the conductor. In steady state, the electric and magnetic forces on an electron in the wire are balanced.

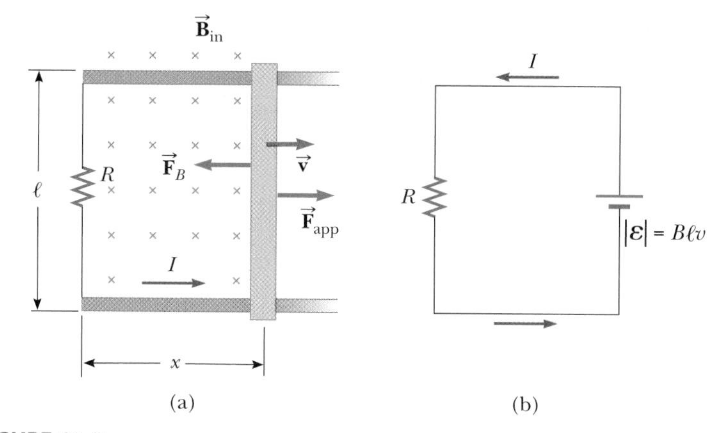

ACTIVE FIGURE 31.8

(a) A conducting bar sliding with a velocity $\vec{v}$ along two conducting rails under the action of an applied force $\vec{F}_{app}$. The magnetic force $\vec{F}_B$ opposes the motion, and a counterclockwise current I is induced in the loop. (b) The equivalent circuit diagram for the setup shown in (a).

Sign in at www.thomsonedu.com and go to ThomsonNOW to adjust the applied force, the magnetic field, and the resistance to see the effects on the motion of the bar.

changing magnetic flux causes an induced current in a closed circuit. Consider a circuit consisting of a conducting bar of length ℓ sliding along two fixed parallel conducting rails as shown in Active Figure 31.8a. For simplicity, let's assume the bar has zero resistance and the stationary part of the circuit has a resistance R. A uniform and constant magnetic field $\vec{B}$ is applied perpendicular to the plane of the circuit. As the bar is pulled to the right with a velocity $\vec{v}$ under the influence of an applied force $\vec{F}_{app}$, free charges in the bar experience a magnetic force directed along the length of the bar. This force sets up an induced current because the charges are free to move in the closed conducting path. In this case, the rate of change of magnetic flux through the circuit and the corresponding induced motional emf across the moving bar are proportional to the change in area of the circuit.

Because the area enclosed by the circuit at any instant is ℓx, where x is the position of the bar, the magnetic flux through that area is

$$\Phi_B = B\ell x$$

Using Faraday's law and noting that x changes with time at a rate $dx/dt = v$, we find that the induced motional emf is

$$\mathcal{E} = -\frac{d\Phi_B}{dt} = -\frac{d}{dt}(B\ell x) = -B\ell\frac{dx}{dt}$$

Motional emf ▶

$$\mathcal{E} = -B\ell v \tag{31.5}$$

Because the resistance of the circuit is R, the magnitude of the induced current is

$$I = \frac{|\mathcal{E}|}{R} = \frac{B\ell v}{R} \tag{31.6}$$

The equivalent circuit diagram for this example is shown in Active Figure 31.8b.

Let's examine the system using energy considerations. Because no battery is in the circuit, you might wonder about the origin of the induced current and the energy delivered to the resistor. We can understand the source of this current and energy by noting that the applied force does work on the conducting bar. Therefore, we model the circuit as a nonisolated system. The movement of the bar through the field causes charges to move along the bar with some average drift velocity; hence, a current is established. The change in energy in the system during some time interval must be equal to the transfer of energy into the system by work, consistent with the general principle of conservation of energy described by Equation 8.2.

Let's verify this mathematically. As the bar moves through the uniform magnetic field $\vec{\mathbf{B}}$, it experiences a magnetic force $\vec{\mathbf{F}}_B$ of magnitude $I\ell B$ (see Section 29.4). Because the bar moves with constant velocity, it is modeled as a particle in equilibrium and the magnetic force must be equal in magnitude and opposite in direction to the applied force, or to the left in Active Figure 31.8a. (If $\vec{\mathbf{F}}_B$ acted in the direction of motion, it would cause the bar to accelerate, violating the principle of conservation of energy.) Using Equation 31.6 and $F_{\text{app}} = F_B = I\ell B$, the power delivered by the applied force is

$$\mathcal{P} = F_{\text{app}}v = (I\ell B)v = \frac{B^2\ell^2v^2}{R} = \frac{\mathcal{E}^2}{R} \qquad \textbf{(31.7)}$$

From Equation 27.21, we see that this power input is equal to the rate at which energy is delivered to the resistor.

Quick Quiz 31.2 In Active Figure 31.8a, a given applied force of magnitude F_{app} results in a constant speed v and a power input $\mathcal{P}$. Imagine that the force is increased so that the constant speed of the bar is doubled to $2v$. Under these conditions, what are the new force and the new power input? (a) $2F$ and $2\mathcal{P}$ (b) $4F$ and $2\mathcal{P}$ (c) $2F$ and $4\mathcal{P}$ (d) $4F$ and $4\mathcal{P}$

EXAMPLE 31.3 Magnetic Force Acting on a Sliding Bar

The conducting bar illustrated in Figure 31.9 moves on two frictionless, parallel rails in the presence of a uniform magnetic field directed into the page. The bar has mass m, and its length is ℓ. The bar is given an initial velocity $\vec{\mathbf{v}}_i$ to the right and is released at $t = 0$.

(A) Using Newton's laws, find the velocity of the bar as a function of time.

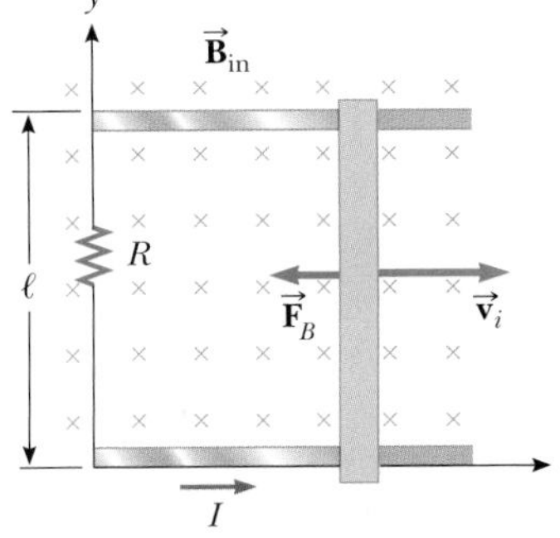

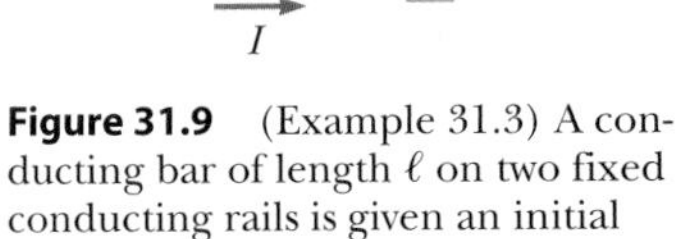

Figure 31.9 (Example 31.3) A conducting bar of length ℓ on two fixed conducting rails is given an initial velocity $\vec{\mathbf{v}}_i$ to the right.

SOLUTION

Conceptualize As the bar slides to the right in Figure 31.9, a counterclockwise current is established in the circuit consisting of the bar, the rails, and the resistor. The upward current in the bar results in a magnetic force to the left on the bar as shown in the figure. Therefore, the bar must slow down, so our mathematical solution should demonstrate that.

Categorize The text already categorizes this problem as one that uses Newton's laws. We model the bar as a particle under a net force.

Analyze From Equation 29.10, the magnetic force is $F_B = -I\ell B$, where the negative sign indicates that the force is to the left. The magnetic force is the *only* horizontal force acting on the bar.

Apply Newton's second law to the bar in the horizontal direction:

$$F_x = ma = m\frac{dv}{dt} = -I\ell B$$

Substitute $I = B\ell v/R$ from Equation 31.6:

$$m\frac{dv}{dt} = -\frac{B^2\ell^2}{R}v$$

Rearrange the equation so that all occurrences of the variable v are on the left and those of t are on the right:

$$\frac{dv}{v} = -\left(\frac{B^2\ell^2}{mR}\right)dt$$

Integrate this equation using the initial condition that $v = v_i$ at $t = 0$ and noting that $(B^2\ell^2/mR)$ is a constant:

$$\int_{v_i}^{v}\frac{dv}{v} = -\frac{B^2\ell^2}{mR}\int_0^t dt$$

$$\ln\left(\frac{v}{v_i}\right) = -\left(\frac{B^2\ell^2}{mR}\right)t$$

Define the constant $\tau = mR/B^2\ell^2$ and solve for the velocity:

$$(1) \quad v = v_i e^{-t/\tau}$$

Finalize This expression for v indicates that the velocity of the bar decreases with time under the action of the magnetic force as expected from our conceptualization of the problem.

(B) Show that the same result is found by using an energy approach.

SOLUTION

Categorize The text of this part of the problem tells us to use an energy approach for the same situation. We model the entire circuit in Figure 31.9 as an isolated system.

Finalize Consider the sliding bar as one system component possessing kinetic energy, which decreases because energy is transferring *out* of the bar by electrical transmission through the rails. The resistor is another system component possessing internal energy, which rises because energy is transferring *into* the resistor. Because energy is not leaving the system, the rate of energy transfer out of the bar equals the rate of energy transfer into the resistor.

Equate the power entering the resistor to that leaving the bar:

$$\mathcal{P}_{\text{resistor}} = -\mathcal{P}_{\text{bar}}$$

Substitute for the electrical power delivered to the resistor and the time rate of change of kinetic energy for the bar:

$$I^2R = -\frac{d}{dt}\left(\tfrac{1}{2}mv^2\right)$$

Use Equation 31.6 for the current and carry out the derivative:

$$\frac{B^2\ell^2v^2}{R} = -mv\frac{dv}{dt}$$

Rearrange terms:

$$\frac{dv}{v} = -\left(\frac{B^2\ell^2}{mR}\right)dt$$

Finalize This result is the same expression found in part (A).

What If? Suppose you wished to increase the distance through which the bar moves between the time it is initially projected and the time it essentially comes to rest. You can do so by changing one of three variables: v_i, R, or B by a factor of 2 or $\frac{1}{2}$. Which variable should you change to maximize the distance, and would you double it or halve it?

Answer Increasing v_i would make the bar move farther. Increasing R would decrease the current and therefore the magnetic force, making the bar move farther. Decreasing B would decrease the magnetic force and make the bar move farther. Which method is most effective, though?

Use Equation (1) to find the distance the bar moves by integration:

$$v = \frac{dx}{dt} = v_i e^{-t/\tau}$$

$$x = \int_0^\infty v_i e^{-t/\tau}\,dt = -v_i\tau e^{-t/\tau}\Big|_0^\infty$$

$$= -v_i\tau(0-1) = v_i\tau = v_i\left(\frac{mR}{B^2\ell^2}\right)$$

This expression shows that doubling v_i or R will double the distance. Changing B by a factor of $\frac{1}{2}$, however, causes the distance to be four times as great!

EXAMPLE 31.4 Motional emf Induced in a Rotating Bar

A conducting bar of length ℓ rotates with a constant angular speed ω about a pivot at one end. A uniform magnetic field $\vec{\mathbf{B}}$ is directed perpendicular to the plane of rotation as shown in Figure 31.10. Find the motional emf induced between the ends of the bar.

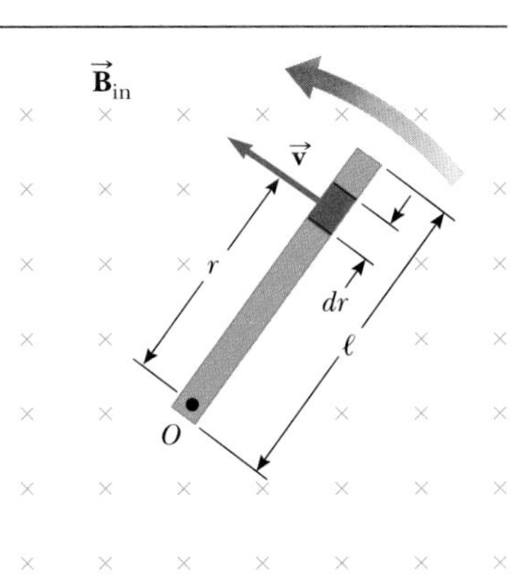

Figure 31.10 (Example 31.4) A conducting bar rotating around a pivot at one end in a uniform magnetic field that is perpendicular to the plane of rotation. A motional emf is induced across the ends of the bar.

SOLUTION

Conceptualize The rotating bar is different in nature than the sliding bar in Active Figure 31.8. Consider a small segment of the bar, however. It is a short length of conductor moving in a magnetic field and has an emf generated in it. By thinking of each small segment as a source of emf, we see that all segments are in series and the emfs add.

Categorize Based on the conceptualization of the problem, we approach this example as we did Example 31.3, with the added feature that the short segments of the bar are traveling in circular paths.

Analyze Evaluate the magnitude of the emf induced in a segment of the bar of length dr having a velocity $\vec{\mathbf{v}}$ from Equation 31.5:

$$d\mathcal{E} = Bv\,dr$$

Find the total emf between the ends of the bar by adding the emfs induced across all segments:

$$\mathcal{E} = \int Bv\,dr$$

The tangential speed v of an element is related to the angular speed ω through the relationship $v = r\omega$ (Eq. 10.10); use that fact and integrate:

$$\mathcal{E} = B\int v\,dr = B\omega\int_0^{\ell} r\,dr = \frac{1}{2}B\omega\ell^2$$

Finalize In Equation 31.5 for a sliding bar, we can increase $\mathcal{E}$ by increasing B, ℓ, or v. Increasing any one of these variables by a given factor increases $\mathcal{E}$ by the same factor. Therefore, you would choose whichever of these three variables is most convenient to increase. For the rotating rod, however, there is an advantage to increasing the length of the rod to raise the emf because ℓ is squared. Doubling the length gives four times the emf, whereas doubling the angular speed only doubles the emf.

What If? Suppose, after reading through this example, you come up with a brilliant idea. A Ferris wheel has radial metallic spokes between the hub and the circular rim. These spokes move in the magnetic field of the Earth, so each spoke acts like the bar in Figure 31.10. You plan to use the emf generated by the rotation of the Ferris wheel to power the lightbulbs on the wheel. Will this idea work?

Answer Let's estimate the emf that is generated in this situation. We know the magnitude of the magnetic field of the Earth from Table 29.1: $B = 0.5 \times 10^{-4}$ T. A typical spoke on a Ferris wheel might have a length on the order of 10 m. Suppose the period of rotation is on the order of 10 s.

Determine the angular speed of the spoke:

$$\omega = \frac{2\pi}{T} = \frac{2\pi}{10\text{ s}} = 0.63\text{ s}^{-1} \sim 1\text{ s}^{-1}$$

Assume the magnetic field lines of the Earth are horizontal at the location of the Ferris wheel and perpendicular to the spokes. Find the emf generated:

$$\mathcal{E} = \frac{1}{2}B\omega\ell^2 = \frac{1}{2}(0.5 \times 10^{-4}\text{ T})(1\text{ s}^{-1})(10\text{ m})^2$$
$$= 2.5 \times 10^{-3}\text{ V} \sim 1\text{ mV}$$

This value is a tiny emf, far smaller than that required to operate lightbulbs.

An additional difficulty is related to energy. Even assuming you could find lightbulbs that operate using a potential difference on the order of millivolts, a spoke must be part of a circuit to provide a voltage to the lightbulbs. Consequently, the spoke must carry a current. Because this current-carrying spoke is in a magnetic field, a magnetic force is exerted on the spoke in the direction opposite its direction of motion. As a result, the motor of the Ferris wheel must supply more energy to perform work against this magnetic drag force. The motor must ultimately provide the energy that is operating the lightbulbs, and you have not gained anything for free!

31.3 Lenz's Law

Faraday's law (Eq. 31.1) indicates that the induced emf and the change in flux have opposite algebraic signs. This feature has a very real physical interpretation that has come to be known as **Lenz's law:**[1]

Lenz's law ▶

> The induced current in a loop is in the direction that creates a magnetic field that opposes the change in magnetic flux through the area enclosed by the loop.

That is, the induced current tends to keep the original magnetic flux through the loop from changing. We shall show that this law is a consequence of the law of conservation of energy.

To understand Lenz's law, let's return to the example of a bar moving to the right on two parallel rails in the presence of a uniform magnetic field (the *external* magnetic field; Fig. 31.11a.) As the bar moves to the right, the magnetic flux through the area enclosed by the circuit increases with time because the area increases. Lenz's law states that the induced current must be directed so that the magnetic field it produces opposes the change in the external magnetic flux. Because the magnetic flux due to an external field directed into the page is increasing, the induced current—if it is to oppose this change—must produce a field directed out of the page. Hence, the induced current must be directed counterclockwise when the bar moves to the right. (Use the right-hand rule to verify this direction.) If the bar is moving to the left as in Figure 31.11b, the external magnetic flux through the area enclosed by the loop decreases with time. Because the field is directed into the page, the direction of the induced current must be clockwise if it is to produce a field that also is directed into the page. In either case, the induced current attempts to maintain the original flux through the area enclosed by the current loop.

Let's examine this situation using energy considerations. Suppose the bar is given a slight push to the right. In the preceding analysis, we found that this motion sets up a counterclockwise current in the loop. What happens if we assume the current is clockwise such that the direction of the magnetic force exerted on the bar is to the right? This force would accelerate the rod and increase its velocity, which in turn would cause the area enclosed by the loop to increase more rapidly. The result would be an increase in the induced current, which would cause an increase in the force, which would produce an increase in the current, and so on. In effect, the system would acquire energy with no input of energy. This behavior is clearly inconsistent with all experience and violates the law of conservation of energy. Therefore, the current must be counterclockwise.

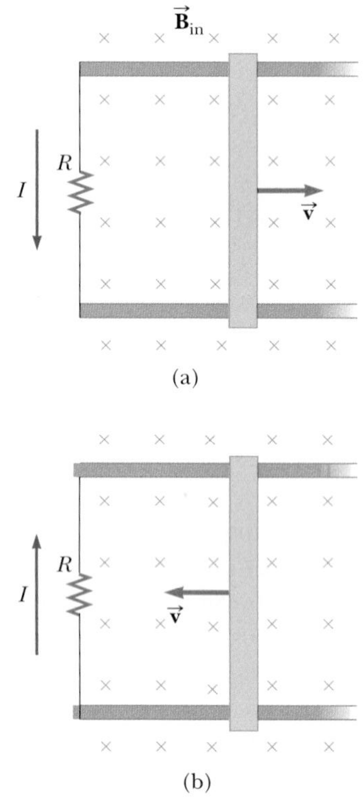

Figure 31.11 (a) As the conducting bar slides on the two fixed conducting rails, the magnetic flux due to the external magnetic field into the page through the area enclosed by the loop increases in time. By Lenz's law, the induced current must be counterclockwise to produce a counteracting magnetic field directed out of the page. (b) When the bar moves to the left, the induced current must be clockwise. Why?

Quick Quiz 31.3 Figure 31.12 shows a circular loop of wire falling toward a wire carrying a current to the left. What is the direction of the induced current in the loop of wire? (a) clockwise (b) counterclockwise (c) zero (d) impossible to determine

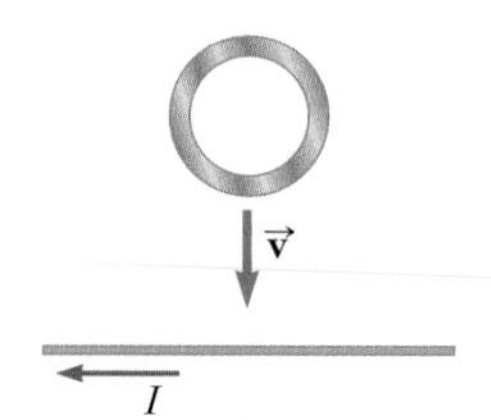

Figure 31.12 (Quick Quiz 31.3)

[1] Developed by German physicist Heinrich Lenz (1804–1865).

CONCEPTUAL EXAMPLE 31.5 Application of Lenz's Law

A magnet is placed near a metal loop as shown in Figure 31.13a.

(A) Find the direction of the induced current in the loop when the magnet is pushed toward the loop.

SOLUTION

As the magnet moves to the right toward the loop, the external magnetic flux through the loop increases with time. To counteract this increase in flux due to a field toward the right, the induced current produces its own magnetic field to the left as illustrated in Figure 31.13b; hence, the induced current is in the direction shown. Knowing that like magnetic poles repel each other, we conclude that the left face of the current loop acts like a north pole and the right face acts like a south pole.

(B) Find the direction of the induced current in the loop when the magnet is pulled away from the loop.

SOLUTION

If the magnet moves to the left as in Figure 31.13c, its flux through the area enclosed by the loop decreases in time. Now the induced current in the loop is in the direction shown in Figure 31.13d because this current direction produces a magnetic field in the same direction as the external field. In this case, the left face of the loop is a south pole and the right face is a north pole.

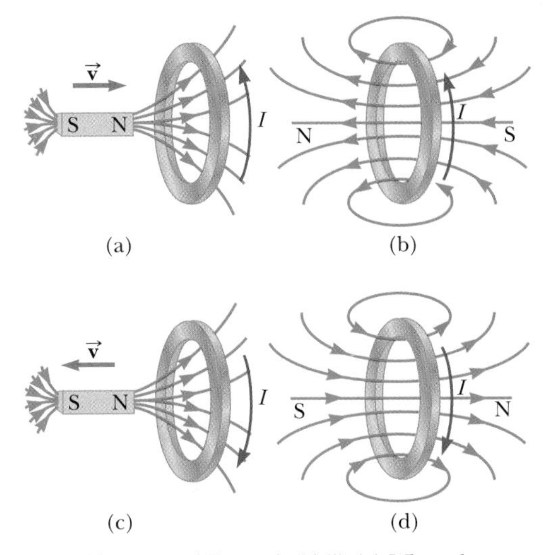

Figure 31.13 (Conceptual Example 31.5) (a) When the magnet is moved toward the stationary conducting loop, a current is induced in the direction shown. The magnetic field lines shown are those due to the bar magnet. (b) This induced current produces its own magnetic field directed to the left that counteracts the increasing external flux. The magnetic field lines shown are those due to the induced current in the ring. (c) When the magnet is moved away from the stationary conducting loop, a current is induced in the direction shown. The magnetic field lines shown are those due to the bar magnet. (d) This induced current produces a magnetic field directed to the right and so counteracts the decreasing external flux. The magnetic field lines shown are those due to the induced current in the ring.

CONCEPTUAL EXAMPLE 31.6 A Loop Moving Through a Magnetic Field

A rectangular metallic loop of dimensions ℓ and w and resistance R moves with constant speed v to the right, as in Figure 31.14a. The loop passes through a uniform magnetic field $\vec{\mathbf{B}}$ directed into the page and extending a distance $3w$ along the x axis. Define x as the position of the right side of the loop along the x axis.

(A) Plot as a function of x the magnetic flux through the area enclosed by the loop.

SOLUTION

Figure 31.14b shows the flux through the area enclosed by the loop as a function of x. Before the loop enters the field, the flux through the loop is zero. As the loop enters the field, the flux increases linearly with position until the left edge of the loop is just inside the field. Finally, the flux through the loop decreases linearly to zero as the loop leaves the field.

(B) Plot as a function of x the induced motional emf in the loop.

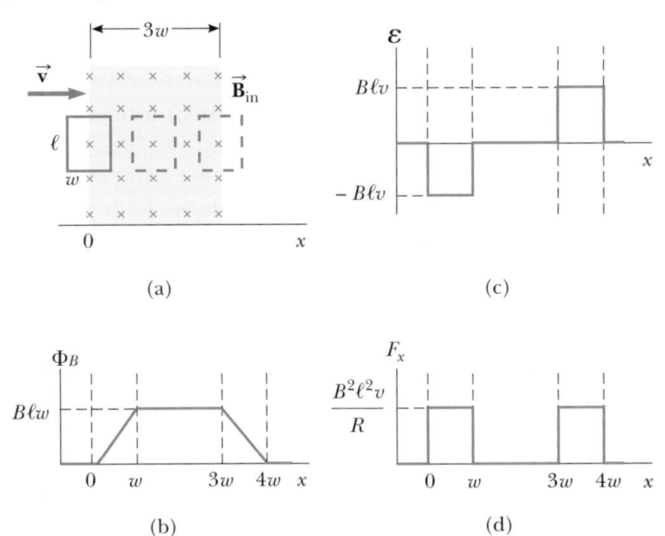

Figure 31.14 (Conceptual Example 31.6) (a) A conducting rectangular loop of width w and length ℓ moving with a velocity $\vec{v}$ through a uniform magnetic field extending a distance $3w$. (b) Magnetic flux through the area enclosed by the loop as a function of loop position. (c) Induced emf as a function of loop position. (d) Applied force required for constant velocity as a function of loop position.

SOLUTION

Before the loop enters the field, no motional emf is induced in it because no field is present (Fig. 31.14c). As the right side of the loop enters the field, the magnetic flux directed into the page increases. Hence, according to Lenz's law, the induced current is counterclockwise because it must produce its own magnetic field directed out of the page. The motional emf $-B\ell v$ (from Eq. 31.5) arises from the magnetic force experienced by charges in the right side of the loop. When the loop is entirely in the field, the change in magnetic flux through the loop is zero; hence, the motional emf vanishes. That happens because once the left side of the loop enters the field, the motional emf induced in it cancels the motional emf present in the right side of the loop. As the right side of the loop leaves the field, the flux through the loop begins to decrease, a clockwise current is induced, and the induced emf is $B\ell v$. As soon as the left side leaves the field, the emf decreases to zero.

(C) Plot as a function of x the external applied force necessary to counter the magnetic force and keep v constant.

SOLUTION

The external force that must be applied to the loop to maintain this motion is plotted in Figure 31.14d. Before the loop enters the field, no magnetic force acts on it; hence, the applied force must be zero if v is constant. When the right side of the loop enters the field, the applied force necessary to maintain constant speed must be equal in magnitude and opposite in direction to the magnetic force exerted on that side. When the loop is entirely in the field, the flux through the loop is not changing with time. Hence, the net emf induced in the loop is zero and the current also is zero. Therefore, no external force is needed to maintain the motion. Finally, as the right side leaves the field, the applied force must be equal in magnitude and opposite in direction to the magnetic force acting on the left side of the loop.

From this analysis, we conclude that power is supplied only when the loop is either entering or leaving the field. Furthermore, this example shows that the motional emf induced in the loop can be zero even when there is motion through the field! A motional emf is induced *only* when the magnetic flux through the loop *changes in time.*

31.4 Induced emf and Electric Fields

We have seen that a changing magnetic flux induces an emf and a current in a conducting loop. In our study of electricity, we related a current to an electric field that applies electric forces on charged particles. In the same way, we can relate an induced current in a conducting loop to an electric field by claiming that **an electric field is created in the conductor as a result of the changing magnetic flux.**

We also noted in our study of electricity that the existence of an electric field is independent of the presence of any test charges. This independence suggests that even in the absence of a conducting loop, a changing magnetic field generates an electric field in empty space.

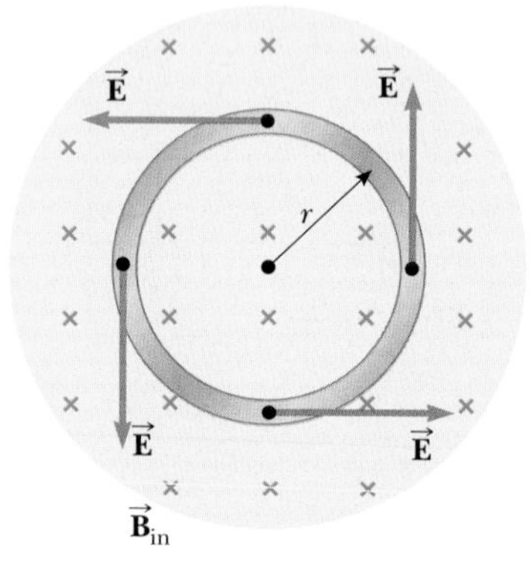

Figure 31.15 A conducting loop of radius r in a uniform magnetic field perpendicular to the plane of the loop. If $\vec{\mathbf{B}}$ changes in time, an electric field is induced in a direction tangent to the circumference of the loop.

PITFALL PREVENTION 31.2
Induced Electric Fields

The changing magnetic field does *not* need to exist at the location of the induced electric field. In Figure 31.15, even a loop outside the region of magnetic field experiences an induced electric field.

This induced electric field is *nonconservative,* unlike the electrostatic field produced by stationary charges. To illustrate this point, consider a conducting loop of radius r situated in a uniform magnetic field that is perpendicular to the plane of the loop as in Figure 31.15. If the magnetic field changes with time, an emf $\mathcal{E} = -d\Phi_B/dt$ is, according to Faraday's law (Eq. 31.1), induced in the loop. The induction of a current in the loop implies the presence of an induced electric field $\vec{\mathbf{E}}$, which must be tangent to the loop because that is the direction in which the charges in the wire move in response to the electric force. The work done by the electric field in moving a test charge q once around the loop is equal to $q\mathcal{E}$. Because the electric force acting on the charge is $q\vec{\mathbf{E}}$, the work done by the electric field in moving the charge once around the loop is $qE(2\pi r)$, where $2\pi r$ is the circumference of the loop. These two expressions for the work done must be equal; therefore,

$$q\mathcal{E} = qE(2\pi r)$$

$$E = \frac{\mathcal{E}}{2\pi r}$$

Using this result along with Equation 31.1 and that $\Phi_B = BA = B\pi r^2$ for a circular loop, the induced electric field can be expressed as

$$E = -\frac{1}{2\pi r}\frac{d\Phi_B}{dt} = -\frac{r}{2}\frac{dB}{dt} \tag{31.8}$$

If the time variation of the magnetic field is specified, the induced electric field can be calculated from Equation 31.8.

The emf for any closed path can be expressed as the line integral of $\vec{\mathbf{E}} \cdot d\vec{\mathbf{s}}$ over that path: $\mathcal{E} = \oint \vec{\mathbf{E}} \cdot d\vec{\mathbf{s}}$. In more general cases, E may not be constant and the path may not be a circle. Hence, Faraday's law of induction, $\mathcal{E} = -d\Phi_B/dt$, can be written in the general form

$$\oint \vec{\mathbf{E}} \cdot d\vec{\mathbf{s}} = -\frac{d\Phi_B}{dt} \quad (31.9)$$

◀ Faraday's law in general form

The induced electric field $\vec{\mathbf{E}}$ in Equation 31.9 is a nonconservative field that is generated by a changing magnetic field. The field $\vec{\mathbf{E}}$ that satisfies Equation 31.9 cannot possibly be an electrostatic field because were the field electrostatic and hence conservative, the line integral of $\vec{\mathbf{E}} \cdot d\vec{\mathbf{s}}$ over a closed loop would be zero (Section 25.1), which would be in contradiction to Equation 31.9.

EXAMPLE 31.7 Electric Field Induced by a Changing Magnetic Field in a Solenoid

A long solenoid of radius R has n turns of wire per unit length and carries a time-varying current that varies sinusoidally as $I = I_{max} \cos \omega t$, where I_{max} is the maximum current and ω is the angular frequency of the alternating current source (Fig. 31.16).

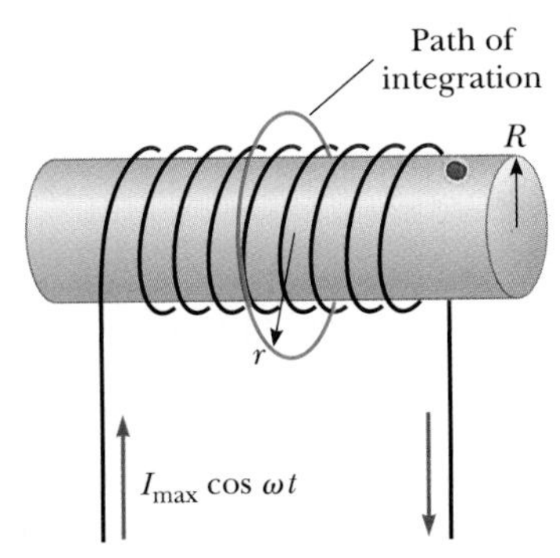

Figure 31.16 (Example 31.7) A long solenoid carrying a time-varying current given by $I = I_{max} \cos \omega t$. An electric field is induced both inside and outside the solenoid.

(A) Determine the magnitude of the induced electric field outside the solenoid at a distance $r > R$ from its long central axis.

SOLUTION

Conceptualize Figure 31.16 shows the physical situation. As the current in the coil changes, imagine a changing magnetic field at all points in space as well as an induced electric field.

Categorize Because the current varies in time, the magnetic field is changing, leading to an induced electric field as opposed to the electrostatic electric fields due to stationary electric charges.

Analyze First consider an external point and take the path for the line integral to be a circle of radius r centered on the solenoid as illustrated in Figure 31.16.

Evaluate the right side of Equation 31.9, noting that $\vec{\mathbf{B}}$ is perpendicular to the circle bounded by the path of integration and that this magnetic field exists only inside the solenoid:

$$(1) \quad -\frac{d\Phi_B}{dt} = -\frac{d}{dt}(B\pi R^2) = -\pi R^2 \frac{dB}{dt}$$

Evaluate the magnetic field in the solenoid from Equation 30.17:

$$(2) \quad B = \mu_0 n I = \mu_0 n I_{max} \cos \omega t$$

Substitute Equation (2) into Equation (1):

$$(3) \quad -\frac{d\Phi_B}{dt} = -\pi R^2 \mu_0 n I_{max} \frac{d}{dt}(\cos \omega t) = \pi R^2 \mu_0 n I_{max} \omega \sin \omega t$$

Evaluate the left side of Equation 31.9, noting that the magnitude of $\vec{\mathbf{E}}$ is constant on the path of integration and $\vec{\mathbf{E}}$ is tangent to it:

$$(4) \quad \oint \vec{\mathbf{E}} \cdot d\vec{\mathbf{s}} = E(2\pi r)$$

Substitute Equations (3) and (4) into Equation 31.9:

$$E(2\pi r) = \pi R^2 \mu_0 n I_{max} \omega \sin \omega t$$

Solve for the magnitude of the electric field: $$E = \frac{\mu_0 n I_{max} \omega R^2}{2r} \sin \omega t \quad (\text{for } r > R)$$

Finalize This result shows that the amplitude of the electric field outside the solenoid falls off as $1/r$ and varies sinusoidally with time. As we will learn in Chapter 34, the time-varying electric field creates an additional contribution to the magnetic field. The magnetic field can be somewhat stronger than we first stated, both inside and outside the solenoid. The correction to the magnetic field is small if the angular frequency ω is small. At high frequencies, however, a new phenomenon can dominate: The electric and magnetic fields, each re-creating the other, constitute an electromagnetic wave radiated by the solenoid as we will study in Chapter 34.

(B) What is the magnitude of the induced electric field inside the solenoid, a distance r from its axis?

SOLUTION

Analyze For an interior point ($r < R$), the magnetic flux through an integration loop is given by $\Phi_B = B\pi r^2$.

Evaluate the right side of Equation 31.9: $$(5) \quad -\frac{d\Phi_B}{dt} = -\frac{d}{dt}(B\pi r^2) = -\pi r^2 \frac{dB}{dt}$$

Substitute Equation (2) into Equation (5): $$(6) \quad -\frac{d\Phi_B}{dt} = -\pi r^2 \mu_0 n I_{max} \frac{d}{dt}(\cos \omega t) = \pi r^2 \mu_0 n I_{max} \omega \sin \omega t$$

Substitute Equations (4) and (6) into Equation 31.9: $$E(2\pi r) = \pi r^2 \mu_0 n I_{max} \omega \sin \omega t$$

Solve for the magnitude of the electric field: $$E = \frac{\mu_0 n I_{max} \omega}{2} r \sin \omega t \quad (\text{for } r < R)$$

Finalize This result shows that the amplitude of the electric field induced inside the solenoid by the changing magnetic flux through the solenoid increases linearly with r and varies sinusoidally with time.

31.5 Generators and Motors

Electric generators take in energy by work and transfer it out by electrical transmission. To understand how they operate, let us consider the **alternating-current (AC) generator.** In its simplest form, it consists of a loop of wire rotated by some external means in a magnetic field (Active Fig. 31.17a).

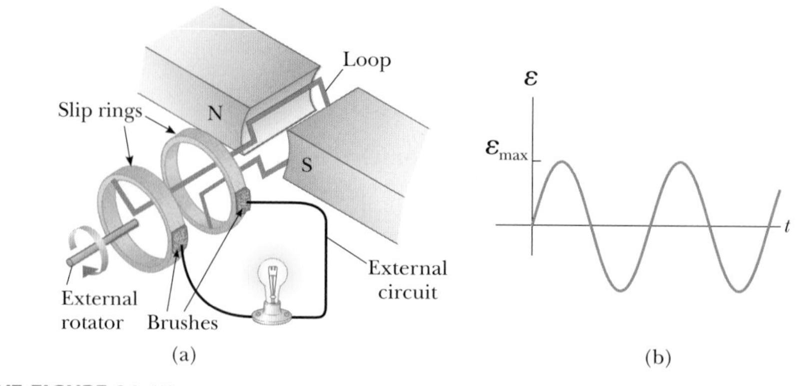

ACTIVE FIGURE 31.17

(a) Schematic diagram of an AC generator. An emf is induced in a loop that rotates in a magnetic field. (b) The alternating emf induced in the loop plotted as a function of time.

Sign in at www.thomsonedu.com and go to ThomsonNOW to adjust the speed of rotation and the strength of the field to see the effects on the emf generated.

In commercial power plants, the energy required to rotate the loop can be derived from a variety of sources. For example, in a hydroelectric plant, falling water directed against the blades of a turbine produces the rotary motion; in a coal-fired plant, the energy released by burning coal is used to convert water to steam, and this steam is directed against the turbine blades.

As a loop rotates in a magnetic field, the magnetic flux through the area enclosed by the loop changes with time, and this change induces an emf and a current in the loop according to Faraday's law. The ends of the loop are connected to slip rings that rotate with the loop. Connections from these slip rings, which act as output terminals of the generator, to the external circuit are made by stationary metallic brushes in contact with the slip rings.

Instead of a single turn, suppose a coil with N turns (a more practical situation), with the same area A, rotates in a magnetic field with a constant angular speed ω. If θ is the angle between the magnetic field and the normal to the plane of the coil as in Figure 31.18, the magnetic flux through the coil at any time t is

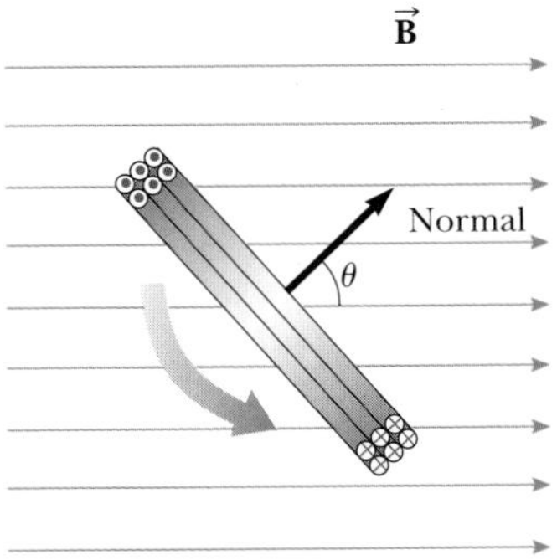

$$\Phi_B = BA\cos\theta = BA\cos\omega t$$

where we have used the relationship $\theta = \omega t$ between angular position and angular speed (see Eq. 10.3). (We have set the clock so that $t = 0$ when $\theta = 0$.) Hence, the induced emf in the coil is

$$\mathcal{E} = -N\frac{d\Phi_B}{dt} = -NAB\frac{d}{dt}(\cos\omega t) = NAB\omega\sin\omega t \qquad (31.10)$$

This result shows that the emf varies sinusoidally with time as plotted in Active Figure 31.17b. Equation 31.10 shows that the maximum emf has the value

$$\mathcal{E}_{max} = NAB\omega \qquad (31.11)$$

which occurs when $\omega t = 90°$ or $270°$. In other words, $\mathcal{E} = \mathcal{E}_{max}$ when the magnetic field is in the plane of the coil and the time rate of change of flux is a maximum. Furthermore, the emf is zero when $\omega t = 0$ or $180°$, that is, when $\vec{\mathbf{B}}$ is perpendicular to the plane of the coil and the time rate of change of flux is zero.

The frequency for commercial generators in the United States and Canada is 60 Hz, whereas in some European countries it is 50 Hz. (Recall that $\omega = 2\pi f$, where f is the frequency in hertz.)

Figure 31.18 A loop enclosing an area A and containing N turns, rotating with constant angular speed ω in a magnetic field. The emf induced in the loop varies sinusoidally in time.

Quick Quiz 31.4 In an AC generator, a coil with N turns of wire spins in a magnetic field. Of the following choices, which does *not* cause an increase in the emf generated in the coil? (a) replacing the coil wire with one of lower resistance (b) spinning the coil faster (c) increasing the magnetic field (d) increasing the number of turns of wire on the coil

EXAMPLE 31.8 emf Induced in a Generator

The coil in an AC generator consists of 8 turns of wire, each of area $A = 0.090\,0\ \text{m}^2$, and the total resistance of the wire is 12.0 Ω. The coil rotates in a 0.500-T magnetic field at a constant frequency of 60.0 Hz.

(A) Find the maximum induced emf in the coil.

SOLUTION

Conceptualize Study Active Figure 31.17 to make sure you understand the operation of an AC generator.

Categorize We evaluate parameters using equations developed in this section, so we categorize this example as a substitution problem.

Use Equation 31.11 to find the maximum induced emf: $\mathcal{E}_{max} = NAB\omega = NAB(2\pi f)$

Substitute numerical values: $$\mathcal{E}_{max} = 8(0.090\ 0\ \text{m}^2)(0.500\ \text{T})(2\pi)(60.0\ \text{Hz}) = 136\ \text{V}$$

(B) What is the maximum induced current in the coil when the output terminals are connected to a low-resistance conductor?

SOLUTION

Use Equation 27.7 and the result to part (A): $$I_{max} = \frac{\mathcal{E}_{max}}{R} = \frac{136\ \text{V}}{12.0\ \Omega} = 11.3\ \text{A}$$

The **direct-current (DC) generator** is illustrated in Active Figure 31.19a. Such generators are used, for instance, in older cars to charge the storage batteries. The components are essentially the same as those of the AC generator except that the contacts to the rotating coil are made using a split ring called a *commutator.*

In this configuration, the output voltage always has the same polarity and pulsates with time as shown in Active Figure 31.19b. We can understand why by noting that the contacts to the split ring reverse their roles every half cycle. At the same time, the polarity of the induced emf reverses; hence, the polarity of the split ring (which is the same as the polarity of the output voltage) remains the same.

A pulsating DC current is not suitable for most applications. To obtain a steadier DC current, commercial DC generators use many coils and commutators distributed so that the sinusoidal pulses from the various coils are out of phase. When these pulses are superimposed, the DC output is almost free of fluctuations.

A **motor** is a device into which energy is transferred by electrical transmission while energy is transferred out by work. A motor is essentially a generator operating in reverse. Instead of generating a current by rotating a coil, a current is supplied to the coil by a battery and the torque acting on the current-carrying coil (Section 29.5) causes it to rotate.

Useful mechanical work can be done by attaching the rotating coil to some external device. As the coil rotates in a magnetic field, however, the changing magnetic flux induces an emf in the coil; this induced emf always acts to reduce the current in the coil. If that were not the case, Lenz's law would be violated. The back emf increases in magnitude as the rotational speed of the coil increases. (The phrase *back emf* is used to indicate an emf that tends to reduce the supplied current.) Because the voltage available to supply current equals the difference between the supply voltage and the back emf, the current in the rotating coil is limited by the back emf.

When a motor is turned on, there is initially no back emf, and the current is very large because it is limited only by the resistance of the coil. As the coil begins

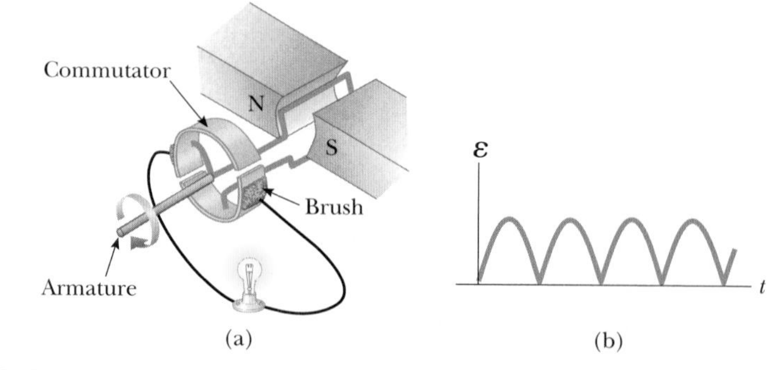

ACTIVE FIGURE 31.19

(a) Schematic diagram of a DC generator. (b) The magnitude of the emf varies in time, but the polarity never changes.

Sign in at www.thomsonedu.com and go to ThomsonNOW to adjust the speed of rotation and the strength of the field to see the effects on the emf generated.

to rotate, the induced back emf opposes the applied voltage and the current in the coil decreases. If the mechanical load increases, the motor slows down, which causes the back emf to decrease. This reduction in the back emf increases the current in the coil and therefore also increases the power needed from the external voltage source. For this reason, the power requirements for running a motor are greater for heavy loads than for light ones. If the motor is allowed to run under no mechanical load, the back emf reduces the current to a value just large enough to overcome energy losses due to internal energy and friction. If a very heavy load jams the motor so that it cannot rotate, the lack of a back emf can lead to dangerously high current in the motor's wire. This dangerous situation is explored in the **What If?** section of Example 31.9.

A modern application of motors in automobiles is seen in the development of *hybrid drive systems*. In these automobiles, a gasoline engine and an electric motor are combined to increase the fuel economy of the vehicle and reduce its emissions. Figure 31.20 shows the engine compartment of a Toyota Prius, one of a small number of hybrids available in the United States. In this automobile, power to the wheels can come from either the gasoline engine or the electric motor. In normal driving, the electric motor accelerates the vehicle from rest until it is moving at a speed of about 15 mi/h (24 km/h). During this acceleration period, the engine is not running, so gasoline is not used and there is no emission. At higher speeds, the motor and engine work together so that the engine always operates at or near its most efficient speed. The result is a significantly higher gasoline mileage than that obtained by a traditional gasoline-powered automobile. When a hybrid vehicle brakes, the motor acts as a generator and returns some of the vehicle's kinetic energy back to the battery as stored energy. In a normal vehicle, this kinetic energy is simply lost as it is transformed to internal energy in the brakes and roadway.

John W. Jewett, Jr.

Figure 31.20 The engine compartment of the Toyota Prius, a hybrid vehicle.

EXAMPLE 31.9 The Induced Current in a Motor

A motor contains a coil with a total resistance of 10 Ω and is supplied by a voltage of 120 V. When the motor is running at its maximum speed, the back emf is 70 V.

(A) Find the current in the coil at the instant the motor is turned on.

SOLUTION

Conceptualize Think about the motor just after it is turned on. It has not yet moved, so there is no back emf generated. As a result, the current in the motor is high. After the motor begins to turn, a back emf is generated and the current decreases.

Categorize We need to combine our new understanding about motors with the relationship between current, voltage, and resistance.

Analyze Evaluate the current in the coil from Equation 27.7 with no back emf generated:

$$I = \frac{\mathcal{E}}{R} = \frac{120\ \text{V}}{10\ \Omega} = 12\ \text{A}$$

(B) Find the current in the coil when the motor has reached maximum speed.

SOLUTION

Evaluate the current in the coil with the maximum back emf generated:

$$I = \frac{\mathcal{E} - \mathcal{E}_{\text{back}}}{R} = \frac{120\ \text{V} - 70\ \text{V}}{10\ \Omega} = \frac{50\ \text{V}}{10\ \Omega} = 5.0\ \text{A}$$

Finalize The current drawn by the motor when operating at its maximum speed is significantly less than that drawn before it begins to turn.

What If? Suppose this motor is in a circular saw. When you are operating the saw, the blade becomes jammed in a piece of wood and the motor cannot turn. By what percentage does the power input to the motor increase when it is jammed?

Answer You may have everyday experiences with motors becoming warm when they are prevented from turning. That is due to the increased power input to the motor. The higher rate of energy transfer results in an increase in the internal energy of the coil, an undesirable effect.

Set up the ratio of power input to the motor when jammed, which is that calculated in part (A), to that when it is not jammed, part (B):

$$\frac{\mathcal{P}_{\text{jammed}}}{\mathcal{P}_{\text{not jammed}}} = \frac{I_A{}^2 R}{I_B{}^2 R} = \frac{I_A{}^2}{I_B{}^2}$$

Substituting numerical values gives

$$\frac{\mathcal{P}_{\text{jammed}}}{\mathcal{P}_{\text{not jammed}}} = \frac{(12\text{ A})^2}{(5.0\text{ A})^2} = 5.76$$

which represents a 476% increase in the input power! Such a high power input can cause the coil to become so hot that it is damaged.

31.6 Eddy Currents

As we have seen, an emf and a current are induced in a circuit by a changing magnetic flux. In the same manner, circulating currents called **eddy currents** are induced in bulk pieces of metal moving through a magnetic field. This phenomenon can be demonstrated by allowing a flat copper or aluminum plate attached at the end of a rigid bar to swing back and forth through a magnetic field (Fig. 31.21). As the plate enters the field, the changing magnetic flux induces an emf in the plate, which in turn causes the free electrons in the plate to move, producing the swirling eddy currents. According to Lenz's law, the direction of the eddy currents is such that they create magnetic fields that oppose the change that causes the currents. For this reason, the eddy currents must produce effective magnetic poles on the plate, which are repelled by the poles of the magnet; this situation gives rise to a repulsive force that opposes the motion of the plate. (If the opposite were true, the plate would accelerate and its energy would increase after each swing, in violation of the law of conservation of energy.)

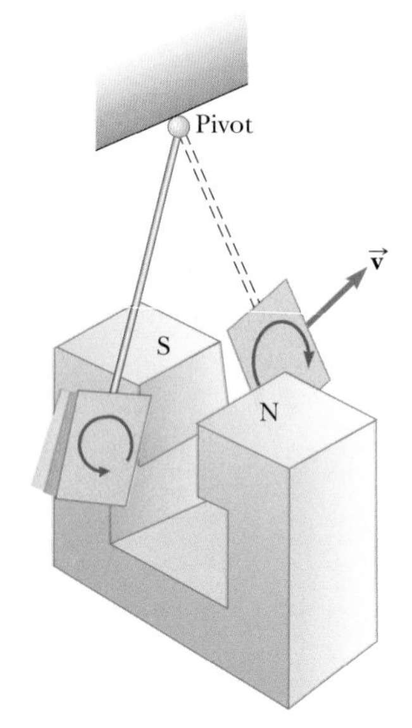

Figure 31.21 Formation of eddy currents in a conducting plate moving through a magnetic field. As the plate enters or leaves the field, the changing magnetic flux induces an emf, which causes eddy currents in the plate.

As indicated in Active Figure 31.22a, with $\vec{\mathbf{B}}$ directed into the page, the induced eddy current is counterclockwise as the swinging plate enters the field at position 1 because the flux due to the external magnetic field into the page through the plate is increasing. Hence, by Lenz's law, the induced current must provide its own magnetic field out of the page. The opposite is true as the plate leaves the field at position 2, where the current is clockwise. Because the induced eddy current always produces a magnetic retarding force $\vec{\mathbf{F}}_B$ when the plate enters or leaves the field, the swinging plate eventually comes to rest.

If slots are cut in the plate as shown in Active Figure 31.22b, the eddy currents and the corresponding retarding force are greatly reduced. We can understand this reduction in force by realizing that the cuts in the plate prevent the formation of any large current loops.

The braking systems on many subway and rapid-transit cars make use of electromagnetic induction and eddy currents. An electromagnet attached to the train is positioned near the steel rails. (An electromagnet is essentially a solenoid with an iron core.) The braking action occurs when a large current is passed through the electromagnet. The relative motion of the magnet and rails induces eddy currents in the rails, and the direction of these currents produces a drag force on the moving train. Because the eddy currents decrease steadily in magnitude as the train slows

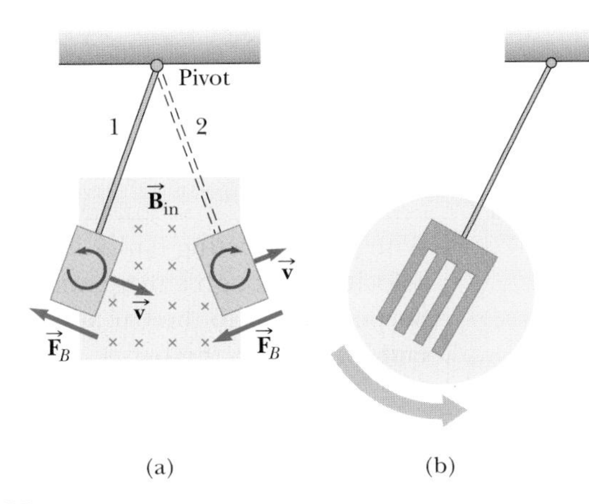

ACTIVE FIGURE 31.22

(a) As the conducting plate enters the field (position 1), the eddy currents are counterclockwise. As the plate leaves the field (position 2), the currents are clockwise. In either case, the force on the plate is opposite the velocity and eventually the plate comes to rest. (b) When slots are cut in the conducting plate, the eddy currents are reduced and the plate swings more freely through the magnetic field.

Sign in at www.thomsonedu.com and go to ThomsonNOW to choose to let a solid or a slotted plate swing through the magnetic field and observe the effect.

down, the braking effect is quite smooth. As a safety measure, some power tools use eddy currents to stop rapidly spinning blades once the device is turned off.

Eddy currents are often undesirable because they represent a transformation of mechanical energy to internal energy. To reduce this energy loss, conducting parts are often laminated; that is, they are built up in thin layers separated by a nonconducting material such as lacquer or a metal oxide. This layered structure prevents large current loops and effectively confines the currents to small loops in individual layers. Such a laminated structure is used in transformer cores (see Section 33.8) and motors to minimize eddy currents and thereby increase the efficiency of these devices.

Quick Quiz 31.5 In an equal-arm balance from the early 20th century (Fig. 31.23), an aluminum sheet hangs from one of the arms and passes between the poles of a magnet, causing the oscillations of the balance to decay rapidly. In the absence of such magnetic braking, the oscillation might continue for a long time, and the experimenter would have to wait to take a reading. Why do the oscillations decay? (a) because the aluminum sheet is attracted to the magnet (b) because currents in the aluminum sheet set up a magnetic field that opposes the oscillations (c) because aluminum is paramagnetic.

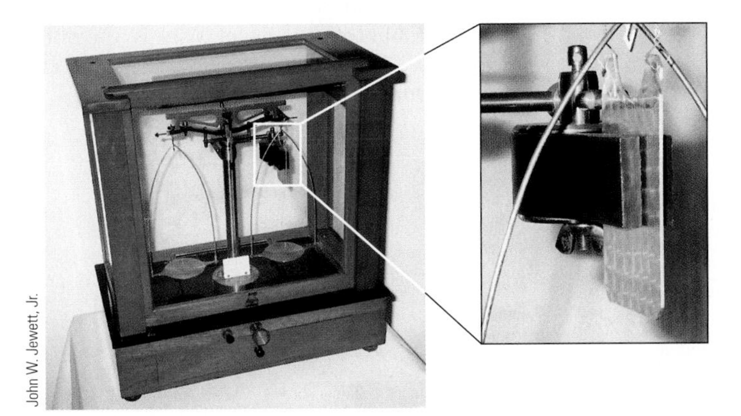

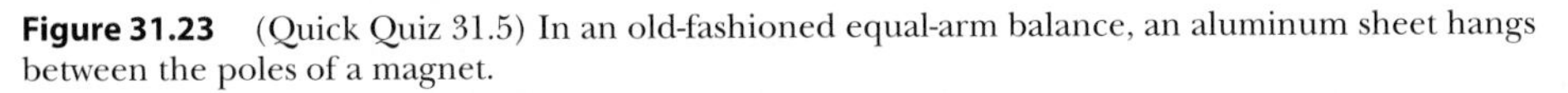

Figure 31.23 (Quick Quiz 31.5) In an old-fashioned equal-arm balance, an aluminum sheet hangs between the poles of a magnet.

Summary

ThomsonNOW™ Sign in at **www.thomsonedu.com** and go to ThomsonNOW to take a practice test for this chapter.

CONCEPTS AND PRINCIPLES

Faraday's law of induction states that the emf induced in a loop is directly proportional to the time rate of change of magnetic flux through the loop, or

$$\mathcal{E} = -\frac{d\Phi_B}{dt} \qquad (31.1)$$

where $\Phi_B = \oint \vec{\mathbf{B}} \cdot d\vec{\mathbf{A}}$ is the magnetic flux through the loop.

When a conducting bar of length ℓ moves at a velocity $\vec{\mathbf{v}}$ through a magnetic field $\vec{\mathbf{B}}$, where $\vec{\mathbf{B}}$ is perpendicular to the bar and to $\vec{\mathbf{v}}$, the **motional emf** induced in the bar is

$$\mathcal{E} = -B\ell v \qquad (31.5)$$

Lenz's law states that the induced current and induced emf in a conductor are in such a direction as to set up a magnetic field that opposes the change that produced them.

A general form of **Faraday's law of induction** is

$$\oint \vec{\mathbf{E}} \cdot d\vec{\mathbf{s}} = -\frac{d\Phi_B}{dt} \qquad (31.9)$$

where $\vec{\mathbf{E}}$ is the nonconservative electric field that is produced by the changing magnetic flux.

Questions

☐ denotes answer available in *Student Solutions Manual/Study Guide;* **O** denotes objective question

1. What is the difference between magnetic flux and magnetic field?

2. O Figure Q31.2 is a graph of the magnetic flux through a certain coil of wire as a function of time, during an interval while the radius of the coil is increased, the coil is rotated through 1.5 revolutions, and the external source of the magnetic field is turned off, in that order. Rank the electromotive force induced in the coil at the instants marked A through F from the largest positive value to the largest-magnitude negative value. In your ranking, note any cases of equality and also any instants when the emf is zero.

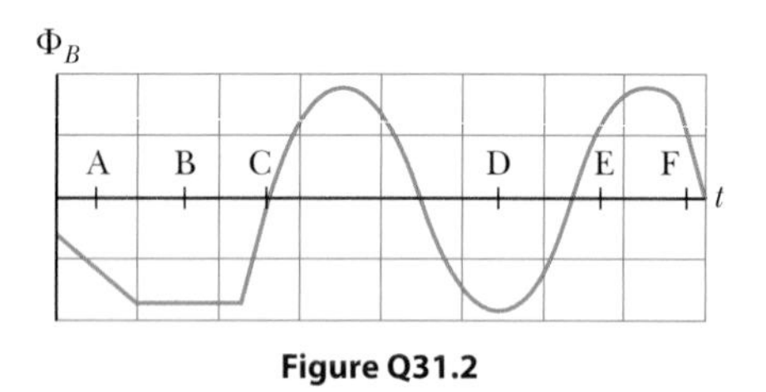

Figure Q31.2

3. O A flat coil of wire is placed in a uniform magnetic field that is in the y direction. **(i)** The magnetic flux through the coil is a maximum if the coil is (a) in the xy plane (b) in either the xy or the yz plane (c) in the xz plane (d) in any orientation, because it is a constant **(ii)** For what orientation is the flux zero? Choose the best answer from the same possibilities.

4. O A square, flat coil of wire is pulled at constant velocity through a region of uniform magnetic field directed perpendicular to the plane of the coil as shown in Figure Q31.4. **(i)** Is current induced in the coil? (a) yes, clockwise (b) yes, counterclockwise (c) no **(ii)** Does charge separation occur in the coil? (a) yes, with the top positive (b) yes, with the top negative (c) no

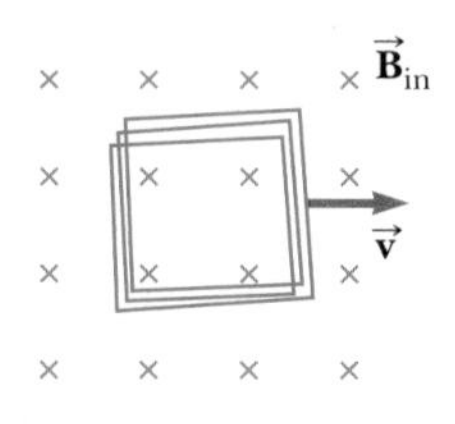

Figure Q31.4 Questions 4 and 6.

5. The bar in Figure Q31.5 moves on rails to the right with a velocity $\vec{\mathbf{v}}$, and the uniform, constant magnetic field is directed out of the page. Why is the induced current clockwise? If the bar were moving to the left, what would be the direction of the induced current?

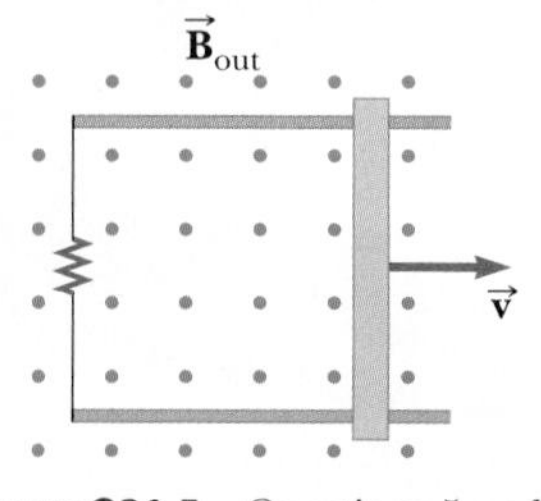

Figure Q31.5 Questions 5 and 6.

6. O (i) As the square coil of wire in Figure Q31.4 moves perpendicular to the field, is an external force required to keep it moving with constant speed? **(ii)** Answer the same question for the bar in Figure Q31.5. **(iii)** Answer the same question for the bar in Figure Q31.6.

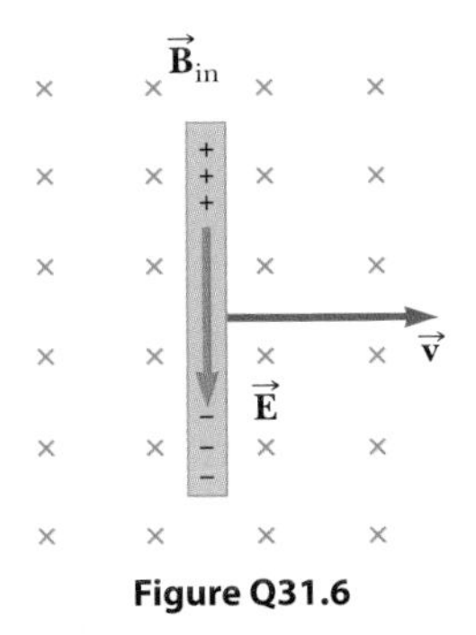

Figure Q31.6

7. In a hydroelectric dam, how is energy produced that is then transferred out by electrical transmission? That is, how is the energy of motion of the water converted to energy that is transmitted by AC electricity?

8. A piece of aluminum is dropped vertically downward between the poles of an electromagnet. Does the magnetic field affect the velocity of the aluminum?

9. **O** What happens to the amplitude of the induced emf when the rate of rotation of a generator coil is doubled? (a) It becomes 4 times larger. (b) It becomes 2 times larger. (c) It is unchanged. (d) It becomes $\frac{1}{2}$ as large. (e) It becomes $\frac{1}{4}$ as large.

10. When the switch in Figure Q31.10a is closed, a current is set up in the coil and the metal ring springs upward (Fig. Q31.10b). Explain this behavior.

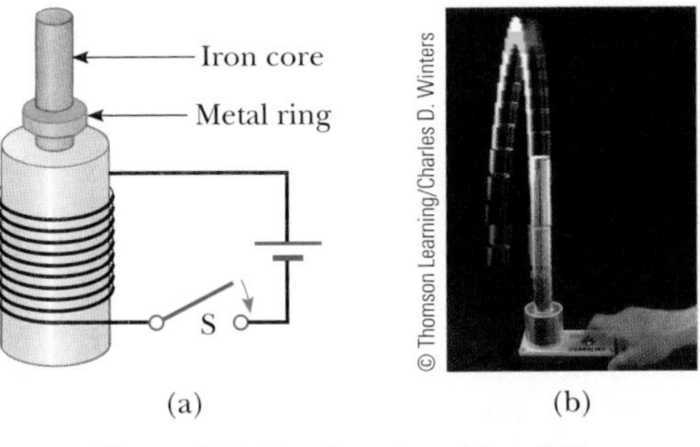

Figure Q31.10 Questions 10 and 11.

11. Assume the battery in Figure Q31.10a is replaced by an AC source and the switch is held closed. If held down, the metal ring on top of the solenoid becomes hot. Why?

12. **O** A bar magnet is held in a vertical orientation above a loop of wire that lies in a horizontal plane as shown in Figure Q31.12. The south pole of the magnet is on the bottom end, closest to the loop of wire. The magnet is dropped toward the loop. **(i)** While the magnet is falling toward the loop, what is the direction of current in the resistor? (a) to the left (b) to the right (c) there is no current (d) both to the left and to the right (e) downward **(ii)** After the magnet has passed through the loop and moves away from it, what is the direction of current in the resistor? Choose from the same possibilities. **(iii)** Now assume the magnet, producing a symmetrical field, is held in a horizontal orientation and then dropped. While it is approaching the loop, what is the direction of current in the resistor? Choose from the same possibilities.

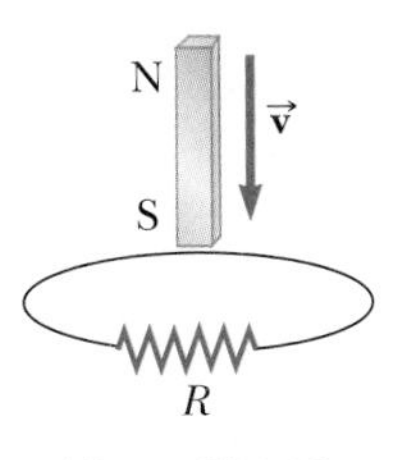

Figure Q31.12

13. **O** What is the direction of the current in the resistor in Figure Q31.13 **(i)** at an instant immediately after the switch is thrown closed, **(ii)** after the switch has been closed for several seconds, and **(iii)** at an instant after the switch has then been thrown open? Choose each answer from these possibilities: (a) left (b) right (c) both left and right (d) The current is zero.

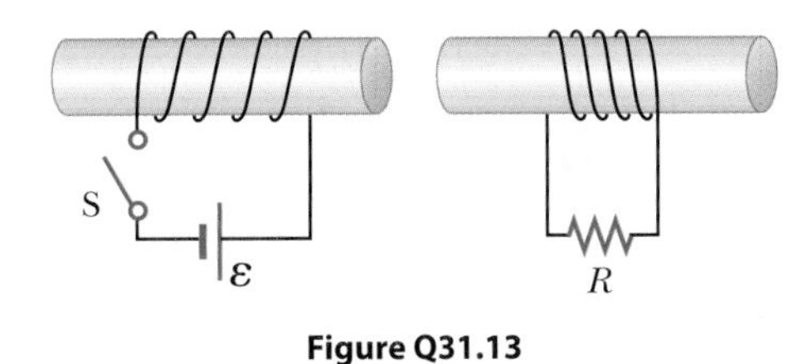

Figure Q31.13

14. In Section 7.7, we defined conservative and nonconservative forces. In Chapter 23, we stated that an electric charge creates an electric field that produces a conservative force. Argue now that induction creates an electric field that produces a nonconservative force.

Problems

WebAssign The Problems from this chapter may be assigned online in WebAssign.

ThomsonNOW Sign in at **www.thomsonedu.com** and go to ThomsonNOW to assess your understanding of this chapter's topics with additional quizzing and conceptual questions.

1, 2, 3 denotes straightforward, intermediate, challenging; ☐ denotes full solution available in *Student Solutions Manual/Study Guide*; ▲ denotes coached solution with hints available at **www.thomsonedu.com**; denotes developing symbolic reasoning; ● denotes asking for qualitative reasoning; denotes computer useful in solving problem

Section 31.1 Faraday's Law of Induction

Section 31.3 Lenz's Law

1. *Transcranial magnetic stimulation* is a noninvasive technique used to stimulate regions of the human brain. A small coil is placed on the scalp, and a brief burst of current in the coil produces a rapidly changing magnetic field inside the brain. The induced emf can stimulate neuronal activity. (a) One such device generates an upward magnetic field

within the brain that rises from zero to 1.50 T in 120 ms. Determine the induced emf around a horizontal circle of tissue of radius 1.60 mm. (b) **What If?** The field next changes to 0.500 T downward in 80.0 ms. How does the emf induced in this process compare with that in part (a)?

2. A flat loop of wire consisting of a single turn of cross-sectional area 8.00 cm^2 is perpendicular to a magnetic field that increases uniformly in magnitude from 0.500 T to 2.50 T in 1.00 s. What is the resulting induced current if the loop has a resistance of 2.00 Ω?

3. A 25-turn circular coil of wire has diameter 1.00 m. It is placed with its axis along the direction of the Earth's magnetic field of 50.0 μT and then in 0.200 s is flipped 180°. An average emf of what magnitude is generated in the coil?

4. ● Your physics teacher asks you to help her set up a demonstration of Faraday's law for the class. As shown in Figure P31.4, the apparatus consists of a strong, permanent magnet producing a field of 110 mT between its poles, a 12-turn coil of radius 2.10 cm cemented onto a wood frame with a handle, some flexible connecting wires, and an ammeter. The idea is to pull the coil out of the center of the magnetic field as quickly as you can and read the average current registered on the meter. The equivalent resistance of the coil, leads, and meter is 2.30 Ω. You can flip the coil out of the field in about 180 ms. The ammeter has a full-scale sensitivity of 1 000 μA. (a) Is this meter sensitive enough to show the induced current clearly? Explain your reasoning. (b) Does the meter in the diagram register a positive or a negative current? Explain your reasoning.

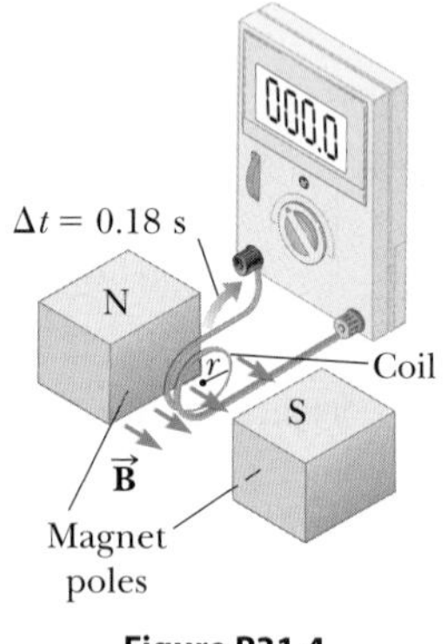

Figure P31.4

5. A rectangular loop of area A is placed in a region where the magnetic field is perpendicular to the plane of the loop. The magnitude of the field is allowed to vary in time according to $B = B_{max}e^{-t/\tau}$, where B_{max} and τ are constants. The field has the constant value B_{max} for $t < 0$. (a) Use Faraday's law to show that the emf induced in the loop is given by

$$\mathcal{E} = \frac{AB_{max}}{\tau}e^{-t/\tau}$$

(b) Obtain a numerical value for $\mathcal{E}$ at $t = 4.00$ s when $A = 0.160$ m^2, $B_{max} = 0.350$ T, and $\tau = 2.00$ s. (c) For the values of A, B_{max}, and τ given in part (b), what is the maximum value of $\mathcal{E}$?

6. To monitor the breathing of a hospital patient, a thin belt is girded around the patient's chest. The belt is a 200-turn coil. When the patient inhales, the area encircled by the coil increases by 39.0 cm^2. The magnitude of the Earth's magnetic field is 50.0 μT and makes an angle of 28.0° with the plane of the coil. Assuming a patient takes 1.80 s to inhale, find the average induced emf in the coil during this time interval.

7. ▲ A strong electromagnet produces a uniform magnetic field of 1.60 T over a cross-sectional area of 0.200 m^2. A coil having 200 turns and a total resistance of 20.0 Ω is placed around the electromagnet. The current in the electromagnet is then smoothly reduced until it reaches zero in 20.0 ms. What is the current induced in the coil?

8. A loop of wire in the shape of a rectangle of width w and length L and a long, straight wire carrying a current I lie on a tabletop as shown in Figure P31.8. (a) Determine the magnetic flux through the loop due to the current I. (b) Suppose the current is changing with time according to $I = a + bt$, where a and b are constants. Determine the emf that is induced in the loop if $b = 10.0$ A/s, $h = 1.00$ cm, $w = 10.0$ cm, and $L = 100$ cm. What is the direction of the induced current in the rectangle?

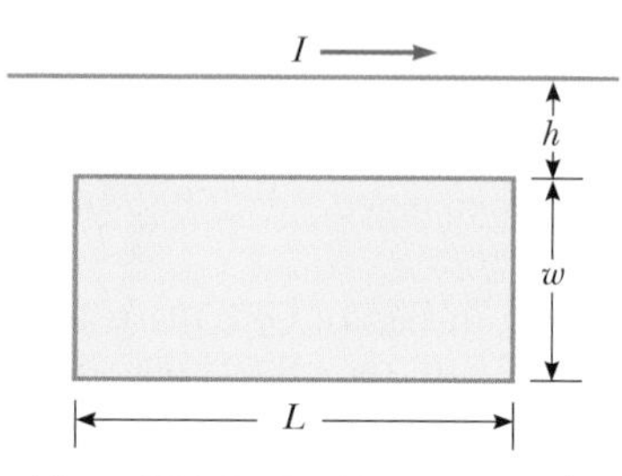

Figure P31.8 Problems 8 and 67.

9. ▲ An aluminum ring of radius 5.00 cm and resistance 3.00×10^{-4} Ω is placed around one end of a long air-core solenoid with 1 000 turns per meter and radius 3.00 cm as shown in Figure P31.9. Assume the axial component of the field produced by the solenoid is one-half as strong over the area of the end of the solenoid as at the center of the solenoid. Also assume the solenoid produces negligible field outside its cross-sectional area. The current in the solenoid is increasing at a rate of 270 A/s. (a) What is the induced current in the ring? At the center of the ring, what are (b) the magnitude and (c) the direction of the magnetic field produced by the induced current in the ring?

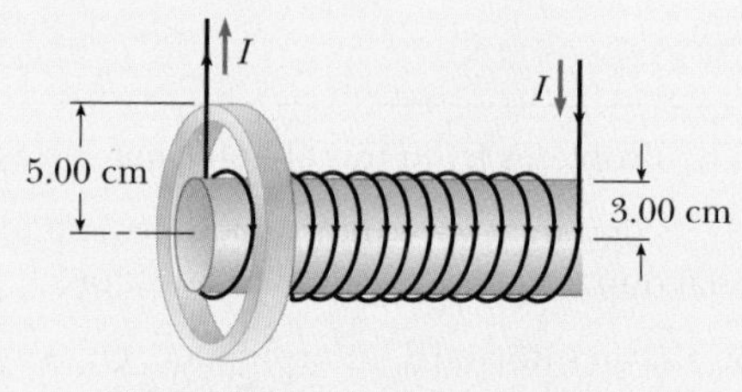

Figure P31.9 Problems 9 and 10.

10. An aluminum ring of radius r_1 and resistance R is placed around one end of a long air-core solenoid with n turns per meter and smaller radius r_2 as shown in Figure P31.9. Assume the axial component of the field produced by the solenoid over the area of the end of the solenoid is one-half as strong as at the center of the solenoid. Also assume the solenoid produces negligible field outside its cross-sectional area. The current in the solenoid is increasing at a rate of $\Delta I/\Delta t$. (a) What is the induced current in the ring? (b) At the center of the ring, what is the magnetic field produced by the induced current in the ring? (c) What is the direction of this field?

11. A coil of 15 turns and radius 10.0 cm surrounds a long solenoid of radius 2.00 cm and 1.00×10^3 turns/meter (Fig. P31.11). The current in the solenoid changes as $I = (5.00 \text{ A}) \sin(120t)$. Find the induced emf in the 15-turn coil as a function of time.

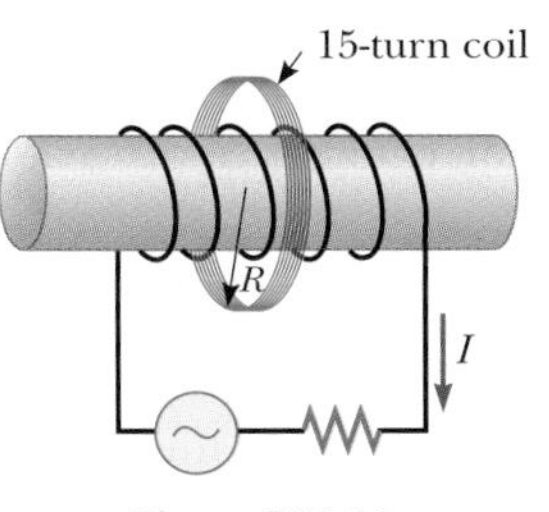

Figure P31.11

12. Two circular coils lie in the same plane. The following equation describes the emf induced in the smaller coil by a changing current in the larger coil. (a) Calculate this emf. (b) Write the statement of a problem, including data, for which the equation gives the solution.

$$\mathcal{E} = -20 \frac{d}{dt}\left[\frac{130\left(4\pi \times 10^{-7} \frac{\text{T}\cdot\text{m}}{\text{A}}\right)\left(3\text{ A} - \frac{(6\text{ A})t}{13 \times 10^{-6}\text{ s}}\right)}{2(0.40\text{ m})}\pi(0.03\text{ m})^2 \cos 0°\right]$$

13. Find the current through section PQ of length $a = 65.0$ cm in Figure P31.13. The circuit is located in a magnetic field whose magnitude varies with time according to the expression $B = (1.00 \times 10^{-3} \text{ T/s})t$. Assume the resistance per length of the wire is 0.100 Ω/m.

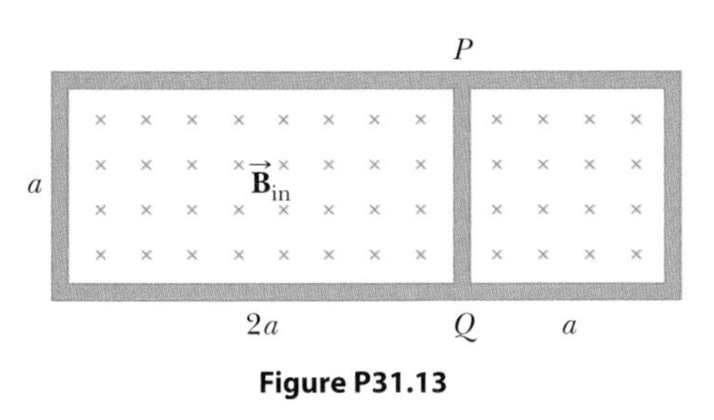

Figure P31.13

14. A 30-turn circular coil of radius 4.00 cm and resistance 1.00 Ω is placed in a magnetic field directed perpendicular to the plane of the coil. The magnitude of the magnetic field varies in time according to the expression $B = 0.010\,0t + 0.040\,0t^2$, where t is in seconds and B is in teslas. Calculate the induced emf in the coil at $t = 5.00$ s.

15. A long solenoid has $n = 400$ turns per meter and carries a current given by $I = (30.0 \text{ A})(1 - e^{-1.60t})$. Inside the solenoid and coaxial with it is a coil that has a radius of 6.00 cm and consists of a total of $N = 250$ turns of fine wire (Fig. P31.15). What emf is induced in the coil by the changing current?

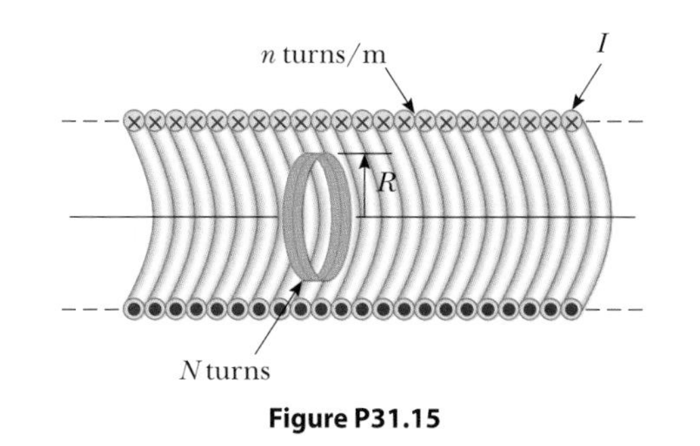

Figure P31.15

16. ● When a wire carries an AC current with a known frequency, you can use a *Rogowski coil* to determine the amplitude I_{max} of the current without disconnecting the wire to shunt the current though a meter. The Rogowski coil, shown in Figure P31.16, simply clips around the wire. It consists of a toroidal conductor wrapped around a circular return cord. Let n represent the number of turns in the toroid per unit distance along it. Let A represent the cross-sectional area of the toroid. Let $I(t) = I_{max} \sin \omega t$ represent the current to be measured. (a) Show that the amplitude of the emf induced in the Rogowski coil is $\mathcal{E}_{max} = \mu_0 n A \omega I_{max}$. (b) Explain why the wire carrying the unknown current need not be at the center of the Rogowski coil and why the coil will not respond to nearby currents that it does not enclose.

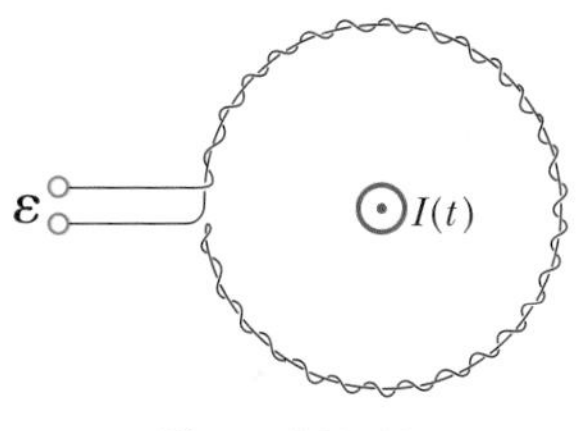

Figure P31.16

17. A coil formed by wrapping 50 turns of wire in the shape of a square is positioned in a magnetic field so that the normal to the plane of the coil makes an angle of 30.0° with the direction of the field. When the magnetic field is increased uniformly from 200 μT to 600 μT in 0.400 s, an emf of magnitude 80.0 mV is induced in the coil. What is the total length of the wire?

18. A toroid having a rectangular cross section ($a = 2.00$ cm by $b = 3.00$ cm) and inner radius $R = 4.00$ cm consists of 500 turns of wire that carries a sinusoidal current $I = I_{max} \sin \omega t$, with $I_{max} = 50.0$ A and a frequency $f = \omega/2\pi = 60.0$ Hz. A coil that consists of 20 turns of wire links with the toroid as shown in Figure P31.18. Determine the emf induced in the coil as a function of time.

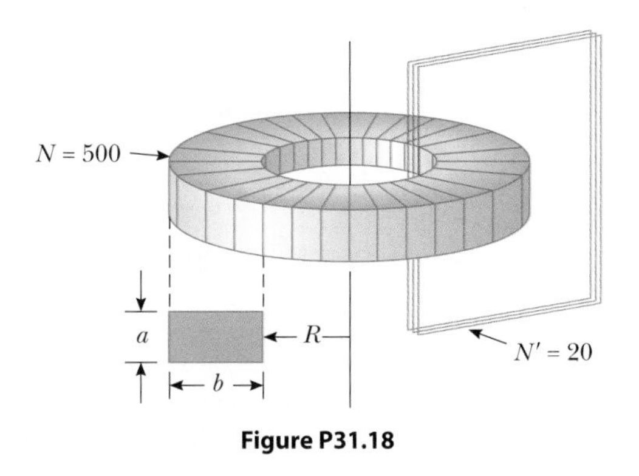

Figure P31.18

19. A piece of insulated wire is shaped into a figure 8 as shown in Figure P31.19. The radius of the upper circle is 5.00 cm and that of the lower circle is 9.00 cm. The wire has a uniform resistance per unit length of 3.00 Ω/m. A uniform magnetic field is applied perpendicular to the plane of the two circles, in the direction shown. The magnetic field is increasing at a constant rate of 2.00 T/s. Find the magnitude and direction of the induced current in the wire.

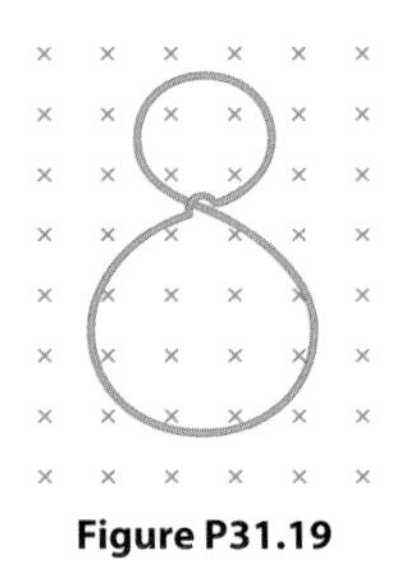

Figure P31.19

Section 31.2 Motional emf

Section 31.3 Lenz's Law

Problem 61 in Chapter 29 can be assigned with this section.

20. An automobile has a vertical radio antenna 1.20 m long. The automobile travels at 65.0 km/h on a horizontal road where the Earth's magnetic field is 50.0 μT directed toward the north and downward at an angle of 65.0° below the horizontal. (a) Specify the direction the automobile should move so as to generate the maximum motional emf in the antenna, with the top of the antenna positive relative to the bottom. (b) Calculate the magnitude of this induced emf.

21. ● A small airplane with a wingspan of 14.0 m is flying due north at a speed of 70.0 m/s over a region where the vertical component of the Earth's magnetic field is 1.20 μT downward. (a) What potential difference is developed between the wingtips? Which wingtip is at higher potential? (b) **What If?** How would the answer change if the plane turned to fly due east? (c) Can this emf be used to power a light in the passenger compartment? Explain your answer.

22. Consider the arrangement shown in Figure P31.22. Assume $R = 6.00\ \Omega$, $\ell = 1.20$ m, and a uniform 2.50-T magnetic field is directed into the page. At what speed should the bar be moved to produce a current of 0.500 A in the resistor?

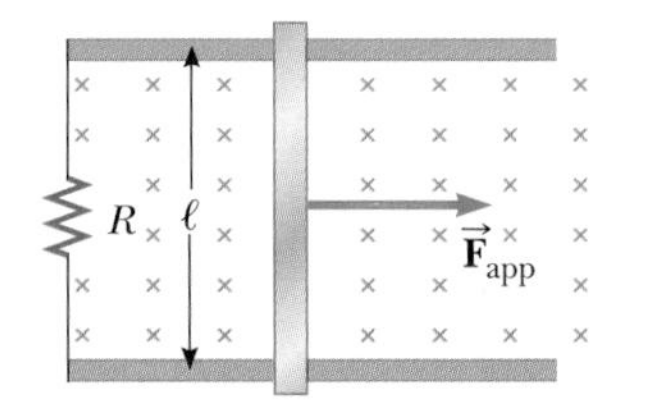

Figure P31.22 Problems 22, 23, and 24.

23. Figure P31.22 shows a top view of a bar that can slide without friction. The resistor is 6.00 Ω, and a 2.50-T magnetic field is directed perpendicularly downward, into the paper. Let $\ell = 1.20$ m. (a) Calculate the applied force required to move the bar to the right at a constant speed of 2.00 m/s. (b) At what rate is energy delivered to the resistor?

24. ● A conducting rod of length ℓ moves on two horizontal, frictionless rails as shown in Figure P31.22. If a constant force of 1.00 N moves the bar at 2.00 m/s through a magnetic field $\vec{\mathbf{B}}$ that is directed into the page, (a) what is the current in the 8.00-Ω resistor R? (b) What is the rate at which energy is delivered to the resistor? (c) What is the mechanical power delivered by the force $\vec{\mathbf{F}}_{app}$? (d) Explain the relationship between the quantities computed in parts (b) and (c).

25. The *homopolar generator,* also called the *Faraday disk,* is a low-voltage, high-current electric generator. It consists of a rotating conducting disk with one stationary brush (a sliding electrical contact) at its axle and another at a point on its circumference as shown in Figure P31.25. A magnetic field is applied perpendicular to the plane of the disk. Assume the field is 0.900 T, the angular speed is 3 200 rev/min, and the radius of the disk is 0.400 m. Find the emf generated between the brushes. When superconducting coils are used to produce a large magnetic field, a homopolar generator can have a power output of several megawatts. Such a generator is useful, for example, in purifying metals by electrolysis. If a voltage is applied to the output terminals of the generator, it runs in reverse as a *homopolar motor* capable of providing great torque, useful in ship propulsion.

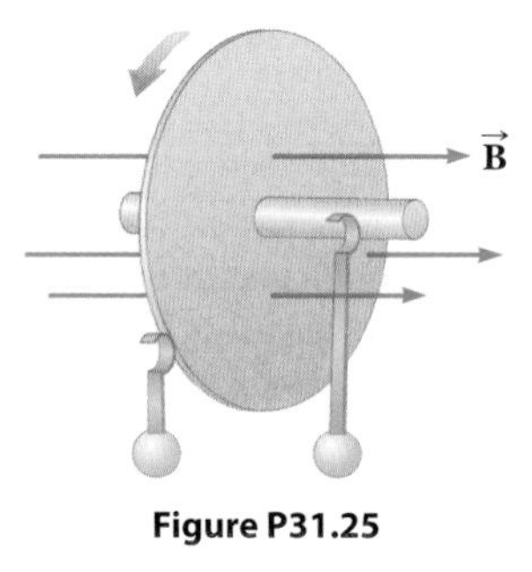

Figure P31.25

26. **Review problem.** As he starts to restring his acoustic guitar, a student attaches a single string, with linear density 3.00×10^{-3} kg/m, between two fixed points 64.0 cm apart, applies tension 267 N, and is distracted by a video game. His roommate attaches voltmeter leads to the ends of the metallic string and places a magnet across the string as shown in Figure P31.26. The magnet does not touch the string, but produces a uniform field of 4.50 mT

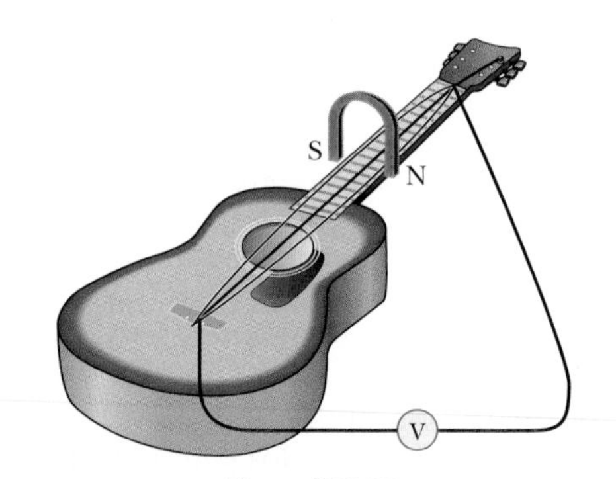

Figure P31.26

over a 2.00-cm length at the center of the string and negligible field elsewhere. Strumming the string sets it vibrating at its fundamental (lowest) frequency. The section of the string in the magnetic field moves perpendicular to the field with a uniform amplitude of 1.50 cm. Find (a) the frequency and (b) the amplitude of the electromotive force induced between the ends of the string.

27. A helicopter has blades of length 3.00 m, extending out from a central hub and rotating at 2.00 rev/s. If the vertical component of the Earth's magnetic field is 50.0 μT, what is the emf induced between the blade tip and the center hub?

28. Use Lenz's law to answer the following questions concerning the direction of induced currents. (a) What is the direction of the induced current in resistor R in Figure P31.28a when the bar magnet is moved to the left? (b) What is the direction of the current induced in the resistor R immediately after the switch S in Figure P31.28b is closed? (c) What is the direction of the induced current in R when the current I in Figure P31.28c decreases rapidly to zero? (d) A copper bar is moved to the right while its axis is maintained in a direction perpendicular to a magnetic field as shown in Figure P31.28d. If the top of the bar becomes positive relative to the bottom, what is the direction of the magnetic field?

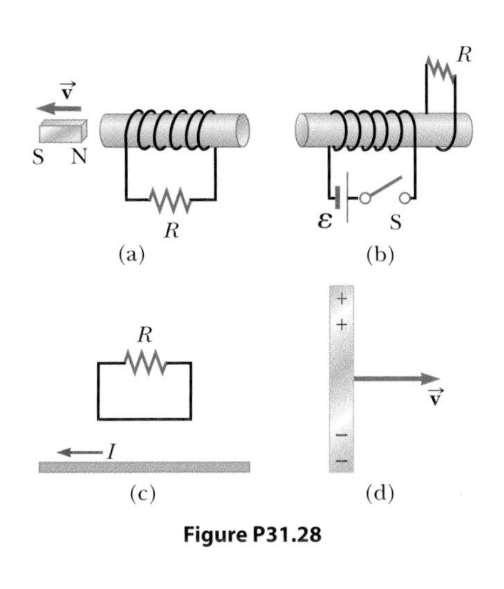

Figure P31.28

29. A rectangular coil with resistance R has N turns, each of length ℓ and width w as shown in Figure P31.29. The coil moves into a uniform magnetic field $\vec{\mathbf{B}}$ with constant velocity $\vec{\mathbf{v}}$. What are the magnitude and direction of the total magnetic force on the coil (a) as it enters the magnetic field, (b) as it moves within the field, and (c) as it leaves the field?

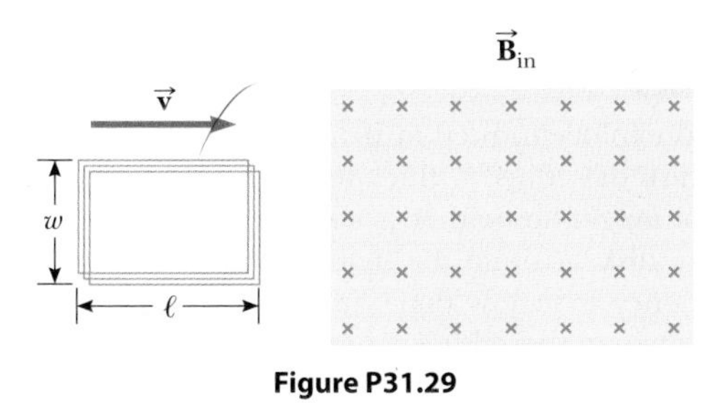

Figure P31.29

30. ● In Figure P31.30, the bar magnet is moved toward the loop. Is $V_a - V_b$ positive, negative, or zero? Explain your reasoning.

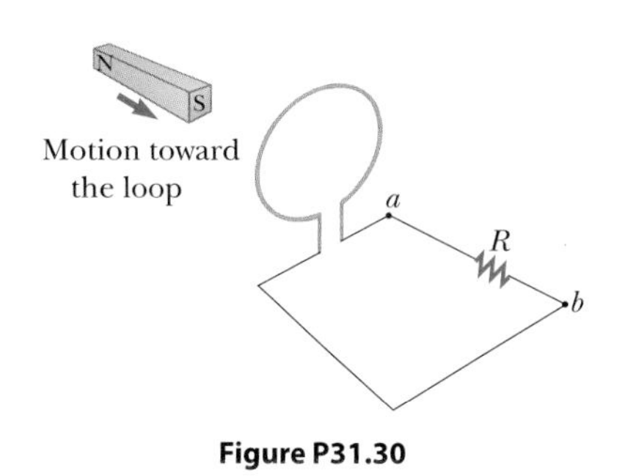

Figure P31.30

31. Two parallel rails with negligible resistance are 10.0 cm apart and are connected by a 5.00-Ω resistor. The circuit also contains two metal rods having resistances of 10.0 Ω and 15.0 Ω sliding along the rails (Fig. P31.31). The rods are pulled away from the resistor at constant speeds of 4.00 m/s and 2.00 m/s, respectively. A uniform magnetic field of magnitude 0.010 0 T is applied perpendicular to the plane of the rails. Determine the current in the 5.00-Ω resistor.

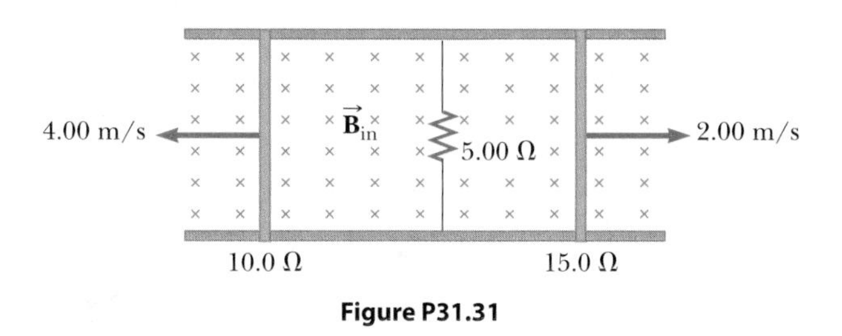

Figure P31.31

Section 31.4 Induced emf and Electric Fields

32. For the situation shown in Figure P31.32, the magnetic field changes with time according to the expression $B = (2.00t^3 - 4.00t^2 + 0.800)$ T, and $r_2 = 2R = 5.00$ cm. (a) Calculate the magnitude and direction of the force exerted on an electron located at point P_2 when $t = 2.00$ s. (b) At what instant is this force equal to zero?

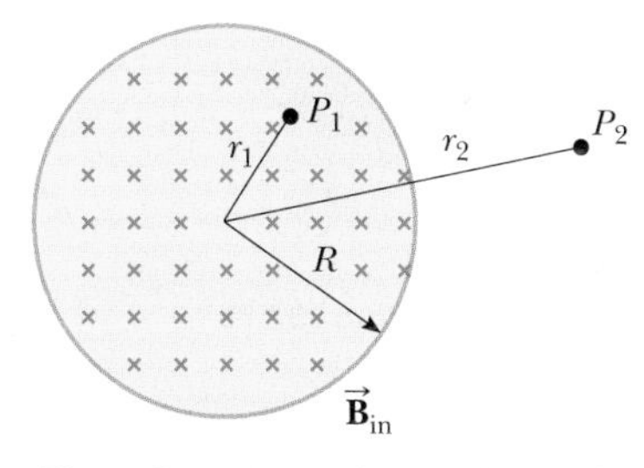

Figure P31.32 Problems 32 and 33.

33. A magnetic field directed into the page changes with time according to $B = (0.030\ 0t^2 + 1.40)$ T, where t is in seconds. The field has a circular cross section of radius $R = 2.50$ cm (Fig. P31.32). What are the magnitude and direction of the electric field at point P_1 when $t = 3.00$ s and $r_1 = 0.020\ 0$ m?

34. A long solenoid with 1 000 turns per meter and radius 2.00 cm carries an oscillating current given by $I = (5.00 \text{ A}) \sin (100\pi t)$. What is the electric field induced at a radius $r = 1.00$ cm from the axis of the solenoid? What is the direction of this electric field when the current is increasing counterclockwise in the coil?

Section 31.5 Generators and Motors

Problems 40 and 54 in Chapter 29 can be assigned with this section.

35. ▲ A coil of area 0.100 m^2 is rotating at 60.0 rev/s with the axis of rotation perpendicular to a 0.200-T magnetic field. (a) If the coil has 1 000 turns, what is the maximum emf generated in it? (b) What is the orientation of the coil with respect to the magnetic field when the maximum induced emf occurs?

36. In a 250-turn automobile alternator, the magnetic flux in each turn is $\Phi_B = (2.50 \times 10^{-4} \text{ Wb}) \cos \omega t$, where ω is the angular speed of the alternator. The alternator is geared to rotate three times for each engine revolution. When the engine is running at an angular speed of 1 000 rev/min, determine (a) the induced emf in the alternator as a function of time and (b) the maximum emf in the alternator.

37. A long solenoid, with its axis along the x axis, consists of 200 turns per meter of wire that carries a steady current of 15.0 A. A coil is formed by wrapping 30 turns of thin wire around a circular frame that has a radius of 8.00 cm. The coil is placed inside the solenoid and mounted on an axis that is a diameter of the coil and coincides with the y axis. The coil is then rotated with an angular speed of 4.00π rad/s. The plane of the coil is in the yz plane at $t = 0$. Determine the emf generated in the coil as a function of time.

38. A bar magnet is spun at constant angular speed ω around an axis as shown in Figure P31.38. A stationary, flat, rectangular conducting loop surrounds the magnet, and at $t = 0$, the magnet is oriented as shown. Make a qualitative graph of the induced current in the loop as a function of time, plotting counterclockwise currents as positive and clockwise currents as negative.

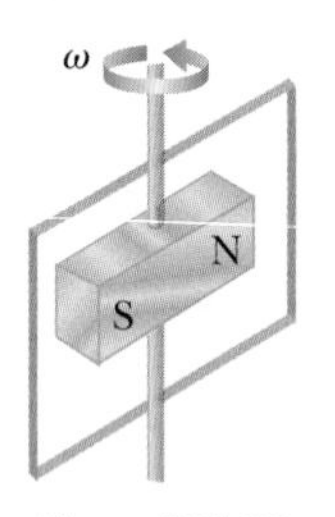

Figure P31.38

39. A motor in normal operation carries a direct current of 0.850 A when connected to a 120-V power supply. The resistance of the motor windings is 11.8 Ω. While in normal operation, (a) what is the back emf generated by the motor? (b) At what rate is internal energy produced in the windings? (c) **What If?** Suppose a malfunction stops the motor shaft from rotating. At what rate will internal energy be produced in the windings in this case? (Most motors have a thermal switch that will turn off the motor to prevent overheating when this stalling occurs.)

40. The rotating loop in an AC generator is a square 10.0 cm on each side. It is rotated at 60.0 Hz in a uniform field of 0.800 T. Calculate (a) the flux through the loop as a function of time, (b) the emf induced in the loop, (c) the current induced in the loop for a loop resistance of 1.00 Ω, (d) the power delivered to the loop, and (e) the torque that must be exerted to rotate the loop.

Section 31.6 Eddy Currents

41. ● Figure P31.41 represents an electromagnetic brake that uses eddy currents. An electromagnet hangs from a railroad car near one rail. To stop the car, a large current is sent through the coils of the electromagnet. The moving electromagnet induces eddy currents in the rails, whose fields oppose the change in the electromagnet's field. The magnetic fields of the eddy currents exert force on the current in the electromagnet, thereby slowing the car. The direction of the car's motion and the direction of the current in the electromagnet are shown correctly in the picture. Determine which of the eddy currents shown on the rails is correct. Explain your answer.

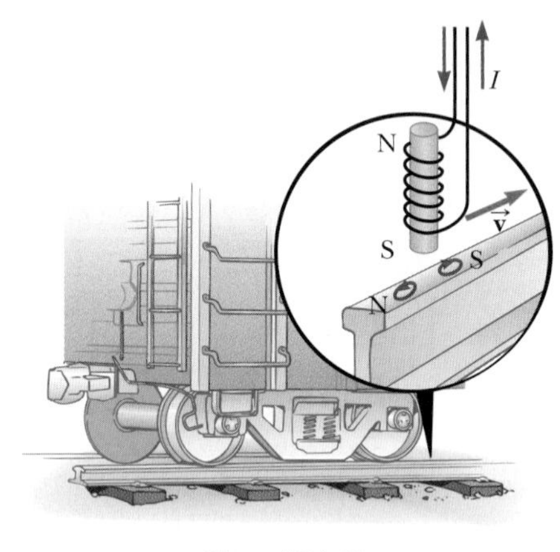

Figure P31.41

42. An *induction furnace* uses electromagnetic induction to produce eddy currents in a conductor, thereby raising the conductor's temperature. Commercial units operate at frequencies ranging from 60 Hz to about 1 MHz and deliver powers from a few watts to several megawatts. Induction heating can be used for warming a metal pan on a kitchen stove. It can be used to avoid oxidation and contamination of the metal when welding in a vacuum enclosure. At high frequencies, induced currents occur only near the surface of the conductor, in a phenomenon called the "skin effect." By creating an induced current for a short time interval at an appropriately high frequency, one can heat a sample down to a controlled depth. For example, the surface of a farm tiller can be tempered to make it hard and brittle for effective cutting while keeping the interior metal soft and ductile to resist breakage.

To explore induction heating, consider a flat conducting disk of radius R, thickness b, and resistivity ρ. A sinusoidal magnetic field $B_{\max} \cos \omega t$ is applied perpendicular to the disk. Assume the field is uniform in space and the frequency is so low that the skin effect is not important. Also assume the eddy currents occur in circles concentric with the disk. (a) Calculate the average power delivered to the disk. (b) **What If?** By what factor does the power change when the amplitude of the field doubles? (c) When the frequency doubles? (d) When the radius of the disk doubles?

43. ▲ ● A conducting rectangular loop of mass M, resistance R, and dimensions w by ℓ falls from rest into a magnetic field $\vec{\mathbf{B}}$ as shown in Figure P31.43. During the time interval before the top edge of the loop reaches the field, the loop approaches a terminal speed v_T. (a) Show that

$$v_T = \frac{MgR}{B^2w^2}$$

(b) Why is v_T proportional to R? (c) Why is it inversely proportional to B^2?

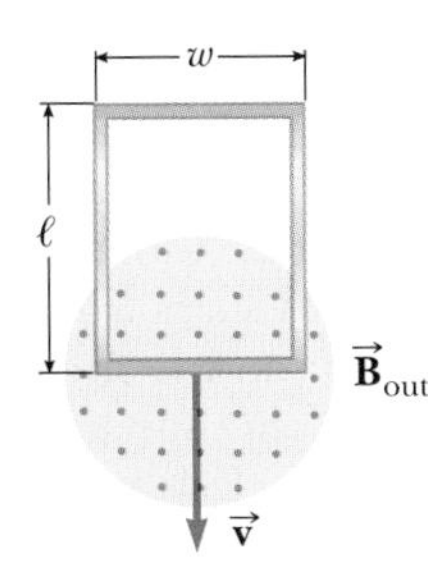

Figure P31.43

Additional Problems

44. ● Consider the apparatus shown in Figure P31.44 in which a conducting bar can be moved along two rails connected to a lightbulb. The whole system is immersed in a magnetic field of 0.400 T perpendicularly into the page. The vertical distance between the horizontal rails is 0.800 m. The resistance of the lightbulb is 48.0 Ω, assumed to be constant. The bar and rails have negligible resistance. The bar is moved toward the right by a constant force of magnitude 0.600 N. (a) What is the direction of the induced current in the circuit? (b) If the speed of the bar is 15.0 m/s at a particular instant, what is the value of the induced current? (c) Argue that the constant force causes the speed of the bar to increase and approach a certain terminal speed. Find the value of this maximum speed. (d) What power is delivered to the lightbulb when the bar is moving at its terminal speed? (e) We have assumed the resistance of the lightbulb is constant. In reality, as the power delivered to the lightbulb increases, the filament temperature increases and the resistance increases. Explain conceptually (not algebraically) whether the terminal speed found in part (c) changes if the resistance increases. If the terminal speed changes, does it increase or decrease? (f) With the assumption that the resistance of the lightbulb increases as the current increases, explain mathematically whether the power found in part (d) changes because of the increasing resistance. If it changes, is the actual power larger or smaller than the value previously found?

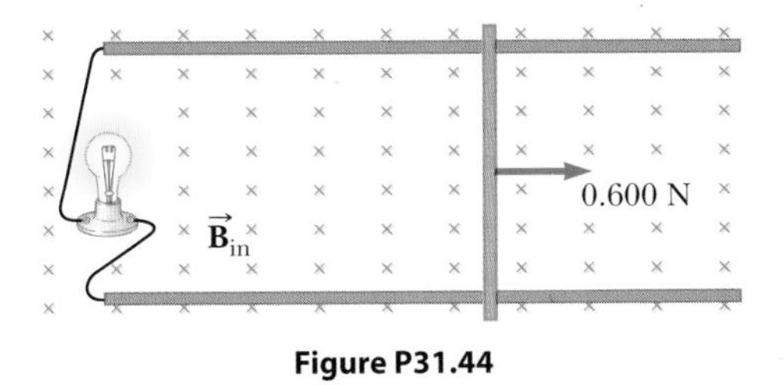

Figure P31.44

45. A guitar's steel string vibrates (Fig. 31.5a). The component of magnetic field perpendicular to the area of a pickup coil nearby is given by

$$B = 50.0 \text{ mT} + (3.20 \text{ mT}) \sin (1\,046\pi t)$$

The circular pickup coil has 30 turns and radius 2.70 mm. Find the emf induced in the coil as a function of time.

46. Strong magnetic fields are used in such medical procedures as magnetic resonance imaging, or MRI. A technician wearing a brass bracelet enclosing area 0.005 00 m^2 places her hand in a solenoid whose magnetic field is 5.00 T directed perpendicular to the plane of the bracelet. The electrical resistance around the bracelet's circumference is 0.020 0 Ω. An unexpected power failure causes the field to drop to 1.50 T in a time interval of 20.0 ms. Find (a) the current induced in the bracelet and (b) the power delivered to the bracelet. *Note:* As this problem implies, you should not wear any metal objects when working in regions of strong magnetic fields.

47. Figure P31.47 is a graph of the induced emf versus time for a coil of N turns rotating with angular speed ω in a uniform magnetic field directed perpendicular to the coil's axis of rotation. **What If?** Copy this sketch (on a larger scale) and on the same set of axes show the graph of emf versus t (a) if the number of turns in the coil is doubled, (b) if instead the angular speed is doubled, and (c) if the angular speed is doubled while the number of turns in the coil is halved.

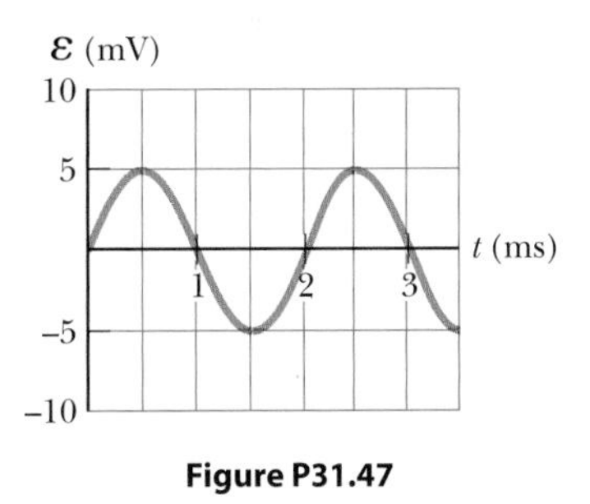

Figure P31.47

48. Two infinitely long solenoids (seen in cross section) pass through a circuit as shown in Figure P31.48. The magnitude of $\vec{\mathbf{B}}$ inside each is the same and is increasing at the rate of 100 T/s. What is the current in each resistor?

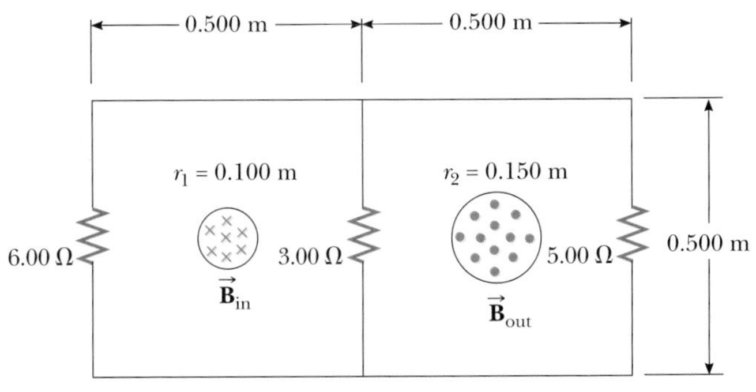

Figure P31.48

49. A conducting rod of length $\ell = 35.0$ cm is free to slide on two parallel conducting bars as shown in Figure P31.49. Two resistors $R_1 = 2.00\ \Omega$ and $R_2 = 5.00\ \Omega$ are connected across the ends of the bars to form a loop. A constant magnetic field $B = 2.50$ T is directed perpendicularly into the page. An external agent pulls the rod to the left with a constant speed of $v = 8.00$ m/s. Find (a) the currents in both resistors, (b) the total power delivered to the resistance of the circuit, and (c) the magnitude of the applied force that is needed to move the rod with this constant velocity.

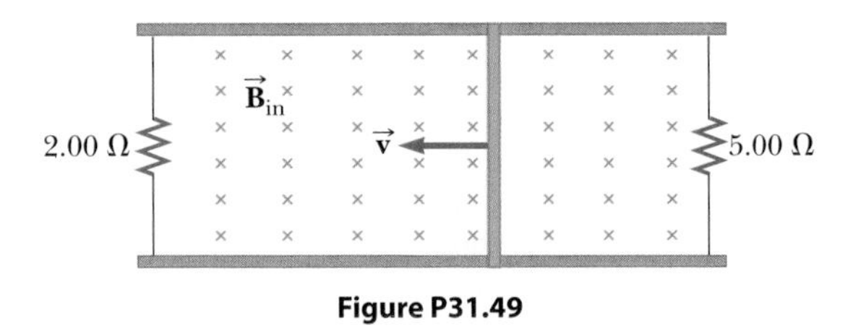

Figure P31.49

50. A bar of mass m, length d, and resistance R slides without friction in a horizontal plane, moving on parallel rails as shown in Figure P31.50. A battery that maintains a constant emf $\mathcal{E}$ is connected between the rails, and a constant magnetic field $\vec{\mathbf{B}}$ is directed perpendicularly to the plane of the page. Assuming the bar starts from rest, show that at time t it moves with a speed

$$v = \frac{\mathcal{E}}{Bd}\left(1 - e^{-B^2d^2t/mR}\right)$$

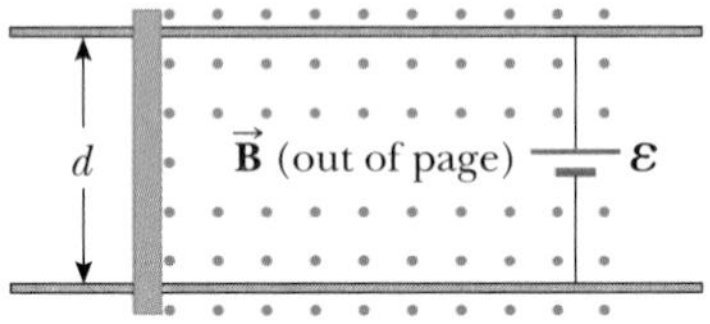

Figure P31.50

51. Suppose you wrap wire onto the core from a roll of cellophane tape to make a coil. How can you use a bar magnet to produce an induced voltage in the coil? What is the order of magnitude of the emf you generate? State the quantities you take as data and their values.

52. Magnetic field values are often determined by using a device known as a *search coil.* This technique depends on the measurement of the total charge passing through a coil in a time interval during which the magnetic flux linking the windings changes either because of the coil's motion or because of a change in the value of B. (a) Show that as the flux through the coil changes from Φ_1 to Φ_2, the charge transferred through the coil is given by $Q = N(\Phi_2 - \Phi_1)/R$, where R is the resistance of the coil and a sensitive ammeter connected across it and N is the number of turns. (b) As a specific example, calculate B when a 100-turn coil of resistance 200 Ω and cross-sectional area 40.0 cm² produces the following results. A total charge of 5.00×10^{-4} C passes through the coil when it is rotated in a uniform field from a position where the plane of the coil is perpendicular to the field to a position where the coil's plane is parallel to the field.

53. The plane of a square loop of wire with edge length $a = 0.200$ m is perpendicular to the Earth's magnetic field at a point where $B = 15.0\ \mu$T as shown in Figure P31.53. The total resistance of the loop and the wires connecting it to a sensitive ammeter is 0.500 Ω. If the loop is suddenly collapsed by horizontal forces as shown, what total charge passes through the ammeter?

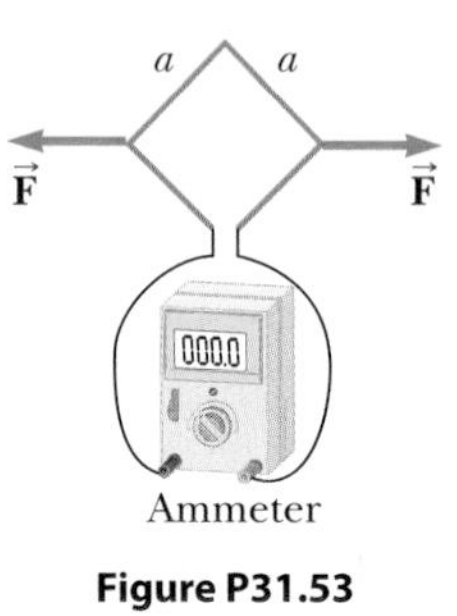

Figure P31.53

54. Review problem. A particle with a mass of 2.00×10^{-16} kg and a charge of 30.0 nC starts from rest, is accelerated by a strong electric field, and is fired from a small source inside a region of uniform constant magnetic field 0.600 T. The velocity of the particle is perpendicular to the field. The circular orbit of the particle encloses a magnetic flux of 15.0 μWb. (a) Calculate the speed of the particle. (b) Calculate the potential difference through which the particle accelerated inside the source.

55. ● In Figure P31.55, the rolling axle, 1.50 m long, is pushed along horizontal rails at a constant speed $v = 3.00$ m/s. A resistor $R = 0.400\ \Omega$ is connected to the rails at points a and b, directly opposite each other. The wheels make good electrical contact with the rails, so the axle, rails, and R form a closed-loop circuit. The only significant resistance in the circuit is R. A uniform magnetic field $B = 0.080\ 0$ T is vertically downward. (a) Find the induced current I in the resistor. (b) What horizontal force F is required to keep the axle rolling at constant speed? (c) Which end of the resistor, a or b, is at the higher electric potential? (d) **What If?** After the axle rolls past the resistor, does the current in R reverse direction? Explain your answer.

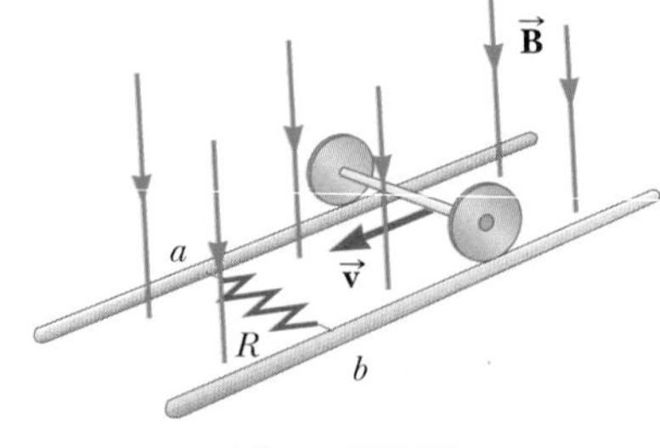

Figure P31.55

56. A conducting rod moves with a constant velocity $\vec{\mathbf{v}}$ in a direction perpendicular to a long, straight wire carrying a current I as shown in Figure P31.56. Show that the magnitude of the emf generated between the ends of the rod is

$$|\mathcal{E}| = \frac{\mu_0 v I \ell}{2\pi r}$$

In this case, note that the emf decreases with increasing r as you might expect.

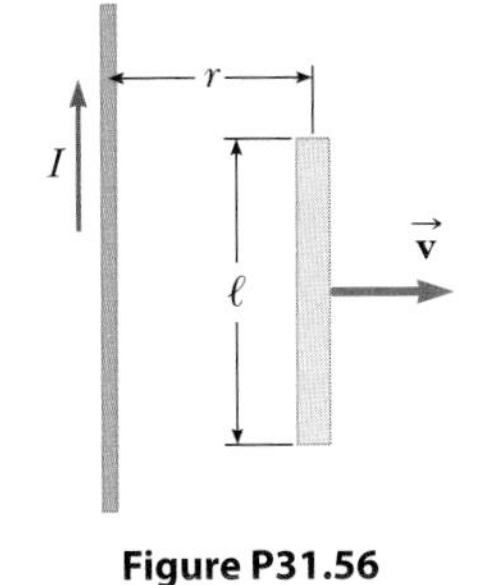

Figure P31.56

57. ● In Figure P31.57, a uniform magnetic field decreases at a constant rate $dB/dt = -K$, where K is a positive constant. A circular loop of wire of radius a containing a resistance R and a capacitance C is placed with its plane normal to the field. (a) Find the charge Q on the capacitor when it is fully charged. (b) Which plate is at the higher potential? (c) Discuss the force that causes the separation of charges.

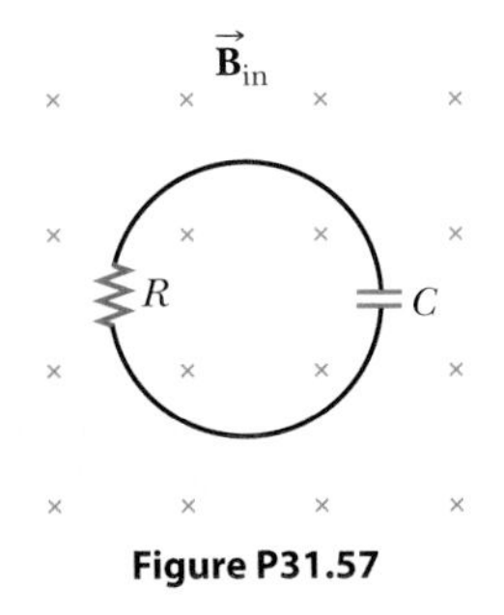

Figure P31.57

58. ● Figure P31.58 shows a compact, circular coil with 220 turns and radius 12.0 cm immersed in a uniform magnetic field parallel to the axis of the coil. The rate of change of the field has the constant magnitude 20.0 mT/s. (a) The following question cannot be answered with the information given. *Is the coil carrying clockwise or counterclockwise current?* What additional information is necessary to answer that question? (b) The coil overheats if more than 160 W of power is delivered to it. What resistance would the coil have at this critical point? To run cooler, should it have lower or higher resistance?

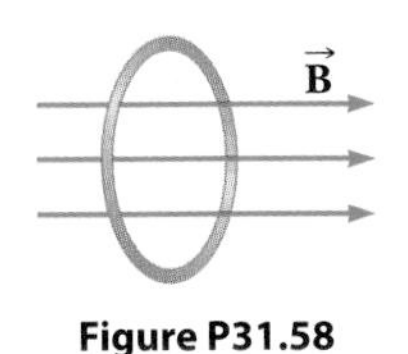

Figure P31.58

59. A rectangular coil of 60 turns, dimensions 0.100 m by 0.200 m and total resistance 10.0 Ω, rotates with angular speed 30.0 rad/s about the y axis in a region where a 1.00-T magnetic field is directed along the x axis. The rotation is initiated so that the plane of the coil is perpendicular to the direction of $\vec{\mathbf{B}}$ at $t = 0$. Calculate (a) the maximum induced emf in the coil, (b) the maximum rate of change of magnetic flux through the coil, (c) the induced emf at $t = 0.050\,0$ s, and (d) the torque exerted by the magnetic field on the coil at the instant when the emf is a maximum.

60. A small, circular washer of radius 0.500 cm is held directly below a long, straight wire carrying a current of 10.0 A. The washer is located 0.500 m above the top of a table (Fig. P31.60). (a) If the washer is dropped from rest, what is the magnitude of the average induced emf in the washer over the time interval between its release and the moment it hits the tabletop? Assume the magnetic field is nearly constant over the area of the washer and equal to the magnetic field at the center of the washer. (b) What is the direction of the induced current in the washer?

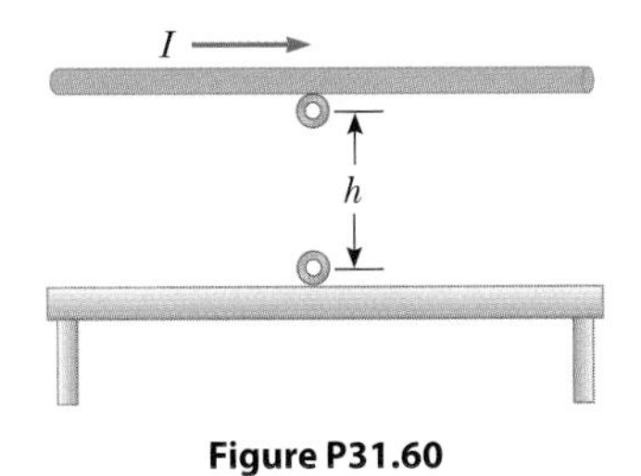

Figure P31.60

61. A conducting rod of length ℓ moves with velocity $\vec{\mathbf{v}}$ parallel to a long wire carrying a steady current I. The axis of the rod is maintained perpendicular to the wire with the near end a distance r away as shown in Figure P31.61. Show that the magnitude of the emf induced in the rod is

$$|\mathcal{E}| = \frac{\mu_0 I v}{2\pi} \ln\left(1 + \frac{\ell}{r}\right)$$

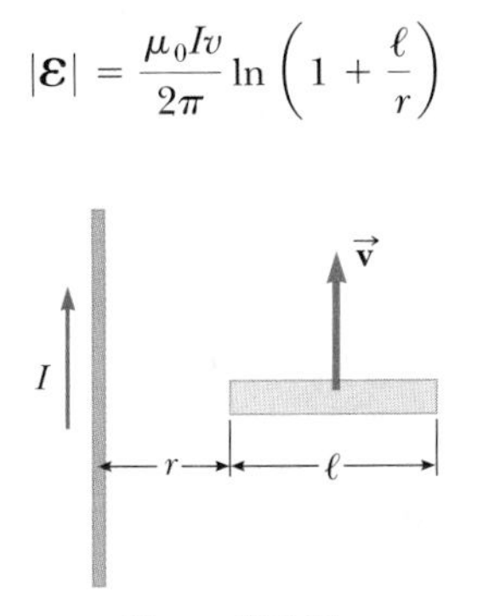

Figure P31.61

62. A rectangular loop of dimensions ℓ and w moves with a constant velocity $\vec{\mathbf{v}}$ away from a long wire that carries a current I in the plane of the loop (Fig. P31.62). The total resistance of the loop is R. Derive an expression that gives the current in the loop at the instant the near side is a distance r from the wire.

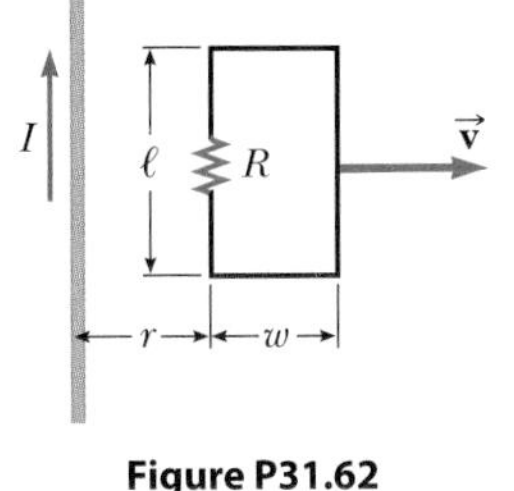

Figure P31.62

63. The magnetic flux through a metal ring varies with time t according to $\Phi_B = 3(at^3 - bt^2)\ \mathrm{T \cdot m^2}$, with $a = 2.00\ \mathrm{s^{-3}}$ and $b = 6.00\ \mathrm{s^{-2}}$. The resistance of the ring is 3.00 Ω. Determine the maximum current induced in the ring during the interval from $t = 0$ to $t = 2.00$ s.

64. **Review problem.** The bar of mass m in Figure P31.64 is pulled horizontally across parallel, frictionless rails by a massless string that passes over a light, frictionless pulley and is attached to a suspended object of mass M. The uniform magnetic field has a magnitude B, and the distance between the rails is ℓ. The only significant electrical resistance is the load resistor R shown connecting the rails at one end. Derive an expression that gives the horizontal speed of the bar as a function of time, assuming the suspended object is released with the bar at rest at $t = 0$.

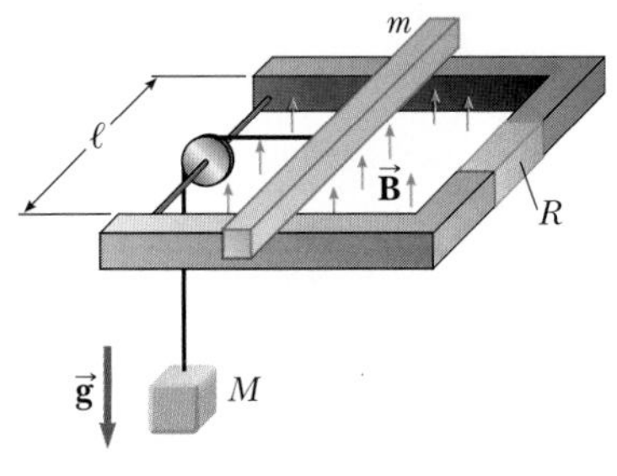

Figure P31.64

65. A *betatron* is a device that accelerates electrons to energies in the MeV range by means of electromagnetic induction. Electrons in a vacuum chamber are held in a circular orbit by a magnetic field perpendicular to the orbital plane. The magnetic field is gradually increased to induce an electric field around the orbit. (a) Show that the electric field is in the correct direction to make the electrons speed up. (b) Assume the radius of the orbit remains constant. Show that the average magnetic field over the area enclosed by the orbit must be twice as large as the magnetic field at the circle's circumference.

66. A thin wire 30.0 cm long is held parallel to and 80.0 cm above a long, thin wire carrying 200 A and resting on the horizontal floor (Fig. P31.66). The 30.0-cm wire is released at the instant $t = 0$ and falls, remaining parallel to the current-carrying wire as it falls. Assume the falling wire accelerates at 9.80 m/s^2. (a) Derive an equation for the emf induced in it as a function of time. (b) What is the minimum value of the emf? (c) What is the maximum value? (d) What is the induced emf 0.300 s after the wire is released?

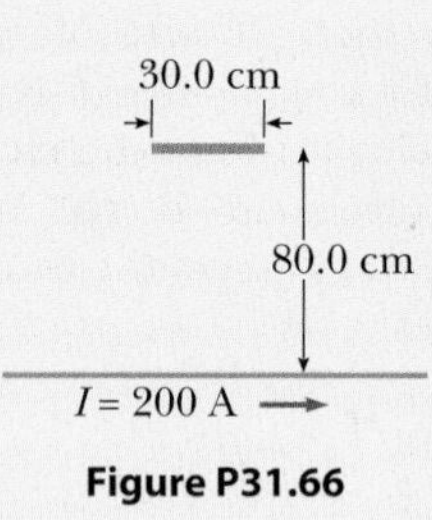

Figure P31.66

67. ▲ A long, straight wire carries a current that is given by $I = I_{max} \sin(\omega t + \phi)$. The wire lies in the plane of a rectangular coil of N turns of wire, as shown in Figure P31.8. The quantities I_{max}, ω, and ϕ are all constants. Determine the emf induced in the coil by the magnetic field created by the current in the straight wire. Assume $I_{max} = 50.0$ A, $\omega = 200\pi$ s^{-1}, $N = 100$, $h = w = 5.00$ cm, and $L = 20.0$ cm.

Answers to Quick Quizzes

31.1 (c). In all cases except this one, there is a change in the magnetic flux through the loop.

31.2 (c). The force on the wire is of magnitude $F_{app} = F_B = I\ell B$, with I given by Equation 31.6. Therefore, the force is proportional to the speed and the force doubles. Because $\mathcal{P} = F_{app}v$, the doubling of the force *and* the speed results in the power being four times as large.

31.3 (b). At the position of the loop, the magnetic field lines due to the wire point into the page. The loop is entering a region of stronger magnetic field as it drops toward the wire, so the flux is increasing. The induced current must set up a magnetic field that opposes this increase. To do so, it creates a magnetic field directed out of the page. By the right-hand rule for current loops, a counterclockwise current in the loop is required.

31.4 (a). Although reducing the resistance may increase the current the generator provides to a load, it does not alter the emf. Equation 31.11 shows that the emf depends on ω, B, and N, so all other choices increase the emf.

31.5 (b). When the aluminum sheet moves between the poles of the magnet, eddy currents are established in the aluminum. According to Lenz's law, these currents are in a direction so as to oppose the original change, which is the movement of the aluminum sheet in the magnetic field. The same principle is used in common laboratory triple-beam balances. See if you can find the magnet and the aluminum sheet the next time you use a triple-beam balance.

A treasure hunter uses a metal detector to search for buried objects at a beach. At the end of the metal detector is a coil of wire that is part of a circuit. When the coil comes near a metal object, the inductance of the coil is affected and the current in the circuit changes. This change triggers a signal in the earphones worn by the treasure hunter. We investigate inductance in this chapter. (Stone/Getty Images)

32 Inductance

In Chapter 31, we saw that an emf and a current are induced in a loop of wire when the magnetic flux through the area enclosed by the loop changes with time. This phenomenon of electromagnetic induction has some practical consequences. In this chapter, we first describe an effect known as *self-induction,* in which a time-varying current in a circuit produces an induced emf opposing the emf that initially set up the time-varying current. Self-induction is the basis of the *inductor,* an electrical circuit element. We discuss the energy stored in the magnetic field of an inductor and the energy density associated with the magnetic field.

Next, we study how an emf is induced in a coil as a result of a changing magnetic flux produced by a second coil, which is the basic principle of *mutual induction.* Finally, we examine the characteristics of circuits that contain inductors, resistors, and capacitors in various combinations.

32.1 Self-Induction and Inductance

In this chapter, we need to distinguish carefully between emfs and currents that are caused by physical sources such as batteries and those that are induced by changing magnetic fields. When we use a term (such as *emf* or *current*) without an adjective, we are describing the parameters associated with a physical source. We

JOSEPH HENRY
American Physicist (1797–1878)
Henry became the first director of the Smithsonian Institution and first president of the Academy of Natural Science. He improved the design of the electromagnet and constructed one of the first motors. He also discovered the phenomenon of self-induction, but he failed to publish his findings. The unit of inductance, the henry, is named in his honor.

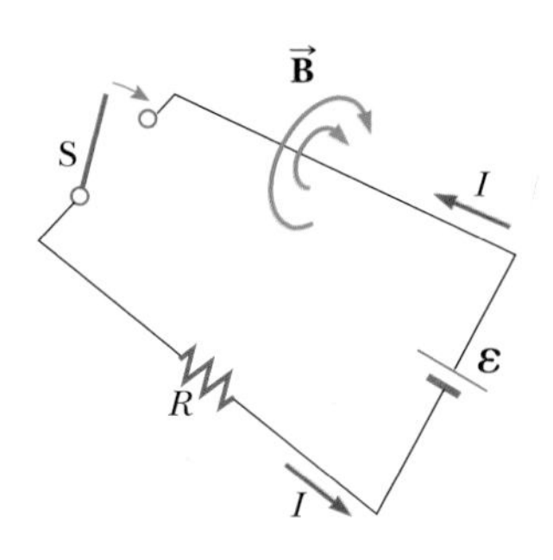

Figure 32.1 After the switch is closed, the current produces a magnetic flux through the area enclosed by the loop. As the current increases toward its equilibrium value, this magnetic flux changes in time and induces an emf in the loop.

use the adjective *induced* to describe those emfs and currents caused by a changing magnetic field.

Consider a circuit consisting of a switch, a resistor, and a source of emf as shown in Figure 32.1. The circuit diagram is represented in perspective to show the orientations of some of the magnetic field lines due to the current in the circuit. When the switch is thrown to its closed position, the current does not immediately jump from zero to its maximum value $\mathcal{E}/R$. Faraday's law of electromagnetic induction (Eq. 31.1) can be used to describe this effect as follows. As the current increases with time, the magnetic flux through the circuit loop due to this current also increases with time. This increasing flux creates an induced emf in the circuit. The direction of the induced emf is such that it would cause an induced current in the loop (if the loop did not already carry a current), which would establish a magnetic field opposing the change in the original magnetic field. Therefore, the direction of the induced emf is opposite the direction of the emf of the battery, which results in a gradual rather than instantaneous increase in the current to its final equilibrium value. Because of the direction of the induced emf, it is also called a *back emf*, similar to that in a motor as discussed in Chapter 31. This effect is called **self-induction** because the changing flux through the circuit and the resultant induced emf arise from the circuit itself. The emf $\mathcal{E}_L$ set up in this case is called a **self-induced emf.**

To obtain a quantitative description of self-induction, recall from Faraday's law that the induced emf is equal to the negative of the time rate of change of the magnetic flux. The magnetic flux is proportional to the magnetic field, which in turn is proportional to the current in the circuit. Therefore, **a self-induced emf is always proportional to the time rate of change of the current.** For any loop of wire, we can write this proportionality as

$$\mathcal{E}_L = -L\frac{dI}{dt} \tag{32.1}$$

where L is a proportionality constant—called the **inductance** of the loop—that depends on the geometry of the loop and other physical characteristics. If we consider a closely spaced coil of N turns (a toroid or an ideal solenoid) carrying a current I and containing N turns, Faraday's law tells us that $\mathcal{E}_L = -N\,d\Phi_B/dt$. Combining this expression with Equation 32.1 gives

Inductance of an N-turn coil ▶

$$L = \frac{N\Phi_B}{I} \tag{32.2}$$

where it is assumed the same magnetic flux passes through each turn and L is the inductance of the entire coil.

From Equation 32.1, we can also write the inductance as the ratio

Inductance ▶

$$L = -\frac{\mathcal{E}_L}{dI/dt} \tag{32.3}$$

Recall that resistance is a measure of the opposition to current ($R = \Delta V/I$); in comparison, Equation 32.3 shows us that inductance is a measure of the opposition to a *change* in current.

The SI unit of inductance is the **henry** (H), which as we can see from Equation 32.3 is 1 volt-second per ampere: $1\text{ H} = 1\text{ V}\cdot\text{s/A}$.

As shown in Example 32.1, the inductance of a coil depends on its geometry. This dependence is analogous to the capacitance of a capacitor depending on the geometry of its plates as we found in Chapter 26. Inductance calculations can be quite difficult to perform for complicated geometries, but the examples below involve simple situations for which inductances are easily evaluated.

Quick Quiz 32.1 A coil with zero resistance has its ends labeled *a* and *b*. The potential at *a* is higher than at *b*. Which of the following could be consistent with this situation? (a) The current is constant and is directed from *a* to *b*. (b) The current is constant and is directed from *b* to *a*. (c) The current is increasing and is directed from *a* to *b*. (d) The current is decreasing and is directed from *a* to *b*. (e) The current is increasing and is directed from *b* to *a*. (f) The current is decreasing and is directed from *b* to *a*.

EXAMPLE 32.1 Inductance of a Solenoid

Consider a uniformly wound solenoid having *N* turns and length ℓ. Assume ℓ is much longer than the radius of the windings and the core of the solenoid is air.

(A) Find the inductance of the solenoid.

SOLUTION

Conceptualize The magnetic field lines from each turn of the solenoid pass through all the turns, so an induced emf in each coil opposes changes in the current.

Categorize Because the solenoid is long, we can use the results for an ideal solenoid obtained in Chapter 30.

Analyze Find the magnetic flux through each turn of area *A* in the solenoid, using the expression for the magnetic field from Equation 30.17:

$$\Phi_B = BA = \mu_0 nIA = \mu_0 \frac{N}{\ell} IA$$

Substitute this expression into Equation 32.2:

$$L = \frac{N\Phi_B}{I} = \mu_0 \frac{N^2}{\ell} A \qquad \textbf{(32.4)}$$

(B) Calculate the inductance of the solenoid if it contains 300 turns, its length is 25.0 cm, and its cross-sectional area is 4.00 cm^2.

SOLUTION

Substitute numerical values into Equation 32.4:

$$L = (4\pi \times 10^{-7}\text{ T}\cdot\text{m/A})\frac{(300)^2}{25.0 \times 10^{-2}\text{ m}}(4.00 \times 10^{-4}\text{ m}^2)$$

$$= 1.81 \times 10^{-4}\text{ T}\cdot\text{m}^2/\text{A} = 0.181\text{ mH}$$

(C) Calculate the self-induced emf in the solenoid if the current it carries decreases at the rate of 50.0 A/s.

SOLUTION

Substitute $dI/dt = -50.0$ A/s into Equation 32.1:

$$\mathcal{E}_L = -L\frac{dI}{dt} = -(1.81 \times 10^{-4}\text{ H})(-50.0\text{ A/s})$$

$$= 9.05\text{ mV}$$

Finalize The result for part (A) shows that L depends on geometry and is proportional to the square of the number of turns. Because $N = n\ell$, we can also express the result in the form

$$L = \mu_0 \frac{(n\ell)^2}{\ell} A = \mu_0 n^2 A\ell = \mu_0 n^2 V \tag{32.5}$$

where $V = A\ell$ is the interior volume of the solenoid.

32.2 *RL* Circuits

If a circuit contains a coil such as a solenoid, the inductance of the coil prevents the current in the circuit from increasing or decreasing instantaneously. A circuit element that has a large inductance is called an **inductor** and has the circuit symbol —ooo—. We always assume the inductance of the remainder of a circuit is negligible compared with that of the inductor. Keep in mind, however, that even a circuit without a coil has some inductance that can affect the circuit's behavior.

Because the inductance of an inductor results in a back emf, **an inductor in a circuit opposes changes in the current in that circuit.** The inductor attempts to keep the current the same as it was before the change occurred. If the battery voltage in the circuit is increased so that the current rises, the inductor opposes this change and the rise is not instantaneous. If the battery voltage is decreased, the inductor causes a slow drop in the current rather than an immediate drop. Therefore, the inductor causes the circuit to be "sluggish" as it reacts to changes in the voltage.

Consider the circuit shown in Active Figure 32.2, which contains a battery of negligible internal resistance. This circuit is an ***RL* circuit** because the elements connected to the battery are a resistor and an inductor. The curved lines on switch S_2 suggest this switch can never be open; it is always set to either a or b. (If the switch is connected to neither a nor b, any current in the circuit suddenly stops.) Suppose S_2 is set to a and switch S_1 is open for $t < 0$ and then thrown closed at $t = 0$. The current in the circuit begins to increase, and a back emf (Eq. 32.1) that opposes the increasing current is induced in the inductor.

With this point in mind, let's apply Kirchhoff's loop rule to this circuit, traversing the circuit in the clockwise direction:

$$\mathcal{E} - IR - L\frac{dI}{dt} = 0 \tag{32.6}$$

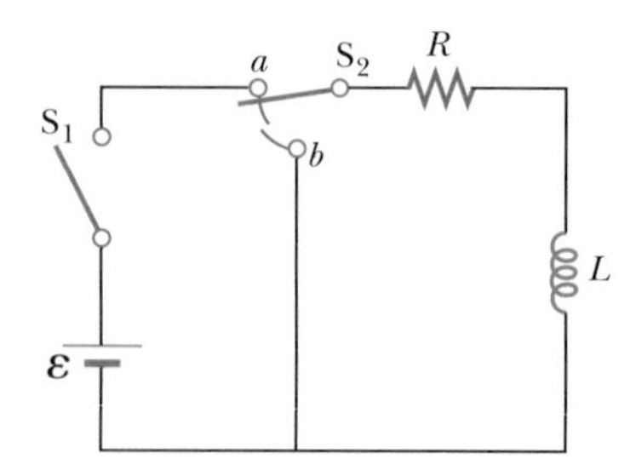

ACTIVE FIGURE 32.2

An *RL* circuit. When switch S_2 is in position a, the battery is in the circuit. When switch S_1 is thrown closed, the current increases and an emf that opposes the increasing current is induced in the inductor. When the switch is thrown to position b, the battery is no longer part of the circuit and the current decreases. The switch is designed so that it is never open, which would cause the current to stop.

Sign in at www.thomsonedu.com and go to ThomsonNOW to adjust the values of R and L and see the effect on the current. A graphical display as in Active Figure 32.3 is available.

where IR is the voltage drop across the resistor. (Kirchhoff's rules were developed for circuits with steady currents, but they can also be applied to a circuit in which the current is changing if we imagine them to represent the circuit at one *instant* of time.) Now let's find a solution to this differential equation, which is similar to that for the *RC* circuit (see Section 28.4).

A mathematical solution of Equation 32.6 represents the current in the circuit as a function of time. To find this solution, we change variables for convenience, letting $x = (\mathcal{E}/R) - I$, so $dx = -dI$. With these substitutions, Equation 32.6 becomes

$$x + \frac{L}{R}\frac{dx}{dt} = 0$$

Rearranging and integrating this last expression gives

$$\int_{x_0}^{x} \frac{dx}{x} = -\frac{R}{L}\int_0^t dt$$

$$\ln \frac{x}{x_0} = -\frac{R}{L}t$$

where x_0 is the value of x at time $t = 0$. Taking the antilogarithm of this result gives

$$x = x_0 e^{-Rt/L}$$

Because $I = 0$ at $t = 0$, note from the definition of x that $x_0 = \mathcal{E}/R$. Hence, this last expression is equivalent to

$$\frac{\mathcal{E}}{R} - I = \frac{\mathcal{E}}{R} e^{-Rt/L}$$

$$I = \frac{\mathcal{E}}{R}(1 - e^{-Rt/L})$$

This expression shows how the inductor affects the current. The current does not increase instantly to its final equilibrium value when the switch is closed, but instead increases according to an exponential function. If the inductance is removed from the circuit, which corresponds to letting L approach zero, the exponential term becomes zero and there is no time dependence of the current in this case; the current increases instantaneously to its final equilibrium value in the absence of the inductance.

We can also write this expression as

$$I = \frac{\mathcal{E}}{R}(1 - e^{-t/\tau}) \quad (32.7)$$

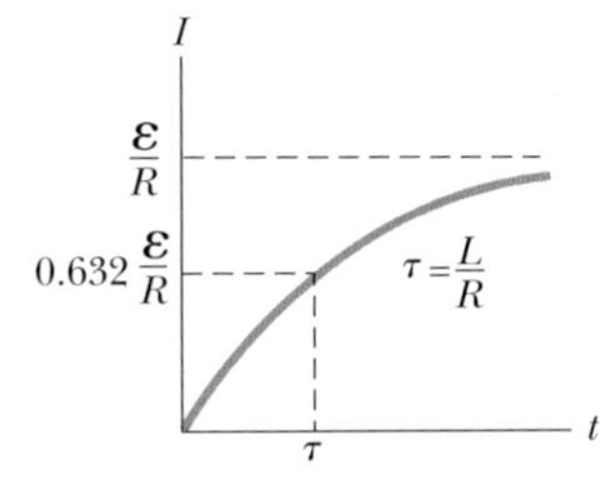

ACTIVE FIGURE 32.3

Plot of the current versus time for the RL circuit shown in Active Figure 32.2. When switch S_1 is thrown closed at $t = 0$, the current increases toward its maximum value $\mathcal{E}/R$. The time constant τ is the time interval required for I to reach 63.2% of its maximum value.

Sign in at www.thomsonedu.com and go to ThomsonNOW to observe this graph develop after switch S_1 in Active Figure 32.2 is thrown closed.

where the constant τ is the **time constant** of the RL circuit:

$$\tau = \frac{L}{R} \quad (32.8)$$

◀ Time constant of an *RL* circuit

Physically, τ is the time interval required for the current in the circuit to reach $(1 - e^{-1}) = 0.632 = 63.2\%$ of its final value $\mathcal{E}/R$. The time constant is a useful parameter for comparing the time responses of various circuits.

Active Figure 32.3 shows a graph of the current versus time in the RL circuit. Notice that the equilibrium value of the current, which occurs as t approaches infinity, is $\mathcal{E}/R$. That can be seen by setting dI/dt equal to zero in Equation 32.6 and solving for the current I. (At equilibrium, the change in the current is zero.) Therefore, the current initially increases very rapidly and then gradually approaches the equilibrium value $\mathcal{E}/R$ as t approaches infinity.

Let's also investigate the time rate of change of the current. Taking the first time derivative of Equation 32.7 gives

$$\frac{dI}{dt} = \frac{\mathcal{E}}{L} e^{-t/\tau} \quad (32.9)$$

This result shows that the time rate of change of the current is a maximum (equal to $\mathcal{E}/L$) at $t = 0$ and falls off exponentially to zero as t approaches infinity (Fig. 32.4).

Now consider the RL circuit in Active Figure 32.2 again. Suppose switch S_2 has been set at position a long enough (and switch S_1 remains closed) to allow the current to reach its equilibrium value $\mathcal{E}/R$. In this situation, the circuit is described by the outer loop in Active Figure 32.2. If S_2 is thrown from a to b, the circuit is now described by only the right-hand loop in Active Figure 32.2. Therefore, the battery has been eliminated from the circuit. Setting $\mathcal{E} = 0$ in Equation 32.6 gives

$$IR + L\frac{dI}{dt} = 0$$

It is left as a problem (Problem 10) to show that the solution of this differential equation is

$$I = \frac{\mathcal{E}}{R} e^{-t/\tau} = I_i e^{-t/\tau} \quad (32.10)$$

where $\mathcal{E}$ is the emf of the battery and $I_i = \mathcal{E}/R$ is the initial current at the instant the switch is thrown to b.

If the circuit did not contain an inductor, the current would immediately decrease to zero when the battery is removed. When the inductor is present, it

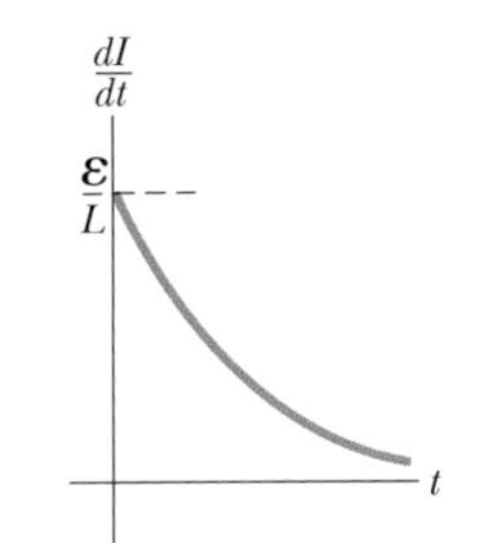

Figure 32.4 Plot of dI/dt versus time for the RL circuit shown in Active Figure 32.2. The time rate of change of current is a maximum at $t = 0$, which is the instant at which switch S_1 is thrown closed. The rate decreases exponentially with time as I increases toward its maximum value.

ACTIVE FIGURE 32.5

Current versus time for the right-hand loop of the circuit shown in Active Figure 32.2. For $t < 0$, switch S_2 is at position *a*. At $t = 0$, the switch is thrown to position *b* and the current has its maximum value $\mathcal{E}/R$.

Sign in at www.thomsonedu.com and go to ThomsonNOW to observe this graph develop after the switch in Active Figure 32.2 is thrown to position *b*.

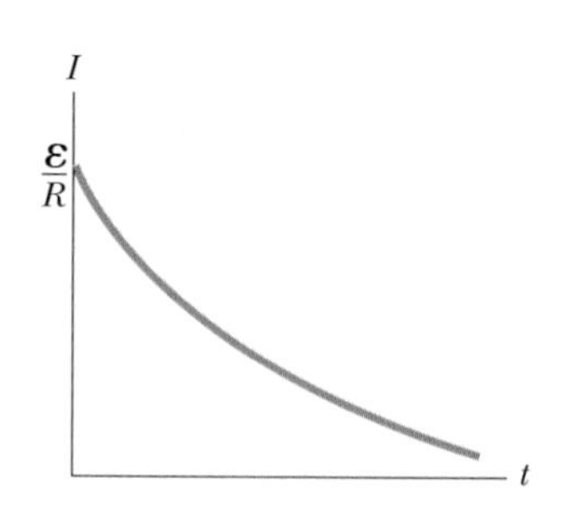

opposes the decrease in the current and causes the current to decrease exponentially. A graph of the current in the circuit versus time (Active Fig. 32.5) shows that the current is continuously decreasing with time.

Quick Quiz 32.2 Consider the circuit in Active Figure 32.2 with S_1 open and S_2 at position *a*. Switch S_1 is now thrown closed. **(i)** At the instant it is closed, across which circuit element is the voltage equal to the emf of the battery? (a) the resistor (b) the inductor (c) both the inductor and resistor **(ii)** After a very long time, across which circuit element is the voltage equal to the emf of the battery? Choose from among the same answers.

EXAMPLE 32.2 Time Constant of an *RL* Circuit

Consider the circuit in Active Figure 32.2 again. Suppose the circuit elements have the following values: $\mathcal{E} = 12.0$ V, $R = 6.00\ \Omega$, and $L = 30.0$ mH.

(A) Find the time constant of the circuit.

SOLUTION

Conceptualize You should understand the behavior of this circuit from the discussion in this section.

Categorize We evaluate the results using equations developed in this section, so this example is a substitution problem.

Evaluate the time constant from Equation 32.8:

$$\tau = \frac{L}{R} = \frac{30.0 \times 10^{-3}\ \text{H}}{6.00\ \Omega} = 5.00\ \text{ms}$$

(B) Switch S_2 is at position *a*, and switch S_1 is thrown closed at $t = 0$. Calculate the current in the circuit at $t = 2.00$ ms.

SOLUTION

Evaluate the current at $t = 2.00$ ms from Equation 32.7:

$$I = \frac{\mathcal{E}}{R}(1 - e^{-t/\tau}) = \frac{12.0\ \text{V}}{6.00\ \Omega}(1 - e^{-2.00\ \text{ms}/5.00\ \text{ms}}) = 2.00\ \text{A}\ (1 - e^{-0.400})$$

$$= 0.659\ \text{A}$$

(C) Compare the potential difference across the resistor with that across the inductor.

SOLUTION

At the instant the switch is closed, there is no current and therefore no potential difference across the resistor. At this instant, the battery voltage appears entirely across the inductor in the form of a back emf of 12.0 V as the inductor tries to maintain the zero-current condition. (The top end of the inductor in Active Fig. 32.2 is at a higher electric potential than the bottom end.) As time passes, the emf across the inductor decreases and the current in the resistor (and hence the voltage across it) increases as shown in Figure 32.6. The sum of the two voltages at all times is 12.0 V.

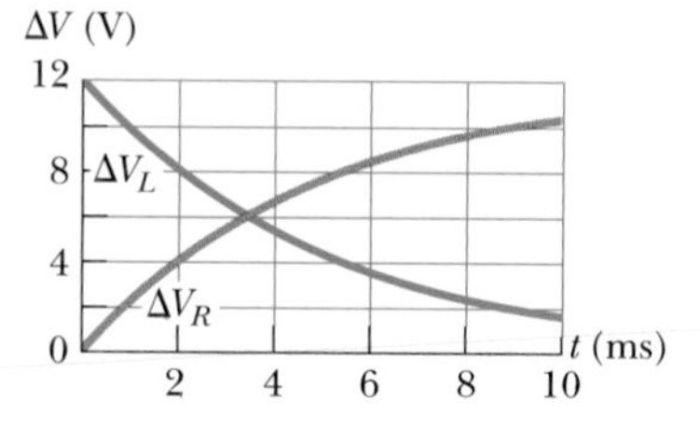

Figure 32.6 (Example 32.2) The time behavior of the voltages across the resistor and inductor in Active Figure 32.2 given the values provided in this example.

What If? In Figure 32.6, the voltages across the resistor and inductor are equal at 3.4 ms. What if you wanted to delay the condition in which the voltages are equal to some later instant, such as $t = 10.0$ ms? Which parameter, L or R, would require the least adjustment, in terms of a percentage change, to achieve that?

Answer Figure 32.6 shows that the voltages are equal when the voltage across the inductor has fallen to half its original value. Therefore, the time interval required for the voltages to become equal is the *half-life* $t_{1/2}$ of the decay. We introduced the half-life in the **What If?** section of Example 28.10 to describe the exponential decay in RC circuits, where $t_{1/2} = 0.693\tau$.

From the desired half-life of 10.0 ms, use the result from Example 28.10 to find the time constant of the circuit:

$$\tau = \frac{t_{1/2}}{0.693} = \frac{10.0 \text{ ms}}{0.693} = 14.4 \text{ ms}$$

Hold L fixed and find the value of R that gives this time constant:

$$\tau = \frac{L}{R} \rightarrow R = \frac{L}{\tau} = \frac{30.0 \times 10^{-3}\text{ H}}{14.4 \text{ ms}} = 2.08\ \Omega$$

Now hold R fixed and find the appropriate value of L:

$$\tau = \frac{L}{R} \rightarrow L = \tau R = (14.4 \text{ ms})(6.00\ \Omega) = 86.4 \times 10^{-3}\text{ H}$$

The change in R corresponds to a 65% decrease compared with the initial resistance. The change in L represents a 188% increase in inductance! Therefore, a much smaller percentage adjustment in R can achieve the desired effect than would an adjustment in L.

32.3 Energy in a Magnetic Field

A battery in a circuit containing an inductor must provide more energy than in a circuit without the inductor. Part of the energy supplied by the battery appears as internal energy in the resistance in the circuit, and the remaining energy is stored in the magnetic field of the inductor. Multiplying each term in Equation 32.6 by I and rearranging the expression gives

$$I\mathcal{E} = I^2R + LI\frac{dI}{dt} \quad (32.11)$$

Recognizing $I\mathcal{E}$ as the rate at which energy is supplied by the battery and I^2R as the rate at which energy is delivered to the resistor, we see that $LI(dI/dt)$ must represent the rate at which energy is being stored in the inductor. If U is the energy stored in the inductor at any time, we can write the rate dU/dt at which energy is stored as

$$\frac{dU}{dt} = LI\frac{dI}{dt}$$

To find the total energy stored in the inductor at any instant, let's rewrite this expression as $dU = LI\,dI$ and integrate:

$$U = \int dU = \int_0^I LI\,dI = L\int_0^I I\,dI$$

$$U = \tfrac{1}{2}LI^2 \quad (32.12)$$

◀ Energy stored in an inductor

where L is constant and has been removed from the integral. Equation 32.12 represents the energy stored in the magnetic field of the inductor when the current is I. It is similar in form to Equation 26.11 for the energy stored in the electric field of a capacitor, $U = \frac{1}{2}C(\Delta V)^2$. In either case, energy is required to establish a field.

PITFALL PREVENTION 32.1
Capacitors, Resistors, and Inductors Store Energy Differently

Different energy-storage mechanisms are at work in capacitors, inductors, and resistors. A charged capacitor stores energy as electrical potential energy. An inductor stores energy as what we could call magnetic potential energy when it carries current. Energy delivered to a resistor is transformed to internal energy.

We can also determine the energy density of a magnetic field. For simplicity, consider a solenoid whose inductance is given by Equation 32.5:

$$L = \mu_0 n^2 V$$

The magnetic field of a solenoid is given by Equation 30.17:

$$B = \mu_0 n I$$

Substituting the expression for L and $I = B/\mu_0 n$ into Equation 32.12 gives

$$U = \tfrac{1}{2}LI^2 = \tfrac{1}{2}\mu_0 n^2 V\left(\frac{B}{\mu_0 n}\right)^2 = \frac{B^2}{2\mu_0}V \qquad \textbf{(32.13)}$$

The magnetic energy density, or the energy stored per unit volume in the magnetic field of the inductor, is

Magnetic energy density ▶

$$u_B = \frac{U}{V} = \frac{B^2}{2\mu_0} \qquad \textbf{(32.14)}$$

Although this expression was derived for the special case of a solenoid, it is valid for any region of space in which a magnetic field exists. Equation 32.14 is similar in form to Equation 26.13 for the energy per unit volume stored in an electric field, $u_E = \frac{1}{2}\epsilon_0 E^2$. In both cases, the energy density is proportional to the square of the field magnitude.

Quick Quiz 32.3 You are performing an experiment that requires the highest-possible magnetic energy density in the interior of a very long current-carrying solenoid. Which of the following adjustments increases the energy density? (More than one choice may be correct.) (a) increasing the number of turns per unit length on the solenoid (b) increasing the cross-sectional area of the solenoid (c) increasing only the length of the solenoid while keeping the number of turns per unit length fixed (d) increasing the current in the solenoid

EXAMPLE 32.3 What Happens to the Energy in the Inductor?

Consider once again the *RL* circuit shown in Active Figure 32.2, with switch S_2 at position *a* and the current having reached its steady-state value. When S_2 is thrown to position *b*, the current in the right-hand loop decays exponentially with time according to the expression $I = I_i e^{-t/\tau}$, where $I_i = \mathcal{E}/R$ is the initial current in the circuit and $\tau = L/R$ is the time constant. Show that all the energy initially stored in the magnetic field of the inductor appears as internal energy in the resistor as the current decays to zero.

SOLUTION

Conceptualize Before S_2 is thrown to *b*, energy is being delivered at a constant rate to the resistor from the battery and energy is stored in the magnetic field of the inductor. After $t = 0$, when S_2 is thrown to *b*, the battery can no longer provide energy and energy is delivered to the resistor only from the inductor.

Categorize We model the right-hand loop of the circuit as an isolated system so that energy is transferred between components of the system but does not leave the system.

Analyze The energy in the magnetic field of the inductor at any time is U. The rate dU/dt at which energy leaves the inductor and is delivered to the resistor is equal to I^2R, where I is the instantaneous current.

Substitute the current given by Equation 32.10 into $dU/dt = I^2R$:

$$\frac{dU}{dt} = I^2R = (I_i e^{-Rt/L})^2 R = I_i^2 R e^{-2Rt/L}$$

Solve for dU and integrate this expression over the limits $t = 0$ to $t \rightarrow \infty$:

$$U = \int_0^\infty I_i^2 R e^{-2Rt/L}\, dt = I_i^2 R \int_0^\infty e^{-2Rt/L}\, dt$$

The value of the definite integral can be shown to be $L/2R$ (see Problem 26). Use this result to evaluate U:

$$U = I_i^2 R\left(\frac{L}{2R}\right) = \frac{1}{2}LI_i^2$$

Finalize This result is equal to the initial energy stored in the magnetic field of the inductor, given by Equation 32.12, as we set out to prove.

EXAMPLE 32.4 **The Coaxial Cable**

Coaxial cables are often used to connect electrical devices, such as your stereo system, and in receiving signals in television cable systems. Model a long coaxial cable as two thin, concentric, cylindrical conducting shells of radii a and b and length ℓ as in Figure 32.7. The conducting shells carry the same current I in opposite directions. Calculate the inductance L of this cable.

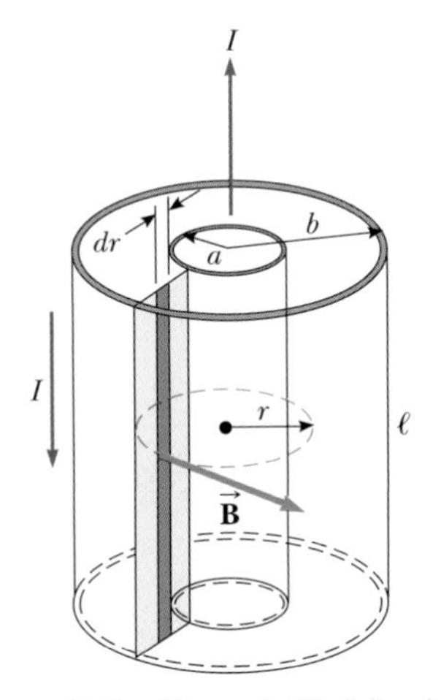

Figure 32.7 (Example 32.4) Section of a long coaxial cable. The inner and outer conductors carry equal currents in opposite directions.

SOLUTION

Conceptualize Consider Figure 32.7. Although we do not have a visible coil in this geometry, imagine a thin, radial slice of the coaxial cable such as the light gold rectangle in Figure 32.7. If the inner and outer conductors are connected at the ends of the cable (above and below the figure), this slice represents one large conducting loop. The current in the loop sets up a magnetic field between the inner and outer conductors that passes through this loop. If the current changes, the magnetic field changes and the induced emf opposes the original change in the current in the conductors.

Categorize We categorize this situation as one in which we must return to the fundamental definition of inductance, Equation 32.2.

Analyze We must find the magnetic flux through the light gold rectangle in Figure 32.7. Ampère's law (see Section 30.3) tells us that the magnetic field in the region between the shells is due to the inner conductor and that its magnitude is $B = \mu_0 I/2\pi r$, where r is measured from the common center of the shells. The magnetic field is zero outside the outer shell ($r > b$) because the net current passing through the area enclosed by a circular path surrounding the cable is zero; hence, from Ampère's law, $\oint \vec{\mathbf{B}} \cdot d\vec{\mathbf{s}} = 0$. The magnetic field is zero inside the inner shell because the shell is hollow and no current is present within a radius $r < a$.

The magnetic field is perpendicular to the light gold rectangle of length ℓ and width $b - a$, the cross section of interest. Because the magnetic field varies with radial position across this rectangle, we must use calculus to find the total magnetic flux.

Divide the light gold rectangle into strips of width dr such as the darker strip in Figure 32.7. Evaluate the magnetic flux through such a strip:

$$\Phi_B = \int B\,dA = \int B\ell\,dr$$

Substitute for the magnetic field and integrate over the entire light gold rectangle:

$$\Phi_B = \int_a^b \frac{\mu_0 I}{2\pi r}\ell\,dr = \frac{\mu_0 I\ell}{2\pi}\int_a^b \frac{dr}{r} = \frac{\mu_0 I\ell}{2\pi}\ln\left(\frac{b}{a}\right)$$

Use Equation 32.2 to find the inductance of the cable:

$$L = \frac{\Phi_B}{I} = \frac{\mu_0 \ell}{2\pi}\ln\left(\frac{b}{a}\right)$$

Finalize The inductance increases if ℓ increases, if b increases, or if a decreases. This result is consistent with our conceptualization: any of these changes increases the size of the loop represented by our radial slice and through which the magnetic field passes, increasing the inductance.

32.4 Mutual Inductance

Very often, the magnetic flux through the area enclosed by a circuit varies with time because of time-varying currents in nearby circuits. This condition induces an emf through a process known as *mutual induction,* so named because it depends on the interaction of two circuits.

Consider the two closely wound coils of wire shown in cross-sectional view in Figure 32.8. The current I_1 in coil 1, which has N_1 turns, creates a magnetic field. Some of the magnetic field lines pass through coil 2, which has N_2 turns. The magnetic flux caused by the current in coil 1 and passing through coil 2 is represented by Φ_{12}. In analogy to Equation 32.2, we can identify the **mutual inductance** M_{12} of coil 2 with respect to coil 1:

Definition of mutual inductance ▶

$$M_{12} = \frac{N_2 \Phi_{12}}{I_1} \tag{32.15}$$

Mutual inductance depends on the geometry of both circuits and on their orientation with respect to each other. As the circuit separation distance increases, the mutual inductance decreases because the flux linking the circuits decreases.

If the current I_1 varies with time, we see from Faraday's law and Equation 32.15 that the emf induced by coil 1 in coil 2 is

$$\mathcal{E}_2 = -N_2 \frac{d\Phi_{12}}{dt} = -N_2 \frac{d}{dt}\left(\frac{M_{12} I_1}{N_2}\right) = -M_{12}\frac{dI_1}{dt} \tag{32.16}$$

Figure 32.8 A cross-sectional view of two adjacent coils. A current in coil 1 sets up a magnetic field, and some of the magnetic field lines pass through coil 2.

In the preceding discussion, it was assumed the current is in coil 1. Let's also imagine a current I_2 in coil 2. The preceding discussion can be repeated to show that there is a mutual inductance M_{21}. If the current I_2 varies with time, the emf induced by coil 2 in coil 1 is

$$\mathcal{E}_1 = -M_{21}\frac{dI_2}{dt} \tag{32.17}$$

In mutual induction, the emf induced in one coil is always proportional to the rate at which the current in the other coil is changing. Although the proportionality constants M_{12} and M_{21} have been treated separately, it can be shown that they are equal. Therefore, with $M_{12} = M_{21} = M$, Equations 32.16 and 32.17 become

$$\mathcal{E}_2 = -M\frac{dI_1}{dt} \quad \text{and} \quad \mathcal{E}_1 = -M\frac{dI_2}{dt}$$

These two equations are similar in form to Equation 32.1 for the self-induced emf $\mathcal{E} = -L\,(dI/dt)$. The unit of mutual inductance is the henry.

Quick Quiz 32.4 In Figure 32.8, coil 1 is moved closer to coil 2, with the orientation of both coils remaining fixed. Because of this movement, the mutual induction of the two coils (a) increases, (b) decreases, or (c) is unaffected.

EXAMPLE 32.5 "Wireless" Battery Charger

An electric toothbrush has a base designed to hold the toothbrush handle when not in use. As shown in Figure 32.9a, the handle has a cylindrical hole that fits loosely over a matching cylinder on the base. When the handle is placed on the base, a changing current in a solenoid inside the base cylinder induces a current in a coil inside the handle. This induced current charges the battery in the handle.

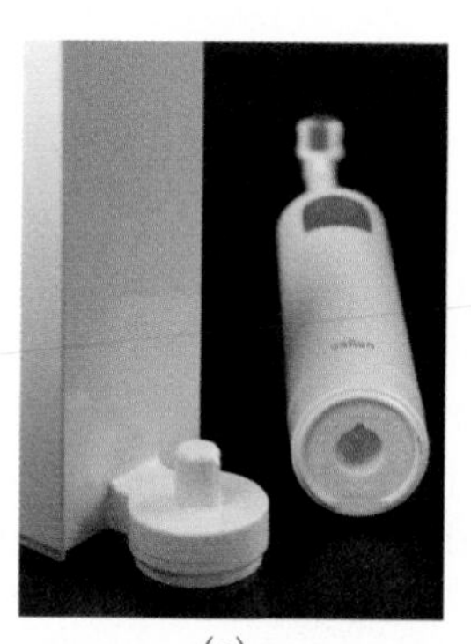

(a) (b)

Figure 32.9 (Example 32.5) (a) This electric toothbrush uses the mutual induction of solenoids as part of its battery-charging system. (b) A coil of N_H turns wrapped around the center of a solenoid of N_B turns.

We can model the base as a solenoid of length ℓ with N_B turns (Fig. 32.9b), carrying a current I, and having a cross-sectional area A. The handle coil contains N_H turns and completely surrounds the base coil. Find the mutual inductance of the system.

SOLUTION

Conceptualize Be sure you can identify the two coils in the situation and understand that a changing current in one coil induces a current in the second coil.

Categorize We will evaluate the result using concepts discussed in this section, so we categorize this example as a substitution problem.

Use Equation 30.17 to express the magnetic field in the interior of the base solenoid:

$$B = \mu_0 \frac{N_B}{\ell} I$$

Find the mutual inductance, noting that the magnetic flux Φ_{BH} through the handle's coil caused by the magnetic field of the base coil is BA:

$$M = \frac{N_H \Phi_{BH}}{I} = \frac{N_H BA}{I} = \mu_0 \frac{N_B N_H}{\ell} A$$

Wireless charging is used in a number of other "cordless" devices. One significant example is the inductive charging used by some manufacturers of electric cars that avoids direct metal-to-metal contact between the car and the charging apparatus.

32.5 Oscillations in an *LC* Circuit

When a capacitor is connected to an inductor as illustrated in Figure 32.10, the combination is an ***LC* circuit.** If the capacitor is initially charged and the switch is then closed, both the current in the circuit and the charge on the capacitor oscillate between maximum positive and negative values. If the resistance of the circuit is zero, no energy is transformed to internal energy. In the following analysis, the resistance in the circuit is neglected. We also assume an idealized situation in which energy is not radiated away from the circuit. This radiation mechanism is discussed in Chapter 34.

Assume the capacitor has an initial charge Q_{max} (the maximum charge) and the switch is open for $t < 0$ and then closed at $t = 0$. Let's investigate what happens from an energy viewpoint.

When the capacitor is fully charged, the energy U in the circuit is stored in the capacitor's electric field and is equal to $Q_{max}^2/2C$ (Eq. 26.11). At this time, the current in the circuit is zero; therefore, no energy is stored in the inductor. After the switch is closed, the rate at which charges leave or enter the capacitor plates (which is also the rate at which the charge on the capacitor changes) is equal to the current in the circuit. After the switch is closed and the capacitor begins to discharge, the energy stored in its electric field decreases. The capacitor's discharge represents a current in the circuit, and some energy is now stored in the magnetic field of the inductor. Therefore, energy is transferred from the electric field of the capacitor to the magnetic field of the inductor. When the capacitor is fully discharged, it stores no energy. At this time, the current reaches its maximum value and all the energy in the circuit is stored in the inductor. The current continues in the same direction, decreasing in magnitude, with the capacitor eventually becoming fully charged again but with the polarity of its plates now opposite the initial polarity. This process is followed by another discharge until the circuit returns to its original state of maximum charge Q_{max} and the plate polarity shown in Figure 32.10. The energy continues to oscillate between inductor and capacitor.

The oscillations of the *LC* circuit are an electromagnetic analog to the mechanical oscillations of the block–spring system studied in Chapter 15. Much of what

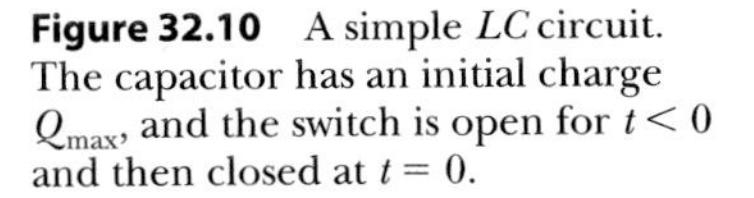

Figure 32.10 A simple *LC* circuit. The capacitor has an initial charge Q_{max}, and the switch is open for $t < 0$ and then closed at $t = 0$.

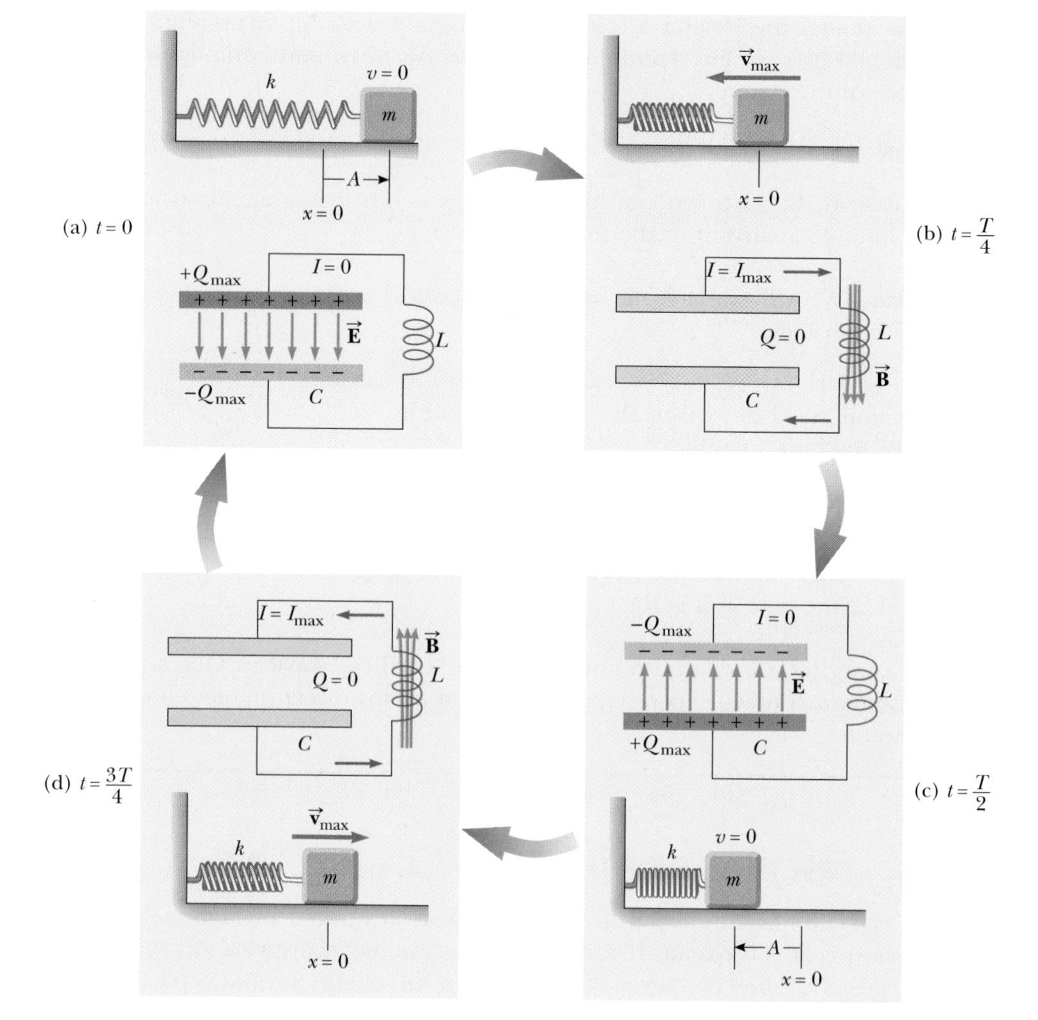

ACTIVE FIGURE 32.11

Energy transfer in a resistanceless, nonradiating LC circuit. The capacitor has a charge Q_{max} at $t = 0$, the instant at which the switch is closed. The mechanical analog of this circuit is a block–spring system.

Sign in at www.thomsonedu.com and go to ThomsonNOW to adjust the values of C and L and see the effect on the oscillating current. The block on the spring oscillates in a mechanical analog of the electrical oscillations. A graphical display as in Active Figure 32.12 is available, as is an energy bar graph.

was discussed there is applicable to LC oscillations. For example, we investigated the effect of driving a mechanical oscillator with an external force, which leads to the phenomenon of *resonance.* The same phenomenon is observed in the LC circuit. (See Section 33.7.)

A representation of the energy transfer in an LC circuit is shown in Active Figure 32.11. As mentioned, the behavior of the circuit is analogous to that of the oscillating block–spring system studied in Chapter 15. The potential energy $\frac{1}{2}kx^2$ stored in a stretched spring is analogous to the potential energy $Q_{max}^2/2C$ stored in the capacitor. The kinetic energy $\frac{1}{2}mv^2$ of the moving block is analogous to the magnetic energy $\frac{1}{2}LI^2$ stored in the inductor, which requires the presence of moving charges. In Active Figure 32.11a, all the energy is stored as electric potential energy in the capacitor at $t = 0$ (because $I = 0$), just as all the energy in a block–spring system is initially stored as potential energy in the spring if it is stretched and released at $t = 0$. In Active Figure 32.11b, all the energy is stored as magnetic energy $\frac{1}{2}LI_{max}^2$ in the inductor, where I_{max} is the maximum current. Active Figures 32.11c and 32.11d show subsequent quarter-cycle situations in which the energy is all electric or all magnetic. At intermediate points, part of the energy is electric and part is magnetic.

Consider some arbitrary time t after the switch is closed so that the capacitor has a charge $Q < Q_{max}$ and the current is $I < I_{max}$. At this time, both circuit elements store energy, but the sum of the two energies must equal the total initial energy U stored in the fully charged capacitor at $t = 0$:

Total energy stored in an LC circuit ▶

$$U = U_C + U_L = \frac{Q^2}{2C} + \tfrac{1}{2}LI^2 \qquad (32.18)$$

Because we have assumed the circuit resistance to be zero and we ignore electromagnetic radiation, no energy is transformed to internal energy and none is transferred out of the system of the circuit. Therefore, *the total energy of the system must remain constant in time.* We describe the constant energy of the system mathematically by setting $dU/dt = 0$. Therefore, by differentiating Equation 32.18 with respect to time while noting that Q and I vary with time gives

$$\frac{dU}{dt} = \frac{d}{dt}\left(\frac{Q^2}{2C} + \tfrac{1}{2}LI^2\right) = \frac{Q}{C}\frac{dQ}{dt} + LI\frac{dI}{dt} = 0 \qquad (32.19)$$

We can reduce this result to a differential equation in one variable by remembering that the current in the circuit is equal to the rate at which the charge on the capacitor changes: $I = dQ/dt$. It then follows that $dI/dt = d^2Q/dt^2$. Substitution of these relationships into Equation 32.19 gives

$$\frac{Q}{C} + L\frac{d^2Q}{dt^2} = 0$$

$$\frac{d^2Q}{dt^2} = -\frac{1}{LC}Q \qquad (32.20)$$

Let's solve for Q by noting that this expression is of the same form as the analogous Equations 15.3 and 15.5 for a block–spring system:

$$\frac{d^2x}{dt^2} = -\frac{k}{m}x = -\omega^2 x$$

where k is the spring constant, m is the mass of the block, and $\omega = \sqrt{k/m}$. The solution of this mechanical equation has the general form (Eq. 15.6):

$$x = A\cos(\omega t + \phi)$$

where A is the amplitude of the simple harmonic motion (the maximum value of x), ω is the angular frequency of this motion, and ϕ is the phase constant; the values of A and ϕ depend on the initial conditions. Because Equation 32.20 is of the same mathematical form as the differential equation of the simple harmonic oscillator, it has the solution

$$Q = Q_{\max}\cos(\omega t + \phi) \qquad (32.21)$$

◀ Charge as a function of time for an ideal *LC* circuit

where $Q_{\max}$ is the maximum charge of the capacitor and the angular frequency ω is

$$\omega = \frac{1}{\sqrt{LC}} \qquad (32.22)$$

◀ Angular frequency of oscillation in an *LC* circuit

Note that the angular frequency of the oscillations depends solely on the inductance and capacitance of the circuit. Equation 32.22 gives the *natural frequency* of oscillation of the LC circuit.

Because Q varies sinusoidally with time, the current in the circuit also varies sinusoidally. We can show that by differentiating Equation 32.21 with respect to time:

$$I = \frac{dQ}{dt} = -\omega Q_{\max}\sin(\omega t + \phi) \qquad (32.23)$$

◀ Current as a function of time for an ideal *LC* current

To determine the value of the phase angle ϕ, let's examine the initial conditions, which in our situation require that at $t = 0$, $I = 0$, and $Q = Q_{\max}$. Setting $I = 0$ at $t = 0$ in Equation 32.23 gives

$$0 = -\omega Q_{\max}\sin\phi$$

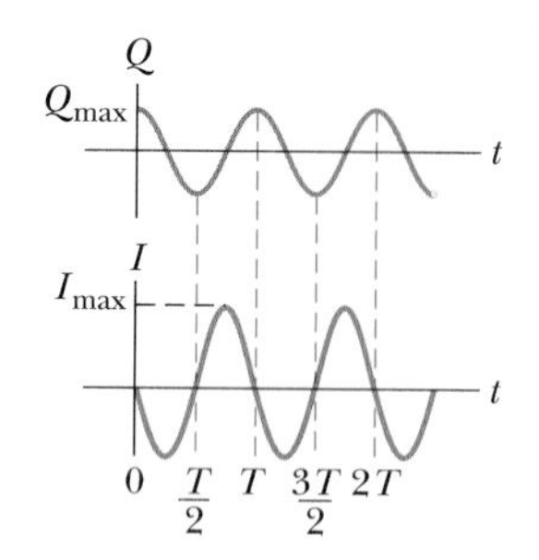

ACTIVE FIGURE 32.12

Graphs of charge versus time and current versus time for a resistanceless, nonradiating *LC* circuit. Notice that *Q* and *I* are 90° out of phase with each other.

Sign in at www.thomsonedu.com and go to ThomsonNOW to observe this graph develop for the *LC* circuit in Active Figure 32.11.

which shows that $\phi = 0$. This value for ϕ also is consistent with Equation 32.21 and the condition that $Q = Q_{max}$ at $t = 0$. Therefore, in our case, the expressions for Q and I are

$$Q = Q_{max} \cos \omega t \quad (32.24)$$

$$I = -\omega Q_{max} \sin \omega t = -I_{max} \sin \omega t \quad (32.25)$$

Graphs of Q versus t and I versus t are shown in Active Figure 32.12. The charge on the capacitor oscillates between the extreme values Q_{max} and $-Q_{max}$, and the current oscillates between I_{max} and $-I_{max}$. Furthermore, the current is 90° out of phase with the charge. That is, when the charge is a maximum, the current is zero, and when the charge is zero, the current has its maximum value.

Let's return to the energy discussion of the *LC* circuit. Substituting Equations 32.24 and 32.25 in Equation 32.18, we find that the total energy is

$$U = U_C + U_L = \frac{Q_{max}^2}{2C} \cos^2 \omega t + \tfrac{1}{2} L I_{max}^2 \sin^2 \omega t \quad (32.26)$$

This expression contains all the features described qualitatively at the beginning of this section. It shows that the energy of the *LC* circuit continuously oscillates between energy stored in the capacitor's electric field and energy stored in the inductor's magnetic field. When the energy stored in the capacitor has its maximum value $Q_{max}^2/2C$, the energy stored in the inductor is zero. When the energy stored in the inductor has its maximum value $\frac{1}{2}LI_{max}^2$, the energy stored in the capacitor is zero.

Plots of the time variations of U_C and U_L are shown in Figure 32.13. The sum $U_C + U_L$ is a constant and is equal to the total energy $Q_{max}^2/2C$, or $\frac{1}{2}LI_{max}^2$. Analytical verification is straightforward. The amplitudes of the two graphs in Figure 32.13 must be equal because the maximum energy stored in the capacitor (when $I = 0$) must equal the maximum energy stored in the inductor (when $Q = 0$). This equality is expressed mathematically as

$$\frac{Q_{max}^2}{2C} = \frac{LI_{max}^2}{2}$$

Using this expression in Equation 32.26 for the total energy gives

$$U = \frac{Q_{max}^2}{2C} (\cos^2 \omega t + \sin^2 \omega t) = \frac{Q_{max}^2}{2C} \quad (32.27)$$

because $\cos^2 \omega t + \sin^2 \omega t = 1$.

In our idealized situation, the oscillations in the circuit persist indefinitely; the total energy U of the circuit, however, remains constant only if energy transfers and transformations are neglected. In actual circuits, there is always some resistance and some energy is therefore transformed to internal energy. We mentioned at the beginning of this section that we are also ignoring radiation from the circuit. In reality, radiation is inevitable in this type of circuit, and the total energy in the circuit continuously decreases as a result of this process.

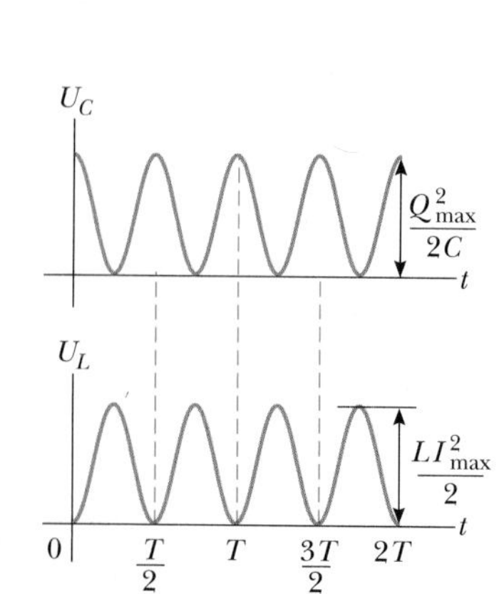

Figure 32.13 Plots of U_C versus t and U_L versus t for a resistanceless, nonradiating *LC* circuit. The sum of the two curves is a constant and is equal to the total energy stored in the circuit.

Quick Quiz 32.5 **(i)** At an instant of time during the oscillations of an *LC* circuit, the current is at its maximum value. At this instant, what happens to the voltage across the capacitor? (a) It is different from that across the inductor. (b) It is zero. (c) It has its maximum value. (d) It is impossible to determine. **(ii)** At an instant of time during the oscillations of an *LC* circuit, the current is momentarily zero. From the same choices, describe the voltage across the capacitor at this instant.

EXAMPLE 32.6 Oscillations in an *LC* Circuit

In Figure 32.14, the battery has an emf of 12.0 V, the inductance is 2.81 mH, and the capacitance is 9.00 pF. The switch has been set to position a for a long time so that the capacitor is charged. The switch is then thrown to position b, removing the battery from the circuit and connecting the capacitor directly across the inductor.

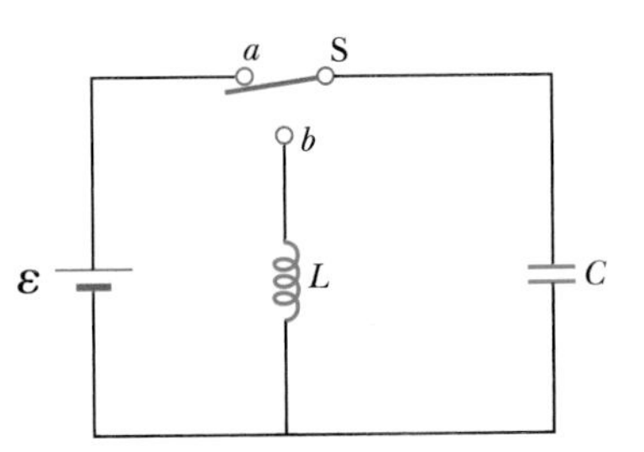

Figure 32.14 (Example 32.6) First the capacitor is fully charged with the switch set to position a. Then, the switch is thrown to position b and the battery is no longer in the circuit.

(A) Find the frequency of oscillation of the circuit.

SOLUTION

Conceptualize When the switch is thrown to position b, the active part of the circuit is the right-hand loop, which is an LC circuit.

Categorize We use equations developed in this section, so we categorize this example as a substitution problem.

Use Equation 32.22 to find the frequency:

$$f = \frac{\omega}{2\pi} = \frac{1}{2\pi\sqrt{LC}}$$

Substitute numerical values:

$$f = \frac{1}{2\pi[(2.81 \times 10^{-3}\text{ H})(9.00 \times 10^{-12}\text{ F})]^{1/2}} = \boxed{1.00 \times 10^{6}\text{ Hz}}$$

(B) What are the maximum values of charge on the capacitor and current in the circuit?

SOLUTION

Find the initial charge on the capacitor, which equals the maximum charge:

$$Q_{\text{max}} = C\,\Delta V = (9.00 \times 10^{-12}\text{ F})(12.0\text{ V}) = \boxed{1.08 \times 10^{-10}\text{ C}}$$

Use Equation 32.25 to find the maximum current from the maximum charge:

$$I_{\text{max}} = \omega Q_{\text{max}} = 2\pi f Q_{\text{max}} = (2\pi \times 10^{6}\text{ s}^{-1})(1.08 \times 10^{-10}\text{ C})$$
$$= \boxed{6.79 \times 10^{-4}\text{ A}}$$

32.6 The *RLC* Circuit

Let's now turn our attention to a more realistic circuit consisting of a resistor, an inductor, and a capacitor connected in series as shown in Active Figure 32.15. We assume the resistance of the resistor represents all the resistance in the circuit. Suppose the switch is at position a so that the capacitor has an initial charge Q_{max}. The switch is now thrown to position b. After this instant, the total energy stored in the capacitor and inductor at any time is given by Equation 32.18. This total energy, however, is no longer constant as it was in the LC circuit because the resistor causes transformation to internal energy. (We continue to ignore electromagnetic radiation from the circuit in this discussion.) Because the rate of energy transformation to internal energy within a resistor is I^2R,

$$\frac{dU}{dt} = -I^2R$$

where the negative sign signifies that the energy U of the circuit is decreasing in time. Substituting this result into Equation 32.19 gives

$$LI\frac{dI}{dt} + \frac{Q}{C}\frac{dQ}{dt} = -I^2R \qquad \textbf{(32.28)}$$

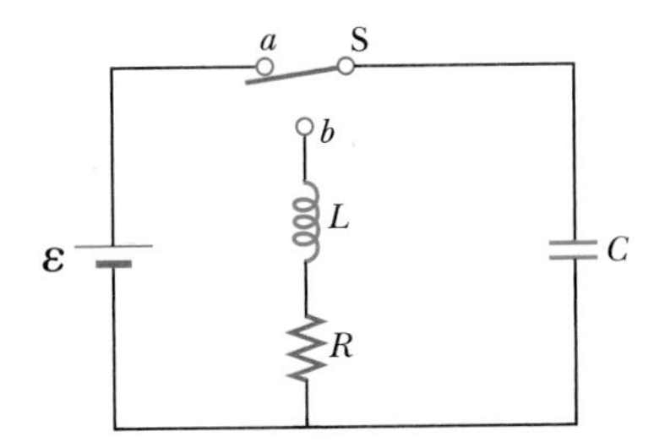

ACTIVE FIGURE 32.15

A series RLC circuit. The switch is set to position a, and the capacitor is charged. The switch is then thrown to position b.

Sign in at www.thomsonedu.com and go to ThomsonNOW to adjust the values of R, L, and C and see the effect on the decaying charge on the capacitor. A graphical display as in Active Figure 32.16a is available, as is an energy bar graph.

To convert this equation into a form that allows us to compare the electrical oscillations with their mechanical analog, we first use $I = dQ/dt$ and move all terms to the left-hand side to obtain

$$LI\frac{d^2Q}{dt^2} + I^2R + \frac{Q}{C}I = 0$$

Now divide through by I:

$$L\frac{d^2Q}{dt^2} + IR + \frac{Q}{C} = 0$$

$$L\frac{d^2Q}{dt^2} + R\frac{dQ}{dt} + \frac{Q}{C} = 0 \tag{32.29}$$

The *RLC* circuit is analogous to the damped harmonic oscillator discussed in Section 15.6 and illustrated in Figure 15.20. The equation of motion for a damped block–spring system is, from Equation 15.31,

$$m\frac{d^2x}{dt^2} + b\frac{dx}{dt} + kx = 0 \tag{32.30}$$

Comparing Equations 32.29 and 32.30, we see that Q corresponds to the position x of the block at any instant, L to the mass m of the block, R to the damping coefficient b, and C to $1/k$, where k is the force constant of the spring. These and other relationships are listed in Table 32.1.

TABLE 32.1

Analogies Between Electrical and Mechanical Systems

Electric Circuit		**One-Dimensional Mechanical System**
Charge	$Q \leftrightarrow x$	Position
Current	$I \leftrightarrow v_x$	Velocity
Potential difference	$\Delta V \leftrightarrow F_x$	Force
Resistance	$R \leftrightarrow b$	Viscous damping coefficient
Capacitance	$C \leftrightarrow 1/k$	(k = spring constant)
Inductance	$L \leftrightarrow m$	Mass
Current = time derivative of charge	$I = \frac{dQ}{dt} \leftrightarrow v_x = \frac{dx}{dt}$	Velocity = time derivative of position
Rate of change of current = second time derivative of charge	$\frac{dI}{dt} = \frac{d^2Q}{dt^2} \leftrightarrow a_x = \frac{dv_x}{dt} = \frac{d^2x}{dt^2}$	Acceleration = second time derivative of position
Energy in inductor	$U_L = \frac{1}{2}LI^2 \leftrightarrow K = \frac{1}{2}mv^2$	Kinetic energy of moving object
Energy in capacitor	$U_C = \frac{1}{2}\frac{Q^2}{C} \leftrightarrow U = \frac{1}{2}kx^2$	Potential energy stored in a spring
Rate of energy loss due to resistance	$I^2R \leftrightarrow bv^2$	Rate of energy loss due to friction
RLC circuit	$L\frac{d^2Q}{dt^2} + R\frac{dQ}{dt} + \frac{Q}{C} = 0 \leftrightarrow m\frac{d^2x}{dt^2} + b\frac{dx}{dt} + kx = 0$	Damped object on a spring

Because the analytical solution of Equation 32.29 is cumbersome, we give only a qualitative description of the circuit behavior. In the simplest case, when $R = 0$, Equation 32.29 reduces to that of a simple *LC* circuit as expected, and the charge and the current oscillate sinusoidally in time. This situation is equivalent to removing all damping in the mechanical oscillator.

When R is small, a situation that is analogous to light damping in the mechanical oscillator, the solution of Equation 32.29 is

$$Q = Q_{\text{max}} e^{-Rt/2L} \cos \omega_d t \qquad (32.31)$$

where ω_d, the angular frequency at which the circuit oscillates, is given by

$$\omega_d = \left[\frac{1}{LC} - \left(\frac{R}{2L}\right)^2\right]^{1/2} \qquad (32.32)$$

That is, the value of the charge on the capacitor undergoes a damped harmonic oscillation in analogy with a block–spring system moving in a viscous medium. Equation 32.32 shows that when $R \ll \sqrt{4L/C}$ (so that the second term in the brackets is much smaller than the first), the frequency ω_d of the damped oscillator is close to that of the undamped oscillator, $1/\sqrt{LC}$. Because $I = dQ/dt$, it follows that the current also undergoes damped harmonic oscillation. A plot of the charge versus time for the damped oscillator is shown in Active Figure 32.16a and an oscilloscope trace for a real *RLC* circuit is shown in Active Figure 32.16b. The maximum value of Q decreases after each oscillation, just as the amplitude of a damped block–spring system decreases in time.

For larger values of R, the oscillations damp out more rapidly; in fact, there exists a critical resistance value $R_c = \sqrt{4L/C}$ above which no oscillations occur. A system with $R = R_c$ is said to be *critically damped*. When R exceeds R_c, the system is said to be *overdamped*.

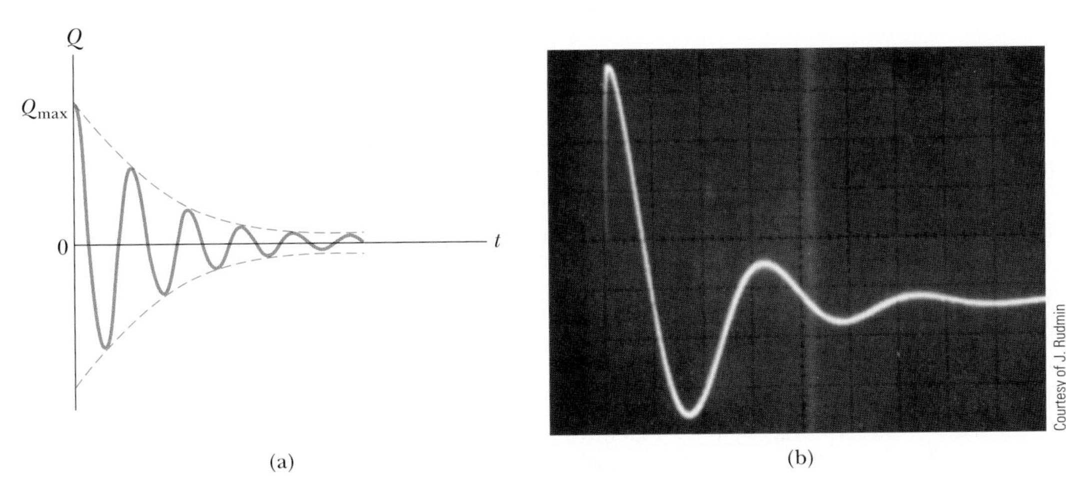

(a) (b)

ACTIVE FIGURE 32.16

(a) Charge versus time for a damped *RLC* circuit. The charge decays in this way when $R < \sqrt{4L/C}$. The Q-versus-t curve represents a plot of Equation 32.31. (b) Oscilloscope pattern showing the decay in the oscillations of an *RLC* circuit.

Sign in at www.thomsonedu.com and go to ThomsonNOW to observe this graph develop for the damped *RLC* circuit in Active Figure 32.15.

Summary

CONCEPTS AND PRINCIPLES

When the current in a loop of wire changes with time, an emf is induced in the loop according to Faraday's law. The **self-induced emf** is

$$\mathcal{E}_L = -L\frac{dI}{dt} \qquad (32.1)$$

where L is the **inductance** of the loop. Inductance is a measure of how much opposition a loop offers to a change in the current in the loop. Inductance has the SI unit of **henry** (H), where 1 H = 1 V · s/A.

The inductance of any coil is

$$L = \frac{N\Phi_B}{I} \qquad (32.2)$$

where N is the total number of turns and Φ_B is the magnetic flux through the coil. The inductance of a device depends on its geometry. For example, the inductance of an air-core solenoid is

$$L = \mu_0\frac{N^2}{\ell}A \qquad (32.4)$$

where ℓ is the length of the solenoid and A is the cross-sectional area.

If a resistor and inductor are connected in series to a battery of emf $\mathcal{E}$ at time $t = 0$, the current in the circuit varies in time according to the expression

$$I = \frac{\mathcal{E}}{R}(1 - e^{-t/\tau}) \qquad (32.7)$$

where $\tau = L/R$ is the **time constant** of the RL circuit. If we replace the battery in the circuit by a resistanceless wire, the current decays exponentially with time according to the expression

$$I = \frac{\mathcal{E}}{R}e^{-t/\tau} \qquad (32.10)$$

where $\mathcal{E}/R$ is the initial current in the circuit.

The energy stored in the magnetic field of an inductor carrying a current I is

$$U = \tfrac{1}{2}LI^2 \qquad (32.12)$$

This energy is the magnetic counterpart to the energy stored in the electric field of a charged capacitor.

The energy density at a point where the magnetic field is B is

$$u_B = \frac{B^2}{2\mu_0} \qquad (32.14)$$

The **mutual inductance** of a system of two coils is

$$M_{12} = \frac{N_2\Phi_{12}}{I_1} = M_{21} = \frac{N_1\Phi_{21}}{I_2} = M \qquad (32.15)$$

This mutual inductance allows us to relate the induced emf in a coil to the changing source current in a nearby coil using the relationships

$$\mathcal{E}_2 = -M_{12}\frac{dI_1}{dt} \quad \text{and} \quad \mathcal{E}_1 = -M_{21}\frac{dI_2}{dt} \qquad (32.16, 32.17)$$

In an LC circuit that has zero resistance and does not radiate electromagnetically (an idealization), the values of the charge on the capacitor and the current in the circuit vary sinusoidally in time at an angular frequency given by

$$\omega = \frac{1}{\sqrt{LC}} \qquad (32.22)$$

The energy in an LC circuit continuously transfers between energy stored in the capacitor and energy stored in the inductor.

In an RLC circuit with small resistance, the charge on the capacitor varies with time according to

$$Q = Q_{\text{max}}e^{-Rt/2L}\cos\omega_d t \qquad (32.31)$$

where

$$\omega_d = \left[\frac{1}{LC} - \left(\frac{R}{2L}\right)^2\right]^{1/2} \qquad (32.32)$$

Questions

☐ denotes answer available in *Student Solutions Manual/Study Guide;* **O** denotes objective question

1. The current in a circuit containing a coil, a resistor, and a battery has reached a constant value. Does the coil have an inductance? Does the coil affect the value of the current?
2. What parameters affect the inductance of a coil? Does the inductance of a coil depend on the current in the coil?
3. **O** Initially, an inductor with no resistance carries a constant current. Then the current is brought to a new constant value twice as large. *After* this change, what has happened to the emf in the inductor? (a) It is larger than before the change by a factor of 4. (b) It is larger by a factor of 2. (c) It has the same nonzero value. (d) It continues to be zero. (e) It has decreased.
4. **O** A long, fine wire is wound into a coil with inductance 5 mH. The coil is connected across the terminals of a battery, and the current is measured a few seconds after the connection is made. The wire is unwound and wound again into a different coil with $L = 10$ mH. This second coil is connected across the same battery, and the current is measured in the same way. Compared with the current in the first coil, is the current in the second coil (a) four times as large, (b) twice as large, (c) unchanged, (d) half as large, or (e) one-fourth as large?
5. **O** Two solenoidal coils, A and B, are wound using equal lengths of the same kind of wire. The length of the axis of each coil is large compared with its diameter. The axial length of coil A is twice as large as that of coil B, and coil A has twice as many turns as coil B. What is the ratio of the inductance of coil A to that of coil B? (a) 8 (b) 4 (c) 2 (d) 1 (e) $\frac{1}{2}$ (f) $\frac{1}{4}$ (g) $\frac{1}{8}$
6. A switch controls the current in a circuit that has a large inductance. Is a spark (Fig. Q32.6) more likely to be produced at the switch when the switch is being closed, when it is being opened, or doesn't it matter? The electric arc can melt and oxidize the contact surfaces, resulting in high resistivity of the contacts and eventual destruction of the switch. Before electronic ignitions were invented, distributor contact points in automobiles had to be replaced regularly. Switches in power distribution networks and switches controlling large motors, generators, and electromagnets can suffer from arcing and can be very dangerous to operate.

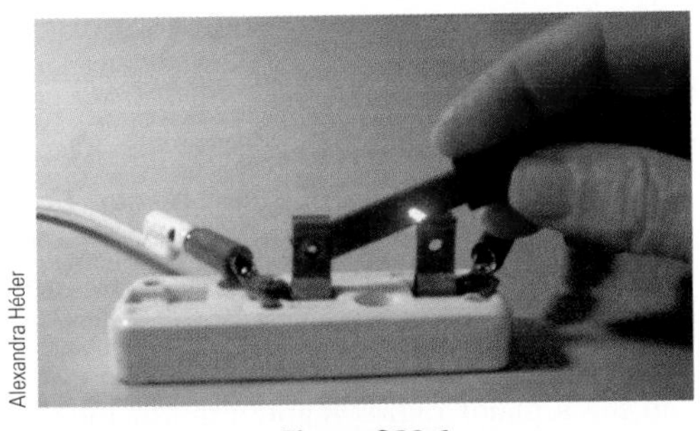

Figure Q32.6

7. **O** In Figure Q32.7, the switch is left in position a for a long time interval and is then quickly thrown to position b. Rank the magnitudes of the voltages across the four circuit elements a short time thereafter from the largest to the smallest.

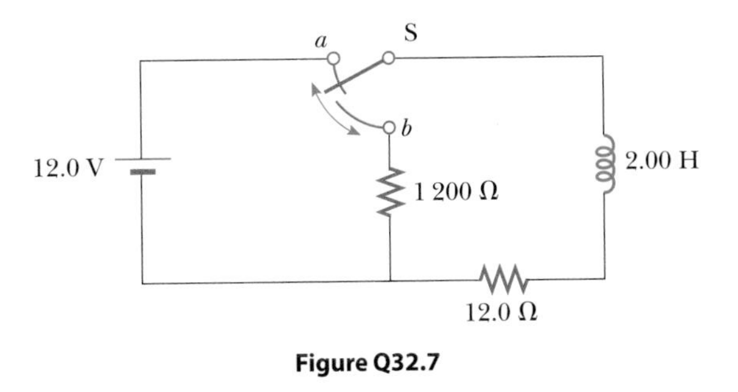

Figure Q32.7

8. Consider the four circuits shown in Figure Q32.8, each consisting of a battery, a switch, a lightbulb, a resistor, and either a capacitor or an inductor. Assume the capacitor has a large capacitance and the inductor has a large inductance but no resistance. The lightbulb has high efficiency, glowing whenever it carries electric current. **(i)** Describe what the lightbulb does in each of circuits (a), (b), (c), and (d) after the switch is thrown closed. **(ii)** Describe what the lightbulb does in each circuit after, having been closed for a long time interval, the switch is thrown open.

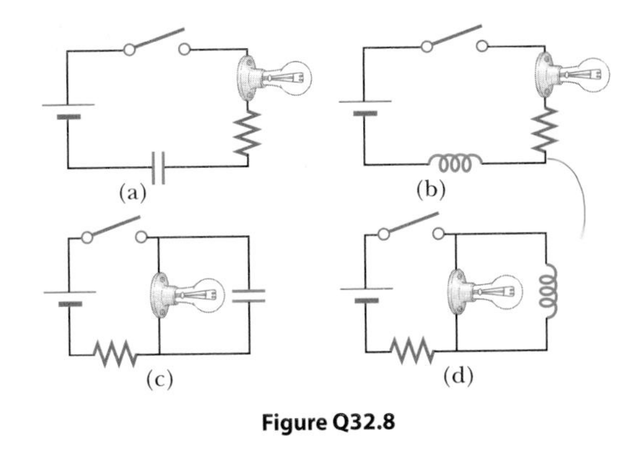

Figure Q32.8

9. **O** *Don't do this; it's dangerous and illegal.* Suppose a criminal wants to steal energy from the electric company by placing a flat, rectangular coil of wire close to, but not touching, one long, straight, horizontal wire in a transmission line. The long, straight wire carries a sinusoidally varying current. Which of the following statements is true? (a) The method works best if the coil is in a vertical plane surrounding the straight wire. (b) The method works best if the coil is in a vertical plane with the two long sides of the rectangle parallel to the long wire and equally far from it. (c) The method works best if the coil and the long wire are in the same horizontal plane with one long side of the rectangle close to the wire. (d) The method works for any orientation of the coil. (e) The method cannot work without contact between the coil and the long wire.
10. Consider this thesis: "Joseph Henry, America's first professional physicist, caused the most recent basic change in

the human view of the Universe when he discovered self-induction during a school vacation at the Albany Academy about 1830. Before that time, one could think of the Universe as composed of only one thing: matter. The energy that temporarily maintains the current after a battery is removed from a coil, on the other hand, is not energy that belongs to any chunk of matter. It is energy in the massless magnetic field surrounding the coil. With Henry's discovery, Nature forced us to admit that the Universe consists of fields as well as matter." Argue for or against the statement. In your view, what makes up the Universe?

11. **O** If the current in an inductor is doubled, by what factor is the stored energy multiplied? (a) 4 (b) 2 (c) 1 (d) $\frac{1}{2}$ (e) $\frac{1}{4}$

12. **O** A solenoidal inductor for a printed circuit board is being redesigned. To save weight, the number of turns is reduced by one-half with the geometric dimensions kept the same. By how much must the current change if the energy stored in the inductor is to remain the same? (a) It must be four times larger (b) It must be two times larger (c) It must be larger by a factor of $\sqrt{2}$. (d) It should be left the same. (e) It should be one-half as large. (f) No change in the current can compensate for the reduction in the number of turns.

13. Discuss the similarities between the energy stored in the electric field of a charged capacitor and the energy stored in the magnetic field of a current-carrying coil.

14. The open switch in Figure Q32.14 is thrown closed at $t = 0$. Before the switch is closed, the capacitor is uncharged and all currents are zero. Determine the currents in L, C, and R and the potential differences across L, C, and R (a) at the instant after the switch is closed and (b) long after it is closed.

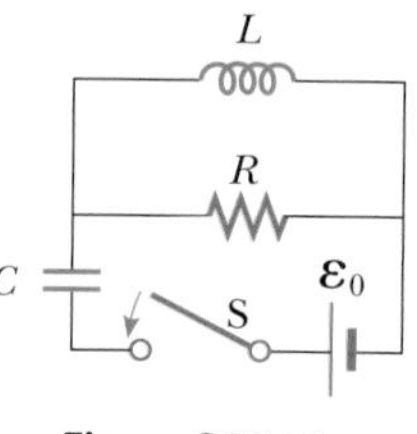

Figure Q32.14

15. **O** The centers of two circular loops are separated by a fixed distance. **(i)** For what relative orientation of the loops is their mutual inductance a maximum? (a) coaxial and lying in parallel planes (b) lying in the same plane (c) lying in perpendicular planes, with the center of one on the axis of the other (d) The orientation makes no difference. **(ii)** For what relative orientation is their mutual inductance a minimum? Choose from the same possibilities.

16. In the LC circuit shown in Figure 32.10, the charge on the capacitor is sometimes zero, but at such instants the current in the circuit is not zero. How is this behavior possible?

17. How can you tell whether an RLC circuit is overdamped or underdamped?

18. Can an object exert a force on itself? When a coil induces an emf in itself, does it exert a force on itself?

Problems

WebAssign The Problems from this chapter may be assigned online in WebAssign.

ThomsonNOW Sign in at **www.thomsonedu.com** and go to ThomsonNOW to assess your understanding of this chapter's topics with additional quizzing and conceptual questions.

1, 2, 3 denotes straightforward, intermediate, challenging; ☐ denotes full solution available in *Student Solutions Manual/Study Guide*; ▲ denotes coached solution with hints available at **www.thomsonedu.com**; ▪ denotes developing symbolic reasoning; ● denotes asking for qualitative reasoning; ▪ denotes computer useful in solving problem

Section 32.1 Self-Induction and Inductance

1. A 2.00-H inductor carries a steady current of 0.500 A. When the switch in the circuit is opened, the current is effectively zero after 10.0 ms. What is the average induced emf in the inductor during this time interval?

2. A coiled telephone cord forms a spiral having 70 turns, a diameter of 1.30 cm and an unstretched length of 60.0 cm. Determine the inductance of one conductor in the unstretched cord.

3. ▲ A 10.0-mH inductor carries a current $I = I_{max} \sin \omega t$, with $I_{max} = 5.00$ A and $\omega/2\pi = 60.0$ Hz. What is the self-induced emf as a function of time?

4. An emf of 24.0 mV is induced in a 500-turn coil at an instant when the current is 4.00 A and is changing at the rate of 10.0 A/s. What is the magnetic flux through each turn of the coil?

5. An inductor in the form of a solenoid contains 420 turns, is 16.0 cm in length, and has a cross-sectional area of 3.00 cm^2. What uniform rate of decrease of current through the inductor induces an emf of 175 μV?

6. The current in a 90.0-mH inductor changes with time as $I = 1.00t^2 - 6.00t$ (in SI units). Find the magnitude of the induced emf at (a) $t = 1.00$ s and (b) $t = 4.00$ s. (c) At what time is the emf zero?

7. ● A 40.0-mA current is carried by a uniformly wound air-core solenoid with 450 turns, a 15.0-mm diameter, and 12.0-cm length. Compute (a) the magnetic field inside the solenoid, (b) the magnetic flux through each turn, and (c) the inductance of the solenoid. (d) **What If?** If the current were different, which of these quantities would change?

8. A toroid has a major radius R and a minor radius r and is tightly wound with N turns of wire as shown in Figure P32.8. If $R >> r$, the magnetic field in the region enclosed by the wire of the torus, of cross-sectional area $A = \pi r^2$, is essentially the same as the magnetic field of a

solenoid that has been bent into a large circle of radius R. Modeling the field as the uniform field of a long solenoid, show that the inductance of such a toroid is approximately

$$L \approx \frac{\mu_0 N^2 A}{2\pi R}$$

(An exact expression of the inductance of a toroid with a rectangular cross section is derived in Problem 57.)

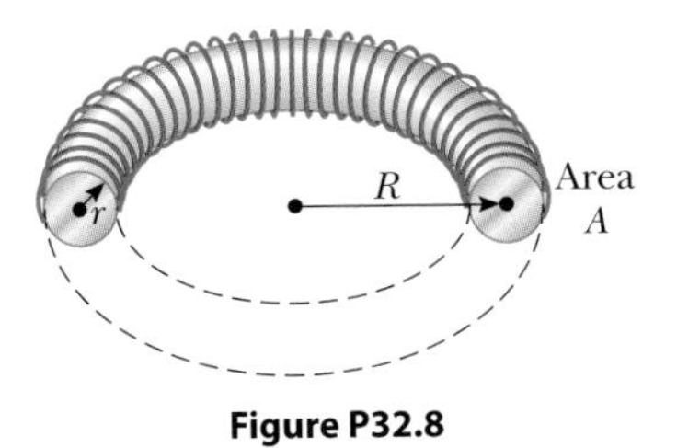

Figure P32.8

9. A self-induced emf in a solenoid of inductance L changes in time as $\mathcal{E} = \mathcal{E}_0 e^{-kt}$. Find the total charge that passes through the solenoid, assuming the charge is finite.

Section 32.2 *RL* Circuits

10. Show that $I = I_i e^{-t/\tau}$ is a solution of the differential equation

$$IR + L\frac{dI}{dt} = 0$$

where I_i is the current at $t = 0$ and $\tau = L/R$.

11. A 12.0-V battery is connected into a series circuit containing a 10.0-Ω resistor and a 2.00-H inductor. In what time interval will the current reach (a) 50.0% and (b) 90.0% of its final value?

12. ● In the circuit diagrammed in Figure P32.12, take $\mathcal{E}$ = 12.0 V and R = 24.0 Ω. Assume the switch is open for $t <$ 0 and is closed at t = 0. On a single set of axes, sketch graphs of the current in the circuit as a function of time for $t \geq 0$, assuming (a) the inductance in the circuit is essentially zero, (b) the inductance has an intermediate value, and (c) the inductance has a very large value. Label the initial and final values of the current.

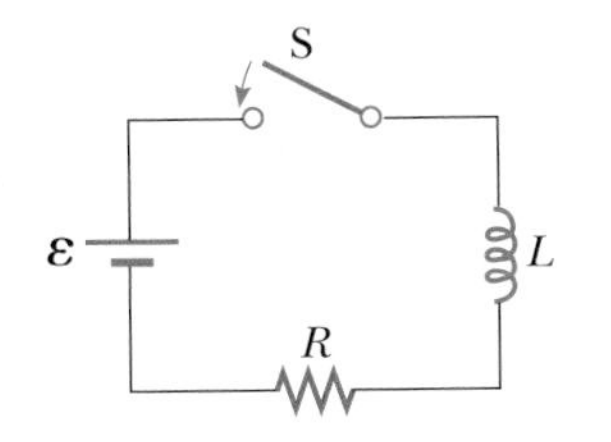

Figure P32.12 Problems 12, 13, 14, and 15.

13. Consider the circuit in Figure P32.12, taking $\mathcal{E}$ = 6.00 V, L = 8.00 mH, and R = 4.00 Ω. (a) What is the inductive time constant of the circuit? (b) Calculate the current in the circuit 250 μs after the switch is closed. (c) What is the value of the final steady-state current? (d) After what time interval does the current reach 80.0% of its maximum value?

14. In the circuit shown in Figure P32.12, let L = 7.00 H, R = 9.00 Ω, and $\mathcal{E}$ = 120 V. What is the self-induced emf 0.200 s after the switch is closed?

15. ▲ For the RL circuit shown in Figure P32.12, let the inductance be 3.00 H, the resistance 8.00 Ω, and the battery emf 36.0 V. (a) Calculate the ratio of the potential difference across the resistor to the emf across the inductor when the current is 2.00 A. (b) Calculate the emf across the inductor when the current is 4.50 A.

16. A 12.0-V battery is connected in series with a resistor and an inductor. The circuit has a time constant of 500 μs, and the maximum current is 200 mA. What is the value of the inductance of the inductor?

17. An inductor that has an inductance of 15.0 H and a resistance of 30.0 Ω is connected across a 100-V battery. What is the rate of increase of the current (a) at t = 0 and (b) at t = 1.50 s?

18. The switch in Figure P32.18 is open for $t <$ 0 and is then thrown closed at time t = 0. Find the current in the inductor and the current in the switch as functions of time thereafter.

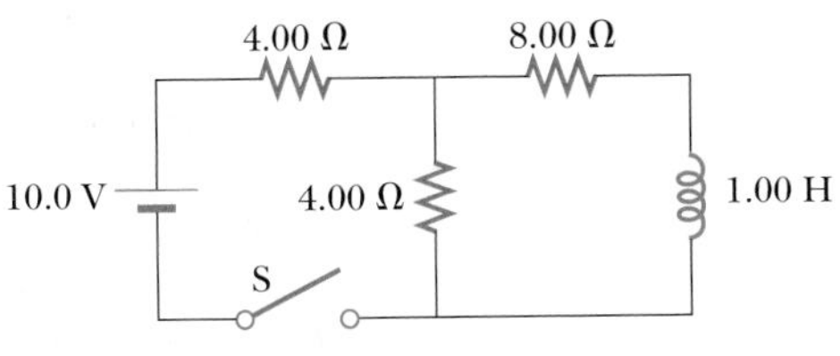

Figure P32.18 Problems 18 and 52.

19. A series RL circuit with L = 3.00 H and a series RC circuit with C = 3.00 μF have equal time constants. If the two circuits contain the same resistance R, (a) what is the value of R and (b) what is the time constant?

20. A current pulse is fed to the partial circuit shown in Figure P32.20. The current begins at zero, becomes 10.0 A between t = 0 and t = 200 μs, and then is zero once again. Determine the current in the inductor as a function of time.

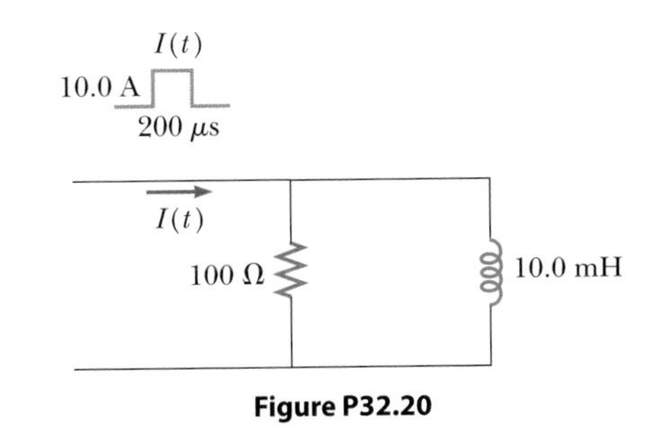

Figure P32.20

21. ▲ A 140-mH inductor and a 4.90-Ω resistor are connected with a switch to a 6.00-V battery as shown in Figure P32.21. (a) After the switch is thrown to a (connecting the battery), what time interval elapses before the current reaches 220 mA? (b) What is the current in the inductor 10.0 s after the switch is closed? (c) Now the switch is

quickly thrown from a to b. What time interval elapses before the current falls to 160 mA?

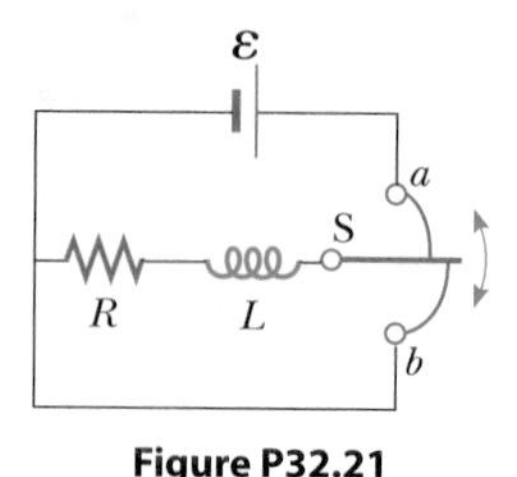

Figure P32.21

22. ● Two ideal inductors, L_1 and L_2, have *zero* internal resistance and are far apart, so their magnetic fields do not influence each other. (a) Assuming these inductors are connected in series, show that they are equivalent to a single ideal inductor having $L_{eq} = L_1 + L_2$. (b) Assuming these same two inductors are connected in parallel, show that they are equivalent to a single ideal inductor having $1/L_{eq} = 1/L_1 + 1/L_2$. (c) **What If?** Now consider two inductors L_1 and L_2 that have *nonzero* internal resistances R_1 and R_2, respectively. Assume they are still far apart so that their mutual inductance is zero. Assuming these inductors are connected in series, show that they are equivalent to a single inductor having $L_{eq} = L_1 + L_2$ and $R_{eq} = R_1 + R_2$. (d) If these same inductors are now connected in parallel, is it necessarily true that they are equivalent to a single ideal inductor having $1/L_{eq} = 1/L_1 + 1/L_2$ and $1/R_{eq} = 1/R_1 + 1/R_2$? Explain your answer.

Section 32.3 Energy in a Magnetic Field

23. An air-core solenoid with 68 turns is 8.00 cm long and has a diameter of 1.20 cm. How much energy is stored in its magnetic field when it carries a current of 0.770 A?

24. The magnetic field inside a superconducting solenoid is 4.50 T. The solenoid has an inner diameter of 6.20 cm and a length of 26.0 cm. Determine (a) the magnetic energy density in the field and (b) the energy stored in the magnetic field within the solenoid.

25. ▲ On a clear day at a certain location, a 100-V/m vertical electric field exists near the Earth's surface. At the same place, the Earth's magnetic field has a magnitude of 0.500×10^{-4} T. Compute the energy densities of the two fields.

26. Complete the calculation in Example 32.3 by proving that

$$\int_0^{\infty} e^{-2Rt/L}\, dt = \frac{L}{2R}$$

27. ● A flat coil of wire has an inductance of 40.0 mH and a resistance of 5.00 Ω. It is connected to a 22.0-V battery at the instant $t = 0$. Consider the moment when the current is 3.00 A. (a) At what rate is energy being delivered by the battery? (b) What is the power being delivered to the resistor? (c) At what rate is energy being stored in the magnetic field of the coil? (d) What is the relationship among these three power values? Is this relationship true at other instants as well? Explain the relationship at the moment immediately after $t = 0$ and at a moment several seconds later.

28. A 10.0-V battery, a 5.00-Ω resistor, and a 10.0-H inductor are connected in series. After the current in the circuit has reached its maximum value, calculate (a) the power being supplied by the battery, (b) the power being delivered to the resistor, (c) the power being delivered to the inductor, and (d) the energy stored in the magnetic field of the inductor.

29. Assume the magnitude of the magnetic field outside a sphere of radius R is $B = B_0(R/r)^2$, where B_0 is a constant. Determine the total energy stored in the magnetic field outside the sphere and evaluate your result for $B_0 = 5.00 \times 10^{-5}$ T and $R = 6.00 \times 10^6$ m, values appropriate for the Earth's magnetic field.

Section 32.4 Mutual Inductance

30. Two coils are close to each other. The first coil carries a current given by $I(t) = (5.00\text{ A})e^{-0.025\,0t}\sin(377t)$. At $t = 0.800$ s, the emf measured across the second coil is -3.20 V. What is the mutual inductance of the coils?

31. Two coils, held in fixed positions, have a mutual inductance of 100 μH. What is the peak emf in one coil when a sinusoidal current given by $I(t) = (10.0\text{ A})\sin(1\,000t)$ is in the other coil?

32. On a printed circuit board, a relatively long, straight conductor and a conducting rectangular loop lie in the same plane as shown in Figure P31.8 in Chapter 31. Taking $h = 0.400$ mm, $w = 1.30$ mm, and $L = 2.70$ mm, find their mutual inductance.

33. Two solenoids A and B, spaced close to each other and sharing the same cylindrical axis, have 400 and 700 turns, respectively. A current of 3.50 A in coil A produces an average flux of 300 μWb through each turn of A and a flux of 90.0 μWb through each turn of B. (a) Calculate the mutual inductance of the two solenoids. (b) What is the inductance of A? (c) What emf is induced in B when the current in A increases at the rate of 0.500 A/s?

34. ● A solenoid has N_1 turns, radius R_1, and length ℓ. It is so long that its magnetic field is uniform nearly everywhere inside it and is nearly zero outside. A second solenoid has N_2 turns, radius $R_2 < R_1$, and the same length. It lies inside the first solenoid, with their axes parallel. (a) Assume solenoid 1 carries variable current I. Compute the mutual inductance characterizing the emf induced in solenoid 2. (b) Now assume solenoid 2 carries current I. Compute the mutual inductance to which the emf in solenoid 1 is proportional. (c) State how the results of parts (a) and (b) compare with each other.

35. A large coil of radius R_1 and having N_1 turns is coaxial with a small coil of radius R_2 and having N_2 turns. The centers of the coils are separated by a distance x that is much larger than R_2. What is the mutual inductance of the coils? *Suggestion:* John von Neumann proved that the same answer must result from considering the flux through the first coil of the magnetic field produced by the second coil or from considering the flux through the second coil of the magnetic field produced by the first coil. In this problem, it is easy to calculate the flux through the small coil, but it is difficult to calculate the flux through the large coil because to do so, you would have to know the magnetic field away from the axis.

36. Two inductors having inductances L_1 and L_2 are connected in parallel as shown in Figure P32.36a. The mutual inductance between the two inductors is M. Deter-

mine the equivalent inductance L_{eq} for the system (Fig. P32.36b).

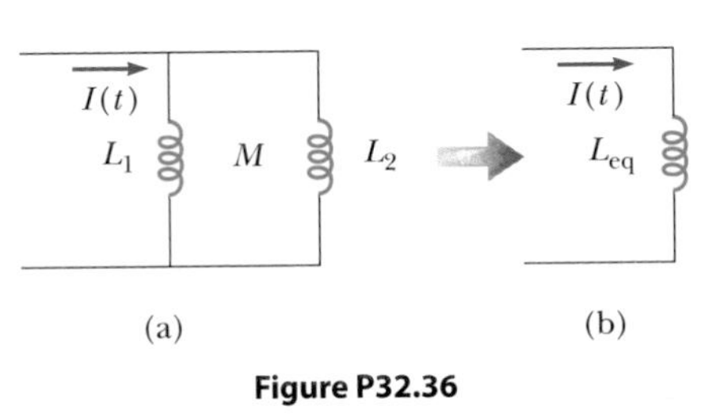

Figure P32.36

Section 32.5 Oscillations in an *LC* Circuit

37. A 1.00-μF capacitor is charged by a 40.0-V power supply. The fully charged capacitor is then discharged through a 10.0-mH inductor. Find the maximum current in the resulting oscillations.

38. An *LC* circuit consists of a 20.0-mH inductor and a 0.500-μF capacitor. If the maximum instantaneous current is 0.100 A, what is the greatest potential difference across the capacitor?

39. In the circuit of Figure P32.39, the battery emf is 50.0 V, the resistance is 250 Ω, and the capacitance is 0.500 μF. The switch S is closed for a long time interval, and zero potential difference is measured across the capacitor. After the switch is opened, the potential difference across the capacitor reaches a maximum value of 150 V. What is the value of the inductance?

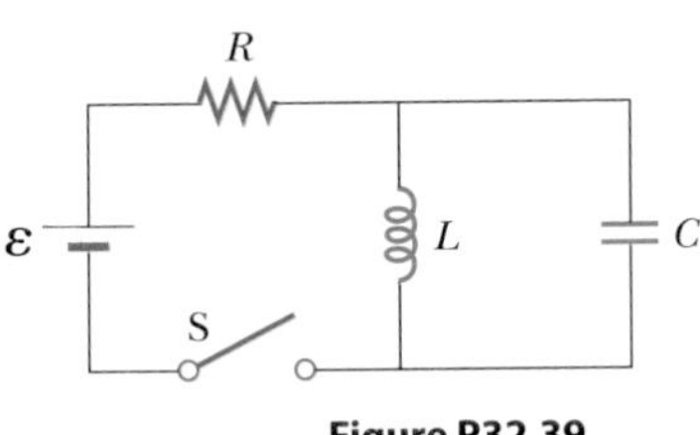

Figure P32.39

40. An *LC* circuit like the one in Figure 32.10 contains an 82.0-mH inductor and a 17.0-μF capacitor that initially carries a 180-μC charge. The switch is open for $t < 0$ and then thrown closed at $t = 0$. (a) Find the frequency (in hertz) of the resulting oscillations. At $t = 1.00$ ms, find (b) the charge on the capacitor and (c) the current in the circuit.

41. A fixed inductance $L = 1.05$ μH is used in series with a variable capacitor in the tuning section of a radiotelephone on a ship. What capacitance tunes the circuit to the signal from a transmitter broadcasting at 6.30 MHz?

42. The switch in Figure P32.42 is connected to point *a* for a long time interval. After the switch is thrown to point *b*, what are (a) the frequency of oscillation of the *LC* circuit, (b) the maximum charge that appears on the capacitor, (c) the maximum current in the inductor, and (d) the total energy the circuit possesses at $t = 3.00$ s?

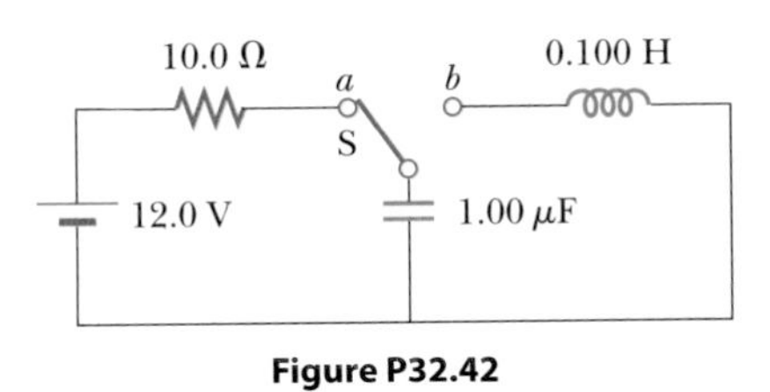

Figure P32.42

43. ▲ An *LC* circuit like that in Figure 32.10 consists of a 3.30-H inductor and an 840-pF capacitor that initially carries a 105-μC charge. The switch is open for $t < 0$ and then thrown closed at $t = 0$. Compute the following quantities at $t = 2.00$ ms: (a) the energy stored in the capacitor, (b) the energy stored in the inductor, and (c) the total energy in the circuit.

Section 32.6 The *RLC* Circuit

44. In Active Figure 32.15, let $R = 7.60$ Ω, $L = 2.20$ mH, and $C = 1.80$ μF. (a) Calculate the frequency of the damped oscillation of the circuit. (b) What is the critical resistance?

45. Consider an *LC* circuit in which $L = 500$ mH and $C = 0.100$ μF. (a) What is the resonance frequency ω_0? (b) If a resistance of 1.00 kΩ is introduced into this circuit, what is the frequency of the (damped) oscillations? (c) What is the percent difference between the two frequencies?

46. Show that Equation 32.28 in the text is Kirchhoff's loop rule as applied to the circuit in Active Figure 32.15.

47. Electrical oscillations are initiated in a series circuit containing a capacitance *C*, inductance *L*, and resistance *R*. (a) If $R \ll \sqrt{4L/C}$ (weak damping), what time interval elapses before the amplitude of the current oscillation falls to 50.0% of its initial value? (b) Over what time interval does the energy decrease to 50.0% of its initial value?

Additional Problems

48. **Review problem.** This problem extends the reasoning of Section 26.4, Problem 29 in Chapter 26, Problem 33 in Chapter 30, and Section 32.3. (a) Consider a capacitor with vacuum between its large, closely spaced, oppositely charged parallel plates. Show that the force on one plate can be accounted for by thinking of the electric field between the plates as exerting a "negative pressure" equal to the energy density of the electric field. (b) Consider two infinite plane sheets carrying electric currents in opposite directions with equal linear current densities J_s. Calculate the force per area acting on one sheet due to the magnetic field, of magnitude $\mu_0 J_s/2$, created by the other sheet. (c) Calculate the net magnetic field between the sheets and the field outside of the volume between them. (d) Calculate the energy density in the magnetic field between the sheets. (e) Show that the force on one sheet can be accounted for by thinking of the magnetic field between the sheets as exerting a positive pressure equal to its energy density. This result for magnetic pressure applies to all current configurations, not only to sheets of current.

49. A 1.00-mH inductor and a 1.00-μF capacitor are connected in series. The current in the circuit is described by $I = 20.0t$, where *t* is in seconds and *I* is in amperes. The capacitor initially has no charge. Determine (a) the voltage across the inductor as a function of time, (b) the voltage across the capacitor as a function of time, and (c) the time when the energy stored in the capacitor first exceeds that in the inductor.

50. An inductor having inductance *L* and a capacitor having capacitance *C* are connected in series. The current in the circuit increases linearly in time as described by $I = Kt$,

where K is a constant. The capacitor is initially uncharged. Determine (a) the voltage across the inductor as a function of time, (b) the voltage across the capacitor as a function of time, and (c) the time when the energy stored in the capacitor first exceeds that in the inductor.

51. A capacitor in a series LC circuit has an initial charge Q and is being discharged. Find, in terms of L and C, the flux through each of the N turns in the coil when the charge on the capacitor is $Q/2$.

52. ● In the circuit diagrammed in Figure P32.18, assume that the switch has been closed for a long time interval and is opened at $t = 0$. (a) Before the switch is opened, does the inductor behave as an open circuit, a short circuit, a resistor of some particular resistance, or none of these choices? What current does the inductor carry? (b) How much energy is stored in the inductor for $t < 0$? (c) After the switch is opened, what happens to the energy previously stored in the inductor? (d) Sketch a graph of the current in the inductor for $t \geq 0$. Label the initial and final values and the time constant.

53. ● At the moment $t = 0$, a 24.0-V battery is connected to a 5.00-mH coil and a 6.00-Ω resistor. (a) Immediately thereafter, how does the potential difference across the resistor compare to the emf across the coil? (b) Answer the same question about the circuit several seconds later. (c) Is there an instant at which these two voltages are equal in magnitude? If so, when? Is there more than one such instant? (d) After a 4.00-A current is established in the resistor and coil, the battery is suddenly replaced by a short circuit. Answer questions (a), (b), and (c) again with reference to this new circuit.

54. When the current in the portion of the circuit shown in Figure P32.54 is 2.00 A and increases at a rate of 0.500 A/s, the measured potential difference is $\Delta V_{ab} = 9.00$ V. When the current is 2.00 A and decreases at the rate of 0.500 A/s, the measured potential difference is $\Delta V_{ab} = 5.00$ V. Calculate the values of L and R.

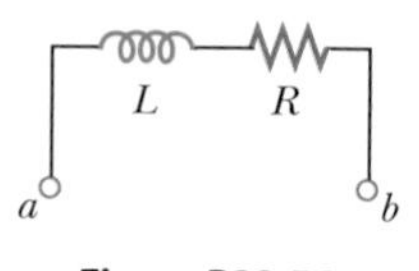

Figure P32.54

55. A time-varying current I is sent through a 50.0-mH inductor as shown in Figure P32.55. Make a graph of the potential at point b relative to the potential at point a.

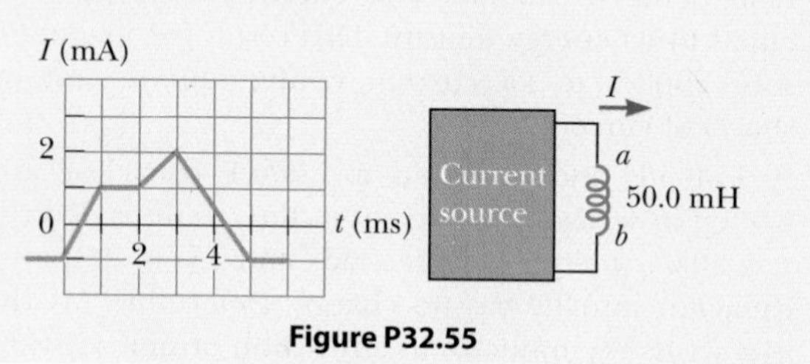

Figure P32.55

56. ● Consider a series circuit consisting of a 500-μF capacitor, a 32.0-mH inductor, and a resistor R. Explain what you can say about the angular frequency of oscillations for (a) $R = 0$, (b) $R = 4.00$ Ω, (c) $R = 15.0$ Ω, and (d) $R = 17.0$ Ω. Relate the mathematical description of the angular frequency to the experimentally measurable angular frequency.

57. ● The toroid in Figure P32.57 consists of N turns and has a rectangular cross section. Its inner and outer radii are a and b, respectively. (a) Show that the inductance of the toroid is

$$L = \frac{\mu_0 N^2 h}{2\pi} \ln \frac{b}{a}$$

(b) Using this result, compute the inductance of a 500-turn toroid for which $a = 10.0$ cm, $b = 12.0$ cm, and $h = 1.00$ cm. (c) **What If?** In Problem 8, an approximate equation for the inductance of a toroid with $R \gg r$ was derived. To get a feel for the accuracy of that result, use the expression in Problem 8 to compute the approximate inductance of the toroid described in part (b). How does that result compare with the answer to part (b)?

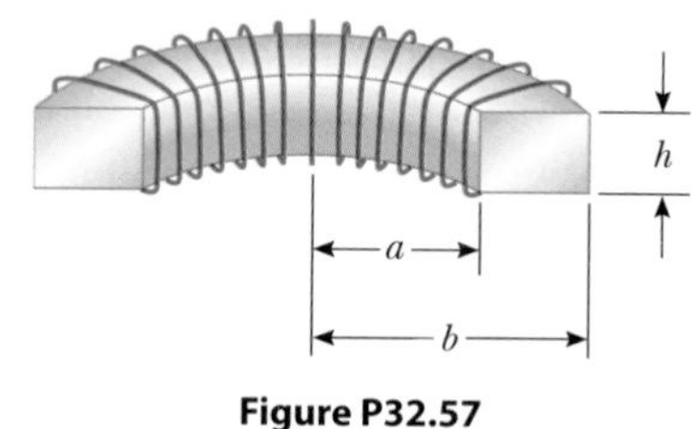

Figure P32.57

58. (a) A flat, circular coil does not actually produce a uniform magnetic field in the area it encloses. Nevertheless, estimate the inductance of a flat, compact, circular coil, with radius R and N turns, by assuming the field at its center is uniform over its area. (b) A circuit on a laboratory table consists of a 1.5-volt battery, a 270-Ω resistor, a switch, and three 30-cm-long patch cords connecting them. Suppose the circuit is arranged to be circular. Think of it as a flat coil with one turn. Compute the order of magnitude of its inductance and (c) of the time constant describing how fast the current increases when you close the switch.

59. At $t = 0$, the open switch in Figure P32.59 is thrown closed. Using Kirchhoff's rules for the instantaneous currents and voltages in this two-loop circuit, show that the current in the inductor at time $t > 0$ is

$$I(t) = \frac{\mathcal{E}}{R_1}\left[1 - e^{-(R'/L)t}\right]$$

where $R' = R_1 R_2/(R_1 + R_2)$.

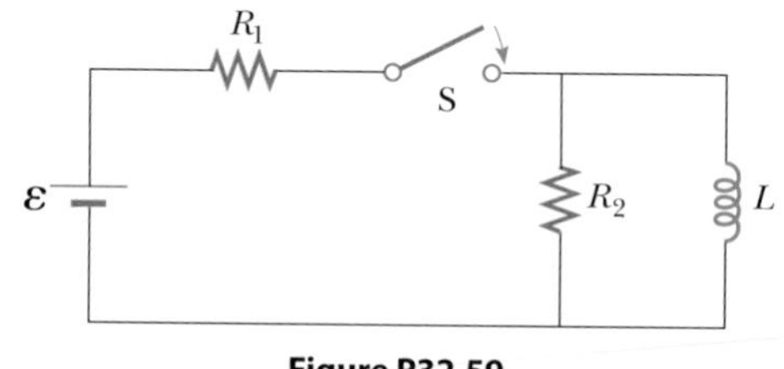

Figure P32.59

60. A wire of nonmagnetic material, with radius R, carries current uniformly distributed over its cross section. The total current carried by the wire is I. Show that the magnetic energy per unit length inside the wire is $\mu_0 I^2/16\pi$.

61. In Figure P32.61, the switch is closed for $t < 0$ and steady-state conditions are established. The switch is opened at $t = 0$. (a) Find the initial emf $\mathcal{E}_0$ across L immediately after $t = 0$. Which end of the coil, a or b, is at the higher voltage? (b) Make freehand graphs of the currents in R_1 and in R_2 as a function of time, treating the steady-state directions as positive. Show values before and after $t = 0$. (c) At what moment after $t = 0$ does the current in R_2 have the value 2.00 mA?

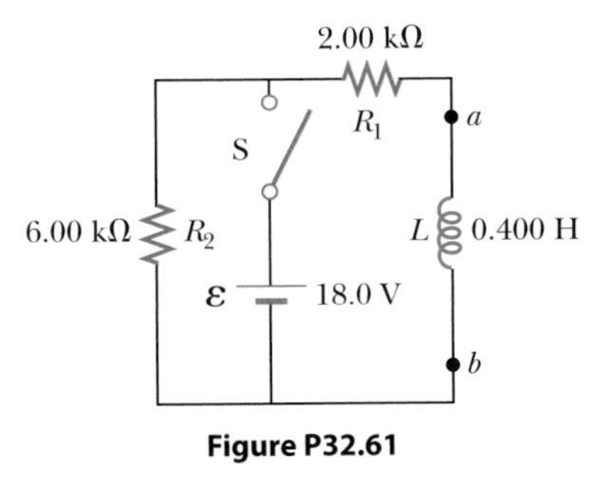

Figure P32.61

62. ● The lead-in wires from a television antenna are often constructed in the form of two parallel wires (Fig. P32.62). The two wires carry currents of equal magnitude in opposite directions. Assume the wires carry the current uniformly distributed over their surfaces and no magnetic field exists inside the wires. (a) Why does this configuration of conductors have an inductance? (b) What constitutes the flux loop for this configuration? (c) Show that the inductance of a length x of this type of lead-in is

$$L = \frac{\mu_0 x}{\pi} \ln\left(\frac{w - a}{a}\right)$$

where w is the center-to-center separation of the wires and a is their radius.

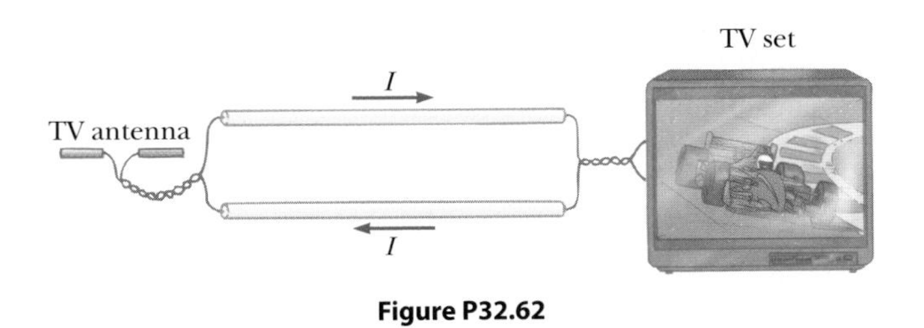

Figure P32.62

63. To prevent damage from arcing in an electric motor, a discharge resistor is sometimes placed in parallel with the armature. If the motor is suddenly unplugged while running, this resistor limits the voltage that appears across the armature coils. Consider a 12.0-V DC motor with an armature that has a resistance of 7.50 Ω and an inductance of 450 mH. Assume the magnitude of the self-induced emf in the armature coils is 10.0 V when the motor is running at normal speed. (The equivalent circuit for the armature is shown in Fig. P32.63.) Calculate the maximum resistance R that limits the voltage across the armature to 80.0 V when the motor is unplugged.

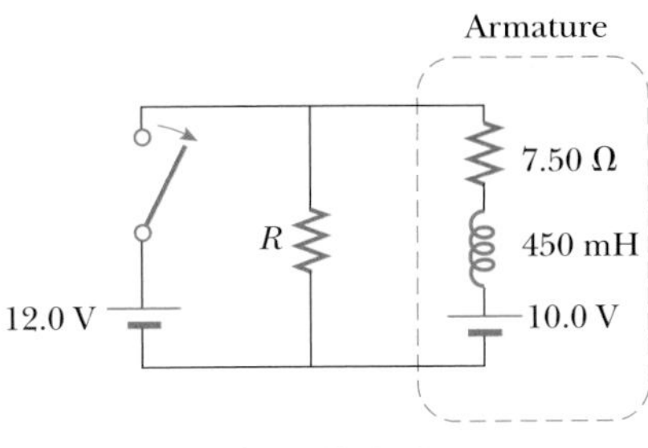

Figure P32.63

Review problems. Problems 64 through 67 apply ideas from this and earlier chapters to some properties of superconductors, which were introduced in Section 27.5.

64. *The resistance of a superconductor.* In an experiment carried out by S. C. Collins between 1955 and 1958, a current was maintained in a superconducting lead ring for 2.50 yr with no observed loss. If the inductance of the ring were 3.14×10^{-8} H and the sensitivity of the experiment were 1 part in 10^9, what was the maximum resistance of the ring? *Suggestion:* Treat the ring as an *RL* circuit carrying decaying current and recall that $e^{-x} \approx 1 - x$ for small x.

65. A novel method of storing energy has been proposed. A huge underground superconducting coil, 1.00 km in diameter, would be fabricated. It would carry a maximum current of 50.0 kA through each winding of a 150-turn Nb_3Sn solenoid. (a) If the inductance of this huge coil were 50.0 H, what would be the total energy stored? (b) What would be the compressive force per meter length acting between two adjacent windings 0.250 m apart?

66. *Superconducting power transmission.* The use of superconductors has been proposed for power transmission lines. A single coaxial cable (Fig. P32.66) could carry 1.00×10^3 MW (the output of a large power plant) at 200 kV, DC, over a distance of 1 000 km without loss. An inner wire of radius 2.00 cm, made from the superconductor Nb_3Sn, carries the current I in one direction. A surrounding superconducting cylinder of radius 5.00 cm would carry the return current I. In such a system, what is the magnetic field (a) at the surface of the inner conductor and (b) at the inner surface of the outer conductor? (c) How much energy would be stored in the space between the conductors in a 1 000-km superconducting line? (d) What is the pressure exerted on the outer conductor?

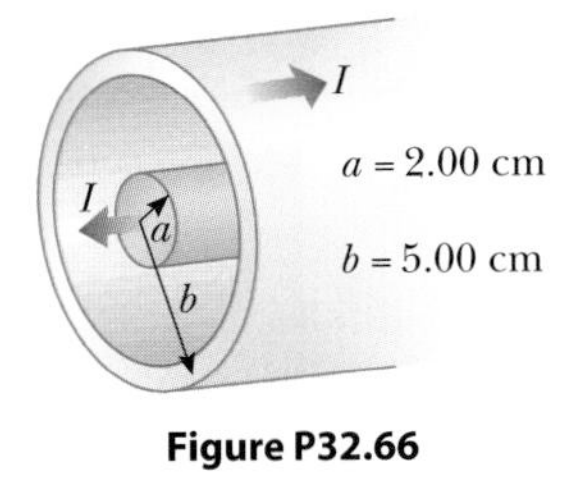

Figure P32.66

67. ● *The Meissner effect.* Compare this problem with Problem 57 in Chapter 26, pertaining to the force attracting a perfect dielectric into a strong electric field. A fundamental property of a type I superconducting material is *perfect*

diamagnetism, or demonstration of the *Meissner effect,* illustrated in Figure 30.27 in Section 30.6 and described as follows. The superconducting material has $\vec{\mathbf{B}} = 0$ everywhere inside it. If a sample of the material is placed into an externally produced magnetic field or is cooled to become superconducting while it is in a magnetic field, electric currents appear on the surface of the sample. The currents have precisely the strength and orientation required to make the total magnetic field be zero throughout the interior of the sample. This problem will help you to understand the magnetic force that can then act on the superconducting sample.

A vertical solenoid with a length of 120 cm and a diameter of 2.50 cm consists of 1 400 turns of copper wire carrying a counterclockwise current of 2.00 A as shown in Figure P32.67a. (a) Find the magnetic field in the vacuum inside the solenoid. (b) Find the energy density of the magnetic field, noting that the units J/m^3 of energy density are the same as the units N/m^2 of pressure. (c) Now a superconducting bar 2.20 cm in diameter is inserted partway into the solenoid. Its upper end is far outside the solenoid, where the magnetic field is negligible. The lower end of the bar is deep inside the solenoid. Explain how you identify the direction required for the current on the curved surface of the bar so that the total magnetic field is zero within the bar. The field created by the supercurrents is sketched in Figure P32.67b, and the total field is sketched in Figure P32.67c. (d) The field of the solenoid exerts a force on the current in the superconductor. Explain how you determine the direction of the force on the bar. (e) Calculate the magnitude of the force by multiplying the energy density of the solenoid field times the area of the bottom end of the superconducting bar.

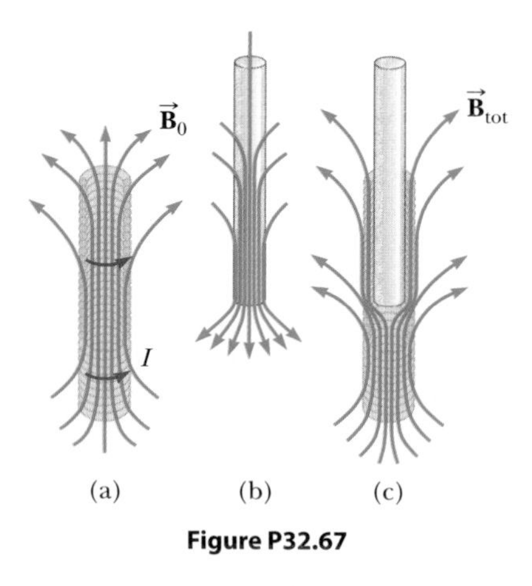

Figure P32.67

Answers to Quick Quizzes

32.1 (c), (f). For the constant current in statements (a) and (b), there is no voltage across the resistanceless inductor. In statement (c), if the current increases, the emf induced in the inductor is in the opposite direction, from b to a, making a higher in potential than b. Similarly, in statement (f), the decreasing current induces an emf in the same direction as the current, from b to a, again making the potential higher at a than at b.

32.2 **(i),** (b). As the switch is closed, there is no current, so there is no voltage across the resistor. **(ii),** (a). After a long time, the current has reached its final value and the inductor has no further effect on the circuit.

32.3 (a), (d). Because the energy density depends on the magnitude of the magnetic field, you must increase the magnetic field to increase the energy density. For a solenoid, $B = \mu_0 nI$, where n is the number of turns per unit length. In choice (a), increasing n increases the magnetic field. In choice (b), the change in cross-sectional area has no effect on the magnetic field. In choice (c), increasing the length but keeping n fixed has no effect on the magnetic field. Increasing the current in choice (d) increases the magnetic field in the solenoid.

32.4 (a). M increases because the magnetic flux through coil 2 increases.

32.5 **(i),** (b). If the current is at its maximum value, the charge on the capacitor is zero. **(ii),** (c). If the current is zero, this moment is the instant at which the capacitor is fully charged and the current is about to reverse direction.

These large transformers are used to increase the voltage at a power plant for distribution of energy by electrical transmission to the power grid. Voltages can be changed relatively easily because power is distributed by alternating current rather than direct current. (Lester Lefkowitz/Getty Images)

33 Alternating Current Circuits

In this chapter, we describe alternating-current (AC) circuits. Every time you turn on a television set, a stereo, or any of a multitude of other electrical appliances in a home, you are calling on alternating currents to provide the power to operate them. We begin our study by investigating the characteristics of simple series circuits that contain resistors, inductors, and capacitors and that are driven by a sinusoidal voltage. The primary aim of this chapter can be summarized as follows: if an AC source applies an alternating voltage to a series circuit containing resistors, inductors, and capacitors, we want to know the amplitude and time characteristics of the alternating current. We conclude this chapter with two sections concerning transformers, power transmission, and electrical filters.

33.1 AC Sources

An AC circuit consists of circuit elements and a power source that provides an alternating voltage Δv. This time-varying voltage from the source is described by

$$\Delta v = \Delta V_{\max} \sin \omega t$$

where $\Delta V_{\max}$ is the maximum output voltage of the source, or the **voltage amplitude.** There are various possibilities for AC sources, including generators as discussed in Section 31.5 and electrical oscillators. In a home, each electrical outlet

PITFALL PREVENTION 33.1
Time-Varying Values

We use lowercase symbols Δv and i to indicate the instantaneous values of time-varying voltages and currents. Capital letters represent fixed values of voltage and current such as $\Delta V_{\max}$ and $I_{\max}$.

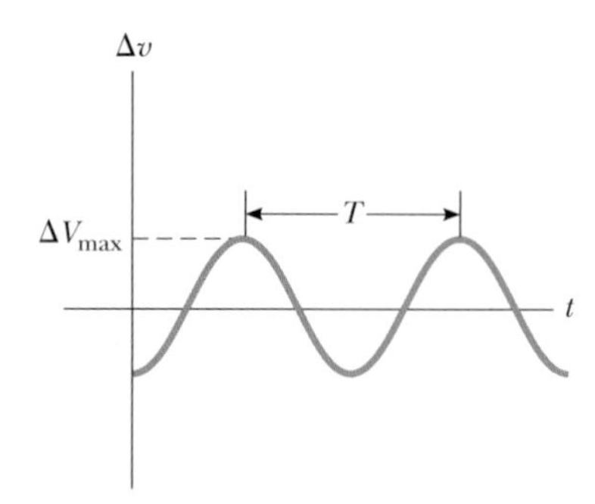

Figure 33.1 The voltage supplied by an AC source is sinusoidal with a period T.

serves as an AC source. Because the output voltage of an AC source varies sinusoidally with time, the voltage is positive during one half of the cycle and negative during the other half as in Figure 33.1. Likewise, the current in any circuit driven by an AC source is an alternating current that also varies sinusoidally with time.

From Equation 15.12, the angular frequency of the AC voltage is

$$\omega = 2\pi f = \frac{2\pi}{T}$$

where f is the frequency of the source and T is the period. The source determines the frequency of the current in any circuit connected to it. Commercial electric-power plants in the United States use a frequency of 60 Hz, which corresponds to an angular frequency of 377 rad/s.

33.2 Resistors in an AC Circuit

Consider a simple AC circuit consisting of a resistor and an AC source as shown in Active Figure 33.2. At any instant, the algebraic sum of the voltages around a closed loop in a circuit must be zero (Kirchhoff's loop rule). Therefore, $\Delta v + \Delta v_R = 0$ or, using Equation 27.7 for the voltage across the resistor,

$$\Delta v - i_R R = 0$$

If we rearrange this expression and substitute $\Delta V_{max} \sin \omega t$ for Δv, the instantaneous current in the resistor is

$$i_R = \frac{\Delta v}{R} = \frac{\Delta V_{max}}{R} \sin \omega t = I_{max} \sin \omega t \quad \textbf{(33.1)}$$

where I_{max} is the maximum current:

Maximum current in a resistor ▶

$$I_{max} = \frac{\Delta V_{max}}{R} \quad \textbf{(33.2)}$$

Equation 33.1 shows that the instantaneous voltage across the resistor is

Voltage across a resistor ▶

$$\Delta v_R = i_R R = I_{max} R \sin \omega t \quad \textbf{(33.3)}$$

A plot of voltage and current versus time for this circuit is shown in Active Figure 33.3a. At point a, the current has a maximum value in one direction, arbitrarily

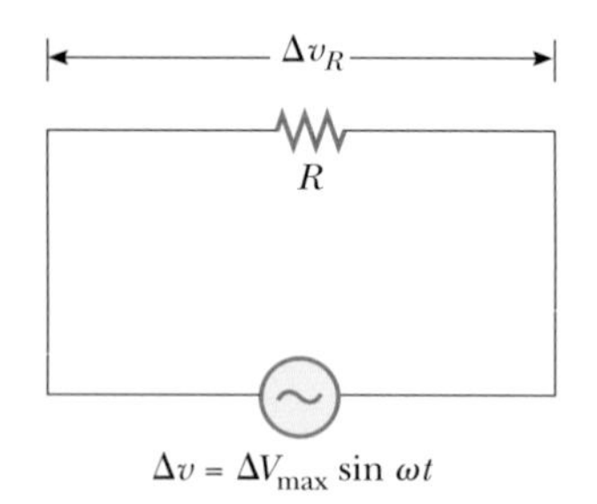

ACTIVE FIGURE 33.2

A circuit consisting of a resistor of resistance R connected to an AC source, designated by the symbol.

Sign in at www.thomsonedu.com and go to ThomsonNOW to adjust the resistance, frequency, and maximum voltage. The results can be studied with the graph and the phasor diagram in Active Figure 33.3.

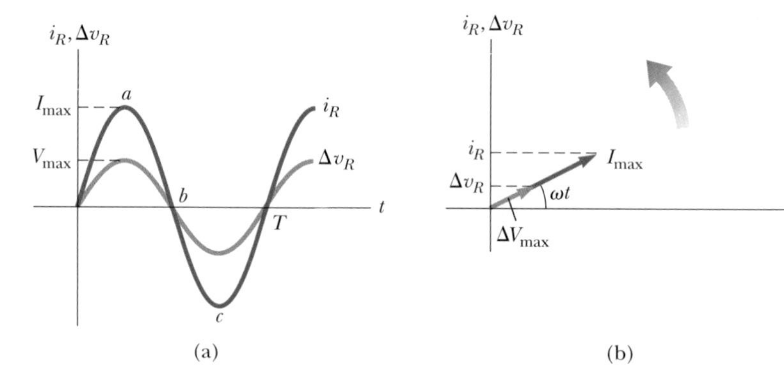

ACTIVE FIGURE 33.3

(a) Plots of the instantaneous current i_R and instantaneous voltage Δv_R across a resistor as functions of time. The current is in phase with the voltage, which means that the current is zero when the voltage is zero, maximum when the voltage is maximum, and minimum when the voltage is minimum. At time $t = T$, one cycle of the time-varying voltage and current has been completed. (b) Phasor diagram for the resistive circuit showing that the current is in phase with the voltage.

Sign in at www.thomsonedu.com and go to ThomsonNOW to adjust the resistance, frequency, and maximum voltage of the circuit in Active Figure 33.2. The results can be studied with the graph and the phasor diagram in this figure.

called the positive direction. Between points *a* and *b*, the current is decreasing in magnitude but is still in the positive direction. At point *b*, the current is momentarily zero; it then begins to increase in the negative direction between points *b* and *c*. At point *c*, the current has reached its maximum value in the negative direction.

The current and voltage are in step with each other because they vary identically with time. Because i_R and Δv_R both vary as $\sin \omega t$ and reach their maximum values at the same time as shown in Active Figure 33.3a, they are said to be **in phase,** similar to the way that two waves can be in phase as discussed in our study of wave motion in Chapter 18. Therefore, **for a sinusoidal applied voltage, the current in a resistor is always in phase with the voltage across the resistor.** For resistors in AC circuits, there are no new concepts to learn. Resistors behave essentially the same way in both DC and AC circuits. That, however, is not the case for capacitors and inductors.

To simplify our analysis of circuits containing two or more elements, we use a graphical representation called a *phasor diagram*. A **phasor** is a vector whose length is proportional to the maximum value of the variable it represents ($\Delta V_{\max}$ for voltage and $I_{\max}$ for current in this discussion). The phasor rotates counterclockwise at an angular speed equal to the angular frequency associated with the variable. The projection of the phasor onto the vertical axis represents the instantaneous value of the quantity it represents.

Active Figure 33.3b shows voltage and current phasors for the circuit of Active Figure 33.2 at some instant of time. The projections of the phasor arrows onto the vertical axis are determined by a sine function of the angle of the phasor with respect to the horizontal axis. For example, the projection of the current phasor in Active Figure 33.3b is $I_{\max} \sin \omega t$. Notice that this expression is the same as Equation 33.1. Therefore, the projections of phasors represent current values that vary sinusoidally in time. We can do the same with time-varying voltages. The advantage of this approach is that the phase relationships among currents and voltages can be represented as vector additions of phasors using the vector addition techniques discussed in Chapter 3.

In the case of the single-loop resistive circuit of Active Figure 33.2, the current and voltage phasors lie along the same line in Active Figure 33.3b because i_R and Δv_R are in phase. The current and voltage in circuits containing capacitors and inductors have different phase relationships.

Quick Quiz 33.1 Consider the voltage phasor in Figure 33.4, shown at three instants of time. **(i)** Choose the part of the figure, (a), (b), or (c), that represents the instant of time at which the instantaneous value of the voltage has the largest magnitude. **(ii)** Choose the part of the figure that represents the instant of time at which the instantaneous value of the voltage has the smallest magnitude.

For the simple resistive circuit in Active Figure 33.2, notice that **the average value of the current over one cycle is zero.** That is, the current is maintained in the positive direction for the same amount of time and at the same magnitude as it is maintained in the negative direction. The direction of the current, however, has no effect on the behavior of the resistor. We can understand this concept by realizing that collisions between electrons and the fixed atoms of the resistor result in an increase in the resistor's temperature. Although this temperature increase depends on the magnitude of the current, it is independent of the current's direction.

We can make this discussion quantitative by recalling that the rate at which energy is delivered to a resistor is the power $\mathcal{P} = i^2R$, where i is the instantaneous current in the resistor. Because this rate is proportional to the square of the current, it makes no difference whether the current is direct or alternating, that is, whether the sign associated with the current is positive or negative. The temperature increase produced by an alternating current having a maximum value $I_{\max}$, however, is not the same as that produced by a direct current equal to $I_{\max}$ because the alternating current has this maximum value for only an instant during each cycle (Fig. 33.5a, page 926). What is of importance in an AC circuit is an average

PITFALL PREVENTION 33.2

A Phasor Is Like a Graph

An alternating voltage can be presented in different representations. One graphical representation is shown in Figure 33.1 in which the voltage is drawn in rectangular coordinates, with voltage on the vertical axis and time on the horizontal axis. Active Figure 33.3b shows another graphical representation. The phase space in which the phasor is drawn is similar to polar coordinate graph paper. The radial coordinate represents the amplitude of the voltage. The angular coordinate is the phase angle. The vertical-axis coordinate of the tip of the phasor represents the instantaneous value of the voltage. The horizontal coordinate represents nothing at all. As shown in Active Figure 33.3b, alternating currents can also be represented by phasors.

To help with this discussion of phasors, review Section 15.4, where we represented the simple harmonic motion of a real object by the projection of an imaginary object's uniform circular motion onto a coordinate axis. A phasor is a direct analog to this representation.

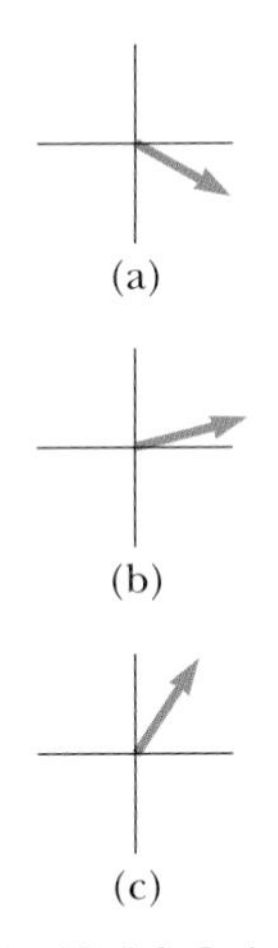

Figure 33.4 (Quick Quiz 33.1) A voltage phasor is shown at three instants of time, (a), (b), and (c).

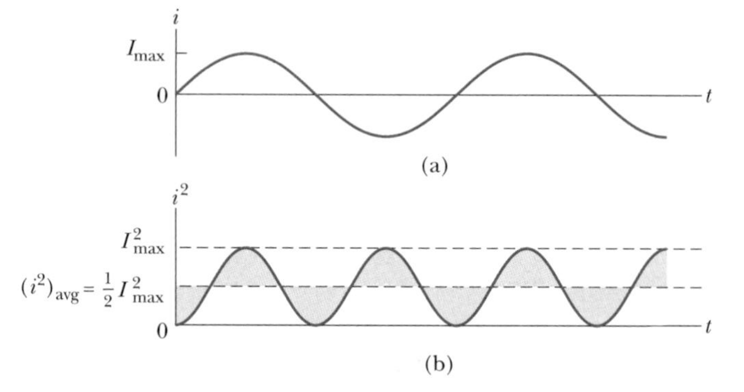

Figure 33.5 (a) Graph of the current in a resistor as a function of time. (b) Graph of the current squared in a resistor as a function of time. Notice that the gray shaded regions *under* the curve and *above* the dashed line for $\frac{1}{2}I^2_{max}$ have the same area as the gray shaded regions *above* the curve and *below* the dashed line for $\frac{1}{2}I^2_{max}$. Therefore, the average value of i^2 is $\frac{1}{2}I^2_{max}$. In general, the average value of $\sin^2 \omega t$ or $\cos^2 \omega t$ over one cycle is $\frac{1}{2}$.

value of current, referred to as the **rms current.** As we learned in Section 21.1, the notation *rms* stands for *root-mean-square,* which in this case means the square root of the mean (average) value of the square of the current: $I_{rms} = \sqrt{(i^2)_{avg}}$. Because i^2 varies as $\sin^2 \omega t$ and because the average value of i^2 is $\frac{1}{2}I^2_{max}$ (see Fig. 33.5b), the rms current is

rms current ▶

$$I_{rms} = \frac{I_{max}}{\sqrt{2}} = 0.707 I_{max} \quad (33.4)$$

This equation states that an alternating current whose maximum value is 2.00 A delivers to a resistor the same power as a direct current that has a value of (0.707)(2.00 A) = 1.41 A. The average power delivered to a resistor that carries an alternating current is

Average power delivered to a resistor ▶

$$\mathcal{P}_{avg} = I^2_{rms} R$$

Alternating voltage is also best discussed in terms of rms voltage, and the relationship is identical to that for current:

rms voltage ▶

$$\Delta V_{rms} = \frac{\Delta V_{max}}{\sqrt{2}} = 0.707\, \Delta V_{max} \quad (33.5)$$

When we speak of measuring a 120-V alternating voltage from an electrical outlet, we are referring to an rms voltage of 120 V. A calculation using Equation 33.5 shows that such an alternating voltage has a maximum value of about 170 V. One reason rms values are often used when discussing alternating currents and voltages is that AC ammeters and voltmeters are designed to read rms values. Furthermore, with rms values, many of the equations we use have the same form as their direct current counterparts.

EXAMPLE 33.1 What Is the rms Current?

The voltage output of an AC source is given by the expression $\Delta v = (200\text{ V})\sin \omega t$. Find the rms current in the circuit when this source is connected to a 100-Ω resistor.

SOLUTION

Conceptualize Active Figure 33.2 shows the physical situation for this problem.

Categorize We evaluate the current with an equation developed in this section, so we categorize this example as a substitution problem.

Comparing this expression for voltage output with the general form $\Delta v = \Delta V_{max} \sin \omega t$ shows that $\Delta V_{max} = 200$ V. Calculate the rms voltage from Equation 33.5:

$$\Delta V_{rms} = \frac{\Delta V_{max}}{\sqrt{2}} = \frac{200 \text{ V}}{\sqrt{2}} = 141 \text{ V}$$

Find the rms current:

$$I_{rms} = \frac{\Delta V_{rms}}{R} = \frac{141 \text{ V}}{100\ \Omega} = 1.41 \text{ A}$$

33.3 Inductors in an AC Circuit

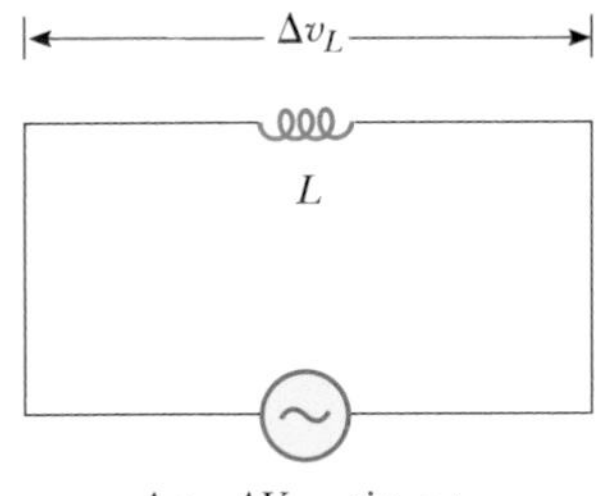

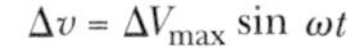

ACTIVE FIGURE 33.6

A circuit consisting of an inductor of inductance L connected to an AC source.

Sign in at www.thomsonedu.com and go to ThomsonNOW to adjust the inductance, frequency, and maximum voltage. The results can be studied with the graph and the phasor diagram in Active Figure 33.7.

Now consider an AC circuit consisting only of an inductor connected to the terminals of an AC source as shown in Active Figure 33.6. If $\Delta v_L = \mathcal{E}_L = -L(di_L/dt)$ is the self-induced instantaneous voltage across the inductor (see Eq. 32.1), Kirchhoff's loop rule applied to this circuit gives $\Delta v + \Delta v_L = 0$, or

$$\Delta v - L\frac{di_L}{dt} = 0$$

Substituting $\Delta V_{max} \sin \omega t$ for Δv and rearranging gives

$$\Delta v = L\frac{di_L}{dt} = \Delta V_{max} \sin \omega t \qquad (33.6)$$

Solving this equation for di_L gives

$$di_L = \frac{\Delta V_{max}}{L} \sin \omega t\, dt$$

Integrating this expression[1] gives the instantaneous current i_L in the inductor as a function of time:

$$i_L = \frac{\Delta V_{max}}{L}\int \sin \omega t\, dt = -\frac{\Delta V_{max}}{\omega L} \cos \omega t \qquad (33.7)$$

Using the trigonometric identity $\cos \omega t = -\sin(\omega t - \pi/2)$, we can express Equation 33.7 as

$$i_L = \frac{\Delta V_{max}}{\omega L} \sin\left(\omega t - \frac{\pi}{2}\right) \qquad (33.8)$$

◀ Current in an inductor

Comparing this result with Equation 33.6 shows that the instantaneous current i_L in the inductor and the instantaneous voltage Δv_L across the inductor are *out* of phase by $\pi/2$ rad $= 90°$.

A plot of voltage and current versus time is shown in Active Figure 33.7a (page 928). When the current i_L in the inductor is a maximum (point *b* in Active Fig. 33.7a), it is momentarily not changing, so the voltage across the inductor is zero (point *d*). At points such as *a* and *e*, the current is zero and the rate of change of current is at a maximum. Therefore, the voltage across the inductor is also at a maximum (points *c* and *f*). Notice that the voltage reaches its maximum value one quarter of a period before the current reaches its maximum value. Therefore, **for a sinusoidal applied voltage, the current in an inductor always lags behind the voltage across the inductor by 90° (one-quarter cycle in time).**

As with the relationship between current and voltage for a resistor, we can represent this relationship for an inductor with a phasor diagram as in Active Figure 33.7b. The phasors are at 90° to each other, representing the 90° phase difference between current and voltage.

[1] We neglect the constant of integration here because it depends on the initial conditions, which are not important for this situation.

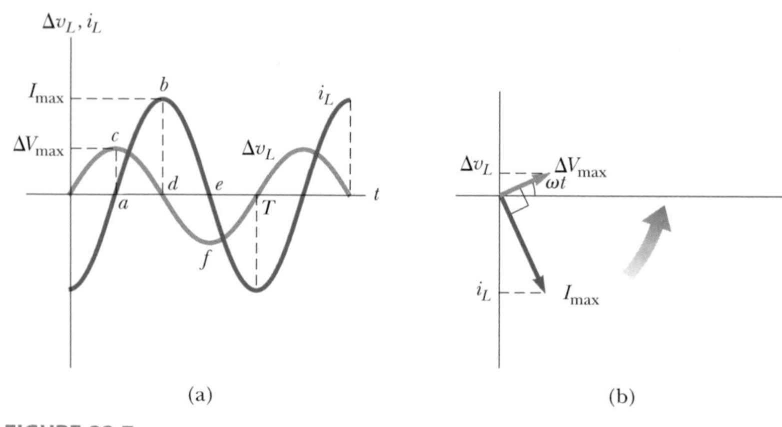

ACTIVE FIGURE 33.7

(a) Plots of the instantaneous current i_L and instantaneous voltage Δv_L across an inductor as functions of time. The current lags behind the voltage by 90°. (b) Phasor diagram for the inductive circuit, showing that the current lags behind the voltage by 90°.

Sign in at www.thomsonedu.com and go to ThomsonNOW to adjust the inductance, frequency, and maximum voltage of the circuit in Active Figure 33.6. The results can be studied with the graph and the phasor diagram in this figure.

Equation 33.7 shows that the current in an inductive circuit reaches its maximum value when $\cos \omega t = \pm 1$:

Maximum current in an inductor ▶

$$I_{max} = \frac{\Delta V_{max}}{\omega L} \quad (33.9)$$

This expression is similar to the relationship between current, voltage, and resistance in a DC circuit, $I = \Delta V/R$ (Eq. 27.7). Because I_{max} has units of amperes and ΔV_{max} has units of volts, ωL must have units of ohms. Therefore, ωL has the same units as resistance and is related to current and voltage in the same way as resistance. It must behave in a manner similar to resistance in the sense that it represents opposition to the flow of charge. Because ωL depends on the applied frequency ω, the inductor *reacts* differently, in terms of offering opposition to current, for different frequencies. For this reason, we define ωL as the **inductive reactance** X_L:

Inductive reactance ▶

$$X_L \equiv \omega L \quad (33.10)$$

Therefore, we can write Equation 33.9 as

$$I_{max} = \frac{\Delta V_{max}}{X_L} \quad (33.11)$$

The expression for the rms current in an inductor is similar to Equation 33.9, with I_{max} replaced by I_{rms} and ΔV_{max} replaced by ΔV_{rms}.

Equation 33.10 indicates that, for a given applied voltage, the inductive reactance increases as the frequency increases. This conclusion is consistent with Faraday's law: the greater the rate of change of current in the inductor, the larger the back emf. The larger back emf translates to an increase in the reactance and a decrease in the current.

Using Equations 33.6 and 33.11, we find that the instantaneous voltage across the inductor is

Voltage across an inductor ▶

$$\Delta v_L = -L\frac{di_L}{dt} = -\Delta V_{max} \sin \omega t = -I_{max} X_L \sin \omega t \quad (33.12)$$

Quick Quiz 33.2 Consider the AC circuit in Figure 33.8. The frequency of the AC source is adjusted while its voltage amplitude is held constant. When does the lightbulb glow the brightest? (a) It glows brightest at high frequencies. (b) It glows brightest at low frequencies. (c) The brightness is the same at all frequencies.

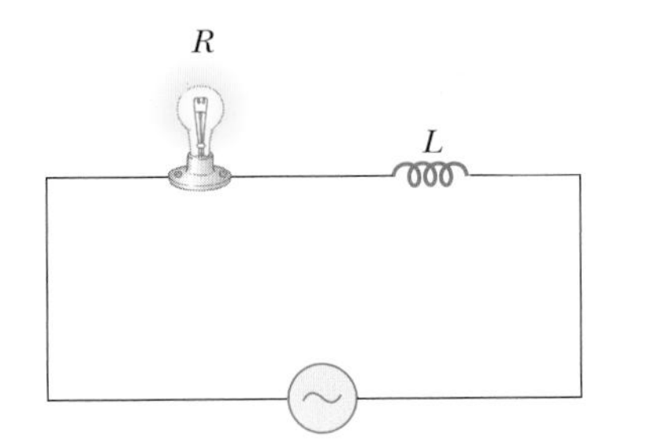

Figure 33.8 (Quick Quiz 33.2) At what frequencies does the lightbulb glow the brightest?

EXAMPLE 33.2 **A Purely Inductive AC Circuit**

In a purely inductive AC circuit, $L = 25.0$ mH and the rms voltage is 150 V. Calculate the inductive reactance and rms current in the circuit if the frequency is 60.0 Hz.

SOLUTION

Conceptualize Active Figure 33.6 shows the physical situation for this problem.

Categorize We evaluate the reactance and the current from equations developed in this section, so we categorize this example as a substitution problem.

Use Equation 33.10 to find the inductive reactance:

$$X_L = \omega L = 2\pi f L = 2\pi(60.0 \text{ Hz})(25.0 \times 10^{-3} \text{ H})$$
$$= 9.42 \ \Omega$$

Use an rms version of Equation 33.11 to find the rms current:

$$I_{\text{rms}} = \frac{\Delta V_{\text{rms}}}{X_L} = \frac{150 \text{ V}}{9.42 \ \Omega} = 15.9 \text{ A}$$

What If? If the frequency increases to 6.00 kHz, what happens to the rms current in the circuit?

Answer If the frequency increases, the inductive reactance also increases because the current is changing at a higher rate. The increase in inductive reactance results in a lower current.

Let's calculate the new inductive reactance and the new rms current:

$$X_L = 2\pi(6.00 \times 10^3 \text{ Hz})(25.0 \times 10^{-3} \text{ H}) = 942 \ \Omega$$

$$I_{\text{rms}} = \frac{150 \text{ V}}{942 \ \Omega} = 0.159 \text{ A}$$

33.4 Capacitors in an AC Circuit

Active Figure 33.9 shows an AC circuit consisting of a capacitor connected across the terminals of an AC source. Kirchhoff's loop rule applied to this circuit gives $\Delta v + \Delta v_C = 0$, or

$$\Delta v - \frac{q}{C} = 0 \qquad \textbf{(33.13)}$$

Substituting $\Delta V_{\text{max}} \sin \omega t$ for Δv and rearranging gives

$$q = C\,\Delta V_{\text{max}} \sin \omega t \qquad \textbf{(33.14)}$$

where q is the instantaneous charge on the capacitor. Differentiating Equation 33.14 with respect to time gives the instantaneous current in the circuit:

$$i_C = \frac{dq}{dt} = \omega C\,\Delta V_{\text{max}} \cos \omega t \qquad \textbf{(33.15)}$$

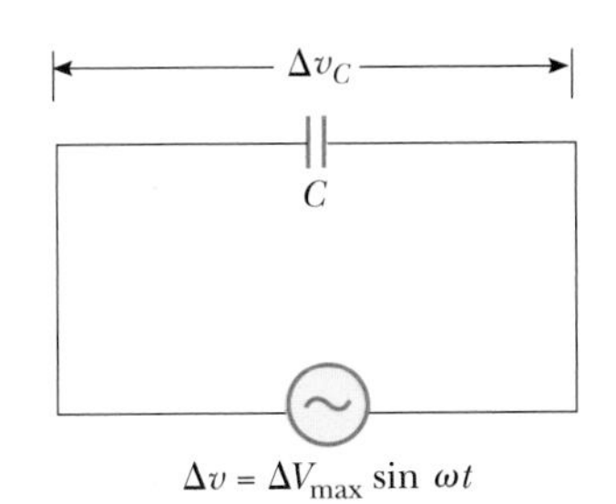

ACTIVE FIGURE 33.9

A circuit consisting of a capacitor of capacitance C connected to an AC source.

Sign in at www.thomsonedu.com and go to ThomsonNOW to adjust the capacitance, frequency, and maximum voltage. The results can be studied with the graph and the phasor diagram in Active Figure 33.10.

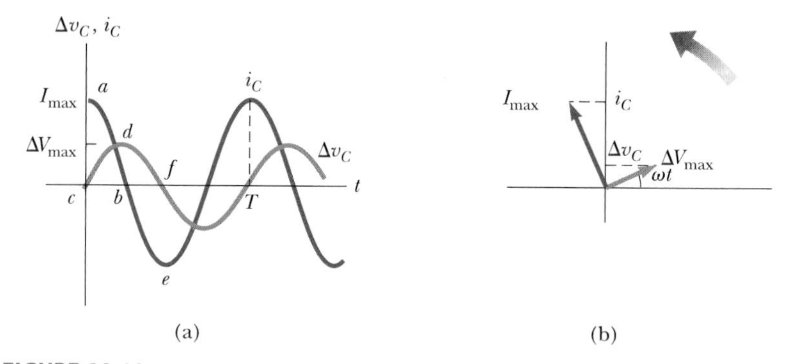

ACTIVE FIGURE 33.10

(a) Plots of the instantaneous current i_C and instantaneous voltage Δv_C across a capacitor as functions of time. The voltage lags behind the current by 90°. (b) Phasor diagram for the capacitive circuit, showing that the current leads the voltage by 90°.

Sign in at www.thomsonedu.com and go to ThomsonNOW to adjust the capacitance, frequency, and maximum voltage of the circuit in Active Figure 33.9. The results can be studied with the graph and the phasor diagram in this figure.

Using the trigonometric identity

$$\cos \omega t = \sin\left(\omega t + \frac{\pi}{2}\right)$$

we can express Equation 33.15 in the alternative form

Current in a capacitor ▶

$$i_C = \omega C \, \Delta V_{max} \sin\left(\omega t + \frac{\pi}{2}\right) \quad \textbf{(33.16)}$$

Comparing this expression with $\Delta v = \Delta V_{max} \sin \omega t$ shows that the current is $\pi/2$ rad $= 90°$ out of phase with the voltage across the capacitor. A plot of current and voltage versus time (Active Fig. 33.10a) shows that the current reaches its maximum value one-quarter of a cycle sooner than the voltage reaches its maximum value.

Consider a point such as *b* where the current is zero at this instant. That occurs when the capacitor reaches its maximum charge so that the voltage across the capacitor is a maximum (point *d*). At points such as *a* and *e*, the current is a maximum, which occurs at those instants when the charge on the capacitor reaches zero and the capacitor begins to recharge with the opposite polarity. When the charge is zero, the voltage across the capacitor is zero (points *c* and *f*). Therefore, the current and voltage are out of phase.

As with inductors, we can represent the current and voltage for a capacitor on a phasor diagram. The phasor diagram in Active Figure 33.10b shows that **for a sinusoidally applied voltage, the current always leads the voltage across a capacitor by 90°.**

Equation 33.15 shows that the current in the circuit reaches its maximum value when $\cos \omega t = \pm 1$:

$$I_{max} = \omega C \, \Delta V_{max} = \frac{\Delta V_{max}}{(1/\omega C)} \quad \textbf{(33.17)}$$

As in the case with inductors, this looks like Equation 27.7, so the denominator plays the role of resistance, with units of ohms. We give the combination $1/\omega C$ the symbol X_C, and because this function varies with frequency, we define it as the **capacitive reactance:**

Capacitive reactance ▶

$$X_C \equiv \frac{1}{\omega C} \quad \textbf{(33.18)}$$

We can now write Equation 33.17 as

Maximum current in a capacitor ▶

$$I_{max} = \frac{\Delta V_{max}}{X_C} \quad \textbf{(33.19)}$$

The rms current is given by an expression similar to Equation 33.19, with I_{max} replaced by I_{rms} and ΔV_{max} replaced by ΔV_{rms}.

Using Equation 33.19, we can express the instantaneous voltage across the capacitor as

$$\Delta v_C = \Delta V_{max} \sin \omega t = I_{max} X_C \sin \omega t \qquad \textbf{(33.20)}$$

◀ Voltage across a capacitor

Equations 33.18 and 33.19 indicate that as the frequency of the voltage source increases, the capacitive reactance decreases and the maximum current therefore increases. The frequency of the current is determined by the frequency of the voltage source driving the circuit. As the frequency approaches zero, the capacitive reactance approaches infinity and the current therefore approaches zero. This conclusion makes sense because the circuit approaches direct current conditions as ω approaches zero and the capacitor represents an open circuit.

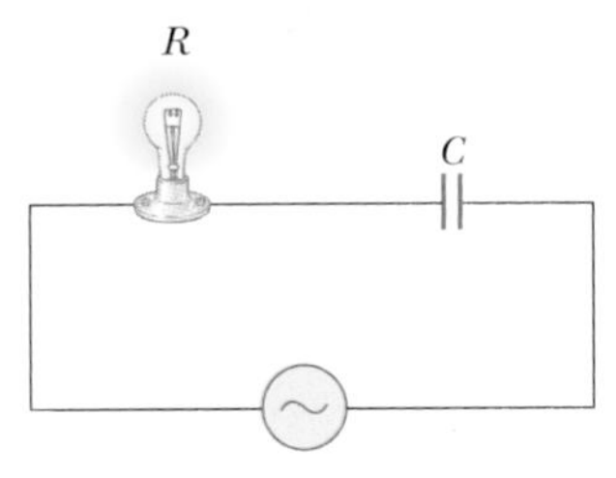

Figure 33.11 (Quick Quiz 33.3)

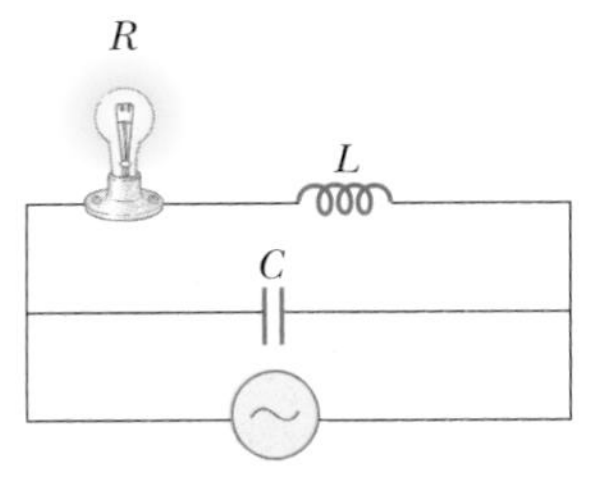

Figure 33.12 (Quick Quiz 33.4)

Quick Quiz 33.3 Consider the AC circuit in Figure 33.11. The frequency of the AC source is adjusted while its voltage amplitude is held constant. When does the lightbulb glow the brightest? (a) It glows brightest at high frequencies. (b) It glows brightest at low frequencies. (c) The brightness is the same at all frequencies.

Quick Quiz 33.4 Consider the AC circuit in Figure 33.12. The frequency of the AC source is adjusted while its voltage amplitude is held constant. When does the lightbulb glow the brightest? (a) It glows brightest at high frequencies. (b) It glows brightest at low frequencies. (c) The brightness is the same at all frequencies.

EXAMPLE 33.3 A Purely Capacitive AC Circuit

An 8.00-μF capacitor is connected to the terminals of a 60.0-Hz AC source whose rms voltage is 150 V. Find the capacitive reactance and the rms current in the circuit.

SOLUTION

Conceptualize Active Figure 33.9 shows the physical situation for this problem.

Categorize We evaluate the reactance and the current from equations developed in this section, so we categorize this example as a substitution problem.

Use Equation 33.18 to find the capacitive reactance:

$$X_C = \frac{1}{\omega C} = \frac{1}{2\pi f C} = \frac{1}{2\pi(60\text{ Hz})(8.00 \times 10^{-6}\text{ F})} = 332\ \Omega$$

Use an rms version of Equation 33.19 to find the rms current:

$$I_{rms} = \frac{\Delta V_{rms}}{X_C} = \frac{150\text{ V}}{332\ \Omega} = 0.452\text{ A}$$

What If? What if the frequency is doubled? What happens to the rms current in the circuit?

Answer If the frequency increases, the capacitive reactance decreases, which is just the opposite from the case of an inductor. The decrease in capacitive reactance results in an increase in the current.

Let's calculate the new capacitive reactance and the new rms current:

$$X_C = \frac{1}{\omega C} = \frac{1}{2\pi(120\text{ Hz})(8.00 \times 10^{-6}\text{ F})} = 166\ \Omega$$

$$I_{rms} = \frac{150\text{ V}}{166\ \Omega} = 0.904\text{ A}$$

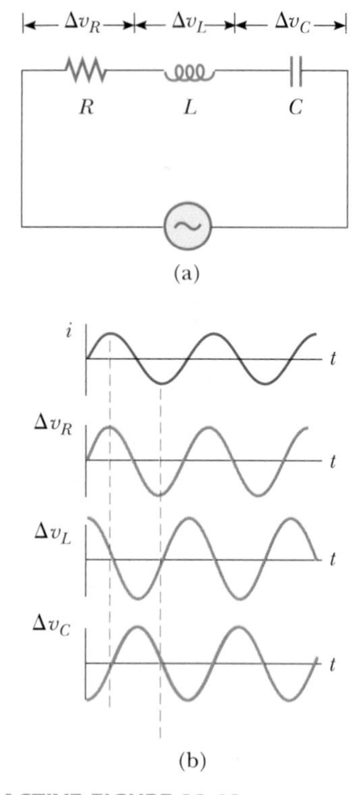

ACTIVE FIGURE 33.13

(a) A series circuit consisting of a resistor, an inductor, and a capacitor connected to an AC source. (b) Phase relationships for instantaneous voltages in the series *RLC* circuit.

Sign in at www.thomsonedu.com and go to ThomsonNOW to adjust the resistance, inductance, and capacitance. The results can be studied with the graph in this figure and the phasor diagram in Active Figure 33.15.

33.5 The *RLC* Series Circuit

Active Figure 33.13a shows a circuit that contains a resistor, an inductor, and a capacitor connected in series across an alternating voltage source. If the applied voltage varies sinusoidally with time, the instantaneous applied voltage is

$$\Delta v = \Delta V_{\max} \sin \omega t$$

while the current varies as

$$i = I_{\max} \sin (\omega t - \phi)$$

where ϕ is some **phase angle** between the current and the applied voltage. Based on our discussions of phase in Sections 33.3 and 33.4, we expect that the current will generally not be in phase with the voltage in an *RLC* circuit. Our aim is to determine ϕ and $I_{\max}$. Active Figure 33.13b shows the voltage versus time across each element in the circuit and their phase relationships.

First, because the elements are in series, the current everywhere in the circuit must be the same at any instant. That is, **the current at all points in a series AC circuit has the same amplitude and phase.** Based on the preceding sections, we know that the voltage across each element has a different amplitude and phase. In particular, the voltage across the resistor is in phase with the current, the voltage across the inductor leads the current by 90°, and the voltage across the capacitor lags behind the current by 90°. Using these phase relationships, we can express the instantaneous voltages across the three circuit elements as

$$\Delta v_R = I_{\max} R \sin \omega t = \Delta V_R \sin \omega t \qquad \textbf{(33.21)}$$

$$\Delta v_L = I_{\max} X_L \sin \left(\omega t + \frac{\pi}{2}\right) = \Delta V_L \cos \omega t \qquad \textbf{(33.22)}$$

$$\Delta v_C = I_{\max} X_C \sin \left(\omega t - \frac{\pi}{2}\right) = -\Delta V_C \cos \omega t \qquad \textbf{(33.23)}$$

The sum of these three voltages must equal the voltage from the AC source, but it is important to recognize that because the three voltages have different phase relationships with the current, they cannot be added directly. Figure 33.14 represents the phasors at an instant at which the current in all three elements is momentarily zero. The zero current is represented by the current phasor along the horizontal axis in each part of the figure. Next the voltage phasor is drawn at the appropriate phase angle to the current for each element.

Because phasors are rotating vectors, the voltage phasors in Figure 33.14 can be combined using vector addition as in Active Figure 33.15. In Active Figure 33.15a, the voltage phasors in Figure 33.14 are combined on the same coordinate axes. Active Figure 33.15b shows the vector addition of the voltage phasors. The voltage phasors ΔV_L and ΔV_C are in *opposite* directions along the same line, so we can construct the difference phasor $\Delta V_L - \Delta V_C$, which is perpendicular to the phasor ΔV_R. This diagram shows that the vector sum of the voltage amplitudes ΔV_R, ΔV_L, and ΔV_C equals a phasor whose length is the maximum applied voltage $\Delta V_{\max}$ and

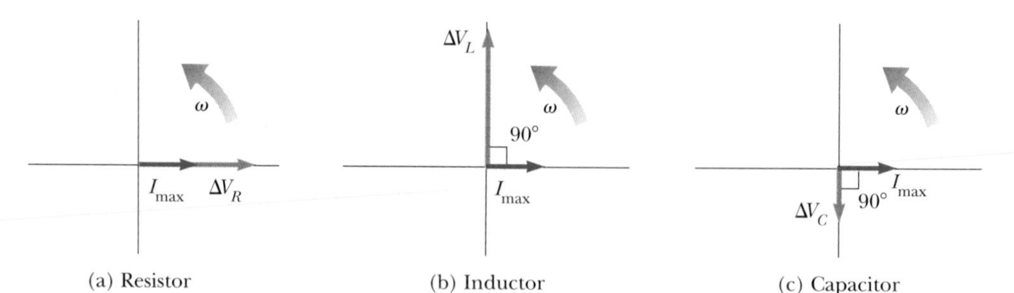

Figure 33.14 Phase relationships between the voltage and current phasors for (a) a resistor, (b) an inductor, and (c) a capacitor connected in series.

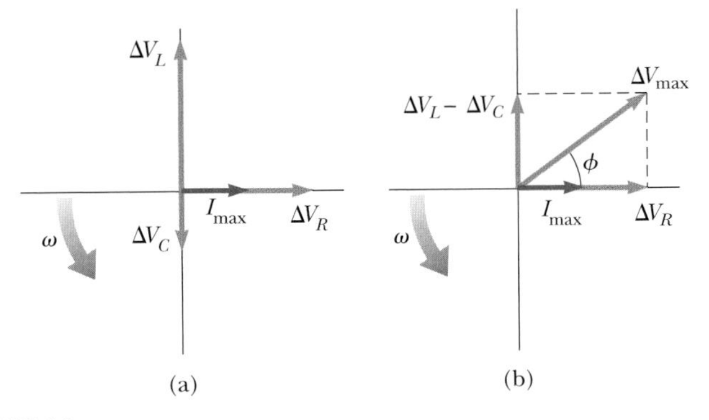

ACTIVE FIGURE 33.15

(a) Phasor diagram for the series *RLC* circuit shown in Active Figure 33.13a. The phasor ΔV_R is in phase with the current phasor I_{max}, the phasor ΔV_L leads I_{max} by 90°, and the phasor ΔV_C lags I_{max} by 90°. (b) The inductance and capacitance phasors are added together and then added vectorially to the resistance phasor. The total voltage ΔV_{max} makes an angle ϕ with I_{max}.

Sign in at www.thomsonedu.com and go to ThomsonNOW to adjust the resistance, inductance, and capacitance of the circuit in Active Figure 33.13a. The results can be studied with the graphs in Active Figure 33.13b and the phasor diagram in this figure.

which makes an angle ϕ with the current phasor I_{max}. From the right triangle in Active Figure 33.15b, we see that

$$\Delta V_{max} = \sqrt{\Delta V_R^{\,2} + (\Delta V_L - \Delta V_C)^2} = \sqrt{(I_{max}R)^2 + (I_{max}X_L - I_{max}X_C)^2}$$

$$\Delta V_{max} = I_{max}\sqrt{R^2 + (X_L - X_C)^2}$$

Therefore, we can express the maximum current as

$$I_{max} = \frac{\Delta V_{max}}{\sqrt{R^2 + (X_L - X_C)^2}} \qquad \textbf{(33.24)}$$

◀ Maximum current in an *RLC* circuit

Once again, this expression has the same mathematical form as Equation 27.7. The denominator of the fraction plays the role of resistance and is called the **impedance** Z of the circuit:

$$Z \equiv \sqrt{R^2 + (X_L - X_C)^2} \qquad \textbf{(33.25)}$$

◀ Impedance

where impedance also has units of ohms. Therefore, Equation 33.24 can be written in the form

$$I_{max} = \frac{\Delta V_{max}}{Z} \qquad \textbf{(33.26)}$$

Equation 33.26 is the AC equivalent of Equation 27.7. Note that the impedance and therefore the current in an AC circuit depend on the resistance, the inductance, the capacitance, and the frequency (because the reactances are frequency dependent).

From the right triangle in the phasor diagram in Active Figure 33.15b, the phase angle ϕ between the current and the voltage is found as follows:

$$\phi = \tan^{-1}\left(\frac{\Delta V_L - \Delta V_C}{\Delta V_R}\right) = \tan^{-1}\left(\frac{I_{max}X_L - I_{max}X_C}{I_{max}R}\right)$$

$$\phi = \tan^{-1}\left(\frac{X_L - X_C}{R}\right) \qquad \textbf{(33.27)}$$

◀ Phase angle

When $X_L > X_C$ (which occurs at high frequencies), the phase angle is positive, signifying that the current lags the applied voltage as in Active Figure 33.15b. We describe this situation by saying that the circuit is *more inductive than capacitive.* When $X_L < X_C$, the phase angle is negative, signifying that the current leads the applied voltage, and the circuit is *more capacitive than inductive.* When $X_L = X_C$, the phase angle is zero and the circuit is *purely resistive.*

Quick Quiz 33.5 Label each part of Figure 33.16, (a), (b), and (c), as representing $X_L > X_C$, $X_L = X_C$, or $X_L < X_C$.

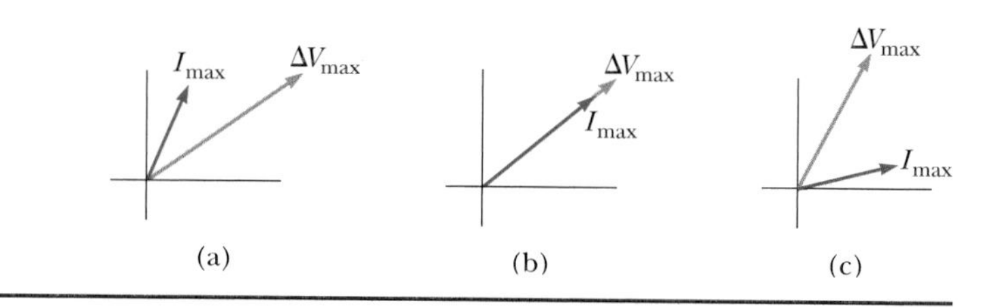

Figure 33.16 (Quick Quiz 33.5) Match the phasor diagrams to the relationships between the reactances.

EXAMPLE 33.4 Analyzing a Series *RLC* Circuit

A series *RLC* circuit has $R = 425\ \Omega$, $L = 1.25$ H, $C = 3.50\ \mu$F. It is connected to an AC source with $f = 60.0$ Hz and $\Delta V_{max} = 150$ V.

(A) Determine the inductive reactance, the capacitive reactance, and the impedance of the circuit.

SOLUTION

Conceptualize The circuit of interest in this example is shown in Active Figure 33.13a. The current in the combination of the resistor, inductor, and capacitor oscillates at a particular phase angle with respect to the applied voltage.

Categorize The circuit is a simple series *RLC* circuit, so we can use the approach discussed in this section.

Analyze Find the angular frequency:

$$\omega = 2\pi f = 2\pi(60.0 \text{ Hz}) = 377 \text{ s}^{-1}$$

Use Equation 33.10 to find the inductive reactance:

$$X_L = \omega L = (377 \text{ s}^{-1})(1.25 \text{ H}) = 471\ \Omega$$

Use Equation 33.18 to find the capacitive reactance:

$$X_C = \frac{1}{\omega C} = \frac{1}{(377 \text{ s}^{-1})(3.50 \times 10^{-6} \text{ F})} = 758\ \Omega$$

Use Equation 33.25 to find the impedance:

$$Z = \sqrt{R^2 + (X_L - X_C)^2}$$
$$= \sqrt{(425\ \Omega)^2 + (471\ \Omega - 758\ \Omega)^2} = 513\ \Omega$$

(B) Find the maximum current in the circuit.

SOLUTION

Use Equation 33.26 to find the maximum current:

$$I_{max} = \frac{\Delta V_{max}}{Z} = \frac{150 \text{ V}}{513\ \Omega} = 0.292 \text{ A}$$

(C) Find the phase angle between the current and voltage.

SOLUTION

Use Equation 33.27 to calculate the phase angle:

$$\phi = \tan^{-1}\left(\frac{X_L - X_C}{R}\right) = \tan^{-1}\left(\frac{471\ \Omega - 758\ \Omega}{425\ \Omega}\right) = -34.0°$$

(D) Find the maximum voltage across each element.

SOLUTION

Use Equations 33.2, 33.11, and 33.19 to calculate the maximum voltages:

$$\Delta V_R = I_{max}R = (0.292 \text{ A})(425\ \Omega) = 124 \text{ V}$$
$$\Delta V_L = I_{max}X_L = (0.292 \text{ A})(471\ \Omega) = 138 \text{ V}$$
$$\Delta V_C = I_{max}X_C = (0.292 \text{ A})(758\ \Omega) = 221 \text{ V}$$

(E) What replacement value of L should an engineer analyzing the circuit choose such that the current leads the applied voltage by 30.0°? All other values in the circuit stay the same.

SOLUTION

Solve Equation 33.27 for the inductive reactance:

$$X_L = X_C + R\tan\phi$$

Substitute Equations 33.10 and 33.18 into this expression:

$$\omega L = \frac{1}{\omega C} + R\tan\phi$$

Solve for L:

$$L = \frac{1}{\omega}\left(\frac{1}{\omega C} + R\tan\phi\right)$$

Substitute the given values:

$$L = \frac{1}{(377\ \text{s}^{-1})}\left[\frac{1}{(377\ \text{s}^{-1})(3.50 \times 10^{-6}\ \text{F})} + (425\ \Omega)\tan(-30.0°)\right]$$

$$L = \boxed{1.36\ \text{H}}$$

Finalize Because the capacitive reactance is larger than the inductive reactance, the circuit is more capacitive than inductive. In this case, the phase angle ϕ is negative, so the current leads the applied voltage.

Using Equations 33.21, 33.22, and 33.23, the instantaneous voltages across the three elements are

$$\Delta v_R = (124\ \text{V})\sin 377t$$

$$\Delta v_L = (138\ \text{V})\cos 377t$$

$$\Delta v_C = (-221\ \text{V})\cos 377t$$

What If? What if you added up the maximum voltages across the three circuit elements? Is that a physically meaningful quantity?

Answer The sum of the maximum voltages across the elements is $\Delta V_R + \Delta V_L + \Delta V_C = 483$ V. This sum is much greater than the maximum voltage of the source, 150 V. The sum of the maximum voltages is a meaningless quantity because when sinusoidally varying quantities are added, *both their amplitudes and their phases* must be taken into account. The maximum voltages across the various elements occur at different times. Therefore, the voltages must be added in a way that takes account of the different phases as shown in Active Figure 33.15.

33.6 Power in an AC Circuit

Now let's take an energy approach to analyzing AC circuits and consider the transfer of energy from the AC source to the circuit. The power delivered by a battery to an external DC circuit is equal to the product of the current and the terminal voltage of the battery. Likewise, the instantaneous power delivered by an AC source to a circuit is the product of the current and the applied voltage. For the RLC circuit shown in Active Figure 33.13a, we can express the instantaneous power $\mathcal{P}$ as

$$\mathcal{P} = i\Delta v = I_{\text{max}}\sin(\omega t - \phi)\,\Delta V_{\text{max}}\sin\omega t$$

$$\mathcal{P} = I_{\text{max}}\Delta V_{\text{max}}\sin\omega t\sin(\omega t - \phi) \qquad \textbf{(33.28)}$$

This result is a complicated function of time and is therefore not very useful from a practical viewpoint. What is generally of interest is the average power over one or more cycles. Such an average can be computed by first using the trigonometric identity $\sin(\omega t - \phi) = \sin\omega t\cos\phi - \cos\omega t\sin\phi$. Substituting this identity into Equation 33.28 gives

$$\mathcal{P} = I_{\text{max}}\Delta V_{\text{max}}\sin^2\omega t\cos\phi - I_{\text{max}}\Delta V_{\text{max}}\sin\omega t\cos\omega t\sin\phi \qquad \textbf{(33.29)}$$

Let's now take the time average of $\mathcal{P}$ over one or more cycles, noting that I_{max}, ΔV_{max}, ϕ, and ω are all constants. The time average of the first term on the right of the equal sign in Equation 33.29 involves the average value of $\sin^2 \omega t$, which is $\frac{1}{2}$. The time average of the second term on the right of the equal sign is identically zero because $\sin \omega t \cos \omega t = \frac{1}{2} \sin 2\omega t$, and the average value of $\sin 2\omega t$ is zero. Therefore, we can express the **average power** $\mathcal{P}_{avg}$ as

$$\mathcal{P}_{avg} = \tfrac{1}{2} I_{max} \Delta V_{max} \cos \phi \tag{33.30}$$

It is convenient to express the average power in terms of the rms current and rms voltage defined by Equations 33.4 and 33.5:

Average power delivered to an *RLC* circuit ▶

$$\mathcal{P}_{avg} = I_{rms}\, \Delta V_{rms} \cos \phi \tag{33.31}$$

where the quantity $\cos \phi$ is called the **power factor.** Active Figure 33.15b shows that the maximum voltage across the resistor is given by $\Delta V_R = \Delta V_{max} \cos \phi = I_{max} R$. Using Equation 33.5 and $\cos \phi = I_{max} R / \Delta V_{max}$, we can express $\mathcal{P}_{avg}$ as

$$\mathcal{P}_{avg} = I_{rms} \Delta V_{rms} \cos \phi = I_{rms} \left(\frac{\Delta V_{max}}{\sqrt{2}} \right) \frac{I_{max} R}{\Delta V_{max}} = I_{rms} \frac{I_{max} R}{\sqrt{2}}$$

Substituting $I_{max} = \sqrt{2} I_{rms}$ from Equation 33.4 gives

$$\mathcal{P}_{avg} = I_{rms}^2 R \tag{33.32}$$

In words, **the average power delivered by the source is converted to internal energy in the resistor,** just as in the case of a DC circuit. When the load is purely resistive, $\phi = 0$, $\cos \phi = 1$, and, from Equation 33.31, we see that

$$\mathcal{P}_{avg} = I_{rms} \Delta V_{rms}$$

Note that **no power losses are associated with pure capacitors and pure inductors in an AC circuit.** To see why that is true, let's first analyze the power in an AC circuit containing only a source and a capacitor. When the current begins to increase in one direction in an AC circuit, charge begins to accumulate on the capacitor and a voltage appears across it. When this voltage reaches its maximum value, the energy stored in the capacitor as electric potential energy is $\frac{1}{2} C (\Delta V_{max})^2$. This energy storage, however, is only momentary. The capacitor is charged and discharged twice during each cycle: charge is delivered to the capacitor during two quarters of the cycle and is returned to the voltage source during the remaining two quarters. Therefore, **the average power supplied by the source is zero.** In other words, **no power losses occur in a capacitor in an AC circuit.**

Now consider the case of an inductor. When the current in an inductor reaches its maximum value, the energy stored in the inductor is a maximum and is given by $\frac{1}{2} L I_{max}^2$. When the current begins to decrease in the circuit, this stored energy in the inductor returns to the source as the inductor attempts to maintain the current in the circuit.

Equation 33.31 shows that the power delivered by an AC source to any circuit depends on the phase, a result that has many interesting applications. For example, a factory that uses large motors in machines, generators, or transformers has a large inductive load (because of all the windings). To deliver greater power to such devices in the factory without using excessively high voltages, technicians introduce capacitance in the circuits to shift the phase.

Quick Quiz 33.6 An AC source drives an *RLC* circuit with a fixed voltage amplitude. If the driving frequency is ω_1, the circuit is more capacitive than inductive and the phase angle is $-10°$. If the driving frequency is ω_2, the circuit is more inductive than capacitive and the phase angle is $+10°$. At what frequency is the largest amount of power delivered to the circuit? (a) It is largest at ω_1. (b) It is largest at ω_2. (c) The same amount of power is delivered at both frequencies.

EXAMPLE 33.5 Average Power in an *RLC* Series Circuit

Calculate the average power delivered to the series *RLC* circuit described in Example 33.4.

SOLUTION

Conceptualize Consider the circuit in Active Figure 33.13a and imagine energy being delivered to the circuit by the AC source. Review Example 33.4 for other details about this circuit.

Categorize We find the result by using equations developed in this section, so we categorize this example as a substitution problem.

Use Equation 33.5 and the maximum voltage from Example 33.4 to find the rms voltage from the source:

$$\Delta V_{\text{rms}} = \frac{\Delta V_{\text{max}}}{\sqrt{2}} = \frac{150\text{ V}}{\sqrt{2}} = 106\text{ V}$$

Similarly, find the rms current in the circuit:

$$I_{\text{rms}} = \frac{I_{\text{max}}}{\sqrt{2}} = \frac{0.292\text{ A}}{\sqrt{2}} = 0.206\text{ A}$$

Use Equation 33.31 to find the power delivered by the source:

$$\mathcal{P}_{\text{avg}} = I_{\text{rms}}V_{\text{rms}}\cos\phi = (0.206\text{ A})(106\text{ V})\cos(-34.0°)$$
$$= 18.1\text{ W}$$

33.7 Resonance in a Series *RLC* Circuit

A series *RLC* circuit is said to be **in resonance** when the driving frequency is such that the rms current has its maximum value. In general, the rms current can be written

$$I_{\text{rms}} = \frac{\Delta V_{\text{rms}}}{Z} \qquad \textbf{(33.33)}$$

where Z is the impedance. Substituting the expression for Z from Equation 33.25 into Equation 33.33 gives

$$I_{\text{rms}} = \frac{\Delta V_{\text{rms}}}{\sqrt{R^2 + (X_L - X_C)^2}} \qquad \textbf{(33.34)}$$

Because the impedance depends on the frequency of the source, the current in the *RLC* circuit also depends on the frequency. The frequency ω_0 at which $X_L - X_C = 0$ is called the **resonance frequency** of the circuit. To find ω_0, we set $X_L = X_C$, which gives $\omega_0 L = 1/\omega_0 C$, or

$$\omega_0 = \frac{1}{\sqrt{LC}} \qquad \textbf{(33.35)}$$

◄ Resonance frequency

This frequency also corresponds to the natural frequency of oscillation of an *LC* circuit (see Section 32.5). Therefore, the rms current in a series *RLC* circuit has its maximum value when the frequency of the applied voltage matches the natural oscillator frequency, which depends only on L and C. Furthermore, at the resonance frequency, the current is in phase with the applied voltage.

Quick Quiz 33.7 What is the impedance of a series *RLC* circuit at resonance? (a) larger than R (b) less than R (c) equal to R (d) impossible to determine

A plot of rms current versus frequency for a series *RLC* circuit is shown in Active Figure 33.17a. The data assume a constant $\Delta V_{\text{rms}} = 5.0$ mV, $L = 5.0\ \mu$H, and $C = 2.0$ nF. The three curves correspond to three values of R. In each case,

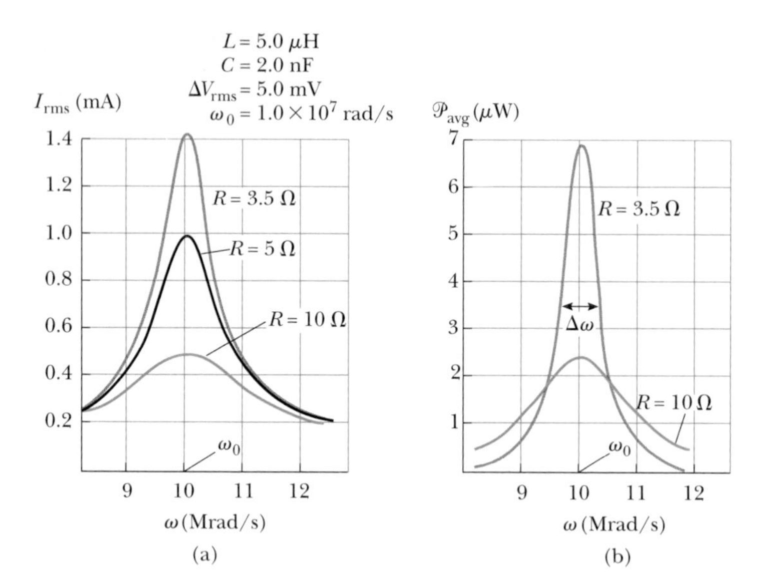

ACTIVE FIGURE 33.17

(a) The rms current versus frequency for a series *RLC* circuit for three values of *R*. The current reaches its maximum value at the resonance frequency ω_0. (b) Average power delivered to the circuit versus frequency for the series *RLC* circuit for two values of *R*.

Sign in at www.thomsonedu.com and go to ThomsonNOW to adjust the resistance, inductance, and capacitance of the circuit in Active Figure 33.13a. You can then determine the current and power for a given frequency or sweep through the frequencies to generate resonance curves as shown in this figure.

the rms current has its maximum value at the resonance frequency ω_0. Furthermore, the curves become narrower and taller as the resistance decreases.

Equation 33.34 shows that when $R = 0$, the current becomes infinite at resonance. Real circuits, however, always have some resistance, which limits the value of the current to some finite value.

We can also calculate the average power as a function of frequency for a series *RLC* circuit. Using Equations 33.32, 33.33, and 33.25 gives

$$\mathcal{P}_{\text{avg}} = I_{\text{rms}}^2 R = \frac{(\Delta V_{\text{rms}})^2}{Z^2} R = \frac{(\Delta V_{\text{rms}})^2 R}{R^2 + (X_L - X_C)^2} \qquad \textbf{(33.36)}$$

Because $X_L = \omega L$, $X_C = 1/\omega C$, and $\omega_0^2 = 1/LC$, the term $(X_L - X_C)^2$ can be expressed as

$$(X_L - X_C)^2 = \left(\omega L - \frac{1}{\omega C}\right)^2 = \frac{L^2}{\omega^2}(\omega^2 - \omega_0^2)^2$$

Using this result in Equation 33.36 gives

Average power as a function of frequency in an *RLC* circuit ▶

$$\mathcal{P}_{\text{avg}} = \frac{(\Delta V_{\text{rms}})^2 R \omega^2}{R^2\omega^2 + L^2(\omega^2 - \omega_0^2)^2} \qquad \textbf{(33.37)}$$

Equation 33.37 shows that **at resonance, when $\omega = \omega_0$, the average power is a maximum** and has the value $(\Delta V_{\text{rms}})^2/R$. Active Figure 33.17b is a plot of average power versus frequency for two values of R in a series *RLC* circuit. As the resistance is made smaller, the curve becomes sharper in the vicinity of the resonance frequency. This curve sharpness is usually described by a dimensionless parameter known as the **quality factor,**[2] denoted by Q:

Quality factor ▶

$$Q = \frac{\omega_0}{\Delta\omega}$$

[2] The quality factor is also defined as the ratio $2\pi E/\Delta E$, where E is the energy stored in the oscillating system and ΔE is the energy decrease per cycle of oscillation due to the resistance.

where $\Delta\omega$ is the width of the curve measured between the two values of ω for which $\mathcal{P}_{avg}$ has one-half its maximum value, called the *half-power points* (see Active Fig. 33.17b.) It is left as a problem (Problem 68) to show that the width at the half-power points has the value $\Delta\omega = R/L$ so that

$$Q = \frac{\omega_0 L}{R} \tag{33.38}$$

A radio's receiving circuit is an important application of a resonant circuit. The radio is tuned to a particular station (which transmits an electromagnetic wave or signal of a specific frequency) by varying a capacitor, which changes the receiving circuit's resonance frequency. When the circuit is driven by the electromagnetic oscillations a radio signal produces in an antenna, the tuner circuit responds with a large amplitude of electrical oscillation only for the station frequency that matches the resonance frequency. Therefore, only the signal from one radio station is passed on to the amplifier and loudspeakers even though signals from all stations are driving the circuit at the same time. Because many signals are often present over a range of frequencies, it is important to design a high-Q circuit to eliminate unwanted signals. In this manner, stations whose frequencies are near but not equal to the resonance frequency give signals at the receiver that are negligibly small relative to the signal that matches the resonance frequency.

EXAMPLE 33.6 A Resonating Series *RLC* Circuit

Consider a series *RLC* circuit for which $R = 150\ \Omega$, $L = 20.0$ mH, $\Delta V_{rms} = 20.0$ V, and $\omega = 5\,000\ s^{-1}$. Determine the value of the capacitance for which the current is a maximum.

SOLUTION

Conceptualize Consider the circuit in Active Figure 33.13a and imagine varying the frequency of the AC source. The current in the circuit has its maximum value at the resonance frequency ω_0.

Categorize We find the result by using equations developed in this section, so we categorize this example as a substitution problem.

Use Equation 33.35 to solve for the required capacitance in terms of the resonance frequency:

$$\omega_0 = \frac{1}{\sqrt{LC}} \rightarrow C = \frac{1}{\omega_0^2 L}$$

Substitute numerical values:

$$C = \frac{1}{(5.00 \times 10^3\ s^{-1})^2(20.0 \times 10^{-3}\ H)} = 2.00\ \mu F$$

33.8 The Transformer and Power Transmission

As discussed in Section 27.6, it is economical to use a high voltage and a low current to minimize the I^2R loss in transmission lines when electric power is transmitted over great distances. Consequently, 350-kV lines are common, and in many areas, even higher-voltage (765-kV) lines are used. At the receiving end of such lines, the consumer requires power at a low voltage (for safety and for efficiency in design). In practice, the voltage is decreased to approximately 20 000 V at a distributing station, then to 4 000 V for delivery to residential areas, and finally to 120 V and 240 V at the customer's site. Therefore, a device is needed that can change the alternating voltage and current without causing appreciable changes in the power delivered. The AC transformer is that device.

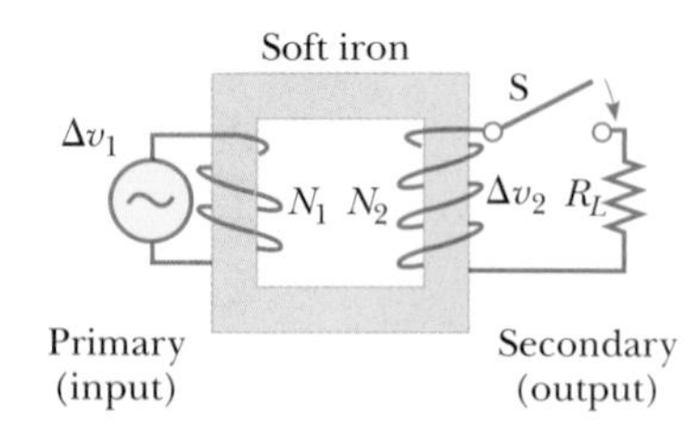

Figure 33.18 An ideal transformer consists of two coils wound on the same iron core. An alternating voltage Δv_1 is applied to the primary coil, and the output voltage Δv_2 is across the resistor of resistance R_L.

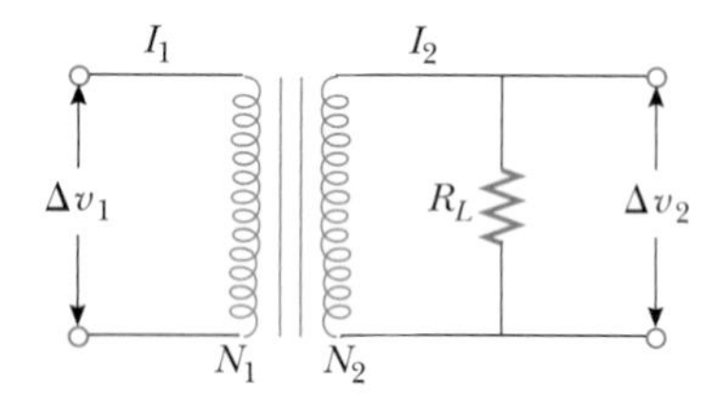

Figure 33.19 Circuit diagram for a transformer.

NIKOLA TESLA
American Physicist (1856–1943)
Tesla was born in Croatia, but he spent most of his professional life as an inventor in the United States. He was a key figure in the development of alternating-current electricity, high-voltage transformers, and the transport of electrical power using AC transmission lines. Tesla's viewpoint was at odds with the ideas of Thomas Edison, who committed himself to the use of direct current in power transmission. Tesla's AC approach won out.

In its simplest form, the **AC transformer** consists of two coils of wire wound around a core of iron as illustrated in Figure 33.18. (Compare this arrangement to Faraday's experiment in Figure 31.2.) The coil on the left, which is connected to the input alternating voltage source and has N_1 turns, is called the *primary winding* (or the *primary*). The coil on the right, consisting of N_2 turns and connected to a load resistor R_L, is called the *secondary winding* (or the *secondary*). The purposes of the iron core are to increase the magnetic flux through the coil and to provide a medium in which nearly all the magnetic field lines through one coil pass through the other coil. Eddy-current losses are reduced by using a laminated core. Transformation of energy to internal energy in the finite resistance of the coil wires is usually quite small. Typical transformers have power efficiencies from 90% to 99%. In the discussion that follows, let's assume we are working with an *ideal transformer*, one in which the energy losses in the windings and core are zero.

Faraday's law states that the voltage Δv_1 across the primary is

$$\Delta v_1 = -N_1 \frac{d\Phi_B}{dt} \tag{33.39}$$

where Φ_B is the magnetic flux through each turn. If we assume all magnetic field lines remain within the iron core, the flux through each turn of the primary equals the flux through each turn of the secondary. Hence, the voltage across the secondary is

$$\Delta v_2 = -N_2 \frac{d\Phi_B}{dt} \tag{33.40}$$

Solving Equation 33.39 for $d\Phi_B/dt$ and substituting the result into Equation 33.40 gives

$$\Delta v_2 = \frac{N_2}{N_1} \Delta v_1 \tag{33.41}$$

When $N_2 > N_1$, the output voltage Δv_2 exceeds the input voltage Δv_1. This configuration is referred to as a *step-up transformer*. When $N_2 < N_1$, the output voltage is less than the input voltage, and we have a *step-down transformer*.

When the switch in the secondary circuit is closed, a current I_2 is induced in the secondary. (In this discussion, uppercase I and ΔV refer to rms values.) If the load in the secondary circuit is a pure resistance, the induced current is in phase with the induced voltage. The power supplied to the secondary circuit must be provided by the AC source connected to the primary circuit as shown in Figure 33.19. In an ideal transformer where there are no losses, the power $I_1 \Delta V_1$ supplied by the source is equal to the power $I_2 \Delta V_2$ in the secondary circuit. That is,

$$I_1 \Delta V_1 = I_2 \Delta V_2 \tag{33.42}$$

The value of the load resistance R_L determines the value of the secondary current because $I_2 = \Delta V_2/R_L$. Furthermore, the current in the primary is $I_1 = \Delta V_1/R_{eq}$, where

$$R_{eq} = \left(\frac{N_1}{N_2}\right)^2 R_L \tag{33.43}$$

is the equivalent resistance of the load resistance when viewed from the primary side. We see from this analysis that a transformer may be used to match resistances between the primary circuit and the load. In this manner, maximum power transfer can be achieved between a given power source and the load resistance. For example, a transformer connected between the 1-kΩ output of an audio amplifier and an 8-Ω speaker ensures that as much of the audio signal as possible is transferred into the speaker. In stereo terminology, this process is called *impedance matching*.

To operate properly, many common household electronic devices require low voltages. A small transformer that plugs directly into the wall like the one illus-

Figure 33.20 The primary winding in this transformer is directly attached to the prongs of the plug. The secondary winding is connected to the power cord on the right, which runs to an electronic device. Many of these power-supply transformers also convert alternating current to direct current.

This transformer is smaller than the one in the opening photograph of this chapter. In addition, it is a step-down transformer. It drops the voltage from 4 000 V to 240 V for delivery to a group of residences.

trated in Figure 33.20 can provide the proper voltage. The photograph shows the two windings wrapped around a common iron core that is found inside all these little "black boxes." This particular transformer converts the 120-V AC in the wall socket to 12.5-V AC. (Can you determine the ratio of the numbers of turns in the two coils?) Some black boxes also make use of diodes to convert the alternating current to direct current. (See Section 33.9.)

EXAMPLE 33.7 The Economics of AC Power

An electricity-generating station needs to deliver energy at a rate of 20 MW to a city 1.0 km away. A common voltage for commercial power generators is 22 kV, but a step-up transformer is used to boost the voltage to 230 kV before transmission.

(A) If the resistance of the wires is 2.0 Ω and the energy costs are about 10¢/kWh, estimate what it costs the utility company for the energy converted to internal energy in the wires during one day.

SOLUTION

Conceptualize The resistance of the wires is in series with the resistance representing the load (homes and businesses). Therefore, there is a voltage drop in the wires, which means that some of the transmitted energy is converted to internal energy in the wires and never reaches the load.

Categorize This problem involves finding the power delivered to a resistive load in an AC circuit. Let's ignore any capacitive or inductive characteristics of the load and set the power factor equal to 1.

Analyze Calculate I_{rms} in the wires from Equation 33.31:

$$I_{\text{rms}} = \frac{\mathcal{P}_{\text{avg}}}{\Delta V_{\text{rms}}} = \frac{20 \times 10^6 \text{ W}}{230 \times 10^3 \text{ V}} = 87 \text{ A}$$

Determine the rate at which energy is delivered to the resistance in the wires from Equation 33.32:

$$\mathcal{P}_{\text{avg}} = I_{\text{rms}}^2 R = (87 \text{ A})^2 (2.0 \ \Omega) = 15 \text{ kW}$$

Calculate the energy T_{ET} delivered to the wires over the course of a day:

$$T_{\text{ET}} = \mathcal{P}_{\text{avg}} \Delta t = (15 \text{ kW})(24 \text{ h}) = 360 \text{ kWh}$$

Find the cost of this energy at a rate of 10¢/kWh:

$$\text{Cost} = (360 \text{ kWh})(\$0.10/\text{kWh}) = \$36$$

(B) Repeat the calculation for the situation in which the power plant delivers the energy at its original voltage of 22 kV.

SOLUTION

Calculate I_{rms} in the wires from Equation 33.31:

$$I_{\text{rms}} = \frac{\mathcal{P}_{\text{avg}}}{\Delta V_{\text{rms}}} = \frac{20 \times 10^6 \text{ W}}{22 \times 10^3 \text{ V}} = 910 \text{ A}$$

From Equation 33.32, determine the rate at which energy is delivered to the resistance in the wires:

$$\mathcal{P}_{\text{avg}} = I_{\text{rms}}^2 R = (910 \text{ A})^2 (2.0 \text{ }\Omega) = 1.7 \times 10^3 \text{ kW}$$

Calculate the energy delivered to the wires over the course of a day:

$$T_{\text{ET}} = \mathcal{P}_{\text{avg}} \Delta t = (1.7 \times 10^3 \text{ kW})(24 \text{ h}) = 4.1 \times 10^4 \text{ kWh}$$

Find the cost of this energy at a rate of 10¢/kWh:

$$\text{Cost} = (4.1 \times 10^4 \text{ kWh})(\$0.10/\text{kWh}) = \$4.1 \times 10^3$$

Finalize Notice the tremendous savings that are possible through the use of transformers and high-voltage transmission lines. Such savings in combination with the efficiency of using alternating current to operate motors led to the universal adoption of alternating current instead of direct current for commercial power grids.

33.9 Rectifiers and Filters

Portable electronic devices such as radios and compact disc players are often powered by direct current supplied by batteries. Many devices come with AC–DC converters such as that shown in Figure 33.20. Such a converter contains a transformer that steps the voltage down from 120 V to, typically, 9 V and a circuit that converts alternating current to direct current. The AC–DC converting process is called **rectification,** and the converting device is called a **rectifier.**

The most important element in a rectifier circuit is a **diode,** a circuit element that conducts current in one direction but not the other. Most diodes used in modern electronics are semiconductor devices. The circuit symbol for a diode is —▶|—, where the arrow indicates the direction of the current in the diode. A diode has low resistance to current in one direction (the direction of the arrow) and high resistance to current in the opposite direction. To understand how a diode rectifies a current, consider Figure 33.21a, which shows a diode and a resistor connected to the secondary of a transformer. The transformer reduces the voltage from 120-V AC to the lower voltage that is needed for the device having a resistance R (the load resistance). Because the diode conducts current in only one direction, the alternating current in the load resistor is reduced to the form shown by the solid curve in Figure 33.21b. The diode conducts current only when the side of the symbol containing the arrowhead has a positive potential relative to the other side. In this situation, the diode acts as a *half-wave rectifier* because current is present in the circuit only during half of each cycle.

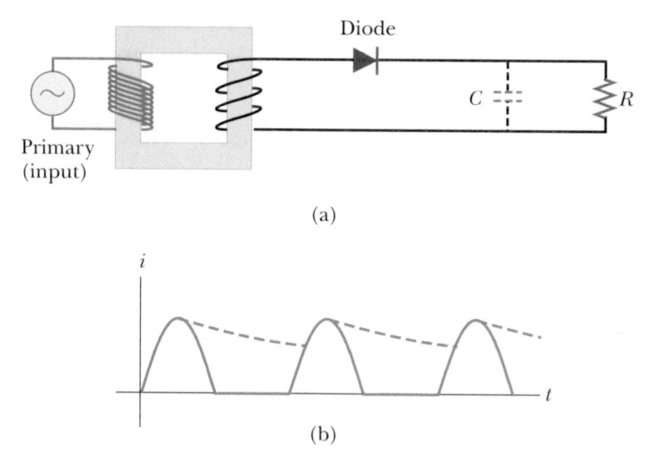

Figure 33.21 (a) A half-wave rectifier with an optional filter capacitor. (b) Current versus time in the resistor. The solid curve represents the current with no filter capacitor, and the dashed curve is the current when the circuit includes the capacitor.

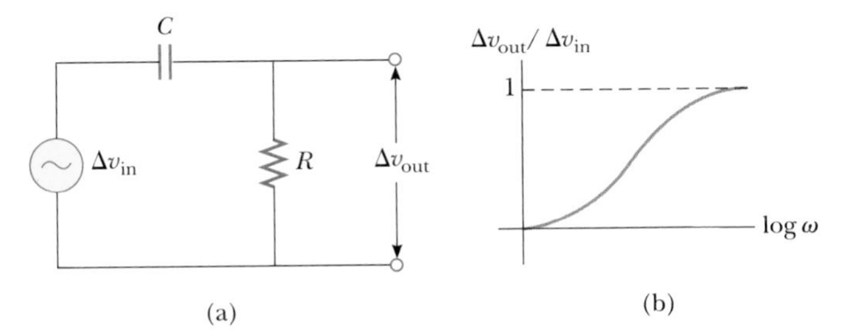

ACTIVE FIGURE 33.22

(a) A simple *RC* high-pass filter. (b) Ratio of output voltage to input voltage for an *RC* high-pass filter as a function of the angular frequency of the AC source.

Sign in at www.thomsonedu.com and go to ThomsonNOW to adjust the resistance and capacitance of the circuit in (a). You can then determine the output voltage for a given frequency or sweep through the frequencies to generate a curve like that in (b).

When a capacitor is added to the circuit as shown by the dashed lines and the capacitor symbol in Figure 33.21a, the circuit is a simple DC power supply. The time variation of the current in the load resistor (the dashed curve in Fig. 33.21b) is close to being zero, as determined by the *RC* time constant of the circuit. As the current in the circuit begins to rise at $t = 0$ in Figure 33.21b, the capacitor charges up. When the current begins to fall, however, the capacitor discharges through the resistor, so the current in the resistor does not fall as quickly as the current from the transformer.

The *RC* circuit in Figure 33.21a is one example of a **filter circuit,** which is used to smooth out or eliminate a time-varying signal. For example, radios are usually powered by a 60-Hz alternating voltage. After rectification, the voltage still contains a small AC component at 60 Hz (sometimes called *ripple*), which must be filtered. By "filtered," we mean that the 60-Hz ripple must be reduced to a value much less than that of the audio signal to be amplified because without filtering, the resulting audio signal includes an annoying hum at 60 Hz.

We can also design filters that respond differently to different frequencies. Consider the simple series *RC* circuit shown in Active Figure 33.22a. The input voltage is across the series combination of the two elements. The output is the voltage across the resistor. A plot of the ratio of the output voltage to the input voltage as a function of the logarithm of angular frequency (see Active Fig. 33.22b) shows that at low frequencies, Δv_{out} is much smaller than Δv_{in}, whereas at high frequencies, the two voltages are equal. Because the circuit preferentially passes signals of higher frequency while blocking low-frequency signals, the circuit is called an *RC* high-pass filter. (See Problem 45 for an analysis of this filter.)

Physically, a high-pass filter works because a capacitor "blocks out" direct current and AC current at low frequencies. At low frequencies, the capacitive reactance is large and much of the applied voltage appears across the capacitor rather than across the output resistor. As the frequency increases, the capacitive reactance drops and more of the applied voltage appears across the resistor.

Now consider the circuit shown in Active Figure 33.23a, where we have interchanged the resistor and capacitor and where the output voltage is taken across the capacitor. At low frequencies, the reactance of the capacitor and the voltage across the capacitor is high. As the frequency increases, the voltage across the capacitor drops. Therefore, this filter is an *RC* low-pass filter. The ratio of output voltage to input voltage (see Problem 46), plotted as a function of the logarithm of ω in Active Figure 33.23b, shows this behavior.

You may be familiar with crossover networks, which are an important part of the speaker systems for high-fidelity audio systems. These networks use low-pass filters to direct low frequencies to a special type of speaker, the "woofer," which is designed to reproduce the low notes accurately. The high frequencies are sent to the "tweeter" speaker.

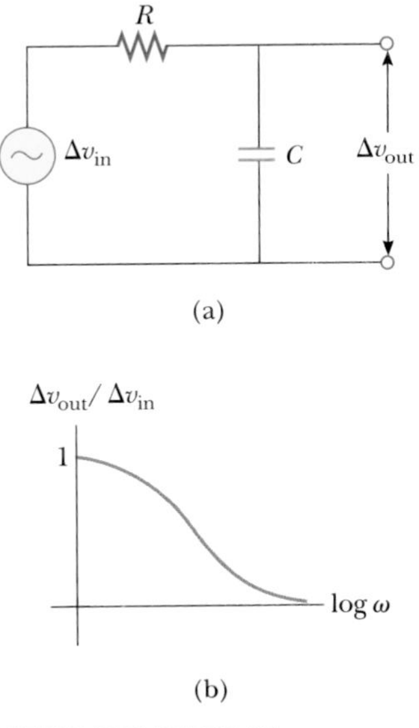

ACTIVE FIGURE 33.23

(a) A simple *RC* low-pass filter.
(b) Ratio of output voltage to input voltage for an *RC* low-pass filter as a function of the angular frequency of the AC source.

Sign in at www.thomsonedu.com and go to ThomsonNOW to adjust the resistance and capacitance of the circuit in (a). You can then determine the output voltage for a given frequency or sweep through the frequencies to generate a curve like that in (b).

Summary

ThomsonNOW™ Sign in at **www.thomsonedu.com** and go to ThomsonNOW to take a practice test for this chapter.

DEFINITIONS

In AC circuits that contain inductors and capacitors, it is useful to define the **inductive reactance** X_L and the **capacitive reactance** X_C as

$$X_L \equiv \omega L \qquad \textbf{(33.10)}$$

$$X_C \equiv \frac{1}{\omega C} \qquad \textbf{(33.18)}$$

where ω is the angular frequency of the AC source. The SI unit of reactance is the ohm.

The **impedance** Z of an RLC series AC circuit is

$$Z \equiv \sqrt{R^2 + (X_L - X_C)^2} \qquad \textbf{(33.25)}$$

This expression illustrates that we cannot simply add the resistance and reactances in a circuit. We must account for the applied voltage and current being out of phase, with the **phase angle** ϕ between the current and voltage being

$$\phi = \tan^{-1}\left(\frac{X_L - X_C}{R}\right) \qquad \textbf{(33.27)}$$

The sign of ϕ can be positive or negative, depending on whether X_L is greater or less than X_C. The phase angle is zero when $X_L = X_C$.

CONCEPTS AND PRINCIPLES

The **rms current** and **rms voltage** in an AC circuit in which the voltages and current vary sinusoidally are given by

$$I_{\text{rms}} = \frac{I_{\text{max}}}{\sqrt{2}} = 0.707 I_{\text{max}} \qquad \textbf{(33.4)}$$

$$\Delta V_{\text{rms}} = \frac{\Delta V_{\text{max}}}{\sqrt{2}} = 0.707\,\Delta V_{\text{max}} \qquad \textbf{(33.5)}$$

where I_{max} and ΔV_{max} are the maximum values.

If an AC circuit consists of a source and a resistor, the current is in phase with the voltage. That is, the current and voltage reach their maximum values at the same time.

If an AC circuit consists of a source and an inductor, the current lags the voltage by 90°. That is, the voltage reaches its maximum value one quarter of a period before the current reaches its maximum value.

If an AC circuit consists of a source and a capacitor, the current leads the voltage by 90°. That is, the current reaches its maximum value one quarter of a period before the voltage reaches its maximum value.

The **average power** delivered by the source in an RLC circuit is

$$\mathcal{P}_{\text{avg}} = I_{\text{rms}}\,\Delta V_{\text{rms}} \cos\phi \qquad \textbf{(33.31)}$$

An equivalent expression for the average power is

$$\mathcal{P}_{\text{avg}} = I_{\text{rms}}^2 R \qquad \textbf{(33.32)}$$

The average power delivered by the source results in increasing internal energy in the resistor. No power loss occurs in an ideal inductor or capacitor.

The rms current in a series RLC circuit is

$$I_{\text{rms}} = \frac{\Delta V_{\text{rms}}}{\sqrt{R^2 + (X_L - X_C)^2}} \qquad \textbf{(33.34)}$$

A series RLC circuit is in resonance when the inductive reactance equals the capacitive reactance. When this condition is met, the rms current given by Equation 33.34 has its maximum value. The **resonance frequency** ω_0 of the circuit is

$$\omega_0 = \frac{1}{\sqrt{LC}} \qquad \textbf{(33.35)}$$

The rms current in a series RLC circuit has its maximum value when the frequency of the source equals ω_0, that is, when the "driving" frequency matches the resonance frequency.

AC transformers allow for easy changes in alternating voltage according to

$$\Delta v_2 = \frac{N_2}{N_1}\,\Delta v_1 \qquad \textbf{(33.41)}$$

where N_1 and N_2 are the numbers of windings on the primary and secondary coils, respectively, and Δv_1 and Δv_2 are the voltages on these coils.

Questions

☐ denotes answer available in *Student Solutions Manual/Study Guide;* **O** denotes objective question

1. **O** **(i)** What is the time average of the "square-wave" potential shown in Figure Q33.1? (a) $\sqrt{2}\,\Delta V_{max}$ (b) ΔV_{max} (c) $\Delta V_{max}/\sqrt{2}$ (d) $\Delta V_{max}/2$ (e) $\Delta V_{max}/4$ **(ii)** What is the rms voltage? Choose from the same possibilities.

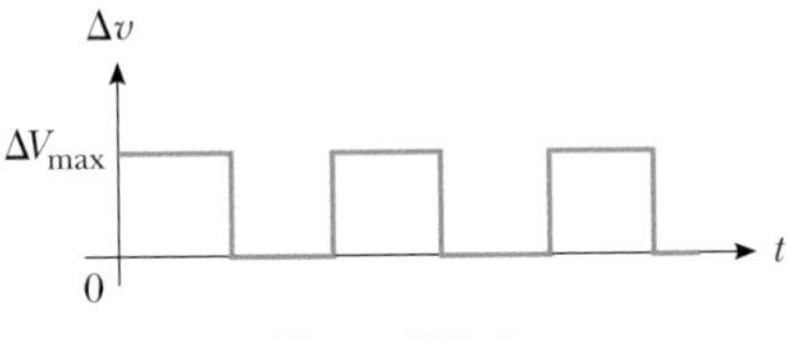

Figure Q33.1

2. **O** Do AC ammeters and voltmeters read (a) peak-to-valley, (b) maximum, (c) rms, or (d) average values?

3. **O** A sinusoidally varying potential difference has amplitude 170 V. **(i)** What is its minimum instantaneous value? (a) 240 V (b) 170 V (c) 120 V (d) 0 (e) −120 V (f) −170 V (g) −240 V **(ii)** What is its average value? **(iii)** What is its rms value? Choose from the same possibilities in each case.

4. Why does a capacitor act as a short circuit at high frequencies? Why does it act as an open circuit at low frequencies?

5. Explain how the mnemonic "ELI the ICE man" can be used to recall whether current leads voltage or voltage leads current in *RLC* circuits. Note that E represents emf $\mathcal{E}$.

6. Why is the sum of the maximum voltages across each element in a series *RLC* circuit usually greater than the maximum applied voltage? Doesn't that inequality violate Kirchhoff's loop rule?

7. Does the phase angle depend on frequency? What is the phase angle when the inductive reactance equals the capacitive reactance?

8. **O** **(i)** When a particular inductor is connected to a source of sinusoidally varying emf with constant amplitude and a frequency of 60 Hz, the rms current is 3 A. What is the rms current if the source frequency is doubled? (a) 12 A (b) 6 A (c) 4.24 A (d) 3 A (e) 2.12 A (f) 1.5 A (g) 0.75 A **(ii)** Repeat part (i) assuming the load is a capacitor instead of an inductor. **(iii)** Repeat part (i) assuming the load is a resistor instead of an inductor.

9. **O** What is the impedance of a series *RLC* circuit at resonance? (a) X_L (b) X_C (c) R (d) $X_L - X_C$ (e) $2X_L$ (f) $\sqrt{2}R$ (g) 0

10. **O** What is the phase angle in a series *RLC* circuit at resonance? (a) 180° (b) 90° (c) 0 (d) −90° (e) None of these answers is necessarily correct.

11. A certain power supply can be modeled as a source of emf in series with both a resistance of 10 Ω and an inductive reactance of 5 Ω. To obtain maximum power delivered to the load, it is found that the load should have a resistance of $R_L = 10\ \Omega$, an inductive reactance of zero, and a capacitive reactance of 5 Ω. (a) With this load, is the circuit in resonance? (b) With this load, what fraction of the average power put out by the source of emf is delivered to the load? (c) To increase the fraction of the power delivered to the load, how could the load be changed? You may wish to review Example 28.2 and Problem 4 in Chapter 28 on maximum power transfer in DC circuits.

12. As shown in Figure 7.5, a person pulls a vacuum cleaner at speed v across a horizontal floor, exerting on it a force of magnitude F directed upward at an angle θ with the horizontal. At what rate is the person doing work on the cleaner? State as completely as you can the analogy between power in this situation and in an electric circuit.

13. **O** A circuit containing a generator, a capacitor, an inductor, and a resistor has a high-Q resonance at 1 000 Hz. From greatest to least, rank the following contributions to the impedance of the circuit at that frequency and at lower and higher frequencies, and note any cases of equality in your ranking. (a) X_C at 500 Hz (b) X_C at 1 000 Hz (c) X_C at 1 500 Hz (d) X_L at 500 Hz (e) X_L at 1 000 Hz (f) X_L at 1 500 Hz (g) R at 500 Hz (h) R at 1 000 Hz (i) R at 1 500 Hz

14. Do some research to answer these questions: Who invented the metal detector? Why? Did it work?

15. Will a transformer operate if a battery is used for the input voltage across the primary? Explain.

16. Explain how the quality factor is related to the response characteristics of a radio receiver. Which variable most strongly influences the quality factor?

17. An ice storm breaks a transmission line and interrupts electric power to a town. A homeowner starts a gasoline-powered 120-V generator and clips its output terminals to "hot" and "ground" terminals of the electrical panel for his house. On a power pole down the block is a transformer designed to step down the voltage for household use. It has a ratio of turns N_1/N_2 of 100 to 1. A repairman climbs the pole. What voltage will he encounter on the input side of the transformer? As this question implies, safety precautions must be taken in the use of home generators and during power failures in general.

Problems

WebAssign The Problems from this chapter may be assigned online in WebAssign.

ThomsonNOW Sign in at **www.thomsonedu.com** and go to ThomsonNOW to assess your understanding of this chapter's topics with additional quizzing and conceptual questions.

1, 2, 3 denotes straightforward, intermediate, challenging; □ denotes full solution available in *Student Solutions Manual/Study Guide;* ▲ denotes coached solution with hints available at **www.thomsonedu.com;** ▭ denotes developing symbolic reasoning; ● denotes asking for qualitative reasoning; ▪ denotes computer useful in solving problem

Section 33.1 AC Sources

Section 33.2 Resistors in an AC Circuit

1. The rms output voltage of an AC source is 200 V and the operating frequency is 100 Hz. Write the equation giving the output voltage as a function of time.

2. (a) What is the resistance of a lightbulb that uses an average power of 75.0 W when connected to a 60.0-Hz power source having a maximum voltage of 170 V? (b) **What If?** What is the resistance of a 100-W lightbulb?

3. An AC power supply produces a maximum voltage $\Delta V_{\max} = 100$ V. This power supply is connected to a 24.0-Ω resistor, and the current and resistor voltage are measured with an ideal AC ammeter and voltmeter as shown in Figure P33.3. What does each meter read? An ideal ammeter has zero resistance and an ideal voltmeter has infinite resistance.

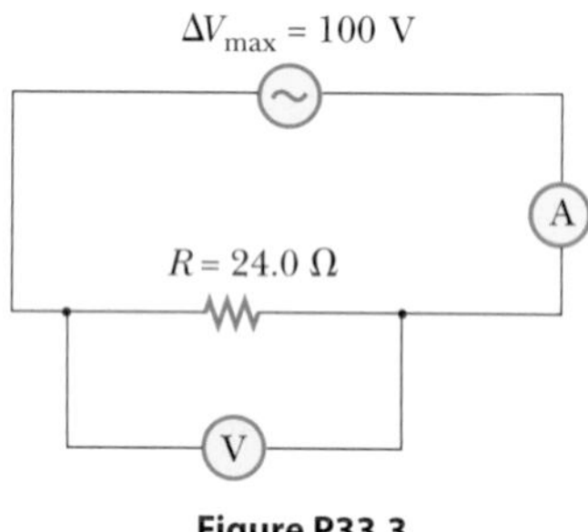

Figure P33.3

4. In the simple AC circuit shown in Active Figure 33.2, $R = 70.0\ \Omega$ and $\Delta v = \Delta V_{\max} \sin \omega t$. (a) If $\Delta v_R = 0.250\ \Delta V_{\max}$ for the first time at $t = 0.010\ 0$ s, what is the angular frequency of the source? (b) What is the next value of t for which $\Delta v_R = 0.250\ \Delta V_{\max}$?

5. □ The current in the circuit shown in Active Figure 33.2 equals 60.0% of the peak current at $t = 7.00$ ms. What is the lowest source frequency that gives this current?

6. An audio amplifier, represented by the AC source and resistor in Figure P33.6, delivers to the speaker alternating voltage at audio frequencies. If the source voltage has an amplitude of 15.0 V, $R = 8.20\ \Omega$, and the speaker is equivalent to a resistance of 10.4 Ω, what is the time-averaged power transferred to it?

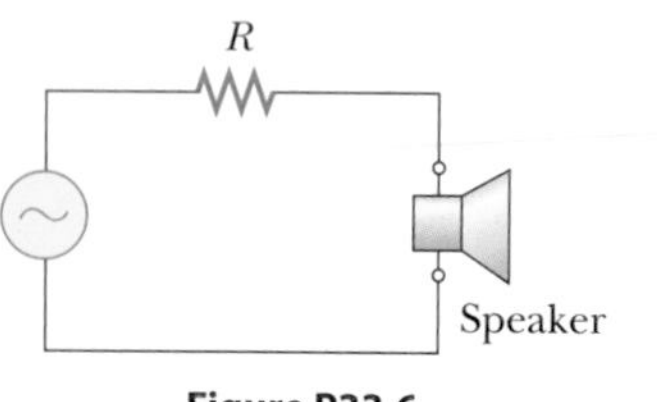

Figure P33.6

Section 33.3 Inductors in an AC Circuit

7. □ In a purely inductive AC circuit as shown in Active Figure 33.6, $\Delta V_{\max} = 100$ V. (a) The maximum current is 7.50 A at 50.0 Hz. Calculate the inductance L. (b) **What If?** At what angular frequency ω is the maximum current 2.50 A?

8. An inductor has a 54.0-Ω reactance at 60.0 Hz. What is the maximum current if this inductor is connected to a 50.0-Hz source that produces a 100-V rms voltage?

9. □ ▲ For the circuit shown in Active Figure 33.6, $\Delta V_{\max} = 80.0$ V, $\omega = 65.0\pi$ rad/s, and $L = 70.0$ mH. Calculate the current in the inductor at $t = 15.5$ ms.

10. A 20.0-mH inductor is connected to a standard electrical outlet ($\Delta V_{\rm rms} = 120$ V, $f = 60.0$ Hz). Determine the energy stored in the inductor at $t = \frac{1}{180}$ s, assuming this energy is zero at $t = 0$.

11. **Review problem.** Determine the maximum magnetic flux through an inductor connected to a standard electrical outlet ($\Delta V_{\rm rms} = 120$ V, $f = 60.0$ Hz).

Section 33.4 Capacitors in an AC Circuit

12. (a) For what frequencies does a 22.0-μF capacitor have a reactance below 175 Ω? (b) **What If?** What is the reactance of a 44.0-μF capacitor over this same frequency range?

13. What is the maximum current in a 2.20-μF capacitor when it is connected across (a) a North American electrical outlet having $\Delta V_{\rm rms} = 120$ V and $f = 60.0$ Hz, and (b) a European electrical outlet having $\Delta V_{\rm rms} = 240$ V and $f = 50.0$ Hz?

14. A capacitor C is connected to a power supply that operates at a frequency f and produces an rms voltage ΔV. What is the maximum charge that appears on either capacitor plate?

15. □ What maximum current is delivered by an AC source with $\Delta V_{\max} = 48.0$ V and $f = 90.0$ Hz when connected across a 3.70-μF capacitor?

16. A 1.00-mF capacitor is connected to a standard electrical outlet ($\Delta V_{\rm rms} = 120$ V, $f = 60.0$ Hz). Determine the current in the wires at $t = \frac{1}{180}$ s, assuming the energy stored in the capacitor is zero at $t = 0$.

Section 33.5 The *RLC* Series Circuit

17. □ An inductor ($L = 400$ mH), a capacitor ($C = 4.43\ \mu$F), and a resistor ($R = 500\ \Omega$) are connected in series. A 50.0-Hz AC source produces a peak current of 250 mA in the circuit. (a) Calculate the required peak voltage $\Delta V_{\max}$. (b) Determine the phase angle by which the current leads or lags the applied voltage.

18. At what frequency does the inductive reactance of a 57.0-μH inductor equal the capacitive reactance of a 57.0-μF capacitor?

19. A series AC circuit contains the following components: a 150-Ω resistor, an inductor of 250 mH, a capacitor of 2.00 μF, and a source with $\Delta V_{max} = 210$ V operating at 50.0 Hz. Calculate the (a) inductive reactance, (b) capacitive reactance, (c) impedance, (d) maximum current, and (e) phase angle between current and source voltage.

20. A sinusoidal voltage $\Delta v(t) = (40.0 \text{ V}) \sin(100t)$ is applied to a series *RLC* circuit with $L = 160$ mH, $C = 99.0$ μF, and $R = 68.0$ Ω. (a) What is the impedance of the circuit? (b) What is the maximum current? (c) Determine the numerical values for I_{max}, ω, and ϕ in the equation $i(t) = I_{max} \sin(\omega t - \phi)$.

21. ▲ An *RLC* circuit consists of a 150-Ω resistor, a 21.0-μF capacitor, and a 460-mH inductor connected in series with a 120-V, 60.0-Hz power supply. (a) What is the phase angle between the current and the applied voltage? (b) Which reaches its maximum earlier, the current or the voltage?

22. Four circuit elements—a capacitor, an inductor, a resistor, and an AC source—are connected together in various ways. First the capacitor is connected to the source, and the rms current is found to be 25.1 mA. The capacitor is disconnected and discharged, and then it is connected in series with the resistor and the source, making the rms current 15.7 mA. The circuit is disconnected and the capacitor discharged. The capacitor is then connected in series with the inductor and the source, making the rms current 68.2 mA. After the circuit is disconnected and the capacitor discharged, all four circuit elements are connected together in a series loop. What is the rms current in the circuit?

23. A person is working near the secondary of a transformer as shown in Figure P33.23. The primary voltage is 120 V at 60.0 Hz. The capacitance C_s, which is the stray capacitance between the hand and the secondary winding, is 20.0 pF. Assuming the person has a body resistance to ground of $R_b = 50.0$ kΩ, determine the rms voltage across the body. *Suggestion:* Model the secondary of the transformer as an AC source.

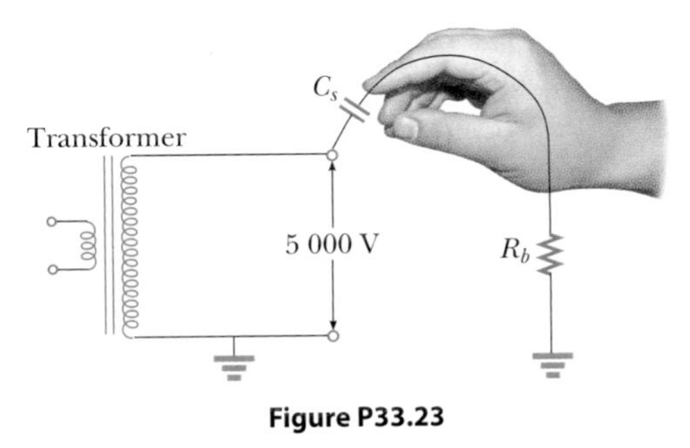

Figure P33.23

24. An AC source with $\Delta V_{max} = 150$ V and $f = 50.0$ Hz is connected between points *a* and *d* in Figure P33.24. Calculate the maximum voltages between (a) points *a* and *b*, (b) points *b* and *c*, (c) points *c* and *d*, and (d) points *b* and *d*.

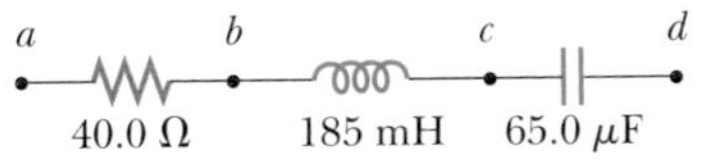

a *b* *c* *d*
40.0 Ω 185 mH 65.0 μF

Figure P33.24 Problems 24 and 64.

25. Draw to scale a phasor diagram and determine Z, X_L, X_C, and ϕ for an AC series circuit for which $R = 300$ Ω, $C = 11.0$ μF, $L = 0.200$ H, and $f = (500/\pi)$ Hz.

26. ● In an *RLC* series circuit that includes a source of alternating current operating at fixed frequency and voltage, the resistance R is equal to the inductive reactance. If the plate separation of the parallel-plate capacitor is reduced to one-half its original value, the current in the circuit doubles. Find the initial capacitive reactance in terms of R. Explain each step in your solution.

Section 33.6 Power in an AC Circuit

27. ▲ An AC voltage of the form $\Delta v = (100 \text{ V}) \sin(1\,000t)$ is applied to a series *RLC* circuit. Assume the resistance is 400 Ω, the capacitance is 5.00 μF, and the inductance is 0.500 H. Find the average power delivered to the circuit.

28. A series *RLC* circuit has a resistance of 45.0 Ω and an impedance of 75.0 Ω. What average power is delivered to this circuit when $\Delta V_{rms} = 210$ V?

29. In a certain series *RLC* circuit, $I_{rms} = 9.00$ A, $\Delta V_{rms} = 180$ V, and the current leads the voltage by 37.0°. (a) What is the total resistance of the circuit? (b) Calculate the reactance of the circuit $(X_L - X_C)$.

30. Suppose you manage a factory that uses many electric motors. The motors create a large inductive load to the electric power line as well as a resistive load. The electric company builds an extra-heavy distribution line to supply you with a component of current that is 90° out of phase with the voltage as well as with current in phase with the voltage. The electric company charges you an extra fee for "reactive volt-amps" in addition to the amount you pay for the energy you use. You can avoid the extra fee by installing a capacitor between the power line and your factory. The following problem models this solution.

In an *RL* circuit, a 120-V (rms), 60.0-Hz source is in series with a 25.0-mH inductor and a 20.0-Ω resistor. What are (a) the rms current and (b) the power factor? (c) What capacitor must be added in series to make the power factor 1? (d) To what value can the supply voltage be reduced if the power supplied is to be the same as before the capacitor was installed?

31. Energy is to be transmitted at the rate of 20.0 kW with only 1.00% loss over a distance of 18.0 km at potential difference ΔV. (a) What is the diameter required for each of the two copper wires in the transmission line? Assume the current density is uniform in the conductors. (b) State how the diameter depends on ΔV. (c) Evaluate the diameter for $\Delta V = 1\,500$ V. (d) If you choose to make the diameter 3.00 mm, what potential difference is required?

32. ● A series circuit consists of an AC generator with an rms voltage of 120 V at a frequency of 60.0 Hz and a magnetic buzzer with a resistance of 100 Ω and an inductance of 100 mH. (a) Find the circuit's power factor. (b) Suppose a higher power factor is desired. Can a power factor of 1.00 be achieved by changing the inductance or any other circuit parameters? (c) Show that a power factor of 1.00 can be attained by inserting a capacitor into the original circuit, and find the value of its capacitance.

33. A diode is a device that allows current to be carried in only one direction (the direction indicated by the arrowhead in its circuit symbol). Find in terms of ΔV and R the average power delivered to the diode circuit of Figure P33.33.

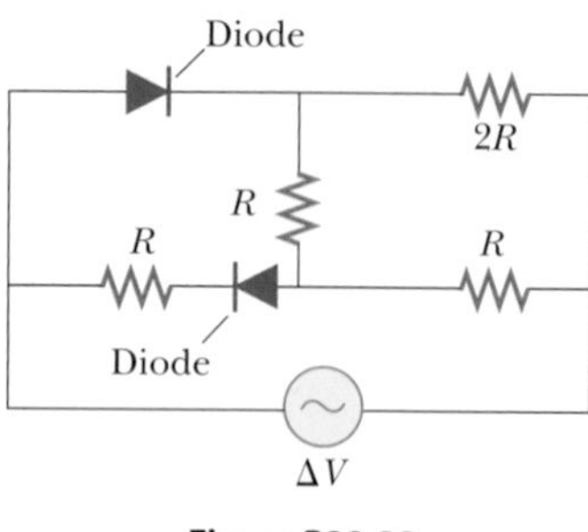

Figure P33.33

Section 33.7 Resonance in a Series *RLC* Circuit

34. A radar transmitter contains an *LC* circuit oscillating at 1.00×10^{10} Hz. (a) What capacitance resonates with a one-turn loop having an inductance of 400 pH at this frequency? (b) The capacitor has square, parallel plates separated by 1.00 mm of air. What should the edge length of the plates be? (c) What is the common reactance of the loop and capacitor at resonance?

35. An *RLC* circuit is used in a radio to tune into an FM station broadcasting at 99.7 MHz. The resistance in the circuit is 12.0 Ω, and the inductance is 1.40 μH. What capacitance should be used?

36. A series *RLC* circuit has components with the following values: $L = 20.0$ mH, $C = 100$ nF, $R = 20.0\ \Omega$, and $\Delta V_{max} = 100$ V, with $\Delta v = \Delta V_{max} \sin \omega t$. Find (a) the resonant frequency, (b) the amplitude of the current at the resonant frequency, (c) the Q of the circuit, and (d) the amplitude of the voltage across the inductor at resonance.

37. A 10.0-Ω resistor, 10.0-mH inductor, and 100-μF capacitor are connected in series to a 50.0-V (rms) source having variable frequency. Find the energy delivered to the circuit during one period if the operating frequency is twice the resonance frequency.

38. A resistor *R*, inductor *L*, and capacitor *C* are connected in series to an AC source of rms voltage ΔV and variable frequency. Find the energy delivered to the circuit during one period if the operating frequency is twice the resonance frequency.

39. Compute the quality factor for the circuits described in Problems 20 and 21. Which circuit has the sharper resonance?

Section 33.8 The Transformer and Power Transmission

40. A step-down transformer is used for recharging the batteries of portable devices such as tape players. The ratio of turns inside the transformer is 13:1, and the transformer is used with 120-V (rms) household service. If a particular ideal transformer draws 0.350 A from the house outlet, what are (a) the voltage and (b) the current supplied to a tape player from the transformer? (c) How much power is delivered?

41. A transformer has $N_1 = 350$ turns and $N_2 = 2\ 000$ turns. If the input voltage is $\Delta v(t) = (170\text{ V}) \cos \omega t$, what rms voltage is developed across the secondary coil?

42. A step-up transformer is designed to have an output voltage of 2 200 V (rms) when the primary is connected across a 110-V (rms) source. (a) If the primary winding has 80 turns, how many turns are required on the secondary? (b) If a load resistor across the secondary draws a current of 1.50 A, what is the current in the primary, assuming ideal conditions? (c) **What If?** If the transformer actually has an efficiency of 95.0%, what is the current in the primary when the secondary current is 1.20 A?

43. ● A transmission line that has a resistance per unit length of $4.50 \times 10^{-4}\ \Omega/\text{m}$ is to be used to transmit 5.00 MW across 400 miles (6.44×10^5 m). The output voltage of the generator is 4.50 kV. (a) What is the line loss if a transformer is used to step up the voltage to 500 kV? (b) What fraction of the input power is lost to the line under these circumstances? (c) **What If?** What difficulties would be encountered in attempting to transmit the 5.00 MW at the generator voltage of 4.50 kV?

Section 33.9 Rectifiers and Filters

44. One particular plug-in power supply for a radio looks similar to the one shown in Figure 33.20 and is marked with the following information: Input 120 V AC 8 W Output 9 V DC 300 mA. Assume these values are accurate to two digits. (a) Find the energy efficiency of the device when the radio is operating. (b) At what rate is energy wasted in the device when the radio is operating? (c) Suppose the input power to the transformer is 8.0 W when the radio is switched off and energy costs \$0.135/kWh from the electric company. Find the cost of having six such transformers around the house, each plugged in for 31 days.

45. Consider the filter circuit shown in Active Figure 33.22a. (a) Show that the ratio of the output voltage to the input voltage is

$$\frac{\Delta v_{out}}{\Delta v_{in}} = \frac{R}{\sqrt{R^2 + \left(\dfrac{1}{\omega C}\right)^2}}$$

(b) What value does this ratio approach as the frequency decreases toward zero? What value does this ratio approach as the frequency increases without limit? (c) At what frequency is the ratio equal to one-half?

46. Consider the filter circuit shown in Active Figure 33.23a. (a) Show that the ratio of the output voltage to the input voltage is

$$\frac{\Delta v_{out}}{\Delta v_{in}} = \frac{1/\omega C}{\sqrt{R^2 + \left(\dfrac{1}{\omega C}\right)^2}}$$

(b) What value does this ratio approach as the frequency decreases toward zero? What value does this ratio approach as the frequency increases without limit? (c) At what frequency is the ratio equal to one-half?

47. ▲ The *RC* high-pass filter shown in Active Figure 33.22a has a resistance $R = 0.500\ \Omega$. (a) What capacitance gives an output signal that has one-half the amplitude of a 300-Hz input signal? (b) What is the ratio $(\Delta v_{out}/\Delta v_{in})$ for a 600-Hz signal? You may use the result of Problem 45.

48. The *RC* low-pass filter shown in Active Figure 33.23a has a resistance $R = 90.0\ \Omega$ and a capacitance $C = 8.00$ nF. Calculate the ratio $(\Delta v_{out}/\Delta v_{in})$ for an input frequency of (a) 600 Hz and (b) 600 kHz. You may use the result of Problem 46.

49. The resistor in Figure P33.49 represents the midrange speaker in a three-speaker system. Assume its resistance to be constant at 8.00 Ω. The source represents an audio amplifier producing signals of uniform amplitude $\Delta V_{max} =$ 10.0 V at all audio frequencies. The inductor and capacitor are to function as a band-pass filter with $\Delta v_{out}/\Delta v_{in} = \frac{1}{2}$ at 200 Hz and at 4 000 Hz. (a) Determine the required values of L and C. (b) Find the maximum value of the ratio $\Delta v_{out}/\Delta v_{in}$. (c) Find the frequency f_0 at which the ratio has its maximum value. (d) Find the phase shift between Δv_{in} and Δv_{out} at 200 Hz, at f_0, and at 4 000 Hz. (e) Find the average power transferred to the speaker at 200 Hz, at f_0, and at 4 000 Hz. (f) Treating the filter as a resonant circuit, find its quality factor.

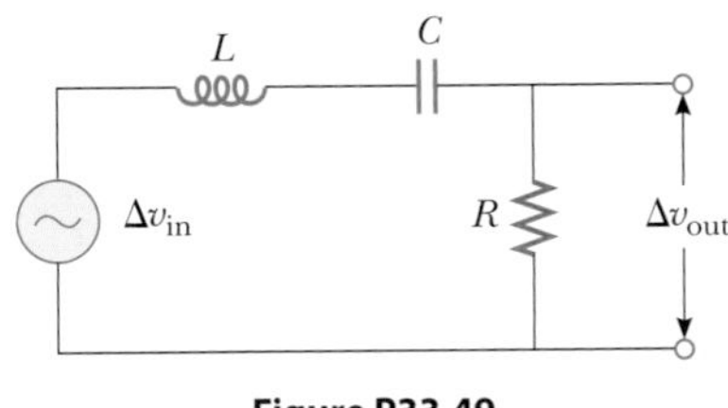

Figure P33.49

Additional Problems

50. Show that the rms value for the sawtooth voltage shown in Figure P33.50 is $\Delta V_{max}/\sqrt{3}$.

Figure P33.50

51. ● A 400-Ω resistor, an inductor, and a capacitor are in series with a generator. The reactance of the inductor is 700 Ω, and the circuit impedance is 760 Ω. (a) Explain what you can and cannot determine about the reactance of the capacitor. (b) If you find that the source power decreases as you raise the frequency, what do you know about the capacitive reactance in the original circuit? (c) Repeat part (a) assuming the resistance is 200 Ω instead of 400 Ω.

52. ● A capacitor, a coil, and two resistors of equal resistance are arranged in an AC circuit as shown in Figure P33.52. An AC generator provides an emf of 20.0 V (rms) at a frequency of 60.0 Hz. When the double-throw switch S is open as shown in the figure, the rms current is 183 mA. When the switch is closed in position 1, the rms current is 298 mA. When the switch is closed in position 2, the rms current is 137 mA. Determine the values of R, C and L. Is more than one set of values possible? Explain.

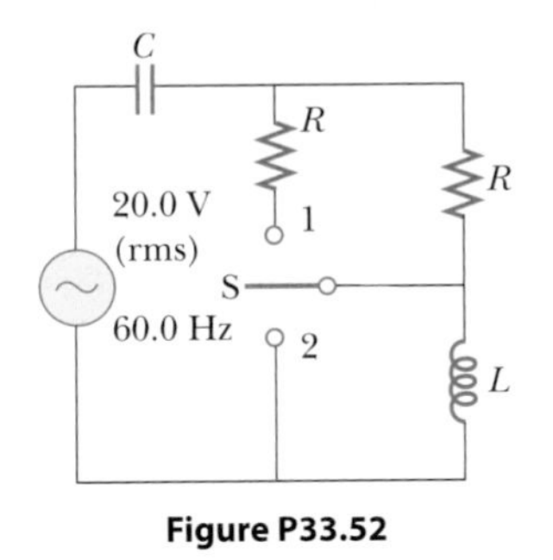

Figure P33.52

53. ▲ A series RLC circuit consists of an 8.00-Ω resistor, a 5.00-μF capacitor, and a 50.0-mH inductor. A variable frequency source applies an emf of 400 V (rms) across the combination. Determine the power delivered to the circuit when the frequency is equal to one-half the resonance frequency.

54. ● A series RLC circuit has resonance angular frequency 2 000 rad/s. When it is operating at some certain frequency, $X_L = 12.0\ \Omega$ and $X_C = 8.00\ \Omega$. (a) Is this certain frequency higher than, lower than, or the same as the resonance frequency? Explain how you can tell. (b) Explain whether it is possible to determine the values of both L and C. (c) If it is possible, find L and C. If this determination is not possible, give a compact expression for the condition that L and C must satisfy.

55. ● **Review problem.** One insulated conductor from a household extension cord has a mass per length of 19.0 g/m. A section of this conductor is held under tension between two clamps. A subsection is located in a magnetic field of magnitude 15.3 mT directed perpendicular to the length of the cord. When the cord carries an AC current of 9.00 A at a frequency of 60.0 Hz, it vibrates in resonance in its simplest standing-wave vibration state. Determine the relationship that must be satisfied between the separation d of the clamps and the tension T in the cord. Determine one possible combination of values for these variables.

56. Sketch a graph of the phase angle for an RLC series circuit as a function of angular frequency from zero to a frequency much higher than the resonance frequency. Identify the value of ϕ at the resonance angular frequency ω_0. Prove that the slope of the graph of ϕ versus ω at the resonance point is $2Q/\omega_0$.

57. In Figure P33.57, find the rms current delivered by the 45.0-V (rms) power supply when (a) the frequency is very large and (b) the frequency is very small.

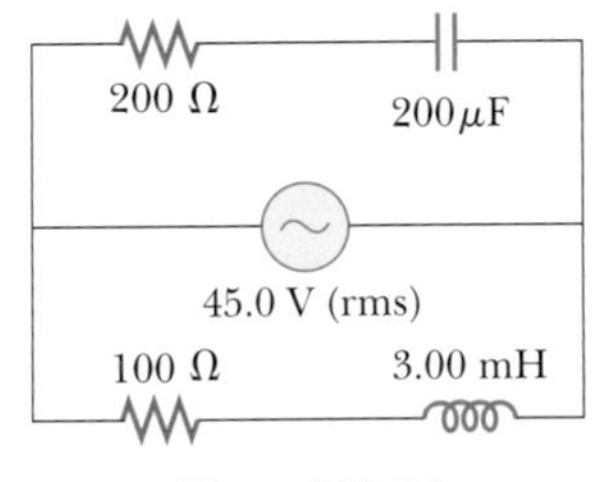

Figure P33.57

58. In the circuit shown in Figure P33.58 (page 950), assume all parameters except C are given. (a) Find the current as a function of time. (b) Find the power delivered to the circuit. (c) Find the current as a function of time after *only* switch 1 is opened. (d) After switch 2 is *also* opened, the current and voltage are in phase. Find the capacitance C. (e) Find the impedance of the circuit when both switches are open. (f) Find the maximum energy stored in the capacitor during oscillations. (g) Find the maximum energy stored in the inductor during oscillations.

(h) Now the frequency of the voltage source is doubled. Find the phase difference between the current and the voltage. (i) Find the frequency that makes the inductive reactance one-half the capacitive reactance.

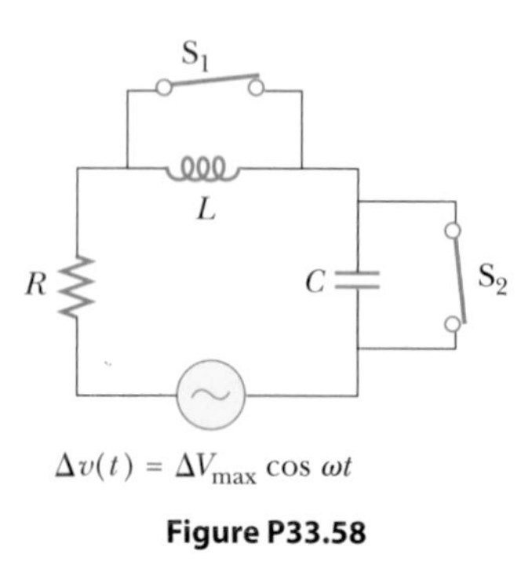

Figure P33.58

59. An 80.0-Ω resistor and a 200-mH inductor are connected in *parallel* across a 100-V (rms), 60.0-Hz source. (a) What is the rms current in the resistor? (b) By what angle does the total current lead or lag behind the voltage?

60. Make an order-of-magnitude estimate of the electric current that the electric company delivers to a town (Fig. P33.60) from a remote generating station. State the data you measure or estimate. If you wish, you may consider a suburban residential community of 20 000 people.

Eddie Hironaka/Getty Images

Figure P33.60

61. Consider a series *RLC* circuit having the following circuit parameters: $R = 200\ \Omega$, $L = 663$ mH, and $C = 26.5\ \mu$F. The applied voltage has an amplitude of 50.0 V and a frequency of 60.0 Hz. Find the following amplitudes. (a) the current I_{max} and its phase relative to the applied voltage Δv (b) the maximum voltage ΔV_R across the resistor and its phase relative to the current (c) the maximum voltage ΔV_C across the capacitor and its phase relative to the current (d) the maximum voltage ΔV_L across the inductor and its phase relative to the current

62. A voltage $\Delta v = (100\text{ V})\sin \omega t$ is applied across a series combination of a 2.00-H inductor, a 10.0-μF capacitor, and a 10.0-Ω resistor. (a) Determine the angular frequency ω_0 at which the power delivered to the resistor is a maximum. (b) Calculate the power delivered at that frequency. (c) Determine the two angular frequencies ω_1 and ω_2 at which the power is one-half the maximum value. *Note:* The Q of the circuit is $\omega_0/(\omega_2 - \omega_1)$.

63. *Impedance matching.* Example 28.2 showed that maximum power is transferred when the internal resistance of a DC source is equal to the resistance of the load. A transformer may be used to provide maximum power transfer between two AC circuits that have different impedances Z_1 and Z_2. (a) Show that the ratio of turns N_1/N_2 needed to meet this condition is

$$\frac{N_1}{N_2} = \sqrt{\frac{Z_1}{Z_2}}$$

(b) Suppose you want to use a transformer as an impedance-matching device between an audio amplifier that has an output impedance of 8.00 kΩ and a speaker that has an input impedance of 8.00 Ω. What should your N_1/N_2 ratio be?

64. ● A power supply with $\Delta V_{rms} = 120$ V is connected between points *a* and *d* in Figure P33.24. At what frequency will it deliver a power of 250 W? Explain your answer.

65. Figure P33.65a shows a parallel *RLC* circuit, and the corresponding phasor diagram is given in Figure P33.65b. The instantaneous voltages (and rms voltages) across each of the three circuit elements are the same, and each is in phase with the current in the resistor. The currents in C and L lead or lag the current in the resistor as shown in Figure P33.65b. (a) Show that the rms current delivered by the source is

$$I_{rms} = \Delta V_{rms}\left[\frac{1}{R^2} + \left(\omega C - \frac{1}{\omega L}\right)^2\right]^{1/2}$$

(b) Show that the phase angle ϕ between ΔV_{rms} and I_{rms} is given by

$$\tan \phi = R\left(\frac{1}{X_C} - \frac{1}{X_L}\right)$$

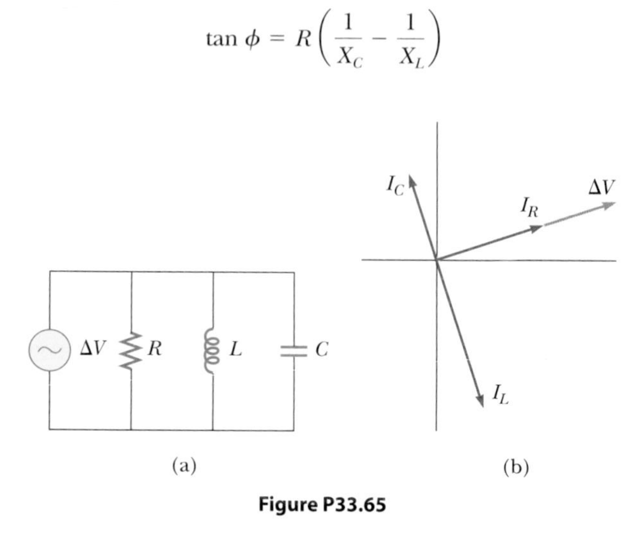

Figure P33.65

66. A certain electric circuit is described by the equations

$$\frac{200\text{ V}}{4.00\text{ A}} = \sqrt{(35.0\ \Omega)^2 + \left[\omega(205\text{ mH}) - \frac{1}{\omega C}\right]^2}$$

$$\omega = 2\pi\,(100\text{ Hz})$$

State a problem for which these equations would appear in the solution, giving the data and identifying the unknown. Evaluate the unknown quantity.

67. A series *RLC* circuit is operating at 2 000 Hz. At this frequency, $X_L = X_C = 1\,884\ \Omega$. The resistance of the circuit is 40.0 Ω. (a) Prepare a table showing the values of X_L, X_C, and Z for f = 300, 600, 800, 1 000, 1 500, 2 000, 3 000, 4 000, 6 000, and 10 000 Hz. (b) Plot on the same set of axes X_L, X_C, and Z as a function of ln f.

68. A series RLC circuit with $R = 1.00\ \Omega$, $L = 1.00$ mH, and $C = 1.00$ nF is connected to an AC source delivering 1.00 V (rms). Make a precise graph of the power delivered to the circuit as a function of the frequency and verify that the full width of the resonance peak at half-maximum is $R/2\pi L$.

69. ● Marie Cornu, a physicist at the Polytechnic Institute in Paris, invented phasors in about 1880. This problem helps you see their general utility in representing oscillations. Two mechanical vibrations are represented by the expressions

$$y_1 = (12.0\text{ cm}) \sin (4.5t)$$

and

$$y_2 = (12.0\text{ cm}) \sin (4.5t + 70°)$$

Find the amplitude and phase constant of the sum of these functions (a) by using a trigonometric identity (as from Appendix B) and (b) by representing the oscillations as phasors. State the result of comparing the answers to (a) and (b). (c) Phasors make it equally easy to add traveling waves. Find the amplitude and phase constant of the sum of the three waves represented by

$$y_1 = (12.0\text{ cm}) \sin (15x - 4.5t + 70°)$$

$$y_2 = (15.5\text{ cm}) \sin (15x - 4.5t - 80°)$$

$$y_3 = (17.0\text{ cm}) \sin (15x - 4.5t + 160°)$$

Answers to Quick Quizzes

33.1 **(i)**, (c). The phasor in (c) has the largest projection onto the vertical axis. **(ii)**, (b). The phasor in (b) has the smallest-magnitude projection onto the vertical axis.

33.2 (b). For low frequencies, the reactance of the inductor is small, so the current is large. Most of the voltage from the source is across the lightbulb, so the power delivered to it is large.

33.3 (a). For high frequencies, the reactance of the capacitor is small, so the current is large. Most of the voltage from the source is across the lightbulb, so the power delivered to it is large.

33.4 (b). For low frequencies, the reactance of the capacitor is large, so very little current exists in the capacitor branch. The reactance of the inductor is small, so current exists in the inductor branch and the lightbulb glows. As the frequency increases, the inductive reactance increases and the capacitive reactance decreases. At high frequencies, more current exists in the capacitor branch than the inductor branch and the lightbulb glows more dimly.

33.5 (a) $X_L < X_C$ (b) $X_L = X_C$ (c) $X_L > X_C$

33.6 (c). The cosine of $-\phi$ is the same as that of $+\phi$, so the $\cos\phi$ factor in Equation 33.31 is the same for both frequencies. The factor ΔV_{rms} is the same because the source voltage is fixed. According to Equation 33.27, changing $+\phi$ to $-\phi$ simply interchanges the values of X_L and X_C. Equation 33.25 tells us that such an interchange does not affect the impedance, so the current I_{rms} in Equation 33.31 is the same for both frequencies.

33.7 (c). At resonance, $X_L = X_C$. According to Equation 33.25, that gives us $Z = R$.

TABLE A.1

Conversion Factors

Length

	m	cm	km	in.	ft	mi
1 meter	1	10^2	10^{-3}	39.37	3.281	6.214×10^{-4}
1 centimeter	10^{-2}	1	10^{-5}	0.393 7	3.281×10^{-2}	6.214×10^{-6}
1 kilometer	10^3	10^5	1	3.937×10^4	3.281×10^3	0.621 4
1 inch	2.540×10^{-2}	2.540	2.540×10^{-5}	1	8.333×10^{-2}	1.578×10^{-5}
1 foot	0.304 8	30.48	3.048×10^{-4}	12	1	1.894×10^{-4}
1 mile	1 609	1.609×10^5	1.609	6.336×10^4	5 280	1

Mass

	kg	g	slug	u
1 kilogram	1	10^3	6.852×10^{-2}	6.024×10^{26}
1 gram	10^{-3}	1	6.852×10^{-5}	6.024×10^{23}
1 slug	14.59	1.459×10^4	1	8.789×10^{27}
1 atomic mass unit	1.660×10^{-27}	1.660×10^{-24}	1.137×10^{-28}	1

Note: 1 metric ton = 1 000 kg.

Time

	s	min	h	day	yr
1 second	1	1.667×10^{-2}	2.778×10^{-4}	1.157×10^{-5}	3.169×10^{-8}
1 minute	60	1	1.667×10^{-2}	6.994×10^{-4}	1.901×10^{-6}
1 hour	3 600	60	1	4.167×10^{-2}	1.141×10^{-4}
1 day	8.640×10^4	1 440	24	1	2.738×10^{-5}
1 year	3.156×10^7	5.259×10^5	8.766×10^3	365.2	1

Speed

	m/s	cm/s	ft/s	mi/h
1 meter per second	1	10^2	3.281	2.237
1 centimeter per second	10^{-2}	1	3.281×10^{-2}	2.237×10^{-2}
1 foot per second	0.304 8	30.48	1	0.681 8
1 mile per hour	0.447 0	44.70	1.467	1

Note: 1 mi/min = 60 mi/h = 88 ft/s.

Force

	N	lb
1 newton	1	0.224 8
1 pound	4.448	1

(*Continued*)

TABLE A.1

Conversion Factors (*Continued*)

Energy, Energy Transfer

	J	ft · lb	eV
1 joule	1	0.737 6	6.242×10^{18}
1 foot-pound	1.356	1	8.464×10^{18}
1 electron volt	1.602×10^{-19}	1.182×10^{-19}	1
1 calorie	4.186	3.087	2.613×10^{19}
1 British thermal unit	1.055×10^{3}	7.779×10^{2}	6.585×10^{21}
1 kilowatt-hour	3.600×10^{6}	2.655×10^{6}	2.247×10^{25}

	cal	Btu	kWh
1 joule	0.238 9	9.481×10^{-4}	2.778×10^{-7}
1 foot-pound	0.323 9	1.285×10^{-3}	3.766×10^{-7}
1 electron volt	3.827×10^{-20}	1.519×10^{-22}	4.450×10^{-26}
1 calorie	1	3.968×10^{-3}	1.163×10^{-6}
1 British thermal unit	2.520×10^{2}	1	2.930×10^{-4}
1 kilowatt-hour	8.601×10^{5}	3.413×10^{2}	1

Pressure

	Pa	atm
1 pascal	1	9.869×10^{-6}
1 atmosphere	1.013×10^{5}	1
1 centimeter mercury[a]	1.333×10^{3}	1.316×10^{-2}
1 pound per square inch	6.895×10^{3}	6.805×10^{-2}
1 pound per square foot	47.88	4.725×10^{-4}

	cm Hg	lb/in.^{2}	lb/ft^2
1 pascal	7.501×10^{-4}	1.450×10^{-4}	2.089×10^{-2}
1 atmosphere	76	14.70	2.116×10^{3}
1 centimeter mercury[a]	1	0.194 3	27.85
1 pound per square inch	5.171	1	144
1 pound per square foot	3.591×10^{-2}	6.944×10^{-3}	1

[a]At 0°C and at a location where the free-fall acceleration has its "standard" value, 9.806 65 m/s^2.

TABLE A.2

Symbols, Dimensions, and Units of Physical Quantities

Quantity	Common Symbol	Unit[a]	Dimensions[b]	Unit in Terms of Base SI Units
Acceleration	$\vec{\mathbf{a}}$	m/s^2	L/T^2	m/s^2
Amount of substance	n	MOLE		mol
Angle	θ, ϕ	radian (rad)	1	
Angular acceleration	$\vec{\boldsymbol{\alpha}}$	rad/s^2	T^{-2}	s^{-2}
Angular frequency	ω	rad/s	T^{-1}	s^{-1}
Angular momentum	$\vec{\mathbf{L}}$	kg · m^2/s	ML^2/T	kg · m^2/s
Angular velocity	$\vec{\boldsymbol{\omega}}$	rad/s	T^{-1}	s^{-1}
Area	A	m^2	L^2	m^2
Atomic number	Z			
Capacitance	C	farad (F)	Q^{2}T^2/ML^2	A^2 · s^4/kg · m^2
Charge	q, Q, e	coulomb (C)	Q	A · s

(*Continued*)

TABLE A.2

Symbols, Dimensions, and Units of Physical Quantities *(Continued)*

Charge density				
Line	λ	C/m	Q/L	A · s/m
Surface	σ	C/m^2	Q/L^2	$A \cdot s/m^2$
Volume	ρ	C/m^3	Q/L^3	$A \cdot s/m^3$
Conductivity	σ	$1/\Omega \cdot m$	Q^2T/ML^3	$A^2 \cdot s^3/kg \cdot m^3$
Current	I	AMPERE	Q/T	A
Current density	J	A/m^2	Q/TL^2	A/m^2
Density	ρ	kg/m^3	M/L^3	kg/m^3
Dielectric constant	κ			
Electric dipole moment	$\vec{\mathbf{p}}$	C · m	QL	A · s · m
Electric field	$\vec{\mathbf{E}}$	V/m	ML/QT^2	$kg \cdot m/A \cdot s^3$
Electric flux	Φ_E	V · m	ML^3/QT^2	$kg \cdot m^3/A \cdot s^3$
Electromotive force	$\mathcal{E}$	volt (V)	ML^2/QT^2	$kg \cdot m^2/A \cdot s^3$
Energy	E, U, K	joule (J)	ML^2/T^2	$kg \cdot m^2/s^2$
Entropy	S	J/K	ML^2/T^2K	$kg \cdot m^2/s^2 \cdot K$
Force	$\vec{\mathbf{F}}$	newton (N)	ML/T^2	$kg \cdot m/s^2$
Frequency	f	hertz (Hz)	T^{-1}	s^{-1}
Heat	Q	joule (J)	ML^2/T^2	$kg \cdot m^2/s^2$
Inductance	L	henry (H)	ML^2/Q^2	$kg \cdot m^2/A^2 \cdot s^2$
Length	ℓ, L	METER	L	m
Displacement	$\Delta x, \Delta\vec{\mathbf{r}}$			
Distance	d, h			
Position	$x, y, z, \vec{\mathbf{r}}$			
Magnetic dipole moment	$\vec{\boldsymbol{\mu}}$	N · m/T	QL^2/T	$A \cdot m^2$
Magnetic field	$\vec{\mathbf{B}}$	tesla (T) ($= Wb/m^2$)	M/QT	$kg/A \cdot s^2$
Magnetic flux	Φ_B	weber (Wb)	ML^2/QT	$kg \cdot m^2/A \cdot s^2$
Mass	m, M	KILOGRAM	M	kg
Molar specific heat	C	J/mol · K		$kg \cdot m^2/s^2 \cdot mol \cdot K$
Moment of inertia	I	$kg \cdot m^2$	ML^2	$kg \cdot m^2$
Momentum	$\vec{\mathbf{p}}$	kg · m/s	ML/T	kg · m/s
Period	T	s	T	s
Permeability of free space	μ_0	N/A^2 ($= H/m$)	ML/Q^2	$kg \cdot m/A^2 \cdot s^2$
Permittivity of free space	ϵ_0	$C^2/N \cdot m^2$ ($= F/m$)	Q^2T^2/ML^3	$A^2 \cdot s^4/kg \cdot m^3$
Potential	V	volt (V) (= J/C)	ML^2/QT^2	$kg \cdot m^2/A \cdot s^3$
Power	$\mathcal{P}$	watt (W) (= J/s)	ML^2/T^3	$kg \cdot m^2/s^3$
Pressure	P	pascal (Pa) ($= N/m^2$)	M/LT^2	$kg/m \cdot s^2$
Resistance	R	ohm (Ω) (= V/A)	ML^2/Q^2T	$kg \cdot m^2/A^2 \cdot s^3$
Specific heat	c	J/kg · K	L^2/T^2K	$m^2/s^2 \cdot K$
Speed	v	m/s	L/T	m/s
Temperature	T	KELVIN	K	K
Time	t	SECOND	T	s
Torque	$\vec{\boldsymbol{\tau}}$	N · m	ML^2/T^2	$kg \cdot m^2/s^2$
Velocity	$\vec{\mathbf{v}}$	m/s	L/T	m/s
Volume	V	m^3	L^3	m^3
Wavelength	λ	m	L	m
Work	W	joule (J) (= N · m)	ML^2/T^2	$kg \cdot m^2/s^2$

[a]The base SI units are given in uppercase letters.

[b]The symbols M, L, T, K, and Q denote mass, length, time, temperature, and charge, respectively.

This appendix in mathematics is intended as a brief review of operations and methods. Early in this course, you should be totally familiar with basic algebraic techniques, analytic geometry, and trigonometry. The sections on differential and integral calculus are more detailed and are intended for students who have difficulty applying calculus concepts to physical situations.

B.1 Scientific Notation

Many quantities used by scientists often have very large or very small values. The speed of light, for example, is about 300 000 000 m/s, and the ink required to make the dot over an *i* in this textbook has a mass of about 0.000 000 001 kg. Obviously, it is very cumbersome to read, write, and keep track of such numbers. We avoid this problem by using a method incorporating powers of the number 10:

$$10^0 = 1$$

$$10^1 = 10$$

$$10^2 = 10 \times 10 = 100$$

$$10^3 = 10 \times 10 \times 10 = 1\,000$$

$$10^4 = 10 \times 10 \times 10 \times 10 = 10\,000$$

$$10^5 = 10 \times 10 \times 10 \times 10 \times 10 = 100\,000$$

and so on. The number of zeros corresponds to the power to which ten is raised, called the **exponent** of ten. For example, the speed of light, 300 000 000 m/s, can be expressed as 3.00×10^8 m/s.

In this method, some representative numbers smaller than unity are the following:

$$10^{-1} = \frac{1}{10} = 0.1$$

$$10^{-2} = \frac{1}{10 \times 10} = 0.01$$

$$10^{-3} = \frac{1}{10 \times 10 \times 10} = 0.001$$

$$10^{-4} = \frac{1}{10 \times 10 \times 10 \times 10} = 0.000\,1$$

$$10^{-5} = \frac{1}{10 \times 10 \times 10 \times 10 \times 10} = 0.000\,01$$

In these cases, the number of places the decimal point is to the left of the digit 1 equals the value of the (negative) exponent. Numbers expressed as some power of ten multiplied by another number between one and ten are said to be in **scientific notation.** For example, the scientific notation for 5 943 000 000 is 5.943×10^9 and that for 0.000 083 2 is 8.32×10^{-5}.

When numbers expressed in scientific notation are being multiplied, the following general rule is very useful:

$$10^n \times 10^m = 10^{n+m} \qquad \textbf{(B.1)}$$

where n and m can be *any* numbers (not necessarily integers). For example, $10^2 \times 10^5 = 10^7$. The rule also applies if one of the exponents is negative: $10^3 \times 10^{-8} = 10^{-5}$.

When dividing numbers expressed in scientific notation, note that

$$\frac{10^n}{10^m} = 10^n \times 10^{-m} = 10^{n-m} \tag{B.2}$$

Exercises

With help from the preceding rules, verify the answers to the following equations:

1. $86\ 400 = 8.64 \times 10^4$
2. $9\ 816\ 762.5 = 9.816\ 762\ 5 \times 10^6$
3. $0.000\ 000\ 039\ 8 = 3.98 \times 10^{-8}$
4. $(4.0 \times 10^8)(9.0 \times 10^9) = 3.6 \times 10^{18}$
5. $(3.0 \times 10^7)(6.0 \times 10^{-12}) = 1.8 \times 10^{-4}$
6. $\dfrac{75 \times 10^{-11}}{5.0 \times 10^{-3}} = 1.5 \times 10^{-7}$
7. $\dfrac{(3 \times 10^6)(8 \times 10^{-2})}{(2 \times 10^{17})(6 \times 10^5)} = 2 \times 10^{-18}$

B.2 Algebra

Some Basic Rules

When algebraic operations are performed, the laws of arithmetic apply. Symbols such as x, y, and z are usually used to represent unspecified quantities, called the **unknowns.**

First, consider the equation

$$8x = 32$$

If we wish to solve for x, we can divide (or multiply) each side of the equation by the same factor without destroying the equality. In this case, if we divide both sides by 8, we have

$$\frac{8x}{8} = \frac{32}{8}$$

$$x = 4$$

Next consider the equation

$$x + 2 = 8$$

In this type of expression, we can add or subtract the same quantity from each side. If we subtract 2 from each side, we have

$$x + 2 - 2 = 8 - 2$$

$$x = 6$$

In general, if $x + a = b$, then $x = b - a$.

Now consider the equation

$$\frac{x}{5} = 9$$

If we multiply each side by 5, we are left with x on the left by itself and 45 on the right:

$$\left(\frac{x}{5}\right)(5) = 9 \times 5$$

$$x = 45$$

In all cases, *whatever operation is performed on the left side of the equality must also be performed on the right side.*

The following rules for multiplying, dividing, adding, and subtracting fractions should be recalled, where a, b, c, and d are four numbers:

	Rule	Example
Multiplying	$\left(\frac{a}{b}\right)\left(\frac{c}{d}\right) = \frac{ac}{bd}$	$\left(\frac{2}{3}\right)\left(\frac{4}{5}\right) = \frac{8}{15}$
Dividing	$\frac{(a/b)}{(c/d)} = \frac{ad}{bc}$	$\frac{2/3}{4/5} = \frac{(2)(5)}{(4)(3)} = \frac{10}{12}$
Adding	$\frac{a}{b} \pm \frac{c}{d} = \frac{ad \pm bc}{bd}$	$\frac{2}{3} - \frac{4}{5} = \frac{(2)(5) - (4)(3)}{(3)(5)} = -\frac{2}{15}$

Exercises

In the following exercises, solve for x.

	Answers
1. $a = \frac{1}{1+x}$	$x = \frac{1-a}{a}$
2. $3x - 5 = 13$	$x = 6$
3. $ax - 5 = bx + 2$	$x = \frac{7}{a-b}$
4. $\frac{5}{2x+6} = \frac{3}{4x+8}$	$x = -\frac{11}{7}$

Powers

When powers of a given quantity x are multiplied, the following rule applies:

$$x^n x^m = x^{n+m} \tag{B.3}$$

For example, $x^2x^4 = x^{2+4} = x^6$.

When dividing the powers of a given quantity, the rule is

$$\frac{x^n}{x^m} = x^{n-m} \tag{B.4}$$

For example, $x^8/x^2 = x^{8-2} = x^6$.

A power that is a fraction, such as $\frac{1}{3}$, corresponds to a root as follows:

$$x^{1/n} = \sqrt[n]{x} \tag{B.5}$$

For example, $4^{1/3} = \sqrt[3]{4} = 1.587\,4$. (A scientific calculator is useful for such calculations.)

Finally, any quantity x^n raised to the mth power is

$$(x^n)^m = x^{nm} \tag{B.6}$$

Table B.1 summarizes the rules of exponents.

TABLE B.1

Rules of Exponents
$x^0 = 1$
$x^1 = x$
$x^n x^m = x^{n+m}$
$x^n/x^m = x^{n-m}$
$x^{1/n} = \sqrt[n]{x}$
$(x^n)^m = x^{nm}$

Exercises

Verify the following equations:

1. $3^2 \times 3^3 = 243$
2. $x^5x^{-8} = x^{-3}$
3. $x^{10}/x^{-5} = x^{15}$
4. $5^{1/3} = 1.709\,976$ (Use your calculator.)
5. $60^{1/4} = 2.783\,158$ (Use your calculator.)
6. $(x^4)^3 = x^{12}$

Factoring

Some useful formulas for factoring an equation are the following:

$$ax + ay + az = a(x + y + z) \quad \text{common factor}$$

$$a^2 + 2ab + b^2 = (a + b)^2 \quad \text{perfect square}$$

$$a^2 - b^2 = (a + b)(a - b) \quad \text{differences of squares}$$

Quadratic Equations

The general form of a quadratic equation is

$$ax^2 + bx + c = 0 \qquad \text{(B.7)}$$

where x is the unknown quantity and a, b, and c are numerical factors referred to as **coefficients** of the equation. This equation has two roots, given by

$$x = \frac{-b \pm \sqrt{b^2 - 4ac}}{2a} \qquad \text{(B.8)}$$

If $b^2 \geq 4ac$, the roots are real.

EXAMPLE B.1

The equation $x^2 + 5x + 4 = 0$ has the following roots corresponding to the two signs of the square-root term:

$$x = \frac{-5 \pm \sqrt{5^2 - (4)(1)(4)}}{2(1)} = \frac{-5 \pm \sqrt{9}}{2} = \frac{-5 \pm 3}{2}$$

$$x_+ = \frac{-5 + 3}{2} = -1 \qquad x_- = \frac{-5 - 3}{2} = -4$$

where x_+ refers to the root corresponding to the positive sign and x_- refers to the root corresponding to the negative sign.

Exercises

Solve the following quadratic equations:

		Answers	
1.	$x^2 + 2x - 3 = 0$	$x_+ = 1$	$x_- = -3$
2.	$2x^2 - 5x + 2 = 0$	$x_+ = 2$	$x_- = \frac{1}{2}$
3.	$2x^2 - 4x - 9 = 0$	$x_+ = 1 + \sqrt{22}/2$	$x_- = 1 - \sqrt{22}/2$

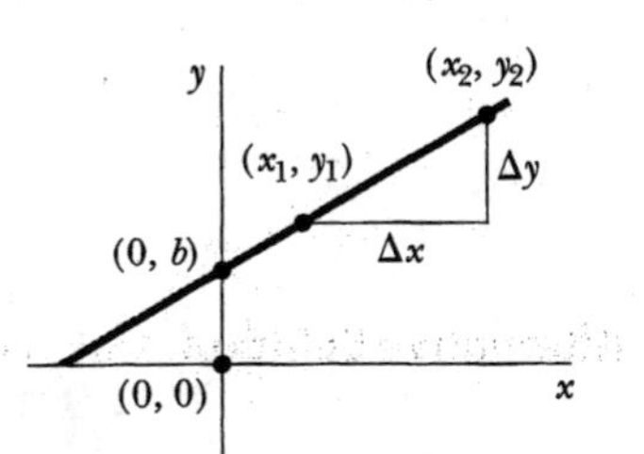

Figure B.1 A straight line graphed on an xy coordinate system. The slope of the line is the ratio of Δy to Δx.

Linear Equations

A linear equation has the general form

$$y = mx + b \qquad \text{(B.9)}$$

where m and b are constants. This equation is referred to as linear because the graph of y versus x is a straight line as shown in Figure B.1. The constant b, called the **y-intercept,** represents the value of y at which the straight line intersects the y axis. The constant m is equal to the **slope** of the straight line. If any two points on the straight line are specified by the coordinates (x_1, y_1) and (x_2, y_2) as in Figure B.1, the slope of the straight line can be expressed as

$$\text{Slope} = \frac{y_2 - y_1}{x_2 - x_1} = \frac{\Delta y}{\Delta x} \qquad \text{(B.10)}$$

Note that m and b can have either positive or negative values. If $m > 0$, the straight line has a *positive* slope as in Figure B.1. If $m < 0$, the straight line has a *negative* slope. In Figure B.1, both m and b are positive. Three other possible situations are shown in Figure B.2.

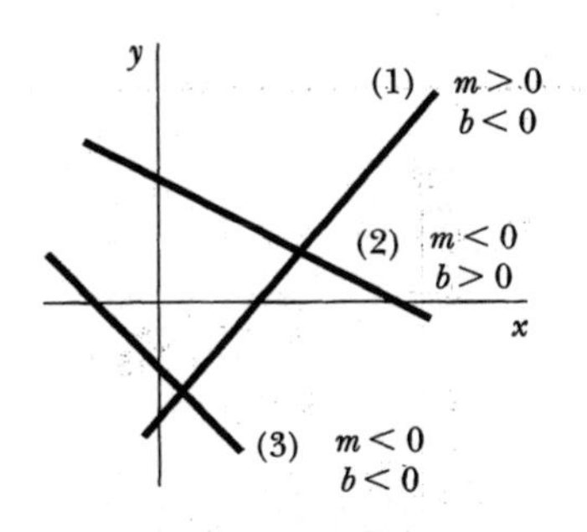

Figure B.2 The brown line has a positive slope and a negative y-intercept. The blue line has a negative slope and a positive y-intercept. The green line has a negative slope and a negative y-intercept.

Exercises

1. Draw graphs of the following straight lines: (a) $y = 5x + 3$ (b) $y = -2x + 4$ (c) $y = -3x - 6$
2. Find the slopes of the straight lines described in Exercise 1.

Answers (a) 5 (b) -2 (c) -3

3. Find the slopes of the straight lines that pass through the following sets of points: (a) $(0, -4)$ and $(4, 2)$ (b) $(0, 0)$ and $(2, -5)$ (c) $(-5, 2)$ and $(4, -2)$

Answers (a) $\frac{3}{2}$ (b) $-\frac{5}{2}$ (c) $-\frac{4}{9}$

Solving Simultaneous Linear Equations

Consider the equation $3x + 5y = 15$, which has two unknowns, x and y. Such an equation does not have a unique solution. For example, $(x = 0, y = 3)$, $(x = 5, y = 0)$, and $(x = 2, y = \frac{9}{5})$ are all solutions to this equation.

If a problem has two unknowns, a unique solution is possible only if we have *two* equations. In general, if a problem has n unknowns, its solution requires n equations. To solve two simultaneous equations involving two unknowns, x and y, we solve one of the equations for x in terms of y and substitute this expression into the other equation.

EXAMPLE B.2

Solve the two simultaneous equations

$$(1) \quad 5x + y = -8$$

$$(2) \quad 2x - 2y = 4$$

Solution From Equation (2), $x = y + 2$. Substitution of this equation into Equation (1) gives

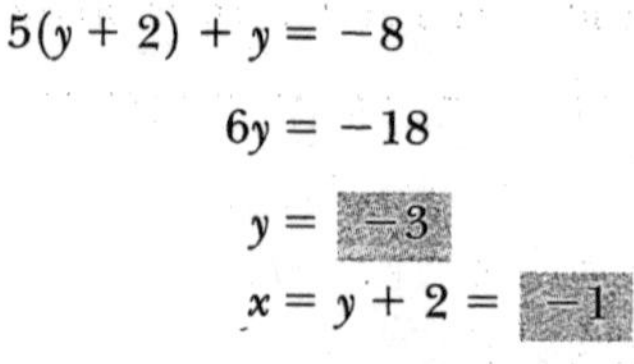

$$5(y + 2) + y = -8$$

$$6y = -18$$

$$y = -3$$

$$x = y + 2 = -1$$

Alternative Solution Multiply each term in Equation (1) by the factor 2 and add the result to Equation (2):

$$10x + 2y = -16$$

$$2x - 2y = 4$$

$$12x \quad = -12$$

$$x = -1$$

$$y = x - 2 = -3$$

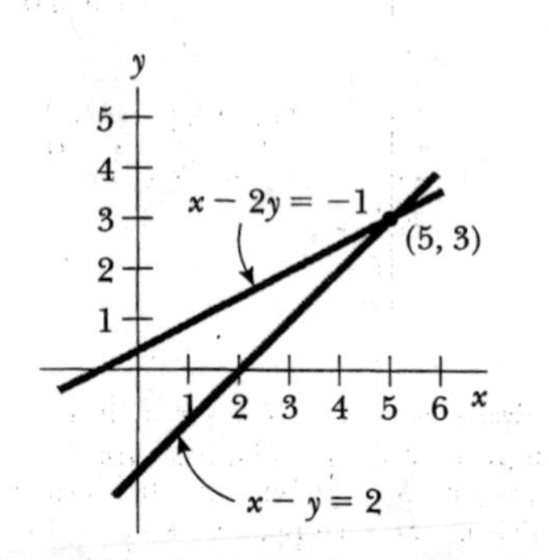

Figure B.3 A graphical solution for two linear equations.

Two linear equations containing two unknowns can also be solved by a graphical method. If the straight lines corresponding to the two equations are plotted in a conventional coordinate system, the intersection of the two lines represents the solution. For example, consider the two equations

$$x - y = 2$$

$$x - 2y = -1$$

These equations are plotted in Figure B.3. The intersection of the two lines has the coordinates $x = 5$ and $y = 3$, which represents the solution to the equations. You should check this solution by the analytical technique discussed earlier.

Exercises

Solve the following pairs of simultaneous equations involving two unknowns:

	Answers
1. $x + y = 8$ $x - y = 2$	$x = 5,\ y = 3$
2. $98 - T = 10a$ $T - 49 = 5a$	$T = 65,\ a = 3.27$
3. $6x + 2y = 6$ $8x - 4y = 28$	$x = 2,\ y = -3$

Logarithms

Suppose a quantity x is expressed as a power of some quantity a:

$$x = a^y \tag{B.11}$$

The number a is called the **base** number. The **logarithm** of x with respect to the base a is equal to the exponent to which the base must be raised to satisfy the expression $x = a^y$:

$$y = \log_a x \tag{B.12}$$

Conversely, the **antilogarithm** of y is the number x:

$$x = \text{antilog}_a\ y \tag{B.13}$$

In practice, the two bases most often used are base 10, called the *common* logarithm base, and base $e = 2.718\ 282$, called Euler's constant or the *natural* logarithm base. When common logarithms are used,

$$y = \log_{10} x \quad (\text{or } x = 10^y) \tag{B.14}$$

When natural logarithms are used,

$$y = \ln x \quad (\text{or } x = e^y) \tag{B.15}$$

For example, $\log_{10} 52 = 1.716$, so $\text{antilog}_{10} 1.716 = 10^{1.716} = 52$. Likewise, $\ln 52 = 3.951$, so $\text{antiln } 3.951 = e^{3.951} = 52$.

In general, note you can convert between base 10 and base e with the equality

$$\ln x = (2.302\ 585) \log_{10} x \tag{B.16}$$

Finally, some useful properties of logarithms are the following:

$$\left.\begin{aligned} \log(ab) &= \log a + \log b \\ \log(a/b) &= \log a - \log b \\ \log(a^n) &= n \log a \end{aligned}\right\} \text{any base}$$

$$\ln e = 1$$

$$\ln e^a = a$$

$$\ln\left(\frac{1}{a}\right) = -\ln a$$

B.3 Geometry

The **distance** d between two points having coordinates (x_1, y_1) and (x_2, y_2) is

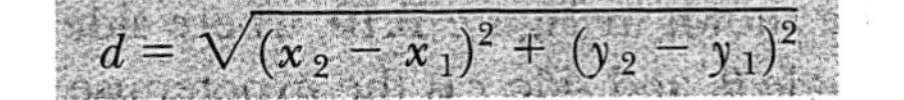

$$d = \sqrt{(x_2 - x_1)^2 + (y_2 - y_1)^2} \tag{B.17}$$

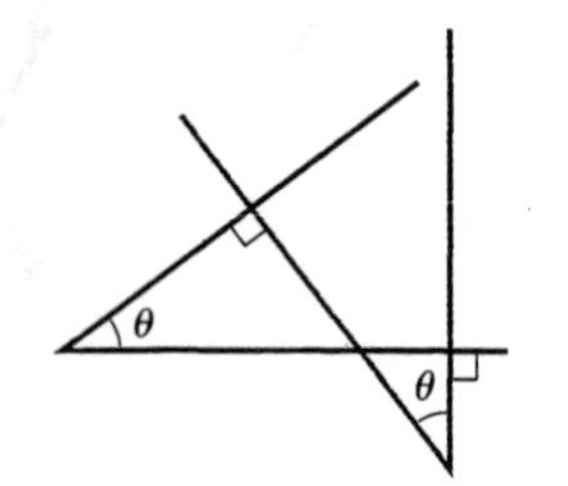

Figure B.4 The angles are equal because their sides are perpendicular.

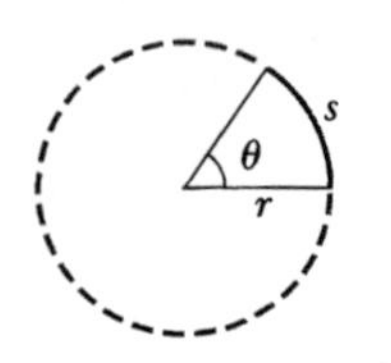

Figure B.5 The angle θ in radians is the ratio of the arc length s to the radius r of the circle.

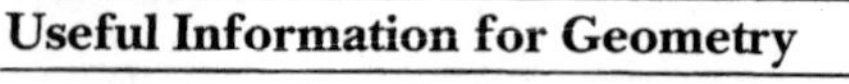

TABLE B.2

Useful Information for Geometry

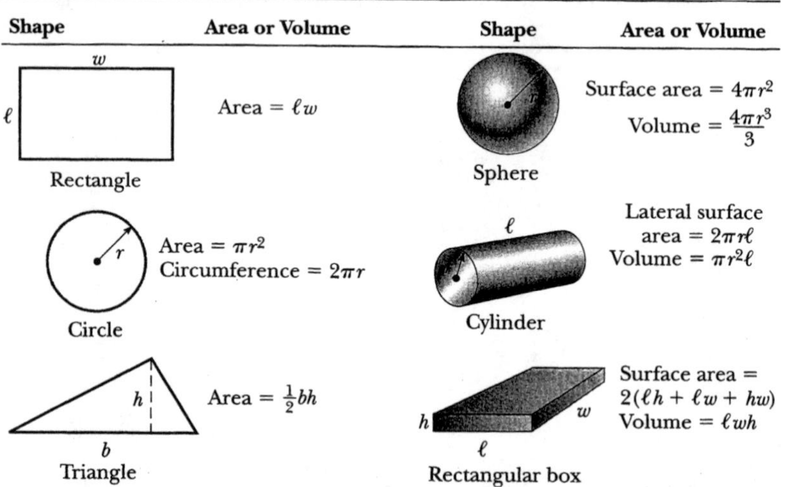

Shape	Area or Volume	Shape	Area or Volume
Rectangle	Area $= \ell w$	Sphere	Surface area $= 4\pi r^2$ Volume $= \frac{4\pi r^3}{3}$
Circle	Area $= \pi r^2$ Circumference $= 2\pi r$	Cylinder	Lateral surface area $= 2\pi r\ell$ Volume $= \pi r^2\ell$
Triangle	Area $= \frac{1}{2}bh$	Rectangular box	Surface area $= 2(\ell h + \ell w + hw)$ Volume $= \ell wh$

Two angles are equal if their sides are perpendicular, right side to right side and left side to left side. For example, the two angles marked θ in Figure B.4 are the same because of the perpendicularity of the sides of the angles. To distinguish the left and right sides of an angle, imagine standing at the angle's apex and facing into the angle.

Radian measure: The arc length s of a circular arc (Fig. B.5) is proportional to the radius r for a fixed value of θ (in radians):

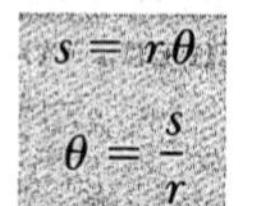

$$s = r\theta$$
$$\theta = \frac{s}{r} \tag{B.18}$$

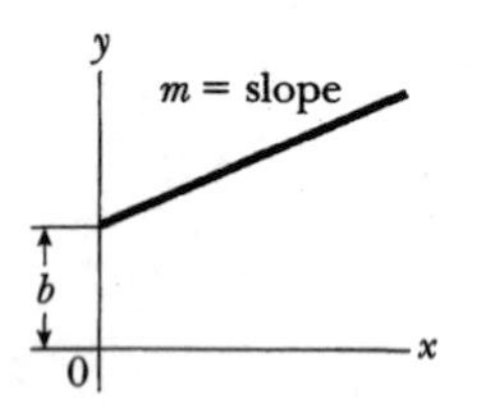

Figure B.6 A straight line with a slope of m and a y-intercept of b.

Table B.2 gives the **areas** and **volumes** for several geometric shapes used throughout this text.

The equation of a **straight line** (Fig. B.6) is

$$y = mx + b \tag{B.19}$$

where b is the y-intercept and m is the slope of the line.

The equation of a **circle** of radius R centered at the origin is

$$x^2 + y^2 = R^2 \tag{B.20}$$

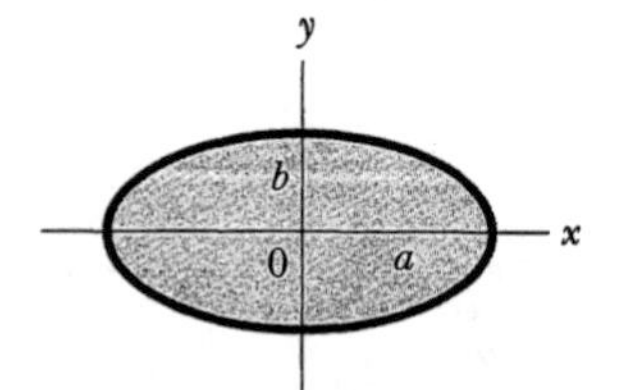

Figure B.7 An ellipse with semimajor axis a and semiminor axis b.

The equation of an **ellipse** having the origin at its center (Fig. B.7) is

$$\frac{x^2}{a^2} + \frac{y^2}{b^2} = 1 \tag{B.21}$$

where a is the length of the semimajor axis (the longer one) and b is the length of the semiminor axis (the shorter one).

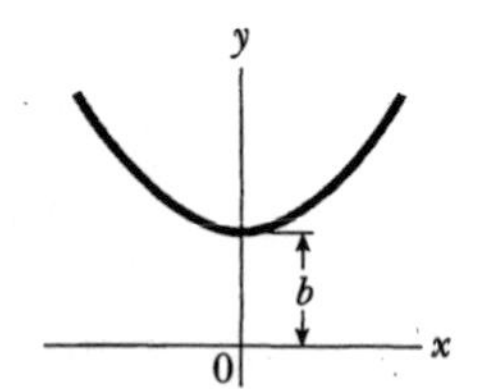

Figure B.8 A parabola with its vertex at $y = b$.

The equation of a **parabola** the vertex of which is at $y = b$ (Fig. B.8) is

$$y = ax^2 + b \tag{B.22}$$

The equation of a **rectangular hyperbola** (Fig. B.9) is

$$xy = \text{constant} \tag{B.23}$$

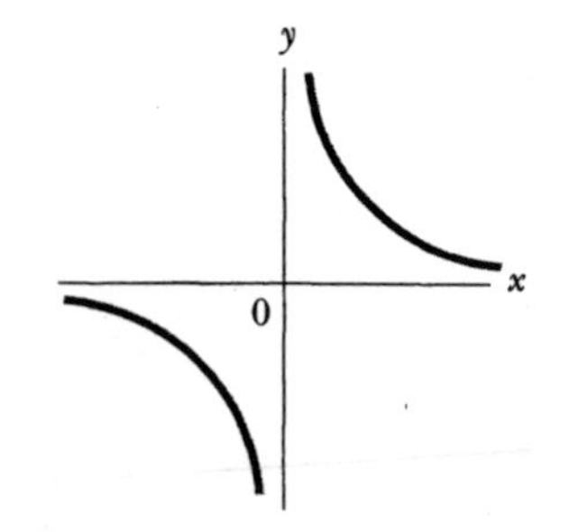

Figure B.9 A hyperbola.

B.4 Trigonometry

That portion of mathematics based on the special properties of the right triangle is called trigonometry. By definition, a right triangle is a triangle containing a 90° angle. Consider the right triangle shown in Figure B.10, where side a is opposite the angle θ, side b is adjacent to the angle θ, and side c is the hypotenuse of the triangle. The three basic trigonometric functions defined by such a triangle are the sine (sin), cosine (cos), and tangent (tan). In terms of the angle θ, these functions are defined as follows:

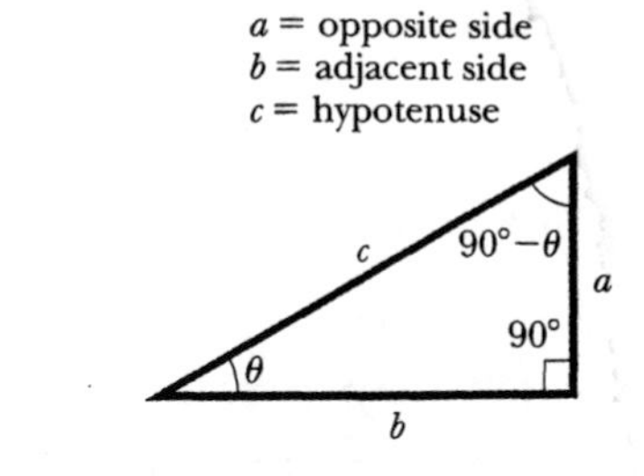

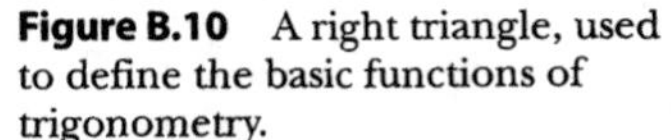

Figure B.10 A right triangle, used to define the basic functions of trigonometry.

$$\sin \theta = \frac{\text{side opposite } \theta}{\text{hypotenuse}} = \frac{a}{c} \qquad \textbf{(B.24)}$$

$$\cos \theta = \frac{\text{side adjacent to } \theta}{\text{hypotenuse}} = \frac{b}{c} \qquad \textbf{(B.25)}$$

$$\tan \theta = \frac{\text{side opposite } \theta}{\text{side adjacent to } \theta} = \frac{a}{b} \qquad \textbf{(B.26)}$$

The Pythagorean theorem provides the following relationship among the sides of a right triangle:

$$c^2 = a^2 + b^2 \qquad \textbf{(B.27)}$$

From the preceding definitions and the Pythagorean theorem, it follows that

$$\sin^2 \theta + \cos^2 \theta = 1$$

$$\tan \theta = \frac{\sin \theta}{\cos \theta}$$

The cosecant, secant, and cotangent functions are defined by

$$\csc \theta = \frac{1}{\sin \theta} \qquad \sec \theta = \frac{1}{\cos \theta} \qquad \cot \theta = \frac{1}{\tan \theta}$$

The following relationships are derived directly from the right triangle shown in Figure B.10:

$$\sin \theta = \cos (90° - \theta)$$

$$\cos \theta = \sin (90° - \theta)$$

$$\cot \theta = \tan (90° - \theta)$$

Some properties of trigonometric functions are the following:

$$\sin (-\theta) = -\sin \theta$$

$$\cos (-\theta) = \cos \theta$$

$$\tan (-\theta) = -\tan \theta$$

The following relationships apply to *any* triangle as shown in Figure B.11:

$$\alpha + \beta + \gamma = 180°$$

Law of cosines
$$\begin{cases} a^2 = b^2 + c^2 - 2bc \cos \alpha \\ b^2 = a^2 + c^2 - 2ac \cos \beta \\ c^2 = a^2 + b^2 - 2ab \cos \gamma \end{cases}$$

Law of sines
$$\frac{a}{\sin \alpha} = \frac{b}{\sin \beta} = \frac{c}{\sin \gamma}$$

Table B.3 (page A-12) lists a number of useful trigonometric identities.

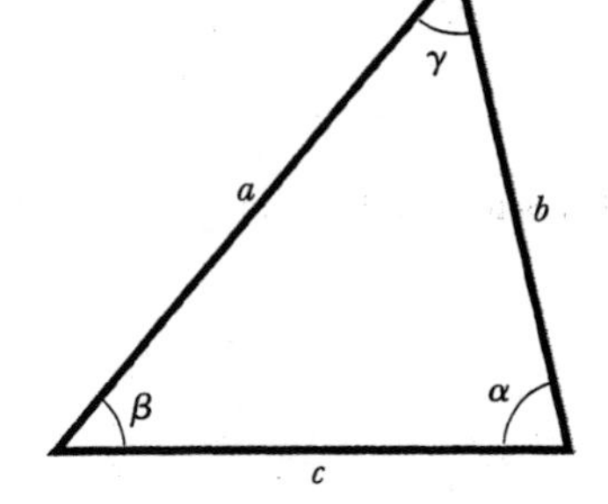

Figure B.11 An arbitrary, nonright triangle.

EXAMPLE **B.3**

Consider the right triangle in Figure B.12 in which $a = 2.00$, $b = 5.00$, and c is unknown. From the Pythagorean theorem, we have

$$c^2 = a^2 + b^2 = 2.00^2 + 5.00^2 = 4.00 + 25.0 = 29.0$$

$$c = \sqrt{29.0} = 5.39$$

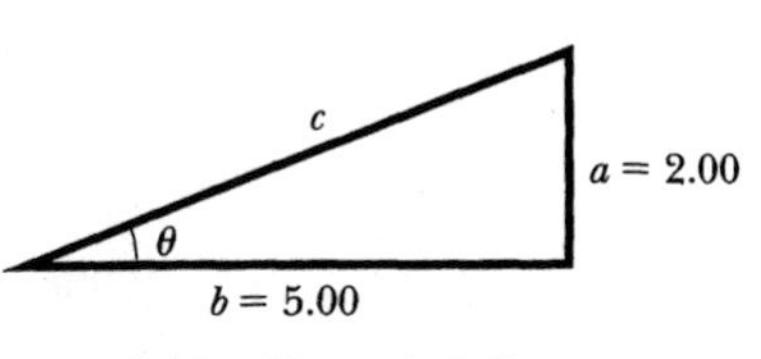

Figure B.12 (Example B.3)

To find the angle θ, note that

$$\tan \theta = \frac{a}{b} = \frac{2.00}{5.00} = 0.400$$

Using a calculator, we find that

$$\theta = \tan^{-1}(0.400) = 21.8°$$

where $\tan^{-1}(0.400)$ is the notation for "angle whose tangent is 0.400," sometimes written as arctan (0.400).

TABLE B.3

Some Trigonometric Identities

$\sin^2 \theta + \cos^2 \theta = 1$	$\csc^2 \theta = 1 + \cot^2 \theta$
$\sec^2 \theta = 1 + \tan^2 \theta$	$\sin^2 \frac{\theta}{2} = \frac{1}{2}(1 - \cos \theta)$
$\sin 2\theta = 2 \sin \theta \cos \theta$	$\cos^2 \frac{\theta}{2} = \frac{1}{2}(1 + \cos \theta)$
$\cos 2\theta = \cos^2 \theta - \sin^2 \theta$	$1 - \cos \theta = 2 \sin^2 \frac{\theta}{2}$
$\tan 2\theta = \frac{2 \tan \theta}{1 - \tan^2 \theta}$	$\tan \frac{\theta}{2} = \sqrt{\frac{1 - \cos \theta}{1 + \cos \theta}}$

$\sin(A \pm B) = \sin A \cos B \pm \cos A \sin B$

$\cos(A \pm B) = \cos A \cos B \mp \sin A \sin B$

$\sin A \pm \sin B = 2 \sin[\frac{1}{2}(A \pm B)] \cos[\frac{1}{2}(A \mp B)]$

$\cos A + \cos B = 2 \cos[\frac{1}{2}(A + B)] \cos[\frac{1}{2}(A - B)]$

$\cos A - \cos B = 2 \sin[\frac{1}{2}(A + B)] \sin[\frac{1}{2}(B - A)]$

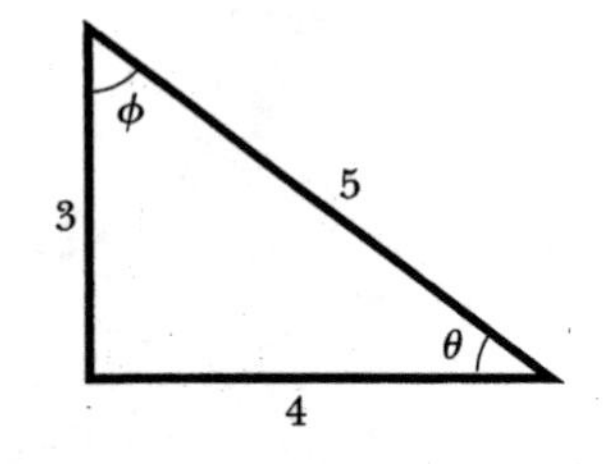

Figure B.13 (Exercise 1)

Exercises

1. In Figure B.13, identify (a) the side opposite θ (b) the side adjacent to ϕ and then find (c) $\cos \theta$, (d) $\sin \phi$, and (e) $\tan \phi$.

Answers (a) 3 (b) 3 (c) $\frac{4}{5}$ (d) $\frac{4}{5}$ (e) $\frac{4}{3}$

2. In a certain right triangle, the two sides that are perpendicular to each other are 5.00 m and 7.00 m long. What is the length of the third side?

Answer 8.60 m

3. A right triangle has a hypotenuse of length 3.0 m, and one of its angles is 30°. (a) What is the length of the side opposite the 30° angle? (b) What is the side adjacent to the 30° angle?

Answers (a) 1.5 m (b) 2.6 m

B.5 Series Expansions

$$(a + b)^n = a^n + \frac{n}{1!} a^{n-1} b + \frac{n(n-1)}{2!} a^{n-2} b^2 + \cdots$$

$$(1 + x)^n = 1 + nx + \frac{n(n-1)}{2!} x^2 + \cdots$$

$$e^x = 1 + x + \frac{x^2}{2!} + \frac{x^3}{3!} + \cdots$$

$$\ln(1 \pm x) = \pm x - \tfrac{1}{2}x^2 \pm \tfrac{1}{3}x^3 - \cdots$$

$$\left.\begin{aligned} \sin x &= x - \frac{x^3}{3!} + \frac{x^5}{5!} - \cdots \\ \cos x &= 1 - \frac{x^2}{2!} + \frac{x^4}{4!} - \cdots \\ \tan x &= x + \frac{x^3}{3} + \frac{2x^5}{15} + \cdots \quad |x| < \frac{\pi}{2} \end{aligned}\right\} \quad x \text{ in radians}$$

For $x \ll 1$, the following approximations can be used:[1]

$$(1 + x)^n \approx 1 + nx \qquad \sin x \approx x$$

$$e^x \approx 1 + x \qquad \cos x \approx 1$$

$$\ln(1 \pm x) \approx \pm x \qquad \tan x \approx x$$

B.6 Differential Calculus

In various branches of science, it is sometimes necessary to use the basic tools of calculus, invented by Newton, to describe physical phenomena. The use of calculus is fundamental in the treatment of various problems in Newtonian mechanics, electricity, and magnetism. In this section, we simply state some basic properties and "rules of thumb" that should be a useful review to the student.

First, a **function** must be specified that relates one variable to another (e.g., a coordinate as a function of time). Suppose one of the variables is called y (the dependent variable), and the other x (the independent variable). We might have a function relationship such as

$$y(x) = ax^3 + bx^2 + cx + d$$

If a, b, c, and d are specified constants, y can be calculated for any value of x. We usually deal with continuous functions, that is, those for which y varies "smoothly" with x.

The **derivative** of y with respect to x is defined as the limit as Δx approaches zero of the slopes of chords drawn between two points on the y versus x curve. Mathematically, we write this definition as

$$\frac{dy}{dx} = \lim_{\Delta x \to 0} \frac{\Delta y}{\Delta x} = \lim_{\Delta x \to 0} \frac{y(x + \Delta x) - y(x)}{\Delta x} \qquad \textbf{(B.28)}$$

where Δy and Δx are defined as $\Delta x = x_2 - x_1$ and $\Delta y = y_2 - y_1$ (Fig. B.14). Note that dy/dx *does not* mean dy divided by dx, but rather is simply a notation of the limiting process of the derivative as defined by Equation B.28.

A useful expression to remember when $y(x) = ax^n$, where a is a *constant* and n is *any* positive or negative number (integer or fraction), is

$$\frac{dy}{dx} = nax^{n-1} \qquad \textbf{(B.29)}$$

If $y(x)$ is a polynomial or algebraic function of x, we apply Equation B.29 to *each* term in the polynomial and take $d[\text{constant}]/dx = 0$. In Examples B.4 through B.7, we evaluate the derivatives of several functions.

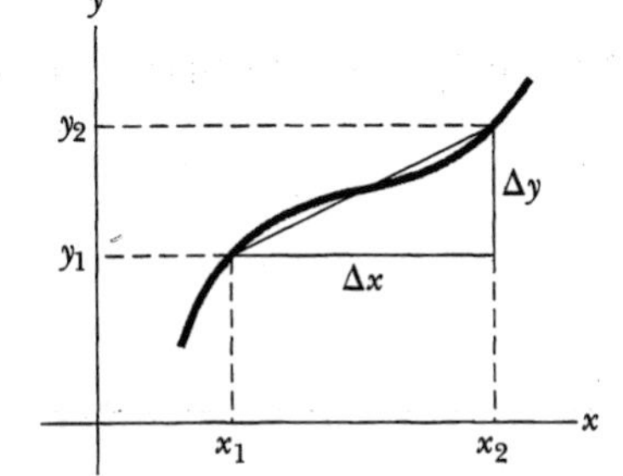

Figure B.14 The lengths Δx and Δy are used to define the derivative of this function at a point.

[1]The approximations for the functions sin x, cos x, and tan x are for $x \leq 0.1$ rad.

TABLE B.4

Derivative for Several Functions

$$\frac{d}{dx}(a) = 0$$

$$\frac{d}{dx}(ax^n) = nax^{n-1}$$

$$\frac{d}{dx}(e^{ax}) = ae^{ax}$$

$$\frac{d}{dx}(\sin ax) = a\cos ax$$

$$\frac{d}{dx}(\cos ax) = -a\sin ax$$

$$\frac{d}{dx}(\tan ax) = a\sec^2 ax$$

$$\frac{d}{dx}(\cot ax) = -a\csc^2 ax$$

$$\frac{d}{dx}(\sec x) = \tan x\sec x$$

$$\frac{d}{dx}(\csc x) = -\cot x\csc x$$

$$\frac{d}{dx}(\ln ax) = \frac{1}{x}$$

$$\frac{d}{dx}(\sin^{-1} ax) = \frac{a}{\sqrt{1-a^2x^2}}$$

$$\frac{d}{dx}(\cos^{-1} ax) = \frac{-a}{\sqrt{1-a^2x^2}}$$

$$\frac{d}{dx}(\tan^{-1} ax) = \frac{a}{1+a^2x^2}$$

Note: The symbols a and n represent constants.

Special Properties of the Derivative

A. Derivative of the product of two functions If a function $f(x)$ is given by the product of two functions—say, $g(x)$ and $h(x)$—the derivative of $f(x)$ is defined as

$$\frac{d}{dx}f(x) = \frac{d}{dx}[g(x)h(x)] = g\frac{dh}{dx} + h\frac{dg}{dx} \tag{B.30}$$

B. Derivative of the sum of two functions If a function $f(x)$ is equal to the sum of two functions, the derivative of the sum is equal to the sum of the derivatives:

$$\frac{d}{dx}f(x) = \frac{d}{dx}[g(x) + h(x)] = \frac{dg}{dx} + \frac{dh}{dx} \tag{B.31}$$

C. Chain rule of differential calculus If $y = f(x)$ and $x = g(z)$, then dy/dz can be written as the product of two derivatives:

$$\frac{dy}{dz} = \frac{dy}{dx}\frac{dx}{dz} \tag{B.32}$$

D. The second derivative The second derivative of y with respect to x is defined as the derivative of the function dy/dx (the derivative of the derivative). It is usually written as

$$\frac{d^2y}{dx^2} = \frac{d}{dx}\left(\frac{dy}{dx}\right) \tag{B.33}$$

Some of the more commonly used derivatives of functions are listed in Table B.4.

EXAMPLE B.4

Suppose $y(x)$ (that is, y as a function of x) is given by

$$y(x) = ax^3 + bx + c$$

where a and b are constants. It follows that

$$y(x + \Delta x) = a(x + \Delta x)^3 + b(x + \Delta x) + c$$

$$= a(x^3 + 3x^2\,\Delta x + 3x\,\Delta x^2 + \Delta x^3) + b(x + \Delta x) + c$$

so

$$\Delta y = y(x + \Delta x) - y(x) = a(3x^2\,\Delta x + 3x\,\Delta x^2 + \Delta x^3) + b\,\Delta x$$

Substituting this into Equation B.28 gives

$$\frac{dy}{dx} = \lim_{\Delta x\to 0}\frac{\Delta y}{\Delta x} = \lim_{\Delta x\to 0}[3ax^2 + 3ax\,\Delta x + a\,\Delta x^2] + b$$

$$\frac{dy}{dx} = 3ax^2 + b$$

EXAMPLE B.5

Find the derivative of

$$y(x) = 8x^5 + 4x^3 + 2x + 7$$

Solution Applying Equation B.29 to each term independently and remembering that d/dx (constant) = 0, we have

$$\frac{dy}{dx} = 8(5)x^4 + 4(3)x^2 + 2(1)x^0 + 0$$

$$\frac{dy}{dx} = 40x^4 + 12x^2 + 2$$

EXAMPLE B.6

Find the derivative of $y(x) = x^3/(x+1)^2$ with respect to x.

Solution We can rewrite this function as $y(x) = x^3(x+1)^{-2}$ and apply Equation B.30:

$$\frac{dy}{dx} = (x+1)^{-2}\frac{d}{dx}(x^3) + x^3\frac{d}{dx}(x+1)^{-2}$$

$$= (x+1)^{-2}3x^2 + x^3(-2)(x+1)^{-3}$$

$$\frac{dy}{dx} = \frac{3x^2}{(x+1)^2} - \frac{2x^3}{(x+1)^3}$$

EXAMPLE B.7

A useful formula that follows from Equation B.30 is the derivative of the quotient of two functions. Show that

$$\frac{d}{dx}\left[\frac{g(x)}{h(x)}\right] = \frac{h\dfrac{dg}{dx} - g\dfrac{dh}{dx}}{h^2}$$

Solution We can write the quotient as gh^{-1} and then apply Equations B.29 and B.30:

$$\frac{d}{dx}\left(\frac{g}{h}\right) = \frac{d}{dx}(gh^{-1}) = g\frac{d}{dx}(h^{-1}) + h^{-1}\frac{d}{dx}(g)$$

$$= -gh^{-2}\frac{dh}{dx} + h^{-1}\frac{dg}{dx}$$

$$= \frac{h\dfrac{dg}{dx} - g\dfrac{dh}{dx}}{h^2}$$

B.7 Integral Calculus

We think of integration as the inverse of differentiation. As an example, consider the expression

$$f(x) = \frac{dy}{dx} = 3ax^2 + b \tag{B.34}$$

which was the result of differentiating the function

$$y(x) = ax^3 + bx + c$$

in Example B.4. We can write Equation B.34 as $dy = f(x)\,dx = (3ax^2 + b)\,dx$ and obtain $y(x)$ by "summing" over all values of x. Mathematically, we write this inverse operation as

$$y(x) = \int f(x)\,dx$$

For the function $f(x)$ given by Equation B.34, we have

$$y(x) = \int (3ax^2 + b)\,dx = ax^3 + bx + c$$

where c is a constant of the integration. This type of integral is called an *indefinite integral* because its value depends on the choice of c.

A general **indefinite integral** $I(x)$ is defined as

$$I(x) = \int f(x)\,dx \tag{B.35}$$

where $f(x)$ is called the *integrand* and $f(x) = dI(x)/dx$.

For a *general continuous* function $f(x)$, the integral can be described as the area under the curve bounded by $f(x)$ and the x axis, between two specified values of x, say, x_1 and x_2, as in Figure B.15.

The area of the blue element in Figure B.15 is approximately $f(x_i)\,\Delta x_i$. If we sum all these area elements between x_1 and x_2 and take the limit of this sum as $\Delta x_i \rightarrow 0$, we obtain the *true* area under the curve bounded by $f(x)$ and the x axis, between the limits x_1 and x_2:

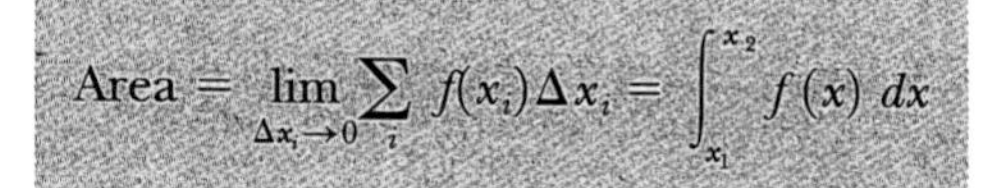

$$\text{Area} = \lim_{\Delta x_i \to 0} \sum_i f(x_i)\,\Delta x_i = \int_{x_1}^{x_2} f(x)\,dx \tag{B.36}$$

Integrals of the type defined by Equation B.36 are called **definite integrals.**

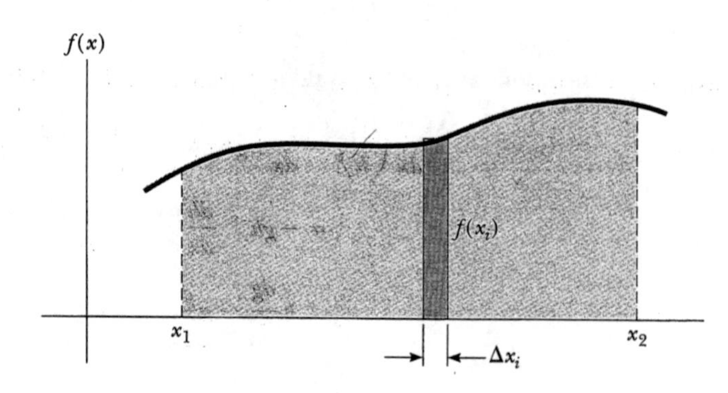

Figure B.15 The definite integral of a function is the area under the curve of the function between the limits x_1 and x_2.

One common integral that arises in practical situations has the form

$$\int x^n\,dx = \frac{x^{n+1}}{n+1} + c \quad (n \neq -1) \qquad \textbf{(B.37)}$$

This result is obvious, being that differentiation of the right-hand side with respect to x gives $f(x) = x^n$ directly. If the limits of the integration are known, this integral becomes a *definite integral* and is written

$$\int_{x_1}^{x_2} x^n\,dx = \left.\frac{x^{n+1}}{n+1}\right|_{x_1}^{x_2} = \frac{x_2^{\,n+1} - x_1^{\,n+1}}{n+1} \quad (n \neq -1) \qquad \textbf{(B.38)}$$

EXAMPLES

1. $\displaystyle\int_0^a x^2\,dx = \frac{x^3}{3}\Big]_0^a = \frac{a^3}{3}$

2. $\displaystyle\int_0^b x^{3/2}\,dx = \frac{x^{5/2}}{5/2}\Big]_0^b = \tfrac{2}{5}b^{5/2}$

3. $\displaystyle\int_3^5 x\,dx = \frac{x^2}{2}\Big]_3^5 = \frac{5^2 - 3^2}{2} = 8$

Partial Integration

Sometimes it is useful to apply the method of *partial integration* (also called "integrating by parts") to evaluate certain integrals. This method uses the property

$$\int u\,dv = uv - \int v\,du \qquad \textbf{(B.39)}$$

where u and v are *carefully* chosen so as to reduce a complex integral to a simpler one. In many cases, several reductions have to be made. Consider the function

$$I(x) = \int x^2 e^x\,dx$$

which can be evaluated by integrating by parts twice. First, if we choose $u = x^2$, $v = e^x$, we obtain

$$\int x^2 e^x\,dx = \int x^2\,d(e^x) = x^2 e^x - 2\int e^x x\,dx + c_1$$

Now, in the second term, choose $u = x$, $v = e^x$, which gives

$$\int x^2 e^x\,dx = x^2 e^x - 2x\,e^x + 2\int e^x\,dx + c_1$$

or

$$\int x^2 e^x\,dx = x^2 e^x - 2xe^x + 2e^x + c_2$$

TABLE B.5

Some Indefinite Integrals (An arbitrary constant should be added to each of these integrals.)

$$\int x^n\,dx = \frac{x^{n+1}}{n+1} \quad (\text{provided } n \neq 1)$$

$$\int \frac{dx}{x} = \int x^{-1}\,dx = \ln x$$

$$\int \frac{dx}{a+bx} = \frac{1}{b}\ln(a+bx)$$

$$\int \frac{x\,dx}{a+bx} = \frac{x}{b} - \frac{a}{b^2}\ln(a+bx)$$

$$\int \frac{dx}{x(x+a)} = -\frac{1}{a}\ln\frac{x+a}{x}$$

$$\int \frac{dx}{(a+bx)^2} = -\frac{1}{b(a+bx)}$$

$$\int \frac{dx}{a^2+x^2} = \frac{1}{a}\tan^{-1}\frac{x}{a}$$

$$\int \frac{dx}{a^2-x^2} = \frac{1}{2a}\ln\frac{a+x}{a-x} \quad (a^2 - x^2 > 0)$$

$$\int \frac{dx}{x^2-a^2} = \frac{1}{2a}\ln\frac{x-a}{x+a} \quad (x^2 - a^2 > 0)$$

$$\int \frac{x\,dx}{a^2 \pm x^2} = \pm\tfrac{1}{2}\ln(a^2 \pm x^2)$$

$$\int \frac{dx}{\sqrt{a^2-x^2}} = \sin^{-1}\frac{x}{a} = -\cos^{-1}\frac{x}{a} \quad (a^2 - x^2 > 0)$$

$$\int \frac{dx}{\sqrt{x^2+a^2}} = \ln(x + \sqrt{x^2 \pm a^2})$$

$$\int \frac{x\,dx}{\sqrt{a^2-x^2}} = -\sqrt{a^2-x^2}$$

$$\int \frac{x\,dx}{\sqrt{x^2 \pm a^2}} = \sqrt{x^2 \pm a^2}$$

$$\int \sqrt{a^2-x^2}\,dx = \tfrac{1}{2}\left(x\sqrt{a^2-x^2} + a^2\sin^{-1}\frac{x}{a}\right)$$

$$\int x\sqrt{a^2-x^2}\,dx = -\tfrac{1}{3}(a^2-x^2)^{3/2}$$

$$\int \sqrt{x^2 \pm a^2}\,dx = \tfrac{1}{2}\left[x\sqrt{x^2 \pm a^2} \pm a^2\ln\left(x + \sqrt{x^2 \pm a^2}\right)\right]$$

$$\int x\left(\sqrt{x^2 \pm a^2}\right)dx = \tfrac{1}{3}(x^2 \pm a^2)^{3/2}$$

$$\int e^{ax}\,dx = \frac{1}{a}e^{ax}$$

$$\int \ln ax\,dx = (x\ln ax) - x$$

$$\int xe^{ax}\,dx = \frac{e^{ax}}{a^2}(ax-1)$$

$$\int \frac{dx}{a+be^{cx}} = \frac{x}{a} - \frac{1}{ac}\ln(a+be^{cx})$$

$$\int \sin ax\,dx = \frac{1}{a}\cos ax$$

$$\int \cos ax\,dx = \frac{1}{a}\sin ax$$

$$\int \tan ax\,dx = -\frac{1}{a}\ln(\cos ax) = \frac{1}{a}\ln(\sec ax)$$

$$\int \cot ax\,dx = \frac{1}{a}\ln(\sin ax)$$

$$\int \sec ax\,dx = \frac{1}{a}\ln(\sec ax + \tan ax) = \frac{1}{a}\ln\left[\tan\left(\frac{ax}{2} + \frac{\pi}{4}\right)\right]$$

$$\int \csc ax\,dx = \frac{1}{a}\ln(\csc ax - \cot ax) = \frac{1}{a}\ln\left(\tan\frac{ax}{2}\right)$$

$$\int \sin^2 ax\,dx = \frac{x}{2} + \frac{\sin 2ax}{4a}$$

$$\int \cos^2 ax\,dx = \frac{x}{2} + \frac{\sin 2ax}{4a}$$

$$\int \frac{dx}{\sin^2 ax} = -\frac{1}{a}\cot ax$$

$$\int \frac{dx}{\cos^2 ax} = \frac{1}{a}\tan ax$$

$$\int \tan^2 ax\,dx = \frac{1}{a}(\tan ax) - x$$

$$\int \cot^2 ax\,dx = -\frac{1}{a}(\cot ax) - x$$

$$\int \sin^{-1} ax\,dx = x(\sin^{-1} ax) + \frac{\sqrt{1-a^2x^2}}{a}$$

$$\int \cos^{-1} ax\,dx = x(\cos^{-1} ax) - \frac{\sqrt{1-a^2x^2}}{a}$$

$$\int \frac{dx}{(x^2+a^2)^{3/2}} = \frac{x}{a^2\sqrt{x^2+a^2}}$$

$$\int \frac{x\,dx}{(x^2+a^2)^{3/2}} = -\frac{1}{\sqrt{x^2+a^2}}$$

TABLE B.6

Gauss's Probability Integral and Other Definite Integrals

$$\int_0^\infty x^n e^{-ax}\,dx = \frac{n!}{a^{n+1}}$$

$$I_0 = \int_0^\infty e^{-ax^2}\,dx = \frac{1}{2}\sqrt{\frac{\pi}{a}} \qquad \text{(Gauss's probability integral)}$$

$$I_1 = \int_0^\infty x e^{-ax^2}\,dx = \frac{1}{2a}$$

$$I_2 = \int_0^\infty x^2 e^{-ax^2}\,dx = -\frac{dI_0}{da} = \frac{1}{4}\sqrt{\frac{\pi}{a^3}}$$

$$I_3 = \int_0^\infty x^3 e^{-ax^2}\,dx = -\frac{dI_1}{da} = \frac{1}{2a^2}$$

$$I_4 = \int_0^\infty x^4 e^{-ax^2}\,dx = \frac{d^2 I_0}{da^2} = \frac{3}{8}\sqrt{\frac{\pi}{a^5}}$$

$$I_5 = \int_0^\infty x^5 e^{-ax^2}\,dx = \frac{d^2 I_1}{da^2} = \frac{1}{a^3}$$

$$\vdots$$

$$I_{2n} = (-1)^n \frac{d^n}{da^n} I_0$$

$$I_{2n+1} = (-1)^n \frac{d^n}{da^n} I_1$$

The Perfect Differential

Another useful method to remember is that of the *perfect differential,* in which we look for a change of variable such that the differential of the function is the differential of the independent variable appearing in the integrand. For example, consider the integral

$$I(x) = \int \cos^2 x \sin x \, dx$$

This integral becomes easy to evaluate if we rewrite the differential as $d(\cos x) = -\sin x\, dx$. The integral then becomes

$$\int \cos^2 x \sin x \, dx = -\int \cos^2 x \, d(\cos x)$$

If we now change variables, letting $y = \cos x$, we obtain

$$\int \cos^2 x \sin x \, dx = -\int y^2\, dy = -\frac{y^3}{3} + c = -\frac{\cos^3 x}{3} + c$$

Table B.5 (page A-18) lists some useful indefinite integrals. Table B.6 gives Gauss's probability integral and other definite integrals. A more complete list can be found in various handbooks, such as *The Handbook of Chemistry and Physics* (Boca Raton, FL: CRC Press, published annually).

B.8 Propagation of Uncertainty

In laboratory experiments, a common activity is to take measurements that act as raw data. These measurements are of several types—length, time interval, temperature, voltage, and so on—and are taken by a variety of instruments. Regardless of the measurement and the quality of the instrumentation, **there is always uncertainty associated with a physical measurement.** This uncertainty is a combination of that associated with the instrument and that related to the system being measured. An example of the former is the inability to exactly determine the position of a length measurement between the lines on a meterstick. An example of uncertainty related to the system being measured is the variation of temperature within a sample of water so that a single temperature for the sample is difficult to determine.

Uncertainties can be expressed in two ways. **Absolute uncertainty** refers to an uncertainty expressed in the same units as the measurement. Therefore, the length of a computer disk label might be expressed as (5.5 ± 0.1) cm. The uncertainty of ± 0.1 cm by itself is not descriptive enough for some purposes, however. This uncertainty is large if the measurement is 1.0 cm, but it is small if the measurement is 100 m. To give a more descriptive account of the uncertainty, **fractional uncertainty** or **percent uncertainty** is used. In this type of description, the uncertainty is divided by the actual measurement. Therefore, the length of the computer disk label could be expressed as

$$\ell = 5.5 \text{ cm} \pm \frac{0.1 \text{ cm}}{5.5 \text{ cm}} = 5.5 \text{ cm} \pm 0.018 \quad \text{(fractional uncertainty)}$$

or as

$$\ell = 5.5 \text{ cm} \pm 1.8\% \quad \text{(percent uncertainty)}$$

When combining measurements in a calculation, the percent uncertainty in the final result is generally larger than the uncertainty in the individual measurements. This is called **propagation of uncertainty** and is one of the challenges of experimental physics.

Some simple rules can provide a reasonable estimate of the uncertainty in a calculated result:

Multiplication and division: When measurements with uncertainties are multiplied or divided, add the *percent uncertainties* to obtain the percent uncertainty in the result.

Example: The Area of a Rectangular Plate

$$A = \ell w = (5.5 \text{ cm} \pm 1.8\%) \times (6.4 \text{ cm} \pm 1.6\%) = 35 \text{ cm}^2 \pm 3.4\%$$
$$= (35 \pm 1) \text{ cm}^2$$

Addition and subtraction: When measurements with uncertainties are added or subtracted, add the *absolute uncertainties* to obtain the absolute uncertainty in the result.

Example: A Change in Temperature

$$\Delta T = T_2 - T_1 = (99.2 \pm 1.5)^\circ\text{C} - (27.6 \pm 1.5)^\circ\text{C} = (71.6 \pm 3.0)^\circ\text{C}$$
$$= 71.6^\circ\text{C} \pm 4.2\%$$

Powers: If a measurement is taken to a power, the percent uncertainty is multiplied by that power to obtain the percent uncertainty in the result.

Example: The Volume of a Sphere

$$V = \tfrac{4}{3}\pi r^3 = \tfrac{4}{3}\pi(6.20 \text{ cm} \pm 2.0\%)^3 = 998 \text{ cm}^3 \pm 6.0\%$$
$$= (998 \pm 60) \text{ cm}^3$$

For complicated calculations, many uncertainties are added together, which can cause the uncertainty in the final result to be undesirably large. Experiments should be designed such that calculations are as simple as possible.

Notice that uncertainties in a calculation always add. As a result, an experiment involving a subtraction should be avoided if possible, especially if the measurements being subtracted are close together. The result of such a calculation is a small difference in the measurements and uncertainties that add together. It is possible that the uncertainty in the result could be larger than the result itself!

Group I	Group II	Transition elements						
H 1 1.007 9 $1s$								
Li 3 6.941 $2s^1$	**Be** 4 9.0122 $2s^2$							
Na 11 22.990 $3s^1$	**Mg** 12 24.305 $3s^2$							
K 19 39.098 $4s^1$	**Ca** 20 40.078 $4s^2$	**Sc** 21 44.956 $3d^14s^2$	**Ti** 22 47.867 $3d^24s^2$	**V** 23 50.942 $3d^34s^2$	**Cr** 24 51.996 $3d^54s^1$	**Mn** 25 54.938 $3d^54s^2$	**Fe** 26 55.845 $3d^64s^2$	**Co** 27 58.933 $3d^74s^2$
Rb 37 85.468 $5s^1$	**Sr** 38 87.62 $5s^2$	**Y** 39 88.906 $4d^15s^2$	**Zr** 40 91.224 $4d^25s^2$	**Nb** 41 92.906 $4d^45s^1$	**Mo** 42 95.94 $4d^55s^1$	**Tc** 43 (98) $4d^55s^2$	**Ru** 44 101.07 $4d^75s^1$	**Rh** 45 102.91 $4d^85s^1$
Cs 55 132.91 $6s^1$	**Ba** 56 137.33 $6s^2$	57–71*	**Hf** 72 178.49 $5d^26s^2$	**Ta** 73 180.95 $5d^36s^2$	**W** 74 183.84 $5d^46s^2$	**Re** 75 186.21 $5d^56s^2$	**Os** 76 190.23 $5d^66s^2$	**Ir** 77 192.2 $5d^76s^2$
Fr 87 (223) $7s^1$	**Ra** 88 (226) $7s^2$	89–103**	**Rf** 104 (261) $6d^27s^2$	**Db** 105 (262) $6d^37s^2$	**Sg** 106 (266)	**Bh** 107 (264)	**Hs** 108 (277)	**Mt** 109 (268)

Symbol — **Ca** 20 — Atomic number
Atomic mass† — 40.078
$4s^2$ — Electron configuration

*Lanthanide series	**La** 57 138.91 $5d^16s^2$	**Ce** 58 140.12 $5d^14f^16s^2$	**Pr** 59 140.91 $4f^36s^2$	**Nd** 60 144.24 $4f^46s^2$	**Pm** 61 (145) $4f^56s^2$	**Sm** 62 150.36 $4f^66s^2$
**Actinide series	**Ac** 89 (227) $6d^17s^2$	**Th** 90 232.04 $6d^27s^2$	**Pa** 91 231.04 $5f^26d^17s^2$	**U** 92 238.03 $5f^36d^17s^2$	**Np** 93 (237) $5f^46d^17s^2$	**Pu** 94 (244) $5f^66d^07s^2$

Note: Atomic mass values given are averaged over isotopes in the percentages in which they exist in nature.
† For an unstable element, mass number of the most stable known isotope is given in parentheses.
†† Elements 112 and 114 have not yet been named.
††† For a description of the atomic data, visit *physics.nist.gov/PhysRefData/Elements/per_text.html*

			Group III	Group IV	Group V	Group VI	Group VII	Group 0
							H 1 1.007 9 $1s^1$	**He** 2 4.002 6 $1s^2$
			B 5 10.811 $2p^1$	**C** 6 12.011 $2p^2$	**N** 7 14.007 $2p^3$	**O** 8 15.999 $2p^4$	**F** 9 18.998 $2p^5$	**Ne** 10 20.180 $2p^6$
			Al 13 26.982 $3p^1$	**Si** 14 28.086 $3p^2$	**P** 15 30.974 $3p^3$	**S** 16 32.066 $3p^4$	**Cl** 17 35.453 $3p^5$	**Ar** 18 39.948 $3p^6$
Ni 28 58.693 $3d^84s^2$	**Cu** 29 63.546 $3d^{10}4s^1$	**Zn** 30 65.41 $3d^{10}4s^2$	**Ga** 31 69.723 $4p^1$	**Ge** 32 72.64 $4p^2$	**As** 33 74.922 $4p^3$	**Se** 34 78.96 $4p^4$	**Br** 35 79.904 $4p^5$	**Kr** 36 83.80 $4p^6$
Pd 46 106.42 $4d^{10}$	**Ag** 47 107.87 $4d^{10}5s^1$	**Cd** 48 112.41 $4d^{10}5s^2$	**In** 49 114.82 $5p^1$	**Sn** 50 118.71 $5p^2$	**Sb** 51 121.76 $5p^3$	**Te** 52 127.60 $5p^4$	**I** 53 126.90 $5p^5$	**Xe** 54 131.29 $5p^6$
Pt 78 195.08 $5d^96s^1$	**Au** 79 196.97 $5d^{10}6s^1$	**Hg** 80 200.59 $5d^{10}6s^2$	**Tl** 81 204.38 $6p^1$	**Pb** 82 207.2 $6p^2$	**Bi** 83 208.98 $6p^3$	**Po** 84 (209) $6p^4$	**At** 85 (210) $6p^5$	**Rn** 86 (222) $6p^6$
Ds 110 (271)	**Rg** 111 (272)	112†† (285)		114†† (289)				

Eu 63 151.96 $4f^76s^2$	**Gd** 64 157.25 $4f^75d^16s^2$	**Tb** 65 158.93 $4f^85d^16s^2$	**Dy** 66 162.50 $4f^{10}6s^2$	**Ho** 67 164.93 $4f^{11}6s^2$	**Er** 68 167.26 $4f^{12}6s^2$	**Tm** 69 168.93 $4f^{13}6s^2$	**Yb** 70 173.04 $4f^{14}6s^2$	**Lu** 71 174.97 $4f^{14}5d^16s^2$
Am 95 (243) $5f^77s^2$	**Cm** 96 (247) $5f^76d^17s^2$	**Bk** 97 (247) $5f^86d^17s^2$	**Cf** 98 (251) $5f^{10}7s^2$	**Es** 99 (252) $5f^{11}7s^2$	**Fm** 100 (257) $5f^{12}7s^2$	**Md** 101 (258) $5f^{13}7s^2$	**No** 102 (259) $5f^{14}7s^2$	**Lr** 103 (262) $6d^15f^{14}7s^2$

TABLE D.1

SI Units

Base Quantity	SI Base Unit Name	SI Base Unit Symbol
Length	meter	m
Mass	kilogram	kg
Time	second	s
Electric current	ampere	A
Temperature	kelvin	K
Amount of substance	mole	mol
Luminous intensity	candela	cd

TABLE D.2

Some Derived SI Units

Quantity	Name	Symbol	Expression in Terms of Base Units	Expression in Terms of Other SI Units
Plane angle	radian	rad	m/m	
Frequency	hertz	Hz	s^{-1}	
Force	newton	N	$kg \cdot m/s^2$	J/m
Pressure	pasçal	Pa	$kg/m \cdot s^2$	N/m^2
Energy	joule	J	$kg \cdot m^2/s^2$	$N \cdot m$
Power	watt	W	$kg \cdot m^2/s^3$	J/s
Electric charge	coulomb	C	$A \cdot s$	
Electric potential	volt	V	$kg \cdot m^2/A \cdot s^3$	W/A
Capacitance	farad	F	$A^2 \cdot s^4/kg \cdot m^2$	C/V
Electric resistance	ohm	Ω	$kg \cdot m^2/A^2 \cdot s^3$	V/A
Magnetic flux	weber	Wb	$kg \cdot m^2/A \cdot s^2$	$V \cdot s$
Magnetic field	tesla	T	$kg/A \cdot s^2$	
Inductance	henry	H	$kg \cdot m^2/A^2 \cdot s^2$	$T \cdot m^2/A$

CHAPTER 11

1. $-7.00\hat{\mathbf{i}} + 16.0\hat{\mathbf{j}} - 10.0\hat{\mathbf{k}}$
3. (a) $-17.0\hat{\mathbf{k}}$ (b) 70.6°
5. 0.343 N · m horizontally north
7. 45.0°
9. $F_3 = F_1 + F_2$; no
11. $17.5\hat{\mathbf{k}}$ kg · m²/s
13. $(60.0\hat{\mathbf{k}})$ kg · m²/s
15. $mvR[\cos(vt/R) + 1]\hat{\mathbf{k}}$
17. (a) zero (b) $(-mv_i^3 \sin^2\theta \cos\theta/2g)\hat{\mathbf{k}}$ (c) $(-2mv_i^3 \sin^2\theta \cos\theta/g)\hat{\mathbf{k}}$ (d) The downward gravitational force exerts a torque in the $-z$ direction.
19. (a) $-m\ell gt \cos\theta\hat{\mathbf{k}}$ (b) The planet exerts a gravitational torque on the ball. (c) $-mg\ell \cos\theta\hat{\mathbf{k}}$
23. (a) 0.360 kg · m²/s (b) 0.540 kg · m²/s
25. (a) 0.433 kg · m²/s (b) 1.73 kg · m²/s
27. (a) 1.57×10^8 kg · m²/s (b) 6.26×10^3 s = 1.74 h
29. (a) $\omega_f = \omega_i I_1/(I_1 + I_2)$ (b) $I_1/(I_1 + I_2)$
31. (a) 11.1 rad/s counterclockwise (b) No. 507 J is transformed into internal energy. (c) No. The turntable bearing promptly imparts impulse 44.9 kg · m/s north into the turntable-clay system and thereafter keeps changing the system momentum.
33. 7.14 rev/min
35. (a) Mechanical energy is not conserved; some chemical energy is converted into mechanical energy. Momentum is not conserved. The turntable bearing exerts an external northward force on the axle. Angular momentum is conserved. (b) 0.360 rad/s counterclockwise (c) 99.9 J
37. (a) $mv\ell$ down (b) $M/(M + m)$
39. (a) $\omega = 2mv_i d/[M + 2m]R^2$ (b) No; some mechanical energy changes into internal energy. (c) Momentum is not conserved. The axle exerts a backward force on the cylinder.
41. $\sim 10^{-13}$ rad/s
43. 5.45×10^{22} N · m
45. (a) $1.67\hat{\mathbf{i}}$ m/s (b) 0.033 5 = 3.35% (c) $1.67\hat{\mathbf{i}}$ m/s (d) 15.8 rad/s (e) 1.00 = 100%
47. (a) $7md^2/3$ (b) $mgd\hat{\mathbf{k}}$ (c) $3g/7d$ counterclockwise (d) $2g/7$ upward (e) mgd (f) $\sqrt{6g/7d}$ (g) $m\sqrt{14gd^3/3}$ (h) $\sqrt{2gd/21}$
49. 0.910 km/s
51. (a) $v_i r_i/r$ (b) $T = (mv_i^2 r_i^2)r^{-3}$ (c) $\frac{1}{2}mv_i^2(r_i^2/r^2 - 1)$ (d) 4.50 m/s, 10.1 N, 0.450 J
53. (a) 3 750 kg · m²/s (b) 1.88 kJ (c) 3 750 kg · m²/s (d) 10.0 m/s (e) 7.50 kJ (f) 5.62 kJ
55. (a) $2mv_0$ (b) $2v_0/3$ (c) $4m\ell v_0/3$ (d) $4v_0/9\ell$ (e) mv_0^2 (f) $26mv_0^2/27$ (g) No horizontal forces act on the bola from outside after release, so the horizontal momentum stays constant. Its center of mass moves steadily with the horizontal velocity it had at release. No torques about its axis of rotation act on the bola, so its spin angular momentum stays constant. Internal forces cannot affect momentum conservation and angular momentum conservation, but they can affect mechanical energy. Energy $mv_0^2/27$ changes from mechanical energy into internal energy as the bola takes its stable configuration.
57. An increase of 0.550 s. It is not a significant change.

CHAPTER 12

1. $[(m_1 + m_b)d + m_1\ell/2]/m_2$
3. (3.85 cm, 6.85 cm)
5. (−1.50 m, −1.50 m)
7. (2.54 m, 4.75 m)
9. 177 kg
11. (a) $f_s = 268$ N, $n = 1\,300$ N (b) 0.324
13. 2.94 kN on each rear wheel and 4.41 kN on each front wheel
15. (a) 29.9 N (b) 22.2 N
17. (a) 1.73 rad/s² (b) 1.56 rad/s (c) $(-4.72\hat{\mathbf{i}} + 6.62\hat{\mathbf{j}})$ kN (d) $38.9\hat{\mathbf{j}}$ kN
19. 2.82 m
21. 88.2 N and 58.8 N
23. 4.90 mm
25. 23.8 μm
27. (a) 3.14×10^4 N (b) 6.28×10^4 N
29. 1.65×10^8 N/m²
31. 0.860 mm
33. $n_A = 5.98 \times 10^5$ N, $n_B = 4.80 \times 10^5$ N
35. 9.00 ft
37. (a)

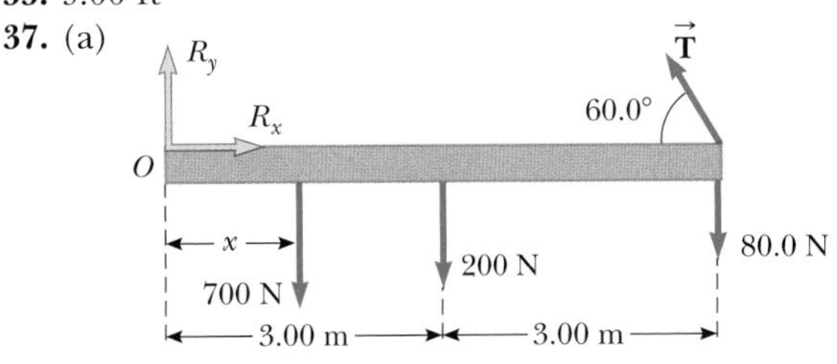

(b) $T = 343$ N, $R_x = 171$ N to the right, $R_y = 683$ N up (c) 5.13 m
39. (a) $T = F_g(L + d)/[\sin\theta\,(2L + d)]$ (b) $R_x = F_g(L + d)\cot\theta/(2L + d)$, $R_y = F_g L/(2L + d)$
41. $\vec{\mathbf{F}}_A = (-6.47 \times 10^5\hat{\mathbf{i}} + 1.27 \times 10^5\hat{\mathbf{j}})$ N, $\vec{\mathbf{F}}_B = 6.47 \times 10^5\hat{\mathbf{i}}$ N
43. 5.08 kN, $R_x = 4.77$ kN, $R_y = 8.26$ kN
45. (a) 20.1 cm to the left of the front edge; $\mu_k = 0.571$ (b) 0.501 m
47. (a) $M = (m/2)(2\mu_s \sin\theta - \cos\theta)(\cos\theta - \mu_s \sin\theta)^{-1}$ (b) $R = (m + M)g(1 + \mu_s^2)^{1/2}$ $F = g[M^2 + \mu_s^2(m + M)^2]^{1/2}$
49. (b) *AB* compression 732 N, *AC* tension 634 N, *BC* compression 897 N
51. (a) 133 N (b) $n_A = 429$ N and $n_B = 257$ N (c) $R_x = 133$ N and $R_y = -257$ N
55. 1.09 m
57. (a) 4 500 N (b) 4.50×10^6 N/m² (c) The board will break.
59. (a) $P_y = (F_g/L)(d - ah/g)$ (b) 0.306 m (c) $(-306\hat{\mathbf{i}} + 553\hat{\mathbf{j}})$ N

CHAPTER 13

1. $\sim 10^{-7}$ N toward you
3. (a) 2.50×10^{-5} N toward the 500-kg object (b) between the objects and 0.245 m from the 500-kg object
5. $(-100\hat{\mathbf{i}} + 59.3\hat{\mathbf{j}})$ pN
7. 7.41×10^{-10} N
9. 0.613 m/s² toward the Earth
11. $\rho_{\text{Moon}}/\rho_{\text{Earth}} = \frac{2}{3}$
13. 1.26×10^{32} kg
15. 1.90×10^{27} kg
17. 8.92×10^7 m
19. After 3.93 yr, Mercury would be farther from the Sun than Pluto.

21. $\vec{\mathbf{g}} = \frac{Gm}{\ell^2}\left(\frac{1}{2} + \sqrt{2}\right)$ toward the opposite corner

23. (a) $\vec{\mathbf{g}} = 2MGr(r^2 + a^2)^{-3/2}$ toward the center of mass (b) At $r = 0$, the fields of the two objects are equal in magnitude and opposite in direction, to add to zero. (d) When r is much greater than a, the fact that the two masses are separate is unimportant. They create a total field like that of a single object of mass $2M$.

25. (a) 1.84×10^9 kg/m³ (b) 3.27×10^6 m/s² (c) -2.08×10^{13} J

27. (a) -1.67×10^{-14} J (b) Each object will slowly accelerate toward the center of the triangle, where the three will simultaneously collide.

29. (b) 340 s

31. 1.66×10^4 m/s

35. (a) 5.30×10^3 s (b) 7.79 km/s (c) 6.43×10^9 J

37. (b) 1.00×10^7 m (c) 1.00×10^4 m/s

39. (a) 0.980 (b) 127 yr (c) -2.13×10^{17} J

43. (b) $2[Gm^3(1/2r - 1/R)]^{1/2}$

45. (a) -7.04×10^4 J (b) -1.57×10^5 J (c) 13.2 m/s

47. 7.79×10^{14} kg

49. $\omega = 0.057\,2$ rad/s or 1 rev in 110 s

51. (a) $m_2(2G/d)^{1/2}(m_1 + m_2)^{-1/2}$ and $m_1(2G/d)^{1/2}(m_1 + m_2)^{-1/2}$; relative speed $(2G/d)^{1/2}(m_1 + m_2)^{1/2}$ (b) 1.07×10^{32} J and 2.67×10^{31} J

53. (a) 200 Myr (b) $\sim 10^{41}$ kg; $\sim 10^{11}$ stars

55. $(GM_E/4R_E)^{1/2}$

59. $(800 + 1.73 \times 10^{-4})\hat{\mathbf{i}}$ m/s and $(800 - 1.73 \times 10^{-4})\hat{\mathbf{i}}$ m/s

61. 18.2 ms

CHAPTER 14

1. 0.111 kg

3. 6.24 MPa

5. 1.62 m

7. 7.74×10^{-3} m²

9. 271 kN horizontally backward

11. 5.88×10^6 N down; 196 kN outward; 588 kN outward

13. 0.722 mm

15. 10.5 m; no because some alcohol and water evaporate

17. 98.6 kPa

19. (a) 1.57 Pa, 1.55×10^{-2} atm, 11.8 mm Hg (b) The fluid level in the tap should rise. (c) blockage of flow of the cerebrospinal fluid

21. 0.258 N down

23. (a) $1.017\,9 \times 10^3$ N down, $1.029\,7 \times 10^3$ N up (b) 86.2 N (c) By either method of evaluation, the buoyant force is 11.8 N up.

25. (a) 1.20×10^3 N/s (b) 0

27. (a) 7.00 cm (b) 2.80 kg

31. 1 430 m³

33. 1 250 kg/m³ and 500 kg/m³

35. (a) 17.7 m/s (b) 1.73 mm

37. 31.6 m/s

39. 0.247 cm

41. (a) 2.28 N toward Holland (b) 1.74×10^6 s

43. (a) 1 atm + 15.0 MPa (b) 2.95 m/s (c) 4.34 kPa

45. 2.51×10^{-3} m³/s

47. (a) 4.43 m/s (b) The siphon can be no higher than 10.3 m.

49. 12.6 m/s

51. 1.91 m

55. 0.604 m

57. If the helicopter could create the air it expels downward, the mass flow rate of the air would have to be at least 233 kg/s. In reality, the rotor takes in air from above, which is moving over a larger area with lower speed, and blows it downward at higher speed. The amount of this air has to be at least a few times larger than 233 kg every second.

61. 17.3 N and 31.7 N

63. 90.04%

65. 758 Pa

67. 4.43 m/s

69. (a) 1.25 cm (b) 13.8 m/s

71. (c) 1.70 m²

CHAPTER 15

1. (a) The motion repeats precisely. (b) 1.81 s (c) No, the force is not in the form of Hooke's law

3. (a) 1.50 Hz, 0.667 s (b) 4.00 m (c) π rad (d) 2.83 m

5. (b) 18.8 cm/s, 0.333 s (c) 178 cm/s², 0.500 s (d) 12.0 cm

7. 40.9 N/m

9. 18.8 m/s, 7.11 km/s²

11. (a) 40.0 cm/s, 160 cm/s² (b) 32.0 cm/s, −96.0 cm/s² (c) 0.232 s

13. 0.628 m/s

15. 2.23 m/s

17. (a) 28.0 mJ (b) 1.02 m/s (c) 12.2 mJ (d) 15.8 mJ

19. 2.60 cm and −2.60 cm

21. (a) at 0.218 s and at 1.09 s (b) 0.014 6 W

23. (b) 0.628 s

25. Assuming simple harmonic motion, (a) 0.820 m/s, (b) 2.57 rad/s², and (c) 0.641 N. More precisely, (a) 0.817 m/s, (b) 2.54 rad/s², and (c) 0.634 N. The answers agree to two digits. The answers computed from conservation of energy and from Newton's second law are more precisely correct. With this amplitude, the motion of the pendulum is approximately simple harmonic.

29. 0.944 kg · m²

33. (a) 5.00×10^{-7} kg · m² (b) 3.16×10^{-4} N · m/rad

35. 1.00×10^{-3} s⁻¹

37. (a) 7.00 Hz (b) 2.00% (c) 10.6 s

39. (a) 1.00 s (b) 5.09 cm

41. 318 N

43. 1.74 Hz

45. (a) 2.09 s (b) 0.477 Hz (c) 36.0 cm/s (d) $(0.064\,8\ \text{m}^2/\text{s}^2)\,m$ (e) $(9.00/\text{s}^2)\,m$ (f) Period, frequency, and maximum speed are all independent of mass in this situation. The energy and the force constant are directly proportional to mass.

47. (a) $2Mg$, $Mg(1 + y/L)$ (b) $T = (4\pi/3)(2L/g)^{1/2}$, 2.68 s

49. 6.62 cm

51. 9.19×10^{13} Hz

53. (a)

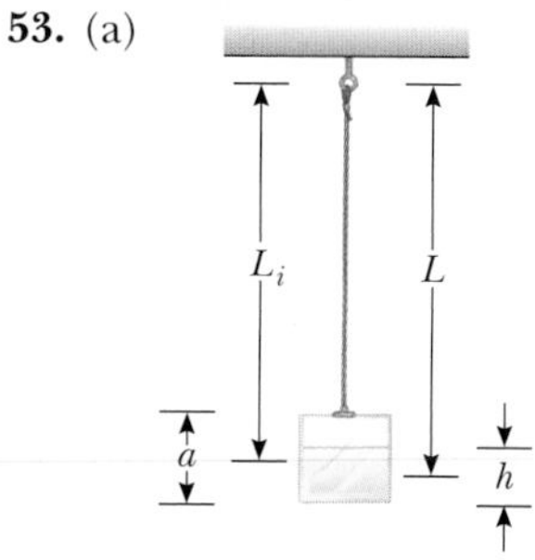

(b) $\dfrac{dT}{dt} = \dfrac{\pi\, dM/dt}{2\rho a^2 g^{1/2}[L_i + (dM/dt)t/2\rho a^2]^{1/2}}$

(c) $T = 2\pi g^{-1/2}\left[L_i + \left(\dfrac{dM}{dt}\right)\left(\dfrac{t}{2\rho a^2}\right)\right]^{1/2}$

55. $f = (2\pi L)^{-1}\left(gL + \dfrac{kh^2}{M}\right)^{1/2}$

57. (b) 1.23 Hz

59. (a) 3.00 s (b) 14.3 J (c) 25.5°

61. If the cyclist goes over washboard bumps at one certain speed, they can excite a resonance vibration of the bike, so large in amplitude as to make the rider lose control. ~ 10^1 m

69. (b) after 42.2 minutes

CHAPTER 16

1. $y = 6\,[(x - 4.5t)^2 + 3]^{-1}$

3. (a) the P wave (b) 665 s

5. (a) $(3.33\hat{\mathbf{i}})$ m/s (b) −5.48 cm (c) 0.667 m, 5.00 Hz (d) 11.0 m/s

7. 0.319 m

9. 2.00 cm, 2.98 m, 0.576 Hz, 1.72 m/s

11. (a) 31.4 rad/s (b) 1.57 rad/m (c) $y = (0.120 \text{ m}) \sin (1.57x - 31.4t)$ where x is in meters and t is in seconds (d) 3.77 m/s (e) 118 m/s^2

13. (a) 0.250 m (b) 40.0 rad/s (c) 0.300 rad/m (d) 20.9 m (e) 133 m/s (f) $+x$

15. (a) $y = (8.00 \text{ cm}) \sin (7.85x + 6\pi t)$ (b) $y = (8.00 \text{ cm}) \sin (7.85x + 6\pi t - 0.785)$

17. (a) −1.51 m/s, 0 (b) 16.0 m, 0.500 s, 32.0 m/s

19. (a) 0.500 Hz, 3.14 rad/s (b) 3.14 rad/m (c) $(0.100 \text{ m}) \sin (3.14\, x/\text{m} - 3.14\, t/\text{s})$ (d) $(0.100 \text{ m}) \sin (-3.14\, t/\text{s})$ (e) $(0.100 \text{ m}) \sin (4.71 \text{ rad} - 3.14\, t/\text{s})$ (f) 0.314 m/s

21. 80.0 N

23. 520 m/s

25. 1.64 m/s^2

27. 13.5 N

29. 185 m/s

31. 0.329 s

35. 55.1 Hz

37. (a) 62.5 m/s (b) 7.85 m (c) 7.96 Hz (d) 21.1 W

39. $\sqrt{2}\,\mathcal{P}_0$

41. (a) $A = 40$ (b) $A = 7.00$, $B = 0$, $C = 3.00$. One can take the dot product of the given equation with each one of $\hat{\mathbf{i}}, \hat{\mathbf{j}}$, and $\hat{\mathbf{k}}$. (c) $A = 0$, $B = 7.00$ mm, $C = 3.00$/m, $D = 4.00$/s, $E = 2.00$. Consider the average value of both sides of the given equation to find A. Then consider the maximum value of both sides to find B. You can evaluate the partial derivative of both sides of the given equation with respect to x and separately with respect to t to obtain equations yielding C and D upon chosen substitutions for x and t. Then substitute $x = 0$ and $t = 0$ to obtain E.

45. ~ 1 min

47. 0.456 m/s

49. (a) 39.2 N (b) 0.892 m (c) 83.6 m/s

51. (a) The energy a wave crest carries is constant in the absence of absorption. Then the rate at which energy moves beyond a fixed distance from the source, which is the power of the wave, is constant. The power is proportional to the square of the amplitude and to the wave speed. The speed decreases as the wave moves into shallower water near shore, so the amplitude must increase. (b) 8.31 m (c) As the water depth goes to zero, our model would predict zero speed and infinite amplitude. The amplitude must be finite as the wave comes ashore. As the speed decreases, the wavelength also decreases. When it becomes comparable to the water depth, or smaller, the expression $v = \sqrt{gd}$ no longer applies.

53. (a) $\mathcal{P} = (0.050\,0 \text{ kg/s})v_{y,\max}^2$ (b) The power is proportional to the square of the maximum element speed. (c) $(7.5 \times 10^{-4} \text{ kg})\, v_{y,\max}^2 = \frac{1}{2}m_3 v_{y,\max}^2$ (d) $(0.300 \text{ kg})\, v_{y,\max}^2$

55. 0.084 3 rad

59. (a) $(0.707)2(L/g)^{1/2}$ (b) $L/4$

61. 3.86×10^{-4}

63. (a) $\dfrac{\mu\omega^3}{2k}A_0^{\,2}e^{-2bx}$ (b) $\dfrac{\mu\omega^3}{2k}A_0^{\,2}$ (c) e^{-2bx}

65. (a) $\mu_0 + (\mu_L - \mu_0)x/L$

CHAPTER 17

1. 5.56 km. As long as the speed of light is much greater than the speed of sound, its actual value does not matter.

3. 0.196 s

5. 7.82 m

7. (a) 826 m (b) 1.47 s

9. (a) 0.625 mm (b) 1.50 mm to 75.0 μm

11. (a) 2.00 μm, 40.0 cm, 54.6 m/s (b) −0.433 μm (c) 1.72 mm/s

13. $\Delta P = (0.200 \text{ N/m}^2) \sin (62.8x/\text{m} - 2.16 \times 10^4 t/\text{s})$

15. 5.81 m

17. 66.0 dB

19. (a) 3.75 W/m^2 (b) 0.600 W/m^2

21. (a) 2.34 m and 0.390 m (b) 0.161 N/m^2 for both notes (c) 4.25×10^{-7} m and 7.09×10^{-8} m (d) The wavelengths and displacement amplitudes would be larger by a factor of 1.09. The answer to part (b) would be unchanged.

23. (a) 1.32×10^{-4} W/m^2 (b) 81.2 dB

25. (a) 0.691 m (b) 691 km

27. 65.6 dB

29. (a) 30.0 m (b) 9.49×10^5 m

31. (a) 332 J (b) 46.4 dB

33. (a) 3.04 kHz (b) 2.08 kHz (c) 2.62 kHz, 2.40 kHz

35. 26.4 m/s

37. 19.3 m

39. (a) 56.3 s (b) 56.6 km farther along

41. 2.82×10^8 m/s

43. It is unreasonable, implying a sound level of 123 dB. Nearly all the missing mechanical energy becomes internal energy in the latch.

45. (a) f is a few hundred hertz. λ ~ 1 m, duration ~ 0.1 s. (b) Yes. The frequency can be close to 1 000 Hz. If the person clapping his or her hands is at the base of the pyramid, the echo can drop somewhat in frequency and in loudness as sound returns, with the later cycles coming from the smaller and more distant upper risers. The sound could imitate some particular bird and could in fact be a recording of the call.

49. (a) 0.515/min (b) 0.614/min

51. (a) 55.8 m/s (b) 2 500 Hz

53. 1 204.2 Hz

55. (a) 0.642 W (b) 0.004 28 = 0.428%

57. (a) The sound through the metal arrives first. (b) (365 m/s) Δt (c) 46.3 m (d) The answer becomes

$$\ell = \frac{\Delta t}{\dfrac{1}{331\text{ m/s}} - \dfrac{1}{v_r}}$$

where v_r is the speed of sound in the rod. As v_r goes to infinity, the travel time in the rod becomes negligible. The answer approaches (331 m/s) Δt, which is the distance the sound travels in air during the delay time.
59. (a) 0.948° (b) 4.40°
61. 1.34×10^4 N
63. (a) 6.45 (b) 0

CHAPTER 18

1. (a) −1.65 cm (b) −6.02 cm (c) 1.15 cm
3. (a) $+x$, $-x$ (b) 0.750 s (c) 1.00 m
5. (a) 9.24 m (b) 600 Hz
7. (a) 2 (b) 9.28 m and 1.99 m
9. (a) 156° (b) 0.058 4 cm
11. 15.7 m, 31.8 Hz, 500 m/s
13. At 0.089 1 m, 0.303 m, 0.518 m, 0.732 m, 0.947 m, 1.16 m from one speaker
15. (a) 4.24 cm (b) 6.00 cm (c) 6.00 cm (d) 0.500 cm, 1.50 cm, 2.50 cm
17. 0.786 Hz, 1.57 Hz, 2.36 Hz, 3.14 Hz
19. (a) 350 Hz (b) 400 kg
21. (a) 163 N (b) 660 Hz
23. $\dfrac{Mg}{4Lf^2 \tan\theta}$
25. (a) 3 loops (b) 16.7 Hz (c) 1 loop
27. (a) 3.66 m/s (b) 0.200 Hz
29. (a) 0.357 m (b) 0.715 m
31. 0.656 m and 1.64 m
33. n(206 Hz) for $n = 1$ to 9 and n(84.5 Hz) for $n = 2$ to 23
35. 50.0 Hz, 1.70 m
37. (a) 350 m/s (b) 1.14 m
39. (21.5 ± 0.1) m. The data suggest 0.6-Hz uncertainty in the frequency measurements, which is only a little more than 1%.
41. (a) 1.59 kHz (b) odd-numbered harmonics (c) 1.11 kHz
43. 5.64 beats/s
45. (a) 1.99 beats/s (b) 3.38 m/s
47. The second harmonic of E is close to the third harmonic of A, and the fourth harmonic of C# is close to the fifth harmonic of A.
49. (a) The yo-yo's downward speed is $dL/dt = (0.8\text{ m/s}^2)(1.2\text{ s}) = 0.960$ m/s. The instantaneous wavelength of the fundamental string wave is given by $d_{NN} = \lambda/2 = L$, so $\lambda = 2L$ and $d\lambda/dt = 2\,dL/dt = 2(0.96\text{ m/s}) = 1.92$ m/s. (b) For the second harmonic, the wavelength is equal to the length of the string. Then the rate of change of wavelength is equal to $dL/dt = 0.960$ m/s, half as much as for the first harmonic. (c) A yo-yo of different mass will hold the string under different tension to make each string wave vibrate with a different frequency, but the geometrical argument given in parts (a) and (b) still applies to the wavelength. The answers are unchanged: $d\lambda_1/dt = 1.92$ m/s and $d\lambda_2/dt = 0.960$ m/s.
51. (a) 34.8 m/s (b) 0.977 m
53. 3.85 m/s away from the station or 3.77 m/s toward the station
55. (a) 59.9 Hz (b) 20.0 cm
57. (a) $\frac{1}{2}$ (b) $[n/(n+1)]^2 T$ (c) $\frac{9}{16}$
59. $y_1 + y_2 = 11.2 \sin(2.00x - 10.0t + 63.4°)$
61. (a) 78.9 N (b) 211 Hz

CHAPTER 19

1. (a) −274°C (b) 1.27 atm (c) 1.74 atm
3. (a) −320°F (b) 77.3 K
5. 3.27 cm
7. (a) 0.176 mm (b) 8.78 μm (c) 0.093 0 cm³
9. (a) −179°C is attainable. (b) −376°C is below 0 K and unattainable.
11. (a) 99.8 mL (b) about 6% of the volume change of the acetone
13. (a) 99.4 cm³ (b) 0.943 cm
15. 5 336 images
17. (a) 400 kPa (b) 449 kPa
19. 1.50×10^{29} molecules
21. 472 K
23. (a) 41.6 mol (b) 1.20 kg, nearly in agreement with the tabulated density
25. (a) 1.17 g (b) 11.5 mN (c) 1.01 kN (d) The molecules must be moving very fast.
27. 4.39 kg
29. (a) 7.13 m (b) The open end of the tube should be at the bottom after the bird surfaces so that the water can drain out. There is no other requirement. Air does not tend to bubble out of a narrow tube.
31. (a) 94.97 cm (b) 95.03 cm
33. 3.55 cm
35. It falls by 0.094 3 Hz.
37. (a) Expansion makes density drop. (b) $5 \times 10^{-5}(°\text{C})^{-1}$
39. (a) $h = nRT/(mg + P_0A)$ (b) 0.661 m
41. We assume $\alpha\,\Delta T$ is much less than 1.
43. Yes, as long as the coefficients of expansion remain constant. The lengths L_C and L_S at 0°C need to satisfy $17L_C = 11L_S$. Then the steel rod must be longer. With $L_S - L_C = 5.00$ cm, the only possibility is $L_S = 14.2$ cm and $L_C = 9.17$ cm.
45. (a) 0.340% (b) 0.480%
47. 2.74 m
49. (b) 1.33 kg/m³
53. No. Steel would need to be 2.30 times stronger.
55. (a) $L_f = L_i e^{\alpha\Delta T}$ (b) 2.00×10^{-4}%; 59.4%
57. (a) 6.17×10^{-3} kg/m (b) 632 N (c) 580 N; 192 Hz
59. 4.54 m

CHAPTER 20

1. (10.0 + 0.117)°C
3. 0.234 kJ/kg · °C
5. 1.78×10^4 kg
7. 29.6°C
9. (a) 0.435 cal/g · °C (b) We cannot make a definite identification. The material might be an unknown alloy or a material not listed in the table. It might be beryllium.
11. 23.6°C
13. 1.22×10^5 J
15. 0.294 g
17. 0.414 kg
19. (a) 0°C (b) 114 g
21. −1.18 MJ

23. −466 J

25. (a) $-4P_iV_i$ (b) It is proportional to the square of the volume, according to $T = (P_i/nRV_i)V^2$.

27. $Q = -720$ J

29.

	Q	W	ΔE_{int}
BC	−	0	−
CA	−	+	−
AB	+	−	+

31. (a) 7.50 kJ (b) 900 K

33. −3.10 kJ, 37.6 kJ

35. (a) 0.041 0 m^3 (b) +5.48 kJ (c) −5.48 kJ

37. 10.0 kW

39. 51.2°C

41. 74.8 kJ

43. (a) 0.964 kg or more (b) The test samples and the inner surface of the insulation can be prewarmed to 37.0°C as the box is assembled. Then nothing changes in temperature during the test period, and the masses of the test samples and insulation make no difference.

45. 3.49×10^3 K

47. Intensity is defined as power per area perpendicular to the direction of energy flow. The direction of sunlight is along the line from the Sun to the object. The perpendicular area is the projected flat, circular area enclosed by the *terminator,* the line that separates day and night on the object. The object radiates infrared light outward in all directions. The area perpendicular to this energy flow is its spherical surface area. The steady-state surface temperature is 279 K = 6°C. We find this temperature to be chilly, well below comfortable room temperatures.

49. 2.27 km

51. (a) 16.8 L (b) 0.351 L/s

53. $c = \mathcal{P}/\rho R \Delta T$

55. 5.87×10^4°C

57. 5.31 h

59. 1.44 kg

61. 38.6 m^3/d

63. 9.32 kW

65. (a) The equation $dT/dr = \mathcal{P}/4\pi kr^2$ represents the law of thermal conduction, incorporating the definition of thermal conductivity, applied to a spherical surface within the shell. The rate of energy transfer $\mathcal{P}$ must be the same for all radii so that each bit of material stays at a temperature that is constant in time. (b) We separate the variables T and r in the thermal conduction equation and integrate the equation between points on the interior and exterior surfaces. (c) 18.5 W (d) With $\mathcal{P}$ now known, we separate the variables again and integrate between a point on the interior surface and any point within the shell. (e) $T = 5°\text{C} + 184 \text{ cm} \cdot °\text{C}\,[1/(3 \text{ cm}) - 1/r]$ (f) 29.5°C

CHAPTER 21

1. (a) 4.00 u = 6.64×10^{-24} g (b) 55.9 u = 9.28×10^{-23} g (c) 207 u = 3.44×10^{-22} g

3. 0.943 N, 1.57 Pa

5. 3.21×10^{12} molecules

7. 3.32 mol

9. (a) 3.54×10^{23} atoms (b) 6.07×10^{-21} J (c) 1.35 km/s

11. (a) 8.76×10^{-21} J for both (b) 1.62 km/s for helium and 514 m/s for argon

13. (a) 3.46 kJ (b) 2.45 kJ (c) −1.01 kJ

15. Between 10^{-2}°C and 10^{-3}°C

17. $13.5PV$

19. (a) 1.39 atm (b) 366 K, 253 K (c) 0, −4.66 kJ, −4.66 kJ

21. 227 K

23. (a)

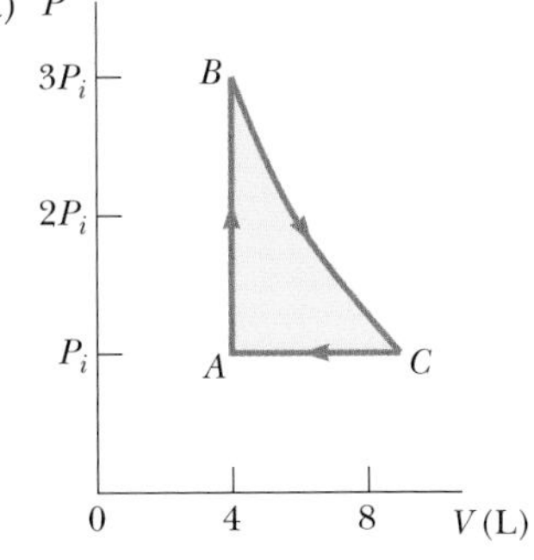

(b) 8.77 L (c) 900 K (d) 300 K (e) −336 J

25. (a) 28.0 kJ (b) 46.0 kJ (c) isothermal process: $P_f = 10.0$ atm; adiabatic process: $P_f = 25.1$ atm

27. (a) 9.95 cal/K, 13.9 cal/K (b) 13.9 cal/K, 17.9 cal/K

29. Sulfur dioxide is the gas in Table 21.2 with the greatest molecular mass. If the effective spring constants for various chemical bonds are comparable, SO_2 can then be expected to have low frequencies of atomic vibration. Vibration can be excited at lower temperature for sulfur dioxide than for the other gases. Some vibration may be going on at 300 K.

31. (a) 6.80 m/s (b) 7.41 m/s (c) 7.00 m/s

35. (a) 2.37×10^4 K (b) 1.06×10^3 K

37. (b) 0.278

39. (a) 100 kPa, 66.5 L, 400 K, 5.82 kJ, 7.48 kJ, −1.66 kJ
(b) 133 kPa, 49.9 L, 400 K, 5.82 kJ, 5.82 kJ, 0
(c) 120 kPa, 41.6 L, 300 K, 0, −909 J, +909 J
(d) 120 kPa, 43.3 L, 312 K, 722 J, 0, +722 J

41. (b) 447 J/kg·°C agrees with the tabulated value within 0.3%. (c) 127 J/kg·°C agrees with the tabulated value within 2%.

43. (b) The expressions are equal because $PV = nRT$ and $\gamma = (C_V + R)/C_V = 1 + R/C_V$ give $R = (\gamma - 1)C_V$, so $PV = n(\gamma - 1)C_VT$ and $PV/(\gamma - 1) = nC_VT$

45. 510 K and 290 K

47. 0.623

49. (a) Pressure increases as volume decreases.
(d) 0.500 atm^{-1}, 0.300 atm^{-1}

51. (a) 7.27×10^{-20} J (b) 2.20 km/s (c) 3 510 K. The evaporating molecules are exceptional, at the high-speed tail of the distribution of molecular speeds. The average speed of molecules in the liquid and in the vapor is appropriate only to room temperature.

53. (a) 0.514 m^3 (b) 2.06 m^3 (c) 2.38×10^3 K (d) −480 kJ (e) 2.28 MJ

55. 1.09×10^{-3}, 2.69×10^{-2}, 0.529, 1.00, 0.199, 1.01×10^{-41}, $1.25 \times 10^{-1\,082}$

59. (a) 0.203 mol (b) $T_B = T_C = 900$ K, $V_C = 15.0$ L

(c, d)	P, atm	V, L	T, K	E_{int}, kJ
A	1.00	5.00	300	0.760
B	3.00	5.00	900	2.28
C	1.00	15.0	900	2.28
A	1.00	5.00	300	0.760

(e) Lock the piston in place and put the cylinder into an oven at 900 K. Keep the gas in the oven while gradually letting the gas expand to lift a load on the piston as far as it can. Move the cylinder from the oven back to the 300-K room and let the gas cool and contract.

(f, g)	Q, kJ	W, kJ	ΔE_{int}, kJ
AB	1.52	0	1.52
BC	1.67	−1.67	0
CA	−2.53	+1.01	−1.52
$ABCA$	0.656	−0.656	0

61. (b) 1.60×10^4 K

CHAPTER 22

1. (a) 6.94% (b) 335 J
3. (a) 10.7 kJ (b) 0.533 s
5. 55.4%
7. 77.8 W
9. (a) 67.2% (b) 58.8 kW
11. The actual efficiency of 0.069 8 is less than four-tenths of the Carnot efficiency of 0.177.
13. (a) 741 J (b) 459 J
15. (a) 564 K (b) 212 kW (c) 47.5%
17. (b) $1 - T_c/T_h$, the same as for a single reversible engine (c) $(T_c + T_h)/2$ (d) $(T_hT_c)^{1/2}$
19. 9.00
23. 72.2 J
25. 23.1 mW
27. (a) 244 kPa (b) 192 J
29. (a) 51.2% (b) 36.2%
33. 195 J/K
35. 1.02 kJ/K
37. ~ 10^0 W/K from metabolism; much more if you are using high-power electric appliances or an automobile
39. 5.76 J/K; the temperature is constant if the gas is ideal.
41. (a) 1 (b) 6
43. (a)

Result	Number of ways to draw
All R	1
2 R, 1 G	3
1 R, 2 G	3
All G	1

(b)

Result	Number of ways to draw
All R	1
4R, 1G	5
3R, 2G	10
2R, 3G	10
1R, 4G	5
All G	1

45. (a) 214 J, 64.3 J (b) −35.7 J, −35.7 J. The net effect would be the transport of energy by heat from the cold to the hot reservoir without expenditure of external work. (c) 333 J, 233 J (d) 83.3 J, 83.3 J, 0. The net effect would be converting energy, taken in by heat, entirely into energy output by work in a cyclic process. (e) −0.111 J/K. The entropy of the Universe would have decreased.
47. (a) 5.00 kW (b) 763 W
49. (a) $2nRT_i \ln 2$ (b) 0.273
51. 5.97×10^4 kg/s
53. (a) 8.48 kW (b) 1.52 kW (c) 1.09×10^4 J/K (d) The COP drops by 20.0%.
55. (a) $10.5nRT_i$ (b) $8.50nRT_i$ (c) 0.190 (d) This efficiency is much less than the 0.833 for a Carnot engine operating between the temperatures used here.
57. (a) $nC_P \ln 3$ (b) Both ask for the change in entropy between the same two states of the same system. Entropy is a state variable. The change in entropy does not depend on path, but only on original and final states.
61. (a) 20.0°C (c) $\Delta S = +4.88$ J/K (d) The mixing is irreversible. It is clear that warm water and cool water do not come unmixed, and the entropy change is positive.

CHAPTER 23

1. (a) +160 zC, 1.01 u (b) +160 zC, 23.0 u (c) −160 zC, 35.5 u (d) +320 zC, 40.1 u (e) −480 zC, 14.0 u (f) +640 zC, 14.0 u (g) +1.12 aC, 14.0 u (h) −160 zC, 18.0 u
3. The force is ~ 10^{26} N.
5. (a) 1.59 nN away from the other (b) 1.24×10^{36} times larger (c) 8.61×10^{-11} C/kg
7. 0.872 N at 330°
9. (a) 2.16×10^{-5} N toward the other (b) 8.99×10^{-7} N away from the other
11. (a) 82.2 nN toward the other particle (b) 2.19 Mm/s
13. (a) 55.8 pN/C down (b) 102 nN/C up
15. The field at the origin can be to the right if the unknown charge is $-9Q$, or the field can be to the left if and only if the unknown charge is $+27Q$.
17. (a) $5.91k_eq/a^2$ at 58.8° (b) $5.91k_eq^2/a^2$ at 58.8°
19. (a) $k_eQx\hat{\mathbf{i}}/(R^2 + x^2)^{3/2}$ (b) As long as the charge is symmetrically placed, the number of charges does not matter. A continuous ring corresponds to n becoming larger without limit.
21. 1.59×10^6 N/C toward the rod
23. (a) $6.64\hat{\mathbf{i}}$ MN/C (b) $24.1\hat{\mathbf{i}}$ MN/C (c) $6.40\hat{\mathbf{i}}$ MN/C (d) $0.664\hat{\mathbf{i}}$ MN/C, taking the axis of the ring as the x axis
25. (a) 93.6 MN/C; the near-field approximation is 104 MN/C, about 11% high. (b) 0.516 MN/C; the charged-particle approximation is 0.519 MN/C, about 0.6% high.
27. $-21.6\hat{\mathbf{i}}$ MN/C
31. (a) 86.4 pC for each (b) 324 pC, 459 pC, 459 pC, 432 pC (c) 57.6 pC, 106 pC, 154 pC, 96.0 pC
33.

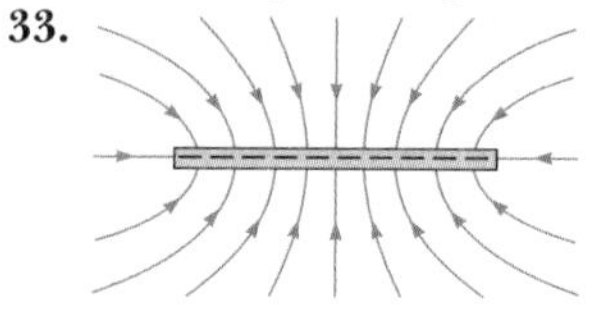

35. (a) The field is zero at the center of the triangle. (b) $1.73\, k_eq\hat{\mathbf{j}}/a^2$
37. (a) 61.3 Gm/s² (b) 19.5 μs (c) 11.7 m (d) 1.20 fJ
39. K/ed in the direction of motion
41. (a) 111 ns (b) 5.68 mm (c) $(450\hat{\mathbf{i}} + 102\hat{\mathbf{j}})$ km/s

43. (a) 21.8 μm (b) 2.43 cm
45. (a) 10.9 nC (b) 5.44 mN
47. 40.9 N at 263°
49. $Q = 2L\sqrt{\frac{k(L - L_i)}{k_e}}$
53. $-707\hat{\mathbf{j}}$ mN
55. (a) $\theta_1 = \theta_2$
57. (a) 0.307 s (b) Yes. Ignoring gravity makes a difference of 2.28%.
59. (a) $\vec{\mathbf{F}} = 1.90(k_e q^2/s^2)(\hat{\mathbf{i}} + \hat{\mathbf{j}} + \hat{\mathbf{k}})$ (b) $\vec{\mathbf{F}} = 3.29(k_e q^2/s^2)$ in the direction away from the diagonally opposite vertex
65. $\frac{k_e \lambda_0}{2x_0}(-\hat{\mathbf{i}})$

CHAPTER 24

1. 4.14 MN/C
3. (a) aA (b) bA (c) 0
5. 1.87 kN · m²/C
7. (a) −6.89 MN · m²/C (b) The number of lines entering exceeds the number leaving by 2.91 times or more.
9. $-Q/\epsilon_0$ for S_1; 0 for S_2; $-2Q/\epsilon_0$ for S_3; 0 for S_4
11. (a) $+Q/2\epsilon_0$ (b) $-Q/2\epsilon_0$
13. −18.8 kN · m²/C
15. 0 if $R \le d$; $(2\lambda/\epsilon_0)\sqrt{R^2 - d^2}$ if $R > d$
17. (a) 3.20 MN · m²/C (b) 19.2 MN · m²/C (c) The answer to part (a) could change, but the answer to part (b) would stay the same.
19. 2.33×10^{21} N/C
21. 508 kN/C up
23. −2.48 μC/m²
25. 5.94×10^5 m/s
27. $\vec{\mathbf{E}} = \rho r/2\epsilon_0$ away from the axis
29. (a) 0 (b) 7.19 MN/C away from the center
31. (a) 51.4 kN/C outward (b) 646 N · m²/C
33. (a) 0 (b) 5 400 N/C outward (c) 540 N/C outward
35. (a) +708 nC/m² and −708 nC/m² (b) +177 nC and −177 nC
37. 2.00 N
39. (a) $-\lambda, +3\lambda$ (b) $3\lambda/2\pi\epsilon_0 r$ radially outward
41. (a) 80.0 nC/m² on each face (b) $9.04\hat{\mathbf{k}}$ kN/C (c) $-9.04\hat{\mathbf{k}}$ kN/C
43. (b) $Q/2\epsilon_0$ (c) Q/ϵ_0
45. (a) The charge on the exterior surface is −55.7 nC distributed uniformly. (b) The charge on the interior surface is +55.7 nC. It might have any distribution. (c) The charge within the shell is −55.7 nC. It might have any distribution.
47. (a) $\rho r/3\epsilon_0$, $Q/4\pi\epsilon_0 r^2$, 0, $Q/4\pi\epsilon_0 r^2$, all radially outward (b) $-Q/4\pi b^2$ and $+Q/4\pi c^2$
49. $\theta = \tan^{-1}[qQ/(2\pi\epsilon_0 dmv^2)]$
51. (a) σ/ϵ_0 away from both plates (b) 0 (c) σ/ϵ_0 away from both plates
53. $\sigma/2\epsilon_0$ radially outward
57. $\vec{\mathbf{E}} = a/2\epsilon_0$ radially outward
61. (b) $\vec{\mathbf{g}} = GM_E r/R_E{}^3$ radially inward
63. (a) −4.00 nC (b) +9.56 nC (c) +4.00 nC and +5.56 nC
65. (a) If the volume charge density is nonzero, the field cannot be uniform in magnitude. (b) The field must be uniform in magnitude along any line in the direction of the field. The field magnitude can vary between points in a plane perpendicular to the field lines.

CHAPTER 25

1. (a) 152 km/s (b) 6.49 Mm/s
3. 1.67 MN/C
5. 38.9 V; the origin
7. (a) $2QE/k$ (b) QE/k (c) $2\pi\sqrt{m/k}$ (d) $2(QE - \mu_k mg)/k$
9. (a) 0.400 m/s (b) It is the same. Each bit of the rod feels a force of the same size as before.
11. (a) 1.44×10^{-7} V (b) -7.19×10^{-8} V (c) -1.44×10^{-7} V, $+7.19 \times 10^{-8}$ V
13. (a) 6.00 m (b) −2.00 μC
15. −11.0 MV
17. 8.95 J
21. (a) no point at a finite distance from the particles (b) $2k_e q/a$
23. (a) 10.8 m/s and 1.55 m/s (b) Greater. The conducting spheres will polarize each other, with most of the positive charge of one and of the negative charge of the other on their inside faces. Immediately before they collide, their centers of charge will be closer than their geometric centers, so they will have less electric potential energy and more kinetic energy.
25. $5k_e q^2/9d$
27. $\left[\left(1 + \sqrt{\tfrac{1}{8}}\right)\frac{k_e q^2}{mL}\right]^{1/2}$
29. (a) 10.0 V, −11.0 V, −32.0 V (b) 7.00 N/C in the +x direction
31. $\vec{\mathbf{E}} = (-5 + 6xy)\hat{\mathbf{i}} + (3x^2 - 2z^2)\hat{\mathbf{j}} - 4yz\hat{\mathbf{k}}$; 7.07 N/C
33. $E_y = \frac{k_e Q}{y\sqrt{\ell^2 + y^2}}$
35. (a) C/m² (b) $k_e\alpha[L - d\ln(1 + L/d)]$
37. −1.51 MV
39. (a) 0, 1.67 MV (b) 5.84 MN/C away, 1.17 MV (c) 11.9 MN/C away, 1.67 MV
41. (a) 248 nC/m² (b) 496 nC/m²
43. (a) 450 kV (b) 7.51 μC
45. (a) 1.42 mm (b) 9.20 kV/m
47. 253 MeV
49. (a) −27.2 eV (b) −6.80 eV (c) 0
51. (a) Yes. The inverse proportionality of potential to radius is sufficient to show that $200R = 150(R + 10\text{ cm})$, so $R = 30.0$ cm. Then $Q = 6.67$ nC. (b) Almost but not quite. Two possibilities exist: $R = 29.1$ cm with $Q = 6.79$ nC and $R = 3.44$ cm with $Q = 804$ pC.
53. 4.00 nC at (−1.00 m, 0) and −5.01 nC at (0, 2.00 m)
55. $k_e Q^2/2R$
57. $V_2 - V_1 = (-\lambda/2\pi\epsilon_0)\ln(r_2/r_1)$
61. (b) $E_r = 2k_e p\cos\theta/r^3$; $E_\theta = k_e p\sin\theta/r^3$; yes; no (c) $V = k_e py(x^2 + y^2)^{-3/2}$; $\vec{\mathbf{E}} = 3k_e pxy(x^2 + y^2)^{-5/2}\hat{\mathbf{i}} + k_e p(2y^2 - x^2)(x^2 + y^2)^{-5/2}\hat{\mathbf{j}}$
63. $V = \pi k_e C\left[R\sqrt{x^2 + R^2} + x^2\ln\left(\frac{x}{R + \sqrt{x^2 + R^2}}\right)\right]$
65. (a) 488 V (b) 78.1 aJ (c) 306 km/s (d) 390 Gm/s² toward the negative plate (e) 651 aN toward the negative plate (f) 4.07 kN/C
67. Outside the sphere, $E_x = 3E_0 a^3 xz(x^2 + y^2 + z^2)^{-5/2}$, $E_y = 3E_0 a^3 yz(x^2 + y^2 + z^2)^{-5/2}$, and $E_z = E_0 + E_0 a^3(2z^2 - x^2 - y^2)(x^2 + y^2 + z^2)^{-5/2}$. Inside the sphere, $E_x = E_y = E_z = 0$.

CHAPTER 26

1. (a) 48.0 μC (b) 6.00 μC
3. (a) 1.33 μC/m^2 (b) 13.3 pF
5. (a) 11.1 kV/m toward the negative plate (b) 98.3 nC/m^2 (c) 3.74 pF (d) 74.7 pC
7. 4.42 μm
9. (a) 2.68 nF (b) 3.02 kV
11. (a) 15.6 pF (b) 256 kV
13. (a) 3.53 μF (b) 6.35 V and 2.65 V (c) 31.8 μC on each
15. 6.00 pF and 3.00 pF
17. (a) 5.96 μF (b) 89.5 μC on 20 μF, 63.2 μC on 6 μF, 26.3 μC on 15 μF and on 3 μF
19. 120 μC; 80.0 μC and 40.0 μC
21. ten
23. 6.04 μF
25. 12.9 μF
27. (a) 216 μJ (b) 54.0 μJ
31. (a) 1.50 μC (b) 1.83 kV
35. 9.79 kg
37. (a) 81.3 pF (b) 2.40 kV
39. 1.04 m
41. 22.5 V
43. (b) -8.78×10^6 N/C·m; $-5.53 \times 10^{-2}\hat{\mathbf{i}}$ N
45. 19.0 kV
47. (a) 11.2 pF (b) 134 pC (c) 16.7 pF (d) 66.9 pC
49. (a) 40.0 μJ (b) 500 V
51. 0.188 m^2
55. Gasoline has 194 times the specific energy content of the battery and 727 000 times that of the capacitor.
57. (a) $Q_0^2 d(\ell - x)/(2\ell^3 \epsilon_0)$ (b) $Q_0^2 d/(2\ell^3\epsilon_0)$ to the right (c) $Q_0^2/(2\ell^4\epsilon_0)$ (d) $Q_0^2/(2\ell^4\epsilon_0)$; they are precisely the same.
59. 4.29 μF
61. (a) The additional energy comes from work done by the electric field in the wires as it forces more charge onto the already-charged plates. (b) The charge increases according to $Q/Q_0 = \kappa$.
63. 750 μC on C_1 and 250 μC on C_2
65. $\frac{4}{3}C$

CHAPTER 27

1. 7.50×10^{15} electrons
3. (a) $0.632 I_0\tau$ (b) $0.999\ 95 I_0\tau$ (c) $I_0\tau$
5. (a) 17.0 A (b) 85.0 kA/m^2
7. (a) 2.55 A/m^2 (b) 5.31×10^{10} m^{-3} (c) 1.20×10^{10} s
9. (a) 221 nm (b) No. The deuterons are so far apart that one does not produce a significant potential at the location of the next.
11. 6.43 A
13. (a) 1.82 m (b) 280 μm
15. $6.00 \times 10^{-15}/\Omega \cdot$m
17. 0.180 V/m
19. (a) 31.5 n$\Omega \cdot$m (b) 6.35 MA/m^2 (c) 49.9 mA (d) 659 μm/s (e) 0.400 V
21. 0.125
23. 5.00 A, 24.0 Ω
25. 5.49 Ω
27. 36.1%
29. (a) 3.17 m (b) 340 W
31. (a) 0.660 kWh (b) $0.039 6
33. $0.232
35. $0.269/day
37. (a) 184 W (b) 461°C
39. ~ $1
41. Any diameter d and length ℓ related by $d^2 = (4.77 \times 10^{-8}\text{ m})\ell$, such as length 0.900 m and diameter 0.207 mm. Yes.
45. Experimental resistivity = 1.47 $\mu\Omega \cdot$m $\pm$4%, in agreement with 1.50 $\mu\Omega \cdot$m
47. (a) 8.00 V/m in the x direction (b) 0.637 Ω (c) 6.28 A (d) 200 MA/m^2 in the x direction
49. (a) 667 A (b) 50.0 km
51.

Material	$\alpha' = \alpha/(1 - 20\alpha)$
Silver	$4.1 \times 10^{-3}/°C$
Copper	$4.2 \times 10^{-3}/°C$
Gold	$3.6 \times 10^{-3}/°C$
Aluminum	$4.2 \times 10^{-3}/°C$
Tungsten	$4.9 \times 10^{-3}/°C$
Iron	$5.6 \times 10^{-3}/°C$
Platinum	$4.25 \times 10^{-3}/°C$
Lead	$4.2 \times 10^{-3}/°C$
Nichrome	$0.4 \times 10^{-3}/°C$
Carbon	$-0.5 \times 10^{-3}/°C$
Germanium	$-24 \times 10^{-3}/°C$
Silicon	$-30 \times 10^{-3}/°C$

53. It is exact. The resistance can be written $R = \rho L^2/V$ and the stretched length as $L = L_i(1 + \delta)$. Then the result follows directly.
55. (b) Charge is conducted by current in the direction of decreasing potential. Energy is conducted by heat in the direction of decreasing temperature.
59. Coat the surfaces of entry and exit with a material of much higher conductivity than the bulk material of the object. The electric potential will be essentially uniform over each of these electrodes. Current will be distributed over the whole area where each electrode is in contact with the resistive object.
61. (a) $\dfrac{\epsilon_0 \ell}{2d}(\ell + 2x + \kappa\ell - 2\kappa x)$

(b) $\dfrac{\epsilon_0 \ell v\,\Delta V(\kappa - 1)}{d}$ clockwise
63. 2.71 MΩ
65. 2 020°C

CHAPTER 28

1. (a) 6.73 Ω (b) 1.97 Ω
3. (a) 12.4 V (b) 9.65 V
5. (a) 17.1 Ω (b) 1.99 A for 4 Ω and 9 Ω, 1.17 A for 7 Ω, 0.818 A for 10 Ω
7. (a) 227 mA (b) 5.68 V
9. (a) 75.0 V (b) 25.0 W, 6.25 W, and 6.25 W; 37.5 W
11. $R_1 = 1.00$ kΩ, $R_2 = 2.00$ kΩ, $R_3 = 3.00$ kΩ
13. It decreases. Closing the switch opens a new path with resistance of only 20 Ω. $R = 14.0\ \Omega$
15. 14.2 W to 2 Ω, 28.4 W to 4 Ω, 1.33 W to 3 Ω, 4.00 W to 1 Ω
17. 846 mA down in the 8-Ω resistor; 462 mA down in the middle branch; 1.31 A up in the right-hand branch
19. (a) -222 J and 1.88 kJ (b) 687 J, 128 J, 25.6 J, 616 J, 205 J (c) 1.66 kJ of chemical energy is transformed into internal energy.

21. 0.395 A and 1.50 V

23. 1.00 A up in 200 Ω, 4.00 A up in 70 Ω, 3.00 A up in 80 Ω, 8.00 A down in 20 Ω, 200 V

25. (a) 909 mA (b) −1.82 V = $V_b - V_a$

27. (a) 5.00 s (b) 150 μC (c) 4.06 μA

29. (a) −61.6 mA (b) 0.235 μC (c) 1.96 A

31. (a) 6.00 V (b) 8.29 μs

33. 0.302 Ω

35. 16.6 kΩ

37. (a) 12.5 A, 6.25 A, 8.33 A (b) No. Together they would require 27.1 A.

39. (a) 1.02 A down (b) 0.364 A down (c) 1.38 A up (d) 0 (e) 66.0 μC

41. 2.22 h

43. *a* is 4.00 V higher

45. 87.3 %

47. 6.00 Ω, 3.00 Ω

49. (a) $I_1 = \dfrac{IR_2}{R_1 + R_2}$, $I_2 = \dfrac{IR_1}{R_1 + R_2}$

51. (a) $R \le 1\,050\ \Omega$ (b) $R \ge 10.0\ \Omega$

53. (a) 9.93 μC (b) 33.7 nA (c) 334 nW (d) 337 nW

55. (a) 40.0 W (b) 80.0 V, 40.0 V, 40.0 V

57. (a) 9.30 V, 2.51 Ω (b) 186 V and 3.70 A (c) 1.09 A (d) 143 W (e) 0.162 Ω (f) 3.00 mW (g) 2.21 W (h) The power output of the emf depends on the resistance connected to it. A question about "the rest of the power" is not meaningful when it compares circuits with different currents. The net emf produces more current in the circuit where the copper wire is used. The net emf delivers more power when the copper wire is used, 687 W rather than 203 W without the wire. Nearly all this power results in extra internal energy in the internal resistance of the batteries, which rapidly rise to a high temperature. The circuit with the copper wire is unsafe because the batteries overheat. The circuit without the copper wire is unsafe because it delivers an electric shock to the experimenter.

61. (a) 0 in 3 kΩ and 333 μA in 12 kΩ and 15 kΩ (b) 50.0 μC (c) $(278\ \mu\text{A})e^{-t/180\text{ ms}}$ (d) 290 ms

63. (a) $R_x = R_2 - R_1/4$ (b) $R_x = 2.75\ \Omega$. The station is inadequately grounded.

65. (a) $2\Delta t/3$ (b) $3\Delta t$

CHAPTER 29

1. (a) up (b) toward you, out of the plane of the paper (c) no deflection (d) into the plane of the paper

3. $(-20.9\hat{\mathbf{j}})$ mT

5. 48.9° or 131°

7. 2.34 aN

9. (a) 49.6 aN south (b) 1.29 km

11. $r_\alpha = r_d = \sqrt{2}r_p$

13. (a) 5.00 cm (b) 8.78×10^6 m/s

15. 7.88 pT

17. 244 kV/m

19. 0.278 m

21. (a) 4.31×10^7 rad/s (b) 51.7 Mm/s

23. 70.1 mT

25. 0.245 T east

27. (a) 4.73 N (b) 5.46 N (c) 4.73 N

29. 1.07 m/s

31. $2\pi rIB \sin\theta$ up

33. 2.98 μN west

35. 9.98 N · m clockwise as seen looking down from above

37. (a) Minimum: pointing north at 48.0° below the horizontal; maximum: pointing south at 48.0° above the horizontal. (b) 1.07 μJ

39. The magnetic moment cannot go to infinity. Its maximum value is 5.37 mA · m² for a single-turn circle. Smaller by 21% and by 40% are the magnetic moments for the single-turn square and triangle. Circular coils with several turns have magnetic moments inversely proportional to the number of turns, approaching zero as the number of turns goes to infinity.

41. 43.1 μT

43. (a) The electric current experiences a magnetic force. (c) no, no, no

45. 12.5 km. It will not hit the Earth, but it will perform a hairpin turn and go back parallel to its original direction.

47. (a) -8.00×10^{-21} kg · m/s (b) 8.90°

49. (a) $(3.52\hat{\mathbf{i}} - 1.60\hat{\mathbf{j}})$ aN (b) 24.4°

51. 128 mT north at an angle of 78.7° below the horizontal

53. 0.588 T

55. 0.713 A counterclockwise as seen from above

57. 2.75 Mrad/s

59. 3.70×10^{-24} N · m

61. (a) 1.33 m/s (b) Positive ions moving toward you in magnetic field to the right feel upward magnetic force and migrate upward in the blood vessel. Negative ions moving toward you feel downward magnetic force and accumulate at the bottom of this section of vessel. Therefore, both species can participate in the generation of the emf.

63. (a) $v = qBh/m$. If its speed is slightly less than the critical value, the particle moves in a semicircle of radius h and leaves the field with velocity $-v\hat{\mathbf{j}}$. If its speed is incrementally greater, the particle moves in a quarter circle of the same radius and moves along the boundary outside the field with velocity $v\hat{\mathbf{i}}$. (b) The particle moves in a smaller semicircle of radius mv/qB, attaining final velocity $-v\hat{\mathbf{j}}$. (c) The particle moves in a circular arc of radius $r = mv/qB$, leaving the field with velocity $v\sin\theta\,\hat{\mathbf{i}} + v\cos\theta\,\hat{\mathbf{j}}$, where $\theta = \sin^{-1}(h/r)$.

65. (a) For small angular displacements, the torque on the dipole is equal to a negative constant times the displacement.

(b) $f = \dfrac{1}{2\pi}\sqrt{\dfrac{\mu B}{I}}$

(c) The equilibrium orientation of the needle shows the direction of the field. In a stronger field, the frequency is higher. The frequency is easy to measure precisely over a wide range of values. 2.04 mT.

CHAPTER 30

1. 12.5 T

3. (a) 28.3 μT into the paper (b) 24.7 μT into the paper

5. $\dfrac{\mu_0 I}{4\pi x}$ into the paper

7. (a) $2I_1$ out of the page (b) $6I_1$ into the page

9. (a) along the line ($y = -0.420$ m, $z = 0$) (b) $(-34.7\hat{\mathbf{j}})$ mN (c) $(17.3\hat{\mathbf{j}})$ kN/C

11. at *A*, 53.3 μT toward the bottom of the page; at *B*, 20.0 μT toward the bottom of the page; at *C*, zero.

13. (a) $4.5\dfrac{\mu_0 I}{\pi L}$

(b) Stronger. Each of the two sides meeting at the nearby vertex contributes more than twice as much to the net field at the new point.

15. $(-13.0\hat{\mathbf{j}})\ \mu\text{T}$

17. $(-27.0\hat{\mathbf{i}})\ \mu\text{N}$

19. parallel to the wires and 0.167 m below the upper wire

21. (a) opposite directions (b) 67.8 A (c) Smaller. A smaller gravitational force would be pulling down on the wires, therefore tending to reduce the angle.

23. 20.0 μT toward the bottom of the page

25. at *a*, 200 μT toward the top of the page; at *b*, 133 μT toward the bottom of the page

27. (a) 6.34 mN/m inward (b) Greater. The magnetic field increases toward the outside of the bundle, where more net current lies inside a particular radius. The larger field exerts a stronger force on the strand we choose to monitor.

29. (a) 0

(b) $\dfrac{\mu_0 I}{2\pi R}$ tangent to the wall in a counterclockwise sense

(c) $\dfrac{\mu_0 I^2}{(2\pi R)^2}$ inward

31. (a) $\mu_0 b r_1{}^2/3$ (b) $\mu_0 b R^3/3r_2$

35. 31.8 mA

37. 226 μN away from the center of the loop, 0

39. (a) 3.13 mWb (b) 0

41. (a) 7.40 μWb (b) 2.27 μWb

43. 2.02

45. (a) 8.63×10^{45} electrons (b) 4.01×10^{20} kg

47. $\dfrac{\mu_0 I}{2\pi w} \ln\left(1 + \dfrac{w}{b}\right)\hat{\mathbf{k}}$

49. $(-12.0\hat{\mathbf{k}})$ mN

51. 143 pT

57. (a) 2.46 N upward (b) The magnetic field at the center of the loop or on its axis is much weaker than the magnetic field immediately outside the wire. The wire has negligible curvature on the scale of 1 mm, so we model the lower loop as a long, straight wire to find the field it creates at the location of the upper wire. (c) 107 m/s^2 upward

59. (a) 274 μT (b) $(-274\hat{\mathbf{j}})\ \mu\text{T}$ (c) $(1.15\hat{\mathbf{i}})$ mN (d) $(0.384\hat{\mathbf{i}})\ \text{m/s}^2$ (e) acceleration is constant (f) $(0.999\hat{\mathbf{i}})$ m/s

61. $\dfrac{\mu_0 I_1 I_2 L}{\pi R}$ to the right

65. $\frac{1}{3}\rho\mu_0\omega R^2$

67. (a) $\dfrac{\mu_0 I(2r^2 - a^2)}{\pi r(4r^2 - a^2)}$ to the left

(b) $\dfrac{\mu_0 I(2r^2 + a^2)}{\pi r(4r^2 + a^2)}$ toward the top of the page

CHAPTER 31

1. (a) 101 μV tending to produce clockwise current as seen from above (b) It is twice as large in magnitude and in the opposite sense.

3. 9.82 mV

5. (b) 3.79 mV (c) 28.0 mV

7. 160 A

9. (a) 1.60 A counterclockwise (b) 20.1 μT (c) left

11. $-(14.2\ \text{mV})\cos(120t)$

13. 283 μA upward

15. $(68.2\ \text{mV})e^{-1.6t}$, tending to produce counterclockwise current

17. 272 m

19. 13.3 mA counterclockwise in the lower loop and clockwise in the upper loop

21. (a) 1.18 mV. The wingtip on the pilot's left is positive. (b) no change (c) No. If we try to connect the wings into a circuit with the lightbulb, we run an extra insulated wire along the wing. In a uniform field, the total emf generated in the one-turn coil is zero.

23. (a) 3.00 N to the right (b) 6.00 W

25. 24.1 V with the outer contact positive

27. 2.83 mV

29. (a) $F = N^2B^2w^2v/R$ to the left (b) 0 (c) $F = N^2B^2w^2v/R$ to the left

31. 145 μA upward in the picture

33. 1.80 mN/C upward and to the left, perpendicular to r_1

35. (a) 7.54 kV (b) The plane of the loop is parallel to $\vec{\mathbf{B}}$.

37. $(28.6\ \text{mV})\sin(4\pi t)$

39. (a) 110 V (b) 8.53 W (c) 1.22 kW

41. Both are correct. The current in the magnet creates an upward magnetic field, so the N and S poles on the solenoid core are shown correctly. On the rail in front of the brake, the upward magnetic flux increases as the coil approaches, so a current is induced here to create downward magnetic field. This current is clockwise, so the S pole on the rail is shown correctly. On the rail behind the brake, the upward magnetic flux is decreasing. The induced current in the rail will produce upward magnetic field by being counterclockwise as the picture correctly shows.

43. (b) Larger *R* makes current smaller, so the loop must travel faster to maintain equality of magnetic force and weight. (c) The magnetic force is proportional to the product of field and current, while the current is itself proportional to field. If *B* becomes two times smaller, the speed must become four times larger to compensate.

45. $-(7.22\ \text{mV})\cos(2\pi\ 523t/\text{s})$

47.

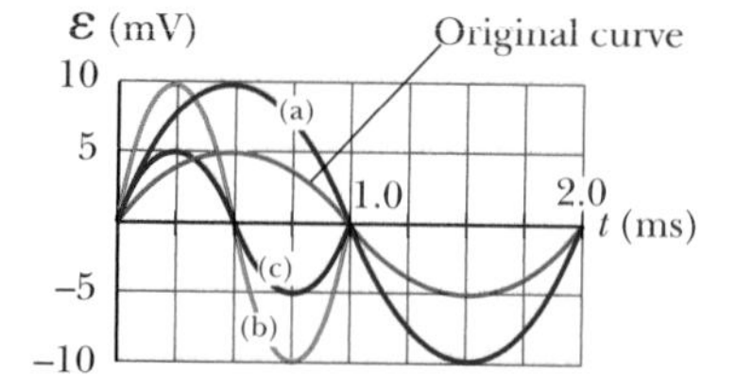

(a) Doubling *N* doubles amplitude. (b) Doubling ω doubles the amplitude and halves the period. (c) Doubling ω and halving *N* leaves the amplitude the same and cuts the period in half.

49. (a) 3.50 A up in 2 Ω, and 1.40 A up in 5 Ω (b) 34.3 W (c) 4.29 N

51. ~10^{-4} V, by reversing a 20-turn coil of diameter 3 cm in 0.1 s in a field of 10^{-3} T

53. 1.20 μC

55. (a) 0.900 A from b toward a (b) 0.108 N (c) b (d) No. Instead of decreasing downward magnetic flux to induce clockwise current, the new loop will see increasing downward flux to cause counterclockwise current, but the current in the resistor is still from b to a.

57. (a) $C\pi a^2 K$ (b) the upper plate (c) The changing magnetic field within the loop induces an electric field around the circumference, which pushes on charged particles in the wire.

59. (a) 36.0 V (b) 600 mWb/s (c) 35.9 V (d) 4.32 N · m

63. 6.00 A

67. $(-87.1 \text{ mV}) \cos(200\pi t + \phi)$

CHAPTER 32

1. 100 V

3. $-(18.8 \text{ V}) \cos(377t)$

5. -0.421 A/s

7. (a) 188 μT (b) 33.3 nT · m^2 (c) 0.375 mH (d) B and Φ_B are proportional to current; L is independent of current

9. $\mathcal{E}_0/k^2L$

11. (a) 0.139 s (b) 0.461 s

13. (a) 2.00 ms (b) 0.176 A (c) 1.50 A (d) 3.22 ms

15. (a) 0.800 (b) 0

17. (a) 6.67 A/s (b) 0.332 A/s

19. (a) 1.00 kΩ (b) 3.00 ms

21. (a) 5.66 ms (b) 1.22 A (c) 58.1 ms

23. 2.44 μJ

25. 44.2 nJ/m^3 for the $\vec{\mathbf{E}}$ field and 995 μJ/m^3 for the $\vec{\mathbf{B}}$ field

27. (a) 66.0 W (b) 45.0 W (c) 21.0 W (d) At all instants after the connection is made, the battery power is equal to the sum of the power delivered to the resistor and the power delivered to the magnetic field. Immediately after $t = 0$, the resistor power is nearly zero and nearly all the battery power is going into the magnetic field. Long after the connection is made, the magnetic field is absorbing no more power and the battery power is going into the resistor.

29. $\dfrac{2\pi B_0^2 R^3}{\mu_0} = 2.70 \times 10^{18}$ J

31. 1.00 V

33. (a) 18.0 mH (b) 34.3 mH (c) -9.00 mV

35. $M = \dfrac{N_1 N_2 \pi \mu_0 R_1^2 R_2^2}{2(x^2 + R_1^2)^{3/2}}$

37. 400 mA

39. 281 mH

41. 608 pF

43. (a) 6.03 J (b) 0.529 J (c) 6.56 J

45. (a) 4.47 krad/s (b) 4.36 krad/s (c) 2.53%

47. (a) $0.693(2L/R)$ (b) $0.347(2L/R)$

49. (a) -20.0 mV (b) $-(10.0 \text{ MV/s}^2)t^2$ (c) 63.2 μs

51. $(Q/2N)(3L/C)^{1/2}$

53. (a) Immediately after the circuit is connected, the potential difference across the resistor is zero and the emf across the coil is 24.0 V. (b) After several seconds, the potential difference across the resistor is 24.0 V and that across the coil is 0. (c) The two voltages are equal to each other, both being 12.0 V, only once, at 0.578 ms after the circuit is connected. (d) As the current decays, the potential difference across the resistor is always equal to the emf across the coil.

55.

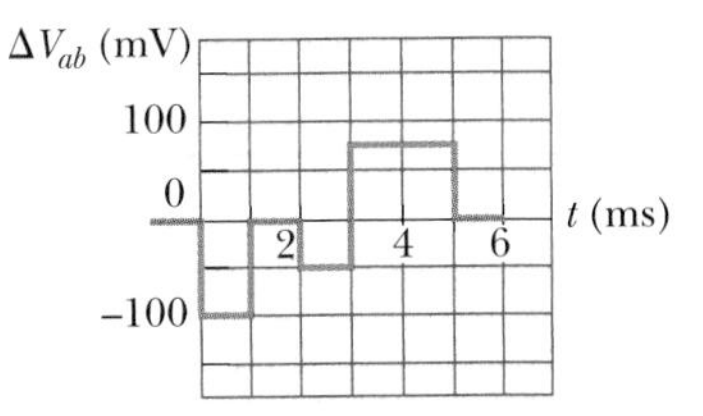

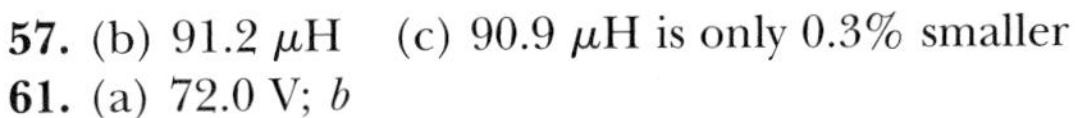

57. (b) 91.2 μH (c) 90.9 μH is only 0.3% smaller

61. (a) 72.0 V; b
(b)

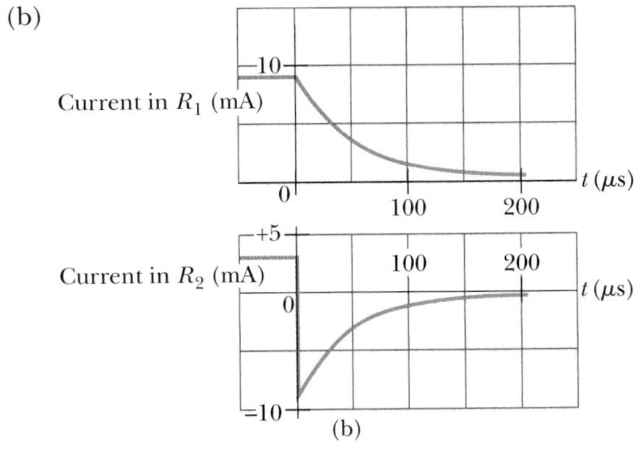

(c) 75.2 μs

63. 300 Ω

65. (a) 62.5 GJ (b) 2 000 N

67. (a) 2.93 mT up (b) 3.42 Pa (c) The supercurrents must be clockwise to produce a downward magnetic field that cancels the upward field of the current in the windings. (d) The field of the windings is upward and radially outward around the top of the solenoid. It exerts a force radially inward and upward on each bit of the clockwise supercurrent. The total force on the supercurrents in the bar is upward. (e) 1.30 mN

CHAPTER 33

1. $\Delta v(t) = (283 \text{ V}) \sin(628t)$

3. 2.95 A, 70.7 V

5. 14.6 Hz

7. (a) 42.4 mH (b) 942 rad/s

9. 5.60 A

11. 0.450 Wb

13. (a) 141 mA (b) 235 mA

15. 100 mA

17. (a) 194 V (b) current leads by 49.9°

19. (a) 78.5 Ω (b) 1.59 kΩ (c) 1.52 kΩ (d) 138 mA (e) $-84.3°$

21. (a) 17.4° (b) The voltage leads the current.

23. 1.88 V

25.

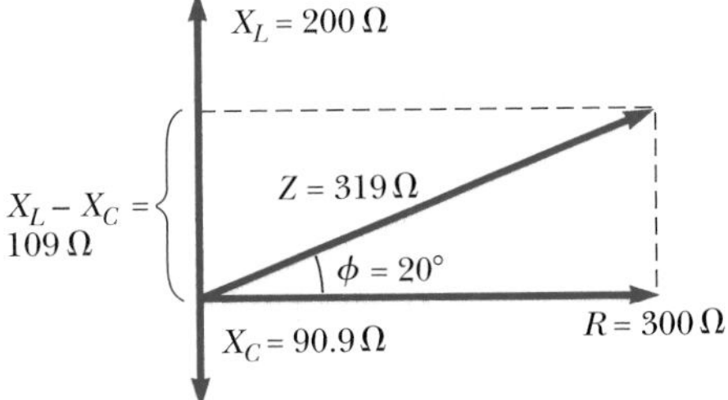

27. 8.00 W

29. (a) 16.0 Ω (b) -12.0 Ω

31. (a) 39.5 V · m/ΔV (b) The diameter is inversely proportional to the potential difference. (c) 26.3 mm (d) 13.2 kV

33. $11(\Delta V_{\text{rms}})^2/14R$
35. 1.82 pF
37. 242 mJ
39. 0.591 and 0.987; the circuit in Problem 21
41. 687 V
43. (a) 29.0 kW (b) 5.80×10^{-3} (c) If the generator were limited to 4 500 V, no more than 17.5 kW could be delivered to the load, never 5 000 kW.
45. (b) 0; 1 (c) $f_h = (10.88RC)^{-1}$
47. (a) 613 μF (b) 0.756
49. (a) 580 μH and 54.6 μF (b) 1 (c) 894 Hz (d) Δv_{out} leads Δv_{in} by 60.0° at 200 Hz. Δv_{out} and Δv_{in} are in phase at 894 Hz. Δv_{out} lags Δv_{in} by 60.0° at 4 000 Hz. (e) 1.56 W, 6.25 W, 1.56 W (f) 0.408
51. (a) X_C could be 53.8 Ω or it could be 1.35 kΩ. (b) X_C must be 53.8 Ω. (c) X_C must be 1.43 kΩ.
53. 56.7 W
55. Tension T and separation d must be related by $T = (274 \text{ N/m}^2)d^2$. One possibility is $T = 10.9$ N and $d = 0.200$ m.
57. (a) 225 mA (b) 450 mA
59. (a) 1.25 A (b) The current lags the voltage by 46.7°.
61. (a) 200 mA; voltage leads by 36.8° (b) 40.0 V; $\phi = 0°$ (c) 20.0 V; $\phi = -90.0°$ (d) 50.0 V; $\phi = +90.0°$
63. (b) 31.6
67. (a)

f (Hz)	X_L (Ω)	X_C (Ω)	Z (Ω)
300	283	12 600	12 300
600	565	6 280	5 720
800	754	4 710	3 960
1 000	942	3 770	2 830
1 500	1 410	2 510	1 100
2 000	1 880	1 880	40.0
3 000	2 830	1 260	1 570
4 000	3 770	942	2 830
6 000	5 650	628	5 020
10 000	9 420	377	9 040

(b)

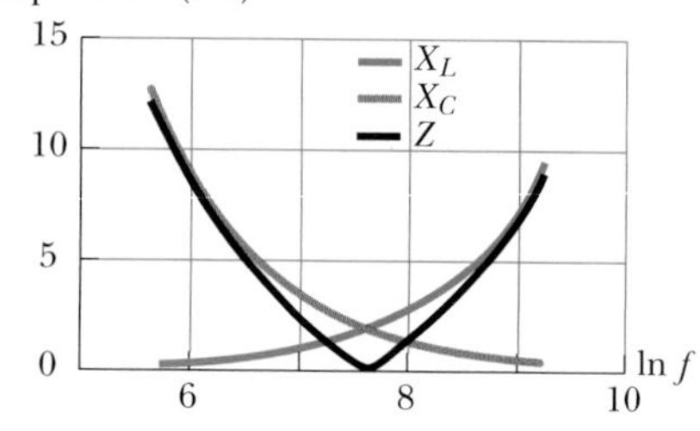

69. (a) and (b) 19.7 cm at 35.0°. The answers are identical. (c) 9.36 cm at 169°

CHAPTER 34

1. (a) 11.3 GV · m/s (b) 0.100 A
3. 1.85 aT up
5. $(-2.87\hat{\mathbf{j}} + 5.75\hat{\mathbf{k}})$ Gm/s²
7. (a) the year 2.69×10^3 (b) 499 s (c) 2.56 s (d) 0.133 s (e) 33.3 μs
9. (a) 6.00 MHz (b) $(-73.3\hat{\mathbf{k}})$ nT (c) $\vec{\mathbf{B}} = [(-73.3\hat{\mathbf{k}})\text{ nT}]\cos(0.126x - 3.77 \times 10^7 t)$
11. (a) 0.333 μT (b) 0.628 μm (c) 477 THz
13. 75.0 MHz
15. 3.33 μJ/m³
17. 307 μW/m²
19. 3.33×10^3 m²
21. (a) 332 kW/m² radially inward (b) 1.88 kV/m and 222 μT
23. (a) $\vec{\mathbf{E}} \cdot \vec{\mathbf{B}} = 0$ (b) $(11.5\hat{\mathbf{i}} - 28.6\hat{\mathbf{j}})$ W/m²
25. (a) 2.33 mT (b) 650 MW/m² (c) 510 W
27. (a) 88.8 nW/m² (b) 11.3 MW
29. 83.3 nPa
31. (a) 1.90 kN/C (b) 50.0 pJ (c) 1.67×10^{-19} kg · m/s
33. (a) 590 W/m² (b) 2.10×10^{16} W (c) 70.1 MN (d) The gravitational force is ~ 10^{13} times stronger and in the opposite direction. (e) On the Earth, the Sun's gravitational force is also ~ 10^{13} times stronger than the light-pressure force and in the opposite direction.
35. (a) 134 m (b) 46.9 m
37. (a) away along the perpendicular bisector of the line segment joining the antennas (b) along the extensions of the line segment joining the antennas
39. (a) $\vec{\mathbf{E}} = \frac{1}{2}\mu_0 c J_{\text{max}}[\cos(kx - \omega t)]\hat{\mathbf{j}}$
(b) $\vec{\mathbf{S}} = \frac{1}{4}\mu_0 c J_{\text{max}}^2[\cos^2(kx - \omega t)]\hat{\mathbf{i}}$
(c) $I = \dfrac{\mu_0 c J_{\text{max}}^2}{8}$ (d) 3.48 A/m
41. (a) 6.00 pm (b) 7.50 cm
43. (a) 4.17 m to 4.55 m (b) 3.41 m to 3.66 m (c) 1.61 m to 1.67 m
45. 1.00 Mm = 621 mi; not very practical
47. (a) 3.85×10^{26} W (b) 1.02 kV/m and 3.39 μT
49. (a)

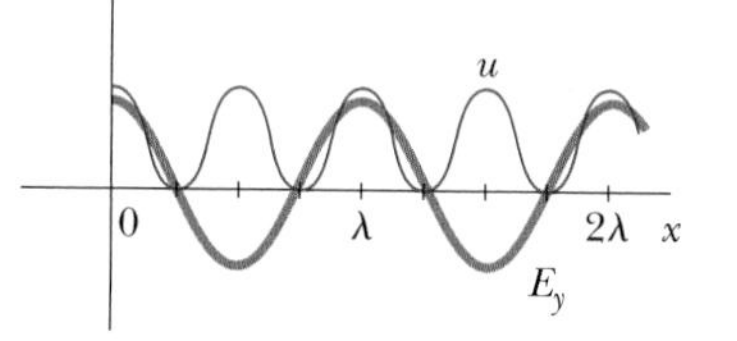

(b), (c) $u_E = u_B = \frac{1}{2}\epsilon_0 E_{\text{max}}^2 \cos^2(kx)$
(d) $u = \epsilon_0 E_{\text{max}}^2 \cos^2(kx)$ (e) $E_\lambda = \frac{1}{2}A\lambda\epsilon_0 E_{\text{max}}^2$
(f) $I = \frac{1}{2}c\epsilon_0 E_{\text{max}}^2 = \frac{1}{2}\sqrt{\dfrac{\epsilon_0}{\mu_0}}\,E_{\text{max}}^2$. This result agrees with $I = \dfrac{E_{\text{max}}^2}{2\mu_0 c}$ in Equation 34.24.
51. (a) 6.67×10^{-16} T (b) 5.31×10^{-17} W/m² (c) 1.67×10^{-14} W (d) 5.56×10^{-23} N
53. 95.1 mV/m
55. (a) $B_{\text{max}} = 583$ nT, $k = 419$ rad/m, $\omega = 126$ Grad/s; $\vec{\mathbf{B}}$ vibrates in xz plane (b) $\vec{\mathbf{S}}_{\text{avg}} = (40.6\hat{\mathbf{i}})$ W/m² (c) 271 nPa (d) $(406\hat{\mathbf{i}})$ nm/s²
57. (a) 22.6 h (b) 30.6 s
59. (a) 8.32×10^7 W/m² (b) 1.05 kW
61. (b) 17.6 Tm/s², 1.75×10^{-27} W (c) 1.80×10^{-24} W
63. (a) $2\pi^2 r^2 f B_{\text{max}} \cos\theta$, where θ is the angle between the magnetic field and the normal to the loop (b) The loop

Locator note: **boldface** indicates a definition; *italics* indicates a figure; *t* indicates a table.

Standard Abbreviations and Symbols for Units

Symbol	Unit	Symbol	Unit
A	ampere	K	kelvin
u	atomic mass unit	kg	kilogram
atm	atmosphere	kmol	kilomole
Btu	British thermal unit	L	liter
C	coulomb	lb	pound
°C	degree Celsius	ly	lightyear
cal	calorie	m	meter
d	day	min	minute
eV	electron volt	mol	mole
°F	degree Fahrenheit	N	newton
F	farad	Pa	pascal
ft	foot	rad	radian
G	gauss	rev	revolution
g	gram	s	second
H	henry	T	tesla
h	hour	V	volt
hp	horsepower	W	watt
Hz	hertz	Wb	weber
in.	inch	yr	year
J	joule	Ω	ohm

Mathematical Symbols Used in the Text and Their Meaning

Symbol	Meaning
$=$	is equal to
$\equiv$	is defined as
$\neq$	is not equal to
$\propto$	is proportional to
$\sim$	is on the order of
$>$	is greater than
$<$	is less than
$\gg (\ll)$	is much greater (less) than
$\approx$	is approximately equal to
Δx	the change in x
$\sum_{i=1}^{N} x_i$	the sum of all quantities x_i from $i = 1$ to $i = N$
$\lvert x \rvert$	the magnitude of x (always a nonnegative quantity)
$\Delta x \rightarrow 0$	Δx approaches zero
$\frac{dx}{dt}$	the derivative of x with respect to t
$\frac{\partial x}{\partial t}$	the partial derivative of x with respect to t
$\int$	integral